William Temple Bows

TREES AND SHRUBS
HARDY IN THE BRITISH ISLES

TREES AND SHRUBS
HARDY IN THE BRITISH ISLES

BY W. J. BEAN, C.V.O., I.S.O., V.M.H.

FORMERLY CURATOR, ROYAL BOTANIC GARDENS, KEW
VEITCH MEMORIAL MEDALLIST (1922 AND 1934)

VOL. III

LONDON
JOHN MURRAY, ALBEMARLE STREET, W.

First Edition (2 vols) . . . 1914
Third Volume (*First Edition*) . . 1933
Seventh Edition
    Volume I 1950
    Volumes II and III . . . 1951

MADE AND PRINTED IN GREAT BRITAIN BY
OLIVER AND BOYD LTD. AND PUBLISHED BY
JOHN MURRAY (PUBLISHERS) LTD.

CONTENTS

VOLUME III

PLATES

The names of the trees and shrubs illustrated in their place in the
text are printed in SMALL CAPITALS in the INDEXES

VOLUME III

Following page 664

PART II—*continued*

DESCRIPTIVE LIST OF GENERA AND SPECIES

RAPHIOLEPIS. ROSACEÆ

A genus of some three or four species of evergreen shrubs natives of Japan and China. Leaves stout and leathery, alternate, shortly stalked. Flowers in terminal racemes or panicles; petals five, stamens fifteen to twenty; ovary two-celled. The following kinds succeed in good well-drained loamy soil.

R. DELACOURI, *André*

An evergreen shrub of free, bushy growth, of rounded well-furnished habit, probably 6 to 8 ft. high ultimately; young shoots at first downy, soon becoming glabrous. Leaves obovate, toothed at the terminal half, wedge-shaped at the base, tapered more abruptly to the blunt or rounded apex; 1½ to 3½ ins. long, ¾ to 1½ ins. wide; of leathery texture, quite glabrous; stalk ¼ to ⅜ in. long. Flowers borne in erect terminal panicles 3 or 4 ins. high, of pyramidal shape; each flower is ½ to ¾ in. wide, the five obovate petals of a lovely rosy pink; flower-stalks downy; calyx with five awl-shaped downy lobes.

A hybrid between R. umbellata and R. indica, raised by Mr Delacour, gardener at the Villa Allerton, Cannes, towards the end of last century. It was named and figured in the *Revue Horticole*, 1900, p. 698. A number of forms varying in leaf and colour of flower were raised, the one selected having " corolles entièrement rosées, du ton le plus frais et le plus charmant, rappelant le rose de Chine." I first saw it in flower in Mr Chenault's garden at Orleans in 1913 and obtained it for the Kew collection. It is a very charming evergreen and judging by its behaviour during the trying winter of 1928-9 it is hardy enough for most parts of the country. Spring would appear to be its normal flowering season, but it is curiously variable in that respect. Lady Moore records it as being " covered with fully open flowers " at Glasnevin on 14th January 1922, and blossom may usually be seen some time in late summer and autumn. It transplants badly and it is advisable for it to be pot-grown until given a permanent place. R. umbellata differs from it in its stiffer leaves, sturdier growths, and white flowers; R. indica by its narrowly lanceolate leaves.

R. INDICA, *Lindley*

(R. salicifolia, *Lindley*)

This species is not very hardy, but can be grown successfully on a warm sunny wall. It has narrow, toothed, lanceolate leaves, 2 or 3 ins. long and short terminal, very pretty racemes of white flowers ⅝ in. wide, tinged, especially towards the centre, with pink. The numerous pink, erect stamens are a notable feature of the inflorescence, which is 2 to 3 ins. long.

Native of China; introduced about the beginning of the nineteenth century. It was figured in the Bot. Mag., t. 1726 as Cratægus indica. An admirable shrub for the south-western counties. Its habit is quite free and graceful when satisfactorily placed.

3

R. UMBELLATA. *Makino*

(R. japonica, *Siebold*; R. japonica integerrima, *Hooker fil.*; Bot. Mag., t. 5510)

An evergreen shrub of sturdy, rounded form, up to 10 ft. in height, with downy young wood.

RAPHIOLEPIS UMBELLATA

Leaves very stout and leathery, broadly oval or obovate, tapering at the base to a stout stalk ½ in. long, round or biunt-pointed, the terminal part usually shallow-toothed, the lower entire; 1½ to 3½ ins. long, about two-thirds as much wide. When young, the leaf is covered on both sides with a loose felt of grey down which rapidly falls away, leaving the surfaces quite glabrous, or with a few pieces of down about the midrib. Flowers fragrant, white, ¾ in. across, produced in a stiff terminal, panicle or raceme 3 or 4 ins. high, in June. Calyx very woolly, funnel-shaped, with five narrow, pointed lobes. Fruit pear-shaped, blue-black, erect, ½ in. long, one-seeded.

Native of Japan and Korea; introduced about 1862. This striking shrub would appear to be hardier than is generally supposed; it is quite healthy in the open at Kew, but no doubt likes a sheltered spot. It is a handsome shrub, well worth growing for the sake of its pure white scented blossoms. Propagated by seeds, or cuttings made of half-ripened shoots.

RHAMNUS. BUCKTHORN. RHAMNACEÆ

There are few groups of trees and shrubs comprising so many hardy species as Rhamnus that possess so little garden value. They have scarcely any beauty of flower, the blossoms being small, and either green, yellowish green, or brownish. The fruits are more attractive, being often very abundant and reddish when approaching ripeness. When fully ripe they are usually black or very dark purple.

The genus contains about sixty species of evergreen or deciduous trees and shrubs, the hardy ones widely spread over northern temperate latitudes. The leaves are normally alternate, but occasionally opposite ; the flowers perfect or unisexual, with the sexes on the same or separate trees. Flowers with a four- or five-lobed calyx and the same number of petals and stamens ; petals sometimes absent. Fruit a drupe, roundish or top-shaped, usually from ⅙ to ⅓ in. in diameter, enclosing two to four seeds. Good ordinary distinguishing features of the buckthorns are :— the number of veins of the leaf, and whether they are parallel or converging ; the absence or presence of marginal teeth ; the arrangement of the flowers—whether in stalked or stalkless clusters ; and the presence or absence of spines at the tips of the side twigs. Various members of the genus yield yellow or green dyes, and most of them have laxative or purgative properties in bark and fruit.

They are easily cultivated in any ordinary soil. Some do not strike root readily from cuttings, but can be layered ; seeds afford the best means of propagation when obtainable. The best species for gardens are :—*Alaternus*, as a dense evergreen ; *fallax* and *imeretina*, for fine foliage ; *pumila* and *rupestris*, as dwarf shrubs ; and *Purshiana*, for its medicinal interest and as a handsome tree.

R. ALATERNUS, *Linnæus*

An evergreen, sometimes unisexual shrub of rounded, bushy habit reaching 10 to 12 ft. in height, occasionally twice as high ; young branchlets covered with a close, minute down. Leaves oval or oblong, sometimes inclined to obovate, ¾ to 2 ins. long, ½ to 1 in. wide ; tapered at both ends and with a short abrupt apex, margins thickened and more or less toothed, especially when young, often conspicuously three-nerved at the base ; dark glossy green and glabrous except for some down on the lower part of the midrib above, and for tufts in the lowermost vein-axils beneath ; chief veins two to five each side the midrib ; stalks ⅛ to ¼ in. long, downy. Flowers yellowish green, very small (⅛ in. diameter), crowded on short, axillary, umbel-like racemes, scarcely ½ in. long, expanding in April. Fruit black, ¼ in. long.

Native of S.W. Europe ; introduced early in the seventeenth century, if not before. The alaternus is a useful, cheerful-looking evergreen of much the same character as phillyrea, but with alternate leaves. It has no beauty of flower, and little of fruit, although the latter are occasionally produced in such abundance as to be noticeable ; but it makes a dense mass of pleasant greenery. Easily propagated by cuttings, and perfectly hardy.

Var. ANGUSTIFOLIA (R. Perrieri, *Hort.*).—A very distinct variety with lanceolate or linear-oval, conspicuously toothed leaves, as long as those of the type, but only from ⅛ to ⅜ in. wide. There is a form of it with slightly variegated leaves. This variety is so distinct that the older authors considered it specifically distinct from the ordinary R. Alaternus. It is the R. angustifolia, *Miller*. In my experience it is not so hardy.

Var. INTEGRIFOLIA.—Leaves nearly always without teeth, and more conspicuously nerved than the type.

Var. MACULATA.—A poor form with leaves irregularly and sparsely blotched with yellow.

Var. VARIEGATA.—A form with leaves intermediate in shape between those of the type and var. angustifolia, often somewhat deformed. They are conspicuously margined with creamy white. This is a really well-variegated shrub, but is more tender than the type.

R. ALNIFOLIA, *L'Héritier*

A low deciduous shrub of spreading but compact habit, rarely more than 3 ft. high ; young shoots minutely downy. Leaves oval, tapered about equally at both ends, rather prominently and unevenly round-toothed ; 1½ to 4 ins. long, ⅝ to 2 ins. wide ; glabrous above, slightly downy on the veins beneath ; veins in about six to eight pairs ; stalk ¼ to ½ in. long, downy on the upper side. Flowers yellow-green, produced usually in twos or threes ; petals absent ; calyx lobes and stamens five. Fruit black, ¼ in. across, roundish or top-shaped, containing three seeds.

Native of N. America, on both the eastern and western sides ; introduced in 1778. A neat bush.

R. ARGUTA, *Maximowicz*

A deciduous shrub 6 ft. or more high ; young shoots glabrous, sometimes spine-tipped. Leaves mostly alternate, sometimes opposite, ovate, oval or roundish, mostly pointed, sometimes bluntish at the apex ; tapered, rounded, or slightly heart-shaped at the base ; margins finely and regularly set with sharp, almost bristle-pointed teeth ; veins in four to six pairs ; 1 to 2½ ins. long, half to three-fourths as wide ; bright green and glabrous ; stalk ¼ to 1 in. long. Flowers greenish, produced in axillary clusters or on short leafy spurs, each on a slender, glabrous stalk ½ to 1 in. long. Fruit roundish pear-shaped, ¼ in. long, black.

Native of North China and originally described in 1866 from specimens collected by Dr Tatarinov in 1851. W. Purdom found it in the province of Chili in 1909, and it is probably from his seed that the plants now in cultivation were raised. The species is distinct amongst the Chinese species by the bristle-tipped teeth of its leaves and its long-stalked flowers and fruit.

R. CALIFORNICA, *Eschscholtz*. CALIFORNIAN BUCKTHORN

An evergreen bush, ultimately 10 or 15 ft. high ; young shoots downy the first season. Leaves oblong or oval, mostly rounded at the base, rounded or broadly pointed at the apex, minutely or not at all toothed ; 1 to 4 ins. long, about half as wide ; glabrous above, downy on the veins beneath ; veins parallel, usually in eight to twelve pairs ; stalk ⅛ to ⅜ in. long, downy at first, glabrous the second season. Flowers in downy, short-stalked umbels. Fruit ¼ in. across, dark purple, globose.

Native of western N. America, from Oregon southwards. With some affinity to R. Purshiana in the stalked flower-clusters, this is easily distinguished by its dwarfer, purely shrubby habit, its evergreen foliage, and more globose fruits.

Var. OLEIFOLIA, *Hooker*, has smaller, narrower leaves, oblong-ovate, 1¼ to 2½ ins. long, ½ to 1 in. wide, uniformly toothed. There are, no doubt, forms intermediate between this and the type.

Var. TOMENTELLA, *Brewer* (R. tomentella, *Bentham*).—A very distinct form, the under-surface of the leaves being covered with a close, velvety, yellowish or greyish felt ; young shoots and leaf-stalks the same.

All these buckthorns are interesting evergreens, and have in their bark aperient properties identical with those alluded to under R. Purshiana ; they help to meet the demand for the Cascara Sagrada drug (see R. Purshiana).

R. CATHARTICA, *Linnæus*. COMMON BUCKTHORN

A deciduous shrub, 10 to 20 ft. high, ultimately of tree-like habit ; young shoots slender, glabrous ; lateral branchlets often terminated by a thorn. Leaves bright green, sometimes alternate, often opposite or sub-opposite ; oval or ovate, tapered or rounded and often unequal at the base, pointed at the apex ; finely toothed ; 1 to 2½ ins. long, half as wide ; mostly glabrous, but in one uncommon form (PUBESCENS) downy, especially beneath ; veins three or four each side the midrib, converging towards the apex ; stalk slender, ¼ to 1 in. long. Flowers small, green, produced in the lower leaf-axils, and forming a dense cluster at the base of the young shoot. Fruit black, about ¼ in. across.

Native of Europe, W. and N. Asia, found in Britain, but not commonly. A vigorous shrub, which by pruning away the lower branches may easily be made to assume a tree form. It has no particular merit, although the leaves die off sometimes a pleasing yellow, and a tree laden with the black fruits is striking. Allied to R. davurica (*q.v.*).

R. COSTATA, *Maximowicz*

A deciduous shrub, ultimately 15 ft. high, of spreading habit ; young shoots glabrous, stout. Leaves opposite, ovate-oblong, pointed, tapering below to a narrowly heart-shaped or cuneate base ; unevenly and shallowly toothed, 3 to 5 ins. long, 1¼ to 2½ ins. wide ; pale green on both sides, strongly ribbed, ribs about twenty ; upper surface wrinkled, and furnished with a few hairs when quite young ; under-surface downy, especially on the ribs ; stalk about ⅓ in. long, downy on the upper side. Flowers green, few or solitary on slender, glabrous stalks, ¾ to 1¼ ins. long, produced at the base of the young shoots. Fruit top-shaped, black, ⅓ in. diameter, two-seeded.

Native of Japan ; introduced in 1900. One of the handsomest of buckthorns in foliage, and belonging to the many-veined group, which includes fallax and imeretina. From fallax it is distinguished by its downy leaves, and from both by the long flower-stalk and strongly wrinkled upper-surface of the leaf. It has also a very short leaf-stalk.

R. DAVURICA, *Pallas*. DAHURIAN BUCKTHORN

A deciduous shrub or small tree, ultimately 30 ft. high ; young branchlets glabrous ; lateral twigs sometimes thorn-tipped. Leaves alternate or often nearly opposite ; oblong or oval, tapering at the base, slender-pointed, finely toothed, 1½ to 4 ins. long, ¾ to 1½ ins. wide ; glabrous or somewhat downy beneath ; veins in four to six pairs, converging towards the apex ; stalk slender, ¼ to 1 in. long. Flowers produced from the lower joints of the young shoots in June, forming dense clusters. Fruit black, about ¼ in. diameter.

Native of Siberia, Manchuria, and N. China, very closely allied to R. cathartica. It does not differ from that species in flower or fruit, but its leaves are longer, uniformly wedge-shaped at the base, and with one or two more pairs of veins. Of little garden value except in rough shrubberies.

R. FALLAX, *Boissier*. CARNIOLIAN BUCKTHORN

(R. alpina grandifolia, *Hort.* ; R. carniolica, *Kerner*)

A deciduous shrub, 4 to 10 ft. high, of stiff habit ; young shoots glabrous. Leaves oval or somewhat ovate, heart-shaped or rounded at the base, shortly tapered at the apex, finely and regularly toothed ; 1½ to 5½ ins. long, 1 to 3½ ins. wide ; dark green and glabrous except for minute tufts of hairs in the vein-axils beneath ; veins parallel, in from twelve to over twenty pairs ; stalks ¼ to ⅔ in. long, downy when young on the upper side. Flowers yellowish green, produced in clusters of three to seven from the leaf-axils and joints near the base of the current year's shoots ; petals and stamens four ; stalk ¼ in. or less long. Fruit black, ¼ in. across.

Native of the Alps of S.E. Europe ; much confused in gardens with R. ALPINA, *Linnæus*, a species with a more western distribution (S. France, Spain, and the West Mediterranean region), with fewer (nine to twelve) pairs of veins and proportionately longer leaf-stalks. It is also allied to R. imeretina (*q.v.*), which differs in the leaves being very downy beneath but equally many-veined. R. fallax and R. imeretina are the most handsome-foliaged of deciduous buckthorns.

R. FRANGULA, *Linnæus*. ALDER BUCKTHORN

A deciduous shrub, or a small tree up to 15 or 18 ft. high ; young shoots downy. Leaves oval or obovate, 1 to 3 ins. long, scarcely half as wide ; wedge-shaped or rounded at the base, often with a short abrupt point, not toothed ; dark glossy green and glabrous above, paler and often somewhat downy beneath ; veins parallel, usually in eight or nine pairs ; stalk ¼ to ½ in. long. Flowers clustered two to ten together in the leaf-axils of the young shoots, bisexual, the parts in fives ; calyx and flower-stalk glabrous. Fruit at first changing from green to red, then to dark purple, ¼ in. across, roundish, two-seeded.

Native of Europe, including the south of Britain. It is a rather handsome small fruiting tree with foliage of a cheerful green. Under the name of " dogwood " its wood is used (as charcoal) in the manufacture of the finest gunpowders. The bark has purgative properties.

Var. ANGUSTIFOLIA has narrowly oblong or oblanceolate leaves, from ¼ to 1 in. wide, the margins uneven or jagged.

Var. ASPLENIFOLIA.—A remarkable form with leaves as long as in the type, but only from 1/12 to ⅛ in. wide as a rule.

Var. LATIFOLIA, *Dippel*, found in the Caucasian region, has larger, broader leaves than the type, up to 3½ ins. long and 2 ins. wide. This form must not be confounded with

R. LATIFOLIUS, *L'Héritier*, a species found in the Azores, and perhaps not very hardy in this country, although it thrives in the garden of Bitton Vicarage and at Glasnevin. It has leaves up to 5 ins. long, 3 ins. wide, with ten to sixteen pairs of parallel veins and a stalk 1¼ ins. long. Akin to R. Frangula, it differs not only in its larger, more numerously veined leaves, but also in having a downy flower-stalk and calyx, the former up to ⅔ in. long. Fruit nearly ½ in. across, red, then black. Introduced in 1778 ; now very rare, but worth growing for its handsome foliage. (Bot. Mag., t. 2663.)

R. HYBRIDA, *L'Héritier*

An evergreen or partially evergreen shrub up to 12 ft. high, of spreading habit, more in diameter than it is high ; shoots glabrous. Leaves ovate to oblong, rounded or widely tapered at the base, pointed, 1½ to 4 ins. long, ¾ to 1¾ ins. wide ; shallowly and finely toothed, glabrous on both surfaces, rather pale green ; about seven veins each side the midrib ; leaf-stalk ⅛ to ⅓ in. long. It is regarded as a hybrid between R. Alaternus and R. alpina.

Var. BILLARDI, *Lavallée* (R. Billardi), with small, narrow, more lanceolate leaves, is considered to be a form of R. hybrida, but is very dissimilar, especially in the conspicuous jagged toothing. Its form of leaf suggests that it might have originated from R. Alaternus angustifolia.

R. IMERETINA, *Kirchner*

(Bot. Mag., t. 6721 (as R. libanotica) ; R. colchica, *Sommier and Levrier*)

A deciduous shrub up to 10 ft. high, with very sturdy shoots sparsely downy when young. Leaves oblong or oval, rounded or slightly heart-shaped at the base, taper-pointed, finely toothed ; 4 to 10 ins. long, 2 to 4 ins. wide ; veins parallel in fifteen to twenty-nine pairs ; upper surface dark green and soon glabrous, except in the sunken midrib and veins ; lower surface downy, especially on the veins ; stalk ½ to ¾ in. long, downy. Flowers green, in small, axillary clusters. Fruit ⅔ in. long.

Native of the Western Caucasus up to 8500 ft., and a very handsome, large-leaved, quite hardy shrub—the finest of all the buckthorns. I have measured odd leaves as much as 14 ins. long, and 6 ins. wide. It is much confused in gardens with R. LIBANOTICA, *Boissier*, a nearly allied species found in the Lebanon region of Syria, and distinguished by smaller leaves with only fifteen or fewer pairs of veins ; leaf-stalk ¼ in. long ; fruit ½ in. diameter, black. The leaves of R. imeretina die off a deep bronzy purple in autumn. R. fallax (*q.v.*) is also similar, but is glabrous in shoot and leaf.

R. INFECTORIA, *Linnæus*. AVIGNON BERRY

A deciduous shrub of spreading habit up to 7 ft. high, the side twigs spine-tipped ; young shoots downy. Leaves very variable, mostly oval, but also ovate or obovate ; tapered at both ends, finely toothed, ½ to 1½ ins. long, ¼ to ¾ in. wide ; upper surface dark green, mostly glabrous, or with down on the midrib, lower one smooth or slightly downy ; veins in three or four pairs converging upwards ; stalk ¼ to ⅜ in. long, usually downy. Fruit two-seeded, black.

Native of S.W. Europe. It has longer, firmer-textured leaves than R. saxatilis, but the two are perhaps only varieties of the one species. The fruit is (or was once) used by dyers under the name of *Graine d'Avignon*. There is a rather handsome bush at Kew, 7 ft. high, and 15 ft. in diameter, distinguished by its dense, gnarled branches.

R. JAPONICA, *Maximowicz*

A deciduous shrub up to 8 or 9 ft. high ; lateral branchlets occasionally spine-tipped or reduced to short spurs with the leaves crowded at the end ; young shoots glabrous. Leaves glossy pale green on both sides, obovate, always tapered at the base, broadly pointed or rounded at the apex, finely toothed except sometimes near the base ; 1 to 3 ins. long, ½ to 1 in. wide ; with three to five pairs of veins converging towards the apex ; stalk ¼ to ¾ in. long, more or less downy. Flowers greenish brown, produced in May in dense hemispherical clusters at the end of the short, spur-like branches ; stalks glabrous, ¼ in. long ; calyx lobes four, triangular ; stamens four. Fruit globose, ¼ in. diameter.

Native of Japan ; introduced in 1888. It flowers with great freedom, and the blossoms have a faint pleasant fragrance. It is distinct in its bright green, uniformly obovate leaves produced on spurs.

R. LANCEOLATA, *Pursh*

An erect shrub up to 6 or 7 ft. high, the young shoots glabrous or slightly downy. Leaves ovate-lanceolate, oblong-lanceolate, or oval, broadly wedge-shaped or rounded at the base, with short, slender or bluntish points, finely toothed ; 1 to 3½ ins. long, ½ to 1¼ ins. wide ; glabrous or slightly downy ; veins parallel in six to nine pairs ; stalk up to ⅓ in. long, mostly downy. Flowers produced in twos or threes in the axils of the young leaves, yellowish green ; the parts in fours ; stalks about ⅛ in. long. Fruit black, roundish, ¼ in. diameter, two-seeded.

Native of the eastern and central United States. This buckthorn flowers with extreme freedom, the short-stalked blossoms being crowded along the young shoots and forming cylindrical clusters.

R. PUMILA, *Linnæus*. DWARF BUCKTHORN

A low, sometimes procumbent shrub usually only a few inches high, of stunted habit ; young shoots downy. Leaves variable in outline, sometimes roundish, sometimes narrowly oval, ¾ to 2 ins. long, more or less tapered at the base, mostly finely toothed ; glabrous, or with down along the midrib and veins ; veins parallel in from five to eight pairs ; stalk downy, ⅛ to ⅓ in. long. Flowers pale green, the parts in fours. Fruit globose, blue-black.

Native of the Alps of Europe ; introduced originally from Mount Baldo, in 1752. It inhabits crevices of rocks, and is of the curious gnarled type common in such places. It has some beauty in fruit, and is best adapted for the rock garden, where it makes a neat and pleasing tuft, although less close and compact than in a wild state.

R. PURSHIANA, *De Candolle*. CASCARA SAGRADA

A deciduous tree up to 40 or 50 ft. high in a wild state ; young shoots conspicuously downy. Leaves oblong or oval, rounded at the base, with a short, bluntish apex, either minutely toothed or entire ; 2 to 5 ins. long, 1 to 3 ins. wide ; downy beneath and on the veins above, veins parallel, in ten to fifteen pairs ; stalk ½ to ¾ in. long, downy. Flowers in stalked umbels, opening in July ; sepals and petals five, flower-stalks downy. Fruit top-shaped, ⅓ in. long, black, usually three-seeded.

Native of western N. America ; introduced in 1891. A handsome small tree, although without any beauty of blossom, forming a broad leafy head of erect or spreading branches. It is allied to R. Frangula, but has more numerous parallel veins in each leaf that are downy above, and differs in the distinctly stalked flower-clusters, the common stalk being often ½ in. or more long. R. Purshiana is the source of the well-known drug, " Cascara Sagrada," one of the most popular of aperient medicines. It is obtained from the bark, and so great is the demand that £20,000 worth was sent from the States of Oregon and Washington in 1907. The consequence is that natural supplies are being rapidly used up, and it has been suggested that the cultivation of this tree in the southern and western parts of the British Isles might prove profitable. The bark of trees raised and grown at Kew has been proved to possess the aperient quality as fully as that of wild trees.

R. CAROLINIANA, *Walter*. Indian Cherry.—This is nearly related to R. Purshiana, and may be regarded as its E. American representative. It differs from the above in having narrower, more pointed leaves, with fewer (eight to ten) pairs of parallel veins. It resembles it in having stalked umbels, but the stalks are much shorter.

Introduced in 1819, according to Loudon, but now rarely seen, and perhaps not very hardy. It varies from a shrub to a tree 30 to 40 ft. high. Fruit red, becoming black, ⅜ in. wide, sweet.

R. RUPESTRIS, *Scopoli*

A deciduous shrub of low, spreading habit, from 8 to 30 ins. high; young shoots covered with fine hairs. Leaves oval, or inclined to oblong, or sometimes orbicular, rounded at the base, pointed or rounded at the apex; ¾ to 2 ins. long, about half as wide; minutely or not toothed; dull green and glabrous (or with the veins downy) above, greyish beneath, and finely hairy on the midrib, veins, and stalk; veins parallel, in five to eight pairs. Flowers in downy, stalked umbels of three to eight. Fruit at first red, then black, roundish top-shaped, ¼ in. wide, three-seeded.

Native of S.E. Europe, inhabiting mountain regions. In habit and leaf it resembles R. pumila, but is distinguished by the more hairy shoots and stalked inflorescences. The latter are sometimes borne on short, lateral, leafy twigs springing from the leaf-axils.

R. SAXATILIS, *Jacquin*. ROCK BUCKTHORN

A low, spreading, deciduous shrub, rarely more than 2 ft. high; young shoots minutely downy, lateral branchlets often ending in a spine. Leaves glabrous or nearly so, narrowly oval, ovate or obovate, tapered at the base, often bluntish at the apex, finely toothed; ½ to 1 in. long, ¼ to ½ in. wide; veins two to four each side the midrib, converging towards the apex; stalk ⅛ in. or less long. Flowers very small, greenish yellow. Fruit black, top-shaped, three-seeded.

Native of the mountains of Central and S.E. Europe; introduced in 1752. A curious dwarf or stunted shrub inhabiting rocky places, belonging to the same group as tinctoria and infectoria, but distinguished by its dwarf habit and smaller, glabrous leaves.

R. SPATHULÆFOLIA, *Fischer and Meyer*

A deciduous shrub up to 6 ft. high, with downy shoots and narrow-oval or lanceolate leaves; ¾ to 2½ ins. long, ¼ to ¾ in. wide; slenderly tapered at the base and apex, finely toothed, distinctly downy on both surfaces; veins three to five each side the midrib, converging towards the point; stalk ¼ to ¾ in. long. Fruit black, on a stalk up to ½ in. long.

Native of S.E. Europe, Persia, etc.; introduced in 1880; distinct in its long, narrow, downy leaves, but of no particular merit.

R. TINCTORIA, *Waldstein and Kitaibel*. DYER'S BUCKTHORN

This species belongs to the same group as R. infectoria and R. saxatilis, and is a deciduous shrub up to 4 or 6 ft. high, the side branchlets spine-tipped. It is distinguished from both its allies by the very hairy leaf-stalk. The largest leaves are 2 ins. long by 1 in. wide, the smallest ½ in. long; oval, more or less downy beneath, and with usually three, sometimes four pairs of veins converging towards the apex. Fruit black, top-shaped.

Native of S.E. Europe; introduced in 1820, but of little garden value.

R. UTILIS, *Decaisne*

A deciduous shrub 6 to 9 ft. high; young shoots slender, glabrous occasionally becoming spine-tipped. Leaves oblong to narrowly obovate, mostly tapered at the base, contracted at the apex to a short, slender point, shallowly and bluntly toothed; 1½ to 5 ins. long, ¾ to 2 ins. wide; veins in five to eight pairs, yellowish; glabrous except for yellowish down beneath in the vein-axils and on the veins when young; stalk ¼ to ½ in. long. Flowers yellowish, ¼ in. wide; petals lanceolate. Fruit black, ¼ in. wide, globose-ovoid, each on a stalk ¼ in. long.

Native of Central and Eastern China; long in cultivation, but sometimes confused with R. davurica, which differs in its longer leaf-stalks—often 1 in. long—whilst the leaf-blades are, on the average, shorter. Both species provide the raw material for the production of the dye known as " China green."

RHAPHITHAMNUS CYANOCARPUS, *Miers*. VERBENACEÆ

(Bot. Mag., t. 6849; Citharexylon cyanocarpum, *Hooker*)

An evergreen shrub or small tree, ultimately 20 or 25 ft. high, with a dense growth and very leafy branches; young shoots covered with erect, bristly down, and armed with axillary spines, which on the year-old branches become ½ to 1 in. long, slender and needle-like. Leaves opposite, often in threes, set about ¼ in. apart; ¼ to ¾ in. long, ⅛ to ½ in. wide; broadly ovate, pointed, rounded at the base; dark green and glabrous above, pale beneath, with at first minute bristles especially on the midrib, also on the very short stalk. Flowers pale blue, produced in April singly or in pairs in the leaf-axils of the previous summer's growth, each on a very short, bristly stalk. Corolla slender, tubular, ½ in. long; calyx bell-shaped, 1/12 in. long, toothed; stamens four, included within the corolla. Berry ⅓ to ½ in. diameter, globose, bright blue.

Native of Chile; introduced by W. Lobb about 1843. It is only hardy at Kew against a wall, and one must go to Ireland or the south-west to see it at its best. I remember seeing a fine specimen at Menabilly, in Cornwall, several years ago, which I believe is now over 20 ft. high, growing in deep loamy soil. Its blue fruits are even more ornamental than its flowers.

RHODODENDRON (including AZALEA). ERICACEÆ

No genus of hardy shrubs, unless it be Rosa, has given to gardens such varied attractions as Rhododendron. In the now generally accepted signification of the word, it includes what were formerly known as Azalea. The true rhododendrons had ten stamens or more to each flower, and were evergreen, whilst the azaleas had five stamens, and were mostly deciduous, but there are numerous species in which these characters are mixed. The former section undoubtedly includes a larger number of beautiful types of evergreen shrubs than any other genus; and to the azaleas or mainly deciduous group it would be difficult to find a rival. The leading characteristics of the genus in its broader sense are as follows :—Shrubs or small trees, deciduous or evergreen; leaves alternate, simple, entire ; flowers in usually terminal but sometimes axillary clusters or short racemes, or solitary ; corolla variable in shape, and either saucer-shaped, funnel-shaped, bell-shaped, or tubular, usually five, sometimes six- to ten-lobed, white, yellow, many shades of purple and red, never real blue ; calyx usually five-lobed, sometimes almost or quite obsolete ; stamens five to twenty ; seed-vessel dry, woody, splitting longitudinally ; seeds numerous, minute, and winged.

The true species of the evergreen group are now largely superseded in gardens by the varieties of hybrid origin which originated mainly from catawbiense, ponticum, arboreum, and caucasicum, and to a smaller extent from maximum, Griffithianum, Fortunei, and Thomsoni. The same is the case with the deciduous or azalea group. Here the original wild types, from which the beautiful garden or so-called " Ghent " varieties were obtained by hybridisers, are flavum, calendulaceum, nudi-florum, viscosum ; and latterly, occidentale, molle, and sinense. Many of these azaleas give beautiful autumn colour.

The hardy species are confined to the northern hemisphere, and the greatest aggregation of species occurs in the Chinese-Tibetan-Himalayan region. Eight or nine are found in Europe and Asia Minor, about a dozen (mostly azaleas) in N. America, somewhat more in Japan. A sub-tropical group with which we have here no concern belongs to the East Indies, New Guinea, and Australia.

In the identification and differentiation of the numerous species the shape and size of the calyx and corolla play a great part, as does also the length of the stamens in relation to the corolla and style. The presence or absence of scales on the younger parts of the plants (a condition known as " lepidote "), and the presence or otherwise of down or glands on the shoots, leaves, calyx, stamens, ovary and style, are also valuable points in assisting identification.

Since the preparation of the two first volumes of this work was finished early in 1913, an astonishing development has occurred in the cultivation of rhododendrons in the British Isles. At that time the introductions of E. H. Wilson from Szechuen and Hupeh were comparatively new to gardens, and many of the finest species had not yet flowered there. These Wilsonian rhododendrons have added much interest and beauty to the genus, and most of them are hardy enough to grow in a climate like that of Kew, even the larger-leaved species like calophytum, sutchuenense, discolor, and auriculatum. But, to be seen at their best, many of them require a softer, moister climate, and especially more freedom from late spring frosts. It is in the gardens of mid-Sussex and Hampshire and thence southwards and westwards that their full beauty begins to be revealed. Yet Wilson's work can only be regarded as a kind of prologue to the great rhododendron epic. It is mainly due to the wonderful work and amazing industry of George Forrest, also to his organisation and training of native collectors, that rhododendrons are so prominent in horticulture to-day. He worked chiefly in W. Yunnan, E. Tibet, and N.E. Burma, in latitudes considerably to the south of Wilson's area, and his introductions on the whole are not so hardy. It is rarely other than those that he found at altitudes of approximately 11,000 to 12,000 ft.

and upwards that can be regarded as possibly hardy in a climate like that of Kew. But again it has to be said that it is late spring frost rather than winter cold merely that is the enemy. Wilson's R. discolor, which he found as low as 4000 to 7000 ft. in Szechuen and Hupeh, is so late a starter into growth that it is never caught by late frost. Consequently it is as hardy and free-flowering at Kew as an ordinary garden hybrid. R. Griersonianum, another late grower, which Forrest found at 7000 to 9000 ft. in W. Yunnan, is hardy enough to grow and flower regularly in a sheltered spot at Kew, although of course nothing like so good as it is in a better climate.

George Forrest died at Tengyueh on 5th January 1932, just as he was on the point of returning home from what he had intended should be his last collecting expedition. In later years he had an enthusiastic and successful co-worker in N.E. Burma and S.E. Tibet in Captain F. Kingdon Ward, who has discovered a number of new species and sent home seeds of many others. Through an American collector, J. F. Rock, seeds of many rhododendrons have been received, but amongst them, I believe, are few new species of his own discovery. The late Reginald Farrer also found and introduced a few species. But the first discovery and introduction of the great bulk of the new Asiatic rhododendrons now in gardens are directly due to Forrest and to those who organised and financed his expeditions.

In a work of 860 pages, *The Species of Rhododendron*, prepared by leading specialists and published by the Rhododendron Society in 1930, well over 600 species are described. The labour of identifying and naming the new species of Forrest, Ward, and Farrer fell mainly on the late Sir Isaac B. Balfour, Regius Keeper of the Edinburgh Botanic Garden, who will always live in botanical history as the leading authority of his time on this genus, and as distinguished for the careful, even meticulous nature of his work. But as with many other botanists who have become absorbed in one group of plants, there is no doubt that he attached too much importance to minute differences and that this led him to establish species on what many people regard as insufficient grounds. In the monograph just mentioned, over one hundred of his specific names have already been sunk as synonyms or sub-species, and I think that as time goes on and plants flower in gardens, this number will be considerably increased. I once heard Forrest himself say that probably only 60 per cent. of the Balfourian names would ultimately survive. Although this was probably said on the spur of the moment and not as the result of deliberate calculation, it showed the trend of his thoughts. And, of course, he knew his living plants (as distinct from mere dried material) better than anyone else has ever done.

Cultivation.—The cultivation of pretty nearly all rhododendrons is the same, and the only difference between the deciduous and the evergreen ones is that the former like less shade. Most of the evergreen species and varieties do very well in semi-shade. In this connection Mr E. H. Wilson told me that he found in China the large broad-leaved species grew naturally in shade ; the small-leaved, scaly, resinous ones on the mountain tops in full sun, filling the same place there as heather on British moors. Most of the common race of hybrids and small-leaved species succeed without shade, but the rest prefer it. All those that flower in early spring, and thus become liable to injury by frost, are best in positions shaded from the morning sun. In such spots they have a chance to thaw gradually, and escape the entire destruction that awaits those flowers exposed to the full rays of the bright early sunshine that so frequently follows a frosty night. But as a rule 5° or 6° of frost is fatal to the expanded flowers of rhododendrons. Both rhododendrons and azaleas are especially suited for planting in large masses. Where the garden is large enough special areas may be set apart for them, and in smaller ones they may be planted in beds or broad groups.

Soil.—The best possible soil for these shrubs is one of a peaty nature. The great rhododendron nurseries are on peaty formations. But this is by no means absolutely necessary. A sweet, well-drained loam, especially if it be of a sandy nature and free from calcareous matter, does almost as well, especially if a good proportion of decayed leaves be incorporated with it. Even a heavy loam treated in the same way will suit the stronger growing sorts. Rhododendrons as a whole abhor lime, R. hirsutum and some of its hybrids, which are found in the Alps on a limestone formation, being the only exceptions. They are all moisture-loving, and delight in a continuously cool damp condition at the root. For plants whose roots are not shaded by their own lower branches, a surface mulching of 4 to 6 ins. of leaves is very beneficial, especially in hot weather. If the soil be poor, a proportion of one-third well-rotted manure may be added to the mulch. It may be said that no one item in the cultivation of rhododendrons tends so much to success as the abundance of decayed leaves in and on the soil.

Removal of Flowers.—Wherever time and opportunity allow, the flowers of all rhododendrons and azaleas should be removed as soon as they have faded. The truss will usually break off in one piece between thumb and finger. Most of them are prolific seed-bearers, and the development of the seed-vessel is very detrimental to the progress of the young growths and the next year's crop of blossom. Even in the great trade establishments where the plants are numbered by tens of thousands the managers find it worth while to have the old flowers religiously removed.

Propagation.—Whilst most of these plants are increased by grafting, the processes of seed-sowing, layering, and propagation by cuttings may be largely adopted. The common garden varieties of the true evergreen group, especially those with large leaves, are extremely difficult to increase by cuttings, and are mostly grafted on seedlings of R. ponticum, but in consequence of the continual watch that has to be kept for suckers from the stock, the practice of layering and thus getting them on their own roots is coming into vogue. Owing to the longer time necessary to obtain layered plants, the prices of plants so raised have to be higher. The species of the lepidote (or scaly), smaller-leaved group, such as yunnanense, racemosum, and concinnum, can quite easily be increased by cuttings made in July or August of the shoots of the year, with a " heel " of old wood attached, and placed in gentle heat.

The named varieties of azalea are mainly propagated by grafting on seedlings of R. flavum. All the species and varieties whose branches can be brought to the ground will take root by layering, and all or nearly all can be increased by cuttings. Small shoots with a " heel " should be taken, 2 or 3 ins. long, when the wood is getting fairly firm—which will usually be about the end of July. They should be dibbled firmly in well-drained pots of sand and peat in about equal parts, and when they are all put in, the surface should be covered with ⅛ in. of sand. A gentle bottom heat is desirable, and the cuttings may be covered with a bell-glass. They should not be disturbed until thoroughly well rooted, when they can be potted in small pots or planted in prepared ground.

Seed-sowing.—The seeds of all rhododendrons and azaleas are very small. They should be sown in pots or pans of soil similar in composition to what is recommended for cuttings, pressed firmly down, and the seed simply sprinkled on the top. All the covering they need is a sprinkling of silver sand sufficient to half bury them. The most important operation in raising rhododendron seeds is in the supply of moisture. They need continuously moist but not sodden conditions, and owing to their lightness are very easily disturbed, the finest possible rose, therefore, should be attached to the spout of the watering-pot. If this is not available, it is better to plunge the pots to half their depth in water for a short time, and dispense with surface watering altogether. In order to reduce evaporation the seed-pots may be covered with sheets of glass, or a light canvas screen may be placed over them. When large enough to handle, the seedlings should be pricked off in shallow boxes. Seedling rhododendrons are longer than cuttings in reaching the flowering state. The big-leaved ones may be eight to fifteen years, the smaller-leaved ones from three to five years. The most tender species, like those from the Himalaya, whilst they may be hardy enough when they are a few years old, need winter protection during their babyhood. The raising of hybrid rhododendrons and azaleas may be recommended as most interesting work. The various species and varieties cross-breed very readily.

Up to the early years of the present century, before the incoming of the Chinese host, the cultivation of rhododendrons in general was regarded as easy. There were, of course, comparatively few species then in cultivation. In the list of hardy trees and shrubs grown at Kew in 1896 about thirty species of evergreen rhododendrons are enumerated and less than twenty species of azaleas. In the warmer counties a number of the more tender Himalayan species were grown in addition. Provided these had an open soil free from calcareous substances and sufficient moisture at the root, their cultivation as a whole presented no problems, although a few like lanatum and camelliæflorum were unsatisfactory. The old-fashioned, hardy type of hybrid raised from ponticum, catawbiense, caucasicum, maximum, and arboreum (and in a lesser degree from Thomsonii, Fortunei, and Griffithianum) were, and still are, grown by nurserymen in open fields like other nursery stock.

But it was soon found, even with some of Wilson's introductions, that things were not going to be so easy with the Chinese wild types. I remember them as young plants in Veitch's Coombe Wood Nursery about 1908-10. There, under conditions which suited the old hybrid types perfectly, many looked unhealthy and the fatalities were numerous. The reason of this was largely due to their being exposed to too much direct sunlight. The first cultivator who appreciated and showed the necessity of shade for the newer and especially the large-leaved species was Mr J. C. Williams of Caerhays, Cornwall. Nowhere in the British Isles was there a collection of rhododendron species more comprehensive or more admirably grown than his. The provision of shade presumes as a rule the existence of at least moderately sized trees, and to plant rhododendrons near enough to benefit from the shade given by such trees involves, or may involve, competition at the root. Rhododendrons are all moisture-lovers, both at the root and in the atmosphere, and although in places where the rainfall is fifty to sixty or more inches per annum the soil may keep moist enough for both trees and rhododendrons in association, in the drier and especially eastern counties, the close proximity of such greedy trees as elms, beeches, limes or sycamores makes the cultivation of rhododendrons very unsatisfactory unless artificial watering can be done, and trenches periodically dug deep enough to keep the tree roots at bay. But the common oak is an exception because a large proportion of its roots are deep enough to avoid much interference with the shallow-rooting rhododendrons. The best of all places that can be provided for rhododendrons is oak woodland, not closely or heavily planted, but still thick enough to cover the ground with light shadows. Forrest in his " field notes " often mentions the association of pine trees with rhododendrons in a wild state ; they, too, are never gross feeders and often deep-rooted.

The association of trees and rhododendrons has one other advantage. A canopy of even leafless branches during a light spring frost will sometimes give just sufficient protection to save blossoms and advanced flower-buds from the complete destruction that would be their fate were they fully open to the sky.

As a general rule, small-leaved rhododendrons, especially those of the lapponicum " series," are the ones best adapted for sunny places. Many of them grow on mountain sides, covering great open expanses just as heather does at home or R. ferrugineum in the Alps. But even there they are often immersed in mist and the nights are cool and dewy. My experience in the hot, dry Lower Valley of the Thames is that even the lapponicum types succeed better with some shade, especially during the hot middle hours of the day.

There are some, not perhaps very many, species which even the most expert cultivators in the most favourable districts find it difficult to grow satisfactorily. They try to solve the problem by putting plants in different places and different exposures. Even when success is achieved it is not always clear to them what particular condition or combination of conditions has brought it about. R. lanatum has already been mentioned ; another old instance is that of R. albiflorum, a species from W. North America introduced in the middle of last century which, so far as I know, no one has ever grown really well. Yet in a wild state it is found in association with other plants that are quite easy to grow.

One of the many benefits conferred by Sir Isaac Balfour and his coadjutors at Edinburgh on cultivators of rhododendrons has been the classification of the known species into groups, or what Sir Isaac called " series " and " sub-series." This classification is to some extent tentative and as yet not wholly or permanently fixed. But it has brought a good deal of order and definiteness into what would otherwise have been chaos. In the valuable *Species of Rhododendron* published by the Rhododendron Society, the genus is divided into forty-three series, eleven of which are composed of one to three species only. The great difficulty experienced by the authors has been to define in any way clearly the limits of each series. Whilst very useful keys are made for the species in each series, no attempt has been made to " key " the series themselves. The cultivator of rhododendrons, however, soon acquires a sufficient familiarity with the larger series to place his species in or near the one to which it belongs.

The Rhododendron Society's monograph (to which I am much indebted in the compilation of the following notes) comprises upwards of 860 pages and contains descriptions of some 650 species. Many of these are not in cultivation, but it has been impossible to include all the species that are cultivated in the present work and keep it within reasonable limits. With the kindly help of the late Mr Lionel de Rothschild of Exbury, the first President of the Rhododendron Association, I have made a selection of species for description or mention, which is an attempt to include the most beautiful, the most remarkable, and the better known species, and to represent the genus as broadly as is possible here. Many beautiful species are perforce omitted, but few, I hope, that are not represented by one or more of a closely related or similar type.

As a guide to those contemplating the planting of evergreen hybrid rhododendrons I give below a selection of fifty varieties, all of which are hardy at Kew, and obtainable in nurseries.

Alice, rose pink, May.
Ascot Brilliant, crimson-scarlet, April.
B. de Bruin, bright red, May, June.
Broughtonii, deep rosy red, May.
Corona, various shades of pink, May.
Cunningham's Sulphur, yellow, May.
Doncaster, brilliant red, June.
Duchess of Connaught, white, late May.
Essex Scarlet, brilliant red, June.
Everestianum, rosy lilac, frilled corolla, June.
Fastuosum, double, purple, June.
Florence, pink, pale centre, May, June.
Gomer Waterer, white, late May.
G. R. Sims, brilliant red, June.
Helen Schiffner, white, May.
J. G. Millais, scarlet, April, May.
James Marshall Brooks, rich red, June.
King George, scarlet, May.
Lady Annette de Trafford, cream, chocolate blotch, May, June.

Lady Clementine Mitford, peach colour, with darker edge, May.
Lady Eleanor Cathcart, rose, chocolate blotch, May.
Lady Grey Egerton, French grey, rosy tint, May, June.
Loderi, white or pale pink, very large, May.
Loder's White, pure white, very fine, May.
Lord Palmerston (Cynthia), rich rosy red, May.
Luscombei, rose pink, April, May.
Manglesii, white, May.
Martin Hope Sutton, bright red, June.
Message of Peace, soft pink, large, June.
Michael Waterer, scarlet, June.
Mrs A. Waterer, white, May, June.
Mrs E. C. Stirling, faint pink, May.
Mrs Geo. Paul, pale pink, May.
Mrs Holford, rich salmon pink, May, June.

Mrs John Clutton, good white, June.
Mrs John Millais, white, May.
Mrs L. de Rothschild, rose pink, May.
Mrs J. P. Lade, French grey, May.
Mrs Mendel, pink, May, June.
Ochroleucum, creamy yellow, May.
Pink Pearl, pink, large truss, May.
Princess Mary of Cambridge, rosy purple, white centre, May, June.
Purple Splendour, purple, May, June.

Royal Purple, purple, May, June.
Sappho, white with maroon blotch, lax habit, May, June.
Sigismund Rucker, magenta crimson, spotted, May, June
Snowflake, pure white, June.
The Bride, white, April, May.
The Queen, blush, then white, May, June.
Unknown Warrior, deep rose, May.

Early Varieties.—Flowering in early or mid April: Countess, altaclerense, arboreum Wellsianum; Handsworth early red; Handsworth early white; Rosa Mundi, Smithii album, Russellianum, Caucasicum pictum, Nobleanum (from January to March), George Cunningham (March).

In recent years a large number of hybrids have been raised, mostly in private gardens, between the finest of the Chinese species. During the rhododendron season dozens of them are shown at Vincent Square and many receive a First-class Certificate or an Award of Merit. They are, of course, of a much finer class and more splendid colouring than most of the old-fashioned types represented by the list given above. But the majority of them are best (or only) fitted for gardens of the south and west and are not in the market.

R. ADENOGYNUM, *Diels*

(Bot. Mag., t. 9253)

An evergreen shrub said to grow 9 ft. high in nature, with the stout young shoots woolly at first, becoming glabrous. Leaves with decurved margins, oblong inclined to ovate, pointed, tapered or rounded at the base; 2 to 6 ins. long, $\frac{3}{4}$ to $1\frac{3}{4}$ ins. wide; dark green, finely wrinkled and at maturity glabrous above, covered beneath with a tawny, suède-like felt; stalk without glands, $\frac{1}{2}$ to $1\frac{1}{4}$ ins. long. Flowers opening in April and May in trusses of six to twelve, fragrant. Corolla white, tinged with pink outside, especially at the base, spotted with crimson, bell-shaped, $1\frac{1}{2}$ to $2\frac{1}{2}$ ins. long, 2 to 3 ins. wide, the five lobes rounded. Stamens ten, $\frac{1}{2}$ to $1\frac{1}{4}$ ins. long, stalks white, downy at the base. Ovary glandular but not downy; style $1\frac{1}{3}$ ins. long, very glandular towards the base. Calyx-lobes five, oval, $\frac{3}{16}$ to $\frac{3}{8}$ in. long, very glandular; flower-stalk up to $1\frac{1}{4}$ ins. long, glandular.

Native of N.W. Yunnan, China, on the eastern flank of the Lichiang Range; discovered by Forrest in 1906, at altitudes of 11,000 to 12,000 ft. As he originally found it, it was scattered in small clumps over grassy mountain slopes. It is quite hardy and flowers at Kew, but grows slowly. It is much more vigorous in the Cornish gardens where its flowers are 3 ins. wide. It belongs to the Taliense series.

R. ADENOPHORUM, *Balfour and W. W. Smith*

An evergreen shrub up to 9 ft., shoots downy. Leaves oblong-lanceolate, 2 to 4 ins. long, 1 to 2 ins. wide, pointed, rounded to slightly cordate at the base, covered beneath with a thick, cinnamon-coloured wool covering small glands; stalk $\frac{3}{4}$ in. long. Flowers in an umbellate cluster of about ten, stalks densely glandular and downy; corolla funnel-shaped, 2 ins. long, rose-coloured with crimson markings, five-lobed; calyx with five deep lobes and, like the ovary and style, very glandular.

Native of the mountains of Yunnan, China, up to 12,000 ft. It is hardy at Kew and flowers there in April. Closely akin to R. adenogynum but more glandular.

R. ADENOPODUM, *Franchet*

An evergreen shrub, 4 to 10 ft. high; young shoots thinly felted and glandular. Leaves leathery, 3 to 8 ins. long, oblong oblanceolate with an acute point, glabrous above, but covered beneath with a close white felt; stalk ½ to 1 in. long, felted. Flowers pale rose, 2½ to 3 ins. across, produced in April, about half a score together in rather loose terminal clusters; corolla broadly bell-shaped, with five rounded lobes; stamens ten, as long as the corolla, hairy at the base; flower-stalks and seed-pods hairy; calyx-lobes oblong, ciliate, ⅛ to ¼ in. long.

Native of Central China; introduced from Hupeh to France by the Abbé Farges in 1901, and a year or two later by Wilson for Messrs Veitch. It first flowered with Mr Maurice de Vilmorin at Les Barres in April 1909. The ovary is bristly, the style glabrous.

R. AGASTUM, *Balfour f.*
(Bot. Mag., t. 9577)

An evergreen shrub or small tree up to 20 ft. high; young shoots sticky with small glands. Leaves narrowly oblong, 4 to 6 ins. long, one-third as wide, tapered to a fine point, rounded at the base, glabrous and dull green above, paler below; veins in about fifteen pairs; stalk about 1 in. long. Flowers numerous in a terminal truss 5 ins. across, flattish; corolla funnel-shaped, 1¾ ins. long, 2 ins. across, the five or seven lobes white tinged with pink and spotted with crimson; stamens ten to fourteen, minutely downy; anthers brown.

Native of Yunnan, China, collected by Forrest in 1913. It belongs to the irroratum series and is only likely to thrive permanently in a soft, mild climate. It flowered beautifully with the late Mr Magor at Lamellen in April 1929.

R. ALBIFLORUM, *Hooker*
(Bot. Mag., t. 3670; Azalea albiflora, *O. Kuntze*)

A deciduous shrub, 5 or 6 ft. high in a wild state, the young shoots furnished with short, dark hairs. Leaves narrowly oval, 1 to 2½ ins. long, ½ to ¾ in. wide; tapering towards both ends, thin and glabrous except that, like the very short stalk, they are furnished when young on the midrib with hairs similar to those on the stems. Flowers creamy white, ¾ in. wide, drooping, produced singly or in pairs from lateral buds on the growth of the previous year during June and July, when the young shoots are in full leaf. Corolla open bell-shaped, with five short, rounded lobes; calyx ⅓ in. long, green, the lobes ovate and edged with glands; stamens ten, shorter than the corolla, hairy at the base; flower-stalk ⅓ in. long, glandular-downy.

Native of the Rocky Mountains, up to 6000 ft., from Oregon to British Columbia. It is a pretty species, very distinct because of the large calyx, the axillary flowers, and the dark hairs on the young wood like those of an azalea of the " indica " group, only not so numerous and persistent. Young plants are at Kew, but the species is very rare and is not a thriving plant under cultivation. It flowered with Mr Hornibrook at Abbeyleix, Ireland, in July 1925.

R. ALBRECHTII, *Maximowicz*. ALBRECHT'S AZALEA

(Bot. Mag., t. 9207 ; Azalea Albrechtii, *O. Kuntze*)

A deciduous azalea described as of thin, loose habit and 3 to 5 ft. high in a wild state ; young shoots furnished with partly sticky hairs at first. Leaves often arranged in clusters of five at the end of the twig, dark green, obovate to oblanceolate, tapered to the base, finely bristle-toothed on the margin ; 2 to 4 ins. long, about half as much wide, being broadest above the middle ; upper surface thinly set with appressed hairs ; under surface grey-downy, especially about the midrib and chief veins ; stalk short, hairy. Flowers opening in May in clusters of three to five. Corolla 1½ to 2 ins. wide, bright purplish rose, spotted with green on the upper lobes ; lobes five, roundish obovate ; tube downy at the base. Stamens ten, of unequal length, the longest equalling the corolla, mostly hairy at the base. Ovary covered with pale, glandular, erect hairs ; style glabrous, curved, longer than the stamens. Calyx very small and like the flower-stalk (which is ½ to ¾ in. long) clothed with curled glandular hairs.

Native of Japan ; discovered by the Russian, Dr Albrecht, in 1860. For a long time after that date it remained unknown in cultivation, although seeds under the name were several times obtained for Kew, which invariably proved to be reticulatum, from which species it differs not only in colour but in producing flowers and leaves from separate buds. Major G. H. Johnstone of Trewithen, Cornwall, appears to have been the most successful raiser of it, from Wilson's seeds collected in 1914. A plant from him has proved hardy at Kew in a sheltered place and flowers annually in May. The blossom is very pretty and the leaves turn a good yellow in autumn. It belongs to the same section of azaleas as Vaseyi and canadense (Rhodora) the latter very distinct in having the lower corolla-lobes slit to the base.

R. AMBIGUUM, *Hemsley*

(Bot. Mag., t. 8400)

An evergreen shrub, probably 5 or 6 ft. high, of bushy habit ; young shoots covered with pale yellow, glistening scales. Leaves aromatic, oval, sometimes slightly obovate or ovate, 1½ to 3 ins. long, ⅝ to 1¼ ins. wide ; scattered along the shoot, pointed, rounded or slightly heart-shaped at the base ; dark green and somewhat scaly above, paler and much more scaly beneath ; stalk ¼ to ⅜ in. long. Flowers produced in April and May in terminal trusses of five or six blossoms. Corolla pale yellow with yellow-green spots on the upper side, about 2 ins. diameter, broadly funnel-shaped, slightly scaly outside. Calyx minute and scarcely lobed, scaly ; stamens ten, whitish, hairy near but not at the base ; style glabrous ; ovary scaly ; flower-stalk ⅓ to ½ in. long, scaly.

Native of W. China ; introduced by Wilson in 1904. In its botanical characters it is closely related to the purple R. concinnum, but is distinct in the yellow of its flowers. This being so rare a colour in the evergreen species gives it a certain distinctness, but it is not always a good yellow.

R. AMESIÆ, *Rehder and Wilson*

(Bot. Mag., t. 9221)

An evergreen shrub which Wilson describes as 6 to 12 ft. high as he found it in a wild state ; young shoots densely clothed with wart-like scales. Leaves oval, pointed, rounded to broadly tapered at the base ; 1½ to 3 ins. long, ¾ to

1⅓ ins. wide ; dark green and at first scaly above and downy on the midrib and veins ; paler and densely scaly beneath ; stalk ¼ in. long, scaly and furnished on the upper side with bristle-like hairs. Flowers two or three in a terminal cluster. Corolla 1½ ins. long, 2 ins. wide, dark reddish purple, hairy in the throat ; stamens ten, downy near the base, nearly as long as the corolla ; anthers yellow ; ovary densely scaly ; style 1⅓ ins. long, glabrous. Calyx cup-shaped, the five small triangular or rounded lobes slightly ciliate ; flower-stalk ½ in. long, very scaly.

Native of W. Szechuen ; introduced in 1910. It belongs to the same section of the Triflorum series as polylepis and yanthinum ; distinguishing characters are the absence of scales outside the corolla, the ciliate calyx and the bristly leaf-stalk ; and its decorative value is about the same. Wilson records its distribution as rather local and I do not think there are many plants in cultivation.

R. AMŒNUM, *Planchon*

(R. obtusum amœnum, *Planchon* ; Azalea amœna, *Paxton and Lindley*;
Bot. Mag., t. 4728)

A compact evergreen shrub, 2 to 4 ft. high, its branches often growing horizontally ; young shoots covered with the scale-like, appressed bristles characteristic of the indicum group. Leaves obovate, usually rounded at the apex, tapering at the base, ½ to 1¼ ins. long, ¼ to ½ in. wide ; bristly on both surfaces, more especially above and at the margins, very dark glossy green ; stalk very short, bristly. Flowers 1 in. or less in diameter, rosy purple ; the calyx-lobes narrowly oblong, ⅓ in. long, often like the corolla in shape and colour, and giving the appearance of one flower growing out of another—a character known to gardeners as " hose-in-hose." Flowers in May.

Native of Japan, but, as generally known in gardens, a cultivated form ; introduced in 1845, and long treated as a greenhouse plant. It is, nevertheless, quite hardy at Kew, and a very pleasing evergreen, flowering most profusely, and at all times a neat shrub. Out-of-doors it grows very slowly. I know plants over twenty years old not yet 3 ft. high. This is a valuable characteristic in many positions, especially where a permanently low evergreen mass is desired without the trouble and perhaps unsightliness of a periodical cropping. A group, if not too thickly planted, affords also an admirable shelter for lilies planted between the shrubs.

Var. JAPONICUM.—This is a very dwarf and dainty plant, perhaps the wild type of R. amœnum. The leaves are ½ to ¾ in. long, and the rosy purple flowers are similar in colour and size to those of R. amœnum, but the calyx is green, smaller, and not corolla-like.

R. ANTHOPOGON, *D. Don*
(Bot. Mag., t. 3947)

An evergreen shrub, 2 ft. or less high, of compact habit ; young branchlets hairy and covered with brown scurf. Leaves oval or ovate, 1 to 1½ ins. long, ½ to ¾ in. wide ; dark, rather glossy green above, covered with brown scales beneath ; stalk ¼ in. long. Flowers sulphur-coloured, ½ to ¾ in. across, produced in a small terminal cluster, 1 to 1½ ins. wide. Corolla thin, almost transparent, tube hairy inside expanding at the mouth into five wavy lobes ; calyx-lobes oblong, pale green, ⅓ in. long, fringed at the margin ; stamens five to eight, very short, and included within the tube ; flower-stalk scaly, ⅙ in. or less in length ; style short and thick. Flowers in April.

Native of the high Himalaya from Cashmere eastwards, up to 16,000 ft. altitude, where it covers large areas; introduced in 1820. The whole plant has a strong, aromatic, slightly acrid odour, especially when crushed. It is an interesting little plant, and one of the hardiest of Himalayan species, but not in any way showy.

R. ANTHOSPHÆRUM, *Diels*
(Bot. Mag., t. 9083)

An evergreen shrub or small tree described by Forrest as reaching 20 to 30 ft. high; young shoots glandular and downy. Leaves elliptical-lanceolate, gradually tapered to both ends; 3 to 6 ins. long, one-third as much wide; glabrous, dark dull green above, brownish beneath; stalk ½ to ¾ in. long. Flowers opening in March and April in close trusses of ten or twelve. Corolla bell-shaped, five- to seven-lobed, 2 ins. wide, scarcely so deep, handsomely coloured and of a rich rose-magenta, the shade deepening in the tube, paling on the lobes, with a black crimson blotch at the base. Stamens double the number of the corolla lobes, white near the anthers, rosy downwards, glabrous or downy. Ovary glabrous or nearly so; style glabrous.

Native of N.W. Yunnan, China; found by Forrest in 1906. It is one of the Irroratum series, in a group distinguished by the quite glabrous style, never glandular ovary, and often six- or seven-lobed corolla. I have not seen it in flower, but judging from the plate in the *Botanical Magazine*, which was prepared from a plant that flowered with the late Mr E. J. P. Magor of Lamellen, Cornwall, in 1924, its flowers have a rich colouring of a shade unusual in rhododendrons. It grows at 9500 to 11,000 ft. altitude and should succeed in a climate like that of mid-Sussex.

R. APERANTUM, *Balfour and Ward*
(Plant Introductions of R. Farrer, p. 68—plate)

A dwarf evergreen shrub of the sanguineum group, forming in nature broad spreading mats 6 to 20 ins. high; younger branches thickly set with roundish-ovate, membranous scales (perulæ) up to ¼ in. long, which persist for several years. Leaves oval-obovate, more tapered to the base than the apex; ¾ to 1½ ins. long, ½ to ⅝ in. wide; dark green above, glaucous-white and nearly glabrous beneath; very shortly stalked. Flowers produced in clusters of three to six. Corolla between funnel- and bell-shaped, 1½ to 1¾ ins. long, scarcely as much wide, varying in colour from white to different shades of rose, orange-red, and yellow. Stamens ten, ¾ in. long, glabrous. Ovary covered with branched hairs and glandular bristles. Calyx with small glands on the margins of the shallow lobes; flower-stalks ½ to ⅝ in. long, downy.

Native of N.E. Burma up to 14,000 ft. altitude; discovered by Ward and Farrer; introduced by Forrest. It is quite hardy, very slow in growth, and suitable for the rock garden. On its native mountains it blooms in June. In the sanguineum group it is distinct in having no down beneath the leaf except sometimes on the midrib. (Neriiflorum series.)

R. APODECTUM, *Balfour and W. W. Smith*
(Bot. Mag., t. 9014; R. liratum, *Balfour and Forrest*)

An evergreen shrub up to 6 ft. high, of sturdy habit; young shoots with a thin whitish down at first, grey the second year. Leaves oval, with usually both ends rounded and a short mucro at the apex; 1½ to 3 ins. long, 1 to 1½ ins. wide; dark green and soon glabrous above, covered beneath with a close greyish down ; stalk $\frac{1}{6}$ to $\frac{1}{2}$ in. long. Flowers two to four in a terminal cluster. Corolla elongated bell-shaped, 1 to 1$\frac{1}{4}$ ins. long, nearly as wide, five-lobed, fleshy, the lobes erect ; it varies in colour on different plants from dull orange to crimson. Stamens ten, up to 1 in. long, downy at the base ; anthers deep purple. Ovary covered with fascicled hairs ; style glabrous. Calyx cup-shaped, $\frac{1}{3}$ to $\frac{1}{2}$ in. long, irregularly five-lobed, scarlet to yellowish ; flower-stalk $\frac{1}{2}$ in. long. (Neriiflorum series.)

Native of W. Yunnan, China; introduced by Forrest in 1912-13. It is most nearly related to R. dichroanthum from which it is easily distinguished by its round-based leaves ; both are destitute of glands, both have a large coloured calyx and both vary a good deal in the colour-shades of the flowers. R. apodectum flowers in May and June about a fortnight later than dichro-anthum. It is quite hardy, but a slow grower. It belongs to the great sanguineum group. None of the wild specimens carry more than three flowers in a truss, but cultivated plants may develop larger trusses.

R. ARAIOPHYLLUM, *Balfour and W. W. Smith*

An evergreen · shrub up to 16 ft. high ; young shoots glabrous or soon becoming so. Leaves lanceolate, slenderly pointed, broadly tapered at the base ; 3 to 5 ins. long, $\frac{5}{8}$ to 1$\frac{1}{4}$ ins. wide; glabrous and green on both surfaces ; stalk $\frac{1}{4}$ to $\frac{1}{2}$ in. long. Flowers in a racemose cluster of about eight. Corolla open bell-shaped, 1$\frac{1}{2}$ ins. long, rather more wide ; white often flushed with rose-lavender, with a crimson blotch at the base and similarly coloured spots on the upper lobes, the five lobes are notched in the middle and their margins are uneven. Stamens ten, downy at the base ; ovary minutely downy, style glabrous, red, only as long as the corolla. Calyx little more than a wavy rim glabrous ; flower-stalk glabrous, slender, up to 1 in. long.

Native of W. Yunnan, China ; discovered at 9000 to 10,000 ft. altitude by Forrest in 1913. It belongs to the Irroratum group (of which it is considered to be one of the most charming species) and has the stiff narrow leaves, pointed leaf-buds, and glabrous character common to irroratum and its nearest allies. Hardy from mid-Sussex southwards and westwards, where it blossoms in May.

R. ARBORESCENS, *Torrey*

(Azalea arborescens, *Pursh*)

A deciduous shrub up to 20 ft. high in a wild state ; young shoots glabrous. Leaves obovate or oval, pointed at both ends, 1$\frac{1}{2}$ to 3$\frac{1}{2}$ ins. long, one-third to half as wide ; glossy green and glabrous above except on the midrib ; pale, glaucous, and glabrous beneath ; margins edged with minute bristles. Flowers fragrant, 1$\frac{1}{2}$ ins. long, 2 to 2$\frac{1}{2}$ ins. wide, white tinged with pink ; corolla-tube, hairy-glandular, the lobes spreading ; stamens five, bright red, much protruded ; style still longer ; flower-stalk $\frac{1}{3}$ in. long, glabrous, or sometimes bristly ; calyx-lobes linear, $\frac{1}{8}$ to $\frac{1}{4}$ in. long, very bristly.

Native of eastern N. America in mountainous regions ; discovered by John Bartram, and introduced in 1818. This azalea, although now but little known, is one of the most beautiful of its kind, and is valuable in flowering late (June and July) when the plants have become leafy. It is allied to R. viscosum (whose flowers also expand after the young leaves), differing in its larger size, in the shining foliage, in the only slightly sticky corolla tube and in its longer style and stamens. In drying, the foliage acquires a perfume like that of mown grass.

R. ARBOREUM, *Smith* (Plate 1)

A small evergreen tree ultimately 30 to 40 ft. high, with a thick, sturdy trunk, the branches forming a head as wide as the tree is high, and reaching to the ground. Leaves narrowly oblong, tapering at both ends; 4 to 7 ins. long, 1 to 2 ins. wide; glabrous above, covered beneath with a coat of silvery scales; stalk ½ to 1 in. long. Flowers blood red, borne in a compact hemispherical head, 4 to 5 ins. through, sitting close on the terminal whorl of leaves. Corolla bell-shaped, 1½ to 2 ins. across; stamens ten; calyx very small; flower-stalk downy. Blossoms in early spring.

Native of the outer Himalaya, where it is widely spread; introduced about 1815. This species is one of the most variable of all rhododendrons, but the form just described, with crimson flowers and silvery under-surface of the leaves, may be taken as the type. There are, besides, other forms with leaves covered with a rich reddish felt beneath, and flowers ranging in colour from rosy red to nearly white. Some of these have distinctive names :—

Var. ALBUM.—Flowers white; leaf rust-coloured beneath.

Var. CAMPBELLIÆ.—Flowers purplish rose; leaf reddish beneath.

Var. CINNAMOMEUM (Plate 1).—Flowers almost white; leaf reddish beneath.

Var. LIMBATUM.—Flowers rosy purple; leaf silvery beneath.

Var. NILAGIRACUM.—Flowers deep rose; leaf rust-coloured beneath (figured as a species, t. 9323).

Var. WINDSORII.—Flowers and trusses small; deep crimson.

Of all these forms the only one which succeeded at Kew out-of-doors was var. cinnamomeum, and that grew very slowly and flowered uncertainly. But in Cornwall, S. Wales, Ireland, etc., R. arboreum in all its forms makes some of the chief glories of the gardens. There is a splendid tree at Carclew, near Falmouth, which, when I saw it a good many years ago, was over 30 ft. high, its trunk 4 ft. in girth. At Castlewellan, Co. Down, there is a famous specimen, forming a pyramid of foliage 30 ft. high and 45 ft. through.

R. arboreum, tender though it may be, has played an important part in the evolution of the hardy garden rhododendrons as we know them to-day. Most of the red-flowered varieties—as distinct from the rose, purple, and white ones—owe their colour to this species. They are far too numerous to be even mentioned here, but a selection of the best is given in the introductory notes to the genus. The following are some of the more important primary crosses :—

R. ALTACLERENSE, *Lindley* (Bot. Mag., 3423).—Raised at Highclere, the seat of the Earl of Carnarvon in Berkshire, by crossing arboreum with ponticum; it has beautiful, deep rosy red flowers in large trusses 6 ins. through. Very similar to it is

R. RUSSELLIANUM, *Sweet*, from catawbiense crossed with arboreum, but of a more crimson shade. It is as richly coloured as all but the richest forms of arboreum. Flowers in April.

For other arboreum crosses, see *Nobleanum, pulcherrimum,* (see p. 43) and *venustum* (see p. 44). SMITHII, with rich red flowers, is arboreum+ponticum; and CUNNINGHAMI is arboreum+maximum.

R. ARGYROPHYLLUM, *Franchet*

An evergreen shrub, from 6 to 20 ft. high, the quite young shoots clothed with a loose, white scurf. Leaves oblong-lanceolate, tapered at the base, pointed, 2½ to 5 ins. long, ½ to 1¼ ins. wide; glabrous and bright green above, the lower surface covered with a close white scurf; stalk ½ in. or less long. Flowers in a lax truss of as many as ten. Corolla white, or blush-tinted,

spotted with pink on the upper side ; broadly funnel-shaped, 1½ ins. wide.
Calyx small, with glabrous triangular lobes ; stamens twelve or fourteen,
shorter than the corolla, white with down at the base, like the ovary ; style
quite glabrous ; flower-stalks slender, up to 1½ ins. long ; seed-vessel 1 in. long,
downy. Var. LEIANDRUM, *Hutchinson*, has glabrous stamens. May.

Native of W. China and Tibet ; discovered by the Abbé David ; introduced by Wilson in 1904. Very distinct in the pure white under-surface of
the young leaves. It is near R. hypoglaucum in leaf character, but that
species has a markedly glandular-downy flower-stalk and calyx.

R. ARIZELUM, *Balfour and Forrest*

An evergreen shrub or a small tree up to 20 ft. high ; young shoots, leaf-
stalks, and under surface of leaves covered with a velvety, cinnamon-brown felt,
which is especially richly coloured beneath the leaves ; these are obovate,
tapered at the base, rounded at the apex and with a short mucro there ;
5 to 9 ins. long by 1½ to 3½ ins. wide ; stalk ½ to 1 in. long. Flowers crowded,
fifteen to twenty-five together, in a rounded truss 5 or 6 ins. across, each on
a downy stalk 1 to 1½ ins. long. Corolla bell-shaped, 1½ to 2 ins. wide, eight-
lobed, in colour either white, creamy yellow, or yellow tinged with rose, with
a dark crimson blotch or streaks of crimson at the base. Ovary densely downy
but not glandular ; style glabrous. Calyx very small ; flower-stalk downy like
the ovary.

Native of Yunnan, S.E. Tibet, and N.E. Upper Burma ; first found by
Forrest in 1917, two years later by Farrer and Kingdon Ward. It is closely
akin to the Himalayan R. Falconeri and has the same rich red-brown felt
beneath the wrinkled leaves, but these are not so large and the plant itself is
of smaller dimensions. In flower R. arizelum is easily distinguished by the
absence of glands from the ovary. It is a fine rhododendron which should
succeed in the inland gardens of Sussex and Hants and, of course, farther to
the south and west. (Falconeri series.)

R. AUGUSTINII, *Hemsley*

(Flora and Sylva, vol. iii., p. 162 ; Bot. Mag., t. 8497)

An evergreen shrub, from 4 to 10 ft. high, of bushy habit ; shoots hairy the
first and second years ; scaly the first. Leaves oblong-lanceolate ; 1½ to 4 ins.
long, ½ to 1 in. wide ; tapering to a fine point ; tapered or rounded at the
base ; upper surface dark green, minutely wrinkled, and covered with fine
down ; under-surface scaly, and with pale bristle-like hairs on the midrib ;
stalk up to ¼ in. long, hairy like the midrib. Flowers produced in clusters
of three or four ; corolla 2½ ins. across, broadly funnel-shaped, wavy at the
margins, varying in colour from white to pink, purplish pink, and bluish, with
yellow spots on the uppermost lobes ; stamens ten, reddish brown, hairy near
but not at the base ; flower-stalk ½ to ¾ in. long, scaly like the ovary.

Native of Hupeh, China ; discovered by Henry, whose christian name it
bears. First introduced to France and cultivated by Mr Maurice de Vilmorin
at Les Barres. It is very variable in the shades of its flowers, some of which
are amongst the most pleasing in the genus. The line of hairs on the midrib
beneath is a good distinguishing character. Flowers in May.

R. AUREUM, *Franchet*

(Bot. Mag., t. 8882)

An evergreen shrub 4 ft. and upwards high ; young shoots sprinkled with scales. Leaves ovate-lanceolate to oblong-lanceolate, usually pointed, tapered at the base ; 1½ to 3½ ins. long, ⅜ to 1⅛ ins. wide ; dark glossy green and soon glabrous above, glaucous and closely pitted with tiny glistening scales beneath ; stalks ¼ to ½ in. long. Flowers opening in May in clusters usually of three to five. Corolla funnel-shaped, about 1 in. long, five-lobed, scaly outside, of varying shades of yellow (rich, bright, or tinged with green). Stamens ten, rather longer than the corolla, downy at the base. Ovary densely scaly as is the style also towards the base. Calyx deeply five-lobed, the lobes rounded, more or less scaly like the flower-stalk which is ¼ to ½ in. long.

Native of W. Yunnan, China ; discovered by Delavay about 1886 on the Tali range, where it was met with again by Forrest flowering in May and June 1906. Kingdon Ward has also found and sent home seeds of it. In the Delei Valley he describes it as a very floriferous shrub 6 to 10 ft. high, the trusses on his specimens carrying as many as ten flowers. The blooms, although small, are of a very good yellow in the better forms. It has been placed in the Boothii series, which is composed mostly of yellow-flowered species, but in this the style is about 1 in. long, slender, and not bent as it is in the majority. It is suitable only for southern and western gardens.

R. AURICULATUM, *Hemsley*

(Bot. Mag., t. 8786)

An evergreen shrub or small tree, 10 to 30 ft. high in a wild state ; branchlets very thick and sturdy. Leaves very large, 6 to 13 ins. long, 2 to 5 ins. wide ; oblong, the apex rounded except for a short abrupt point, the base with two well-marked lobes (or auricles) to which the specific name refers ; upper surface dull dark green, hairy on the midrib when young, becoming glabrous ; lower surface clothed with rust-coloured hairs, ultimately whitish brown ; stalk up to 1¾ ins. long, stout, bristly. The leaf-blade is of very leathery texture. Flowers 3 to 4 ins. deep, scarcely as wide at the mouth, funnel-shaped ; white or pink, six to eight in a truss ; flower-stalk stout, 1 to 1½ ins. long, glandular-hairy. Corolla seven- or eight-lobed, downy outside ; stamens fourteen or sixteen, glabrous ; calyx small. Seed-pod 1½ ins. long, ½ in. wide.

Discovered by Henry in W. Hupeh, China ; introduced in 1900 by Wilson, who considered it one of the most distinct and beautiful of Chinese rhododendrons. It is remarkably late in starting into growth, never making a move at Kew until July ; the lower part of the young shoots are then furnished with lurid crimson scales covered with sticky glands. It inhabits semi-wooded places, and Mr Wilson recommends half shade for it. I believe the finest plants in the country are at Caerhays Castle, Cornwall, where it has already borne good seed. In June 1910, I measured a leaf on a young plant at Coombe Wood which was 13 ins. by 5 ins. It does not flower until July or August.

R. AUSTRINUM, *Rehder*

(R. nudiflorum luteum, *Curtis* ; Azalea austrina, *Small*)

A deciduous azalea up to 9 ft. high ; young shoots and leaf-stalks furnished with soft down mixed with which are numerous gland-tipped hairs. Leaves oval to obovate, 1½ to 3½ ins. long, both surfaces downy, especially the lower one ; margins bristly. Flowers slightly fragrant, borne in April eight to fifteen in a cluster. Corolla yellow and orange, with a cylindrical tube ¾ in. long, downy, glandular and more or less purple-stained outside. Stamens five, 2 ins. long, downy below the middle ; anthers yellowish ; ovary covered with whitish hairs, some of them gland-tipped ; style slightly longer than the stamens, downy near the base. Lobes of calyx downy outside, margined with hairs ; flower-stalks ¼ in. long, hairy.

Native of N. Florida, in one county only ; discovered before 1865 by Dr Chapman ; introduced to England by Sargent in 1916. Closely related to R. canescens, it is of course very distinct in its yellow flowers. It has proved hardy at Kew where it flowers in early June.

R. AZALEOIDES, *Dum.-Cours.*

(R. odoratum, *Loddiges* ; R. fragrans, *Paxton* ; Mag. of Bot., x., t. 147)

An evergreen (in hard winters semi-evergreen) bush, 4 to 6 ft. high, of twiggy habit and with interlaced branches ; young shoots downy and viscid. Leaves oblanceolate, 2 to 4 ins. long, ½ to 1½ ins. wide ; tapering gradually towards the base, more abruptly to the short point ; dark glossy green above, glaucous beneath, quite glabrous except when very young ; stalk ⅛ to ¼ in. long. Flowers very fragrant, white, deeply but unequally tinged with purplish lilac, about 1¼ ins. long and wide, produced in June and July in terminal clusters of twelve to twenty blossoms. Corolla funnel-shaped, downy outside and in the throat ; stamens ten, very hairy at the base ; calyx-lobes linear-triangular, ⅛ to ¼ in. long, downy ; flower-stalk ¾ to 1 in. long, downy.

According to Loudon this hybrid was raised about 1820, and he gives R. ponticum and some deciduous azalea as the parents. Others give the parentage as R. maximum+viscosum, which may be correct. It is undoubtedly a hybrid between the two great sections of the genus, and viscosum is, I believe, certainly one parent. It is a most charming shrub, flowering later than most of its kind, and with great freedom. There are few shrubs blooming in June and July so fragrant and pleasing. Increased easily by late July cuttings.

There are probably several hybrids of an origin identical, or nearly so, with that of R. azaleoides ; or, as frequently happens, the progeny raised from the original seed-pod may have varied. Very closely allied to it is

R. GOWENIANUM, *Sweet.*—This has similarly shaped leaves also glaucous beneath, and the flowers are similarly coloured. They differ, however, in being of a darker shade and the calyx-lobes are narrower and more strap-shaped. Raised in the Earl of Carnarvon's garden at Highclere about 1825. (See Sweet's *Brit. Flower Garden*, ser. i., t. 263.)

R. CARTONI (Bot. Reg., t. 1449) was raised from the same batch of seeds as R. Gowenianum, and is very similar.

R. BACHII, *Léveillé*

(Bot. Mag., t. 9375)

This species is closely related to R. ovatum and R. leptothrium. From the former it differs by the calyx lobes being fringed with hairs and from R. leptothrium in the leaves being much more tapered at the base, also in the young shoots being glandular hairy as well as downy. Flowers soft rosy-lilac, 1 to 1½ ins. wide ; corolla with deep obovate lobes ; calyx lobes densely fringed with stalked glands.

Native of Hupeh, China ; introduced by Wilson. Like its two allies, it is too tender for the open air at Kew, but it was grown successfully by the late Lord Wakehurst at Wakehurst in Sussex.

R. BAILEYI, *Balfour fil.* (Plate 2)

(Bot. Mag., t. 8942)

An evergreen bush of rounded shape 3 to 5 ft. high ; young shoots covered with reddish brown scales. Leaves often clustered at the end of the shoot, oval or ovate, broadly wedge-shaped at the base, bluntish at the apex but with a distinct mucro there ; 1 to 2½ ins. long, ½ to 1⅛ ins. wide ; dark glossy green and scurfy above ; pale yellowish brown (at first glaucous) beneath, completely covered with scales ; stalk ⅓ to ⅖ in. long. Flowers produced during May in one or more racemes at and near the end of the shoot, the main-stalk up to 1 in. long ; individual flower-stalks up to 1½ ins. long. A raceme will carry sometimes twelve or more flowers, usually fewer. Corolla flattish, deep red-purple with dark spots on the upper three lobes, 1⅛ ins. wide, five-lobed, the lobes rounded, scaly outside. Stamens ten, with rosy purple stalks, glabrous at the base, more or less downy above ; anthers brown. Ovary covered with whitish scales ; style red-purple, much bent over. Calyx small with five scaly unequal lobes. (Lepidotum series.)

Native of S. Tibet ; introduced by Col. Bailey in 1913. It was scarcely hardy when grown at Kew but flowered freely when protected. It belongs to the Lepidotum group which is characterised by the flattish, open corolla and very scaly leaves, etc. From lepidotum itself it is distinct in the more numerous flowers in the raceme. Closely related and much resembling it is

R. THYODOCUM, *Balfour and Cooper*, introduced in 1914 from Bhotan by Mr R. E. Cooper. Its leaves generally are more obovate in outline, the main-stalk of the raceme usually shorter and carrying only half as many flowers. The down on the stamens seems never to reach so near the anthers as it does in Baileyi. The flowers are closely alike in colour and shape. Both species succeed very well with Mr Armytage-Moore at Rowallane, Co. Down. They have, on the average, the largest leaves in the lepidotum group.

R. BALFOURIANUM, *Diels*

An evergreen shrub up to 8 ft. high in nature ; young shoots and midrib at first scurfy. Leaves oblong or narrowly ovate, sharply pointed, rounded at the base ; 2½ to 4½ ins. long, ¾ to 1½ ins. wide ; dark dullish green above, silvery grey with scurfy down beneath ; stalk ½ to ¾ in. long. Flowers in trusses of six to nine. Corolla bell-shaped, 1¾ ins. deep, rather more wide, five-lobed, pale rose with crimson spottings. Stamens downy at the base, shorter than the corolla ; ovary and lower part of style densely glandular. Calyx deeply lobed, the five lobes ovate, blunt, ¼ in. long, and, like the flower-stalks (which are about 1 in. long), very glandular.

Native of W. Yunnan, where it was found by Forrest on the Tali Range in 1906. It is perfectly hardy at Kew. Closely related to R. adenogynum, it is still very distinct in the pale metallic-looking under surface of the leaf. Here also comes, as belonging to the same Taliense series,

R. BUREAVII, *Franchet*, first found in 1886 by the Abbé Delavay in Yunnan, and by Forrest in 1908. It is a shrub 6 ft. and upwards high, very distinct from adenogynum and Balfourianum in the thick red-brown wool that covers the leaf beneath and the young shoots. The corolla is rose with crimson spots, rather funnel-shaped, 1½ ins. long and wide, five-lobed ; stamens very downy at the base ; the ovary, base of style, calyx and flower-stalk all densely glandular. Judging by wild specimens, the trusses each carry eight to fifteen flowers. The wool persists on the shoots for two years, and with that on the leaves, makes the plant interesting and attractive even without flowers.

R. BARBATUM, *G. Don*

An evergreen shrub or small tree, the bark peeling from the branches and leaving them blue-grey and smooth ; winter buds viscid ; branches yellowish, sometimes glabrous, sometimes bristly.   Leaves in a terminal cluster, oblong, heart-shaped at the base, terminated by a short, fine point ; 4 to 9 ins. long, 1 to 3 ins. wide ; dark dull green and ultimately glabrous above, pale and usually woolly at first beneath ; stalk ½ to 1 in. long, conspicuously bristly on the upper side and at the base of the midrib.   Flowers densely packed in a hemispherical truss about 4 ins. wide, blood-red.   Corolla bell-shaped, 1½ ins. across, five-lobed ; stamens ten ; calyx with five glabrous, ovate lobes, ¼ in. long.

Native of the Himalaya up to 12,000 ft. ; introduced about 1849.   This rhododendron is hardy in a sheltered spot at Kew, where it flowers in April. It is somewhat gaunt of habit, but worth growing for its marvellous richness of colour.   It is, of course, much finer in Cornwall and similar places.   There is some variation in the bristliness of the stems and leaves.   In one form the young wood is furnished with bristles and the leaf-stalk is bristly all round ; bristles up to ½ in. long.

R. BASILICUM, *Balfour and W. W. Smith*

(R. megaphyllum, *Balfour and Forrest* ; R. regale, *Balfour and Ward*)

An evergreen shrub or small tree up to 30 ft. high ; young shoots clothed with red-brown, soft felt.   Leaves oval or obovate, rounded at the apex, less so or broadly tapered at the base ; 6 to 13 ins. long, about half as much wide ; dark green and ultimately glabrous above, covered beneath with a rich red-brown down ; stalk very stout, flattened above, up to 1¼ ins. long.   Flowers opening in June in a wild state, numerously and closely packed in a truss 5 ins. or more wide.   Corolla broadly and obliquely bell-shaped, eight-lobed, 1½ ins. wide, pale yellow flushed with rose and blotched with crimson at the base.   Stamens sixteen, nearly or quite glabrous.   Ovary densely clothed with down ; style glabrous.   Calyx a mere wavy rim ; flower-stalks 1 to 1⅓ ins. long, downy.

Native of W. Yunnan, China ; found by Forrest in 1913 and introduced by him.   This fine rhododendron is one of the noble Falconeri series, in which Mr Tagg distinguishes it by its short flattened leaf-stalk, down along each side of which a thin section of the blade extends (*i.e.* " decurrent ").   Generally in this group the leaf-stalk is cylindrical.   Forrest found it at 11,000 ft. altitude, so it is probably of about the same hardiness as Falconeri.   On young vigorous plants leaves as much as 18 ins. by 8 ins. are sometimes borne.

R. BATEMANII, *Hooker*

(Bot. Mag., t. 5387)

An evergreen shrub up to 20 ft. high ; young shoots at first covered with pale rust-coloured wool.   Leaves lanceolate-oblong, pointed, rounded or broadly tapered at the base ; 4 to 9 ins. long, 1½ to 2½ ins. wide ; dull dark green, ultimately glabrous above, clothed beneath with a soft, pale brown felt ; stalk ¾ to 1 in. long, felted.   Flowers produced in spring, twelve to twenty crowded in a terminal hemispherical truss 5 or 6 ins. wide.   Corolla bell-shaped, 2 ins. wide, soft rosy crimson spotted on the upper side.   Stamens ten, downy at the base; anthers brown. Ovary brown-felted; style 1½ ins. long, glabrous. Calyx small with unequal pointed lobes; flower-stalk 1 in. long, downy.

Native of Bhotan; discovered and introduced by Booth in 1852; flowered by Mr James Bateman at Knypersley Hall, Staffordshire, in February 1863. Lost sight of in most gardens for many years, it has survived in the Earl of Stair's garden at Loch Inch in Wigtownshire, where it is 20 ft. high. It is considered to have some affinity with R. campanulatum but is very distinct in the narrow, pointed leaves, in the rich red of the flowers, and in the very downy ovary and flower-stalk. The late Mr J. G. Millais suggested that it is a hybrid between that species and arboreum, an origin which would explain the differences from campanulatum just enumerated. It is hardy at Kew.

There is another rhododendron which has been preserved in cultivation in the gardens at Loch Inch in a somewhat similar way. This is called there " R. nobile " and is a very handsome plant with bright carmine flowers in trusses about 4 ins. across, opening in April and May. The leaves are covered with felt beneath. The name " nobile," however, really has no standing because Wallich, the Indian botanist who first used it in his herbarium (now preserved at Kew), gummed on to one sheet (No. 1521) flowering specimens of two distinct species, viz., campanulatum and barbatum, and labelled them " R. nobile." He never published a description. The Loch Inch plant therefore has no right to this name and it is something of a mystery how it acquired it. It was quite hardy when grown at Kew.

R. BEESIANUM, *Diels*

An evergreen shrub or small tree up to 20 ft. high; young shoots stout, nearly ½ in. in diameter, soon glabrous. Leaves elliptic-oblong, inclined to oblanceolate, rather abruptly narrowed to a short point, rounded or slightly heart-shaped at the base; 6 ins. to over 1 ft. long, 1½ to 3½ ins. wide; dark green and glabrous above, covered beneath with a thin, close, red-brown, felt-like down; stalk up to 1¼ ins. long, slightly flattened or winged. Flowers in a racemose truss of twenty or more and 5 or 6 ins. across, each flower on a downy stalk 1 to 1½ ins. long. Corolla openly bell-shaped, 2 ins. long and wide, white to deep rich rose with a few crimson markings or a basal blotch, five-lobed. Stamens ten, downy at the base, about 1 in. long; ovary cylindrical, covered with brown down; style glabrous, 1 in. long. Calyx merely a wavy rim.

Native of the eastern flank of the Lichiang Range, Yunnan, China; found by Forrest in 1906 and afterwards at altitudes of 11,000 to 14,000 ft., often in forests of silver fir and pine. It is one of the large-leaved rhododendrons belonging to the Lacteum series and like lacteum itself is somewhat difficult to cultivate. Coming from such considerable elevations, it should succeed from mid-Sussex southwards and westwards, so far as temperature is concerned. But all these large-leaved rhododendrons need above all shelter from wind and from full sunlight. It flowered at Caerhays in April 1927.

R. BOOTHII, *Nuttall*

(Bot. Mag., t. 7149)

An evergreen shrub 6 to 8 ft., sometimes 10 ft. high, of loose habit; young shoots at first very hairy. Leaves leathery, oval-ovate, slenderly pointed; 3½ to 5 ins. long, 1¼ to 2½ ins. wide; dark green and ultimately glabrous above, but sprinkled with long hairs when young and hairy on the margins; scaly beneath; stalk about ¼ in. long and clothed with shaggy hairs like the young shoot. Flowers rich yellow, seven to ten of them closely packed in a terminal cluster, opening in April and May. Corolla 1 to 1½ ins. wide, bell-shaped at the base, separating into five broad, rounded lobes ; scaly outside. Stamens ten, their stout stalks very hairy at the lower half ; anthers standing just clear of the corolla tube. Ovary ¼ in. long, conical, closely covered with scales, surmounted by a glabrous, thick, much decurved style. Calyx membranous, deeply five-lobed, the lobes broadly ovate, rounded, ¼ in. long, sparsely hairy on the margins. Flower-stalks ½ to ¾ in. long, scaly. (Boothii series.)

Native of Bhotan ; discovered and introduced by T. J. Booth in 1852, during the same journey on which R. Nuttallii was found and introduced. Booth was the nephew of Nuttall. He found this rhododendron growing wild mostly on the trunks and forks of trees. For long after its introduction it was very rare, but latterly has been raised in goodly number from seeds produced on cultivated plants. Not hardy near London, it is successfully grown in the open air in the south-west. Its flowers and trusses are small, but attractive in the uncommon colour. This, together with the short stamens, short decurved style, large calyx and hairy young shoots, make it distinct.

R. BRACHYANTHUM, *Franchet*

(Bot. Mag., t. 8750

An evergreen shrub probably 4 to 5 ft. high, of rather stiff habit ; young shoots reddish, scaly, becoming bright brown and smooth the second season. Leaves oblong to narrowly oval, usually tapered at the apex (sometimes rounded) to a mucro, tapered at the base ; 1½ to 2½ ins. long, ½ to 1 in. wide ; dark glossy green above ; slightly scaly and very glaucous beneath ; stalk ⅛ to ¼ in. long. Flowers from three or four to as many as eight or ten in a cluster, each on a slender scaly stalk ¾ to 1½ ins. long. Corolla clear pale yellow or tinged with green, bell-shaped with five broadly ovate, pointed, recurved lobes ; ⅝ in. long, ¾ to 1 in. wide. Stamens ten, shorter than the corolla, clothed with pale hairs to the middle and upwards ; ovary scaly ; style about as long as the stamens, quite smooth, swelling to a broad stigma at the top. Calyx green, scaly outside, very large for the size of the flower, ⅝ to ¾ in. wide with five leaf-like rounded lobes spreading out away from the corolla. (Glaucum series.)

Native of Yunnan, China ; discovered by the Abbé Delavay about 1884, introduced by Forrest twenty-two years later. In its best form this is a charming and distinct species with flowers shaped like those of a campanula and of a pleasing yellow, with a large foliaceous calyx. But in other forms the green-tinted flowers are dull. It seems to be quite hardy and flowers about midsummer. Although so different in colour, the flowers in shape of corolla and size of calyx strongly resemble those of R. glaucum. The seed-vessel in both is hidden by the persistent calyx, and the leaves of both have a strong odour (see also hypolepidotum).

R. BRACHYCARPUM, *Don*

(Bot. Mag., t. 7881)

A robust evergreen shrub, 6 to 10 ft. high ; young shoots downy. Leaves narrowly oblong, 4 or 5 ins. long, 1½ to 1¾ ins. wide ; with a short, abrupt tip and a rounded base ; upper surface glabrous, the lower one more or less felted ; stalk ½ to ¾ in. long, very stout. Flowers creamy white, flushed with pink, produced in a rounded cluster 4 to 6 ins. across ; corolla 2 ins. across, broadly funnel-shaped, five-lobed, the lobes broad and rounded, emarginate, the three upper ones spotted with brownish yellow. Calyx-lobes five, shallow ; stamens ten, hairy at the base, ovary covered with brown down ; flower-stalk ¾ to 1¼ ins. long, slightly downy. Flowers in June.

Native of Japan, where it is said to be abundant above the forest line on Fuji-yama. It is a very hardy shrub of sturdy habit, flowering in June, and very distinct in the colour of its flowers. This species and R. Degronianum are the only two species of (true) rhododendron found wild in Japan.

R. BRACTEATUM, *Rehder and Wilson*

(Bot. Mag., t. 9031)

An evergreen shrub 3 to 6 ft. high ; young shoots not downy, bearing below the leaves proper linear " bracts " (really depauperate leaves) ¼ to ⅝ in. long, some of which persist to the second or even third year. Leaves oval with a tendency to ovate or oblong, rounded at the base, terminated by a short mucro ; ¾ to 2 ins. long by about half as much wide ; dark green and thinly-scaly above, paler and more scaly beneath ; stalk ⅛ to ¼ in. long. Flowers borne three to six in a cluster, the corolla about 1 in. wide, white, strongly blotched and dotted with deep wine red, bell-shaped at the base, the five lobes spread out widely ; stamens ten, the lower half hairy ; ovary very scaly ; style almost or quite glabrous ; calyx small, unequally lobed ; flower-stalks ½ to 1 in. long.

Native of W. Szechuen, China ; introduced in 1908 by Wilson. He and Rehder considered it to be most closely related to R. yanthinum, while later authorities in classification associate it with oreotrepnes, but to neither of them does it bear much resemblance in general appearance when in bloom. The figure in the *Botanical Magazine* was made from a plant growing at Caerhays in Cornwall, where it flowers about mid-June. The crushed leaves have a curious odour resembling that of black currants ; this, with the persistent " bracts " mentioned above, make the species easily recognised. The flowers are not large but they are daintily pretty. (Triflorum series.)

R. BREVISTYLUM, *Franchet*

(R. pholidotum, *Balfour fil.* ; R. porrosquameum, *Balfour fil. and Forrest*)

An evergreen shrub up to 10 ft. high ; young shoots densely scaly. Leaves oblong-lanceolate, slenderly pointed, more or less tapered at the base ; 2 to 4 ins. long, 1 to 1¾ ins. wide ; dark green above, tawny green beneath, rather thinly scaly on both sides ; stalk ¼ to ½ in. long. Flowers in clusters of four to eight, opening in June and July. Corolla widely funnel-shaped, 1½ ins. wide and nearly as long, conspicuously scaly outside, downy at the base inside, pale to deep rose with crimson markings on the upper lobes. Stamens ten, very downy on the lower half ; ovary thickly scaly ; style pubescent towards the base. Calyx small, wavy-lobed, scaly, sometimes slightly ciliate ; flower-stalk up to 1 in. long, scaly.

Native of Yunnan, China, on the Lichiang Range, up to 12,000 to 13,000 ft. altitude, also of W. Szechuen, where it was discovered in the valley of the Upper Mekong by Père R. P. Soulié flowering in July 1875 ; introduced by Forrest in 1906 ; afterwards found by Kingdon Ward. It is a pretty rhododendron belonging to the Heliolepis series and is therefore a close

III   B relation of R. rubiginosum, which differs in its glabrous style and more closely aggregated scales on the lower surface of the leaf. Hardy. Another ally with a glabrous style is

R. DESQUAMATUM, *Balfour and Forrest*, a native of W. Yunnan and N. Burma. It takes its name from the early-falling nature of the leaf-bud scales, not from the absence of scales on the leaves, where, on the under surface, they are really very dense. Flowers opening in May, mauve, spotted, 1½ to 2 ins. wide, the corolla thinly scaly outside. Farrer, who found it in N. Burma, describes it as " a small neat tree, with scarlet-styled, ponticum-coloured azaleas [*sic*] in May." In comparison with brevistylum and heliolepis the leaves are longer in proportion to their width, being sometimes as much as 4½ ins. long and only 1¼ ins. wide. It is hardy and very charming in its best forms. (Syns. catapastum, squarrosum, and stenoplastum, all of *Balfour fil.*) Bot. Mag., t. 9497.

R. BROUGHTONII AUREUM, *Hort.*

A low, rounded evergreen bush, 2 to 3 ft. high, not densely branched ; young shoots downy and rather viscid. Leaves narrowly obovate or oblong,

RHODODENDRON BROUGHTONII AUREUM

2 to 6 ins. long, ¾ to 1¾ ins. wide ; dark dull green above, pale green and prominently net-veined beneath, covered with fine down on both sides. Flower-truss 4 ins. wide, carrying eight to sixteen blossoms, which are 2½ ins. across and of a beautiful soft primrose-yellow, with reddish brown spots on the upper side of the corolla ; stamens ten ; calyx-lobes pale green, of unequal length, oblong ; flower-stalk 1 to 1½ ins. long, downy.

R. SMITHII AUREUM (Paxton's Mag. of Botany, ix., t. 79), is very like the preceding, which is frequently exhibited at flower shows under this name. The true R. Smithii aureum differs in having the leaves very glaucous beneath ; the flowers, too, are of a paler yellow and not so flat and open ; the flower-stalk is longer and more slender, and the calyx-lobes somewhat narrower. The two are, no doubt, very much alike, but easily distinguished by the glaucous leaf of Smithii aureum. R. Broughtonii aureum is the better shrub—more beautiful and growing better. Both are hybrids between an azalea and a true rhododendron. I do not know the parentage of Broughtonii aureum, but that of the other is given as " Rhododendron seedling+Azalea sinensis." From the latter it may derive its glaucous hue. Both can be propagated by cuttings or by grafting on R. ponticum.

It should be mentioned that the names " Broughtonii " and " Smithii " have been given to other and very different rhododendrons. Thus R. BROUGHTONII is a large-leaved, large-flowered garden variety of the true evergreen type, not in the least like the so-called var. aureum ; flowers bright rosy red, in large trusses, very like the well-known " Cynthia " or " Lord Palmerston." R. SMITHII is a hybrid between ponticum and arboreum (*q.v.*), and R. SMITHII ALBUM is an early, white-flowered hybrid of the arboreum type also. These, as well as " Smithii elegans," were all raised by Smith, a nurseryman of Norbiton, near Kingston, who flourished about 1830, and appears to have called most of his rhododendrons after himself, whatever their parentage.

R. BULLATUM, *Franchet*

(Gardeners' Chronicle, 4th Dec. 1909—Supplement)

An evergreen shrub of thin loose habit up to 8 ft. high ; young shoots $\frac{3}{16}$ in. thick, clad with a thick, tawny felt. Leaves thick and leathery, narrowly oval-ovate, rounded or broadly tapered at the base, pointed ; $1\frac{1}{2}$ to $4\frac{1}{2}$ ins. long, $\frac{3}{4}$ to 2 ins. wide ; glossy green and without down at maturity above but with a network of deeply sunken veins giving it a puckered (bullate) surface ; lower surface thickly covered with tawny felt ; stalk up to $\frac{3}{4}$ in. long. Flowers produced during May in terminal clusters usually of two to four, but occasionally five or even six, richly fragrant. Corolla fleshy, scaly outside, waxy-white with a yellow stain inside and tinged with pink outside ; shallowly trumpet-shaped, five-lobed, $2\frac{1}{2}$ to $4\frac{1}{2}$ ins. wide, the lobes $1\frac{1}{2}$ to 2 ins. wide. Stamens ten, shorter than the corolla, shaggy with down at the base. Ovary very woolly ; style scaly and slightly downy towards the base. Calyx deeply five-lobed, the lobes rounded, $\frac{1}{2}$ in. long, scaly outside, shaggy only on the margins. Flower-stalks $\frac{1}{2}$ to $\frac{3}{4}$ in. long, shaggy. (Edgeworthii series.)

Native of W. Yunnan, China ; discovered by Delavay in 1886 at altitudes of 8000 to 11,000 ft. ; introduced by Forrest in 1904. This beautiful and deliciously scented rhododendron is not hardy at Kew ; after surviving unhappily one or two winters, all the plants in the open air were killed by the frosts of January and February 1917. It succeeds admirably at Exbury on the Solent. It resembles and is closely akin to R. Edgeworthii, of which it may be regarded as the Chinese and sturdier, hardier form. R. Edgeworthii is distinguished by having the calyx-lobes shaggy all over the outside ; its style also is shaggy at the lower third but not scaly. Probably intermediate forms may appear. Mr P. D. Williams observed that it resents excessive moisture at the roots.

R. CALENDULACEUM, *Torrey*. FLAME-FLOWER

(Azalea calendulacea, *Michaux*)

A deciduous shrub up to 10 or more feet high ; young shoots bristly-hairy. Leaves obovate or oval, 2 to 4 ins. long, $\frac{3}{4}$ to $1\frac{1}{4}$ ins. wide ; with a few scattered hairs above, downy beneath, especially on the midrib and veins ; leaf-stalk hairy, very short. Flowers of various shades of red, orange, and yellow, scarcely fragrant, produced in showy terminal clusters of five or more. Corolla-tube about ½ in. long, glandular-hairy ; lobes often 1 in. long, often considerably longer than the tube ; calyx-lobes edged with long, erect hairs ; flower-stalk ¼ in. long, glandular-hairy. Flowers in May.

Native of eastern N. America ; introduced in 1806. This is the most brilliantly coloured of all wild azaleas, and is the source of the scarlet and orange-coloured varieties of garden origin. It is itself no longer common in cultivation. It has been much confused, both in books and in gardens, with R. nudiflorum, from which it is distinguished by the proportionately shorter tube of the corolla in comparison with the lobes, by the orange or scarlet (not pink or purplish) flowers, and by the leaf being grey-downy beneath (not merely bristly on the midrib). John Bartram gives this description of his first sight of this azalea in the Carolina Mountains : " I saw the blossoms covering plants on the hill-sides in such incredible profusion that, suddenly opening to view from deep shade, I was alarmed by the apprehension of the hill being on fire."

R. CALIFORNICUM, *Hooker*
(Bot. Mag., t. 4863)

An evergreen shrub up to 12 ft. high, with glabrous young wood ; branches stout and erect. Leaves oval or oblong, 3 to 6 ins. long, 1¼ to 3 ins. wide ; tapering at the base, dark green above, paler beneath, quite glabrous on both surfaces ; stalk ½ to 1 in. long. Flowers rich rosy purple, with red-brown spots on the upper side of the corolla, 2 to 2½ ins. across, produced twenty or more together in a truss during May ; corolla bell-shaped, with five wavy lobes ; stamens ten, shorter than the corolla, downy at the base ; calyx small, with five short, broad lobes, the upper one often long-pointed ; ovary covered with white down ; flower-stalk 1½ to 2 ins. long, glabrous or slightly downy.

Native of California northwards to British Columbia ; introduced by W. Lobb in 1850, but now rare in gardens. It may be considered as the Western form of R. catawbiense, differing in its more erect growth, in having more rosy tinted flowers, and often glabrous flower-stalks. The calyx-lobes in catawbiense are also longer, more pointed, and triangular. It is quite hardy at Kew.

R. CALLIMORPHUM, *Balfour and W. W. Smith*
(Bot. Mag., t. 8789)

An evergreen shrub up to 9 ft. high in a wild state, forming a rounded bush in cultivation as wide as it is high ; young shoots clothed at first with stalked glands. Leaves of thin texture, round to roundish ovate, the base heart-shaped, the apex with a short mucro ; 1 to 3 ins. long, usually not quite so wide ; dark glossy green and with scattered hairs above, glaucous beneath with glands on the midrib and margin ; stalk ⅜ to ⅝ in. long, very glandular. Flowers opening during April and May in a terminal truss of five to eight flowers. Corolla openly bell-shaped, five-lobed, 1½ ins. long and wide, pale rose with a blotch of intense crimson at the base, lobes notched. Stamens ten, their white stalks from ½ to 1 in. long, glabrous except for (occasionally) a few minute hairs at the base ; anthers brown. Ovary covered with red glands, of which a few extend a short way up the style. Calyx very small with shallow triangular lobes, glandular like the flower-stalk which is ¾ in. long. (Thomsonii series.)

Native of W. Yunnan, China ; introduced by Forrest in 1912, first flowered at Caerhays in 1917. It is a pretty plant of neat habit, related to R. campylocarpum and to R. Souliei ; the first of these, of course, has yellow flowers and R. Souliei has a style glandular the whole length, a larger calyx and, more especially, a flat saucer-shaped corolla. It was hardy at Kew when given a sheltered place and some shade, but succeeds better to the south and west. A characteristic feature of the tuft of foliage at the end of each shoot is the gradual reduction in size of the leaves from below upwards, which gives a rather rosette-like effect.

R. CYCLIUM, *Balfour and Forrest*, is closely akin to R. callimorphum and has the same glandular young shoots, leaf-stalks, flower-stalks, calyx, and ovary. The bell-shaped corolla is 1½ ins. wide, of a deeper rose than that of callimorphum, with a blotch of still darker rose at the base. The leaves also are of a thicker, more leathery texture. Discovered by Forrest in W. Yunnan in 1917. It grows well and has flowered during May with the late Marquis of Headfort in his garden near Kells in Co. Meath and is evidently pretty hardy. In the same group comes

R. MYIAGRUM, *Balfour and Forrest*, but it is quite distinct from callimorphum and cyclium in its flowers being white ; they are bell-shaped and 1¼ to 1½ ins. wide. Leaves nearly orbicular, 1 to 2 ins. long. The specific name, meaning " fly-catcher," applies to the flower-stalks, which are furnished with such viscid glands that small flies are caught thereon in great numbers. Forrest's specimens, collected wild in W. Yunnan, are covered with them. Introduced in 1919. Flowers in May and June.

R. CALOPHYTUM, *Franchet*

(Bot. Mag., t. 9173)

An evergreen tree up to 45 ft. high. Leaves obovate to oblanceolate, abruptly pointed, wedge-shaped at the base ; 8 to 12 ins. long, 2 to 3½ ins. wide, glabrous except for some floss on the midrib beneath when young. Flowers up to thirty in trusses 6 to 8 ins. across ; corolla five- to eight-lobed, 2½ ins. wide, not so deep, bell-shaped, white or rosy with a large, conspicuous, dark crimson blotch at the base. Flower-stalk 1½ to 3 ins. long, glabrous ; calyx very small ; stamens sixteen to twenty-two, of very unequal length but shorter than the corolla, slightly downy at the base ; ovary and style glabrous ; stigma very large, ¼ in. wide, yellow ; seed-pod 1 in. long, ⅓ in. wide. Flowers in April.

Native of W. China and Tibet ; discovered by the Abbé David ; introduced by Wilson in 1904. One of the noblest of Chinese rhododendrons. In foliage it has some resemblance to R. sutchuenense, but that species has larger flowers (3 ins. across), much shorter flower-stalks, and stamens downy at the base. Flowers fragrant. The knob-like stigma is very conspicuous.

R. CALOSTROTUM, *Balfour and Ward* (Plate 3)

(Bot. Mag., t. 9001)

An evergreen shrub up to 1 ft. or perhaps more high, of rounded compact shape ; young shoots densely scaly. Leaves oval or obovate, rounded or bluntish at the apex, tapered at the base to a very short stalk ;. ¾ to 1⅛ ins. long, ⅓ to ½ in. wide ; dull grey green at first, turning dark green above, brownish with a dense layer of overlapping scales beneath, edged when young with bristles. Flowers terminal, usually in pairs, opening in May, each on a scaly stalk 1 in. or so long. Corolla open and flattish, 1½ ins. wide, pale pink to magenta purple with deeper spots on the upper side, five-lobed, the lobes overlapping, downy outside. Stamens ten, ½ in. long, purple with a dense tuft of hairs at the base. Ovary covered with pale scales ; style purple with a few hairs at the bottom.

Calyx ¼ in. long, with five broadly ovate, purplish lobes, fringed with hairs and very scaly. (Saluenense series.)

Native of N.E. Burma up to 12,000 ft. altitude ; discovered by Kingdon Ward in 1914 ; introduced by him and Farrer in 1919. It flowered at Kew in April 1923, when only two or three inches high, and is quite hardy there. It appears inclined to grow taller than was at first foreseen. Farrer wrote of it as forming a " close flat carpet " and Ward as a " pigmy with giant flowers," but plenty of plants are now 1 ft. high. So large are the flowers indeed and so freely are they borne that a small plant may be literally hidden with flowers at blossoming time. No more delightful rhododendron for the rock garden has been introduced and perhaps no more delightful shrub, as hardy as it is, will ever come to us from Burma. It produces fertile seed in plenty and as it does not seem particular as to position, succeeding even in sunny places, it should become a popular garden plant.

R. CALOXANTHUM, *Balfour and Farrer*

(Plant Introductions of R. Farrer, p. 76)

An evergreen shrub 3 to 5 ft. high ; young shoots glandular. Leaves broadly oval to roundish, 1½ to 2½ ins. long ; not quite so wide, pale glaucous green beneath, glabrous or nearly so at maturity ; stalk about ½ in. long, glandular. Flowers in trusses of four to nine opening in April and May. Corolla bell-shaped, 1¾ ins. wide, scarcely so long, five-lobed, scarlet in bud, sulphur- to orange-yellow when fully open ; stamens ten, up to 1 in. long, not downy ; ovary densely furnished with stalked glands which extend to the lower third of the pistil. Calyx small and like the flower-stalk (which is about ½ in. long) thickly clad with glands. (Thomsonii series.)

Native of N.E. Upper Burma ; discovered and introduced by Farrer in 1919 at elevations of 11,000 to 12,000 ft. There it grows in dense tangles and flowers in June. Farrer describes the young shoots as being " almost cobalt blue," making its masses very conspicuous in July, but this character has not so far shown itself very markedly on cultivated plants. It resembles R. Wardii in its yellow flowers, but that species is well distinguished by its large calyx. It is more nearly akin to R. campylocarpum, whose leaves are not so wide in proportion to their length and whose style is less glandular or even glabrous. R. caloxanthum has produced some good orange-flowered forms at Caerhays, Exbury, and Bodnant, and ought to be hardy in most parts of the British Isles. Related to it and flowering ordinarily in May is

R. TELOPEUM, *Balfour and Forrest*, which has pale yellow flowers, but they have a faint blotch of crimson at the base of the corolla, the style is quite glabrous and the stamens are downy. In other characteristics very similar. Introduced in 1919 from S.E. Tibet by Forrest, who found it at 12,000 ft. altitude, so it ought to be hardy. A charming truss was shown by Lady Aberconway at Westminster in March 1929 ; it carried about ten flowers, each 1½ ins. wide. Its height is about 3 ft.

R. CAMELLIÆFLORUM, *Hooker fil.*

(Bot. Mag., t. 4932 ; R. Cooperi, *Balfour fil.*)

An evergreen shrub up to 6 ft. high, of sparse straggling habit, often growing wild on the trunks and forks of trees ; young shoots very scaly. Leaves oblong-lanceolate, pointed ; 2½ to 4 ins. long, ¾ to 1½ ins. wide ; dark green above ; almost covered with brown glistening scales beneath, between which, however, the glaucous surface of the leaf is visible ; stalk ¼ to ⅜ in. long. Flowers produced in July, usually in pairs. Corolla 1½ ins. wide, white tinged with rose, the base broadly bell-shaped ; lobes five, rounded, overlapping, scaly outside. Stamens twelve to sixteen, downy towards but not at the broadened base. Ovary scaly ; style ⅝ in. long, with a broad thick stigma ; glabrous except for a few scales near the ovary. Calyx ¼ in. long, scaly at the base, the lobes deep, oval, rounded at the end. Flower-stalk ¼ in. long.

Native of N. India, from E. Nepal to Bhotan, up to 10,000 ft. altitude. It was discovered in Sikkim by J. D. Hooker and introduced in 1851 to Kew, where it is still cultivated under glass. Although occurring at fairly high elevations it is not very hardy, but the late Sir Edmund Loder grew it well at Leonardslee. A plant at Lanarth 3 or 4 ft. wide and as much high, is the best I have seen. It is quite uncommon, which is no matter for great regret, for it is one of the least ornamental and most difficult of rhododendrons ; with a little known species, R. lucidum, *Nuttall*, it constitutes a " series."

R. CAMPANULATUM, *Don*

(Bot. Mag., t. 3759)

An evergreen shrub of stiff, spreading habit, 6 to 12 ft. high, more in diameter ; bark peeling ; young shoots glabrous. Leaves oval, 3 to 5½ ins. long, 1¼ to 2½ ins. wide ; abruptly tapering at the apex ; tapering, rounded, or slightly heart-shaped at the base ; glabrous above, densely covered beneath with a red-brown felt ; stalk ½ to 1 in. long, often reddish. Flowers rosy purple of numerous shades, 2 ins. across, produced during April in rather loose clusters about 4 in. wide. Corolla broadly bell-shaped, with five notched lobes, the upper ones dark purple-spotted ; calyx downy, small and scarcely lobed ; stamens ten, glabrous or sometimes downy towards the base ; flower-stalk about 1 in. long.

Native of the interior Himalaya of Sikkim and Nepal ; introduced in 1825. This is perhaps the hardiest and most satisfactory of Himalayan rhododendrons near London, where it flowers regularly and profusely. In very cold weather (and it withstands uninjured thirty-two degrees of frost) its leaves roll themselves up tightly, giving the shrub a very curious aspect. It is very variable in the colour of the flowers, which are sometimes quite pale, sometimes of a bright bluish purple, sometimes lilac ; in the amount of felt at the back of the leaf ; and in the colour of the leaf-scales that accompany the young bursting shoots, which are sometimes rich crimson, sometimes green. One of the most distinct forms is

Var. WALLICHII, *Hooker fil.* (Bot. Mag., t. 4928), in which the corolla is not spotted, the leaf-scales and leaf-stalks are red, and there is very little felt beneath the leaf.

R. CAMPYLOCARPUM, *Hooker fil.* (Plate 4)

(Bot. Mag., t. 4968)

An evergreen shrub, 4 to 8 ft. high, of neat, bushy habit. Leaves 2½ to 4 ins. long, half as wide ; heart-shaped or rounded at the base, the apex with a short, abrupt tip ; upper surface dark glossy green, lower one vividly blue-white ; stalk ½ to 1 in. long, thickly set with stalked glands when young. Flowers pale yellow, slightly fragrant, in loose terminal clusters of six to eight ; corolla bell-shaped, 2½ to 3 ins. across ; lobes five, rounded ; calyx scarcely ¼ in. across, the five shallow lobes edged with dark, stalked, viscid glands ; flower-stalk about 1 in. long, and, like the ovary and base of style, glandular ; stamens ten, downy at the base.

Native of the Sikkim Himalaya at 12,000 ft. Although not one of the hardiest species, it has lived outside in the sheltered Rhododendron Dell at Kew for over twenty years with no other protection than the situation affords. It is at present the best of the larger species with yellow flowers (apart from Azalea) in cultivation, although the colour, in some forms especially, is too pale and sulphur-like to give hopes of founding upon it a race of golden-flowered kinds. Perhaps the finest example of this rhododendron is in the Earl of Morley's garden at Whiteway, in Devonshire, which some years ago was 8 ft. high. Flowers in May.

R. CAMPYLOGYNUM, *Franchet*

(Bot. Mag., t. 9407 ; R. cæruleo-glaucum, *Balfour* ; R. damascenum, *Balfour* ; R. glauco-aureum, *Balfour*)

A usually dwarf, evergreen shrub, but according to Forrest's field notes, sometimes 2 to 4 ft. or even 6 ft. high, of densely branched, close growth ; young shoots thinly scaly. Leaves obovate, tapered at the base, rounded but with a short mucro at the apex ; margins recurved and crinkled ; $\frac{1}{3}$ to 1 in. long, $\frac{1}{8}$ to $\frac{1}{2}$ in. wide ; dark bright green and glabrous above ; pale green or slightly glaucous beneath and slightly scaly at first ; stalk $\frac{1}{10}$ in. long. Flowers solitary or in twos or threes at the end of the shoot, nodding, each produced on a slender, slightly scaly stalk 1 to $1\frac{1}{2}$ ins. long. Corolla of various shades of purple from rosy to plum-coloured or almost black purple, widely bell-shaped, $\frac{5}{8}$ in. long, five-lobed, the lobes rounded and scarcely recurved. Stamens ten (sometimes eight or twelve), downy and widened towards the base ; anthers yellowish brown. Ovary glandular-scaly ; style glabrous, purple, decurved so as to protrude between the lower lobes of the corolla. Calyx five-lobed ; the lobes $\frac{1}{8}$ in. long, glabrous. (The type species of a " series.")

Native of Yunnan, China ; discovered by Delavay in 1884 ; introduced by Forrest in 1912, later by Kingdon Ward. This pleasing species flowers in May and is admirable for the rock garden by reason of its neat habit and rich purple flowers. As one knows it at present, it is difficult to conceive it attaining 6 ft. in height. It is found at elevations of 15,000 ft. and is very hardy. Closely akin to it is myrtilloides, whose leaves are more freely sprinkled with more persistent scales beneath, also more glaucous there ; it is also apparently always dwarf.

R. CAMTSCHATICUM, *Pallas*

(Bot. Mag., t. 8210 ; Therorhodion camtschaticum, *Small*)

A deciduous shrub growing in low dense tufts 4 to 10 ins. high, producing its flowers on stems up to 6 in. high. It spreads by means of underground suckers. Young shoots furnished with scattered bristles. Leaves stalkless, obovate, $\frac{3}{4}$ to 2 ins. long, $\frac{1}{4}$ to $\frac{3}{4}$ in. wide ; thin in texture, glabrous above, slightly bristly beneath, and conspicuously so on the margin. Flowers solitary or in pairs (rarely in threes) on an erect, slender, glandular-bristly stem, the lateral flower or flowers produced on stalks $\frac{3}{4}$ to $1\frac{1}{2}$ ins. long; corolla $1\frac{1}{2}$ to $1\frac{3}{4}$ ins. across, rosy crimson, with five open, spreading, oblong lobes, the three upper ones spotted. Calyx green, 1 in. across, the lobes narrowly oblong, bristly ; stamens ten, very downy at the bottom.

This remarkable and pretty rhododendron, so distinct from every other, is a native of Kamtschatka and other parts of N.E. Asia. Introduced in 1799. It is still very rare, although many times introduced. Whilst not difficult to cultivate, it requires rather special treatment—the ordinary conditions adapted to Ericaceæ in general do not quite suit it. Found naturally in

boggy places, it needs chiefly more continuous surface moisture than
rhododendrons in general do, although they are well known to love cool, moist
conditions about the roots. I have found that the most successful way to
grow this plant in a dry, hot place like Kew is to plant it in sandy, peaty soil
with which a little chopped sphagnum has been mixed, and after it is planted
to lay sphagnum round it and amongst the stems also. As it is apt to be cut
by late spring frosts it is an advantage to cover the plants with a handlight
for a few weeks until that danger be past, or failing that, to select a spot screened
from the rays of the morning sun. It also succeeds well in the rock garden.

R. CANADENSE, *Torrey*. RHODORA

(R. Rhodora, *Gmelin* ; Rhodora canadense, *Linnæus* ; Bot. Mag., t. 474)

A deciduous shrub, rarely more than 3 to 4 ft. high ; branches erect-
growing ; branchlets glabrous except when quite young. Leaves narrowly
oval, tapering about equally to either end ; mostly 2 to 2½ ins. long, ½ to ¾ in.
wide ; with scattered bristles on the upper surface and margins ; lower surface
downy, becoming, in some plants at least, nearly or quite glabrous before
falling. Flowers bright rosy purple, 1 to 1½ ins. wide, produced in April in a
cluster of about six at the end of naked twigs. The corolla has its three upper
lobes united almost to the end, and erect ; the two lower ones narrow-oblong,
divided to the base, and spreading. Calyx green, the lobes shallow, rounded,
glandular at the margins ; flower-stalks ¼ in. long, glandular : stamens ten,
downy quite at the base ; anthers purple.
Native of eastern N. America ; introduced in 1767. This is one of the
brightest and most pleasing of early-flowering shrubs, and one of the hardiest.
Once considered distinct enough to constitute a separate genus (Rhodora), it
has latterly been united with Rhododendron. But from all the deciduous
species, the curious two-lipped corolla consisting of one broad, erect segment
and two spreading narrow ones, and (from most) the ten stamens distinguish
it. The twigs of the year are remarkable also in thickening gradually towards
the end. Increased by seed. Often growing in swamps in a wild state, it loves
moist position under cultivation.

R. CANESCENS, *Sweet*. MOUNTAIN AZALEA

(Azalea canescens, *Michaux*)

A deciduous shrub up to 10 or 15 ft. high, nearly allied (and joined by intermediate forms) to R. nudiflorum, from which it differs in having the leaves
grey-downy on the midrib and veins beneath, especially when young (not bristly
on the midrib, as in R. nudiflorum) ; in the corolla-tube, flower-stalk, and
seed-vessel being glandular, and in the five stamens not being so much protruded. Flowers pink or rose-coloured, fragrant, borne on the naked shoots.
Native of eastern N. America ; introduced in 1810, according to Loudon,
but much confused with nudiflorum, and to some extent with calendulaceum.
The latter it resembles in the downy under-surface of the leaf, but is quite
different in the colour of the flower.

R. CARNEUM, *Hutchinson*

(Bot. Mag., t. 8634)

An evergreen shrub up to 5 ft. high ; young shoots clad with brown
glistening scales. Leaves obovate to oval, leathery deep green and thinly
wrinkled with scales above, glaucous and scaly beneath ; 2 to 5 ins. long,

1 to 1¾ ins. wide ; stalk up to ⅔ in. long. Flowers produced in May in terminal clusters of two to five blooms. Corolla flesh-coloured, funnel-shaped at the base, 2¼ ins. long, 2½ ins. wide ; with five obovate, rounded lobes, scaly outside. Stamens ten or twelve, up to 1¾ ins. long, densely clad on the lowest third with spreading whitish hairs. Ovary and lower part of style very scaly, the latter 2 ins. long, pink towards the top. Calyx five-lobed, the lobes 1/12 in. long, fringed with long hairs, scaly. Flower-stalks up to ⅝ in. long, covered with yellow scales. (Maddenii series.)

Native of Upper Burma ; discovered at altitudes of about 7500 ft. by Major C. W. Browne, who sent seeds in 1909 to Col. F. B. Longe of Thorpe, Norwich. Plants flowered in 1915. In most places this will need greenhouse conditions, but it is cultivated out-of-doors at Caerhays, Cornwall. Its nearest allies are R. Veitchianum (see p. 67) which has larger white flowers, a calyx much less or not at all fringed with hairs, and much less hairy stamens ; and R. pachypodum which has yellow flowers. A fine plant flowering in the Rhododendron House at Exbury, in April and May 1932, suggested a small flowered, rose-tinted ciliicalyx.

R. CAROLINIANUM, *Rehder*

(R. punctatum var., *Ker*, Bot. Reg., vol. i., t. 37 ; R. punctatum, *Small*, not *Andrews*

This species is closely related to R. minus (syn. punctatum) and wa identified with it as a variety until 1912, when Dr Rehder gave it its present name in *Rhodora*, vol. xiv., p. 97. It was originally introduced to England by John Fraser about 1810, but, according to Rehder, was subsequently lost to cultivation, not being seen again in this country until re-introduced from Mr H. P. Kelsey's nursery, Carolina, in 1895. It is an evergreen shrub of more compact habit than the true minus, young shoots scaly. Leave elliptic to elliptic-obovate, broadly wedge-shaped at the base, tapered at th apex to an often bluntish point ; 1 to 3½ ins. long, ½ to 1¾ ins. wide ; gloss green and soon glabrous above ; densely covered with ultimately dark scale beneath ; midrib yellowish ; stalk stout, ⅛ to ¼ in. long. Flowers four to te in a terminal truss, opening in May. Corolla five-lobed, about 1½ ins. wide pale rosy purple, faintly or not at all spotted, the lobes rather longer than th tube. Stamens ten, with a band of down near the base ; ovary scaly ; styl glabrous ; flower-stalk ½ in. long. (Type species of a " series.")

Native of N. Carolina. The true minus (punctatum) differs from carolinianum in the following particulars : Its leaves are more pointed ; it habit straggling and taller ; the corolla lobes are shorter than the tube an much more scaly outside (in carolinianum the corolla is only slightly or not a all scaly) ; corolla conspicuously spotted.

Var. ALBUM, *Rehder*.—Flowers white or whitish. I have seen this growing and flowering well at Wakehurst. Both it and the type are very hardy.

R. CHAPMANII, *A. Gray*, from the pinelands of W. Florida is nearly related. Th leaves are distinct in their oval shape and rounded apex, 1 to 2 ins. long, more tha half as much wide. Flowers rose coloured. Too tender for Kew, it succeeds well an flowers at Caerhays in April and May. (Carolinianum series.)

R. CATAWBIENSE, *Michaux*

(Bot. Mag., t. 1671)

An evergreen shrub, 6 to 10 ft. high, forming eventually a large spreading bush wider than high—a dense thicket of branches and leaves. Leaves ova or oblong, 3 to 6 ins. long, 1¼ to 2 ins. wide ; broadest above the middl dark glossy green above, pale beneath, glabrous on both sides ; stalk ½ to ¾ ins. long. Flowers lilac-purple, produced in a large cluster 5 or 6 ins. across ; corolla 1½ ins. long, 2½ ins. broad, with five short, rounded spreading lobes ; calyx with five shallow, triangular pointed lobes ; stamens white, downy at the base ; flower-stalks 1 to 1½ ins. long, glandular-downy ; ovary brown-felted ; style red.

Native of the slopes and mountain summits of the south-eastern United States, where it is described as forming dense thickets "through which the traveller can only make his way by following old bear tracks." In the gardens of Britain, to which it was introduced in 1809 by John Fraser, it has proved one of the most valuable evergreen shrubs for ornament ever introduced. In the hands of nurserymen, but chiefly of the Waterers, it has given birth by selection and hybridisation to a most valuable group of evergreen garden rhododendrons—hardy and easily grown—the group which flowers in May and June. The characteristics of this group, as compared with the companion group derived from R. ponticum, are their broad foliage and greater hardiness. The rhododendrons known in gardens as EVERESTIANUM and FASTUOSUM, the former with a frilled corolla, the latter double-flowered, are forms of catawbiense.

R. CAUCASICUM, *Pallas*

An evergreen, low shrub, usually under 3 ft. in height, with slightly downy young shoots. Leaves sometimes rather leathery, glabrous and dark green above, more or less clothed with brownish red felt beneath ; narrowly oval or slightly obovate ; 2 to 4 ins. long, ¾ to 1½ ins. wide ; stalk stout, ¼ in. long. Flowers yellowish white or with a pale lilac tinge, produced during June in terminal clusters. Corolla 2 ins. across ; stamens ten ; calyx very small ; flower-stalk slightly downy, about 1½ ins. long ; seed-pods erect.

Native of the Caucasus ; introduced in 1803. Although its hybrid progeny is numerous in gardens, the true species is itself now scarcely ever seen. It is an interesting dwarf bush, remarkable for its dense habit and slow growth. As it approaches 8000 ft. altitude in a wild state it is very hardy. Nearly allied to it, but quite a distinct species, is

R. CHRYSANTHUM, *Pallas*, found in Siberia and N.E. Asia. It has yellow flowers and differs in its smaller leaves, glabrous but strongly net-veined. Although closely allied botanically to R. caucasicum it is very unsatisfactory under cultivation, so much so, that from my experience with it I should say it was not worth growing. I have never seen it in flower.

Many of the garden varieties of Rhododendron with a blotch of yellow on the otherwise white corolla are derived in part from R. caucasicum. Amongst the more notable hybrids are the following :—

CAUCASICUM PICTUM.—A compact bush up to 6 ft. high, with thinner branches and freer habit than caucasicum. Flowers soft, pale rose, spotted on the upper side, opening in early May or even late April.

CUNNINGHAM'S WHITE.—Raised by James Cunningham of Comely Bank nurseries, Edinburgh, about 1830, from R. caucasicum crossed with ponticum album. According to information received from Mr James Smith of the Darley Dale nurseries, this variety thrives well in a limestone district, in evidence of which are a large number of thriving plants planted by his firm near Buxton. A robust shrub 10 ft. high, flowers white.

NOBLEANUM (*q.v.*), caucasicum × arboreum.

PULCHERRIMUM (see under Nobleanum).

ROSA MUNDI.—Very near caucasicum in leaf and habit, being a dwarf rounded bush, only 2 or 3 ft. high in twenty years ; flowers white with a slight flush and a yellow spot.

STRAMINEUM (Bot. Mag., t. 3422).—A shrub, 5 or 6 ft. high, with the foliage of caucasicum, and pale yellow or straw-coloured flowers.

SULPHUREUM.—Raised at Comely Bank nurseries from caucasicum and arboreum album. Flowers of a pretty sulphur yellow, produced in April and May. One of the best yellow hardy rhododendrons.

VENUSTUM.—A hybrid between caucasicum and R. arboreum, raised by Mr W. Smith, of Norbiton, near Kingston. It flowers in April, and is a beautiful variety, the corolla pale in the centre, deeply suffused towards the margin with rose and blotched with dark purple on the upper side. It is of spreading habit, and grows 4 to 6 ft. high. A very similar plant (R. JACKSONI), said to come from caucasicum crossed with Nobleanum, was raised by Mr Jackson, also of Kingston.

The caucasicum group of rhododendrons is distinguished by the cluster of erect sheathing scales, pale green, membranous and downy, which beset the base of the flower-stalks and the erect, closely-packed cluster of seed-pods.

R. CEPHALANTHUM, *Franchet* (Plate 5)

An evergreen shrub of bushy habit up to 3 or 4 ft. high ; young shoots thickly covered with scurf-like scales and bristly. Leaves oval to oblong, rounded or tapered, and with a short mucro at the apex ; ½ to 1¼ ins. long, ¼ to ½ in. wide ; the margins decurved ; dark glossy green above, clothed beneath with a dense scurfy coating of scales at first whitish, ultimately pale brown ; stalk ⅛ to ¼ in. long. Flowers densely clustered in a terminal head of eight or more blossoms which is 1½ to 2 ins. wide. Each flower is about ⅔ in. long and wide, the corolla white, narrowly tubular at the base, spreading at the mouth into five rounded lobes with crinkled margins, the throat filled with white down. Stamens five, ¼ in. long, enclosed within the corolla tube, slightly downy towards the base ; ovary very scaly ; style short, glabrous ; calyx deeply five-lobed, scarcely half as long as the corolla, the lobes narrowly ovate, scaly outside, fringed with hairs ; flower-stalk ⅛ in. long, scaly.

Native of W. Szechuen and Yunnan, China, at altitudes of 9000 to 10,000 ft. ; discovered by Delavay in 1884 ; introduced by Wilson in 1908 and later by Forrest. It is a very charming dwarf species, very hardy, and flowers in April. It is now the type species of a " series " which is closely related to, and scarcely distinguishable from, the Anthopogon series ; the stamens, however, uniformly number five but vary from five to ten in the Anthopogons. A rhododendron closely akin to cephalanthum is

R. CEPHALANTHOIDES, *Balfour and W. W. Smith*, which has white fragrant flowers similar in size and arrangement to those of its ally. It is well distinguished, however, by its glabrous stamens and by the leaf-bud scales falling early whilst they are persistent in cephalanthum.

Native of Yunnan at 11,000 to 12,000 ft. altitude ; discovered by Forrest in 1906.

R. CHÆTOMALLUM, *Balfour and Forrest*

An evergreen shrub up to 4 or 5 ft. high ; young shoots thickly clothed with twisted, bristly hairs. Leaves obovate, rounded at the end, tapered at the base, dark green and glabrous above except when quite young, velvety with a coat of tawny down beneath ; 2 to 4 ins. long, 1 to 1¾ ins. wide ; stalk ⅛ in. long, stout, hairy like the shoot. Flowers in clusters of six to ten opening in April and May. Corolla bell-shaped, 1¾ ins. long and 2½ ins. wide, deep crimson, five-lobed. Stamens ten, up to 1 in. long, glabrous ; anthers chocolate brown. Ovary densely woolly ; style glabrous. Calyx red, up to ⅜ in. long, with five lobes unequal in shape and size ; flower-stalks bristly, $\frac{1}{2}$ to $\frac{3}{4}$ in. long. (Neriiflorum series.)

Native of N.W. Yunnan and S.E. Tibet ; discovered and introduced by Forrest in 1917-8. It belongs to the hæmatodes group and is a very handsome shrub, differing from R. hæmatodes itself chiefly in the bristly character of the young shoots and in the usually broader and more rounded apex of the leaf. It is a variable plant, one of its most distinct forms being

Var. XANTHANTHUM, *Tagg and Forrest*, which has larger flowers of a creamy yellow colour flushed with rose-pink ; calyx large, cup-shaped. Found on Alpine moorland at 14,000 ft. altitude. (Hardy in Eastern Suffolk.)

R. CHAMPIONÆ, *Hooker*

(Bot. Mag., t. 4609)

An evergreen shrub probably some 6 or 8 ft. high ; young shoots clothed with stiff outstanding hairs, some of which are gland-tipped. Leaves elliptic-lanceolate, pointed, mostly wedge-shaped at the base ; 3 to 5 ins. long, 1 to $1\frac{3}{4}$ ins. wide ; dark green, sprinkled on both surfaces with pale bristles that are especially abundant on the midrib beneath and on the margins ; stalk $\frac{1}{2}$ to $\frac{3}{4}$ in. long, very bristly. Flowers as many as six in a terminal cluster, usually fewer, opening in May. Corolla pink, $3\frac{1}{2}$ ins. wide, the base narrowly tubular and $\frac{3}{4}$ in. long, separating into five oblong, bluntish lobes $1\frac{1}{2}$ to 2 ins. long. Stamens ten, 2 ins. long, downy at the lower half. Calyx-lobes five, linear, very unequal, $\frac{1}{8}$ to $\frac{1}{2}$ in. long, very bristly on the margins ; flower-stalk very bristly, $\frac{3}{4}$ to 1 in. long. (Stamineum series.)

Native of Hong Kong on Mt. Victoria, where it is rare ; found also in the province of Fokien, China, by Mr Dunn in 1905. It was discovered in 1849 by Lt.-Col. Champion, after whose wife it was named by the elder Hooker. Although no longer there it was introduced to Kew in 1881 and flowered in the Temperate House in 1894, but was a shy bloomer. It is a quite tender shrub and I have only seen it in the open air at Caerhays, where it grows in a sheltered enclosure. It has been placed in the Stamineum series, amongst the cultivated species of which it is very distinct in the conspicuously bristly flower-stalks, leaves, and ovary.

R. CHARIANTHUM, *Hutchinson*

(Bot. Mag., t. 8665)

An evergreen shrub of diffuse habit with slightly scaly, not downy young shoots. Leaves oblanceolate, 1 to $2\frac{1}{4}$ ins. long, $\frac{1}{3}$ to $\frac{3}{4}$ in. wide, scaly on both surfaces. Flowers as many as ten together in several clusters forming a truss $3\frac{1}{2}$ ins. wide, opening in April and May. Corolla $1\frac{1}{2}$ ins. wide with a short funnel-shaped base and five ovate lobes, pale lavender rose with a conspicuous cluster of brownish red spots on the upper side. Stamens ten, white, downy at the base with rosy red anthers showing well above the corolla. Calyx small, scarcely lobed and (like the flower-stalk, which is $\frac{1}{2}$ to $\frac{2}{3}$ in. long) slightly scaly. Ovary scaly ; style downy near the base. Seed vessel $\frac{1}{4}$ in. long. (Triflorum series.)

Native of W. Szechuen, China ; introduced by Wilson in 1908 (No. 1274). It very much resembles R. yunnanense, but has none of the bristles on the upper surface of the leaves that characterise that species. The slight downiness of the style is also distinctive. It belongs to the attractive triflorum-yunnanense group including R. Davidsonianum and R. siderophyllum.

R. CHARITOPES, *Balfour and Farrer*

(Bot. Mag., t. 9358)

A dwarf evergreen shrub described by Farrer as 9 to 12 ins. high in a wild state ; young shoots scaly. Leaves obovate, the apex mucronulate, the base wedge-shaped ; 1 to 2¾ ins. long, ½ to 1⅛ ins. wide ; glossy dark green above, pale green and fairly thickly sprinkled over with yellowish shining scales beneath ; stalk ⅛ in. long. Flowers opening in May with us, usually three (sometimes two to four) in a terminal cluster, each on its slender scaly stalk which is ¾ to 1 in. long. Corolla bell-shaped, five-lobed, about 1 in. wide, clear pink, speckled with crimson. Stamens ten, hairy on the lower two-thirds ; ovary densely scaly ; style ⅓ in. long, thick and glabrous. Calyx large for the size of the flower, ⅓ in. long, cut to the base into five ovate lobes, scaly outside. (Glaucum series.)

Native of N.E. Upper Burma, found in the Shing Hong Pass by Farrer in June 1920. It was then in flower and he describes it as a " particularly charming plant with three- (rarely four-) bloomed inflorescences. Flowers of a clear apple-blossom pink flushed more warmly in the upper lobes, and speckled with crimson ; and with a deep rose tube." At first regarded as belonging to the campylogynum " series," it has latterly been associated with glaucum. I saw it in flower at Exbury in 1931 and thought it a very attractive little plant, eminently fitted for the rock garden. It grows at 10,000 to 12,000 ft. altitude and should be fairly hardy. Near R. charitopes comes

R. TSANGPOENSE, *Hutchinson and Ward.*—Corolla pink to deep cerise ; calyx deeply five-lobed. From charitopes it may be distinguished by the very thin, transient sprinkling of scales beneath the leaf. Style short, thick, sharply bent down. Flowered at Nymans, Sussex, in May 1930. Discovered in 1924 by Kingdon Ward near the Tsangpo river. Tibet. Grows 1 to 2 ft. high, dense and tangled in habit.

R. CHASMANTHUM, *Diels*

An evergreen shrub up to 6 ft. high ; young shoots reddish, slightly scaly, not downy. Leaves lanceolate, 2½ to 4 ins. long, ¾ to 1½ ins. wide ; pointed, glabrous above, thinly scaly beneath and softly downy on the midrib. Flowers in a cluster of as many as five from the terminal bud, sometimes supplemented by smaller axillary clusters so that the whole may form a truss of eight or nine flowers. Corolla shortly tubular at the base, spreading into five oblong-ovate lobes and giving the flower a diameter of 1½ to 2 ins., pale lavender to deep lavender-mauve spotted with olive green on the upper part ; scaly on one side. Stamens ten, much exposed, downy at the lower part ; ovary densely scaly ; style glabrous. Calyx five-lobed, scaly ; flower-stalk ⅝ to 1 in. long. Seed vessel cylindrical, ¾ in. long, ⅜ in. wide. (Triflorum series.)

Native of Yunnan, China, and of S.E. Tibet ; first found by the Rev. J. A. Soulié in the latter country in 1893, and in N.W. Yunnan by Père Monbeig in 1907. The plants in cultivation were raised from seed collected by Forrest in 1919. This charming species belongs to the triflorum-Augustinii group and resembles Augustinii itself in having a conspicuous line of down along the midrib beneath, but that rhododendron is well distinguished by its downy shoots. I have seen R. chasmanthum beautifully in flower at Exbury, where it flowers in May a week or two later than R. Augustinii, to which species Mr L. de Rothschild considered that, of the triflorum series, it comes next in quality. Very closely akin to it is

R. CHASMANTHOIDES, *Balfour and Forrest* (Plate 6), which differs somewhat in the broader, more abruptly pointed leaves, and the unlobed calyx. Flowers rose-lavender with well defined, olive-green markings. Collected in S.E. Tibet by Forrest in 1918 ; also native of N.W. Yunnan. A spray shown by Mr J. C. Williams at the Rhododendron Society's Show at Westminster in April 1926 was awarded Second Prize in a class for the Triflorum series in which there were many exhibits.

R. CHRYSEUM, *Balfour and Ward*

(Bot. Mag., t. 9246)

A dwarf, evergreen, much branched shrub, 1 to 2½ ft. high ; young shoots densely covered with a rather loose scurf of reddish scales, which become darker and fewer the second year, the bark of the branchlets becoming finally grey and peeling. Leaves stout, aromatic, oval or inclined to obovate, mostly bluntish at both ends ; ½ to ¾ in. long, $\frac{3}{16}$ to $\frac{5}{16}$ in. wide ; dark green, covered with shining scales above, paler and rather glaucous beneath with the scales less dense ; stalk $\frac{1}{12}$ in. long, scaly. Flowers deep sulphur yellow, four to six in a terminal cluster, opening in May. Corolla ¾ to 1 in. wide, with a funnel-shaped base and five ovate lobes ⅜ in. long, slightly scaly outside, covered with white down in the tube. Stamens five, ½ in. long, each with a tuft of white down at the base ; ovary very scaly ; style glabrous or slightly downy at the base. Calyx very scaly, five-lobed, the lobes oblong, ⅛ in. or less long. (Lapponicum series.)

Native of W. China on the Yunnan-Tibet frontier ; found by Kingdon Ward in 1912 at 13,000 to 14,000 ft. altitude, later by Forrest. It flowered at Caerhays in May 1919. In the original description the corolla is described as golden, but all the flowers I have seen have been too pale to deserve that term. Possibly they vary in depth of shade. It bears a strong resemblance to R. flavidum but that species has ten stamens to each flower. R. chryseum is very hardy and a charming shrub for the rock garden. (See also R. muliense.)

R. CHRYSODORON, *Tagg*

(Bot. Mag., t. 9442)

An evergreen small shrub ; young shoots sparingly bristly. Leaves oval, rounded at the base, also somewhat rounded at the apex but furnished with a conspicuous mucro there ; mostly 2 to 3 ins. long, 1 to 1½ ins. wide ; bright green and glabrous above, glaucous green and scaly beneath, more or less ciliate ; stalk ⅓ to ½ in. long, bristly. Flowers in terminal clusters of about five ; corolla bell-shaped, 1½ ins. long and wide, with five lobes each 1 in. wide, notched about the middle, of a beautiful unspotted canary-yellow ; stamens downy on the lower half ; ovary and flower-stalk very scaly.

Native most probably of W. Yunnan ; introduced by Forrest. There was, however, some confusion in the numbering of his specimens. All yellow rhododendrons are valuable and this is one of the most richly coloured of them. It flowered with the Earl of Stair in 1931 and four years later with Lord Conway. It will probably be hardy only in the south and west.

R. CILIATUM, *Hooker fil.*

An evergreen shrub of stiff, wide-spreading habit, rarely more than 3 to 4 ft. high out-of-doors near London, but 9 ft. high and twice as much in diameter in Cornwall ; young branchlets covered with bristly hairs. Leaves oval or obovate, tapering sometimes equally to both ends, sometimes more gradually towards the base ; 2 to 4 ins. long, ¾ to 1½ ins. wide ; bristly on the upper surface and on the margins, scaly beneath ; stalk bristly, $\frac{1}{4}$ to $\frac{1}{3}$ in. long. Flowers beautiful rosy red in bud, pale pink on opening, becoming almost white with age ; $2\frac{1}{2}$ ins. across, produced three to five in a cluster during March and April ; corolla widely bell-shaped, with broad notched lobes ; calyx-lobes rounded ovate, bristly on the margins, stamens ten, hairy at the base, flower-stalks $\frac{1}{2}$ in. long, bristly.

Native of Sikkim ; introduced to Kew in 1850. It is hardy there, but really needs milder conditions to bring out its best qualities. In Mr Shilson's garden at Tremough, near Falmouth, some years ago I saw a specimen of the larger dimensions given above. Near London it needs a very sheltered position, and in such a spot, although it grows slowly, it frequently gives a very charming display in April if the weather be kind. As a shrub for the cool, unheated greenhouse it makes a fine display in February and March.

R. ciliatum has been extensively used for crossing with other species, but most of its progeny are more tender than itself and are greenhouse plants. Of the hardy ones the best is

R. PRÆCOX, *Carrière*, raised about 1855 by Mr Isaac Davies of the Ormskirk nurseries, by crossing ciliatum with dauricum. The flowers are $1\frac{1}{2}$ to 2 ins. across, of a beautiful, bright rosy purple ; leaves dark glossy green and bristly above, scaly beneath. No early flowering shrub is more lovely than this, but as it comes into flower in March or even February its flowers rarely pass through their natural term of existence, being almost invariably cut off by frost, sometimes before they are fully open. The plant itself, a bush not so spreading in habit or strictly evergreen as ciliatum, and with deeper green foliage, is perfectly hardy.

R. CILIICALYX, *Franchet*

(Bot. Mag., t. 7782)

An evergreen shrub of rather diffuse habit, 8 to 10 ft. high ; young shoots bristly and slightly scaly. Leaves narrowly oval, or oblanceolate, tapered at both ends, pointed ; $2\frac{1}{2}$ to $4\frac{1}{2}$ ins. long, 1 to 2 ins. wide ; dark glossy green above, glaucous-green beneath and thickly sprinkled with golden-brown scales ; stalk $\frac{1}{8}$ to $\frac{1}{2}$ in. long, bristly and slightly scaly. Flowers produced in March and April in a terminal truss of usually three blossoms. Corolla pure white except for a yellow stain on the upper side of the tube ; the base is funnel-shaped, the five rounded wavy lobes spreading and giving the flower a diameter of 4 ins. Stamens ten, about 2 ins. long, white, very hairy at the base. Ovary scaly ; style $2\frac{1}{2}$ ins. long, scaly at the base. Calyx five-lobed, the lobes $\frac{1}{8}$ in. long, conspicuously fringed with white bristles $\frac{1}{8}$ in. long. Flower-stalks $\frac{1}{2}$ in. long, stout, scaly.

Native of W. Yunnan ; discovered by Delavay about 1884 ; introduced from Paris to Kew in 1892. This beautiful species, one of the very finest of white rhododendrons, grows well in the Himalayan House at Kew, where it has protection from more than one or two degrees of frost. Here it is covered with blossom every spring. It is only likely to succeed out-of-doors in the milder parts of Cornwall and similar places. The flowers are sometimes pink and they have a faint sweet fragrance. It is closely related to the much hardier Himalayan R. ciliatum, whose style has no scales and whose habit is dwarfer, more spreading and bushy. The bristly calyx is distinctive. (Maddenii series.)

R. SUPRANUBIUM, *Hutchinson.*—According to the author of the name, this may be regarded as a near Alpine ally of ciliicalyx. It grows in Yunnan at altitudes of 10,000 to 12,000 ft., higher up than most of this group of rhododendrons ; it should therefore be able to withstand considerable cold. It was found by Forrest in 1906, as an evergreen shrub 2 to 5 ft. high, with the usual scaly young shoots, leaves, flower-stalks, and calyx of this group. The oblanceolate to obovate leaves are 2 to 3½ ins. long, ½ to 1⅛ in. wide, glaucous between the scales beneath. Corolla 3 ins. long, with five deep rounded lobes, softly downy outside near the base. Calyx fringed with long pale bristles ; stamens downy at the lower half. Ovary and lower part of style scaly. It differs from ciliicalyx in the corolla being scaly all over the outside. At Caerhays the flowers open towards the end of May. (Maddenii series.)

R. CINNABARINUM, *Hooker fil.*

An evergreen shrub, 6 to 10 ft. high, somewhat thin and sparse of habit, the branches long and slender, scaly when young. Leaves 2 to 4 ins. long, ⅜ to 1¼ ins. broad ; oval, tapering about equally to each end, glabrous, and of a greyish green metallic lustre above, scaly beneath, and varying in colour from glaucous green to reddish brown ; stalk ⅓ in. long. Flowers funnel-shaped, and like those of Lapageria, 1¼ to 2 ins. long, very variable in colour ;

RHODODENDRON CINNABARINUM

ordinarily of a dull cinnabar red, produced during May and June, from five to eight in terminal heads. In other forms the corolla is orange-red outside, yellowish within, sometimes greenish. Calyx with four short, broadish lobes, and one longer narrow one, or sometimes with all five nearly equal, scaly. Stamens ten, scarcely so long as the corolla, hairy at the base ; flower-stalk ½ in. long, scaly.

Native of Sikkim and Bhotan ; introduced in 1849. This distinct and striking species is chiefly remarkable for the variability of the colour of its flowers, and the under-surface of its leaves. But the differences between some of the intermediate forms are so unimportant that botanists regard them all as of one species. In gardens, however, it has been found convenient to distinguish three forms :—

CINNABARINUM (type).—Flowers cinnabar red, corolla-lobes pointed ; calyx-lobes unequal, especially the upper one, which is long and narrow.

BLANDFORDIÆFLORUM.—Flowers red outside, yellow or greenish yellow within (Bot. Mag., t. 4930).

ROYLEI.—Leaves glaucous beneath; flowers intense, rosy red, shorter (about 1¼ ins. long) than the two others; calyx-lobes nearly equal in size and shape. (Bot. Mag., t. 4788.)

The leaves of all forms of cinnabarinum are believed to be poisonous to browsing animals.

R. CITRINIFLORUM, *Balfour and Forrest*

(R. chlanidotum, *Balfour and Forrest*)

A dwarf evergreen shrub of the sanguineum group, 2 to 4 ft. high, with obovate or oblong leaves, tapering to the base; 1½ to 3½ ins. long, ½ to 1½ ins wide; densely clothed beneath with loose tawny wool. Flowers opening in April and early May in clusters of six to eight flowers. Corolla clear unspotted lemon-yellow, bell-shaped, 1¾ ins. long, five-lobed. Stamens ten finely downy at the base. Ovary matted with tawny hairs and glandular bristly. Calyx ⅛ in. long; flower-stalks about 1 in. long, clad with tawny bristles. (Neriiflorum series.)

Native of W. Yunnan, China, up to 13,000 ft. altitude; discovered and introduced by Forrest in 1917. It is well marked in the sanguineum group by its bright lemon-yellow flowers without markings, but often flushed with pink, and should prove a welcome addition to dwarf rhododendrons of that colour. Considering the high altitudes at which it grows wild it should be fairly hardy. It blossoms profusely at Exbury, even as a small plant.

R. CLEMENTINÆ, *Forrest*

(Bot. Mag., t. 9392)

An evergreen shrub 4 ft. and upwards high in a wild state, with stout, stiff young shoots. Leaves oval, mostly heart-shaped at the base, rounded at the apex; 2½ to 5 ins. long, rather more than half as much wide; dull green and without down at maturity above, covered beneath with a soft, thick, pale brown felt; stalk ½ to ¾ in. long. Flowers produced in a terminal truss of seven to fifteen flowers. Corolla bell-shaped, creamy white flushed with rose or bright rose usually dotted with crimson, 2 ins. wide, six- or seven-lobed; stamens double the number of the corolla lobes, scarcely half the length of the corolla downy at the base; ovary and style glabrous. Seed-vessel described as purple-black.

Native of N.W. Yunnan and S.W. Szechuen, China; discovered and introduced by Forrest in 1913. It appears to be one of the most ornamental of the Taliense series to which it belongs and amongst which it is distinct on account of the six or seven lobes of the corolla. As it is found at altitudes of 13,000 ft. and upwards it should be quite hardy.

R. CLOIOPHORUM, *Balfour and Forrest*

An evergreen shrub of the sanguineum group, up to 4 ft. high, with obovate leaves 1½ to 3 ins. long, one-third as much wide; tapered more gradually to the base than the apex, clothed beneath with a pale close down; stalk very short. Flowers in trusses of four to six. Corolla between funnel- and bell-shaped, 1½ ins. long, not quite so wide, five-lobed, " rose-coloured, darkest round the margins, yellowish towards the base " (Forrest). Stamens ten, glabrous, shorter than the corolla. Ovary downy, without glands; style glabrous. Calyx ⅖ in. long, with five unequal lobes that are often deflexed and give it the collar-like appearance to which the specific name refers ; flower-stalks $\frac{1}{2}$ to $\frac{3}{4}$ in. long, covered with loose curling hairs.

Native of W. Yunnan ; discovered in 1917 and introduced by Forrest. From most of the sanguineum group this is distinguished by the combination of its rose-coloured flowers with the thin-textured corolla and the thin appressed down beneath the leaves. (Neriiflorum series.)

Very nearly allied are R. LEUCOPETALUM, with pure white flowers ; R. ASMENISTUM, with white flowers tinged with rose on the margin ; R. MANNOPHORUM, white suffused with rose ; and R. ROSEOTINCTUM, with smaller more bell-shaped flowers deep rose on the margin. The last two are inclined to bear glands on flower-stalk, calyx, and ovary.

R. COLLETTIANUM, *Aitchison*

(Bot. Mag., t. 7019)

An evergreen shrub of dwarf habit in cultivation, but described as 8 to 10 ft. high in nature. Leaves 2 to 3 ins. long, $\frac{1}{3}$ to $\frac{5}{8}$ in. wide ; narrowly oval, pointed at both ends, dark dull green above, covered with brownish scales beneath ; when crushed they have a strong, resinous, aromatic odour ; stalk about $\frac{1}{4}$ in. long. Flowers 1 in. across, white, produced during May in terminal clusters 2 to 2$\frac{1}{2}$ ins. across. Corolla with a funnel-shaped tube, hairy within, the five rounded oblong lobes not fully spreading ; calyx with five narrow, oblong lobes rounded at the end, scaly, and very hairy at the margins ; stamens ten, almost hidden within the corolla-tube, hairy near the bases.

Native of Afghanistan ; discovered in the Kurrum Valley in 1879, and introduced the same year to Kew by the late Sir Henry Collett, after whom it is named. It first flowered in the Kew rock garden in May 1888, and it is for such a position that it appears best adapted.

Closely allied to R. Collettianum, and coming from the same country, is R. AFGHANICUM, *Aitchison*. It is very similar in foliage and inflorescence, but differs in the protruding stamens, and in the calyx-lobes being shorter, more rounded, and not hairy on the margins, as in Collett's species.

R. CONCINNUM, *Hemsley*

(R. coombense, *Hemsley*, Bot. Mag., t. 8280)

An evergreen bush, probably up to 6 ft. in height ; young shoots scaly. Leaves scattered along the branches, aromatic, narrowly oval, tapered towards both ends, but more gradually towards the apex ; 1 to 2 ins. long, $\frac{1}{3}$ to $\frac{5}{8}$ in. wide ; dark green and scaly above, pale and grey beneath, but densely sprinkled with scales that are at first golden, ultimately brownish ; stalk $\frac{1}{4}$ to $\frac{1}{3}$ in. long. Flowers in terminal trusses of about four blossoms, expanding in May. Corolla purple, 1$\frac{1}{2}$ to 2 ins. across ; funnel-shaped, five-lobed, spotted on the upper side with brownish purple ; the lower part slightly scaly outside. Stamens ten, whitish, downy near, but not at, the base ; style glabrous or sometimes downy towards the base ; ovary scaly. Calyx with shallow rounded lobes ; scaly like the flower-stalk, which is $\frac{1}{3}$ to $\frac{5}{8}$ in. long.

Native of Western China ; discovered in 1886 by the Rev. Ernest Faber on Mount Omi ; introduced by Wilson for Messrs Veitch in 1904. It is allied to yanthinum (which differs in its lanceolate calyx-lobes) and to polylepis (*q.v.*). A form named lætevirens is figured in Bot. Mag., t. 8912.

R. CORIACEUM, *Franchet*

(R. foveolatum, *Rehder and Wilson*)

An evergreen shrub or small tree from 10 to 25 ft. high ; young shoots pale grey with down. Leaves oblanceolate, 5 to 10½ ins. long, 1½ to 3½ ins. wide, dark green and glabrous above, grey white and downy beneath ; stalk 1 in. or less long, cylindrical, pale yellowish green like the midrib. Flowers borne rather loosely in a truss fifteen to twenty together. Corolla between funnel- and bell-shaped, 1¾ ins. long and wide, five- to seven-lobed, white or rose-tinted, with a crimson blotch at the base and sometimes similarly coloured spots on the upper lobes. Stamens double the number of corolla lobes, scurfy at the base ; ovary downy ; style glabrous. Calyx a mere rim ; flower-stalks downy, ¾ to 1 in. long.

Native of Yunnan, where it was found in the valley of the Mekong river by the Abbé Soulié in 1898, flowering in March ; afterwards in the same region by Père Monbeig and by Forrest who introduced it. As it occurs up to 13,000 ft. altitude, it should be hardy in climates like that of the inland parts of Sussex and Hampshire. It is a handsome-leaved species of the Falconeri series, distinct therein by reason of the grey-white colouring of various parts, but inferior as regards blossom. The leathery texture of the leaf, to which the specific name refers, is not more marked than in others of this group.

R. CRASSUM, *Franchet*

An evergreen shrub or small tree up to 20 ft. high ; young shoots stout, scaly. Leaves usually crowded at the end of the shoot, leathery, oval, narrowly obovate or oblanceolate, pointed, tapered at the base ; 2½ to 6 ins. long, 1 to 2½ ins. wide ; dark glossy green and wrinkled above, rather glaucous beneath but thickly sown with red-brown scales. Flowers delightfully fragrant, three to six in a terminal cluster, each on a thick scaly stalk, ½ to ¾ in. long. Corolla funnel-shaped, 2½ to 3½ ins. long, creamy white to rosy white, scaly outside, five-lobed, the lobes roundish ovate and 1 in. long. Stamens fifteen to twenty, downy at the lower part. Ovary and style scaly, the latter 2 to 2½ ins. long. Calyx scaly at the base, deeply five-lobed, the lobes ¼ to ½ in. long, glabrous. Seed-vessel very stout, ¾ to 1¼ ins. long, ½ in. wide, ribbed. (Maddenii series.)

Native of W. Yunnan, China ; discovered by Delavay about 1885 ; introduced by Forrest in 1906. This beautiful rhododendron may be regarded as the Yunnan representative of R. Maddenii, a well-known Himalayan species long cultivated in greenhouses. Being much the hardier, it is a valuable acquisition. It has lived in the open air at Kew through a few mild winters and occasionally flowered, but it needs a milder climate. It flowers in June and, starting late into growth escapes late spring frosts, which may account for its comparative hardiness. R. Maddenii differs in having glabrous stamens and the calyx-lobes are only ⅛ in. long. Forrest has introduced a number of forms of R. crassum differing in the shape and size of the leaves, some of which have glabrous stamens. Near it comes

R. MANIPURENSE, *Balfour* (R. Maddenii obtusifolium, *Hutchinson*, Bot. Mag., t. 8212). It has a four- or five-flowered inflorescence, the pure white corolla being 4 ins. long, scaly outside except near the margins of the lobes. It is readily distinguished from Maddenii by the downy stamens and larger calyx. It resembles R. crassum in the downiness of the stamens, but its leaves are wider and more broadened towards the apex (up to 7 ins. long and 3 ins. wide) and the scales of the flower-buds are glabrous ; in crassum they are silky towards the top. Native of Manipur, up to 10,000 ft. altitude ; introduced to Kew in 1882 by Sir George Watt. Not very hardy.

R. CRINIGERUM, *Franchet*

(Bot. Mag., t. 9464 ; R. ixeuticum, *Balfour and W. W. Smith*)

An evergreen shrub up to 12 ft. high in a wild state ; young shoots and leaf-stalks very sticky with glandular bristles. Leaves oblong-lanceolate to oblanceolate, tapered to a narrow, often rounded base, slenderly pointed ; 3 to 7 ins. long, ¾ to 1¾ ins. wide ; dark glossy green and soon glabrous above ; clothed beneath with a soft tawny felt, with many small, ultimately dark glands on the midrib ; leaf-stalk ⅝ in. long. Flowers about twelve in a truss. Corolla bell-shaped, 1½ ins. long, five-lobed, white with a dark blotch at the base and sometimes flushed with rose. Stamens ten, downy at the base. Ovary thickly furnished with stalked glands ; style glabrous except at the base. Calyx deeply five-lobed, the lobes narrowly oblong, ¼ in. long, glandular-bristly and hairy like the flower-stalks which are up to 1 in. long. (Barbatum series.)

Native of N.W. Yunnan, China, and E. Tibet ; discovered in the former province by the Abbé Soulié in 1895 ; introduced in 1914 by Forrest, who found it growing at 12,000 ft. altitude. Not being at first identified with Franchet's crinigerum, it was re-named " ixeuticum " at Edinburgh from Forrest's material and got into cultivation under that name. Mr Lionel de Rothschild stated that some plants have flowered in this country that have cream-coloured, heavily-spotted corollas. It belongs to the barbatum group and is related to glischrum and habrotrichum, but the dense velvety covering beneath the leaf distinguishes it. It seems to be fairly hardy and flowered in the open air at Kew as long ago as April 1923.

R. BAINBRIDGEANUM, *Tagg and Forrest*, was discovered in 1922, as a shrub 4 to 6 ft. high, by Forrest in S.E. Tibet. Nearly related to crinigerum and having similar glandular bristly shoots and leaf-stalks, the flower structure and details are also similar. According to Forrest's notes, the flowers are white flushed with rose or creamy yellow with a crimson blotch at the base. The leaves differ in their proportionately greater width and in being much less pointed, and the wool beneath is thinner and looser.

R. CROCEUM, *Balfour and W. W. Smith* (Plate 7)

(R. prasinocalyx, *Balfour fil.*)

An evergreen shrub described as sometimes a small tree 15 to 20 ft. high ; young shoots and leaves soon glabrous or nearly so. Leaves oval-oblong, generally slightly heart-shaped at the base, rounded to broadly tapered at the apex ; 2½ to 4½ ins. long, 1 to 2½ ins. wide ; pale green beneath ; stalk ½ to 1 in. long. Flowers in clusters of seven or eight, opening in May. Corolla five-lobed, saucer-shaped, 2 to 3 ins. wide, 1½ ins. deep ; clear soft yellow, sometimes with a crimson blotch ; stamens ten, ½ in. long, glabrous ; ovary and pistil glandular from top to bottom. Calyx ⅝ to ¾ in. wide, tinged with yellow, the five lobes ovate-oblong, blunt, edged with minute stalked glands ; flower-stalk up to 1¾ ins. long, slightly glandular to nearly glabrous.

Native of N.W. Yunnan ; discovered and introduced by Forrest in 1913. It belongs to the charming Souliei group of the Thomsonii series, in which its yellow flowers with clearly stalked glands and more or less oblong leaves that are pale green (not glaucous) beneath chiefly distinguish it. (See also R. Wardii.)

R. LITIENSE, *Balfour fil.*, discovered in Yunnan by Forrest in 1913, is nearly akin to croceum. It has oblong leaves 2 to 3½ ins. long and ¾ to 1½ ins. wide, glaucous beneath and clear pale yellow flowers without markings, widely open and about 2 ins.

wide. The distinct calyx is ⅜ to ¾ in. wide, yellowish, with five ovate or oblong lobes edged with numerous small glands. The flower-stalk also is glandular.

R. PURALBUM, *Balfour and W. W. Smith*, is another closely related species, chiefly distinguished in this group by its pure white flowers which are 1½ to 2 ins. wide, with the ovary and pistil covered with glands from top to bottom, as is common to all this group. It is a shrub up to 12 or 15 ft. high, the leaves mostly more or less heart-shaped at the base and 2 to 4 ins. long by 1 to 2 ins. wide. Found by Forrest in Yunnan and introduced by him in 1913. It flowers at Exbury, Hants, in late May and June.

R. CUNEATUM, *W. W. Smith*

(R. calcicola, *Millais*)

An evergreen shrub of rather erect growth 4 to 6 ft. high, scaly. Leaves oval, often inclined to obovate, tapered about equally to both ends ; 1 to 2 ins. long, ½ to 1 in. wide ; dark glossy green and scaly above ; dull and rusty beneath with brownish yellow scales ; stalk ⅛ in. long. Flowers produced in April in terminal clusters of three to six. Corolla widely funnel-shaped, 1 to 1½ ins. long and wide, five-lobed, deep rose coloured, downy in the throat. Stamens ten, their white stalks with a tuft of down towards the base ; anthers brown, well exposed. Ovary scaly ; style slender, glabrous, 1 in. long. Calyx reddish, ¼ to ⅓ in. long, deeply five-lobed, the lobes scaly outside and fringed with bristles ; flower-stalk ½ to ¾ in. long. Seed-vessel ⅓ to ½ in. long, clasped at the base by the persisting enlarged calyx.

Native of the Lichiang Range, Yunnan, China, at 11,000 to 12,000 ft. altitude ; discovered by Forrest in 1906, but I think most of the plants in cultivation were raised from seed he collected in 1913. The species flowered at Caerhays in April 1917, and is quite hardy at Kew. It belongs to the Lapponicum series in which it may be identified by the following combined characters : rose-coloured flowers, glabrous style longer than the stamens, ten downy stamens, large deeply lobed calyx, corolla not scaly outside.

R. CYANOCARPUM, *Franchet*

(R. hedythamnum eglandulosum, *Balfour and Forrest*)

An evergreen shrub 5 to 12 ft. high, with glaucous green young shoots. Leaves oval to roundish, the base sometimes slightly heart-shaped ; 2½ to 4 ins. long, 1¾ to 3 ins. wide ; blue-green, ultimately dark green above, glaucous beneath, glabrous or nearly so ; stalk stout, ½ to 1⅛ ins. long. Flowers in trusses of as many as ten, fragrant. Corolla between funnel-shaped and bell-shaped, about 2 ins. long, varying from white or creamy white tinged with rose to rich rose, five-lobed, the lobes 1 in. wide and notched in the middle ; stamens ten, their stalks smooth, anthers brown ; ovary and style glabrous. Calyx cup-shaped, up to ½ in. long, with five broad lobes, glabrous, glaucous. (Thomsonii series.)

Native of W. Yunnan, China, at 10,000 to 12,000 ft. altitude ; originally discovered by the Abbé Delavay, who only saw the plant in its seed-bearing state. It remained a rather mysterious plant until Forrest, in 1906, collected it in flower on the Tali Range. It was then seen, as Franchet had duly noted, to be closely related to the Himalayan R. Thomsonii, but to differ in the colour of the flowers (those of Thomsonii are blood-red) and in their being fragrant, also in the larger, more oval, and more conspicuously veined leaves. Both have a large, cup-shaped, characteristic calyx and the bluish or bluish-purple seed-vessel to which the specific name refers. The species is in cultivation in southern and western gardens, where it flowers in March and April.

R. DAURICUM, *Linnæus*. DAHURIAN RHODODENDRON

(Bot. Mag., t. 636)

A deciduous or semi-evergreen shrub up to 6 ft. in height; young shoots scaly and downy. Leaves oval, rounded at the apex, tapering or rounded at the base; ½ to 1½ ins. long, ¼ to ⅝ in. wide; dark glossy green and slightly scaly above, paler and scaly beneath. Flowers bright rosy purple, 1 to 1½ ins. across, produced during January and February singly from each one of a cluster of scaly buds at the end of the previous summer's growth, where there are usually but one or two flowers open at a time. Corolla flat, saucer-shaped; calyx-lobes five, short.

Var. SEMPERVIRENS, *Sims*. (syn. atrovirens, *Edwards*). (Bot. Mag., t. 8930.)—An evergreen form.

Native of Siberia, and grown in English gardens since 1780. It is the earliest of rhododendrons to flower, preceding even R. Nobleanum, and showing its blossoms usually in January, sometimes even when snow is on the ground. For this reason, although its beauties are of a modest kind, it is well worth growing in a small group, preferably in some spot sufficiently sheltered to mitigate to some extent the harshness of wind and weather at the inclement season when its blossoms appear.

R. MUCRONULATUM, *Turczaninow* (Bot. Mag., t. 8304), is a close ally of R. dauricum, native of Dahuria, N. China, Manchuria and Japan; introduced in 1907. It resembles R. dauricum in being deciduous and in producing its flowers singly from terminal buds. They are pale rose-purple, about 1½ ins. across, and usually larger than in dauricum. The leaves also are larger, up to 3 ins. long, thinner in texture, more tapering at the apex, often hairy above. The two appear to be united by intermediate forms found wild, which has led some authorities to consider this merely a variety of dauricum.

R. DAVIDII, *Franchet*

An evergreen shrub, 4 to 12 ft. high, leaves and young shoots glabrous, the latter yellowish. Leaves oval-oblong, broadly wedge-shaped at the base, terminated by a short, abrupt tip; 3 to 6 ins. long, ¾ to 2 ins. broad; pale green, net-veined beneath; stalk ½ to ¾ in. long. Flowers produced ten or more together in a raceme up to 6 ins. long; corolla widely bell-shaped, 1¾ to 2 ins. across, seven-lobed, lilac-purple spotted with a deeper shade on the upper side; calyx, flower-stalk, style and ovary glandular; stamens fourteen, not downy.

Native of W. China and Tibet; discovered by the Abbé David, after whom it is named; introduced by Wilson for Messrs Veitch in 1904. An ally of R. Fargesii distinct in the glandular style.

R. DAVIDSONIANUM, *Rehder and Wilson*

(Bot. Mag., t. 8759—as R. siderophyllum)

An evergreen shrub up to 10 ft. high; young shoots at first purplish red, scaly. Leaves narrowly oblong-lanceolate, 1 to 2½ ins. long, ⅓ to ⅞ in. wide, dark glossy green and slightly scaly above, dull brown and densely scaly beneath. Flowers opening in April in clusters of two to five at the end of the shoot and in the terminal leaf-axils, each on a scaly stalk ⅓ to ½ in. long. Corolla about 1¼ ins. long, 1¾ ins. wide, pale rose with a few red dots on the upper side. Stamens ten, paler than the corolla, downy at the base. Ovary covered with minute scales ; style glabrous. Seed-vessel ⅛ in. long. (Triflorum series.)

Native of W. Szechuen, China, up to 10,000 ft. altitude ; introduced by Wilson in 1908. He describes it as very common near Tachien-lu, in sunny exposed places, where it flowers with great freedom. It belongs to the same group as R. yunnanense (Triflorum-yunnanense) but flowers earlier than that species and has more scaly leaves without bristles on the top. A distinctive character is the bending up of the two halves of the leaf from the midrib, giving it in cross section a V-shape. Seen at its best R. Davidsonianum is a very pretty shrub, its flowers delicate in hue and abundant, varying in shade and spotting.

R. LOCHMIUM, *Balfour fil.*, was confused with the above until separated by Balfour (see *Notes, Edinburgh Botanic Garden*, vol. xi., p. 90) and is no doubt still grown in many gardens under its name. The best distinction, perhaps, is in the convex or recurved form of the leaf as distinct from the concave or V-shape of Davidsonianum as noted above. There does not seem much in floral characters to distinguish them. Introduced by Wilson from W. Szechuen in 1908.

R. DEGRONIANUM, *Carrière*

(R. Metternichii pentamerum, Bot. Mag., t. 8403 ;
R. japonicum pentamerum, *Hutchinson*)

An evergreen shrub of compact, rounded shape up to 4 ft. high ; shoots glabrous or nearly so. Leaves oblong-lanceolate to narrowly obovate, decurved at the mucronate apex, 3 to 5 ins. long, 1 to 1¾ ins. wide, glabrous at maturity ; stalk ¾ to 1 in. long. Flowers eight to twelve in a rounded umbel, the corolla five-lobed, about 2¼ ins. across, soft rose-pink, the lobes rounded, 1 in. wide, notched at the apex ; stamens normally ten, white ; anthers yellow.

Native of Japan. The nomenclature of this rhododendron has been much involved and it has been mixed up with R. Metternichii and generally gone by that name in gardens. Carrière's name originally appeared in the *Revue Horticole* in 1869 with a figure of leafy shoots and a description of the leaves only. It is quite hardy and flowers in April. Its compact shape makes it useful for restricted spaces.

R. DELAVAYI, *Franchet*

(Bot. Mag., t. 8137 ; R. pilovittatum, *Balfour and W. W. Smith*)

So near is this rhododendron to R. arboreum that the description given of the latter might be repeated. R. arboreum comes from the Himalaya, R. Delavayi from W. Yunnan and Burma ; if both had come from the same area they would probably never have been separated. Mr H. F. Tagg, in *The Species of Rhododendron*, p. 17, says : " The best distinguishing feature is in the indumentum [*i.e.*, the covering of the under surface of the leaf] ; in R. arboreum it is usually thin and more or less plastered, whereas in R. Delavayi it is of somewhat spongy texture, the surface more or less fissured." This is not much to base a species upon. In nature it varies from a shrub to a tree 40 ft. high, and the flowers (as in arboreum) vary from rose-coloured to deep crimson. The " indumentum " also varies from whitish to fawn-coloured. Originally discovered by Delavay about 1884, it was first introduced to France, and thence to Kew in 1889. I believe the first flowers seen in the British Isles were borne on a plant at Kilmacurragh, Co. Wicklow, in 1904. Although it will keep alive in the open air at Kew, it is of no value there ; whilst it is hardier than the typical blood-red arboreum, it is not so hardy as arboreum cinnamomeum, which has lived in the open air at Kew for the last seventy years and occasionally flowered.

Var. ALBUM, which flowered in the Temperate House at Kew first in May 1912, has pure white flowers except for some reddish brown spots inside. Lord Stair grows a very fine crimson form at Loch Inch in Wigtownshire, almost as good as the best arboreum, and there was one similarly coloured in the Temperate House at Kew.

R. DIAPREPES, *Balfour and W. W. Smith*

(Bot. Mag., t. 9524 ; R. rasile, *Balfour fil.*)

An evergreen shrub 10 to 25 ft. high ; young shoots and leaves quite glabrous. Leaves elliptic-oblong, rounded or rather heart-shaped at the base, bluntish at the apex, described as being sometimes as much as 12 ins. long by 4 ins. wide ; usually, as I have seen them, considerably smaller ; lightish green above, rather glaucous beneath ; stalk 1 to 1¾ ins. long. Flowers rather fragrant, opening in July in trusses of seven to ten. Corolla seven-lobed, 4 to 5 ins. across, funnel-shaped at the base, white or faintly rose-tinted, greenish and downy inside the tube at the base. Stamens eighteen or twenty, downy at the base ; ovary and style glandular from top to bottom.

Native of S.W. Yunnan and N.E. Burma ; found by Forrest in 1913 and introduced by him. Both in leaf and flower this is the finest of the Fortunei series, the latter exceeding even the flower of discolor in size. It scarcely differs from R. decorum (see p. 69) in essential botanical detail, but coming from a more southern habitat is less hardy. It appears in fact to be better suited for the maritime parts of the south and west. The glanded character of calyx, flower-stalk, and corolla seems to vary a good deal in degree, and is sometimes scarcely discernible. R. discolor and R. Fortunei are distinguished by their glabrous stamens.

R. DICHROANTHUM, *Diels*

(Bot. Mag., t. 8815)

An evergreen shrub 2 to 5 ft. high, of stiff close growth ; young shoots at first white with a close down, grey the second season. Leaves obovate to oblanceolate, tapered abruptly at the apex to a short mucro, always more or less wedge-shaped at the base ; 2 to 4 ins. long, ¾ to 1½ ins. wide, dark green and glabrous above, covered beneath with a glaucous white, thin, scurfy down ; stalk ¼ to ½ in. long. Flowers opening in May, six to eight in a terminal truss. Corolla fleshy, elongated-bell-shaped, 1¾ ins. long, scarcely so wide ; the colour is variable in different plants and may be of various shades of orange, often more or less suffused with pink. Stamens ten, scarcely as long as the corolla, slightly downy at the base. Ovary very clothed with white down and fascicled hairs ; style glabrous. Calyx very variable in the size and shape of the lobes ; ¼ to 1 in. long and awl-shaped to roundish ovate ; approximating the corolla in colour ; flower-stalk ½ to 1 in. long, white with down.

Native of Yunnan, China ; discovered by Forrest in 1906 and introduced to cultivation by him. His No. 11597, which he found on the Tali Range and describes as having deep orange flowers, is perhaps the most desirable form, but others are very attractive. Forrest describes some shades as " creamy rose " or " yellowish rose." It is akin to apodectum (*q.v.*) but has more flowers in the truss and the leaves are almost always wedge-shaped at the base and widest above the middle. In its best forms this is one of the most attractive members of the sanguineum group in the Neriiflorum series, and quite hardy.

There are two other species belonging to the sanguineum group which should be mentioned, viz., R. herpesticum and R. scyphocalyx. Both have a fleshy corolla but are easily distinguished from dichroanthum and apodectum by the flower-stalks, calyces, and ovaries being furnished with glands.

R. HERPESTICUM, *Balfour and Ward*, was found by Kingdon Ward in E. Upper Burma at altitudes of 12,000 to 13,000 ft. in 1914 as a " dwarf shrub forming tangled growths covering a good deal of ground " but only one foot in height. The leaves are grey-white beneath like those of dichroanthum ; and the flowers, described as dull yellow to orange-red, are borne in trusses of four or more. Corolla about 1⅛ ins. long. Calyx cupped and coloured. Flowers in April and May.

R. SCYPHOCALYX, *Balfour and Forrest*, from N.E. Burma and W. Yunnan, was found and introduced by Forrest in 1919. It has the same close crust of greyish-white down beneath as herpesticum, but according to collectors' notes grows three to five times as high. The flowers, variable in colour as in all of this section, are " rose orange, yellowish crimson, or coppery yellow." The corolla is larger than in herpesticum, being 1¾ ins. long by 1½ ins. wide, broadly funnel-shaped. The rounded lobes of the large coloured calyx are ¼ in. long. There are four to six, or perhaps more, flowers in a truss, each with its glandular stalk ¾ to 1⅛ ins. long. It does not appear to differ from herpesticum by any character of genuine botanical importance. Farrer found this species during his expedition of 1919-20 to Upper Burma, and describes its " profusion of large pendent trumpets " as " varying from fiery bronze to flame colour, orange, and (rarely) cinnabar scarlet." It flowers at Exbury in May and June.

R. DIDYMUM, *Balfour and Forrest*

(Bot. Mag., t. 9217)

A low, evergreen shrub 1 to 3 ft. high ; young shoots bristly-glandular. Leaves of stout texture, clustered at the end of the short twigs, obovate, rounded or abruptly tapered at the apex, more or less wedge-shaped at the base ; 1 to 2 ins. long, ½ to 1 in. wide ; dark green and at first somewhat bristly above, covered beneath with a permanent grey-white down ; stalk ⅙ to ⅓ in. long. Flowers in clusters of four to eight, opening in June or July. Corolla black-crimson, between funnel- and bell-shaped, about 1 in. long and wide, five-lobed. Stamens ten, with glabrous red stalks and dark brown anthers. Ovary grooved, glandular ; style glabrous, red. Calyx ⅛ in. long, very bristly-glandular like the slender flower-stalk which is ¾ to 1⅛ in. long. (Neriiflorum series.)

Native of S.E. Tibet ; discovered and introduced by Forrest in 1917. The black-crimson colour of its flowers distinguishes it from all the others of the sanguineum group except R. hæmaleum, and from that it can readily be recognised by the glandular bristles on young shoot, calyx, and flower-stalk ; the flowers also are smaller. It should be mentioned, however, that rhododendrons intermediate between the two exist in a wild state ; they may be of hybrid origin as the native areas are known to overlap. In both the colour is rather funereal unless lit up by a gleam of sunshine. It is hardy and may be given a place in the middle elevation of the rock garden, where the light may show through its blossoms.

R. DILATATUM, *Miquel*

(Bot. Mag., t. 7681 ; Azalea dilatata, *Kuntze*)

A deciduous azalea of rather thin habit, probably 4 to 6 ft. high ; branches almost or quite glabrous. Leaves often in threes at the end of the twig, ovate or somewhat diamond shaped ; 1 to 2½ ins. long, ⅝ to 1½ ins. wide ; soon glabrous on both surfaces, bright green above, pale and finely net-veined beneath ;

stalk ⅛ to ½ in. long. Flowers usually in pairs, 2 ins. or rather more across, purple, unspotted ; corolla lobes oblong, rounded at the apex, the three upper ones erect, the lower ones pointed downwards and more deeply cut ; calyx small, almost entire ; flowers-stalk ⅛ in. long, slightly hairy ; stamens five ; ovary covered with glands, not hairy ; style smooth.

Native of Japan ; introduced by Messrs Veitch in 1883. It is very similar in general appearance to R. reticulatum (rhombicum) but from that species as well as Mariesii and Albrechtii it is at once recognised by having only five stamens. Out of flower it is distinguished from reticulatum by its smooth adult leaves. Blossoming in April, it is very charming then. In my experience it is hardier and more amenable to cultivation than R. reticulatum. It can be increased by cuttings.

R. DIPHROCALYX, *Balfour fil.*

(Millais' Rhododendrons, 2nd series, p. 152 ; R. burriflorum, *Balfour fil.*)

An evergreen shrub 5 to 15 ft. high ; young shoots and leaf-stalks clothed with a mixture of glandular bristles and short down. Leaves 2½ to 6 ins. long, 1 to 2¼ ins. wide ; elliptical to oblong, bright green above, pale and rather glaucous beneath, nearly or quite glabrous at maturity except on the midrib ; stalk ½ to ¾ in. long. Flowers opening in April and said to have as many as twenty flowers in a truss. Corolla bell-shaped, 1¼ ins. long, bright red to light rosy crimson with a crimson blotch at the base and crimson spots. Stamens ten, slightly downy at the base ; ovary covered with tawny down as is also the base of the style. Calyx very large, ½ to ¾ in. long, unequally five-lobed, rather bell-shaped, bright red, but conspicuously spotted on one side. Flower-stalk ¾ in. long, clothed with loose wool.

Native of W. Yunnan, China. It first appeared as a " rogue " amongst R. habrotrichum in Mr Magor's garden at Lamellen in Cornwall, where it flowered in 1918. Sir Isaac Balfour appears first to have regarded it as a hybrid. Mr Tagg, however, has united with it the R. burriflorum described as a species by Balfour in the *Edinburgh Botanic Garden Notes*, vol. xiii., p. 34, where it is recorded as having been found by Forrest in W. Yunnan in 1918. It is remarkable for the size and colouring of its corolla-like calyx. Placed in the glischrum section of the Barbatum series, it is distinguished therein by the flower-stalks having no glands, although quite woolly. A handsome rhododendron scarcely hardy enough to succeed at Kew.

R. DISCOLOR, *Franchet*

A shrub, 10 to 18 ft. high, of robust habit, free from down in all its parts ; young shoots stout, yellowish. Leaves oblong or narrowly oval, 3 to 8 ins. long, ¾ to 2½ ins. wide ; tapered about equally at both ends, sometimes heart-shaped at the base, the apex with a short mucro ; upper surface deep green, lower one pale ; stalk ½ to 1¼ ins. long, stout, purple. Flowers white or faintly bluish-tinted ; corolla funnel-shaped, 2½ to 3 ins. long and wide, six- or seven-lobed. Stamens twelve to sixteen, not downy, shorter than the corolla ; ovary and style glandular ; calyx small, glandular on the margins at first ; seed-vessel 1½ ins. long, ½ in. thick.

Native of W. and Central China ; introduced by Wilson in 1900. It belongs to the same group as R. Fortunei, which has its leaves almost uniformly heart-shaped at the base. The foliage of young bushes is of greater size than stated above. The species starts into growth very late and does not flower until June or July. A fine species and quite hardy.

R. EDGARIANUM, *Rehder and Wilson*

(R. oresbium, *Balfour and Forrest*)

An intricately branched, evergreen shrub up to 3 ft. high ; young shoots scurfy. Leaves aromatic, oval, ¼ to ½ in. long, about half as much wide, tapered about equally towards both ends ; dull dark green and scaly above ; pale and with contiguous, shining (at first) scales beneath. Flowers solitary or in pairs, opening in May. Corolla ¾ to 1 in. wide, rose-purple, deeply five-lobed, the lobes oblong, rounded at the end, not scaly outside. Stamens ten, their hairy tufts near the base filling up the tube of the corolla ; anthers pale yellowish brown. Ovary scaly ; style purple, glabrous. Calyx deeply five-lobed, the oval-oblong lobes $\frac{1}{12}$ in. long, more or less scaly outside and fringed with hairs.

Native of W. Szechuen, China, where Wilson found it in 1908, forming heath-like areas at 13,000 to 15,000 ft. altitude. It is one of the numerous and outwardly very similar species of the Lapponicum series in which the following combination of characters may distinguish it ; leaves usually less than ½ in. long ; inflorescence one- or two-flowered ; flower-bud scales dropping early ; flowers purple ; corolla neither downy nor scaly outside ; style glabrous and as long as the stamens. It is very hardy. Very near to it, botanically, is

R. YUNGNINGENSE, *Balfour fil.*, which has all the characters just enumerated but with the calyx lobes scarcely scaly outside and the leaves of oblong-lanceolate shape. It is one of Forrest's discoveries in S.W. Szechuen, where it grows on mountains at 13,000 to 14,000 ft. altitude. In the same alliance comes

R. FASTIGIATUM, *Franchet*, a native of Yunnan and a small shrub of erect habit, with pale purple flowers borne in clusters of four or five. Discovered by Delavay in 1883.

R. EDGEWORTHII, *Hooker fil.*

(Bot. Mag., t. 4936)

In characters of flower, leaf, and branches this rhododendron is so like R. bullatum already described that it is unnecessary to repeat the description in detail. They have the same puckered or bullate upper surface of the leaf, the same tawny felt on the lower surface and young shoots, and the same large, deliciously scented, waxy-white flowers. They differ, however, in two respects : the five large, rounded lobes of the calyx in Edgeworthii are clothed outside with tawny down ; in bullatum the down is confined to the margins, and the main part of the lobes is furnished with scales only ; then the style of Edgeworthii is shaggy with wool on the lower third and not scaly, whereas in bullatum it is scaly and only slightly downy towards the base. R. bullatum is of sturdier habit. (Edgeworthii series.)

Native of the Himalaya in Sikkim and Bhotan ; discovered in the former country by J. D. Hooker in 1849 and introduced to Kew soon after. It is an evergreen shrub of loose, straggling habit a few feet high and often found wild growing in the forks of trees. More tender than bullatum, it can still be grown in the open air in Cornwall ; at Caerhays I have seen it beautifully in flower in late April and May. But for somewhat less favourable localities bullatum is the more reliable species. A very fine race of hybrids has been raised from it, such as " Princess Alice " (a cross with R. ciliatum raised by Veitch in 862), Forsterianum, fragrantissimum, " Lady Alice Fitzwilliam," Sesterianum, etc.

R. ELÆAGNOIDES, *Hooker fil.*

(Hooker's Sikkim Rhododendrons, t. 23 ; R. sinolepidotum, *Balfour fil.* ;
R. cremnastes, *Balfour fil.*)

A dwarf evergreen shrub usually under 1 ft. high, with slender, warty twigs.
Leaves roundish oval or obovate, ¼ to ⅝ in. long, densely covered on both
surfaces with scales that overlap each other beneath. Flowers usually solitary,
each on a slender, loosely scaly stalk up to 1 in. long. Corolla flat and open,
to 1 in. wide. usually of some shade of yellow, five-lobed, densely scaly
outside. Stamens eight or ten, downy near the base. Ovary scaly ; style
glabrous, bent over. Calyx with five broad, spreading, reddish lobes, scaly
outside.

Discovered in Sikkim by J. D. Hooker in 1849 up to altitudes of 16,000 ft.,
flowering there in June and July. Hooker observes that it grows " in widely
extended clumps much as heather does, but never so extensively, emitting in
sunshine a powerful resinous odour." The Himalayan plant seems to be very
rare in cultivation and I do not remember to have seen it in flower. Coming
from such high elevations, it is likely to be most successfully grown in the cool
moist parts of North Britain. Hooker's figure, quoted above, depicts the
flower of a charming bright yellow, but he describes that of some of his collected
specimens as " dirty yellow." (Lepidotum series.)

Two of Balfour's species, viz., R. sinolepidotum, introduced in 1906 by
Forrest from Yunnan, and R. cremnastes, found by Farrer in Upper Burma,
are now united with elæagnoides. The former is in cultivation and flowered at
Edinburgh as long ago as May 1910. Both have rose-coloured or pink flowers
and it has to be mentioned that Hooker records some Sikkim plants as having
" red-purple " blossom. Kingdon Ward in 1926 also found some plants with
yellow flowers, others with purple ones. Forrest's sinolepidotum bears its
flowers sometimes in pairs or threes.

R. ELLIOTTII, *Watt*

(Bot. Mag., t. 9546)

A small evergreen tree, much branched ; young shoots furnished with
short, branched hairs. Leaves narrowly oval-oblong, pointed, narrowed to
the stalk, 4 to 6 ins. long, two-fifths as wide, dull green above, shining beneath,
stalk about 1 in. long, downy when quite young. Flowers in a terminal truss
of about twelve, 5 ins. across, opening in late May and June ; corolla rich
scarlet, funnel-shaped below, spreading at the top into five rounded, notched
lobes which give it a diameter of 2½ ins., freely crimson spotted ; stamens ten,
red, glabrous.

Native of Assam and one of the finest of all red-flowered rhododendrons.
It was discovered by Sir George Watt in 1882, but the plants at cultivation
were raised from seeds collected by Kingdon Ward as lately as 1927. It
succeeds very well at Exbury and will probably need a similar climate elsewhere
in the south and west to bring out its best qualities.

R. EMASCULUM, *W. Watson*

An evergreen shrub up to 6 ft. high, of open bushy growth, young wood
and leaves scaly. Leaves oval, tapered towards both ends, 1 to 2 ins. long,
to 1 in. wide ; dark glossy green above, covered with brown scales beneath ;
stalk ⅛ to ¼ in. long. Flowers solitary or in pairs at the end of the shoot ;

corolla 1½ to 2 ins. wide, five-lobed, the lobes rounded and wavy, pale lilac
purple, unspotted ; calyx scarcely lobed, scaly ; stamens none or aborted
ovary scaly, style glabrous.

A hybrid, the origin of which does not appear to have been recorded
I first saw it in the Coombe Wood Nursery about 1910. It is a pretty, early
flowering shrub easily increased by cuttings and useful for forcing early int
bloom for greenhouse decoration. It is rendered distinct by having no rea
stamens (such as are there being reduced to mere abortions ranged round th
base of the ovary) but its appearance is not improved thereby. Its ancestr
is no doubt shared by R. dauricum, from which it derives its colour, earl
flowering, and often solitary flowers. It is certainly closely akin to R. præco:
(see p. 48) and may have been raised from it. R. emasculum flowers som
two or three weeks later than præcox—in March or early April.

R. ERIOGYNUM, *Balfour and W. W. Smith*
(Bot. Mag., t. 9337)

An evergreen shrub up to 10 ft. high; young shoots soon glabrous. Leave
oblong-elliptic or oblanceolate, the apex pointed or rounded ; 4 to 8 ins. long
1¼ to 3 ins. wide; ultimately glabrous on both surfaces, glittering beneath
with a thin transparent marginal line ; stalk ½ to 1¼ ins. long. Flowers in
truss of twelve to sixteen, opening in June. Corolla bell-shaped, 1¾ ins. deep
2 ins. wide, clear bright red with five deep purple pouches at the base, five
lobed. Stamens ten, 1 in. or more long, downy at the lower third or hal
Ovary densely covered with tawny, starry down, which extends more thinl
up the style. Calyx ⅛ in. long, fleshy, reddish, the lobes wavy.

Native of Yunnan, China ; discovered in 1914 by Forrest at 9000 f
altitude, east of Tali Lake. This beautiful species is only hardy in the sout
and west, some of the most vigorous plants I have seen being at Caerhays an
in Major G. H. Johnstone's garden at Trewithen in Cornwall. It is one c
the Irroratum series and belongs to the group including Kyawi (prophantum
and agapetum which have fine crimson or scarlet blossoms and are curiousl
late in breaking into new growth. R. eriogynum is one of the very best c
the late-flowering species.

R. FACETUM, *Balfour and Ward*, is very closely akin to, and probably n
specifically distinct from eriogynum. Kingdon Ward discovered it in E. Burm
15 to 20 ft. high, in June 1914, just coming into bloom. It comes from a moister regio
than eriogynum and its leaves are of thinner texture and it is probably rather mo
tender. The main and secondary flower-stalks are more or less glandular ; the
are not so in eriogynum. It flowered in the open air at Caerhays in April 1926 an
at Exbury in June 1930. Farrer described it as the " finest blazing crimson-scarl
of any rhododendron I have yet seen."

R. EUDOXUM, *Balfour and Forrest*

An evergreen shrub of the sanguineum group 3 to 6 ft. high ; young shoo
slender. Leaves oval-oblong or somewhat obovate, tapered more gradual
towards the base than the apex ; 2 to 4 ins. long, ¾ to 1½ ins. wide ; dull gree
above, thinly downy beneath and becoming glabrous or nearly so ; stalk abou
¼ in. long. Flowers in a cluster of five to eight, opening in June. Corol
narrowly bell-shaped, 1¼ ins. long and wide, " deep clear crimson-rose with fe
markings " (Forrest), five-lobed. Stamens ten, up to 1 in. long, faintly dowr
near the base. Ovary cylindric, bristly and downy ; style glabrous. Calyx ⅛ i
long, the five rounded lobes margined with glanded hairs. Flower-sta
downy and glandular, up to ¾ in. long. (Neriiflorum series.)

Native of N.W. Yunnan, up to 13,000 ft. altitude; discovered and intro-
ced by Forrest in 1917-18. It and several sub-species constitute a section of
sanguineum group having leaves with little or no down beneath them, and
hin-textured corolla. There are eight subspecies which vary chiefly in the
aracter of the leaf-covering beneath; one of them, GLAPHYRUM, has flowers
ally rose but varying from white to yellow.

R. EXQUISITUM, *Hutchinson*
(Bot. Mag., t. 9597)

An evergreen shrub up to 10 ft. high; young shoots purple, at first slightly
ly, finally glabrous. Leaves scattered on the shoots, 1¾ to 2¼ ins. long,
re than half as wide, dark green and glabrous above, glaucous and scaly
neath; veins in five to nine pairs; stalk scarcely ½ in. long. Flowers eight
ten in a loose, terminal cluster, opening in May. Corolla widely funnel-
ped, nearly 3 ins. wide, deeply five-lobed, the lobes oval-oblong, nearly
n. wide, unspotted and of an exquisite pink; the tubular base is short and
rrow. Stamens ten, downy towards the base; anthers yellowish brown;
ary very densely scaly; style glabrous.
Native of S.W. Szechuen " on open rocky hillsides on the mountains east
Yung-ning," found by Forrest and introduced by him in 1921. It belongs
the Oreotrephes group of the Yunnanense series in which its unspotted
olla is distinctive. Dr Hutchinson regards it as probably the gem of its
ies. It is hardy.

R. FALCONERI, *Hooker fil.*
(Bot. Mag., t. 4924)

A large shrub or a small tree, ultimately over 30 ft. high, with stiff, very
ck, somewhat sparse branches, woolly when young. Leaves oval or oblong,
o 12 ins. long, 2½ to 6 ins. wide (sometimes larger); very stout, thick, and
ongly veined; the upper surface dark green, curiously wrinkled, but
erwise smooth; the lower surface covered with a dense, rust-coloured felt;
lk 1 to 2 ins. long. Flowers about 2 ins. across, creamy white, shaded with
c and marked with a conspicuous dark purple blotch at the base, fragrant,
oduced in spring in large terminal clusters 6 to 9 ins. across; the twenty
more flowers tightly packed. Corolla bell-shaped, 2 ins. long, its lobes
rying in number from eight to ten; calyx scarcely observable; stamens
elve to sixteen, shorter than the corolla; style about as long as the corolla,
ut, and surmounted by the large knob-like stigma; flower-stalk downy,
n. long.
Native of the Himalaya; introduced about 1850. A rhododendron nearly
ntical (sino-Falconeri) has been found in China. This is one of the noblest
all the genus, but not very hardy. It cannot be described as a genuine
ccess in the open air at Kew but it has occasionally flowered there. Yet in
Duchess's garden at Belvoir Castle there used to be a specimen about
ft. high in perfect health, although it suffered in the great frost of February
95. But this garden is elevated, and is in the form of an amphitheatre facing
ith, a very favourable position compared with low-lying, flat country. In
south coast gardens, in Ireland and in Cornwall it is perfectly at home.
Var. EXIMIUM has pink flowers and reddish down on both surfaces of the
ves—a fine variety.
There is a hybrid between Falconeri and niveum to be found in several
rdens in the south and west of England.

R. FARGESII, *Franchet*

An evergreen shrub, 10 ft. high, of bushy habit; leaves oblong-ova rounded at the apex, slightly cordate at the base, 2 to 3½ ins. long, 1½ to 2½ i wide, dull grey-green above, pale and rather glaucous beneath, glabrous maturity on both surfaces; stalk 1 to 1¼ ins. long. Flowers in a terminal tr of six to eight. Corolla widely funnel-shaped, seven-lobed, 2 ins. deep, 2½ i wide, pale rose or purplish pink, often with deeper spots on the upper si Calyx shallowly seven-lobed, glandular-downy like the flower-stalk; stame twelve or fourteen, glabrous, about half as long as the corolla, white w brown anthers; style longer than stamens, glabrous; ovary glandular.

Native of E. Szechuen, China, where it was discovered by Père Farge introduced by Wilson in 1901. It flowers in late April, and is allied to oreodoxa, but that species is well distinguished by the glabrous ovary.

R. FARRERÆ, *Tate*

(Azalea Farreræ, *K. Koch*; A. squamata, *Lindley*, Bot. Reg., vol. 33, t. 3)

A low, deciduous or semi-evergreen azalea; young shoots furnished w brown, appressed, bristly hairs; grey and glabrous the second year. Leav usually two to four at the end of the twigs, ovate to oval or rarely obova pointed; ¾ to 1½ ins. long, ¼ to 1 in. wide; bristly on the midrib beneath wh young, and on the margins otherwise glabrous; distinctly net-veined beneat stalk ¼ in. or less long, hairy like the young shoots. Flowers solitary or tw opening in spring. Corolla 1½ to 2 ins. wide, rose-coloured, of varying depth shade with purple spots on the upper lobes; the tube short, funnel-shape spreading into five oblong, round-ended lobes. Stamens eight or ten, ½ to ¾ long, glabrous. Ovary covered with erect brown bristles; style well protrud glabrous. Calyx small, covered like the very short flower-stalk with brown dov

Native of Hong Kong and the adjacent mainland of China; introduced Captain Farrer of the East India Company in 1829. It was again introduc to the Horticultural Society's garden at Chiswick by Fortune and flower there about 1846. It is very rare in cultivation now. It is found in the sa region as R. Championæ and is only likely to succeed in the very mildest pa of Britain in the open air. It is most nearly related to R. Mariesii (see p. 1 which has a leaf-stalk up to ½ in. long; both these belong to the same group azaleas as Schlippenbachii and rhombicum (the latter now called reticulatur

R. FERRUGINEUM, *Linnæus*. ROSE DES ALPES

(Loddiges' Botanical Cabinet, t. 65)

A dwarf, slow-growing, evergreen shrub of close habit, ultimately 3 or 4 high and wide, forming a dense hemispherical mass; young shoots cover with rust-coloured scales. Leaves narrow-oblong or oval, tapering at bc ends, 1 to 1¾ ins. long, ¼ to ½ in. wide; dark glossy green and slightly sca above, but thickly covered beneath with golden brown, ultimately rust-colour scales. Flowers rosy scarlet or deep rose, ½ to ¾ in. wide and long, produc in June in terminal clusters of six to twelve blossoms; corolla scaly outsi funnel-shaped at the base, with five spreading, oblong lobes; calyx-lobes ve short; stamens ten, hairy at the base; flower-stalk ¼ in. long, scaly.

Native of the European Alps, occupying the zone of vegetation imme ately above the pines and junipers. Said by Aiton to have been introduc in 1752. Visitors to the Alps well know this shrub as the "Alpine rose," oft covering miles of mountain side and making one of the most gorgeous

Alpine pictures in July. It finds the conditions of the Thames Valley too hot and dry for it, but in the cooler midland and northern counties is a charming bush of neat, healthy aspect, flowering freely every summer. It has produced several varieties, some, no doubt, of garden origin, which vary chiefly in the colour of the blossom, but even in a wild state one may notice in a day's walk many variations of colour between rosy pink and rosy scarlet, and on rare occasions a white-flowered plant.

Var. ALBUM.—Flowers white.

Var. ATROCOCCINEUM.—The form whose flowers most nearly approach scarlet.

Var. VARIEGATUM.—Leaves bordered with a thin line of creamy white— of no value.

Var. MYRTIFOLIUM (R. myrtifolium, *Schott and Kotschy* ; R. Kotschyi, *Simk.*), sometimes regarded as a distinct species, was recognised in the Austrian Alps about 1850. It has the general aspect of R. ferrugineum, but is usually smaller in habit ; its leaves average under 1 in. in length, the corolla is downy outside, and it is especially distinguished by the much shorter style. In the typical form the flowers are of the same colour as in ferrugineum, but there is also one with white flowers. (Bot. Mag., t. 9132, as R. Kotschyi.)

R. FICTOLACTEUM, *Balfour fil.*

(Bot. Mag., t. 8372 as R. lacteum ; R. lacteum macrophyllum, *Franchet*)

In our first and second editions this rhododendron was described under the name "lacteum," thereby following the *Botanical Magazine*. It was afterwards shown by Sir Isaac Balfour (see *Gardeners' Chronicle*, 25th March 1916, p. 168) that it was not the true lacteum of Franchet, but the rhododendron Franchet had named R. lacteum macrophyllum. Balfour justly concluded that it was a good species and gave it the above name.

It is an evergreen tree said to be as much as 45 ft. high ; young shoots clothed with brownish down. Leaves varying from narrowly elliptical to oblanceolate and from tapered to slightly heart-shaped at the base, the apex rounded and mucronate ; 5 to 12 ins. long, 2 to 4½ ins. wide ; dark green and glabrous above, covered beneath with a dense brown felt ; stalk ¾ to 1½ ins. long. Flowers opening in April or early May in a truss of twelve to fifteen. Corolla bell-shaped, 1¾ to 2½ ins. wide, white, creamy white, or rose-tinted, with a dark crimson blotch at the base, seven- or eight-lobed. Stamens fourteen or sixteen, unequal in length but all shorter than the corolla, downy at the base ; anthers red-brown. Ovary felted ; style glabrous ; calyx inconspicuous ; flower-stalks 1 to 1½ ins. long.

Discovered in W. China by Delavay about 1884 ; introduced from Paris to Kew in 1889 ; first flowered in this country at South Lodge, Horsham, in 1910. Several later importations of seeds have been made by Forrest and forms superior to the original type in flower and foliage have been raised. The species belongs to the Falconeri series and is hardy at Kew. (See also *lacteum* and *galactinum*.)

R. FLAVIDUM, *Franchet*

(Bot. Mag., t. 8326 ; R. primulinum, *Hemsley*)

An evergreen shrub about 2 ft. high, of rounded, bushy habit, branches densely scaly. Leaves leathery, ovate-oblong, ½ to 1 in. long, ¼ to ⅜ in. wide ; rounded at the base, dark green above, paler beneath, scaly on both surfaces ;

III   C stalk ⅛ in. long. Flowers 1 to 1¼ ins. across, primrose-yellow, becoming paler with age, produced during April in a terminal cluster of three to six. Corolla with a very short, rather downy tube, and flat, spreading, rounded lobes, wavy at the margins. Calyx pale green, the five lobes oblong, ¼ in. long, covered like the flower-stalk (which is ⅛ in. long) with transparent yellowish scales.

RHODODENDRON FLAVIDUM

Native of W. Szechuen, China; introduced to cultivation by Wilson for Messrs Veitch in 1905. This delightful little species is very distinct through the clear pale yellow of its flowers, and is a most promising acquisition for the rock garden or some place where dainty little plants can grow without danger of being overrun by stronger neighbours. The leaves when crushed have a pleasant, aromatic odour.

R. FLOCCIGERUM,
Franchet

(Bot. Mag., t. 9290)

An evergreen shrub 3 to 5 ft. (perhaps ultimately more) high; young shoots clothed at first with brownish red wool. Leaves narrowly oblong-lanceolate, sharply pointed, tapered at the base; 2 to 4½ ins. long, ⅓ to 1 in. wide; dull green and glabrous above, covered with loose brownish red wool beneath; stalk ¼ to ½ in. long. Flowers opening during March and April in trusses of four to eight. Corolla bell-shaped, 1¼ ins. long and wide, five-lobed; in colour it is very variable, ranging from blood-red to yellow tinged with rose. Stamens ten, about 1 in. long, quite glabrous; anthers black-purple. Ovary clothed with whitish felt; style about as long as the stamens, downy only near the ovary (if at all). Calyx ⅛ in. wide, shallowly five-lobed. Flower-stalk ⅓ to ½ in. long, loosely downy.

Native of Yunnan, China, and E. Tibet; discovered by the Abbé Soulié in 1895; introduced in 1914 by Forrest, who found it at altitudes up to 13,000 ft. I first saw it in flower at Caerhays in April 1922, its blooms there being of somewhat the same hue as those of the blood-red R. arboreum. But the colour in this species varies a good deal and a plant at Kew bears flowers of rich salmon red. I have not seen one with flowers of a good yellow, but some of an indeterminate mixture of rose and yellow shades are very poor and dull. One of the best is depicted in the *Botanical Magazine* (loc. cit. supra). The species is hardy enough for Kew. The narrow leaves, covered thickly beneath with loose rufous floss, constitute one of its most distinctive characters in the section to which it has been assigned. (Neriiflorum.)

R. FLORIBUNDUM, *Franchet*

(Bot. Mag., t. 9609)

An evergreen shrub up to 16 ft. high in a wild state ; of stiff erect habit when young ; branchlets clothed with grey down. Leaves of stiff, hard leathery texture, elliptical-lanceolate, tapered at both ends ; margins recurved ; 3 to 6 ins. long, 1 to 1¾ ins. wide ; dark dull green, much wrinkled above, clothed beneath with a dull white felt ; stalk ½ to ¾ in. long. Flowers in a compact truss of eight to twelve flowers, opening in April. Corolla purplish lavender at first, turning paler, with a blackish crimson blotch at the base and spots on the upper side ; bell-shaped, five-lobed, 2 to 3 ins. wide. Stamens ten, anthers brown, ovary clothed with erect white bristles, style 1½ ins. long, glabrous or slightly downy at the base like the stamens. Calyx minutely triangularly lobed and, like the short flower-stalk, felted with white down.

Native of W. Szechuen, China ; discovered by David in 1869 ; introduced by Wilson in 1903. I first saw this species in bloom in Lt.-Col. Roger's garden at Riverhill, near Sevenoaks, in April 1920. The flowers vary in colouring, and the better lavender-coloured forms are very pleasing. Lt.-Col. Stephenson-Clarke has a particularly fine form at Borde Hill, in Sussex, with flowers 3 ins. wide and a large, deep maroon blotch at the base of the corolla. The plant has a curiously stiff, hard appearance that makes it easily recognisable. It is moderately hardy at Kew but is seen to better advantage farther south. (Arboreum series.)

R. FORMOSUM, *Wallich*

(Bot. Mag., t. 4457 ; R. Gibsonii, *Paxton*)

An evergreen shrub of rather open thin habit, 8 or 10 ft. high ; young shoots, leaves, flower-stalks, calyx, and ovary scaly. Leaves oblanceolate to obovate, usually broadest above the middle, tapered at the base, pointed ; 1½ to 3 ins. long, ½ to 1½ ins. wide ; glossy green above, glaucous beneath ; margins and leaf-stalks usually fringed with long hairs when young. Flowers sweetly scented, produced two to four together in May and June. Corolla funnel-shaped, 2 to 2½ ins. long ; white tinged with pink, yellow in the throat, with the five lobes roundish ovate and about 1 in. long. Stamens ten, shorter than the corolla, densely clothed with hairs on the lower half. Ovary six-celled ; style well protruded, scaly at the base. Calyx very small ; flower-stalks up to ½ in. long. (Maddenii series.)

Native of the Khasia Hills, Assam ; introduced about 1845 by Gibson (who collected plants for the then Duke of Devonshire) and named after him by Paxton. But it had been discovered in 1815 and previously named by Wallich in 1832. In the south and south-western counties it succeeds well out-of-doors, but in our average climate needs protection in winter. Being easily cultivated and bearing charmingly fragrant flowers, it has long been a favourite. Some beautiful hybrids have been raised from it crossed with Edgeworthii, *e.g.*, SESTERIANUM and FRAGRANTISSIMUM.

R. JOHNSTONEANUM, *Watt*, was at first considered to be a variety of formosum, but on the basis of its much more bristly shoots, its obovate leaves up to 4 ins. long, and especially its calyx densely fringed with longish hairs, it is now regarded as a distinct species. Flowers white, 2½ ins. long, blotched with yellow at the base, spotted with red. Native of Manipur, Assam ; discovered by Sir George Watt in 1882. It needs cool greenhouse conditions at Kew. Another species closely related to formosum is

R. VEITCHIANUM, *Hooker* (Bot. Mag., t. 4992 ; R. formosum Veitchianum,

Kurz). It is an epiphytic species, being found in nature growing on trees or rocks, rarely or never in ordinary soil. Leaves 2 to 4 ins. long, always broadest above the middle, glaucous beneath. Flowers pure white, 3 ins. long, 4 ins. wide. Native of Burma and Siam ; introduced about 1850 by Thomas Lobb to Veitch's nursery at Exeter. It differs from formosum in the following respects : leaves and flowers larger ; young shoots, leaf-margins and leaf-stalks not bristly-hairy. More tender than formosum, I do not recall having seen it cultivated anywhere in the open air. It belongs to, and is one of the finest of, the ciliicalyx section of the Maddenii group, the calyx usually having a few long hairs on the margin. Crossed with Edgeworthii it has produced R. FORSTERIANUM. These three species belong to the Maddenii-ciliicalyx group.

R. FORRESTII, *Balfour fil.*

(Bot. Mag., t. 9186 ; R. repens, *Balfour and Forrest*)

A slow-growing, creeping, evergreen shrub a few inches high on the level, but capable, according to Forrest, of climbing the faces of moist rocks 3 to 5 ft. high, attaching itself, like ivy, by roots from the stems. Leaves broadly obovate to nearly orbicular, rounded at the apex, usually more or less tapered at the base ; ½ to 1½ ins. long, ⅓ to ⅞ in. wide ; dark glossy green and with conspicuously grooved veins above, pale beneath or more or less stained with purple ; stalk ⅛ to ½ in. long, reddish, slightly downy and glandular. Flowers usually solitary, but sometimes in pairs or threes. Corolla narrowly bell-shaped, 1¾ ins. long and wide, deep crimson, with five rounded deeply notched lobes. Stamens ten, white, glabrous ; anthers dark brown. Ovary conical, clad with pale glands ; style glabrous, longer than the stamens. Calyx small, shallow, fringed with glands. Flower-stalk up to 1 in. long glandular, bearing large bracts at the base. Blossoms in April and May. (Neriiflorum series.)

Native of N.W. Yunnan and S.E. Tibet, up to 14,000 ft. altitude ; discovered by Forrest in 1905 ; introduced by him in 1914. This little rhododendron is remarkably distinct from any other previously introduced in its creeping habit ; and for so small a plant the flowers are extraordinarily large. It is now the type species of a small group. Balfour considered R. repens distinct enough to rank as a species, one of his chief reasons being that the under surface of the leaf was pale green or glaucous whilst that of Forrestii was deep reddish purple. Even if fixed and regular, Dr Stapf (see *Bot. Mag., loc. cit. supra*) considered this too slight a distinction and therefore reduced R. repens to a synonym of Forrestii. The species is quite hardy and seems to grow best with us planted in association with stones as it occurs in nature. Whilst it likes continuous moisture at the root, it must have perfect drainage. The rock garden is consequently suggested as a suitable place for it.

Var. CHAMÆTHAUMA is a rather more erect grower and a taller shrub with oval or obovate leaves 1 to 2½ ins. long, green beneath, and rounded at the apex ; the flowers come four or five in a truss, are broader than those of Forrestii and in colour rose or carmine. Found by Kingdon Ward in S.E. Tibet flowering in June 1924. It seems almost distinct enough to rank as a species, or it may be a natural hybrid.

Two other rhododendrons in the Forrestii alliance differ in much the same way, viz., PORPHYROPHYLLUM and SERPENS, the former being purplish, the latter pale green beneath the leaf. They have the same creeping mode of growth as Forrestii but are of stouter growth, and the flowers differ in being rose-coloured. The leaves, too, are of distinct shape, being oval to oblong-obovate, pointed, the larger ones 2 ins. by ¾ in. wide. Dr Stapf does not consider them specifically distinct. Completing the group comes R. ERASTUM, which also has clear rose-coloured flowers but small, very narrow, linear, oblong leaves, rarely more than 1 in. long and ⅕ to ⅖ in. wide. Probably they would come larger under cultivation but I do not know that any of these rosy-flowered members of the Forrestii group are introduced. R. Forrestii and the other species mentioned here as its close allies form a group in the Neriiflorum series.

R. FORTUNEI, *Lindley*

(Bot. Mag., t. 5596)

An evergreen shrub, ultimately 10 to 12 ft. high, usually less in this country and of wide-spreading habit ; branches stout, soon glabrous. Leaves oblong, with a tapering, rounded, or heart-shaped base, abruptly pointed ; 4 to 8 ins. long, 2 to 3½ ins. wide ; quite glabrous on both surfaces, pale green above, slightly glaucous beneath ; stalk stout, purplish, ½ to 1 in. long. Flowers fragrant, produced in May, somewhat loosely arranged in terminal clusters of eight to twelve ; each blossom is 2½ to 3 ins. across, of a lovely blush tint on opening, becoming paler afterwards ; corolla seven- (or rarely eight-) lobed, flattish ; calyx so small as to be scarcely discernible ; stamens fourteen to sixteen, much shorter than the corolla, glabrous ; ovary and base of style glandular.

Native of E. China ; discovered by Fortune on mountains west of Ning Po, and introduced by him about 1855. It is a beautiful rhododendron, and is of interest in having a seven-lobed corolla and spicily fragrant flowers. It was the first hardy species of true Rhododendron (as distinct from Azalea) received from China—now the headquarters of the genus. For many years it has been grown outside at Kew, and is quite hardy. Propagated by seeds, which it ripens freely, or by grafting on R. ponticum.

Fortune's rhododendron has in recent years acquired a revived interest in giving birth to a new, distinct, and beautiful race of hardy kinds. The first experiments in hybridising this species were made by Mr Luscombe, an amateur residing in Devonshire ; crossing it with R. Thomsoni, he obtained the fine R. Luscombei and Luscombei splendens. Crossing it with garden varieties, he obtained the two kinds afterwards named " Mrs Thiselton-Dyer " and " Frances Thiselton-Dyer." These crosses appear to have been made about 1880. Soon after that date Mr G. Paul of Cheshunt made an extensive series of crosses, with R. Fortunei as the seed-bearing parent. From these, some scores of varieties were obtained that may be said to have laid the foundation of the new Fortunei race, the value of which is that they flower earlier than the great mass of catawbiense and ponticum hybrids, and thus help to extend the rhododendron season. And they have, besides their lovely and delicate colouring, often the additional charm of a fragrance inherited from R. Fortunei.

R. DECORUM, *Franchet*, is closely allied to R. Fortunei, and is perhaps its representative in W. China. It has the same seven-lobed corolla and fragrant blossoms, but it differs in the larger, thicker, grey-green leaves, a more sturdy habit, and in the stamens being downy or glandular at the base. Introduced in 1889. A very attractive species. R. Spooneri, *Hemsley and Wilson*, is apparently identical with R. decorum. (Bot. Mag., t. 8659.)

R. FULGENS, *Hooker fil.*

(Bot. Mag., t. 5317)

An evergreen shrub, 6 to 12 ft. high, with stiff branches and peeling bark. Leaves oval, 3 to 4 ins. long, 1½ to 2 ins. wide ; rounded at the end except for a short, abrupt tip ; somewhat heart-shaped at the base ; covered beneath with a thick reddish brown felt. Flowers blood-red, 1 to 1¼ ins. across, densely packed in hemispherical trusses $3\frac{1}{2}$ ins. wide. Corolla bell-shaped, with five shallow, notched lobes ; calyx very small, shallowly lobed ; stamens ten, much shorter than the corolla, not downy ; ovary glabrous, style crimson.

Native of Nepal and Sikkim at 10,000 to 14,000 ft. ; introduced about 1849. This species is very similar to R. campanulatum in foliage, but is not quite so hardy nor so free in growth. Its flowers are. the richest red of any hardy species except R. Thomsoni (which is of quite a different type) and R. barbatum. They appear during March and April, and provide a feast of colour unequalled in cold districts so early in the year. A suitable spot for it is some sheltered outskirt of woodland, especially where the flowers may be protected from early morning sunlight. At Kew the various titmice are very fond of pecking a hole through the base of the corolla, presumably to get at the honey. An ornamental feature of the plant are the crimson bracts that accompany the young growth in spring.

R. FULVUM, *Balfour and W. W. Smith*
(Bot. Mag., t. 9587)

An evergreen shrub or small tree 9 to 20 ft. high ; young shoots covered with a brownish yellow felt, some of which remains till the following year. Leaves stout and leathery, oblong to oval, abruptly narrowed to a mucro at the apex, tapered to slightly heart-shaped at the base ; 4 to 8 ins. long, $1\frac{1}{2}$ to 3 ins. wide ; very dark green and glabrous above, clothed beneath with a richly cinnamon-coloured felt ; midrib prominent, ultimately naked and pale. Flowers produced in March and April, up to twenty in a globose truss 4 ins. wide. Corolla white to pale or bright rose with a fine crimson blotch at the base, bell-shaped, $1\frac{1}{2}$ ins. long, five- or six-lobed, each lobe $\frac{3}{4}$ in. long and nearly 1 in. wide. Stamens ten, very minutely downy at the base ; anthers dark brown. Ovary and style glabrous. Calyx small, glabrous ; flower-stalk $\frac{1}{2}$ to $\frac{3}{4}$ in. long.

Native of W. Yunnan, China ; discovered and introduced by Forrest in 1912. He found it at altitudes of 10,000 ft. and it has proved quite hardy. The flowers, without being more than ordinary, are attractive enough ; the most striking character of the plant is the felt-like covering of the under surface of the leaf. In Forrest's No. 8989, his original importation, this is rich brown-red, but it has also been described as " pale fawn," and Mr L. de Rothschild alluded to it as " brilliant orange." It is a beautiful feature, more especially when the leaf is young, and would in itself make the species worthy of cultivation.

R. FULVOIDES, *Balfour and Forrest,* is closely akin but, according to Mr Tagg, has an ovary five- or six-chambered, whilst that of fulvum is eight- to ten-chambered. The covering of the leaf beneath is ochre-coloured to buff and more powdery. Flowers in trusses 5 ins. wide, white to pinkish with a crimson blotch at the base of the bell-shaped corolla which is about $1\frac{1}{3}$ ins. wide, opening in April. N.W. Yunnan and S.E. Tibet. (Fulvum series.)

R. GALACTINUM, *Balfour fil.*
(R. lacteum, *Rehder and Wilson,* not of *Franchet*)

This is one of the rhododendrons concerned in the confusion that has surrounded the identity of R. lacteum. It was included under that name by Rehder and Wilson in *Plantæ Wilsonianæ,* vol. i., p. 545, but not with great certainty, as Wilson had seen and collected it in ripe fruit only. Sir Isaac Balfour, in unravelling the confusion between the true lacteum (*q.v.*) and the rhododendron which is now known as " fictolacteum," found that Wilson's plant was neither.

It is an evergreen tree up to 25 ft. high ; young shoots grey-downy at first, glabrous later. Leaves 5 to 10 ins. long, 2 to 4 ins. wide, from oblong-ovate to oblanceolate ; soon glabrous above, densely clothed beneath with pale yellowish grey or pale brown velvety down ; stalk 1 to 1½ ins. long. Flowers about fifteen in a rounded truss opening in April and May. Corolla seven-lobed, bell-shaped, 1¼ ins. long, white tinged with pink outside, with a blotch and spots of crimson inside. Stamens fourteen, white with down at the base ; ovary and style glabrous ; calyx a mere wavy rim.

Native of Szechuen, China ; discovered and introduced by Wilson in 1908. The flowers were unknown until plants flowered in this country in 1923, or possibly before. Like most of the rhododendrons of Wilson's introduction, it is quite hardy at Kew and is well worth growing in similarly unfavourable spots. The true lacteum is very distinct in its yellow flowers and five-lobed corolla. R. fictolacteum differs in its densely downy ovary. (Falconeri series.)

R. GEMMIFERUM, *Hort.*

A hybrid between a true Rhododendron and one of the Azalea group, forming an evergreen bush of rather loose, open habit, up to 6 ft. high. Leaves 2 to 3½ ins. long, 1 to 1½ ins. wide ; obovate to oval, downy beneath when young, but becoming glabrous with age ; dark glossy green above, pale green beneath ; margins recurved. Flowers in a truss 3 ins. across, purplish rose ; corolla funnel-shaped, 1¼ ins. long and wide ; calyx-lobes ⅛ in. long, linear, hairy on the margins ; flower-stalk ½ in. long, sticky and downy. This shrub flowers in May or early June. It is allied to azaleoides and Gowenianum, but its flowers are more uniformly rosy, and the leaves are not glaucous beneath.

R. GENESTIERIANUM, *Forrest*
(Bot. Mag., t. 9310)

An evergreen shrub described by Forrest as being found by him from 4 to 12 ft. high in a wild state ; young shoots glabrous, glaucous. Leaves aggregated at the end of the twig, of thin texture, lanceolate or oblanceolate, slenderly pointed, wedge-shaped at the base ; 2 to 4 (sometimes 6) ins. long, ¼ to 1½ ins. wide ; bright green above, very glaucous beneath, glabrous on both sides except for a few scales beneath ; stalk ¼ to ¾ in. long. Flowers in a distinctly racemose cluster of twelve or more, opening in April. Corolla narrowly bell-shaped, about ½ in. long, of fleshy texture and plum-purple covered with a bloom, the five lobes erect. Stamens ten, glabrous, both they and the anthers purple-red to bright crimson ; ovary purplish, scaly ; style glabrous, bent over. Calyx small, shallowly or not at all lobed, glabrous.

Native of Yunnan, China, and S.E. Tibet ; discovered in 1919 and introduced by Forrest. Although it has been assigned to the Glaucum series, it lacks their large, leafy-lobed, characteristic calyx. In the shape and purple colouring of the corolla it resembles the campylogynum group, but the large number of flowers racemosely arranged and the long, sharply pointed leaves are very distinct. In its glabrous stamens it differs from both groups. Forrest calls it a charming plant, distinct, and very desirable for gardens.

R. PRUNIFLORUM, *Hutchinson and Ward*, has also plum-coloured flowers which are open, bell-shaped, and 1 in. wide and long, but they and the foliage are of the genuine glaucum type, the calyx large and deeply lobed. Found by Kingdon Ward in N.E. Burma in 1926. Flowers in May and June at Exbury, and a very charming species of its type. Growing as a shapely little bush, perhaps 2 or 2½ ft. high, it is very suitable for the rock garden.

R. GIGANTEUM, *Forrest and Tagg*

This is the largest of all known rhododendrons, and Forrest, who discovered it in September 1919 in S.W. Yunnan, at altitudes of 9000 to 10,000 ft., describes it as 80 ft. high, growing in " open forest," and the girth of the trunk as 7 ft. 9 ins. at 5 ft. from the ground. The seeds he sent home germinated in great abundance. He first saw it in blossom in March 1921, and describes the flowers as " deep rose-crimson without markings, but with a slight blotch of deep crimson at the base." Other characters are as follows : young shoots grey-downy ; leaves 9 to 16 ins. long, one-third as much wide, clothed beneath with reddish brown down in the plant's adult state, wholly glabrous and bright green beneath when young ; veins in about two dozen pairs, conspicuous ; trusses of twenty to twenty-five flowers, each flower on a stout downy stalk about 1¼ ins. long ; corolla longish bell-shaped, 2½ ins. long, eight-lobed ; stamens sixteen, smooth ; ovary downy ; style glabrous ; calyx $\frac{1}{10}$ in. long, with eight wavy teeth.

In a young state the plants seem to be very tender and the species will probably succeed only in the south-west and similar places. I suppose Forrest was able to judge by the size of the trees he saw, which were not in bloom, that the species takes many years to reach the blossoming stage. Never-

RHODODENDRON GLAUCUM

theless, the tree will be worth planting in the south-west as a noble evergreen, and the best place evidently would be the base of a bluff, from the top of which one may be able to appreciate the blossom. It would be difficult to do that with even the noblest rhododendron truss if it were poised 40 to 80 ft. in the air. (Grande series.)

R. GLAUCUM, *Hooker fil.* (Plate 8)

(Bot. Mag., t. 4721)

An evergreen shrub, 3 to 6 ft. high, of bushy habit, and usually wider than it is high ; young branches, leaves, flower-stalks, and calyx covered with reddish brown scurf or scales. Leaves oval or oblong, 1 to 3 ins. long, ⅛ to ¾ in. wide ; margins recurved ; upper surface dark dull green, lower one glaucous white or sometimes pale brown when young ; stalk ⅛ to ⅓ in. long. The leaf when crushed has a strong, rather resinous odour. Flowers ¾ to 1¼ ins. wide, rosy red, produced during May in terminal clusters of usually five or six (sometimes eight to ten) ; corolla bell-shaped, with five spreading, rounded lobes, slightly scaly outside ; calyx large, with five ovate, pointed lobes, ⅓ in. long, scaly outside ; stamens ten, downy at the base.

Native of Sikkim and Bhotan up to 12,000 ft. ; introduced about 1850. It is quite hardy in fairly sheltered places, but, like other Himalayan species, is liable to suffer injury by May frosts. It is not showy, but pretty when well in bloom. The hybrid, " Rosy Bell," is derived from this species.

R. GLISCHRUM, *Balfour and W. W. Smith*

(Bot. Mag., t. 9035)

An evergreen tree up to 25 ft. high in nature, mostly seen in cultivation as a shrub of stiff, rather gaunt habit ; young shoots, leaf-stalks, and flower-stalks all glandular-bristly. Leaves narrowly oblong, often inclined to oblanceolate, rather abruptly narrowed at the apex to a slender point ; tapered, rounded, or slightly heart-shaped at the base ; 6 to 12 ins. long, 1½ to 3 ins. wide ; dark green and eventually glabrous above, pale green beneath and more or less furnished all over with bristly down, but especially on the midrib. Flowers borne during May in trusses 5 or 6 ins. across, of up to fifteen or more. Corolla bell-shaped, five-lobed, 2 ins. wide, varying in colour from a dull magenta-pink to a purplish rose with a dark blotch at the base. Stamens ten, 1 to 1¼ ins. long, glandular-downy towards the base. Ovary and base of style clothed with white bristles. Calyx deeply five-lobed, the lobes ⅜ in. long, oblong, blunt, bristly ; flower-stalk 1½ ins. long.

Native of Yunnan, China ; discovered and introduced by Forrest in 1914 ; Farrer found it in Upper Burma in 1919, and describes it as " a neat tree with large trusses of bright pink flowers in May, produced in great abundance." The species varies evidently in the colour quality of its blossom, but most of the plants that have flowered have had an unpleasant magenta shade. There is a better type at Caerhays, judging by a truss Mr J. C. Williams kindly sent to me in May 1924, which carried clear rosy lilac flowers. Forrest also mentions them as " lovely pink." It is hardy in Sussex and Hampshire, but not genuinely so at Kew where it is no longer grown. Its nearest relative, perhaps, is habrotrichum (*q.v.*). It belongs to the Barbatum series. Another species closely akin is

R. GLISCHROIDES, *Tagg and Forrest*, a shrub or small tree up to 15 ft. high, said to be like R. glischrum in habit and flower-structure, but with a glabrous style and white or creamy-white corollas, blotched with crimson at the base, and more or less flushed with rose. The leaf has more numerous veins (eighteen to twenty-five each side the midrib) and beneath it the veins are clothed with fine white hairs in addition to bristles. Native of N.E. Burma at 10,000 to 11,000 ft. altitude, discovered and introduced by Forrest in 1925. Mr L. de Rothschild found it less hardy than glischrum at Exbury, Hants. ; from that species it is easily distinguished by the grey aspect of the young leaves beneath, due to the covering of pale hairs and bristles. Flowers in March.

R. GRANDE, *Wight*

(R. argenteum, *Hooker fil.*, Bot. Mag., t. 5054 ; R. longifolium, *Nuttall*)

An evergreen tree or large shrub up to 30 ft. high ; young shoots stout, clothed with silvery scurf. Leaves stiff and leathery, oblong to oblanceolate, tapered at both ends ; 6 to 15 ins. long, 3 to 6 ins. wide ; dark green and glabrous above, beautifully silvery or covered with dull tawny down beneath ; stalk 1 to 2 ins. long. Flowers sometimes twenty-five to thirty, opening during March and April in a rounded truss 5 to 7 ins. wide. Corolla bell-shaped, 2 to 3 ins. long and wide, ivory white, with conspicuous blotches at the base, eight-lobed. Stamens sixteen, downy at the base. Ovary downy and densely glandular ; style glabrous or nearly so ; stigma large, disk-like. Calyx a mere rim ; flower-stalks glandular, and it may be slightly downy, like the calyx.

Native of the Sikkim Himalaya ; introduced by Joseph Hooker to Kew in

1849 ; also of Bhutan, where it had previously been discovered. One of the most magnificent of rhododendrons, this unfortunately can only be grown in the open air in the mildest counties. The finest examples are to be seen in the Cornish gardens, none better perhaps than at Bosahan. It is, however, often gaunt and ungainly in habit, and seems to be liable to enfeeblement of health by overflowering. Of the Himalayan species it is most nearly akin to R. Falconeri (well distinguished from R. grande by the red-brown felt beneath the leaf) and the two adjoin each other in a wild state, R. Falconeri growing at the higher altitudes. In Cornish gardens there are several rhododendrons which are almost certainly natural hybrids between the two. It is the type species of the Grande series.

Var. ROSEUM, *Hooker fil.*—Flower-buds deep red ; corolla six-lobed, of a bright rose. (*Botanical Magazine*, t. 6948.) Perhaps a natural hybrid.

There seems to be no doubt that the Sikkim plant and the Bhutan ones are distinct, although united under grande by C. B. Clarke. In some Cornish gardens they distinguish three varieties, subspecies, or species as follows :—

Argenteum.—Leaves shining silvery beneath. Flowers dull creamy white with a large blotch at the base ; stigma slightly red ; flower-stalk nearly glabrous.

Grande.—Leaves not silvery or shining beneath but coated with a looser tawny or greyish down. Flowers of a purer, clearer white, with the basal blotch not so large ; stigma yellow ; flower-stalk glandular-downy.

Longifolium.—Leaves long, narrow, of oblanceolate shape.

R. SIDEREUM, *Balfour fil.*, is closely related to R. grande and has leaves brightly silvery beneath, but they are as a rule narrower, only 1¼ to 2¾ ins. wide, and up to 10 or 12 ins. long. Corolla eight-lobed, bell-shaped, creamy-white to yellow with a crimson blotch at the base, and nearly 2 ins. wide. It is a large shrub or even a tree up to 30 ft. high. Forrest, Farrer, and Ward found it in Upper Burma in 1919. As it grows at 10,000 ft. altitude, it should be somewhat hardier than grande, but even so is only likely to succeed in places as mild or milder than the maritime parts of Sussex and Hampshire. The collectors found it blossoming in April and May. Ward remarks that its chief characteristic as he saw it in a wild state was the " peculiarly smooth, shimmering, tawny purple bark," on which neither fungus, fern, nor moss will grow.

R. GRIERSONIANUM, *Balfour and Forrest*
(Bot. Mag., t. 9195)

An evergreen shrub of lax, open growth up to 7 ft. or more high ; young shoots glandular-bristly and hairy. Winter-buds very distinct, being encased by bracts extending well beyond the bud and free at the ends. Leaves oblong-lanceolate, pointed, tapered at the base ; 4 to 7 ins. long, 1 to 1¾ ins. wide ; dull green above, covered with a pale buff wool beneath ; stalk ¾ to 1½ ins. long, glandular and hairy like the young shoots. Flowers opening in June, loosely arranged in trusses of five to twelve flowers. Corolla rosy scarlet, trumpet-shaped, narrowed to a fluted cylindrical tube at the base, five-lobed, 3 ins. wide, 2½ ins. long, the lobes roundish ovate, 1¼ ins. wide, with darker crimson lines running into the throat, very downy outside especially towards the base. Stamens ten, crimson, 1½ to 2 ins. long, slightly downy on the lower half ; anthers very dark brown. Ovary covered with pale tawny felt ; style crimson, downy at the base. Calyx small and like the flower-stalk, which is 1¼ to 1½ ins. long, viscous and downy.

Native of W. Yunnan, China ; discovered by Forrest in the Schweli Valley in 1917 at 9000 ft. altitude. This is undoubtedly one of the finest and most remarkable of Forrest's introductions. Although it is officially united with R. auriculatum to constitute a " series," chiefly I suppose on account of the curiously elongated buds and downy corolla common to both, it is very distinct. R. auriculatum has for instance a seven-lobed corolla. The pinched-in, cylindrical base of the corolla of R. Griersonianum is a marked characteristic. All the flowers I have seen have had some suggestion of rose in their colouring, and Forrest, in the field note to his No. 15815, described them as "bright rose." Other observers call them "geranium scarlet" and "vermilion." At Kew the species has lived and flowered in the open air sheltered by a wall and shrubs from east and north, but it is replaced from time to time as hard winters kill it. In a cool house it has larger leaves and better trusses, the latter carrying sometimes a dozen flowers. There will doubtless be a numerous hybrid progeny from it in a few years of time.

R. GRIFFITHIANUM, *Wight*
(Bot. Mag., t. 5065 ; R. Aucklandii, *Hooker fil.*)

An evergreen shrub, or occasionally a small tree, with erect branches and peeling bark. It is quite devoid of down or hairs in all its parts. Leaves narrowly oblong, 6 to 9 (sometimes 12) ins. long, about one-third as much wide ; rather pale green above, slightly glaucous beneath ; stalk 1 to 1½ ins. long. Flowers white with a pink tinge, slightly fragrant, 5 or 6 ins. diameter, produced loosely in a cluster of about six ; corolla widely bell-shaped, with five large, rounded lobes notched in the middle. Calyx ¾ to 1 in. across, buckler-like, scarcely lobed ; stamens up to sixteen, much shorter than the corolla ; style 1½ ins. long, with a large knob-like stigma ; flower-stalk 1 to 1¾ ins. long.

Native of Sikkim and Bhutan ; introduced in 1849, and in some respects the finest of all rhododendrons, especially in regard to the size and width of the individual flower, which resembles some fine lily, and is occasionally 7 ins. across. The species is not regarded as hardy near London, but claims notice here as one parent of a rapidly increasing group of hybrids quite distinct from all other hardy groups. The following deserve special mention :—

R. KEWENSE, *W. Watson.*—Raised at Kew in 1875 by the late Mr W. Binder, who gave the parentage as Griffithianum × Hookeri, but the latter species is a doubtful parent. The flowers in shape are like Griffithianum, but smaller, being 3½ to 5 ins. across, white, suffused with rose. One form, ROSEUM, has flowers of a decided rose colour. In both, the unexpanded buds are of a lovely rosy crimson. The large crimson bracts which accompany the young growths are another feature that add to the beauty of this hybrid. It is hardy in the south, but needs a sheltered spot. Leaves as in Griffithianum, but smaller.

R. LODERI is a hybrid raised at Leonardslee, in 1900, by Sir Edmund G. Loder, between R. Griffithianum and Fortunei. It is a magnificent rhododendron with pure white or faintly pink flowers 5½ to 6½ ins. across, and as many as ten in a truss.

R. MANGLESII is a hybrid between Griffithianum and R. album elegans, the latter itself a hybrid of the catawbiense group. It has pure white flowers 3 to 4 ins. across, with a few spots of red on the upper side of the corolla.

The variety known as PINK PEARL, one of the most popular hardy rhododendrons of recent times, is derived from R. Griffithianum, as are several other popularly named varieties ; the number is likely to be increased greatly in coming years, especially in the Cornish gardens.

R. HABROTRICHUM, *Balfour and W. W. Smith* (Plate 9)
(Gardeners' Chronicle, 30th July 1921, fig. 23)

A bushy evergreen shrub up to 10 ft. high, or a small tree up to 25 ft. high (Ward) ; young shoots purplish, clothed with bristles up to ¼ in. long and gland-tipped. Leaves ovate-oblong, rounded or heart-shaped at the base, slenderly pointed ; 3 to 6½ ins. long, 1½ to 3 ins. wide ; dark green above, paler green and bristly on the midrib but not on the veins beneath ; margins bristly ; stalk up to 1 in. long, very glandular-bristly. Flowers produced in April in compact trusses about 4 ins. across. Corolla bell-shaped, 1½ to 2 ins. wide, white or pale rose with usually a blotch of purple at the base, five-lobed, the lobes rounded and notched in the middle. Stamens ten, varying from half to nearly as long as the corolla, downy towards the base. Ovary and base of style glandular-bristly. Calyx five-lobed, the lobes ⅜ to ½ in. long, glandular-bristly like the flower-stalk, which is ½ to 1 in. long.

Native of Yunnan, China ; discovered and first introduced by Forrest in 1912-13, later by Kingdon Ward. It flowered at Kew in April 1920, but is scarcely hardy enough to succeed there. It is no longer represented at Kew. It is quite pretty and probably the most attractive of its particular group. R. glischrum, a species of generally similar character, can be distinguished at any time by its leaves, which are longer (up to 10 ins.) but not so wide and with shorter bristles more or less all over the under surface. (Barbatum series.)

R. HÆMALEUM, *Balfour and Forrest*

(Bot. Mag., t. 9263—as R. sanguineum)

An evergreen shrub 2 to 4 ft. high ; young shoots downy when quite young, afterwards grey. Leaves inversely lanceolate, widest above the middle, wedge-shaped at the base ; 1½ to 3½ ins. long, ⅜ to 1 in. wide ; dark green and glabrous above, grey-white beneath with a thin close layer of down except on the prominent midrib ; stalk ¼ to ⅓ in. long. Flowers produced during June in a terminal cluster of three to six. Corolla between funnel- and bell-shaped, 1 to 1½ ins. long and about as much wide, black-crimson, five-lobed, the lobes rounded and ½ in. wide ; at the base are five protuberances or pockets. Stamens ten, nearly or quite glabrous, shorter than the corolla. Ovary thickly clothed with down ; style glabrous. Calyx crimson, ⅙ in. long ; flower-stalk up to 1 in. long, loosely downy. (Neriiflorum series.)

Native of S.E. Tibet ; discovered by Forrest in 1904 ; introduced to cultivation by him in 1917. In the colour of its flowers this is one of the most remarkable of all rhododendrons, and in time may prove valuable in the hybridiser's hands. The crimson of the blossoms will bear dilution. It occurs at altitudes up to 13,000 ft., so, as might be expected, it has proved very hardy. It belongs to the sanguineum group, in which its black-crimson flowers make it conspicuous (but see also R. didymum), but Dr Stapf, in the text accompanying the *Botanical Magazine* plate quoted above, does not consider it specifically distinct from Franchet's original sanguineum which was collected by Soulié in 1895.

R. HÆMATODES, *Franchet*

(Bot. Mag., t. 9165)

An evergreen shrub of close, dwarf habit as seen in cultivation at present but said by Forrest in a field note to be sometimes 6 to 10 ft. high ; young shoots clothed with a dense brown wool. Leaves leathery, obovate, abruptly contracted at the apex to a small mucro, tapered gradually to the base ; 1½ to 3½ ins. long, ¾ to 1½ ins. wide ; dark glossy green above, densely felted with reddish-brown wool beneath ; stalk ¼ to ½ in. long, woolly. Flowers in a terminal cluster of six to ten, opening in mid-May. Corolla funnel-shaped with five broad, rounded, erect lobes ; 1½ to 2 ins. long, nearly as much wide, scarlet to deep, rich, almost blood red. Stamens ten, ½ to ¾ in. long, glabrous or nearly so ; anthers brown. Ovary densely woolly ; style glabrous. Calyx red, unequally five-lobed, up to ⅓ in. long. Flower-stalks slender, downy, ¾ to 1½ ins. long.

Native of Yunnan on the Tali Range, where it was discovered by Delavay in 1885, associated in its wild state with R. neriiflorum ; introduced by Forrest about 1911. It is certainly one of the best of his introductions so far as this country in general is concerned, for it is very hardy. Its dwarf habit and slow growth make it suitable for the rock garden. It is the type species of a section of the Neriiflorum series distinguished mainly by the thick woolly covering on the young shoots and underneath the leaf. The richly coloured flowers are very effective and as a rule come late enough to escape frost. In the var. CALYCINUM, *Franchet*, the coloured calyx is remarkably developed so that the lobes may be as much as ¾ in. long. Nearly related to R. hæmatodes is

R. CATACOSMUM, *Balfour fil.*, which is distinguished from it by the huge calyx being cup-shaped and ¾ in. long ; the leaves are more rounded and the corolla more openly bell-shaped and of a " crimson-rose " colour. Discovered in S.E. Tibet and introduced by Forrest in 1921-2. Mr Tagg describes it as a magnificent member of the hæmatodes group. It is found at 14,000 ft. altitude, so should be very hardy.

R. POCOPHORUM, *Balfour fil.*, is another of the hæmatodes group with flowers described by Forrest as " deep to light crimson," and " deep purplish crimson." It is marked by the glands on the flower-stalks, calyx, and ovary. The flower-stalks are only half the length of those of hæmatodes and catacosmum. Native of S.E. Tibet up to 15,000 ft. altitude ; discovered by Forrest in 1922.

R. HANCEANUM, *Hemsley*

(Bot. Mag., t. 8669)

An evergreen shrub 3 to 4 ft. high ; young shoots glabrous. Leaves lanceolate to narrowly obovate, usually tapered, sometimes rounded at the base, slenderly pointed ; very unequal in size, and varying from ½ to 4 ins. in length, by ¼ to 1¾ ins. in width ; dark green, rather scaly above, pale and freely sprinkled with small scales beneath ; stalk up to ¼ in. long. Flowers numerous in one or two terminal clusters. Corolla about 1 in. long, funnel-shaped, deeply lobed, varying from white to clear yellow. Calyx-lobes $\frac{3}{16}$ in. long, oblong with a rounded end, scaly ; stamens ten, protruded, downy at the lower half ; seed-vessel about half as long again as the persistent, deeply lobed calyx ; style glabrous ; ovary scaly. It blossoms in March or April.

Native of W. China ; discovered by the Rev. E. Faber on Mt. Omi about 1886 ; introduced by Wilson in 1909. Young plants appear to be quite hardy and vigorous. The species is very distinct in its numerous white or yellow flowers, deeply lobed conspicuous calyx, and hard-textured leaves.

R. HEADFORTIANUM, *Hutchinson*

(Bot. Mag., t. 9614)

An evergreen shrub at present 3 to 4 ft. high in cultivation, but probably becoming taller ; young shoots loosely scaly. Leaves narrowly oblong or oblong-lanceolate, 2½ to 5 ins. long, less than half as wide, apex mucronate, soon glabrous above, glaucous and scaly beneath ; stalk ½ to 1 in. long. Flowers solitary ; corolla funnel-shaped, 4 ins. long, nearly as wide across, the five rounded, spreading lobes, cream-coloured, faintly tinged with pink ; at the base are five oblong pouches. Calyx with five deep oval lobes about ½ in. long ; stamens ten, about the length of the corolla-tube, hairy towards the base. Stalk about 1 in. long, very scaly.

Native of S.E. Tibet, in the Tsangpo Gorge and in Assam ; discovered and introduced by Kingdon Ward in 1924. It belongs to the Maddenii series, which contains such magnificent species as Nuttallii, Sinonuttallii, Dalhousie, Taggianum, etc. It was first flowered by the late Marquess of Headfort in 1932. All of this group are more or less tender and will only be hardy in the mildest localities.

R. HELIOLEPIS, *Franchet*

(R. plebeium, *Balfour and W. W. Smith*)

An evergreen shrub up to 10 ft. high ; young shoots greyish, scaly. Leaves ovate-lanceolate, pointed, rounded at the base ; 2 to 4 ins. long, 1 to 1¾ ins. wide ; leaves dark green above, rather tawny green beneath and sprinkled thickly with glistening scales ; stalk ¼ to ¾ in. long. Flowers four to seven in a loose cluster, opening in June. Corolla widely funnel-shaped, 1 to 1⅜ ins. long and wide, scaly outside, rosy red with crimson markings. Stamens ten, ½ to ¾ in. long, densely downy at the base ; ovary densely scaly ; style as long as the stamens, downy at the base. Calyx 1⁄10 in. long, with rounded lobes, scaly like the flower-stalk, which is ½ to ¾ in. long.

Native of Yunnan at 10,000 to 11,000 ft. altitude ; discovered by Delavay flowering in July 1886 ; introduced by Forrest in 1912. In leaf it bears a strong resemblance to the well-known R. rubiginosum, which can be distinguished from it botanically by having a glabrous style. Another rhododendron to which it is akin is R. brevistylum, which has a shorter downy style and leaves not so rounded at the base. R. heliolepis is the type species of one of Sir Isaac Balfour's " series," characterised by the leaves, shoots, ovary, and outside of corolla being scaly.

R. HEMITRICHOTUM, *Balfour and Forrest*

(Journal Royal Hort. Soc., vol. xlviii., t. 23)

An evergreen shrub 2 to 3 (sometimes 4 or 5) ft. high, with slender, softly downy young shoots. Leaves oblong to narrowly ovate or oblanceolate, pointed, tapered at the base to a very short stalk ; margins recurved ; 1 to 1½ (sometimes 2) ins. long, ¼ to ½ (sometimes ¾) in. wide ; dull green and downy above, glaucous and scaly but downy only on the midrib beneath. Flowers produced in April usually in pairs from several of the terminal leaf-axils, constituting altogether a crowded cluster 1½ to 2 ins. wide. Corolla white to pale rose, ½ to ¾ in. wide, funnel-shaped at the base with five broadly ovate lobes. Stamens ten, slightly downy towards the base ; ovary scaly, style glabrous. Calyx saucer-shaped, not lobed, scaly like the flower-stalk which is ¼ in. long. (Scabrifolium series.)

Native of S.W. Szechuen, China, on the Mu-li Mountains at 12,000 ft. altitude, where it was discovered and whence it was introduced by Forrest in 1918-19. It is most closely related to R. mollicomum, also to R. scabrifolium, but is well distinguished from both by the leaves being glaucous beneath and by the glabrous style. Like them it flowers quite young when raised from seed, sometimes in three or four years. It is hardy at Kew, having grown there in the open air since 1922.

R. PUBESCENS, *Balfour and Forrest*, belongs to this same Scabrifolium series and is a bush of similar character to hemitrichotum and mollicomum. It has pinkish white flowers ½ in. or more wide and small linear-oblong leaves ½ to 1 in. long, very bristly-hairy on both surfaces, scaly beneath. Apart from the bristly character of the pubescence it differs from mollicomum in its glabrous style, whilst hemitrichotum differs by the glaucous, nearly glabrous under surface of its leaves. Introduced from S.W. Szechuen by Forrest in 1918-19. Hardy at Kew.

R. HIPPOPHÆOIDES, *Balfour and W. W. Smith*

(Bot. Mag., t. 9156)

An evergreen shrub 4 to 5 ft. high, of erect growth when young, making long slender shoots with half a dozen or more leaves to the inch, scurfy. Leaves mostly oblong or narrowly oval, apex often bluntish or rounded, more tapered at the base; $\frac{3}{4}$ to $1\frac{1}{2}$ ins. long, $\frac{1}{8}$ to $\frac{1}{2}$ in. wide; dark dullish green above, greyish beneath, both surfaces scaly but the lower one more copiously so; stalk $\frac{1}{8}$ to $\frac{1}{8}$ in. long. When crushed, the leaf emits a slightly acrid odour. Flowers four to eight together, crowded in a roundish umbel about $1\frac{1}{2}$ ins. wide, opening normally in March and April. Corolla flattish, saucer-shaped, $\frac{3}{4}$ to 1 in. wide, five-lobed (the lobes roundish), the short tube hairy. Forrest describes the flowers as deep purplish blue, blue-purple, pale bluish rose and blue. One plant at Kew gave rosy pink flowers. Stamens normally ten, purple, about $\frac{1}{8}$ in. long, downy at the base; anthers dark reddish brown. Ovary very scaly, green; style red, glabrous; flower-stalk $\frac{1}{8}$ to $\frac{1}{4}$ in. long, scaly. Calyx $\frac{1}{10}$ in. long, five-lobed, with a few hairs at the rounded end of each lobe. (Lapponicum series.)

Native of Yunnan, China; discovered by Kingdon Ward in 1913; introduced by Forrest. It grows at an altitude of 12,000 ft. and is very hardy. It has proved one of the most satisfactory and amenable of all Chinese rhododendrons in our less favourable climates, growing and flowering freely. It is admirable for grouping. Ripening seed freely as it does, and easily raised from cuttings, it should become as popular as it deserves to be. The flowers are less susceptible to frost than those of larger flowered species.

R. HIRSUTUM, *Linnæus*. ROSE DES ALPES

An evergreen shrub of the same habit as ferrugineum, 2 to 3 ft. high; young shoots bristly and scaly. Leaves narrowly oval, occasionally somewhat obovate or lanceolate, about 1 in. long, $\frac{1}{4}$ to $\frac{1}{2}$ in. wide; bright green above, somewhat scaly beneath, the margins fringed with conspicuous bristles. Flowers rosy pink to rosy scarlet, $\frac{1}{2}$ in. to $\frac{3}{4}$ in. across, produced in June in terminal clusters; corolla slightly scaly outside, funnel-shaped at the base, the lobes spreading. Calyx and flower-stalk bristly and scaly, the latter $\frac{1}{2}$ to 1 in. long.

Native of the European Alps; introduced in 1656. This species although palpably a close ally of R. ferrugineum, and having the same popular name, is in several respects very distinct. The bristly character of the leaves, shoots, and calyx to which the specific name refers is, of course, its most distinctive feature, but it differs also in being greener and less scaly underneath the leaf, and in the usually longer calyx-lobes and flower-stalk. In a wild state it is always found on a limestone formation, and is therefore useful as one of the few species thriving in gardens with a soil of that nature.

Var. ALBIFLORUM.—Flowers white.
Var. LACINIATUM.—Leaves toothed; a curiosity.
Var. LATIFOLIUM.—Leaves broad, almost rounded.

R. HODGSONI, *Hooker fil.*

(Bot. Mag., t. 5552)

An evergreen shrub or small tree up to 20 ft. high; bark peeling. Leaves large, slightly obovate, rounded at the apex, tapering at the base; 6 to 12 ins. long, 3 to 4 ins. wide; very leathery, dark green and glossy above, with brownish red down beneath; stalk very thick, 1 to 2 ins. long. Flowers rosy lilac, 1½ to 2 ins. across, packed in a rounded truss about 6 ins. wide ; corolla bell-shaped, with eight to ten lobes ; stamens about twice as many, shorter than the corolla ; calyx very small ; ovary and flower-stalk downy.

Native of Nepal and Sikkim ; introduced in 1849. It is one of the noblest of all rhododendrons in its foliage. Sir Joseph Hooker observed that its leaves are sometimes 18 ins. long. Fine plants have been grown in the open air at Edinburgh, but it does not succeed so well at Kew.

R. HOOKERI, *Nuttall*

(Bot. Mag., t. 4926 ; Gardeners' Chronicle, 13th May 1882, fig. 96)

An evergreen shrub 10 to 14 ft. high ; young shoots glabrous. Leaves oval-oblong, rounded at both ends with a short mucro at the apex ; 3 to 5 ins. long, about half as much wide ; green and glabrous above, rather glaucous beneath and glabrous except along the veins upon which, at fairly regular intervals, occur little tufts of down ; stalk up to 1⅛ ins. long. Flowers produced in late March or April ten to fifteen in a truss. Corolla blood-red, bell-shaped, 1½ to 2 ins. wide, five-lobed, the lobes rounded and deeply notched in the middle ; stamens ten, quite glabrous ; ovary and style glabrous, the latter longer than the stamens but shorter than the corolla. Calyx cup-shaped, ¼ in. long, smooth, obscurely five-lobed ; flower-stalk ½ to 1 in. long.

Native of Bhotan ; discovered by Thos. J. Booth in 1852. For many years this handsome and richly coloured species was one of the rarest of rhododendrons ; even now, although it is becoming more widely spread in gardens, it is still quite uncommon. It is related to R. Thomsonii, but is well distinguished from that and all other known rhododendrons by the curious tufts of down scattered along the chief veins beneath the leaf, and nowhere else. It is grown out-of-doors, really successfully, in the southern and western maritime counties only, although thirty or forty miles south of London it has survived pretty severe winters. In view of this tenderness it is interesting to note Booth's record that, when and where he first collected it, frost and snow were very severe and continuous ; also that it is associated in the wild with Pinus excelsa, a perfectly hardy pine. (Thomsonii series.)

R. HOULSTONII, *Hemsley and Wilson*

(R. Fortunei Houlstonii, *Rehder and Wilson*)

An evergreen shrub up to 12 ft. high, with stout, glabrous branchlets. Leaves oblong or slightly obovate, 3 to 6 ins. long, ¾ to 2 ins. wide ; narrowed abruptly at the apex to a short point ; tapered or rounded at the base ; both surfaces perfectly smooth, the upper one dark green, the lower very pale ; stalk purple, ½ to 1⅛ ins. long. Flowers eight or more in a truss, flesh-pink, about 3 ins. across. Corolla widely bell-shaped, seven-lobed ; stamens twelve or fourteen, with glabrous stalks ; summit of ovary and base of style hairy-glandular ; flower-stalk covered with viscid stalked glands, 1 in. or more long.

Native of W. Hupeh, China ; introduced about 1900, by Wilson. It is closely allied to R. Fortunei, especially in the smooth, purple-stalked leaves and seven-lobed corolla, but differs in the tapered base of the leaves, stalked glands of the flower-stalk, bell-shaped corolla and longer stamens ; it flowers earlier.

R. HUNNEWELLIANUM, *Rehder and Wilson*

(R. leucolasium, *Diels*)

An evergreen shrub up to 15 ft. high in a wild state ; young shoots covered with a short grey felt. Leaves oblanceolate, slenderly pointed but tapering more gradually towards the base ; 2 to 4½ ins. long, ¼ to 1 in. wide ; dark

green, glabrous above at maturity, clothed beneath with a loose grey felt ; stalk
¼ to ½ in. long. Flowers produced in March or April in clusters of five to
eight. Corolla bell-shaped, five-lobed, 2 to 2¼ ins. wide, 1¾ to 2 ins. deep, pink
to pale rosy-lilac, spotted with maroon on the three upper lobes. Stamens
ten, the longest about as long as the corolla, their stalks white, downy at the
base ; anthers dark brown. Ovary and base of style clad with white
down, the latter nearly 2 ins. long. Calyx small, shallowly lobed, downy ;
flower-stalks ¾ in. long, downy. Seed-vessel ¾ in. long, covered with tawny
down.

Native of W. Szechuen, China ; discovered and introduced by Wilson in
1908. A distinct species on account of its stiff, very narrow leaves, grey-white
beneath. It is perfectly hardy at Kew, but increases slowly in size because of
its being so frequently cut back by late spring frosts,.and for the same reason
flowers there infrequently. It flowered with Lt.-Col. Stephenson Clarke at
Borde Hill, Sussex, in March 1918. Related to floribundum, it differs in its
smaller, narrower leaves, more slenderly tapered at the base. It is named
after the Hunnewell family, well known and ardent patrons of horticulture and
botany in Massachusetts. (Arboreum series.)

R. HYPENANTHUM, *Balfour fil.*

This rhododendron is very closely related to R. Anthopogon and has not
until comparatively recently been distinguished from it (see Balfour in *Notes
Roy. Bot. Garden, Edinburgh*, vol. ix., p. 291). The flowers of what is now
considered to be the true R. Anthopogon are pink to white (often showing
some yellow with age) ; those of R. hypenanthum are pure yellow from the
beginning. This seems to be the most ostensible distinction, but there is
another. In the true R. Anthopogon the scales that surround the base of the
winter leaf-buds fall away as soon as, or soon after, the leaves open ; but in
R. hypenanthum these scales—triangular, overlapping, and ciliate—remain
clasping the twigs for several years. On these two characters R. hypenanthum
mainly stands as a species, but the calyx is also more densely ciliate than
in R. Anthopogon. The description given in vol. ii., p. 341, of early editions
is based on the original conception of R. Anthopogon as a species. It is not
certain which species the figure cited there from the *Botanical Magazine*,
t. 3947 really represents, but except for the points noted above it may serve
just as well for the present one.

Native of W. Himalaya up to 15,000 ft. ; introduced in 1820. It is, of
course, very hardy. The very short, stout, glabrous style is characteristic of the
whole group, also the strongly aromatic odour of the foliage. (Anthopogon
series.)

R. HYPOGLAUCUM, *Hemsley*

(Bot. Mag., t. 8649)

An evergreen shrub up to 10 ft. high, or a small tree. Leaves stiff and
leathery, oval, inclined sometimes to obovate, 2 to 4 ins. long, 1 to 1½ ins. wide,
rather abruptly tapered to a short point, wedge-shaped at the base ; upper
surface dark green and glabrous, lower surface covered with a very close white
scurf ; stalk ¼ to ⅜ in. long, wrinkled. Flowers white, produced eight to ten in
a truss ; corolla widely funnel-shaped, 1¾ ins. wide, scarcely so deep, with five
rounded lobes ; stamens ten or twelve, their stalks glabrous except at the base.
Flower-stalk 1 to 1½ ins. long, and, like the small, scarcely-lobed calyx,
glandular-downy. Ovary glabrous or with a few gland-tipped hairs. Seed-
vessel ¾ in. long, ⅛ in. wide.

Native of W. China; discovered by Henry; introduced by Wilson in 1900. Very distinct in the whiteness of the leaf beneath. If the plants now grown under this name are true, the species would not appear to be so vigorous as many of the Chinese species. According to Wilson, the calyx and flower-stalk are sometimes glabrous. Flowers in May.

R. HYPOLEPIDOTUM, *Balfour and Forrest*

(Bot. Mag., t. 9259 ; R. brachyanthum lepidotum, *Franchet*)

An evergreen, strong-smelling shrub 4 to 6 ft. high ; young shoots scaly. Leaves oval to obovate, mostly rounded at the apex, tapered at the base ; 1 to 2 ins. long, ½ to ¾ in. wide ; scaly and slightly glaucous beneath ; stalk ⅙ in. long. Flowers opening in late May and June in terminal clusters of usually four to eight, sometimes ten, each flower on a scaly stalk 1 to 1½ ins. long. Corolla yellow, bell-shaped, ¾ in. wide, five-lobed, the lobes erect or slightly concave, the tube softly downy inside. Stamens ten, with whitish stalks hairy almost to the top ; anthers brown ; ovary densely scaly ; style stout, ¼ in. long, glabrous. Calyx ¼ in. long, reddish, cut almost to the base into five roundish ovate lobes scaly on the outside and usually on the margin.

Native of W. China and S.E. Tibet ; originally discovered by the Abbé Soulié ; introduced by Forrest and Kingdon Ward. It belongs to the Glaucum series, which is distinguished by a usually large, deeply-lobed calyx ; a short, thick, often recurved style, a bell-shaped corolla, and strongly aromatic foliage. This species is very near brachyanthum, which differs by its leaves being very glaucous and less scaly beneath, and the stamens not furnished with hairs so near to the anthers. Both have only a modest beauty but are reasonably hardy.

R. IMPEDITUM, *Balfour fil. and W. W. Smith*

An evergreen shrub, 6 to 18 ins. high, of tufted habit ; the young shoots, both surfaces of the leaf and calyx all scaly, the scales being pale and giving a dull greyish tinge to the leaf. Leaves oval or ovate, tapered or rounded at the base, ⅜ to ⅝ in. long, ¼ in. wide ; stalk $\frac{1}{12}$ in. long. Flowers slightly fragrant, clustered in twos or threes at the end of the shoot. Corolla 1 in. across, pale purple ; the lobes five or six, ¼ in. long, ovate, rounded at the end, spreading horizontally ; tube very short, bearded with pale hairs ; stamens ten or twelve, hairy at the base, much protruded, purple, with brownish anthers ; style longer than the stamens, also purple ; calyx-lobes ⅛ in. long, oblong-ovate, ciliate, covered with pale scales.

Native of W. China ; introduced by Forrest in 1911 ; flowered at Kew, Edinburgh, and Caerhays in the autumn of 1912, but May is its ordinary season. It is a dainty little plant, in the way of R. intricatum, but well distinguished by the long, protruded stamens. Forrest says it is the dominant species on open pasture-land on the summit of the Sung-Kivee Pass. (R. fastigiatum of our 1st Ed., not of *Franchet*.)

R. IMPERATOR, *Hutchinson and Ward*

A dwarf evergreen shrub forming in a wild state a flat, mat-like growth only a few inches high ; young shoots slightly scaly ; older bark peeling. Leaves aromatic, oblanceolate to narrowly elliptical, rounded to pointed at the mucronate apex, always wedge-shaped at the base ; 1 to 1½ ins. long, ⅛ to ½ in. wide ; glabrous and dark green above, glaucous and very thinly scaly beneath ; midrib yellowish ; margins decurved ; stalk ¼ in. or less long. Flowers solitary or in pairs, opening in May. Corolla funnel-shaped with reflexed lobes, 1 to 1½ ins. wide, scarcely so long, downy all over outside, pinkish purple in various shades, unspotted. Stamens ten, purple, downy quite at the base only ; ovary scaly ; style rather longer than the corolla, slender, glabrous, red. Calyx slightly but distinctly five-lobed ; flower-stalk red, thinly scaly, ½ to 1 in. long.

Native of Upper Burma in the Seinghku district, where it was discovered at 10,000 to 11,000 ft. altitude by Kingdon Ward and introduced by him. He describes it as growing on bare ledges of granite cliffs, fully exposed. It belongs to the Lepidotum series, in which it is distinct amongst the other species here described in the very thin disposition of the scales on the leaves, etc. A very handsome group of young plants flowering freely in a pan was exhibited at Westminster by Lord Swathling on 10th May 1932. It is likely to be quite hardy and to prove a very attractive plant for the rock garden. So far as is known at present it is a rare species ; in the Seinghku valley at any rate its discoverer found only two small patches.

R. INDICUM, *Sweet*. " INDIAN " AZALEA

(Azalea indica, *Linnæus*)

An evergreen shrub, sometimes a dense bush from 3 to 6 ft. high, sometimes low and more or less prostrate ; young shoots slender, stiff, clothed with flattened, appressed, bristle-like hairs pointing towards the end of the branch. Leaves lanceolate to oblanceolate, tapered at the base, pointed, often sparsely toothed ; 1 to 1½ ins. long, ¼ to ¾ in. wide ; dark green and rather glossy above, paler beneath, with appressed red-brown bristles on both sides ; stalk $\frac{1}{12}$ to ⅛ in. long. Flowers opening in June, solitary or in pairs at the end of the shoot. Corolla broadly funnel-shaped, about 1½ ins. long, rather more wide, five-lobed, bright red to scarlet, sometimes rosy red. Stamens five, about the same length as the corolla, slightly downy towards the base. Ovary covered with erect bristles ; style glabrous. Calyx and flower-stalk bristly.

Native of S. Japan ; introduced in 1833 by a Mr M'Killigan to Knight's nursery at Chelsea. It had long been cultivated by the Japanese, and Wilson, when in Japan, found that some two hundred sorts are recognised by them. Although it—or rather its varieties—held a place in European gardens for some years, it was rapidly displaced after the year 1850 by the Chinese species, R. Simsii (*q.v.*), a species with many varieties also, somewhat more tender than R. indicum and better adapted for greenhouse cultivation, especially for forcing early into bloom. These two species and their varieties have been much confused by botanists and have usually been referred to collectively as " Indian Azaleas." R. Simsii is distinguished by its usually ten (sometimes eight) stamens to a flower. The true indicum is now very rare in gardens but it is in the Kew collection. Although not robust in habit, it and the following varieties are fairly hardy there, and this cannot be said of Simsii and its forms :—

Var. BALSAMINÆFLORUM, *Nicholson* (Azalea rosæflora, *R. Dean*).—A miniature shrub usually only a few inches high. Leaves ½ to 1 in. long, ⅛ to ¼ in. wide, glossy green above, grey beneath, bristly on both surfaces. Flowers very double, salmon red, in the bud state very much resembling small rose-buds. It has lived in the open air at Kew for many years but grows slowly and prefers a rather warmer climate. Suitable for the rock garden. Introduced from Japan about 1877.

Var. CRISPIFLORUM, *C. K. Schneider* (Azalea crispiflora, *Hooker*), has thicker leaves than the type, bright rose flowers and wavy margins to the corolla. Introduced by Fortune about 1850. (*Botanical Magazine*, t. 4726).

Var. LACINIATUM, *Wilson*.—Corolla rich red, divided to the base into narrow, strap-shaped segments nearly 1 in. long, $\frac{1}{12}$ to $\frac{1}{8}$ in. wide. Often the two or three upper segments are united half-way down. Calyx five-lobed, the lobes $\frac{1}{8}$ in. long, bristly, pointed. Stamens five, red ; style $1\frac{1}{4}$ ins. long, red. It flowers in the open air at Kew in June, but can be regarded only as a curious monstrosity.

Var. VARIEGATUM, *De Candolle*.—Flowers striped in red and white. Introduced with the type in 1833 to Knight's nursery at Chelsea, and a favourite variety for breeding from in the early days. In England it disappeared from cultivation, but was re-introduced from Japan some years ago as var. matsushima. Rather tender.

About 1878 Charles Maries introduced for Messrs Veitch two varieties very similar to each other named respectively " Daimyo " and " Mikado." They have pale salmon single flowers and proved perfectly hardy at the Coombe Wood Nursery.

R. INSIGNE, *Hemsley and Wilson*

(Gardeners' Chronicle, 23rd June 1923, fig. 168)

An evergreen shrub described by Wilson as from 12 to 18 ft. high in a wild state, but as seen in cultivation a dwarfish rounded bush of stocky growth. Leaves very hard and firm in texture, narrowly elliptical to lanceolate, sharply pointed, tapered at the base ; glossy dark green above, covered beneath with a close silvery down that ultimately turns brown ; 2 to 5 ins. long, $\frac{1}{2}$ to 2 ins. wide ; stalk thick and flattish, $\frac{1}{8}$ to $\frac{3}{4}$ in. long. Flowers opening in May in hemispherical trusses 4 to 5 ins. wide, carrying fifteen or more flowers. Corolla bell-shaped, five-lobed, 2 ins. wide, $1\frac{1}{4}$ to $1\frac{1}{2}$ ins. deep, soft pink, the upper lobes maroon-spotted ; the outside is broadly striped with deep rosy pink. Stamens normally ten, $\frac{1}{4}$ to $\frac{5}{8}$ in. long, downy at the base ; ovary thickly downy ; style glabrous. Calyx small, shallowly five-lobed ; slightly downy like the flower-stalk, which is up to 2 ins. long. (Arboreum series.)

Native of W. Szechuen, China ; introduced in 1908 by Wilson, who found it growing on the limestone bluffs of Mt. Wu. It had, however, been seen by Henry and Pratt long before. It is an attractive and distinct species, considered to have some affinity with arboreum. The deep rosy bands of colour at the back of the corolla (they occur also in Thayerianum) are very effective ; the metallic lustre of the under surface of the leaf is distinctive. At present it is a neat dense bush in gardens and gives no promise of attaining the dimensions indicated in Wilson's field note. It flowered when only 1 ft. high and is very hardy at Kew.

R. INTERMEDIUM, *Tausch*. ROSE DES ALPES

Between R. ferrugineum and hirsutum there is a series of hybrid forms, uniting the two. They vary in the scaliness of the under-surface of the leaf, in the degree of bristliness on the leaf-margins and young shoots, and in the length of the calyx-lobes. The commonest and most intermediate form is R. intermedium itself, found in the Tyrol. Its leaves are very scaly beneath, but not so much so as in R. ferrugineum, and the margins are slightly bristly. Closely allied to this are

R. HALENSE, *Gremblich*, which, however, leans more to ferrugineum ; and
R. HIRSUTIFORME *Gremblich*, which in the scaliness of the leaves resembles

R. ferrugineum, but in the hairiness of the leaf-margin and in the long calyx-lobes very nearly approaches hirsutum. R. intermedium and R. hirsutiforme usually inhabit calcareous localities.

R. INTRICATUM, *Franchet*

(Bot. Mag., t. 8163)

A dwarf evergreen shrub, usually 6 to 12 ins. high, perhaps ultimately 18 ins. ; young shoots scurfy, with reddish scales. Leaves roundish ovate, $\frac{1}{4}$ to $\frac{1}{2}$ in. long, half or more than half as wide, dark green above, pale beneath, both surfaces covered with glistening scales ; leaf-stalk distinctly formed, but only $\frac{1}{12}$ in. long. Flowers in terminal trusses of frequently five or six ; each flower $\frac{3}{8}$ in. across, violet-purple in the bud state, becoming paler and lilac-coloured after opening ; corolla with a short tube and five rounded, spreading lobes ; calyx-lobes five, short, triangular. Stamens ten, almost entirely included within the corolla-tube, downy at the base.

Native of Szechuen, W. China, at 11,000 to 15,000 ft. ; introduced by Wilson for Messrs Veitch in 1904, and one of the most dainty of recent acquisitions. This rhododendron makes a neat little bush of rounded form suggesting a pygmy tree, and it flowers when only a few inches high ; this, together with the colour of the flowers and the profusion in which they are borne, render it a singularly attractive little plant for the rock garden or some such place, where tiny, slow-growing plants are not in danger of being smothered by stronger ones. Coming from high Alpine regions, it is quite hardy. Increased by cuttings of firm young twigs. Under the name of " nigro-punctatum," a near ally, this species was given a first-class certificate by the Royal Horticultural Society, 2nd April 1907. The true R. NIGRO-PUNCTATUM, *Bureau* (Bot. Mag., t. 8529), is similar in its twiggy habit and scaly foliage to R. intricatum. The leaves are oval-oblong or obovate, $\frac{1}{4}$ to $\frac{1}{2}$ in. long, covered with golden-brown scales on both surfaces. Flowers solitary or few in a cluster, scarcely stalked ; corolla violet-purple, $\frac{1}{2}$ in. wide, with five spreading ovate lobes ; calyx-lobes oblong, $\frac{1}{8}$ in. long, margins hairy towards the ends ; stamens ten, $\frac{1}{8}$ in. long, very hairy at the base, both they and the style protruded. Native of China and Tibet ; discovered by Prince Henri d'Orleans in 1890. Although confused with R. intricatum, it is very distinct in the much exposed stamens and larger calyx.

R. IRRORATUM, *Franchet*

(Bot. Mag., t. 7361 ; Gardeners' Chronicle, 3rd June 1911, Supplement)

An evergreen shrub of rather stiff habit up to 12 ft. high ; occasionally a tree twice as high in a wild state ; young shoots minutely downy and glandular. Leaves of firm and rather leathery texture, narrowly elliptical, sharply pointed, tapered at the base ; 2 to 5$\frac{1}{2}$ ins. long, 1 to 1$\frac{3}{4}$ ins. wide ; ultimately glabrous on both surfaces ; veins in thirteen to sixteen pairs ; stalk $\frac{1}{3}$ to $\frac{2}{3}$ in. long. Flowers in a terminal hemispherical truss, 4 ins. wide, of about fifteen blooms opening in April. Corolla bell-shaped, with the five rounded lobes notched and wavy at the margin ; 1$\frac{1}{2}$ to 2 ins. long and wide ; the colouring varies, and although the ground is white, sometimes pure, some-times yellowish, sometimes suffused with rose, it is always or nearly always more or less spotted. Sometimes the spotting is conspicuous but probably never so much so as is shown in the *Gardeners' Chronicle* figure quoted above.

Stamens ten, white or yellowish, about 1 in. long, minutely downy towards the base ; anthers brown. Ovary densely glandular, as is also the style the whole of its length. Calyx with five shallow triangular teeth, covered like the flower-stalk with minute glands ; the latter is ½ to 1 in. long.

Native of Yunnan, China ; discovered by Delavay in 1886. Introduced from Paris to Kew in 1890. Since then seeds have several times been sent home by Forrest giving plants that vary considerably in flower colour ; one form I believe is a good yellow. It is fairly hardy at Kew but the flowers are often destroyed by spring frosts. A pure white form is very attractive. This is the type species of the ill-defined Irroratum series.

R. Kaempferi, *Planchon*

(R. obtusum Kaempferi, *Wilson* ; Azalea indica Kaempferi, *Rehder*)

A semi-evergreen or nearly deciduous azalea, probably 8 or 10 ft. high in favourable localities ; young twigs covered with appressed, forward-pointing bristles. Leaves 1 to 2½ ins. long, ⅓ to 1 in. wide ; oval, or somewhat diamond-shaped, glossy green above, paler beneath, with scattered bristly hairs on both surfaces. Flowers about 2 ins. in diameter, variable in colour, purplish rose, rose-coloured or rosy scarlet ; produced about mid-May, two to four in terminal clusters. Corolla open bell-shaped, with five roundish oval lobes. Calyx-lobes five, narrowly ovate or obovate, hairy outside and at the margins ; stamens five ; flower-stalk silky-hairy, ¼ in. long.

Native of Japan ; introduced to the United States by Prof. Sargent in 1892, thence to Kew two years later. Nearly allied to R. indicum, this species differs in its nearly deciduous habit, the leaves in any case persisting one winter only, also by its more numerous flowers in a cluster, and by the yellow anthers. It is very much hardier, and, excepting R. amœnum, the best and hardiest of the indicum group of azaleas for near London. Whilst it does not suffer by the hardest winter weather, it is, unfortunately, liable to injury by late frosts, which occasionally destroy not only the blossom but the young shoots also. It thrives excellently, and every year makes a great show in the Arnold Arboretum.

R. Keiskei, *Miquel*

(Bot. Mag., t. 8300)

An evergreen shrub only known as yet in a small state under cultivation, but said to be 6 ft. high in nature ; young branches slightly scaly. Leaves 1½ to 2½ ins. long, ¾ to 1¼ ins. wide ; oval-oblong, pointed at the apex, rounded or tapered at the base, more or less scaly on both surfaces, but especially beneath ; stalk about ¼ in. long. Flowers pale, rather dull yellow, 1¼ to 2 ins. across, in clusters of about four or five ; corolla broadly bell-shaped ; calyx undulated into five very shallow lobes ; stamens ten, slightly downy ; flower-stalk scaly, ½ to ¾ in. long. Blossoms in April and May.

Native of Japan ; introduced in 1908, and apparently hardy. Its chief claim to recognition in gardens will be that it is one of the comparatively few species with yellow flowers. The only one of these with which it is likely to be confused is the Himalayan

R. triflorum, *Hooker fil.*, which differs in the leaves being larger, bright green and not scaly above, glaucous beneath, in the more distinctly lobed calyx, the larger pale yellow corolla, and more hairy stamens. R. triflorum has been tried several times out-of-doors at Kew, but does not thrive. In the Isle of Wight Cornwall, and similar places it succeeds admirably.

R. KEYSII, *Nuttall*

(Bot. Mag., t. 4875)

An evergreen shrub, 6 ft. or more high ; the young shoots, the under-surface of the leaves, leaf-stalk, and flower-stalk densely covered with brownish red, glistening scales. Leaves 2 to 4 ins. long, ⅝ to 1¼ ins. wide ; oval-ovate, tapering at both ends ; stalk ⅛ to ⅔ in. long. Flowers crowded in short clusters, several of which are borne during May and June from axillary buds near the end of the previous year's shoot, and at the time of flowering surmounted by the young shoot of the current year. Each flower is ¾ to 1 in. long, ¼ in. wide—a brick-red, cylindrical tube with five small, blunt, yellow teeth at the mouth ; calyx very small ; flower-stalk ¼ in. long.

Native of Bhotan, up to 10,000 ft. This rhododendron, so remarkably distinct from all others known at the time of its introduction (1851) in the curious Correa-like flowers, forms with a recent introduction from China— R. spinuliferum (*q.v.*)—the sub-genus KEYSIA. It is only hardy in the milder parts of the kingdom, and is a botanical curiosity as well as a rather striking garden plant. Several fine examples exist in Ireland and Cornwall.

R. KINGIANUM, *Watt*

(R. arboreum Kingianum, *Hooker fil.*, Bot. Mag., t. 7696)

Botanically, this is, no doubt, no more than a variety of R. arboreum as J. D. Hooker regarded it, for in all really essential characters it does not differ materially. It is, however, very distinct in foliage. As we know it in cultivation it is a compact evergreen shrub with leaves that are broader than those of typical arboreum and much more ovate in outline ; the upper surface is very wrinkled, with sunken veins, puckered (bullate), convex, with the margins decurved, dark glossy green ; the lower surface is covered with a tawny felt. Wild specimens collected in 1881-2 by Sir George Watt in Manipur, at 9000 ft. altitude, have leaves as much as 6 ins. long and 2½ ins. wide and our cultivated plants have them quite as long and even wider. The flowers, borne in hemispherical trusses 4 or 5 ins. wide, are of a deep blood red, the bell-shaped corolla 1½ ins. wide. Flower-stalks glandular-downy ; ovary downy ; style and stamens glabrous ; calyx small, with five broad, rounded lobes. Very similar to Kingianum in foliage is

R. ZEYLANICUM, *Hort.*—It has the same ovate or ovate-elliptical, puckered, convex leaves, with decurved margins and the same tawny felt beneath. The flowers are variously described as rich pink and blood red. There is a good coloured plate of it in Lindley and Paxton's *Flower Garden*, vol. i., t. 7, where it is called " R. Rollissonii, the Ceylon rhododendron, *alias* R. zeylanicum of gardens." This picture was made from a plant which blossomed with Sir Charles Lemon at Carclew, Cornwall, in March 1850, and the flowers as depicted there have a distinct shade of rose in them. I think the two have been confused in gardens, but the flowers of R. zeylanicum, besides their pinkish tinge, open distinctly earlier than those of R. Kingianum. Their habitats, of course, are 1500 miles apart. (Arboreum series.)

R. KYAWI, *Lace and W. W. Smith*

(Bot. Mag., t. 9271 ; R. prophantum, *Balfour and Forrest*)

An evergreen shrub up to 15 or 20 ft. high ; young shoots at first furnished with starry down and glands, afterwards glabrous. Leaves between oblong and oval ; 6 to 12 ins. long, 2 to 4 ins. wide ; dark green and loosely downy above and finally glabrous there ; the under surface at first covered with starry down and glands like the young shoots, much or all of which wears away leaving it pale and shining green ; stalk up to 2¼ ins. long. Flowers opening during July and August in trusses of twelve to sixteen, the main flower-stalk downy and glandular. Corolla fleshy, funnel-shaped, 3 ins. wide by 2¼ ins. deep, rich crimson, downy outside, five-lobed, the lobes 1 in. wide ; there are five darkly coloured pouches at the base. Stamens ten, crimson, up to 1⅝ ins. long, downy at the base. Ovary covered with tawny down ; style 1¾ ins. long, crimson, glandular over most of its length. Calyx ⅜ in. wide, with five broad shallow lobes ; flower-stalk ½ to 1 in. long, bristly glandular.

Native of E. Upper Burma ; discovered in 1912 by Maung Kyaw, a collector in the Burmese Forest Service, after whom it is named ; found again and introduced by Forrest in 1919 and re-named " prophantum." Both in foliage and in flower this is a really magnificent species, although no doubt best when grown in the open air in our mildest parts, such as Logan in Wigtownshire, where I saw healthy plants several feet high in June 1931. It has, however, borne fourteen degrees of frost at Headfort, Co. Meath. It has been placed in the Irroratum series and is closely related to R. eriogynum, having the same starry down on various parts, the same glittering under surface of the adult leaf, and the same habit of growing late in the season ; but the foliage, flowers, and the plant itself are all larger. Another species of the same group very closely akin to Kyawi and probably equalling it in beauty is

R. AGAPETUM, *Balfour and Ward.* I have not seen it in bloom, but the flowers are also crimson-scarlet and about the same size ; the calyx smaller and edged with glands ; the glands and starry down of the style confined to near the base. Discovered by Kingdon Ward in E. Upper Burma at 6000 to 7000 ft. altitude, flowering in July 1914. All this group must be grown in shade.

R. LACTEUM, *Franchet* (Plate 10)

(Bot. Mag., t. 8988 ; not R. lacteum, *Hemsley,* in Bot. Mag., t. 8372)

In the first and second editions of this work (vol. ii., p. 364) a rhododendron is described under this name (also figured in the *Botanical Magazine*) which, from investigations made by the late Sir Isaac Balfour, proves to be distinct from the plant originally called lacteum by Franchet in 1886. Sir Isaac named it FICTOLACTEUM, and as such it appears in our third and subsequent editions. It now remains for the true R. lacteum to be described.

An evergreen shrub or a tree up to 30 ft. high ; young shoots ½ in. thick, at first scurfy, becoming glabrous. Leaves oblong-ovate, shortly pointed, rounded or slightly heart-shaped at the base ; 4 to 8 ins. long, about half as much wide ; dark green and glabrous above, clothed beneath with a fine, close tawny felt, much of which sometimes wears off before the leaf falls ; stalk ¾ to 1½ ins. long. Flowers opening in April, closely packed twenty or thirty together in a truss up to 8 ins. across. Corolla bell-shaped, soft or canary yellow, 2 ins. wide, five-lobed, not markedly blotched. Stamens ten, downy towards the base. Ovary covered with whitish down ; style glabrous. Calyx a mere wavy rim ; flower-stalk downy, ½ to 1 in. long. (Lacteum series.)

Native of Yunnan, China ; discovered by Delavay in 1884 ; introduced by Forrest in 1910 from the Tali Range, where he found it growing at 12,000 ft. He regarded it as the finest yellow rhododendron he had met with, an opinion everyone who has seen the trusses exhibited at the Rhododendron Association's Shows by Mr A. M. Williams, from Werrington in Cornwall, will support. The false " lacteum " differs in having the under surface covered densely with a thick red-brown or buff felt, in the flowers being white (creamy or rose-tinted) with a conspicuous crimson blotch at the base, in the corolla being seven- or eight-lobed and the stamens fourteen or sixteen. I note that, in his original description, Franchet describes the corolla of the true lacteum as six-lobed, and the stamens as being twelve.   Coming from such a high elevation, it should be moderately hardy, but it does not appear easy to grow.   It is very resentful of hot sunshine.   (See also *galactinum.*)

R. LANATUM, *Hooker fil.*

An evergreen shrub rarely more than 6 or 7 ft. high in cultivation, but said to be sometimes a small tree in nature ; young shoots, under surface of leaves, and flower-stalks thickly covered with a pale brown felt.   Leaves obovate to narrowly oval, rounded at the end ; 2½ to 5 ins. long, 1 to 2¼ ins. wide ; upper surface at first covered with whitish wool which ultimately falls away except at the base of the midrib, leaving it dark green ; stalk ¼ to ½ in. long. Flowers in a terminal cluster of usually six or seven but sometimes ten, opening in April.   Corolla 2 to 2½ ins. wide, bell-shaped, five-lobed, pale yellow dotted with red, the lobes rounded, ¾ in. wide.   Stamens ten, downy at the base ; anthers dark brown.   Ovary woolly ;   style glabrous.   Calyx very small ; flower-stalk ½ to ¾ in. long.

Native of the Sikkim Himalaya at 10,000 to 12,000 ft. altitude ;   discovered by J. D. Hooker in 1848, and soon after introduced to Kew, but unfortunately it is not there now.   It is a very distinct species of the Campanulatum series, especially in the more persistent woolliness of its branchlets, under surface of leaves, etc., combined with the pale yellow flowers.   It has never been common, and is still rarely seen in a thoroughly healthy condition.   There is (or used to be) a plant about 7 ft. high at Carclew, in Cornwall, and there are some healthy plants at Bodnant in the Conway Valley, and at Exbury.   Mr Magor of Lamellen, Cornwall, had a fine truss at the Rhododendron Association's Show at Westminster, in April 1930, which showed how charming the species can be.   It is only in such localities as these that it is likely to be a success in the open air.

R. LAPPONICUM, *Wahlenberg*
(Bot. Mag., t. 3106)

A dwarf evergreen shrub, rarely more than 1 to 1½ ft. high, the lower branches often prostrate ; young wood very scaly, becoming warted.   Leaves oblong, rounded or abruptly tapered at the apex ; ¼ to 1 in. long, ⅛ to ¼ in. wide ; rough and dark green above, covered beneath with brownish yellow scales ; stalk 1/12 to ⅛ in. long.   Flowers bright purple, ¾ in. across, produced three to six together in a small cluster.   Calyx and flower-stalk very scaly ; calyx-lobes triangular, fringed ; stamens five to eight, about as long as the corolla, quite devoid of down ; flower-stalk ¼ to ½ in. long.

Native of the high latitudes of Europe, Asia, and N. America ; probably the most northern of rhododendrons.   It is found on mountain tops in eastern N. America.   Introduced in 1825, but long lost to cultivation, until recently re-introduced.   It probably requires exceptionally cool, moist conditions, somewhat similar to those recommended for R. camtschaticum.   It is a very pretty plant when seen at its best, the colour of the flowers being very bright, and with more blue in it than almost any other species.   (See also R. parvifolium.)

R. LEDOIDES, *Balfour and W. W. Smith*
(Bot. Mag., t. 8831 ; R. hedyosmum, *Balfour fil.*)

A neat evergreen shrub 2 to 4 ft. high, of twiggy habit ; young shoots slender, covered with a mass of scurfy overlapping scales, mixed with which are whitish hairs.   Leaves linear or oblong-lanceolate, tapering about equally at both ends ; $\frac{3}{4}$ to $1\frac{1}{4}$ ins. long, $\frac{1}{6}$ to $\frac{5}{16}$ in. wide ; dull green and with some scales above, paler and with a thick scurf of yellowish scales beneath ; margins decurved ; stalk $\frac{1}{12}$ to $\frac{1}{6}$ in. long. Flowers opening in May densely packed, twelve to twenty together, in a hemispherical cluster 1 to $1\frac{1}{2}$ ins. wide. Corolla white, pale pink or rose-coloured, fading with age, about $\frac{1}{3}$ in. long and $\frac{1}{2}$ in. wide, with a tubular base $\frac{1}{4}$ in. long which is downy inside, expanding at the mouth into five lobes. Stamens five, hidden away in the tube of the corolla, their stalks glabrous ; ovary densely scaly ; style red, shorter than the stamens, thick and club-shaped, with a large pink stigma. Calyx small, pale green, with five rounded fringed lobes ; flower-stalk scaly, $\frac{1}{12}$ in. long.

Native of Yunnan, China, up to altitudes of 13,000 ft., discovered and introduced by Forrest in 1913. The leaves when crushed are rather strongly scented. It is one of the Cephalanthum series and a charming hardy species very daphne-like in truss and individual flower. It first flowered at Caerhays in 1917 at three years old, raised from seed.

R. SPHÆRANTHUM, *Balfour and W. W. Smith*, is so similar to ledoides that it scarcely deserves to rank as a species. Balfour relied on the following differentiating characters : main flower-stalk scaly in sphæranthum, minutely downy in ledoides ; corolla scaly outside in sphæranthum, not so in ledoides ; stamens downy towards the base in sphæranthum, glabrous in ledoides. I have noticed, however, on plants grown in Cornwall under Forrest's No. 11246 (the type number for ledoides) a few scales outside the corolla, and traces of pubescence on the stamens. Native of Yunnan, China, up to elevations of 13,000 ft. (*Gardeners' Chronicle*, 23rd May 1925, fig. 146.)

R. LEPIDOTUM, *Wallich*

(Bot. Mag., t. 4657)

A low, evergreen, sometimes nearly deciduous shrub, usually 1 to 2 ft. high in this country, but said to be 4 ft. high in the Himalaya ; young wood, leaves, leaf-stalk, and flower-stalks dotted thickly with minute scales. Leaves oblong, 1 to $1\frac{1}{2}$ ins. long, about $\frac{1}{2}$ in. wide, only hairy on the margins when young. Flowers pink or purple, spotted, produced singly or a few together in June, each about 1 in. across, flat and saucer-shaped, and borne on a stalk 1 to $1\frac{1}{2}$ ins. long ; corolla-tube very short, lobes rounded. Stamens about ten, hairy towards the base ; calyx-lobes $\frac{1}{8}$ in. long, rounded.

Native of the lofty interior ranges of the Nepal and Sikkim Himalaya, up to 16,000 ft. altitude ; and in Yunnan. It is hardy at Kew, and one of the most distinct and interesting of dwarf rhododendrons. Sir Joseph Hooker mentions varieties with golden yellow flowers and greenish yellow flowers, which do not appear to be in cultivation. Seeds are freely borne.

R. LEPTOTHRIUM, *Balfour and Forrest*

(R. australe, *Balfour and Forrest*)

An evergreen, diffusely branched shrub up to 20 ft. high in a wild state, with slender downy twigs becoming grey, the down remaining on at least two years. Leaves thin, oval-lanceolate, rounded at the base, tapering at the apex to a short mucro ; $1\frac{1}{2}$ to 3 ins. long, $\frac{5}{8}$ to 1 in. wide ; at first a pleasing purplish red then dark green and glabrous except for the midrib which is downy above and below ; stalk $\frac{1}{4}$ to $\frac{3}{8}$ in. long, covered with grey down. Flowers solitary from the clustered terminal leaf-axils, opening in May. Corolla deep magenta rose with crimson spots, about $1\frac{3}{4}$ ins. wide, five-lobed, the lobes oblong and as long or longer than the tube which is downy inside. Stamens five, the lower half downy ; ovary covered with sticky glands ; style glabrous. Calyx with five ovate or oblong lobes ⅜ in. long, ciliate; flower-stalks slender, ⅜ in. long, downy, rosy purple.

Native of N.W. Yunnan ; discovered and introduced by Forrest in 1914. I first saw it in flower at Caerhays in May 1920 ; in 1932 it was 12 ft. high there. It belongs to the series of which R. ovatum is the type species, well marked by the solitary axillary flowers, the five stamens, and the large calyx-lobes ; the group is intermediate between the azaleas and true rhododendrons.

R. LEUCASPIS, *Tagg*

(Bot. Mag., t. 9665 ; Gardeners' Chronicle, 23rd Feb. 1929, fig. 67)

An evergreen shrub 1 to 2 ft. high ; young shoots and leaf-stalks bristly. Leaves elliptic to obovate, tapered at the base, rounded at the apex, the mucro at the end often curiously reflexed ; 1½ to 2¾ ins. long, ½ to 1¼ ins. wide ; dark glossy green and sparsely bristly above ; glaucous and thickly set with shining yellowish scales beneath ; stalk ¼ in. long. Flowers terminal, mostly in pairs, sometimes solitary or in threes, opening in April and May. Corolla flat and open, 2 ins. wide, pure white, with five broadly rounded, overlapping lobes ; slightly scaly outside, hairy in the throat. Stamens ten, their white stalks hairy except towards the top ; anthers chocolate-brown. Ovary densely clad with whitish scales ; style thick, curved, whitish, glabrous. Calyx ¼ in. long, with five deep, broadly ovate or obovate lobes, scaly only at the base, fringed with soft hairs ; flower-stalk ¼ in. long, scaly but not bristly.

Native of Tibet ; discovered and introduced by Kingdon Ward in 1925. His note referring to his No. 6273, the seed of which has produced plants that flowered in 1929, reads : " Prostrate shrub, forming a close growth, with stems rising 1 to 2 ft., or forming small erect bushes." Plants less than 1 foot high were shown in flower by Mr L. de Rothschild at Westminster on 12th February 1929, when the species was given an Award of Merit. Plants of about the same size, and in perfect health, I saw blooming very prettily in the rock garden at Exbury in April 1931. It belongs to the Boothii series, in which a flat corolla, large deeply lobed calyx and bent style are notable characteristics, but it is well distinguished by its white flowers, most of the group having yellow ones. Ward found it at 10,000 ft. altitude in the Tsangpo Gorge, but the degree of cold it will bear with us is as yet uncertain. It is evidently hardy enough at Exbury, which is close to the Solent, and flowered when only three years old.

R. LINDLEYI, *T. Moore*

An evergreen shrub of lax habit, often found in nature as an epiphyte on various species of trees ; young shoots slightly scaly, otherwise glabrous. Leaves oblong to oval, rounded at both ends ; 2½ to 6 ins. long, ¾ to 2 ins. wide ; glaucous and scaly beneath ; stalk ¾ in. long. Flowers in clusters of four to six, fragrant. Corolla white, funnel-shaped, 3 to 3½ ins. long and wide, five-lobed. Stamens ten, very downy at the lower half. Ovary and base of style thickly covered with red-brown scales. Calyx ⅜ in. long, deeply five-lobed, the lobes oblong-ovate fringed with whitish hairs ; flower-stalk ½ in. long, scaly, not downy.

Native of Sikkim and Bhutan ; discovered in 1848 by J. D. Hooker who, both in his illustration and description (*Sikkim Rhododendrons*, t. 2), confused it with R. Dalhousiæ. The true plant is very rare, but plants are growing at Caerhays and Heligan in Cornwall, and Millais records his having seen one at

Fermoy, Co. Cork. As it grows in Sikkim at elevations as low as 6000 ft., it is only in such warm localities that it can be grown in the open.

R. DALHOUSIÆ, *Hooker fil.* (*Botanical Magazine*, t. 4718), is also sometimes an epiphyte, sometimes it grows on rocks. It was discovered in Sikkim, in 1848, by J. D. Hooker. The fragrant flowers open in May and June in clusters of three to five, the corolla white tinged with rose, 3 to 4 ins. long, nearly as wide. It differs from Lindleyi in the young shoots being bristly as well as scaly, in the downy flower-stalks, in the calyx-lobes not being fringed with hairs, and in the style being scaly two-thirds up. It comes from the same elevations and is equally tender. The true plant, a fine thing, is very rare, many so-called being really hybrids. One of the best plants in cultivation is at Kew, grafted on ponticum. Crossed with formosum it has produced R. TYERMANNII, and, with ciliatum, "Countess of Haddington." Both species belong to the megacalyx section of the Maddenii series.

R. LINEARIFOLIUM, *Siebold and Zuccarini*

(Azalea linearifolia, *Hooker* ; Bot. Mag., t. 5769)

An evergreen, flattish shrub, 2 to 4 ft. high, with forking, often horizontal branches ; the younger parts covered with bristly hairs, the young wood, leaves, and flower-stalks very thickly so. Leaves crowded at the end of short twigs, narrowly linear ; 2 to 3 ins. long, usually $\frac{1}{8}$ to $\frac{3}{16}$ in. wide at the middle, tapering gradually to each end. Flowers produced during May in a terminal cluster of about three, the corolla having long, narrow lobes of about the same shape as the leaves, and up to 1$\frac{1}{2}$ ins. long, bright rosy lilac, hairy at the base. The calyx has five narrow-linear lobes $\frac{1}{2}$ in. long, thickly covered, like the flower-stalk, with hairs ; stamens five.

A Japanese garden form ; the type being R. macrosepalum, a native of Japan, introduced by Messrs Standish, and first flowered by them in 1867. Although not represented there now it is quite hardy at Kew, and worth growing for its remarkable aspect. The long narrow leaves and corolla-lobes, and the shaggy character of the entire plant render it quite distinct from all other azaleas. Increased by cuttings.

R. LONGESQUAMATUM, *C. K. Schneider*

(Bot. Mag., t. 9430 ; R. Brettii, *Hemsley*)

An evergreen bush about 10 ft. high ; young shoots clothed thickly with brown, shaggy, branched hairs, which persist for two or more seasons. Leaves oblong, inclined to obovate, pointed at the apex, rounded or slightly heart-shaped at the base ; 2$\frac{1}{2}$ to 5 ins. long, 1 to 1$\frac{3}{4}$ ins. wide ; dark green and glabrous except for the midrib, which is shaggy beneath like the young shoots and leaf-stalks—the latter about $\frac{1}{2}$ in. long. The flowers, which open in April, are bell-shaped, 2 ins. across, pink with a dark red blotch, and produced ten or more in a truss. Stamens ten, shorter than the corolla, downy below ; calyx-lobes $\frac{1}{2}$ in. long, hairy and glandular.

Native of Szechuen, China, up to 9000 ft. altitude ; discovered by Wilson, and introduced in 1904. Quite hardy at Coombe Wood and Kew, and said by Mr Wilson to be a very striking and handsome species, not common. The fur-like covering of the young shoots is very marked, as is also the large petaloid calyx, about 1 in. across, glandular and hairy.

R. LONGISTYLUM, *Rehder and Wilson*

An evergreen shrub up to 6 or 7 ft. high, with only slightly scaly young shoots. Leaves narrowly oval or oblanceolate, much tapered towards the base, $\frac{3}{4}$ to 2 ins. long, $\frac{1}{4}$ to $\frac{3}{4}$ in. wide ; dark dullish green and with a fine network of sunken veins above, quite pale and sprinkled thinly with very small scales beneath ; stalk ⅛ to ¼ in. long. Flowers produced in March and April, eight to twelve or more crowded in a terminal cluster. Corolla white or pink, ¾ in. long and wide, with five ovate, bluntish lobes. Stamens ten, unequal, the longest slightly exceeding the corolla, downy at the base ; anthers yellow. Ovary scaly ; style 1 to 1⅛ ins. long, glabrous, often reddish. Calyx pale green, scaly, five-lobed, the lobes ¹⁄₁₂ to ⅛ in. long, fringed with hairs. (Triflorum series.)

Native of W. Szechuen, China ; introduced in 1908 by Wilson, who describes it as growing on cliffs and scrub-clad slopes fully exposed to the sun. Rehder and Wilson write of the great length of the style as " most remarkable " ; but, compared with some of its newer allies, it does not exceed the corolla to any very notable degree. They considered it to be related to R. micranthum, but that species has much smaller, more numerous flowers in a cluster, smooth stamens, and flowers much later. R. longistylum is now placed in the triflorum-yunnanense group, whilst R. micranthum as " showing no particular affinity with any other rhododendron " is in a group by itself. Both are quite hardy near London but neither is remarkable for flower beauty.

R. LUTESCENS, *Franchet*

(Bot. Mag., t. 8851)

An evergreen shrub, 3 to 7 ft. high, of loose habit ; young shoots reddish, slender, scaly. Leaves lanceolate, with a long slender point and a tapered base ; 1½ to 3¼ ins. long, ½ to 1¼ ins. wide ; dark green above, paler and more scaly beneath ; stalk ¼ to ⅓ in. long. Flowers pale yellow, produced singly or occasionally in pairs from several buds at the apex of the shoot, terminal and axillary ; corolla broadly funnel-shaped, 1 in. wide ; stamens ten, protruded, hairy near the base. Ovary, calyx, and flower-stalk scaly, the last ½ in. long ; calyx scarcely lobed.

Native of W. China and Tibet ; discovered by the Abbé David ; introduced by Wilson in 1904. In the curious habit of bearing often a single flower only from each bud, this species resembles dauricum and mucronulatum. Its yellow flowers give it interest, but opening, as they do, in March, they often perish by frost. Wilson's later introductions of this species seem hardier than his first. It is very charming in the milder counties.

R. LUTEUM, *Sweet*

(R. flavum, *G. Don* ; Azalea pontica, *Linnæus*, Bot. Mag., t. 433)

A deciduous shrub of vigorous, rather stiff habit, 8 to 10 ft. high ; young shoots viscous, glandular. Leaves linear-oblong, 2½ to 5 ins. long, ¾ to 1½ ins. wide ; with a short, abrupt tip, more tapering at the base ; at maturity glaucous, hairy beneath along the midrib and at the margins ; stalk hairy, ⅛ in. or less long. Flowers fragrant, rich bright yellow, 1½ to 2 ins. across, crowded in several clusters at the end of the previous year's naked shoots. Corolla-tube ½ in. long, hairy ; calyx-lobes small, ovate, edged with glanded hairs ; stamens five, hairy at the base like the style ; flower-stalk ½ to ¾ in. long, covered with sticky, glandular hairs. Blossoms in May.

Native of the Caucasian region, Asia Minor, etc. ; introduced by Mr Anthony Hove in 1793. This beautiful, perfectly hardy azalea, the only yellow one known until the advent of the Chinese (sinense) type, and the parent or the predominant parent of all the older yellow garden varieties, is still one of the most useful and generally cultivated of all shrubs. It blossoms unfailingly, and with an exquisite fragrance. Coming freely from seed, it is the chief stock used for grafting the choicer varieties on. This probably explains its abundance in gardens, for being a vigorous grower it will, unless watched, often send up strong sucker growths that in time smother out the more finely bred sorts grafted on it.

Var. ALBIFLORUM (Bot. Mag., t. 2383).—A white-flowered form, or perhaps hybrid.

Var. MACRANTHUM.—Flowers rich yellow, 2½ ins. or more wide.

R. MACROSEPALUM, *Maximowicz*

(R. linearifolium macrosepalum, *Makino* ; Azalea macrosepala, *K. Koch*)

According to Wilson, this evergreen azalea is the wild type of the curious R. linearifolium, the latter being really an abnormal form which originated in Japanese gardens. Only comparatively small plants of R. macrosepalum are in this country, but Wilson describes it as a low, laxly branched evergreen azalea of spreading habit, usually less than 3 ft. high, but seen by him in Shikoku thrice as tall. The young shoots are densely clothed with outstanding, occasionally gland-tipped hairs. Leaves lanceolate to ovate or oval, hairy on both surfaces, the larger ones 1½ to 2½ ins. long, ½ to 1½ ins. wide ; stalk up to ¼ in. long, very hairy. Flowers fragrant, opening in May in terminal clusters usually of four to six, but sometimes up to ten. Corolla rose-pink to reddish purple, funnel-shaped at the base, dividing into five lobes and 1½ to 2 ins. wide, not so long. Stamens five normally, usually shorter than the corolla. Ovary clothed with erect white hairs. Calyx green, with five narrow, pointed, strap-shaped, hairy lobes ⅖ to 1⅕ ins. long, sometimes exceeding the corolla in length.

Native of Japan ; introduced to St Petersburg by Maximowicz in 1863 and flowered in 1870, but afterwards apparently lost to cultivation. Wilson reintroduced it in 1914. It is evidently a very variable plant and Wilson enumerates four forms of it, one of which, DIANTHIFLORUM (Azalea dianthiflora, *Carrière*), is or has been cultivated in this country and has double rosy-purple flowers dotted with brown. I saw a plant of R. macrosepalum flowering freely with Mr P. D. Williams at Lanarth in May 1920, which had curious green, hairy, malformed, flattened styles exceeding the corolla in length. It is fairly hardy when grown at Kew. The calyx is quite remarkable.

R. MACULIFERUM, *Franchet*

An evergreen shrub 8 to 10 ft. high in cultivation and of dense, bushy, very leafy habit ; young shoots at first woolly. Leaves oblong, narrowly oval or obovate, rounded or slightly heart-shaped at the base, abruptly narrowed to a short point, 3 to 5½ ins. long, 1 to 2½ ins. wide ; dark green and glabrous above, woolly beneath, but only on the midrib where the wool is dense at the base, fading away upwards until at the upper third it quite disappears ; stalk ½ to 1½ ins. long, downy like the base of the midrib. Flowers opening in March and April in loose trusses 4 ins. wide composed of six to ten blossoms. Corolla five-lobed, bell-shaped, 1½ ins. wide, pale rose to white with a dark crimson, almost black spot at the base, to which the specific name refers. Stamens ten, shorter than the corolla, their stalks downy at the base ; anthers black or nearly so. Ovary cylindrical, $\frac{3}{16}$ in. long, covered with short, pale tawny hairs ; style glabrous. Calyx small, with five triangular lobes ; flower-stalk ¾ to 1 in. long, woolly.

Native of N.W. Hupeh, whence it was introduced to cultivation by Wilson in 1901 ; originally discovered, however, in Szechuen by Farges early in the previous decade. Wilson gives its height at one place as up to 32 ft., but healthy bushes thirty years old at Caerhays do not promise to attain that height or become tree-like. It is a well-marked species by reason of the woolly midrib beneath and the bell-shaped flowers with almost erect lobes and a very conspicuous black-crimson blotch at the base. It blossoms in March and April, not always freely, and is inclined to hide its trusses in the luxuriant foliage. One of the fine plants growing in the Caerhays woods has flowers of a very pure white. Quite hardy. (Barbatum series.)

R. MADDENII, *Hooker fil.*

(Bot. Mag., t. 4805 ; R. Jenkinsii, *Nuttall*)

An evergreen shrub up to 9 ft. high, of open habit ; bark papery ; young shoots grey, clad with red-brown scales. Leaves lanceolate to oblong-lanceolate, sharply pointed, tapered at both ends ; 3 to 6 ins. long, 1¼ to 2½ ins. wide ; dark green above, glaucous beneath but nearly covered with scales ; stalk ½ to 1 in. long. Flowers very fragrant, produced from June to August in clusters of two to four. Corolla white, sometimes flushed with rose on the outside, funnel-shaped, 4 ins. long and wide, five-lobed, the lobes rounded, over 1 in. wide ; scaly outside. Stamens twenty, 2 ins. long, glabrous ; anthers orange-yellow. Ovary and style completely clad with scales. Calyx small for the size of the flower, the five lobes usually about ⅛ in. long, except the back one which may be ½ in. long, scaly outside. Flower-stalk ½ to ¾ in. long.

Native of Sikkim ; discovered and introduced about 1849 by the younger Hooker. It occurs at 5000 to 9000 ft. altitude, and is not hardy in our average climate, but is a delightful shrub in Cornwall and other mild places, one of its good qualities being that it flowers later in the season than most rhododendrons ; another that it is easily grown. It is named after Major Madden, who belonged to the Bengal Civil Service in 1849. Several very beautiful hybrids between this and R. cinnabarinum have been raised, such as "Rose Mangles." Mr L. de Rothschild re-crossed two of these with cinnabarinum and thereby obtained two very beautiful varieties called "Lady Rosebery" and "Lady Chamberlain." Being by descent three-fourths cinnabarinum (which is perfectly hardy at Kew) they should bring some of the beauty and distinction of the tender Maddenii to the cooler gardens of this country. The flowers of "Lady Rosebery" (Plate 11) are shining pink, prettily veined within ; those of "Lady Chamberlain" orange coloured stained with ruby red. Both have been awarded a first-class certificate. (See also R. crassum, p. 52.)

R. CALOPHYLLUM, *Nuttall*, has frequently been united with R. Maddenii, although sometimes as a variety. Dr Hutchinson (see *Notes from the Royal Botanic Garden, Edinburgh*, vol. xii., p. 22) considers them distinct and that the true calophyllum has never been in cultivation. (Maddenii series.)

R. MALLOTUM, *Balfour and Ward*

(Bot. Mag., t. 9419 ; R. æmulorum, *Balfour fil.*)

An evergreen shrub or a small tree, in nature up to 15 ft. high ; young shoots stout, downy. Leaves obovate, 3 to 7 ins. long, half or rather more than half as much wide ; dark dull green and wrinkled above like R. Falconeri ; covered beneath with a rich, soft, brownish red wool ; veins twelve to fifteen on each side of the midrib which is terminated by a yellowish, knob-like, shining mucro. Flowers opening in April in hemispherical trusses about 5 ins. wide, carrying over a dozen blossoms. Corolla tubular-bell-shaped, rosy scarlet to deep crimson, 2 ins. wide, 1½ ins. long, with five notched lobes, each ⅞ in. wide. Stamens ten, ¾ to 1 in. long, glabrous ; anthers dark brown. Ovary silky-hairy ; style glabrous, 1½ ins. long. Calyx very small ; flower-stalk about ½ in. long, very woolly.

Discovered in N.E. Burma by Kingdon Ward in 1914 ; introduced by Forrest from W. Yunnan, China, in 1919. Judging by leaf alone, one would regard it as being akin to R. Falconeri, to which it bears a striking resemblance, but it really belongs to the hæmatodes section of the Neriiflorum series. Mr J. C. Williams sent me a truss during the last days of March 1931, from Caerhays, which I thought to be extremely beautiful ; in this the corolla had a distinct shade of rose. According to Mr E. H. M. Cox the species is hardy in Perthshire, but I imagine it will show its best qualities in the maritime counties of the south and west.

R. MARTINIANUM, *Balfour and Forrest*

An evergreen shrub 3 to 6 ft. high, with slender but stiff young shoots furnished with glands, becoming grey and swollen at the joints the second and third years. Leaves clustered at the end of the shoot, oval inclined to oblong, abruptly tapered towards both ends, ending in a very distinct mucro ; ¾ to 1¾ ins. long, half as much wide ; more or less glandular when young, eventually glabrous or nearly so, rather glaucous beneath ; stalk ¼ in. long, glandular. Flowers two or three together in a terminal cluster each on a glandular stalk up to 1¼ ins. long. Corolla widely funnel-shaped, five-lobed, 1 in. long, 2 ins. wide, pale rose with a dark blotch at the base, the lobes reflexed. Stamens ten, downy at the base ; ovary and base of style glandular. Calyx small, fringed with glands.

Native of Yunnan, China ; discovered and introduced by Forrest in 1914. It is described as a most distinct and beautiful species which will find its most suitable conditions in the southern and western maritime counties. Regarded botanically as a distinct type of the Thomsonii series, it has very little resemblance to R. Thomsonii itself. Flowers in May and June. A noticeable character is the swollen joints of the year-old (and older) branchlets, marking the places where the whorls of leaves were attached.

R. MAXIMUM, *Linnæus*
(Bot. Mag., t. 951)

An evergreen tree, sometimes over 30 ft. high, with a short trunk 1 ft. in diameter in a wild state, but always a shrub under cultivation in Britain, and rarely more than 8 or 10 ft. high ; young wood reddish and scurfy. Leaves narrowly obovate to oblong, 4 to 10 ins. long, 1 to 2½ ins. wide ; dark green above, pale beneath, becoming quite glabrous on both surfaces by autumn ; stalk ½ to 1 in. long, very stout. Flowers produced in a cluster about 4 ins. across ; corolla rose-coloured or purplish pink, spotted with yellow on the upper side, about 1½ ins. across, the lobes rounded ; calyx with ovate, rounded lobes slightly downy, $\frac{3}{16}$ in. long ; stamens ten, flower-stalk viscid and downy, 1 to 1½ ins. long.

Native of the United States ; introduced in 1736, but now rarely seen in gardens. Its trusses are small, but very pretty and delicate in colour. It is useful, moreover, in flowering late—the end of June and in July. Distinct in the comparatively large calyx-lobes.

Var. ALBUM.—Flowers white, smaller ; wild with the type. (R. Purshii, *Don*.)

R. Meddianum, *Forrest*

(Bot. Mag., t. 9636)

An evergreen, stoutly branched shrub up to 6 ft. high, glabrous in all its parts ; young shoots glaucous. Leaves oval or inclined to obovate, broadly tapered to rounded at the base, rounded and with a short mucro at the apex ; 3 to 5 ins. long, 2 to 3 ins. wide ; dark dull green above, paler green beneath ; stalk stout, ½ to 1¼ ins. long. Flowers in a terminal truss of five to ten, opening in March and April. Corolla deep crimson, between bell-shaped and funnel-shaped, 2½ ins. long and wide, five-lobed, the lobes shallow, rounded and notched ; stamens ten, with white stalks, shorter than the corolla. Calyx red, cup-shaped, five-lobed, the obovate lobes ¼ to ½ in. long ; style 1½ ins. long, red ; flower-stalk yellowish. (Thomsonii series.)

Native of W. Yunnan, China, and of N.E. Burma ; discovered by Forrest at 10,000 to 11,000 ft. altitude in 1917 and introduced by him. It is a Chinese representative of R. Thomsonii, from which it differs in its red calyx and green under surface of the leaves. It is a very handsome richly coloured rhododendron. A form with bright scarlet flowers is said to have flowered in Cornwall. The var. ATROKERMESINUM is distinguished by its glandular ovary and larger darker coloured flowers.

R. MEGACALYX, *Balfour and Ward*

(Bot. Mag., t. 9326 ; Gardeners' Chronicle, 25th May 1929, fig. 192)

An evergreen shrub up to 10 ft. or 15 ft. high in a wild state, described by Ward as of " tall, loosely knit " habit. Leaves oblong-oval, often inclined to obovate, mostly rounded at the apex ; 4 to 6 ins. long, 1 to 3 ins. wide ; strongly veined ; dull light green and glabrous above, densely furnished with sunken, yellow-brown scales beneath ; stalk ½ to ¾ in. long, with a shallow groove on the upper side. Flowers drooping, opening in April and May in loose clusters of three to five, with a nutmeg-like fragrance. Corolla funnel-shaped, 4 ins. long and as much wide, pure white or flushed with pinkish purple, stained with pale yellow at the base inside. Stamens ten, shorter than the corolla, downy at the lower part. Ovary and base of style scaly. Calyx very large, bell-shaped, ¾ to 1¼ ins. long, with five deep, rounded ovate lobes ; flower-stalk stout, glabrous, 1 to 1¼ ins. long. Seed-vessel thick, ¾ in. long, enclosed by the persistent calyx.

Native of N.E. Burma, up to elevations of 9000 ft. ; discovered by Kingdon Ward in 1914, afterwards found by Forrest and Farrer. This has to be grown in a cool greenhouse at Kew, where it flowers freely and regularly and is always to be recognised through the winter by its curiously stalked flower-buds. Mr Lionel de Rothschild observed that the later importations of this fine species promise to be hardier than the earliest one, and it may prove to be possible to grow them in the open air in such places as Exbury, near the Solent. It is the type species of a section of the Maddenii series characterised by the flower having ten stamens and a large calyx with broad lobes. R. megacalyx itself is distinguished by the flower-stalks and calyx being free from scales, and by the leaf-stalk being grooved on the upper side.

R. MICRANTHUM, *Turczaninow*

(Bot. Mag., t. 8198)

An evergreen shrub of bushy form, ultimately 4 to 6 ft. high ; branches slender, scaly, and slightly downy when young. Leaves narrowly oval or oblanceolate, tapering at both ends ; ¾ to 1½ ins. long, ¼ to ½ in. wide ; glabrous

III   D above, very scaly beneath; stalk $\frac{1}{8}$ in. or less long. Flowers dull white, $\frac{1}{3}$ to $\frac{1}{2}$ in. across, numerous and densely packed in a short, terminal, rounded raceme $1\frac{1}{4}$ to $1\frac{1}{2}$ ins. across. Corolla bell-shaped at the base, with five flatly spreading, oval lobes as long as the tube; stamens ten, longer than the corolla, not downy; flower-stalk slender, scaly, $\frac{1}{3}$ to $\frac{3}{4}$ in. long.

Native of N. and Central China and Manchuria; introduced by Wilson, in 1901, from W. Hupeh. It is found at elevations of 5500 to 8000 ft. there, and promises to be quite hardy. It is remarkably distinct in its racemes of small, numerous flowers, which open in May, and give the plant at that time a strong resemblance to Ledum latifolium. Still, it is not in the front rank of rhododendrons.

R. MICROPHYTON, *Franchet*

(The Species of Rhododendron, p. 90)

An evergreen azalea 1 to 3 (or occasionally up to 6) ft. high, of bushy, twiggy habit; young shoots densely clothed with pale, reddish-brown, appressed, flattened, forward-pointing bristles. Leaves oval, ovate, or lanceolate, $\frac{1}{2}$ to $1\frac{1}{2}$ ins. long, $\frac{1}{3}$ to $\frac{3}{4}$ in wide, pointed, of a bronzy tinge when young, bright green above when older and sprinkled with bristles; the lower surface paler and with appressed bristles, especially on the midrib; margins bristly; stalk $\frac{1}{12}$ to $\frac{1}{8}$ in. long. Flowers four to six together in terminal clusters opening in April and May. Corolla pale rosy lilac with carmine or crimson spots on the three upper lobes, $\frac{3}{4}$ to $1\frac{1}{4}$ ins. wide and long, five-lobed, the lobes ovate, spreading, contracted at the base to a cylindrical tube, faintly downy inside. Stamens $\frac{5}{8}$ to $\frac{7}{8}$ in. long, downy towards the base; anthers deep rose. Ovary covered with bright brown hairs; style glabrous. Calyx lobes five, varying from $\frac{1}{16}$ to $\frac{1}{6}$ in. long, covered with bright-brown bristles like the flower-stalks, which are $\frac{1}{6}$ in. long.

Native of Yunnan, China; discovered by the Abbé Delavay about 1884, and a little later by Henry. Forrest found it on the eastern flank of the Tali Range in 1906, but the plants I have seen in flower were raised from his 1913 seed (some flowered at Kew under glass in April 1921). It belongs to the indicum group of azaleas, characterised by the forward-pointing appressed bristles on the vegetative parts; the long cylindrical tube of the corolla is distinctive. It is a pretty, free-flowering plant, the flowers sometimes almost white. Only hardy, I think, in the south and west.

R. MINUS, *Michaux*

(R. Cuthbertii, *Small*; R. punctatum, *Andrews*)

An evergreen bush, up to 8 ft. high; young shoots rough with scales. Leaves oval-lanceolate to narrowly obovate, tapering at both ends; $1\frac{1}{2}$ to 3 ins. long, $\frac{1}{2}$ to $1\frac{1}{4}$ ins. wide; dark green and nearly glabrous above, thickly dotted beneath with minute red-brown scales; stalk $\frac{1}{4}$ to $\frac{1}{2}$ in. long. Flowers 1 to $1\frac{1}{2}$ ins. wide, pale pinkish purple, spotted on the upper side with brownish red; corolla funnel-shaped, scaly; stamens ten, hairy at base, protruding somewhat beyond the corolla; calyx-lobes very short; flower-stalk scaly, $\frac{1}{2}$ to $\frac{3}{4}$ in. long. Ovary scaly; style glabrous. Blossoms in May and June.

Native of eastern N. America; introduced in 1786. It is a neat and pretty bush, but not one of the showier sorts, and is, perhaps, of chief interest now as the parent of several useful hybrids, amongst which the following are of especial interest:—

R. ARBUTIFOLIUM, *Hort.* (R. daphnoides).—A neat shrub, 3 or 4 ft. high, with dark dull green leaves (purplish in winter) covered beneath with glistening minute scales, amidst which are sprinkled larger darker ones. Flowers rose-coloured. The other parent is ferrugineum.

R. MYRTIFOLIUM, *Loddiges* (R. ovatum, *Hort.*, not *Planchon*).—The other parent of this is probably hirsutum. Its leaves are not of so dark a green as those of arbutifolium, and the scales beneath are all of the large dark kind. Flowers about 1 in. wide, a delicate rose. It grows 4 or 5 ft. high, and is not so stiff in habit as arbutifolium. Leaves 1½ to 2 ins. long, ¾ in. wide.

R. WILSONI, *Hort.*, not of *Hooker.*—This has longer leaves than either of the preceding (2½ ins. long, ¾ in. wide) and is of freer growth, forming a dense, leafy bush 5 or 6 ft. high. Flowers pale rose, 1¼ ins. wide. A useful, neat, and pretty evergreen, probably a cross with some form of R. ponticum.

R. MOLLE, *G. Don*

(Azalea mollis, *Blume*)

A deciduous bush, of rounded habit, 4 to 8 ft. high, with stiff, erect branches; young shoots sparsely hairy. Leaves narrowly oval or obovate, 2 to 4 ins. long, ¾ to 1¼ ins. wide; dark green and sparsely hairy above, more or less glaucous and slightly hairy beneath when young, especially on the midrib and margins. Flowers six to ten in a cluster, produced during May on the end of leafless shoots, the corolla being of various shades of soft rose, salmon red, and orange red, 2½ to 3½ ins. wide, the lobes oblong; calyx-lobes oblong to linear-oblong, as long as the ovary, conspicuously edged with long whitish hairs; flower-stalk ½ to 1 in. long, hairy.

Native of Japan, perhaps China also, and one of the most beautiful of all deciduous shrubs. It flowers somewhat in advance of the so-called " Ghent " azaleas that have been derived from R. luteum and the American species, and its blossom is apt to be spoilt by late frosts. Still, it often escapes, especially if planted on elevated ground, and then gives one of the most delightful of all colour displays. The flowers have no fragrance. There is now a great variety of shades—almost white, yellow, deep rose, and salmon—among cultivated varieties, which, however much mixed, always harmonise. For some time past it has been the practice among botanists to amalgamate this azalea with R. sinense (*q.v.*). This arrangement has never been accepted in nurseries and gardens, and as there appear to be fairly well-marked differences between them, I have here kept them apart. R. sinense as here interpreted differs from R. molle in the following particulars : The branchlets and undersurface of the leaves are somewhat less hairy than in R. molle, but are, in addition, covered with a dense felt of soft down; the lobes of the corolla are shorter, fuller, and more rounded; and the calyx-lobes are more rounded, shorter (scarcely half the length of the ovary), and not so conspicuously hairy. It appears to be exclusively Chinese, and perhaps less hardy.

Between R. molle and R. sinense a series of intermediate, probably hybrid, forms have become popular in cultivation, especially for forcing. One of the most notable of these is the variety " Anthony Koster," with brilliant yellow blossom.

R. MOLLICOMUM, *Balfour and W. W. Smith*

An evergreen shrub up to 6 ft. high; young shoots very downy. Leaves of stout leathery texture, narrowly oval or oblong, tapered at the base, rather blunt at the apex; ¾ to 2 ins. long, $\frac{3}{16}$ to ½ in. wide; dull green above, downy on both surfaces, especially on the midrib beneath and on the strongly decurved margins; somewhat scaly beneath; stalk ⅛ in. or less long. Flowers opening in April and May usually in pairs from the terminal leaf-axils, each flower on a downy stalk about ¼ in. long, the whole forming a truss 2 or 3 ins.

wide. Corolla pale pink to rosy red, ¾ in. long, 1 in. wide, slenderly funnel-shaped at the base, dividing at the top into five oblong lobes ; slightly scaly outside, slightly downy inside the tube. Stamens ten, well protruded, their slender stalks downy on the lower half. Ovary scaly and downy ; style downy at the base, slender, 1 in. or so long, standing along with the stamens half an inch beyond the corolla. Calyx very small, scarcely lobed, very downy.

Native of Yunnan, China, up to altitudes of 11,000 ft. ; discovered and introduced by Forrest in 1913 ; first flowered at Caerhays in 1917. It is a pretty rhododendron akin to R. scabrifolium, but differs in its smaller flowers and leaves and scarcely lobed calyx. Notable characteristics are the soft down which covers shoots, leaves, flower-stalks and calyx, the protruded stamens and style, and the mixture of scales and down beneath the leaf. It is evidently hardier than is generally supposed, as it has lived and flowered annually in the open air at Kew since 1923. At the same time it is better suited with milder conditions. (Scabrifolium series.)

R. MONOSEMATUM, *Hutchinson*

(Bot. Mag., t. 8675)

An evergreen shrub closely related to R. pachytrichum, of sturdy, bushy habit and probably capable of growing 10 ft. or more high. It differs chiefly from pachytrichum in the young shoots and leaf-stalks being furnished with straight, unbranched, gland-tipped bristles ; in pachytrichum the hairs are curly, branched and not gland-tipped. Leaves oblong, 3 to 6 ins. long, 1 to 1½ ins. wide, green on both surfaces and glabrous except for some hairs at the base of the midrib. Flowers produced in April, a dozen or so together, in hemispherical terminal trusses 4 ins. wide. Corolla bell-shaped, 1¼ ins. wide, white tinged with rose, marked at the base with a black-purple blotch and a few spots. Stamens ten, white, downy at the base ; anthers dark purple. Ovary covered with short glands, mixed with longer whitish hairs, style glabrous. Calyx and flower-stalk very glandular.

Native of Szechuen, China ; introduced by Wilson for Messrs Veitch in 1904. It will be seen from the description given above that it differs from pachytrichum in the glandular character of the hairs on branchlet, leaf-stalk, flower-stalk, calyx, and ovary. It has about the same hardiness and the same garden value. (Barbatum series.)

R. MOUPINENSE, *Franchet*

A dwarf evergreen shrub 2 to 3 ft. high ; young shoots hairy, much of the hairiness disappearing by autumn. Leaves leathery, obovate or oval, rounded or slightly heart-shaped at the base, usually rounded and with a short mucro at the apex ; ¾ to 1½ ins. long, about half as wide ; dark, slightly glossy green, and glabrous except for some minute down on the midrib above ; pale and covered with minute scales beneath ; margins ciliate at first towards the base ; leaf-stalk ⅛ to ¼ in. long, furnished with dark hairs. Flowers fragrant, white or pink with purple or yellowish spots, 2 ins. across, opening in March ; corolla shortly tubular and downy at the base, expanding into five rounded lobes. Stamens ten, shorter than the corolla, downy at the base, anthers purplish brown ; style glabrous or nearly so. Calyx with rounded, ciliate lobes. Seed-vessel ¾ in. long, ⅓ in. wide. Flowers usually about three in a cluster.

Native of Tibet and W. China ; introduced by Wilson in 1909. It is described as growing in the forks of trees. Young plants in cultivation appear to be quite hardy and thriving. It promises to be useful for the rock garden.

R. MUCRONATUM, *G. Don*

(R. ledifolium, *G. Don* ; Azalea ledifolia, Bot. Mag., t. 2901)

A stiff evergreen shrub, 5 or 6 ft. high in favourable localities ; branches rigid, covered densely with dark bristles the first and second seasons. Leaves narrowly oval-lanceolate, 1 to 2½ ins. long, ⅛ to ¾ in. wide ; tapering at both ends, hairy all over especially when young, rather dull green ; stalk ⅛ in. long. Flowers pure white, fragrant, 2½ ins. across, solitary at the end of short lateral twigs, or in pairs or threes ; corolla open bell-shaped, with a short tube ; stamens ten, about as long as the corolla ; calyx with five hairy, viscidly glandular, lanceolate lobes ⅛ in. long ; flower stalk hairy, ½ in. long.

Native of China, Japan, and Korea ; introduced in 1819 from Japan, where it is much cultivated. It is nearly allied to the common greenhouse " Azalea indica," and is largely used as a stock on which the finer varieties of that species are grafted. It is often known even now as " A. indica alba," but is well worthy of the specific rank the elder Hooker gave it in 1829, being distinct in its duller, more hairy leaves, in the outstanding hairs and in the viscid calyx with more erect lobes. In gardens it has not received the notice it deserves as a hardy evergreen. At Kew, in an exposed position, it has stood for over twenty years, and is still only 3 ft. high ; but it thrives best in the most sheltered spots. When covered, as it generally is about the end of May, with its pure white, fragrant flowers it is exceedingly pretty, and is well adapted for positions where a slow-growing dwarf shrub is desirable. In Cornwall and similar places it grows much taller.

R. NARCISSIFLORUM, *Planchon*, is a double, white-flowered variety of R. mucronatum introduced by Fortune from China in 1850. Another double variety with rose-purple flowers sometimes called narcissiflorum is var. PLENUM. China, 1819.

R. MUCRONULATUM, *Turczaninow*

(Bot. Mag., t. 8304)

This rhododendron was briefly mentioned in vol. ii., p. 353, under the note on R. dauricum, of which it was made a variety by Maximowicz. It was introduced in 1907 and has since then developed such fine qualities that it deserves fuller mention than was there given. It is a deciduous shrub of erect, thinnish habit, up to 6 or 8 ft. high, the twigs slender and glabrous except for a few scales. Leaves lanceolate or inclined to oblanceolate, slenderly pointed ; 1¼ to 4 ins. long, ½ to 1¼ ins. wide ; of thin texture ; stalk ⅛ to ¼ in. long. Flowers produced singly from each of a cluster of buds at the end of the naked shoots, sometimes as many as six at the tip of one shoot, often opening successively. Corolla pale rose-purple, opening widely, 1½ to 2 ins. across, five-lobed, downy outside. Stamens ten, their stalks downy at the base ; anthers dark purple. Ovary covered with close, minute scales ; style glabrous. Calyx small, shallowly five-lobed ; flower-stalk scaly, ¼ in. long, hidden by the bracts of the flower-bud. (Dauricum series.)

Native of N. China, Manchuria, Japan, and Korea. Wilson observes that it is very abundant in Korea in thin woods and open country. Under cultivation its flowering season varies according to the weather. At Kew, as a rule, it is at its best from Christmas to the beginning of February. I have seen it in splendid bloom on Christmas Day. The flowers are destroyed by about five degrees of frost, but are often succeeded by a fresh crop. After a hard winter and spring, flowers will open as late as April. This shrub must be included amongst the very best of winter flowerers, for few give so beautiful a display so early in the year. In botanical detail it scarcely differs from dauricum, but in its greater size and vigour, its larger more pointed leaves, and its larger flowers it is very different. It is also superior as a garden shrub.

Var. ACUMINATUM (R. acuminatum, *Hort. Japan*, not *Hooker fil.*), introduced to Kew along with the type in 1907, differs in flowering later and in its more twiggy habit.

R. MULIENSE, *Balfour and Forrest*

An evergreen shrub apparently not more than 3 ft. high ; young shoots slender, densely scurfy. Leaves oblong or oval, mostly rounded at the apex ; $\frac{1}{2}$ to $\frac{7}{8}$ in. long, $\frac{3}{16}$ to $\frac{1}{2}$ in. wide ; dull green above, pale and grey beneath, densely scaly on both sides, the scales below pitted and shining ; very shortly but distinctly stalked. Flowers five or six together in terminal clusters, opening in May and June. Corolla bright yellow, $\frac{3}{4}$ to 1 in. wide, five-lobed, the lobes oval and scaly up the centre outside, downy in the tube ; stamens ten, $\frac{1}{2}$ in. long with a tuft of down near the base. Ovary scaly ; style downy at the base. Calyx five-lobed ; the lobes elliptical, $\frac{1}{8}$ to $\frac{3}{16}$ in. long, scaly outside, fringed with hairs ; flower-stalks $\frac{1}{8}$ in. long, scaly.

Native of S.W. Szechuen, China ; found on the Mu-li Mountains (from which it takes its name) by Forrest in June 1918. It grows at 12,000 to 13,000 ft. altitude, and is quite hardy. It belongs to the yellow-flowered section of the Lapponicum series, which includes chryseum and flavidum. R. chryseum is well distinguished by having usually only five stamens and no down on the style ; whilst flavidum has no scales outside the corolla, and those beneath the leaf are more thinly disposed. R. muliense is a pretty, dwarf species very suitable for rock garden cultivation.

R. MULTIFLORUM, *Hort.*

This is a hybrid between virgatum and ciliatum, and is a neat evergreen bush capable of growing 6 or 8 ft. high and more in breadth. It has obovate or oblong pointed leaves, $1\frac{1}{2}$ to 2 ins. long, $\frac{1}{2}$ to $\frac{3}{4}$ in. wide, dark bright green above, scaly beneath and very shortly stalked. From virgatum it inherits the character of producing its flowers singly from the axils of the leaves. Corolla white, flushed with rose, funnel-shaped, five-lobed, $1\frac{1}{2}$ ins. long and wide. Stamens ten, hairy at the base ; ovary scaly ; style longer than corolla, nearly or quite glabrous. Calyx $\frac{1}{8}$ in. deep, the five rounded lobes fringed with hairs as in ciliatum.

Although this interesting and pretty hybrid succeeds better to the south and west, it is hardy at Kew. It used to grow very well in the Coombe Wood Nursery. Millais mentions a plant in the garden of Sir John Llewellyn, near Swansea, 7 ft. high and 15 ft. in diameter. It flowers in April.

R. MYRTILLOIDES, *Balfour and Ward* (Plate 12)

A dwarf evergreen shrub usually given as under 6 ins. high in nature ; young shoots warted. Leaves narrowly obovate, wedge-shaped at the base, rounded and with a short mucro at the apex ; $\frac{1}{3}$ to $\frac{3}{4}$ in. long, $\frac{1}{3}$ in. or less wide ; dark bright green above, thinly scaly and glaucous beneath ; margins recurved ; stalk very short. Flowers solitary on a slender, glandular-warty stalk 1 to $1\frac{1}{2}$ ins. long. Corolla bell-shaped, plum-coloured outside, maroon inside, about $\frac{1}{2}$ in. long, five-lobed, the lobes rounded. Stamens ten, downy on the lower part ; anthers white. Ovary scaly ; style short, stout, curved downwards. Calyx with five rounded lobes $\frac{1}{12}$ in. long, glabrous outside.

Native of N.E. Burma ; discovered by Kingdon Ward in 1914 growing on granite cliffs up to 15,000 ft. altitude. Farrer came across it in 1919 and describes its flowers as " waxy, with a deep plum-like bloom outside and inside of a hot mahogany red, very delicate and attractive." If the description given above be compared with that of campylogynum, not much will be found to differentiate them. But myrtilloides is evidently permanently dwarfer, although Mr E. H. M. Cox gives its maximum height as 18 ins., the leaves at first are glaucous beneath, the flower is solitary (? always) and rather smaller, and the scaliness is somewhat more obvious and permanent. It is quite hardy, is easily increased by cuttings, and makes dainty tufts for the rock garden. (Campylogynum series.)

R. NERIIFLORUM, *Franchet*

(Bot. Mag., t. 8727)

An evergreen shrub 4 to 6 ft. (occasionally 8 ft.) high ; young shoots reddish, woolly at first. Leaves oblong to narrowly obovate, rounded to abruptly tapered at both ends, mucronate ; 2 to 4 ins. long, 1 to 1½ ins. wide ; dark green above, glaucous-white beneath, glabrous except on the midrib beneath ; stalk ⅓ to ¾ in. long, reddish and downy when young. Flowers six to twelve in a truss 3 to 4 ins. wide, opening in March or April. Corolla rich crimson, tubular-bell-shaped, 1½ to 1¾ ins. long, not so much wide, with five rounded, notched lobes ; stamens ten, white, glabrous, ¾ to 1¼ ins. long ; anthers very dark brown. Ovary felted ; style slightly overtopping the stamens, glabrous except just above the ovary. Calyx membranous, varying in size and very irregular, with five unequal rounded lobes ; flower-stalk about ½ in. long, downy.

Native of Yunnan, China ; discovered by Delavay in 1883 ; introduced by Forrest in 1906 and again in 1910. He found it on the eastern flank of the Tali Range up to 12,000 ft. altitude. This beautiful species (the type of a " series ") is one of the most richly coloured of all Chinese rhododendrons and should be regarded as indispensable to any collection of them where it can be grown. It is hardy in a well-sheltered place at Kew, but grows slowly and is apt to overflower itself there, and is happier thirty or more miles to the south. In its glowing colour it bears comparison with Thomsonii and fulgens and will no doubt prove valuable for hybridising.

R. EUCHAITES, *Balfour and Forrest*, is now regarded as a subspecies of neriiflorum. It is a taller plant (Forrest says 15 to 20 ft. high), even a small tree, and the flowers are larger and brighter in colour. Native of S.W. Yunnan and Burma ; discovered by Forrest in 1913. It flowers in April and is perhaps the best of the Neriiflorum section of the series.

R. NIPHARGUM, *Balfour and Ward*

An evergreen shrub 15 to 25 ft. high ; young shoots stout and as much as ⅜ in. thick, grey-downy. Leaves stout and leathery, oblanceolate, blunt or almost rounded at the apex, long-tapered at the base ; 5 to 9 ins. long, 1½ to 2¾ ins. wide ; dark green and soon glabrous above, covered beneath with a close white felt ; stalk ½ to 1 in. long. Flowers in a compact rounded truss of ten to fifteen, opening in spring. Corolla bell-shaped, five-lobed, 1½ ins. long, rosy white to pale rose, with a crimson blotch at the base and similarly coloured spots on the upper side. Stamens ten, minutely downy at the base, white with dark brown anthers, ovary slender, glabrous or with a little down, tapered at the top to the glabrous style. Calyx very small.

Native of Yunnan, up to 13,000 ft. altitude ; found in June 1913 by Kingdon Ward and during the following month by Forrest. This species has been placed in the same group or " series " as fulvum and fulvoides, both of which, of course, are very different in the colour of the coating on the leaves beneath. At the Rhododendron Association's Show, 5th May 1932, niphargum was exhibited in flower. The snowy whiteness of the leaf's under surface, as suggested by the specific name, is an attractive character. It is a fine foliaged shrub as seen in the Caerhays woods. Hardy in Sussex and Hampshire.

R. UVARIFOLIUM, *Diels* (R. Monbeigii, *Rehder and Wilson*).—According to Mr H. F. Tagg of Edinburgh, the distinctions between this and R. niphargum are chiefly in size and shape of leaf, and these, in wild specimens at any rate, are not very obvious. Both have oblanceolate leaves but they are generally somewhat narrower in uvarifolium (1½ to 2 ins.). Flowers pink with crimson blotch and spots. Native of N.W. Yunnan at 7000 to 8000 ft. altitude ; found by Forrest in 1904, and at about the same period by Père T. Monbeig.

R. NIPPONICUM, *Matsumura*

A deciduous azalea described as of bushy habit and from 3 to 6 ft. high ; the stiff young shoots reddish brown and clothed with glandular bristles. Leaves scarcely stalked, obovate, rounded and often notched at the apex, tapered to the base ; 2 to 6 ins. long, half as much wide ; more or less appressed-bristly above and beneath. Flowers opening about midsummer, six to fifteen in a cluster. Corolla narrowly bell-shaped, scarcely 1 in. long, white with five short, slightly spreading lobes. Stamens ten, unequal in length but all shorter than the corolla, downy below the middle. Ovary glandular-hairy ; style glabrous. Calyx small, with five ovate ciliate lobes ; flower-stalk ½ to ¾ in. long, sticky with glands.

Native of the mountains of Central Japan ; discovered in 1883. Its existence in gardens is apparently due to E. H. Wilson, who found it on the hills around Toge in 1914 and sent seeds to the Arnold Arboretum. It first flowered at Kew in June 1921, but this species is no longer there. The blossom is very disappointing, being small and hidden away in the young growths. But in foliage it is probably the finest of all azaleas and it takes on brilliant orange and crimson tints in autumn. The bright reddish brown bark is also pleasing. Botanically it is distinct in having the stamens and style included within the somewhat tubular corolla.

R. NIVEUM, *Hooker fil.*

(Bot. Mag., t. 4730)

An evergreen shrub of sturdy habit, up to 6 or 8 ft. high in the open air ; young shoots clothed with a whitish felt. Leaves narrowly-oblong, 3 to 7 ins. long, 1 to 2½ ins. wide ; tapering at the base, more rounded at the apex. When the young leaves unfold they are covered all over with a snow-white floss, which falls away from the upper surface, leaving it very deep green, but which persists beneath and turns a pale brown. Flowers purplish lilac, 1 to 1½ ins. across, densely packed in a compact, rounded head, 3 to 4 ins. across. Corolla bell-shaped ; lobes five, rounded, notched ; calyx simply an expanded end to the short, downy flower-stalk ; stamens ten, much shorter than the corolla ; anthers brown.

Native of the Sikkim Himalaya at 10,000 to 12,000 ft. ; introduced in 1849. It is quite hardy in the Rhododendron Dell at Kew, but enjoys a warmer climate. The unusual colour of the flowers among rhododendrons, and the striking snowy white covering to the young leaves, gives this species a certain distinction and makes it well worth growing. It flowers from March to May. Of its several forms, some are much inferior to others.

Var. FULVUM (Bot. Mag., t. 6827) is one of the best. Its leaves are reddish brown beneath, and the flower-truss larger than in the type.

R. NOBLEANUM, *Lindley*

Soon after the first flowering of R. arboreum, which occurred at The Grange, Northington, Hants, in 1825, a number of crosses were made with the various hardy species then in cultivation, especially catawbiense, ponticum, and caucasicum. Of all the plants raised, the one which has acquired the surest place in gardens is R. Nobleanum; this was raised in the Knap Hill nursery by crossing caucasicum with arboreum about 1832. It forms a small tree up to 15 ft. high, the leaves having a thin, brownish felt beneath. Flowers bright and rich rose, in trusses 4 ins. across. Soon after the New Year (still earlier in the warmer parts of the kingdom) the flowers of this hybrid commence to open, and they continue for about two months, according to climatic conditions. Very frequently they are destroyed by frost, but usually some of them escape. If the weather be exceptionally favourable, no tree or shrub gives so brilliant a display in the first two months of the year, and for this reason a few examples are worth growing. If possible, a spot sheltered by trees from the north and east should be given them.

Var. ALBUM.—Raised in the Comely Bank nurseries, Edinburgh, by crossing arboreum album with caucasicum. Mr Fraser, the head of this nursery, informed me that his firm continued to raise new stock of this variety and the original Nobleanum, by re-making the original crosses.

R. PULCHERRIMUM is of an origin similar to that of Nobleanum, and was raised at the same time in the Knap Hill nursery. Its flowers are like those of Nobleanum, but paler. It exists, no doubt, in many gardens under that name.

R. NUDIFLORUM, *Torrey*

(Azalea nudiflora, *Linnæus*, Bot. Reg., t. 120)

A deciduous azalea up to 9 ft. high in its native state; young wood bristly. Leaves mostly obovate, some oblong, tapering at both ends; $1\frac{1}{2}$ to $3\frac{1}{2}$ ins. long, one-third to half as wide; green on both sides with a few scattered hairs above, bristly on the midrib beneath and on the margins. Flowers faintly scented, in clusters of six or more, the corolla-tube hairy, pink $\frac{3}{4}$ in. long; the five lobes paler, expanding and giving the flower a diameter of $1\frac{1}{2}$ to 2 ins.; stalk $\frac{1}{4}$ to $\frac{1}{2}$ in. long, bristly like the small calyx; stamens five, pinkish coloured, standing out well beyond the corolla; seed-vessels $\frac{3}{4}$ in. long, bristly. Blossoms in May.

Native of eastern N. America; introduced by Peter Collinson in 1734. It is one of the chief parents of the great race of garden azaleas, but is itself very rarely seen now. The flowers appear to be variable in colour, even in a wild state, although of some shade of red or pink, or purplish. Of the north American azaleas, whose flowers expand before the leaves, this differs from R. calendulaceum in the longer-tubed, differently coloured corolla, and in the bristly midrib of the leaf, and from R. canescens in the hairy, not glandular, corolla-tube.

R. NUTTALLII, *Booth*

(Bot. Mag., t. 5146 ; Gardeners' Chronicle, 14th July 1883, fig. 10)

An evergreen shrub or small tree from 12 to 30 ft. high, of straggling, thinly branched habit, often growing in nature as an epiphyte on the branches and forks of large trees ; young shoots very stout, scaly. Leaves stout and leathery, oval, tapered at both ends, shortly pointed ; 5 to 12 ins. long, 2½ to 4½ ins. wide ; greyish, strongly reddish veined and thickly sprinkled with scales beneath ; at first reddish above, ultimately pale green, much puckered and wrinkled. Flowers fragrant, usually three to six in a terminal truss (as many as eleven have been known), opening in May horizontally or rather nodding. Corolla funnel-shaped at the base, of wax-like texture, ivory-white suffused with yellow in the throat ; 4 to 5 ins. long and measuring about the same across the five spreading, rounded lobes. Stamens normally ten, 2½ ins. long, downy towards the base ; anthers ⅛ in. long, reddish brown. Ovary and base only of style scaly, the latter up to 3 ins. long. Calyx deeply five-lobed, the lobes oblong, rounded at the end, 1 in. long, ½ in. wide.

Native of Bhotan ; discovered and introduced by T. J. Booth in 1852 and flowered at Kew in 1859. In regard to the individual flower, which suggests a lily in size and texture, this is the most magnificent of rhododendrons. Flowers are frequently 6 ins. wide. Unfortunately it is tender and only suitable for the warmer parts of Cornwall. It is not a strong-rooting shrub and likes a sandy, peaty, well-drained soil. Healthy plants make shoots one foot or more long in a season. Several fine hybrids have been raised from it such as VICTORIANUM, a cross with Dalhousiæ. Very nearly akin to it is

R. SINO-NUTTALLII, *Balfour and Forrest*. In leaf and habit it is the same, but does not, perhaps, attain so large a size, and it may be somewhat hardier. But the flower-stalks and the calyx-lobes are softly-downy (not so in Nuttallii) and the seed-vessels are larger—up to 2½ ins. long and ¾ in. wide, whereas the maximum length in Nuttallii is 1¼ ins. Discovered in 1919 by Forrest in S.E. Tibet, and introduced by him. It flowered in a cool greenhouse at Kew in 1930, and is magnificent in the Rhododendron House at Exbury. (Maddenii-megacalyx series.)

R. OBLONGIFOLIUM, *Millais*

(Azalea oblongifolia, *Small*)

A deciduous azalea up to 6 ft. high ; young shoots more or less bristly. Leaves obovate to oblanceolate, 1½ to 4 ins. long, ½ to 1½ ins. wide. Flowers slightly fragrant, produced after the leaves in seven- to twelve-flowered clusters. Corolla funnel-shaped, pure white, with a cylindrical tube ¾ to 1 in. long and more or less glandular and hairy outside. Stamens five, about 2 ins. long, hairy below the middle ; ovary covered with bristly hairs ; style longer than the stamens. Calyx small, bristly.

Native of Arkansas, Oklahoma, and Texas, growing, according to Rehder, in moist sandy woods or on the margins of sandy bogs or streams ; introduced by means of seeds sent to Britain by Prof. Sargent in 1917. Numerous plants were raised which have proved quite hardy at Kew, where it flowers in July and even later. The leaves are glaucous beneath and bristly on the midrib and margins. It seems to be very close in botanical relationship to viscosum, but Rehder relies on its longer, more oblong calyx-lobes, its downy winter buds and larger leaves. I do not consider it so good a garden azalea as viscosum, but it is worth noting that in Oklahoma it has been found growing on limestone.

R. SERRULATUM, *Millais* (Azalea serrulata, *Small*), is also closely akin and quite hardy. It has very fragrant white flowers. Native of the S.E. United States. In the same group comes

R. ATLANTICUM, *Rehder* (Azalea atlantica, *Ashe*), but distinguished from viscosum by its stoloniferous habit (producing sucker shoots that root on the surface). Grows 2 to 4 ft. high. Flowers white, pink or purplish. Found wild from Delaware south to the Carolinas. Introduced in 1922.

R. OBTUSUM, *Planchon* (Plate 13)

(Azalea obtusa, *Lindley*, Bot. Reg. vol. xxxii., t. 37; R. indicum obtusum, *Maximowicz*)

In former editions of this work, R. obtusum is included as a variety of R. indicum, in which arrangement I followed Maximowicz and other authors. It is only since the publication in 1921 of the *Monograph of Azaleas* by Wilson and Rehder, however, that we have learnt what R. indicum really is. Wilson, after an exhaustive study of the Asiatic azaleas, separated R. obtusum from R. indicum and in his hands it became an important species, for under it he included R. amœnum, *Planchon*, R. Kæmpferi, *Planchon*, and many forms both wild and cultivated.

The typical obtusum is a shrub which has been cultivated for centuries by the Japanese and called by them " Kirishima-tsutsuji." Wilson describes it as a densely branched, twiggy plant seldom more than 3 ft. high, with small, scarlet, slightly scented flowers. This plant, which has mostly obovate rounded leaves and rather pointed corolla lobes, as figured by Lindley in 1846 (*loc. cit. supra*); the one latterly cultivated as " obtusum " has rounded corolla-lobes. Both are cultivated forms of Japanese azaleas.

The really wild plant which Wilson named OBTUSUM JAPONICUM, as well as the var. album and R. Kæmpferi, grow on Mt. Kirishima on the island of Kiushiu, Japan. In Kurume, an important town on this island, R. obtusum has been cultivated for one hundred years past and according to Wilson has, in the hands of Japanese cultivators, developed a great number of beautiful forms ; they profess to recognise 250 of them. Of these, in 1919, Wilson successfully introduced to the Arnold Arboretum fifty of what he considered the best ; they vary in colour from white, creamy white and various shades of pink to carmine, scarlet and crimson. Kurume appears to be remote from the other horticultural centres of Japan and these " Kurume azaleas," which in Wilson's mind were the loveliest of azaleas, have remained practically unknown to the world outside.

R. obtusum is closely allied to R. indicum and the key-constructors are only able to base their distinctions on the leaves which in obtusum are mostly oval or obovate, smaller (up to 1 or 1¼ ins. long), and with none of the sparse toothing often seen in indicum. The flowers also are ordinarily only half as wide (about 1 in.). In most other characters they do not differ essentially. Both are distinguished from R. Simsii by having only five stamens.

Var. ALBUM, *C. K. Schneider* (Azalea ramentacea, *Lindley*).—Flowers pure white ; leaves rather larger than in the type. Introduced by Fortune in 1846.

R. Kæmpferi and R. amœnum are now regarded as varieties of obtusum. The former, considering its deciduous character, its larger leaves and flowers, its great hardiness, the fact that it grows 8 to 10 ft. high in favourable places, and its absolutely distinct appearance in general, seems to deserve specific rank, especially when one considers how trifling are the differences on which so many species of rhododendron have been based in recent years. The brilliant red " Hinodegiri " and the delightfully soft pink " Hinemayo " are forms of obtusum. But neither of them, nor obtusum or its var. album, is genuinely hardy at Kew.

R. OCCIDENTALE, *A. Gray*

(Bot. Mag., t. 5005 ; Azalea occidentalis, *Torrey*)

A deciduous, rounded bush, 8 ft. or more high ; young shoots slightly downy. Leaves oval or obovate, 2 to 4 ins. long, ¾ to 1½ ins. wide ; tapering at the base, often rounded at the apex ; upper surface glossy green and furnished with scattered hairs ; lower surface pale, rather glaucous, downy (at least when young) ; stalk downy, ¼ in. or less long. Flowers fragrant, white with a blotch of yellow on the upper side, 2½ to 3 ins. across, produced in terminal clusters of six to twelve after the leaves, during June and July. Corolla-tube 1 in. or more long, downy ; stamens and style protruded, 2 to 2½ ins. long ; calyx-lobes edged with long hairs ; flower-stalk ¾ to 1 in. long.

Native of western N. America ; introduced by Wm. Lobb for Messrs Veitch about 1851. This beautiful azalea is the only species of its section found west of the Rocky Mountains. It has many points of resemblance to, and appears to be the Western representative of, R. arborescens, but has larger yellow-blotched flowers and its foliage is quite hairy beneath ; the calyx also is shorter. It does not blossom until the great azalea season is over, or until it is itself in almost full leaf. It is one of the best summer-flowering shrubs, although it has taken horticulturists a long time to find that out. In 1857, Lindley, then the high priest of gardening, pronounced it to be " of little value." Mr Waterer of Knap Hill and Mr Koster of Boskoop, by crossing it with the bright-coloured azaleas that flower earlier, have laid the foundation of a beautiful race of late-flowering varieties.

R. OLDHAMII, *Maximowicz*. FORMOSAN AZALEA

(Bot. Mag., t. 9059 ; Azalea Oldhamii, *Hort.*)

An evergreen much branched shrub, 5 to 10 ft. high ; young shoots densely clothed with outstanding reddish hairs and some flattish bristles. Leaves elliptic to elliptic-ovate or oval, pointed, tapered at the base ; 1 to 3½ ins. long, ½ to 1½ ins. wide ; dull green and downy on both surfaces, especially beneath, wrinkled and rough to the touch above ; stalk up to ½ in. long, bristly and hairy like the young shoots. Flowers in a terminal cluster of two to four. Corolla 2 ins. wide, funnel-shaped at the base, spreading out into five rounded lobes ¾ in. long, orange-red except on the upper lobes which are stained with pink and dotted with dark purple. Stamens ten, ½ to 1 in. long, red, with purple anthers and a downy base. Ovary bristly ; style smooth, red, 1½ ins. long. Calyx green, with rounded or ovate and pointed lobes up to ¼ in. long, usually smaller ; covered like the flower-stalk with glandular, sticky hairs.

Native of Formosa only ; discovered by Richard Oldham, the Kew collector, in 1864. First introduced for Messrs Veitch by Chas. Maries in 1878. I do not think any of his generation of plants survived, and the species was, no doubt, lost to cultivation until Wilson reintroduced it in 1918. In the past it has flowered in a cool greenhouse at Kew at such diverse seasons as February and August, but its normal time is April. In the open air there it will not survive even mild winters, and is only likely to be hardy in the south and west. It is handsome in flower, but not more so than many of the so-called " Indian " azaleas (R. Simsii) to which it is related, but easily distinguished by its larger leaves and the soft, spreading, frequently glandular hairs (not appressed flattened bristles) on the young shoots. Wilson calls it the " common red-flowered azalea of Formosa " ; it is found on that island from sea level up to 8500 ft.

R. OLEIFOLIUM, *Franchet*

(Bot. Mag., t. 8802 ; R. sinovirgatum, *Balfour*)

An evergreen shrub 2 to 4 ft. high (probably more in mild localities) ; young shoots clothed with dark brown scales. Leaves narrowly elliptical or oblong-lanceolate, wedge-shaped at the base, pointed, margins recurved ; 1 to 2¼ ins. long, ⅓ to ⅔ in. wide ; dark green above, glaucous beneath and sprinkled with shining brown scales ; midrib conspicuously raised beneath ; leaf-stalk ⅛ to ¼ in. long. Flowers produced in April singly or in pairs from the uppermost leaf-axils of the previous season's growths, the flower-buds ½ in. long, slender and pointed. Corolla scaly outside, pale rose or white, 1 to 1½ ins. long, funnel-shaped at the base, where it is downy outside, dividing upwards into five broadly ovate lobes. Stamens ten, rosy purple, downy near the base ; anthers pale brown. Ovary scaly ; style scaly and downy at the base. Calyx triangularly lobed ; flower-stalk ⅛ in. long, but quite hidden by the bracts.

Native of Yunnan, China ; discovered by Delavay about 1884 ; introduced by Forrest in 1906. This is one of that interesting group of scaly rhododendrons (to which virgatum and racemosum also belong) whose flowers spring from the leaf-axils along (sometimes nearly the whole length of) the shoot. Neither of those species has a corolla that is downy outside. R. oleifolium is moderately hardy at Kew but is not so satisfactory there as racemosum. It is worth growing where dwarf shrubs are desirable. (Virgatum series.)

R. ORBICULARE, *Decaisne*

(Bot. Mag., t. 8775 ; R. rotundifolium, *David*)

An evergreen shrub up to 6 or 9 ft. high ; young shoots stout, purplish, glandular. Leaves almost orbicular, but usually somewhat longer than broad, 2 to 4 ins. long ; deeply auricled at the base, rounded at the apex, with a minute tip formed by a slight prolongation and thickening of the midrib ; quite glabrous, dark green above, glaucous beneath ; stalk 1½ to 2 ins. long, very stout. Flowers rosy red, ten or more forming a truss 6 ins. across ; flower-stalks glabrous, up to 2¼ ins. long. Corolla 2 to 2½ ins. across, widely bell-shaped, seven-lobed ; calyx minute, glabrous ; stamens about fourteen, glabrous, shorter than the corolla ; ovary glandular ; style glabrous.

Native of Szechuen, China ; introduced for Messrs Veitch by Wilson in 1904. A very pretty and distinct rhododendron of which there are fine specimens at Caerhays, rounded, hemispherical bushes 6 ft. in diameter, very dense in habit. Apparently best adapted for the S.W. counties. Flowers April, May.

R. OREODOXA, *Franchet*

(Bot. Mag., t. 8518 ; R. hæmatochilum, *Craib*)

An evergreen shrub with stout twigs up to ¼ in. thick, sparsely set with glandular hairs when young, soon glabrous. Leaves oblong, rounded to heart-shaped at the base ; rounded, with a short blunt tip at the apex ; up to 3½ ins. long by 1⅜ ins. wide ; glabrous and dark green above, paler beneath ; veins in thirteen to fifteen pairs ; stalk ⅓ to ⅔ in. long. Flowers eight to ten in a rounded truss 4 ins. across. Corolla broadly funnel-shaped, seven-lobed, 2 ins. wide, the tube scarcely 1 in. long. In the bud state the flower is almost blood-red, changing when open to carmine, then to a lilac shade. Stamens fourteen, about as long as the corolla-tube, white and glabrous ; anthers purplish bro wn

Ovary and style glabrous, the latter longer than the stamens. Calyx indistinctly lobed, and, like the flower-stalk, glandular.

Native of W. Szechuen, China; introduced by Wilson about 1904; first flowered in the Coombe Wood nursery in the spring of 1913. The change in colour of the corolla with age is rather marked. It differs from its allies, R. Sheltonæ (considered to be a geographical form of vernicosum) and R. Davidii, in its glabrous style and ovary.

R. OREOTREPHES, *W. W. Smith*

(Bot. Mag., t. 8784; R. depile, *Balfour fil.*; R. hypotrichum, *Balfour fil.*, R. phæochlorum, *Balfour fil.*)

In a wild state this evergreen species is described by Forrest as being sometimes 15 to 25 ft. high and tree-like; under cultivation it does not promise to get beyond the shrubby state and 6 or 8 ft. high; except for a few glandular scales the young shoots are glabrous. Leaves mostly oval, and rounded to tapered at both ends; 1½ to 3 ins. long, ¾ to 1½ ins. wide; dull grey-green and glabrous above; glaucous (sometimes very glaucous) and scaly beneath; stalk ¼ to ½ in. long. Flowers four to eleven in a terminal truss opening in April and May. Corolla funnel-shaped below, spreading out into five roundish-ovate lobes and giving the flower a diameter of 2 to 2½ ins., usually pale lavender-rose, but variable in shade, freely spotted on the upper side with brownish crimson. Stamens ten, about 1 in. long, white, hairy towards the base; style longer, quite glabrous; ovary scaly. Calyx small, shallowly lobed; flower-stalk ½ to ¾ in. long, glabrous or slightly scaly. Seedvessel cylindrical, scaly, ½ in. long. (Triflorum series.)

Native of Yunnan, China; discovered and introduced by Forrest in 1906. The flowers of this rhododendron vary a good deal in depth of shade from pearl grey lavender to deep rosy lavender. The glaucousness of the foliage varies also; in some plants it is very noticeable even on the upper surface and Mr J. C. Williams compared the best forms in this respect to sea-holly. At Kew it loses much of its foliage in winter but is quite hardy. In spring when the delicately coloured flowers are associated with the glaucous young growth, it is a very attractive shrub. Very near this species is

R. TIMETIUM, *Balfour and Forrest*, an evergreen shrub 3 to 4 ft. high, with pink, slightly spotted flowers, and leaves whose scales are farther apart underneath. Introduced from W. Szechuen by Forrest in 1918. Flowers in May. Another species closely related is

R. ARTOSQUAMEUM, *Balfour and Forrest*, a shrub of the same size and character but with the leaves distinctly heart-shaped at the base. Introduced from S.E. Tibet by Forrest about 1917. Flowers rosy-lilac; blossoms in May.

R. ORTHOCLADUM, *Balfour and Forrest*

An evergreen shrub of densely twiggy, bushy, rounded shape; young shoots very slender, densely scurfy. Leaves narrowly oblong or lanceolate, tapered at both ends; ⅓ to ¾ in. long, $\frac{1}{12}$ to ⅕ in. wide; dark green and scaly above, grey-green and furnished with glistening yellowish scales beneath, amongst which are sprinkled larger brown ones; stalk $\frac{1}{12}$ to ⅛ in. long. Flowers two to four closely packed in terminal clusters 1 in. wide. Corolla pale mauve, ¾ in. wide, with a very short, downy tube, five-lobed, the lobes rounded, ovate, ¼ in. long. Stamens ten, purple, about ¼ in. long, with a tuft of down near the base; anthers red. Ovary scaly; style glabrous, reddish, shorter than the stamens. Calyx minute, with small lobes covered thickly with glistening scales like the flower-stalk, which is only $\frac{1}{12}$ in. long.

Native of Yunnan, China; discovered and introduced by Forrest in 1913. This is a pleasing dwarf shrub with some resemblance to R. scintillans, but paler in colour of blossom and with a much shorter style. It is quite hardy at Kew, grows well and flowers freely towards the end of April, and is noticeable for its dense neat habit and rounded shape. Scarcely differing from orthocladum in essential botanical characters is

R. THYMIFOLIUM, *Maximowicz*, originally found by the Russian traveller Przewalsky in the Kansu province, China, in 1873, but its leaves are only about ⅓ in. long and ⅛ in. wide, narrowly elliptical or lanceolate and the scales beneath uniformly glistening and yellowish (not bicoloured). Flowers usually solitary, mauve, ¾ in. wide. Both belong to the Lapponicum series.

R. OVATUM, *Maximowicz*

(Azalea ovata, *Lindley*; Bot. Mag., t. 5064)

An evergreen shrub of bushy habit, 2 to 4 ft., perhaps more, high; young wood, leaf-stalks, and midrib on the upper side downy. Leaves dark green and glossy, ovate, pointed, the base tapered or rounded; ¾ to 2¼ ins. long, ⅜ to 1¼ ins. wide; stalk ⅛ to ¾ in. long. Flowers solitary from buds near the end of the preceding year's shoots, produced about the end of May; pale purple to pink, specked with darker spots on the upper lobe of the corolla, 1 in. across, flat and open; stamens five; calyx-lobes oblong, ₁₆/₃ in. long; flower-stalk ¼ to ½ in. long, glandular-hairy. (See R. Bachii, *Léveillé*.)

Native of China; introduced about 1844 by Fortune, and latterly by Wilson from Hupeh. The colour of the flowers varies from almost white to pink and purplish. Exceedingly rare in gardens. It is allied to the West American albiflorum, but that species has ten stamens. It must not be confounded with the R. ovatum of gardens, which is the same as R. myrtifolium (p. 99) a hybrid between hirsutum and minus.

R. OXYPHYLLUM, *Franchet* (Plate 14)

(Gardeners' Chronicle, 6th Aug. 1921, fig. 30)

An evergreen shrub of open habit, said to be up to 16 or 18 ft. high or even tree-like; free from down in all its parts except towards, but not at, the base of the stamens and outside the flower-bud scales. Leaves firm and leathery, clustered at the end of the season's growth, oblanceolate and broadest above the middle, narrowly wedge-shaped at the base; 2 to 6 ins. long, 1 to 2½ ins. wide; dark brightish green above, pale beneath; stalk ½ to ¾ in. long. Flowers produced in several clusters near the apex of the shoot in April, each cluster consisting usually of three to five blossoms, fragrant. Corolla 3 ins. wide, 2½ ins. long, the lower part tubular-funnel-shaped, the upper part cut into five narrowly obovate, pointed lobes which are 1½ ins. long, ¾ in. wide; pure white except for a yellow blotch on the upper side of the throat. Stamens ten, 1½ to 1¾ ins. long, white, slender; style, 1½ ins. long. Seed-pod 1½ ins. long, very slender.

Native of S. Yunnan, China; first discovered in 1885 by Prince Henri of Orleans, afterwards introduced by Forrest. This is perhaps the most beautiful of the Stamineum series and it is distinct in the deep lobing of the corolla and in the number of its few-flowered axillary inflorescences, the whole making a cluster of twelve or more flowers. Lord Wakehurst showed a plant, 2½ ft. high and flowering freely, at Westminster on 5th April 1921. This had been grown under glass, even at Wakehurst, and the species is not likely to succeed in the open air in this country except in Cornwall and similar places.

R. PACHYPODUM, *Balfour and W. W. Smith*

An evergreen shrub up to 6 ft. high; young shoots densely scaly. Leaves stiff and leathery, oblanceolate to narrowly obovate, the largest 4 ins. long by $1\frac{1}{2}$ ins. wide, glaucous and very scaly beneath; stalk $\frac{1}{5}$ to $\frac{2}{5}$ in. long, slightly hairy when young. Flowers borne two or three together, each on a stout scaly stalk about $\frac{1}{2}$ in. long. Corolla yellow, funnel-shaped at the base, $1\frac{1}{2}$ to 2 ins. long, scaly outside, downy at the base inside, the five lobes rounded-oblong, $\frac{5}{8}$ in. long. Stamens ten, downy at the lower half. Ovary six-celled, densely scaly like the lower two-thirds of the style which is 2 ins. long. Calyx five-lobed, scaly and fringed with hairs. (Maddenii series.)

Native of Yunnan, where it reaches 9000 to 10,000 ft. altitude on the Tali Range; introduced by Forrest in 1913-14. In botanical characters this resembles very closely R. carneum, but of course its yellow flowers make it very distinct from the fresh-coloured ones of that species. Considering the altitude at which it grows wild, it should also be hardier. It is cultivated at Caerhays, Cornwall, where it flowers in March. It belongs to the ciliicalyx section of its series, as does also

R. BURMANICUM, *Hutchinson*, a native of Mt. Victoria, S.W. Burma; introduced by Lady Wheeler Cuffe to the Glasnevin Botanic Garden, where it first flowered in May 1914. The very fragrant flowers are yellow, often more or less tinged with green, but at their best a good yellow. They come in clusters of three to six, the corolla about 2 ins. long, scaly all over outside; calyx small, fringed with bristles. Closely related to pachypodum in botanical characters, it can be distinguished by the green under surface of the leaves (between the scales) and the more numerous flowers in a cluster. It is only likely to succeed in the open air in Cornwall and similar localities.

R. PACHYTRICHUM, *Franchet*

An evergreen shrub or small tree up to 20 ft. high; young shoots conspicuously furnished with a dense coat of brown curly bristles $\frac{1}{8}$ in. long. Leaves 3 to 6 ins. long, 1 to 2 ins. wide, narrowly oblong or inclined to obovate, abruptly narrowed at the apex to a short fine point, rounded at the base, dark green and soon glabrous above, bristly on the margins at first, and on the midrib beneath; stalk $\frac{1}{3}$ to 1 in. long, with the same mossy character as the young shoot. Flowers white or pale rose, in compact trusses, 3 to 4 ins. across; corolla $1\frac{1}{2}$ ins. wide, scarcely so deep, bell-shaped; stamens ten, shorter than the corolla, downy at the base; ovary bristly; calyx small, glabrous or nearly so, triangular-lobed; flower-stalk mossy, $\frac{5}{8}$ in. long. April.

Native of W. China and Tibet; discovered by the Abbé David; introduced by Wilson for Messrs Veitch in 1903. A very distinct species allied to strigillosum, but that species has rich red flowers and glabrous stamens. According to Wilson, R. pachytrichum occurs up to 10,000 ft. altitude, so is, no doubt, capable of withstanding great winter cold, but it appears to be spring tender.

R. PARMULATUM, *Cowan*

(Bot. Mag., t. 9624)

An evergreen shrub up to 3 or 4 ft. high; young shoots glabrous. Leaves oval, rounded at the apex to a short mucro, almost similarly rounded at the base to the stalk, $1\frac{1}{2}$ to $2\frac{1}{4}$ ins. long, about half as wide, glabrous above, loosely papillose beneath (not downy), stalk $\frac{1}{5}$ to $\frac{2}{5}$ in. long. Flowers in trusses of about six ; corolla widely campanulate, 1¾ ins. deep, 2¼ ins. wide across the five bilobed, reflexed lobes which are 1 in. wide, white flushed pink, veined with crimson and with deeper coloured pouches at the base ; calyx a flat, circular disk, ½ in. wide with a crimson ring ; stamens ten, shorter than the tube, anthers dark brown ; ovary glabrous.

Native of S.E. Tibet ; discovered by Kingdon Ward in 1924. The plant figured in the Bot. Mag. flowered with the late Colonel Stephenson R. Clarke at Borde Hill in Sussex in April 1939. The flowers are very charming with their various colourings. The plant itself will no doubt thrive best in mild regions of the south and west.

R. PARVIFOLIUM, *Adams*

An evergreen shrub of sparse habit and thin, wiry, erect or spreading branches, 2 ft. to 3 ft. high ; young wood scurfy. Leaves slightly aromatic when crushed ; ½ to ¾ in. long, ⅛ to ¼ in. wide ; narrowly oblong-obovate, dark green above, pale beneath, scaly on both sides. Flowers rosy purple, ¼ to ¾ in. across, borne in a small terminal cluster of four to six ; stamens ten, hairy at the base ; calyx-lobes small, angular, slightly ciliate.

Native of Siberia, Korea, etc. This species is allied to R. lapponicum, and is often supplied for it, but is distinguished by the more numerous hairy stamens. It blossoms early, from January to March according to the mildness or otherwise of the weather. It may be seen probably in finest condition in this country at the Edinburgh Botanic Garden, where I saw it some years ago on a ledge in the rock garden. The practice there is to peg down the stems and cover them with soil ; they then root into it, and in this way produce a much better furnished mass of branches than the plant left to itself can do.

R. PENTAPHYLLUM, *Maximowicz*

(R. nikoense, *Nakai* ; R. quinquefolium roseum, *Rehder*)

A deciduous, sometimes tree-like azalea up to 20 ft. high ; young shoots often in tiers, thinly hairy when young, red-brown, becoming grey the second season. Leaves produced in a whorl of five at the end of the shoot, oval to oval-lanceolate, pointed, wedge-shaped at the base ; 1¼ to 2½ ins. long, half as much wide ; midrib downy on both surfaces ; margins toothed and ciliate ; stalk ⅛ to ¼ in. long, thinly glandular-hairy. Flowers terminal, opening in April or May, solitary or in pairs. Corolla bright rose-pink, not spotted, 2 ins. wide, with five spreading, rounded, often notched lobes. Stamens ten, of unequal length, downy at the base ; anthers yellow ; ovary and style glabrous. Calyx with five triangular teeth ⅛ in. or less long ; flower-stalk ½ in. long, varying from densely glandular to quite glabrous.

Native of Japan, where it grows in woodland, and is fond of partial shade. Wilson, who saw it wild in the Nikko region, wrote highly of its beauty both in bloom and in autumn, when the leaves change to rich orange and crimson. Whether the plant sent out by the Yokohama Nursery Co. as " Azalea quinquefolia pink " is the same, I am not sure. But Wilson described quinquefolium as having pure white flowers spotted above the centre with green ; the leading distinction, however, between it and R. pentaphyllum being that it produces flowers and leafy shoots from the same bud, whereas in pentaphyllum they come from separate buds. The latter succeeds on Long Island, New York, so will be hardy in most parts of Britain. It has been placed in the canadense (i.e., R. Rhodora) section of the Azalea series.

R. POLYLEPIS, *Franchet*

(R. Harrovianum, *Hemsley*, Bot. Mag., t. 8309)

An evergreen shrub, 5 or 6 ft., perhaps more, high ; young branches scaly. Leaves aromatic, narrowly oval-lanceolate, 1¼ to 3 ins. long, dark shining green and glabrous above, densely scaly beneath ; stalk ¼ in. long. Flowers 2 ins. across, pale purple, spotted with yellow on the upper side ; stamens ten, hairy at the base, protruded beyond the corolla ; calyx-lobes very short and rounded ; flower-stalk ¾ in. long and, like the calyx and ovary, scaly.

Native of W. China ; introduced for Messrs Veitch by Wilson about 1904. It is closely allied to R. concinnum, being distinguished chiefly by the protruding stamens and usually wrinkled leaves. An inferior species.

R. PONTICUM, *Linnæus*

(Bot. Mag., t. 650)

An evergreen shrub, 8 to 15 ft. high, twice as wide as it is high, sometimes forming a trunk 1 ft. through like a small tree ; branchlets soon glabrous. Leaves 4 to 8 ins. long, 1 to 2½ ins. wide ; narrow oblong or oblanceolate, very dark glossy green above, paler beneath, quite glabrous on both surfaces. Flowers purple, suffused more or less with pink, 2 ins. across, produced during June in terminal heads 4 to 6 ins. wide ; calyx small, with five thickened, shallow lobes ; ovary glabrous.

Native of Spain and Portugal, but more especially of that portion of Armenia known to the ancients as Pontus ; introduced in 1763. No rhododendron has obtained so secure a footing in Britain as this, and it now shares with the cherry laurel the distinction of being the commonest of introduced evergreens. It is certainly a most useful shrub. In thin woodland it will make thick masses of evergreen undergrowth, which give a fine display of blossom annually. In thicker woods it will also live, but it is apt to become thin and ungainly, and does not flower well. The worst possible use to which it is put (and it shares the indignity with the cherry laurel), is being cropped over annually and made to form a low flat surface. But where such a low evergreen covering is desired in semi-shady spots, it is one of the best available, although it is better to use a naturally dwarf shrub like Berberis Aquifolium. It is seen at its best in open spots fully exposed to the sun, where it can take its natural form and spread in its own way, and from its habit of taking root at the branches there is scarcely a limit to its extension. It must be said, indeed, that in spite of its great beauty the Pontic rhododendron needs occasionally the curb of a strong hand. I know more than one demesne in the south of England which is overrun with the shrub to such an extent as to have become monotonous.

Hundreds of thousands of young plants are used every year as stocks on which the garden varieties are grafted, and to this practice, no doubt, the presence of great drifts of this shrub in many gardens is due. For when planted out and left unwatched the stock frequently sends up sucker-growths, and it then becomes only a matter of time before the finer bred and less assertive scion is overwhelmed.

From catawbiense, which is the only species with which it is likely to be confused, R. ponticum is distinguished by its long, narrow leaves, the deeper narrow lobes of the corolla and glabrous ovary ; catawbiense never grows rampant, as ponticum does.

R. ponticum has been used to a considerable extent by hybridisers, but the hybrids are not generally so valuable and hardy as those derived from catawbiense. One of the best is altaclerense (see under arboreum). Of its own varieties the following may be mentioned :—

Var. ALBUM.—Flowers white. This variety is now very rarely seen.

Var. CHEIRANTHIFOLIUM.—Flowers pale purple ; the plant dwarf and compact ; leaves 2 or 3 ins. long, ⅓ to ½ in. wide, very wavy at the margins.

Var. LANCIFOLIUM (R. lancifolium, *Moench*).—A small edition of the type ; leaves 2 to 4 ins. long, ½ to ¾ in. wide. Flowers in small trusses, almost white in the centre, suffused with purple towards the margin. The plant is dwarf and compact, rarely more than 6 to 8 ft. high. It is distinguished from cheiranthifolium by the leaves being flat, not wavy.

Var. VARIEGATUM.—Leaves smaller and narrower than in the type, edged with creamy white.

R. PRÆSTANS, *Balfour and W. W. Smith*

This is one of the Grande series of rhododendrons and in general appearance most nearly approaches R. sinogrande, having similarly immense leathery leaves of the same shining black-green colour, but distinct in being broadest near the apex and tapering thence to rather flattened leaf-stalk, as thick as one's little finger, whereas in sinogrande the widest part is at or just above the middle. Young plants bear leaves up to 2 ft. long and 1 ft. wide and at that age are almost as remarkable as those of sinogrande, but they get smaller as the plant gets older. Balfour gives the maximum length in wild specimens as being about 15 ins. The under surface is covered with a grey or fawn-coloured, thin, " plastered " scurf such as we see in the " argenteum " form of grande, but not so silvery. The midrib and veins are yellowish above and the leaf-stalk (in young plants) up to 2 ins. in length. I do not know that this species has blossomed under cultivation, but the flowers are described as being fifteen to twenty in a truss ; the obliquely bell-shaped corolla " magenta-rose or flushed with that colour, crimson blotched " (Forrest), nearly 2 ins. long, eight-lobed ; stamens sixteen, up to 1 in. long, glabrous ; style glabrous ; calyx minute ; flower-stalk 1 to 1¼ ins. long.

Forrest found this species in Yunnan, China, on the mountains between the Mekong and Yangtze rivers and described it as a shrub 20 to 30 ft. high. That was in 1914. It must be included amongst his most remarkable discoveries. It grows at altitudes of 13,000 ft., and whilst no doubt showing its best in the gardens of the south-west, should be hardy enough to succeed in such places as mid-Sussex and Hampshire, and the warmer parts of Surrey.

R. CORYPHÆUM, *Balfour fil.* (syn. R. semnum, *Balfour fil.*), is regarded by Mr H. F. Tagg of Edinburgh as so closely akin to R. præstans that it may have to be included in it. It has creamy-white flowers, but in essential botanical characters there is little difference. Found by Forrest, in 1918, on the mountains between the Mekong and Salween rivers in Yunnan at 12,000 ft. altitude. The leaf-stalk, short and very stout, is marked by the upper side being very much flattened.

R. PRÆTERITUM, *Hutchinson*

An evergreen shrub probably 10 ft. or more high ; young shoots downy. Leaves oblong, rounded or slightly heart-shaped at the base, abruptly narrowed at the apex to a short mucro ; 3 to 5½ ins. long, 1¼ to 1¾ ins. wide ; dark dull green above, pale green and ultimately glabrous beneath except on the midrib ; stalk ⅓ to ⅝ in. long. Flowers opening in March about eight in a truss 4 ins. wide. Corolla bell-shaped, 1¼ to 1½ ins. long and wide, pink or pinkish white, five-lobed, each lobe notched, ¾ to 1 in. wide. Stamens ten,

⅜ to 1¼ ins. long, slightly downy towards the base ; anthers chocolate-purple. Ovary and style quite glabrous. Calyx shallowly five-lobed, glabrous ; flower-stalks ½ to ¾ in. long, loosely downy at first. Native of China, probably of W. Hupeh ; introduced by Wilson for Messrs Veitch in 1900. This species is placed in the oreodoxa section of the Fortunei series ; from oreodoxa itself it differs in having a five-lobed corolla and only ten stamens ; the flower-stalks of oreodoxa are also glandular. It was at first confused with maculiferum, from which it is clearly distinguished by having no blotch on the corolla and a quite smooth ovary. It is very hardy and has about the same garden value as R. Fargesii ; on account of its early opening the blossom is liable to damage by frost.

R. PRÆVERNUM, *Hutchinson*

(Gardeners' Chronicle, 24th March 1923, fig. 74)

Some students of the genus Rhododendron are doubtful whether this can be considered as specifically distinct from R. sutchuenense. To my mind it is certainly distinct enough to have its own name, if not a specific at least a varietal one. It is a native of W. Hupeh and was originally found by Wilson when collecting there for Messrs Veitch in 1900. Most of the plants in cultivation belong to his No. 509, raised from seed collected by him in 1907. Compared with R. sutchuenense it is quite distinct in habit, being much dwarfer and more spreading. The oblanceolate leaves are smaller, 4 to 7 ins. long, 1 to 2 ins. wide, abruptly tapered at the apex, gradually tapered to a stalk ¾ to 1 in. long ; they are quite glabrous at maturity, even on the midrib, which is downy beneath in sutchuenense. The truss carries about ten flowers, the bell-shaped corolla 2 ins. long and wide, white or pink marked with a fine wine-red blotch at the base and very downy there. In sutchuenense the corolla has no blotch but is freely spotted on the upper side. Stamens fifteen, downy near the base ; anthers dark brown. Ovary and style glabrous. Calyx very small ; flower-stalk 1 in. long. To sum up : R. prævernum differs from sutchuenense in its closer dwarfer growth, narrower leaves more tapered at the base and not downy on the midrib beneath, flowers smaller and with a heavy blotch at the base. It is a very beautiful shrub, perfectly hardy at Kew, and often setting a fine lot of flower-buds there. The date of flowering is dependent on the season and varies from February to April. At the earlier date, of course, there is much danger of flower injury by frost. (Fortunei series.)

There are rhododendrons intermediate or natural hybrids between these two. One called R. sutchuenense Geraldii, *Hutchinson*, has all the characters of sutchuenense with the corolla blotch of prævernum.

R. PRATTII, *Franchet*

(Bot. Mag., t. 9414 ; R. Faberi *of gardens*, not of *Hemsley*)

A stiff evergreen shrub up to 12 ft. high in a wild state ; young shoots clothed with loose brown down, becoming glabrous. Leaves stiff and hard in texture, oval or broadly ovate to ovate-oblong, abruptly narrowed at the apex to a short point ; rounded or slightly heart-shaped at the base ; 3 to 8 ins. long, 1½ to 3½ ins. wide ; glossy dark green and soon nearly or quite glabrous above, thinly downy beneath in two layers, the upper one brown and wearing off in great part, the under one paler, close, and permanent ; stalk ⅝ to 1⅛ ins. long. Flowers produced in April and May a dozen to twenty together in a truss 3 or 4 ins. wide. Corolla white, pink-tinged, with a crimson blotch and spots at the base, 1½ to 2 ins. long and wide, bell-shaped, downy inside towards the base, five-lobed, the lobes ½ in. long. Stamens ten, ⅓ to 1 in. long, downy at the base ; ovary felted ; style glabrous or glanded at the base, longer than the stamens. Calyx divided almost to the base into five ovate membranous lobes ⅓ to ⅝ in. long, downy outside and glandular-ciliate. Flower-stalks ¾ to 1 in. long, covered with tawny, glandular down.

Native of W. Szechuen, China ; discovered by Pratt near Tatsienlu ; introduced by Wilson in 1904. It is quite hardy at Kew and flowers regularly ; the foliage is handsome, but the colouring is not particularly effective. The large membranous calyx is distinctive. Wilson describes it as a woodland species and it undoubtedly needs partial shade. It has been very much confused in gardens with R. Faberi, *Hemsley*, owing to its having been wrongly identified with that species in the *Plantæ Wilsonianæ*, vol. i., p. 533, and distributed from the Coombe Wood Nursery under that name. The true R. Faberi is distinct in the thicker woolly tomentum beneath the leaf and is probably not in cultivation. Both species belong to the Taliense series.

R. PROSTRATUM, *W. W. Smith*

(Bot. Mag., t. 8747)

A prostrate evergreen shrub a few inches only high in nature (but probably taller under cultivation) growing in stony Alpine pasture or trailing over rocks ; young shoots scaly and clothed with hairs. Leaves oblong or oval, rounded or blunt at both ends ; ½ to ¾ in. long, scarcely half as much wide ; glossy dark green and glabrous above, covered with reddish scales beneath ; margins thinly furnished with hairs ; stalk 1/10 in. long. Flowers solitary or in pairs, more rarely in threes, produced in April at the end of the shoot, each on a very hairy stalk ½ to ¾ in. long. Corolla flat and open, 1¼ to 1½ ins. wide, rosy purple, spotted on the upper side, five-lobed, the lobes rounded. Stamens ten, rosy purple, hairy at the base ; anthers dark brown ; ovary scaly ; style glabrous. Calyx deeply five-lobed, the lobes obovate, ¼ in. long, rounded at the end, hairy at the margins. (Saluenense series.)

Native of Yunnan, China ; discovered and introduced by Forrest in 1910. A very pleasing species, distinct in its dwarf prostrate habit and conspicuous hairiness of the young shoots, leaf margins, calyx, and flower-stalks. The flowers are richly coloured and large for the size of the plant. An appropriate plant for a moist spot with peaty or at any rate lime-free soil in the rock garden. It is quite hardy. Nearly related to it is

R. CHAMEUNUM, *Balfour and Forrest* (syns. R. colobodes, *Balfour fil.*, and R. sericocalyx, *Balfour fil.*), a more erect shrub 1 to 2 ft. high with the same bristly flower-stalks ; corolla more downy outside and deep purple rose, the calyx also softly downy outside. Native of W. Yunnan, founded by Forrest in 1914. Also closely related to R. saluenense.

R. PROTISTUM, *Balfour and Forrest*

Some young plants of this fine species, grew vigorously in a cool, scarcely heated greenhouse at Kew, and were very noticeable for their whorl-like tiers of large spreading leaves. Although Forrest found it (in 1919) up to altitudes of 13,000 ft. in N.W. Yunnan, it has very much the appearance of being only likely to succeed in the open air in the maritime parts of the south and west. It is described as a large shrub or a tree 25 to 45 ft. high, with stout branches and leaves 8 to 18 ins. long by 4 to 7½ ins. wide ; they are of oblanceolate shape, rounded at the apex, tapered to a thick, cylindrical stalk

1 in. or rather more long, of thin texture and quite glabrous on the young cultivated plants. The leaves are notable also for the number of lateral veins, which may be counted up to more than thirty ; and the way they are sunk on the upper surface so as to leave the intervening parts of the blade puckered. Flowers in trusses of twenty to thirty, opening in May in Yunnan. Corolla bell-shaped, 2 ins. long, eight-lobed, fleshy, creamy-white, flushed with rose. Stamens sixteen ; ovary covered with pinkish down ; style glabrous. Flower-stalk 1½ ins. long and downy like the small calyx.

This species belongs to the Grande series and seems to be very nearly allied to R. giganteum, which, however, has crimson flowers. Whilst the foliage of both is glabrous in our juvenile plants, it becomes downy in adult ones. I do not know that protistum has flowered in cultivation and we may have to wait some years before seeing them. In the striking character of its foliage it is scarcely surpassed.

R. PRUNIFOLIUM, *Millais*

(Azalea prunifolia, *Small*)

A deciduous azalea up to 9 ft. high in a wild state ; young shoots glabrous, purplish red, becoming greyish later. Leaves oval, or obovate to oblong ; 1½ to 4 ins. long, ½ to 1½ ins. wide ; green and glabrous on both surfaces except on the midrib which is slightly downy above and very sparingly bristly beneath, margins ciliate ; stalk ⅛ to ¼ in. long. Flowers produced in July in clusters of four or five. Corolla crimson, funnel-shaped, the tube ¾ to 1 in. long, glabrous or nearly so outside, downy inside. Stamens five, 2 to 2½ ins. long, the lower half downy ; ovary covered with pale bristly not glandular hairs ; calyx very small, flower-stalks hairy.

Native of Georgia and Alabama ; found in shady ravines on the banks of streams ; introduced to England by Prof. Sargent in 1918. Rehder describes it as the most glabrous of all American azaleas and very distinct in being entirely without glandular pubescence except occasionally on the outside of the corolla lobes. It will, no doubt, be best suited for southern and western gardens and should be welcome for its crimson, late-opening flowers. It blossomed in July 1931 with Lt.-Col. Stephenson Clarke at Borde Hill in Sussex. It must not be confused with R. pruniflorum, one of the glaucum series (*see under* R. Genestierianum, p. 71).

R. PRZEWALSKII, *Maximowicz*

(R. kialense, *Franchet*)

An evergreen shrub of very compact, slow growth, forming a close hemispherical bush ; young shoots bright yellow, glabrous, stiff, and stout. Leaves oval or obovate, 2 to 4 ins. long, 1 to 1½ ins. wide ; tapered or rounded at the base, pointed ; dark green and glabrous above, more or less scurfy, and with netted veins beneath ; stalk yellow. Flowers white or pink, spotted with rose purple, borne in compact trusses 3 ins. across ; corolla five-lobed, 1¼ ins. across, broadly funnel-shaped ; stamens ten, smooth-stalked or very slightly downy at the base ; ovary and style glabrous ; flower-stalk about ½ in. long and like the small inconspicuously lobed calyx, glabrous.

Native of W. China ; first collected in Kansu by the Russian traveller Przewalsky, in 1880 ; introduced to cultivation by way of St Petersburg. Wilson, who found it further south in 1904, observes that it reaches higher altitudes in W. China than any other broad-leaved rhododendron. He found it up to 14,500 ft. Its yellow buds, young shoots, and leaf-stalks combined with its dense close habit make cultivated plants very distinct, but it appears to be very shy-flowering. Some plants have the young shoots balsamic scented.

R. PULCHRUM, *Sweet*

(R. indicum Smithii, *Wilson* ; R. phœnicum, *G. Don*)

This azalea is one of the indicum group and has mostly been known as a variety of R. indicum itself. It differs, however, in having ten stamens and is known only as a cultivated plant, not having yet been found in a wild state. It was introduced from Canton, China, to the Horticultural Society's Garden early in the nineteenth century. According to Wilson it is, at the present time, used in great numbers as a stock on which the " Indian " azaleas (R. Simsii) are grafted by Belgian growers. I have never seen what may be regarded as the type in bloom and it is said to be shy-flowering. It is closely related to R. Simsii (*q.v.*) but has a larger calyx.

A vigorous evergreen shrub probably 6 ft. or more high, the young shoots covered with the flattened, appressed, forward-pointing bristles characteristic of its group. Leaves narrowly obovate to ovate-lanceolate, 1 to 3 ins. long, with appressed hairs on both surfaces. Flowers produced in May, two to four together. Corolla funnel-shaped, five-lobed, 2 to 2½ ins. wide, purple. Stamens ten, downy at the base ; ovary clothed with erect bristles ; style glabrous. Calyx-lobes awl-shaped, ⅓ to ½ in. long, the outside and margins hairy. Flower-stalk ½ in. long, hairy.

Var. CALYCINUM, *Wilson* (" Omurasaki ").—Flower rose-purple spotted with crimson. Long cultivated in Japan ; introduced to England in 1849.

Var. MAXWELLII (R. Maxwellii, *Millais*).—Flowers carmine red.

These two varieties are perhaps the only forms of R. pulchrum at present in cultivation here. Neither is very hardy, although the former lived outside at Kew for some years and Maxwellii succeeds admirably in mid-Sussex. The names here used are those adopted by Wilson in his monograph of the Old World azaleas, but Rehder has lately made them all varieties of R. pulchrum, *Sweet*.

R. QUINQUEFOLIUM, *Bisset and Moore*

A deciduous azalea of low, bushy habit, 4 to 20 ft. high ; shoots glabrous, branches erect, forked. Leaves produced in whorls of five (with sometimes one or two very small ones in addition) at the end of the shoot only ; broadly obovate or somewhat diamond-shaped, rounded at the apex, except for a short, abrupt tip, tapering at the base to a very short bristly stalk ; they vary in size in each set of five, the largest being 1½ to 2 ins. long by 1 in. wide, the smallest not half as large ; upper surface sparsely hairy when young, the lower one hairy about the margin and along the midrib ; both sides pale green, often with a purplish margin. Flowers solitary, in pairs or in threes, produced with the young leaves from the terminal bud ; corolla broadly funnel-shaped, 1½ ins. across, pinkish or white, the lobes ovate ; calyx-lobes short, triangular ; stamens ten, hairy at the base ; flower-stalk 1 in. long, hairy.

Native of Japan ; discovered by Mr Bisset in 1876 ; introduced about twenty years later by Lord Redesdale. This azalea is most distinct and attractive in its foliage, especially in spring when the leaves are of a tender green bordered with purple, each whorl of five forming an umbrella-like group at the top of a slender twig. It flowers in April.

R. RACEMOSUM, *Franchet*

(Bot. Mag., t. 7301)

An evergreen shrub, at least 5 or 6 ft. high, of tufted habit when young and small, but, when well established in good soil, sending up vigorous erect shoots, 12 ins. or more long in a year ; young wood scaly. Leaves ¾ to 2 ins.

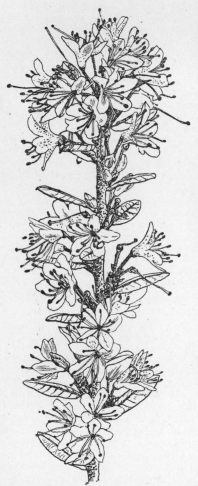

long, about half as wide, obovate or oval, rounded or abruptly tapering at both ends, thickly dotted beneath with brownish scales on a vividly glaucous surface. Flowers produced in April and May in axillary and terminal clusters, from three to six in a cluster. Corolla soft pink, 1 to 1¼ ins. across, widely bell-shaped, the tube shorter than the five oblong rounded lobes ; calyx minute, and, like the flower-stalk, covered with scales ; stamens ten, downy at the base.

Native of W. China, first raised in the Jardin des Plantes at Paris in 1889 ; where I saw it in November and brought to Kew some seedlings. The seed had been gathered and sent to Paris by Père Delavay. It has since proved one of the most distinct and pretty of the dwarfer Chinese rhododendrons. Its most remarkable feature is the production of flowers from the leaf-axils along the previous year's wood. Often from 6 to more than 12 ins. of the shoot will be laden with blossom—very different from the single rounded truss which in Rhododendron is usually seen terminating the shoot. This shrub produces good seed in abundance, which affords an easy means of increase. It can also be propagated from cuttings. It is a charming plant for grouping in low shrubberies.

RHODODENDRON RACEMOSUM

R. RADICANS, *Balfour and Forrest*

An evergreen shrub 2 to 4 ins. high, forming neat close tufts ; young shoots scaly, slender. Leaves oblanceolate, tapered at the end to a conspicuous mucro and at the base to a scaly stalk $\frac{1}{20}$ in. long ; ¼ to ½ in. long, $\frac{1}{12}$ to $\frac{3}{16}$ in. wide ; dark bright green and glabrous or nearly so above, very scaly beneath. Flowers terminal, solitary, on a scaly stalk ½ to 1 in. long. Corolla purple, ¾ in. wide, deeply five-lobed, downy and scaly outside. Stamens ten, woolly near the base ; ovary scaly ; style glabrous. Calyx with ovate, pointed lobes ⅙ in. long, ciliate, scaly.

Native of S.E. Tibet ; found by Forrest in 1921 on open, stony moorland, up to 15,000 ft. altitude. This charming little rhododendron, one of the pygmies of the genus, is very hardy and excellently adapted for the rock garden. Nearly akin to it and of a similar type is

R. KELETICUM, *Balfour and Forrest*, an evergreen shrub up to 12 ins. high, with slender, scaly young shoots and oval or obovate leaves about ½ in. long, bright green and glabrous above, pale and densely scaly beneath, with a few bristles on the margin. Flowers mostly solitary, sometimes in pairs, the corolla purplish crimson, ⅝ in. wide, downy and scaly outside. Calyx deeply five-lobed ; the lobes $\frac{3}{16}$ in. long, ovate, glabrous, except for some marginal down. Stamens ten, downy at the base ; ovary scaly ; style glabrous. Flower-stalk ½ to 1 in. long, scaly.

Native of S.E. Tibet ; discovered and introduced in 1919 by Forrest, who found it growing on " open, peaty, stony pasture, and on cliffs and screes." It is a quite hardy and attractive rock garden plant with broader leaves than R. radicans, rather taller, and with a calyx not at all (or only slightly) scaly. Both these species are included in the Saluenense series.

R. RAVUM, *Balfour and W. W. Smith*

(Bot. Mag., t. 9561 ; R. cheilanthum, *Balfour fil.*; R. sclerocladum, *Balfour and Forrest*)

An evergreen shrub usually 2 to 4 ft. high ; young shoots very scaly. Leaves oval, oblong or narrowly obovate, tapered at the base, rounded or tapered at the apex, with a distinct mucro there ; ¾ to 2 ins. long, ¼ to ⅞ in. wide ; dark green and scaly above, very densely scaly and rather tawny beneath ; stalk ¼ in. or less long. Flowers opening in May, four to six together in a terminal cluster. Corolla deep rose, narrowly funnel-shaped, ¾ to 1 in. long, 1 in. wide, the short tube (hairy inside) expanding into five deep lobes. Stamens ten, downy at the base. Ovary covered with yellowish scales ; style slender, overtopping the stamens, downy towards the base. Calyx ⅛ to ¼ in. long, deeply five-lobed, the lobes oblong, fringed all round with hairs, scaly at the lower part ; flower-stalks about ¼ in. long, scaly.

Native of Yunnan, China, at 10,000 to 11,000 ft. altitude. This is one of the Lapponicum series, standing in the section with a style downy in the lower part, a four- or five-flowered truss, rose-coloured blossom, and calyx-lobes scaly outside. It was discovered and introduced by Forrest in 1913, and has proved quite hardy.

R. RETICULATUM, *D. Don*

(R. rhombicum, *Miquel*, Bot. Mag., t. 6972)

A deciduous azalea 5 to 12 ft. high with stiff, erect, somewhat sparse branches, covered with a loose brownish wool when young. Leaves diamond-shaped, 1 to 2½ ins. long, ¾ to 1½ ins. wide ; dark dull green and very hairy above when young, becoming almost or quite glabrous by autumn ; paler and very finely net-veined beneath ; stalk ⅛ to ⅓ in. long, brown-woolly. Flowers solitary or in pairs (rarely twice as many) purple, almost or quite unspotted, 1½ to 2 ins. across ; corolla-lobes oblong, ½ in. wide, the three upper ones erect, the two smaller ones more deeply divided and pointed downwards ; calyx small, five-toothed, very hairy like the flower-stalk, which is about ¼ in. long ; stamens usually ten ; ovary and style hairy.

Native of Japan ; long cultivated at Kew but rare in gardens. It flowers on the leafless twigs in late April. Although hardy, it likes a sheltered position and a sandy, peaty soil. The unusual colour of the flowers, which has a distinct suggestion of blue, gives the species a claim to more general recognition. The unfolding leaves have a purplish tinge, which they again assume before falling in autumn.   Hardy enough in the adult stage, small plants are better with some protection in winter until two or three years old.

RHODODENDRON RETICULATUM

R. MARIESII, *Hemsley* (Bot. Mag., t. 8206), is a close ally.   It is a native of Central China (Hupeh), whence it was introduced to Kew in 1886 by Prof. A. Henry but it is no longer represented there.   As it occurs below 4000 ft., it is likely to be hardy in the mildest parts of the kingdom only.   The corolla has the same five deeply cut lobes, the three upper ones erect, as in reticulatum, but they are conspicuously spotted at the base, and the leaf is broadest below the middle.

R. RHABDOTUM, *Balfour and Cooper*
(Bot. Mag., t. 9447)

An evergreen shrub or small tree up to about 12 ft. high ; young shoots scaly, slightly bristly, becoming glabrous and purplish later.   Leaves 4 to 7½ ins. long, about one-third as wide, ovate-oblong, tapering at the apex to a fine point, glabrous above, glaucous green and scaly beneath.   Flowers in a terminal cluster of about four ; corolla with a funnel-shaped base and five spreading wavy lobes giving it a diameter of 4 ins., white with broad strips of crimson running down outside the tube nearly to the base ; stamens about as long as the corolla, downy towards the base.

Native of Bhotan, discovered by Mr R. E. Cooper in 1915, first flowered in August 1931, by Lord Aberconway. Seed was first introduced by Kingdon Ward. The late Mr Lionel de Rothschild was given a First-Class Certificate for it in 1934. It belongs to the noble Maddeni series, but will only be hardy in our mildest districts. It is sometimes found growing wild as an epiphyte.

R. RIRIEI, *Hemsley and Wilson*

An evergreen shrub up to 18 ft. high ; branchlets furnished with a loose white scurf when quite young. Leaves narrowly oval or broadly oblanceolate, 3 to 6 ins. long, 1 to 2 ins. wide ; tapered at both ends, usually more abruptly towards the apex ; glabrous and green above, covered beneath with a very close scurf, at first white, turning grey ; midrib yellow below. Flowers purple with a black spot at base, 2 ins. across, in trusses of eight or more. Corolla broadly bell-shaped, five-lobed ; ovary covered with pale greyish wool ; pistil glabrous, nearly 2 ins. long ; flower-stalk about ⅔ in. long ; seed-vessel very large, 1¼ ins. long, ⅖ in. wide. Stamens ten, glabrous.

Discovered and introduced in 1904 from Mt. Omi, W. China, by Wilson. Cultivated at Kew until 1949, but very rare. From the other West Chinese rhododendrons with white scurf beneath the leaf (hypoglaucum and argyrophyllum) this is distinguished by its large seed-vessels.

R. ROSEUM, *Rehder*

(Azalea rosea, *Loiseleur* ; A. nudiflora rosea, *Sweet* ; A. prinophylla, *Small*)

A deciduous azalea 3 to 9 ft. high ; young shoots downy and usually sparingly bristly. Leaves dull or bluish green, oval to obovate ; 1½ to 2½ ins. long, slightly downy above, densely grey-woolly beneath ; margins ciliate. Flowers fragrant, produced during May, in clusters of five to nine. Corolla bright pink, with a cylindrical tube ¾ in. long, covered outside with thin down and gland-tipped hairs, and with five ovate abruptly pointed lobes. Stamens five, 1½ ins. long, downy below the middle ; ovary covered with pale silky down ; style overtopping the stamens, downy towards the base ; calyx and flower-stalk downy.

Native of eastern N. America ; probably introduced early in the nineteenth century or even earlier as it grows in the older settled States, but always much confused with nudiflorum and canescens. To nudiflorum it is closely related, but Rehder distinguishes it by its " pubescent winter-buds and pubescent bluish green leaves, shorter stamens and more or less glandular corolla with larger broader lobes and wider tube." Being found wild in States of New York, Massachusetts, etc., this azalea is quite hardy and may be in cultivation in old collections under Sweet's name given above. Seeds of this species were sent to England by Sargent in 1922. It is found on limestone in the New York State.

R. ALABAMENSE, *Rehder*, is a near ally with white flowers, fragrant and nearly 2 ins. wide. Leaves downy and rather glaucous beneath. One collector calls the flowers " snowy white." Introduced in 1922 from Alabama. Probably only hardy enough for the south and west. It has also been called " Azalea nudiflora alba."

R. ROXIEANUM, *Forrest*
(Bot. Mag., t. 9383)

An evergreen shrub 4 ft. and upwards high in nature, of slow-growing, congested habit ; young shoots as a rule short, clothed with reddish brown wool and mostly hidden by the closely packed leaves, which are of linear-oblong or oblanceolate shape, pointed, tapered at the base to a very short stalk ; 2 to 4 ins. long, ⅓ to ¾ in. wide ; dark glossy green above, covered thickly beneath with a reddish brown wool ; margins much recurved. Flowers packed, ten to fifteen together and opening in May, in terminal trusses about 3 ins. wide. Corolla bell-shaped, 1 to 1½ ins. long, five-lobed, white or creamy-white, flushed with rose and spotted with crimson. Stamens ten, ½ in. long, their lower two-thirds covered with pale hairs. Ovary clothed with down which sometimes extends to the base of the style. Calyx very small ; flower-stalks hairy.

Native of Yunnan, China ; discovered by Forrest in 1913. It belongs to a section of the Taliense series marked by its narrow leaves, small calyx, and congested growths and flower-trusses. According to Forrest's field notes, he found plants 10 ft. high, which, judging by the rate of growth under cultivation, must be of very great age. Belonging to the same group and likely to prove of more interest in gardens is

R. PROTEOIDES, *Balfour and W. W. Smith*, found by Forrest in 1917, apparently always under 3 ft. high and mostly only 1 to 2 ft. Its flowers, crowded in trusses of about eight, are creamy yellow spotted with crimson and sometimes flushed with rose. The leaves are oblong, oval, or obovate, with much recurved margins ; ¾ to 2 ins. long by ¼ to ½ in. wide ; thickly covered beneath with reddish wool, the stalk very short and curiously thick. The stamens, calyx, ovary, and style are much the same as in Roxieanum, but the leaves are only half the length and blunt or rounded at the end. Judging by wild specimens this species—with its dense, dwarf habit, its small leaves and rounded trusses of yellow flowers 2 to 3 ins. wide—should make a pleasing shrub in positions suitable for one of its size, such as on a broad ledge in the rock garden. Both these species are hardy at Kew.

R. RUBIGINOSUM, *Franchet*
(Bot. Mag., t. 7621)

A stiff-habited, erect-growing evergreen shrub, 6 to 20 ft. high, branchlets becoming warty. Leaves 1½ to 3½ ins. long, ½ to 1 in. wide ; narrowly oval, tapering gradually to each end ; upper surface glabrous, dull green, lower one covered with reddish brown scales ; stalk ¼ to ½ in. long. Flowers in terminal clusters of four to seven, produced in April and May. Corolla 1½ to 2 ins. wide, rosy lilac, spotted with maroon on the upper side, the tube funnel-shaped, lobes wavy-margined ; calyx shallowly five-lobed, small, warty ; flower-stalk ¾ in. long ; stamens downy at the base.

Native of the Tsangchan Mountain in Yunnan, S.W. China ; introduced to Paris in 1889 by the Abbé Delavay, and thence to England. It is a somewhat stiff, dull-foliaged shrub, and bears a great resemblance to the American R. carolinianum differing in its taller growth, mostly narrower more tapering leaves, and larger flowers. It is hardy under ordinary circumstances, although a few plants at Kew died through the killing of the bark at ground-level during the trying winter of 1908-9, but this only occurred in a low-lying, damp situation. Several plants were also lost during the winter of 1946-47. It succeeds in the chalky soil at Highdown, Goring-on-Sea, Sussex.

R. RUBROPILOSUM, *Hayata*
(R. caryophyllum, *Hayata*)

An evergreen azalea up to 9 ft. high in a wild state ; young shoots covered densely with flattened, appressed, grey to red-brown hairs. Leaves oblong-lanceolate to oval-lanceolate, ½ to 1¾ ins. long. ½ to ¾ in. wide, slightly hairy above, thickly furnished beneath with forward-pointing bristly hairs, especially on the midrib. Corolla funnel-shaped, with five spreading lobes, pink spotted with dark rose, ¾ to 1 in. wide. Stamens seven to ten, shorter than the corolla, downy near the base as is also the longer style. Calyx and flower-stalk very bristly. The flowers come in clusters of three or four.

Native of Formosa, up to 10,000 ft. altitude. Wilson, who visited its native habitat in 1918, found many plants flowering in October. During the same journey he introduced the species to cultivation by means of seeds. It is not likely to be hardy except in such climates as that of Cornwall. It belongs to the indicum group of azaleas, differing from indicum itself in the more numerous stamens and in the downy style ; the latter character distinguishes it also from tosaënse and Simsii. Mr W. R. Price, who visited Formosa in 1912, also found it blooming in October. (Azalea (obtusum) series.)

R. RUPICOLA, *W. W. Smith*

An evergreen shrub 2 to 4 ft. high, young shoots, leaves (on both sides), outside of calyx-lobes, ovary, and flower-stalks all very scaly. Leaves oval, often inclined to oblong, rounded but with a tiny mucro at the apex ; $\frac{1}{2}$ to $\frac{3}{4}$ in. long, $\frac{1}{6}$ to $\frac{1}{3}$ in. wide ; dark green above, yellowish grey between the scales beneath ; stalk $\frac{1}{12}$ to $\frac{1}{8}$ in. long. Flowers opening in April and May in a terminal cluster of three to five, each on a very short stalk. Corolla $\frac{7}{8}$ in. wide, of a rich plum-purple, the tube very short and clothed inside with white hairs, five-lobed, the lobes ovate-oblong, rounded at the end, spreading, sprinkled more or less with scales outside, mostly up the middle. Stamens normally ten, but sometimes as few as seven, purple, $\frac{1}{2}$ in. long, tufted with white down near the base ; anthers pale brown. Ovary scaly towards the top ; style overtopping the stamens, purple, glabrous. Calyx $\frac{1}{8}$ in. long, deeply five-lobed, the lobes oblong, deep purple, fringed at the margin.

Native of Yunnan, China ; discovered and introduced by Forrest in 1910. Its flowers, although small, are of a wonderfully rich purple, this colour extending to all the parts except the anthers. Coming from an altitude of 14,000 ft., it is naturally hardy, but nevertheless appears to prefer the conditions of the south and west. The also richly purple-flowered russatum differs in having much larger leaves and a downy style.

R. ACHROANTHUM, *Balfour and W. W. Smith*, is in the same alliance but the flowers are paler and have some red in the colouring. More important differential characters are the five or six stamens and the grey ovary coated from top to bottom with scales. Introduced from Yunnan by Forrest in 1914. (Lapponicum series.)

R. RUSSATUM, *Balfour and Forrest*

(R. cantabile, *Balfour fil.*, Bot. Mag., t. 8963)

A dwarf evergreen shrub, ultimately a yard or more high, of bushy, densely leafy habit ; young shoots covered with red and yellow scales. Leaves borne along nearly the whole of the shoots, half a dozen to the inch ; oval or ovate, round-ended ; $\frac{3}{4}$ to $1\frac{3}{4}$ ins. long, half as much wide ; dark dull green above, rusty yellow beneath, both surfaces very scaly ; stalk $\frac{1}{10}$ to $\frac{1}{8}$ in. long. Flowers opening in March and April in close clusters of five to ten. Corolla a vivid purple-blue, about 1 in. wide, with five spreading lobes and a funnel-shaped base that is hairy in the throat. Stamens ten, conspicuously exposed, hairy towards the base, the stalks reddish ; anthers brown. Ovary scaly ; style red, hairy at the base. Calyx deeply cut into five ovate or oblong lobes about $\frac{1}{8}$ in. long, fringed with hairs. The inflorescence as a whole is nearly or quite stalkless, but the individual flower-stalks are $\frac{1}{8}$ to $\frac{1}{4}$ in. long, scaly.

Native of Yunnan, China ; discovered at an altitude of 12,000 ft. and introduced by Forrest in 1913. It belongs to the Lapponicum series and is one of the most richly coloured and desirable of them. R. cantabile, originally regarded as a distinct species by Balfour, represents a form with usually more flowers in a truss, but others are intermediate in this respect. Quite hardy at Kew.

R. SANGUINEUM, *Franchet*

(Bot. Mag. t. 9263; R. hæmaleum, *Balfour and Forrest*)

An evergreen shrub up to 3 ft. high; shoots turning grey the second year. Leaves oblong-obovate to oval, usually tapered more gradually to the base; 2 to 3½ ins. long, ½ to 1¼ ins. wide; dark green and glabrous above, covered with a grey-white, close down beneath; stalk ⅛ to ⅓ in. long. Flowers opening in May, June, and July in clusters of six or more. Corolla fleshy, bright crimson (the Abbé Soulié, who discovered the species in 1895, says "fleur rouge de sang"), bell-shaped, 1¼ to 1½ ins. long, five-lobed. Stamens ten, up to 1 in. long, glabrous. Ovary hairy, style glabrous. Calyx small with red lobes; flower-stalk ½ to 1 in. long, loosely downy.

Native of W. Szechuen, China, and S.E. Tibet; introduced by Forrest. It is the type species of a large sub-series of shrubby rhododendrons, usually of low stature, to which (as being the longest known) it gives its name and in which some thirty so-called species have been included. There is a very large assembly of them at Exbury, Hants, but Mr de Rothschild found that they do not flower at an early age. The nearest akin to sanguineum itself, mentioned here, are hæmaleum and didymum, both with black-crimson flowers, but there is no doubt some names will eventually be suppressed. Dr Stapf has already united hæmaleum with sanguineum (see *Botanical Magazine* as quoted above), but for garden purposes at least both names should be retained. R. sanguineum and its allies are included by Mr Tagg in the Neriiflorum series. Hardy at Kew.

R. SARGENTIANUM, *Rehder and Wilson*

(Bot. Mag., t. 8871)

A low evergreen shrub up to 2 ft. high and 3 ft. or more across, with numerous erect branches which, when young, are covered with down and dark scurf. Leaves aromatic when crushed, oval, ⅓ to ⅔ in. long, half as much wide; dark glossy green and soon glabrous above, very scurfy beneath; leaf-stalk about ⅛ in. long. Flowers produced in May, six to twelve together in a loose terminal cluster, each bloom on a stalk ⅕ to ⅜ in. long, thickly covered with yellowish scurf. Corolla pale yellow, ½ in. long and wide, the base a cylindrical tube hairy inside, spreading at the mouth into five lobes, scaly outside. Stamens five, glabrous, hidden in the corolla-tube; ovary scaly; style shorter than the stamens. Calyx ⅛ in. long, its five oblong lobes scurfy and margined with hairs.

Native of W. Szechuen, China; discovered and introduced by Wilson in 1903-4. This is a rather dainty little shrub, found at high altitudes (11,000 ft.) and very hardy. Very suitable for the rock garden. It belongs to the Cephalanthum series in which its scaly, yellow corolla distinguishes it. Allied also to R. Anthopogon and other species with a slender tube to the corolla, in which the stamens and short, sturdy style are enclosed. Named after C. S. Sargent, first Director of the Arnold Arboretum, Mass.

R. SALUENENSE, *Franchet*

(Bot. Mag., t. 9095; R. amaurophyllum, *Balfour*; R. humicola, *Wilding*)

An evergreen shrub 1½ to 2 ft. high; young shoots scaly and conspicuously bristly. Leaves oblong to oval, with a distinct mucro at the abruptly tapered or rounded apex and a bristly scaly stalk $\frac{1}{12}$ in. long; ¾ to 1 in. long, ¼ to ½ in.

wide ; dark glossy green with minute scales above, more tawny, paler and scaly beneath. Flowers produced in April and May in pairs or threes from the end of the shoot. Corolla rosy-purple or purplish crimson with darker spots, widely open, 1½ to 1¾ ins. wide, with five broad, rounded, overlapping lobes, very scaly and softly downy outside ; downy in the throat. Stamens ten, purplish, with a tuft of down at the base. Ovary densely scaly ; style glabrous. Calyx ⅓ in. wide, with five ovate, conspicuously fringed lobes. Flower-stalks ¼ to ½ in. long, bristly and scaly.

Native of N.W. Yunnan ; discovered in 1894 by the Abbé Soulié ; introduced by Forrest in 1914. It grows at elevations of 12,000 to 14,000 ft. and is quite hardy. It is the type of the Saluenense series whose leading characters are : a low or prostrate habit ; a scaliness and often bristliness of young shoot, leaf-stalk, calyx, and flower-stalk ; flowers solitary or in twos or threes ; a more or less widely open corolla ; and a large, distinctly lobed calyx which often persists at the base of the seed-vessel. It is a very charming series of great garden value, comprising amongst others prostratum, calostrotum, radicans, and keleticum, all very hardy. The last three have no bristles on young shoot or flower-stalk.

R. SCABRIFOLIUM, *Franchet*

(Bot. Mag., t. 7159)

An evergreen shrub of thin, lanky habit, 6 to 8 ft. high, young shoots slender but rather rigid, clothed with pale wool and long hairs. Leaves distributed along the branchlets, narrowly oval to oblong-lanceolate, pointed, tapered at the base ; 1½ to 3½ ins. long, ¾ to 1 in. wide ; dark green and with stiff short hairs above ; paler, scaly, and hairy beneath especially on the prominent midrib and veins ; stalk ⅛ to ¼ in. long. Flowers produced in April and May from several of the axils of the terminal leaves in two- to four-flowered umbels, the whole forming a many-flowered cluster 3 or 4 ins. wide. Corolla white or pale pink, 1¼ ins. wide, with a short tube and five ovate, blunt, spreading lobes ½ in. long. Stamens ten, with pink stalks ½ in. long, downy at the base. Ovary scaly and clothed with short, whitish hairs ; style ¾ in. long, hairy towards the base. Calyx hairy and scaly, ⅛ in. long, with five deep, pointed lobes ; flower-stalks ¾ to 1½ ins. long.

Native of Yunnan, China ; discovered by Delavay in 1883, introduced to the Jardin des Plantes at Paris in 1885, whence plants were sent to Kew in 1888 that flowered two years later. It is an interesting and (in its clothing of stiff hairs and flatly open flowers) a distinct species, but not one of the more attractive ones. It was re-discovered and introduced in 1913 by Forrest, who found it in W. China in open situations up to 11,000 ft. altitude. It is, however, rather tender. The " type " species of its series.

R. SCABRUM, *G. Don*

(R. sublanceolatum, *Miquel*; Bot. Mag., t. 8478)

An evergreen azalea of the indicum group, stiffly branched, bushy, probably up to 6 ft. high, the branchlets having the dark forward-pointing bristles of this group. Leaves 1 to 3 ins. long, ½ to 1½ ins. wide ; oblanceolate, or oval, tapered at the base, terminated by a short mucro ; glabrous and dark green above, paler and with dark appressed hairs like those of the stem beneath and on the margins ; stalk ¼ to ½ in. long. Flowers often three in a cluster, broadly funnel-shaped ; the corolla varies in shade from purplish red to the richest blood-red ; 2½ to 3 ins. wide, 2 ins. long ; the lobes five, rounded, and about ⅞ in. wide ; calyx-lobes obovate, rounded at the apex, hairy on the margins, ₃/₁₆ to ¼ in. long ; stamens ten, nearly as long as the corolla, downy towards the base ; style glabrous ; flower-stalk hairy.

Native of Japan ; introduced about 1909 by Mr Notcutt, of Woodbridge. Its best forms are some of the richest coloured of all azaleas, but it is not very hardy, and needs a slightly warmer climate than that of Kew. It differs from R. indicum in the calyx being glabrous except at the margins, and in the more rounded calyx-lobes. The stamens, too, are almost invariably ten.

R. SCHLIPPENBACHII, *Maximowicz*

(Bot. Mag., t. 7373 (Azalea))

A deciduous shrub, up to 10 or 15 ft. high ; twigs bristly when young. Leaves in a terminal cluster of about five, each 2½ to 5 ins. long, 1½ to 3 ins. wide ; obovate or somewhat diamond-shaped, tapering at the base, blunt or slightly notched at the apex ; glabrous on both surfaces except for a few scattered bristles above and loose down beneath when young. Flowers 3 to 3½ ins. across, soft rose, spotted on the three upper lobes of the corolla with reddish brown, and produced in clusters of three to six. Calyx and flower-stalk very clammy, the latter about 1 in. long.

Native of Manchuria, Korea, etc., first discovered by Richard Oldham in 1863, and afterwards by Baron Schlippenbach ; introduced by the late J. H. Veitch in 1893. It is a plant of exquisite beauty, and its fine leaves, suffused with purplish red when young, are the largest and most striking among azaleas. Unfortunately it suffers from a defect very common to Manchurian shrubs and trees : it is excited into growth by early warmth only to have its young growths destroyed by frost. I have seen this happen twice in one season, an experience no plant can long survive. So far as winter frost is concerned it is apparently quite hardy, but I consider it a hopeless subject except in warm or elevated districts, where spring frosts do little harm, or where artificial protection until May can be given. There is a beautiful plant at Borde Hill, Sussex, which was 10 ft. high and wide when I saw it some years ago.

R. SCINTILLANS, *Balfour and W. W. Smith*

An evergreen shrub up to 3½ ft. high, of twiggy habit ; young shoots very slender, erect, densely scaly. Leaves oblong-lanceolate, abruptly pointed, tapered at the base ; ¼ to ¾ in. long, ⅛ to ⅜ in. wide ; dark green above, greyish beneath, very scaly on both sides ; stalk ₁/₁₆ to ⅛ in. long. Flowers three to six in a terminal cluster 1½ ins. wide, opening in April. Corolla lavender-blue to purplish blue, ¾ to 1 in. wide, five-lobed, the ovate lobes reaching to within ¼ in. of the base ; throat downy ; stamens ten, downy at the base, ½ in. long. Ovary scaly ; style purple, distinctly longer than the stamens, glabrous. Calyx very small but distinctly lobed, scaly, fringed towards the end of the lobes ; flower-stalk very short and scaly.

Native of Yunnan, China, up to 14,000 ft. altitude ; discovered and introduced by Forrest in 1913. Of the large and puzzling Lapponicum group, this is one of the very finest species, especially if the most richly coloured, purple-blue forms are selected. It is very hardy and should eventually become a common garden shrub. Like its allies it is quite easily propagated by cuttings. It gives a fine display every April in the rock garden at Exbury, Hants.

R. SEARSIÆ, *Rehder and Wilson*

(Bot. Mag., t. 8993)

An evergreen shrub 6 to 10 ft. high ; young shoots freely set with pale scales, prominently warted the following year. Leaves narrowly oblong or oblanceolate, slenderly pointed, much tapered at each end ; 2 to 3½ ins. long, ½ to ⅞ in. wide ; dark green and at first scaly above, becoming glabrous ; glaucous beneath, freely sprinkled with small yellowish scales, amongst which are scattered large brown ones ; margins slightly decurved ; stalk ¼ to ⅓ in. long, scaly. Flowers produced during late April and May in terminal clusters of four to eight, occasionally augmented by others from the uppermost leaf-axils ; common flower-stalk ¼ to ½ in. long ; individual stalks ⅓ to ⅔ in. long, scaly. Corolla 1 to 1½ ins. long, 1½ to 2 ins. wide, the base funnel-shaped, the five lobes ovate-oblong, rounded at the end ; pale lavender to almost white spotted with pale green, not scaly outside. Calyx very scaly, small, five-lobed with two lobes enlarged and fringed with hairs. Stamens ten, of varying length, downy towards but not at the base ; anthers pale brown ; style glabrous, slightly overtopping the stamens.

Native of W. Szechuen, China ; discovered and introduced by Wilson in 1908. It is one of the Triflorum-yunnanense group, differing from yunnanense itself in having no bristly hairs on the upper leaf surface. The mixture of yellow and brown scales beneath on a glaucous ground, combined with the two fringed calyx-lobes, is also distinctive. A pretty and quite hardy species.

R. SELENSE, *Franchet*

(R. panteumorphum, *Balfour and W. W. Smith*)

An evergreen shrub 4 to 7 ft. high ; young shoots at first glandular. Leaves oval to obovate, rounded with a distinct mucro at the apex, rounded to tapered at the base ; 1½ to 3½ ins. long, ¾ to 1½ ins. wide ; dark green and glabrous at maturity, pale beneath, stalk up to ⅝ in. long. Flowers in a truss of four to eight. Corolla bell-shaped, about 1½ ins. long and wide, five-lobed, from white to various depths of rose, unspotted or with a crimson blotch ; stamens ten, downy at the base ; ovary glandular, style glabrous ; calyx small and like the flower-stalks (which are ½ to 1 in. long), glandular. (Thomsonii series.)

Native of W. Yunnan, China ; discovered on the mountains between the Mekong and Salween Rivers by the Abbé Soulié in 1895 ; introduced from the same region by Forrest in 1917. It is the type species of a considerable group of species in the Thomsonii series which are distinguished mainly by their slender twigs, thin-textured leaves, small calyx and tapered rather funnel-shaped corolla.

R. RHAIBOCARPUM, *Balfour and W. W. Smith*, is nearly related, but the young shoots and leaf-stalks are very bristly glandular. The corolla is white, more or less flushed with rose and marked with a blotch of crimson at the base. Found in 1914 by Forrest in N.W. Yunnan. R. PROBUM, *Balfour and Forrest*, now regarded as a sub-species of selense, has creamy white flowers. This group flowers in April and May.

R. SEMIBARBATUM, *Maximowicz*

(Bot. Mag., t. 9147)

A deciduous shrub 2 to 8 ft. high with downy and hairy, glandular young shoots, becoming when older smooth and dark brown. Leaves oval to ovate, very variable in size and from ¾ to 2 ins. long by ⅓ to 1 in. wide, rounded or

nearly so at the base, bluntish at the apex, minutely toothed on the margins
and slightly bristly on midrib and veins beneath; stalk ⅙ to ⅓ in. long, downy
and bristly. Flowers solitary, white or yellowish white, ¾ in. wide; lobes
five, rounded, spreading widely from the short tube, freely dotted with red at
the base; stamens five, very unequal, the three lower ones glabrous or nearly
so, the other two much shorter and nearly covered with bristles; calyx with
five ovate lobes 1/12 in. long, glandular and bristly like the short flower-stalk;
ovary globose, bristly on the upper half style, glabrous.

Native of Japan, originally introduced to the Botanic Garden at St
Petersburg. In 1914, Wilson sent seeds to the Arnold Arboretum from which
plants were raised. Botanically it is very distinct and interesting with considerable affinities to Azalea. In the " Species of Rhododendron " it constitutes, in itself, a series. As a garden plant it has little to recommend it,
being evidently not easy to grow.

R. SEROTINUM, *Hutchinson*
(Bot. Mag., t. 8841)

An evergreen shrub of loose straggling habit; young shoots and leaves
glabrous. Leaves oval-oblong, rounded to shallowly cordate at the base,
rounded and mucronate at the apex; 3 to 7 ins. long, 1¼ to 2¾ ins. wide;
dull green above, rather glaucous beneath; stalk ¾ to 1½ ins. long. Truss
composed of six to eight flowers which are fragrant. Corolla 3 to 3½ ins. wide,
funnel-shaped at the base, seven-lobed, the lobes spreading, notched in the
middle, white flushed with rose and glandular outside, blotched and stained
with red inside the funnel. Stamens fourteen to sixteen, of unequal length,
their stalks white and downy at the base; anthers pale brown. Ovary and
style glandular. Calyx small, ⅓ in. wide, with shallow rounded lobes; flower-
stalk slightly glandular, 1 to 1¾ ins. long.

Native of W. China; although no longer there it was introduced to Kew
from the Jardin des Plantes, Paris, in 1889. It came as R. decorum and
remained under that name until the true decorum of Wilson's introduction
flowered and showed the differences. The real decorum, as is now well known,
is a sturdy, compact bush; serotinum is so lanky and so loth to branch that a
plant was trained up a pillar at Kew as a sort of climber. The blotch at the
base of the corolla and the reddish stains are further distinctions. Lastly it
flowers in September, a fact which explains its specific name. Otherwise the
two are very much alike in their blossom. It is quite hardy and gives a noble
truss of blossom as the figure above quoted shows. (Fortunei series.)

R. SERPYLLIFOLIUM, *Miquel*
(Bot. Mag., t. 7503 ; Azalea serpyllifolia, *A. Gray*)

A low evergreen azalea, perhaps 2 or 3 ft. high, with the slender wiry stems
covered thickly with appressed, linear, dark brown bristles, that point towards
the end of the shoot. Leaves narrowly oval or obovate, ¼ to ¾ in. long, ⅛ to ¼
in. wide; dark green, and thinly furnished above and on the margins with
bristly hairs, paler and with a few bristles beneath, base tapering to a very
short stalk. Flowers mostly solitary at the end of short twigs, ¾ in. across,
pale rose, or almost white; corolla with five oblong lobes; stamens five, calyx
and ovary bristly. Blossoms in May.

Native of Japan. This quaint and pretty little shrub, an ally of R. indicum,
is not often seen, as it is scarcely hardy in the London district. The ideal
place for it would be some ledge in a rock garden in the milder localities of

the south and west. It is distinguished among the " indica " group of azaleas by its tiny evergreen foliage, and thin, straggling branches.

R. SETOSUM, *Don*

(Bot. Mag., t. 8523)

A dwarf evergreen shrub, 6 to 12 ins. high, of close, bushy habit ; young shoots densely clothed with pale bristles and minute down. Leaves oblong, tapered at the base, rounded at the apex, ⅜ to ⅝ in. long, bristly on the margins, very scaly above, rather glaucous and less scaly beneath. Flowers three to eight in a terminal cluster ; corolla 1 in. across, reddish purple, lobed to two-thirds of its depth ; calyx comparatively large, scaly and downy, with five ovate lobes ¼ in. long ; stamens ten, hairy at the base ; flower-stalk scaly, slender, ¼ in. long.

Native of the Himalaya up to 16,000 ft. The plant is very distinct in its bristly character and strong resinous odour. Introduced in 1825, this curious alpine species is now very rare. It thrives well in the Edinburgh Botanic Garden, but in the south misses its winter covering of snow, and is often excited into growth too early.

R. SHEPHERDII, *Nuttall*

(Bot. Mag., t 5125)

It seems doubtful if the real R. Shepherdii be now in cultivation, but as plants under the name exist in gardens and as the name itself is familiar to rhododendron lovers, a few words may be given to it. The true plant was discovered in 1852 on the Oola Mountains in Bhotan by Booth, on the notable journey during which he found R. Nuttallii, Boothii, and Hookeri. Nuttall, when describing the various new species of the journey, was only able to put on record the characters of the leaves and leaf-buds of Shepherdii. According to the *Botanical Magazine* of 1859, the figure which appeared there was made from a plant which Nuttall himself had flowered at Nutgrove in Cheshire. As no authentic specimen of the wild R. Shepherdii appears to exist in the leading herbaria, this figure must be regarded as the base on which this rhododendron as a species stands.

The cultivated R. Shepherdii I only know through having seen it at Kilmacurragh, Co. Wicklow. It was then a healthy bush about 12 ft. high, its leaves oblong or oblanceolate, narrowed abruptly at the apex to a short point, 4 to 6 ins. long, 1 to 2 ins. wide, brown and papillose beneath. Flowers opening in February or March in a compact hemispherical truss 4 ins. wide, the bell-shaped corolla 1½ ins. long and wide, five-lobed, and deep scarlet spotted with dark red on the upper lobes. Stamens ten, ½ to 1 in. long, glabrous. Ovary covered with erect bristles ; style quite glabrous. Calyx large, membranous, ⅝ in. wide, deeply five-lobed, the lobes unequal in size, ¼ in. or more deep, glabrous, margins jagged.

The Kilmacurragh rhododendron is very handsome and is evidently related to barbatum, especially in the red flowers, the glabrous stamens and style, the bristly ovary and large membranous jagged calyx ; but it has neither the deeply impressed leaf-veins nor the bristly leaf-stalks of that species. The rhododendron figured in the *Botanical Magazine* differs chiefly in the ovary which is described as glabrous. Mr H. F. Tagg has placed it in the Irroratum " series."

R. SIDEROPHYLLUM, *Franchet*

An evergreen shrub, 4 to 9 ft. high; young wood slightly scaly. Leaves aromatic, oval-lanceolate, tapering about equally to each end; 1½ to 2½ ins. long, ⅜ to ⅝ in. wide; bright green and slightly scaly above, paler and scaly beneath, the scales yellowish; stalk ⅛ in. long. Flowers 1¼ to 1½ ins. across, of a pale blush tint with two groups of dark brown spots on the upper side, produced during May in terminal and axillary clusters of six to eight; corolla flat, open, short-tubed; two lower lobes deeper than the upper ones; stamens ten, pinkish white, hairy at the base, anthers dark red; ovary scaly; style 1¼ ins. long, glabrous; flower-stalk ¾ in. long, scaly.

Native of W. China; introduced by Wilson in 1904. It belongs to the same group as yunnanense, and its flowers are equally pretty. But the leaves are never bristly above, as they often are in yunnanense, they are more scaly beneath, the stamens are not so much protruded beyond the corolla as in that species; the flowers are smaller and earlier. It frequently produces a considerable number of flower-clusters densely packed at the end of the shoot.

R. SIMSII, *Planchon*. "INDIAN" AZALEA

(R. indicum, *Hort.*; Azalea indica, *Sims*, not *Linnæus*)

To this species belong almost all the common azaleas of greenhouses, of which there are now so many varieties with single or double flowers varying in colour from pure white to rose and scarlet; they are mostly grown under the name of "indicum." These varieties are rather outside the province of this work, although many of them can be grown in the open air in the mildest parts of the country. According to Wilson the typical R. Simsii grows throughout the temperate parts of China and in South Formosa. He says "it delights in rocky places, preferably cliffs, thin dry woods and thickets, its wealth of flowers making it one of the most conspicuous of all shrubs."

It is an evergreen bush up to 5 (occasionally 7 or 8) ft. high, and of twiggy habit; young shoots clothed with appressed, flattened, forward-pointing hairs. Leaves lanceolate to narrowly obovate or narrowly elliptical; 1½ to 3½ ins. long, ⅓ to ¾ in. wide; dark green, bristly on both surfaces. Flowers opening in May in clusters of usually two or three, sometimes more; corolla funnel-shaped, 2 to 3 ins. wide, rosy red to dark red. Stamens normally ten, rarely eight, never fewer; ovary bristly, style glabrous. Calyx variable and said by Wilson to be sometimes merely an inconspicuous rim, sometimes ¼ in. long, the margins ciliate.

R. Simsii is very much confused with R. indicum in botanical and horticultural literature and nearly always the plants in cultivation are known by the latter name. The true R. indicum is a very rare plant in gardens, but is readily distinguished by having only five stamens to a flower; it is, moreover, a native only of Japan. There are dried specimens of R. Simsii at Kew collected in the orangery in the Jardin du Luxembourg, Paris, in 1822 and 1823, which seem to be the oldest known in this country. Single-flowered forms with red flowers are growing well in Cornish gardens. Neither the species nor any of its varieties is hardy near London. Wilson observes that up to about 1845 forms of indicum were more plentiful in gardens than those of Simsii, but that from 1850 onwards the former rapidly dropped out of cultivation, their place being taken by the latter, which at the present time constitute almost the whole of the so-called "Indian azaleas" in gardens. Their cultivation is an important industry in Belgium. The modern varieties have leaves and flowers very much larger than occur in the wild type.

The spray with a red flower figured in the *Botanical Magazine*, t. 1480, as " Azalea indica " has ten stamens and is really R. Simsii.

R. SINENSE, *Sweet*

(Azalea sinensis, *Loddiges*)

Under R. molle (*q.v.*) the differences between it and R. sinense are pointed out. The present species is confined to China, and is much less common in cultivation and perhaps not so hardy. It is a deciduous shrub, the young twigs and the under-surface of the leaves being covered with a dense velvet-like felt. Leaves up to 4½ ins. long and 1¼ ins. wide, green or glaucous beneath. Flowers yellow of various shades. Fortune introduced this shrub in 1845 (it had previously been brought to England in 1824), and is very eloquent of its beauty as seen wild in China, especially on the hills about Ningpo, where, he wrote, " the yellow Azalea sinensis seemed to paint the hill sides, so large were the flowers, so vivid the colours." The true plant is now very uncommon, but hybrids between it and molle are abundant.

R. SINOGRANDE, *Balfour and W. W. Smith.* (Plate 15)

(Bot. Mag., t. 8973)

An evergreen shrub or a tree up to 35 ft. high, the young shoots silvery grey, very stout, and up to 1 in. thick. Leaves oval or oblong, occasionally obovate, rounded at both ends ; ordinarily 10 to 20 ins. long, 6 to 12 ins. wide ; at first grey scurfy above, ultimately dark green and glabrous, silvery grey beneath with a closely appressed scurf, not downy or hairy in the ordinary sense of those words ; midrib very prominent beneath as are also the fourteen to sixteen pairs of roughly parallel veins springing from it ; stalk very stout (up to ½ in. thick) 1 to 2 ins. long. Flowers in a racemose truss of twenty to thirty, and about 9 ins. wide. Corolla bell-shaped, fleshy, dull creamy white to soft yellow, marked with red patches at the base, 2 ins. wide, eight- to ten-lobed, the lobes ¾ in. wide, notched. Stamens eighteen or twenty, downy towards the base, shorter than the corolla. Ovary covered with reddish down ; style glabrous ; stigma ⅖ in. wide. Calyx woolly, fringed with small teeth ; flower-stalks 1½ ins. long, densely woolly.

Native of W. Yunnan (China), N.E. Burma, and S.E. Tibet ; discovered and introduced by Forrest in 1912-13. Botanically this is the Chinese representative of the Himalayan R. grande, but in leaf, at any rate, it is a much finer species and in that respect the most splendid and remarkable of all rhododendrons. In the Cornish woods, where it first faced the English climate, it is now growing extraordinarily well, and leaves 2⅓ ft. long and 1 ft. or more wide have been produced. It first flowered at Heligan in May 1919, and the flowers strongly resemble those of grande but differ in not having club-shaped, sticky glands on flower-stalk and ovary. The species will survive mild winters at Kew but is probably not worth struggling with there in the open air. As it has been found at 14,000 ft. altitude, the hardier forms (No. 20387 of Forrest is said to be one) should succeed in Hampshire and Sussex, even in the inland parts ; also in the warmer parts of Surrey. But probably, to see it at its best, we shall always have to go to the south and west or places with a similar climate.

Var. BOREALE, a northern form, is described as having a corolla " soft yellow throughout without markings, or pale yellow with a crimson blotch at the base."

R. SMIRNOWI, *Trautvetter*

(Bot. Mag., t. 7495)

A sturdy evergreen shrub, 4 to 6 ft. high in cultivation, usually wider than it is high, but described in a wild state as a tree-like shrub 15 to 20 ft. high ; young shoots thick, and clothed with a soft white felt. Leaves narrowly oblong, tapered at the base, blunt at the apex ; 4 to 7 ins. long, 1 to 2 ins. wide ; thick and leathery, dark green, soon becoming glabrous above ; lower surface covered with a thick, soft felt, at first almost pure white, finally pale brown ; stalk ¼ to ¾ in. long. Flowers bright purplish rose, 2 to 3 ins. across, produced during May in fine trusses 5 or 6 ins. through ; corolla broadly funnel-shaped, the five rounded lobes with beautifully frilled margins ; calyx very small, with five rounded lobes ; flower-stalks 1 to 1½ ins. long, slightly downy.

Native of the South Caucasus, where it was discovered by Baron Ungern-Sternberg in 1885, and introduced to Kew the following year. The species is distinct because of the very thick white felt on the lower surface of the leaf, resembling in this respect R. Ungerni (*q.v.*) and R. niveum. It is a very hardy species, and should be given a trial where only the hardiest evergreens thrive. By hybridisation it may produce a useful race of very hardy varieties.

R. SOULIEI, *Franchet*

(Bot. Mag., t. 8622 ; Gardeners' Chronicle, 1909, i., fig. 167 (and supplement))

An evergreen bush, 5 to 10 ft. high ; young shoots purplish, they and flower-stalks glandular and viscid. Leaves 2 to 3½ ins. long, 1 to 2 ins. wide ; broadly ovate, with a heart-shaped base and a blunt, glandular tip ; of a distinct glaucous, somewhat metallic hue, quite glabrous on both surfaces ; stalk glandular when young, ½ to ¾ in. long. Flowers in a terminal cluster (about six on each) white or beautiful pale rose, 2 to 3 ins. in diameter ; the corolla very open and saucer-shaped, five- or six-lobed ; calyx about ½ in. across, with five unequal, oblong blunt lobes, purplish green, thickly clothed outside and on the margins with dark glands ; stamens eight or ten ; ovary and style glandular ; flower-stalks 1½ to 2 ins. long.

Native of W. China ; introduced by Wilson for Messrs Veitch in 1905, from near Tatien-lu, where, at altitudes of 9000 to 10,000 ft., it is found entirely covering large areas. It flowers in early and mid-May, and commences to bloom at four years old from seed. Apparently very hardy and a charming addition to cultivated rhododendrons ; distinct on account of its glaucous, heart-shaped foliage and flat, saucer-shaped flowers.

R. SPECIOSUM, *Sweet*

(Azalea speciosa, *Willdenow* ; A. nudiflora coccinea, *Aiton* ; Bot. Mag., t. 180)

A deciduous azalea up to 6 ft. high ; young shoots finely downy and bristly. Leaves obovate, oval, or oblong ; 1½ to 2½ ins. long, half as much wide ; upper surface bristly, lower one finely downy with bristles on the midrib ; margins bristly ; stalk ⅛ in. long. Flowers opening in April and May, up to as many as fifteen in a truss. Corolla funnel-shaped, about 1¾ ins. long, the tube slender, cylindric, and downy outside ; scarlet or bright red with an orange-coloured blotch on the upper lobe. Stamens five, 2 ins. long, downy below the middle. Ovary clothed with bristly, not glandular hairs ; style 2 ins. or more long, downy at the base. Calyx with five very small, ciliate, ovate or oblong lobes. Flower-stalks bristly.

Native of the S.E. United States from Georgia to S. Carolina. This, the most brilliantly coloured of all American azaleas, was in cultivation as long ago as 1789, and was figured in the *Botanical Magazine* in 1792. Old plants may still be in gardens, but the name appears to have been lost. It was in cultivation at Kew in 1881 as " Azalea nudiflora coccinea." Plants were sent to England by Professor Sargent in 1916, as " R. flammeum." It has been confused with R. calendulaceum, but differs in the slender corolla-tube which is not glandular as it is in that species. The flowers also are more numerous in the truss, and the colour " is always scarlet or bright red and never varies to yellow " (Rehder). R. calendulaceum is a more northern shrub and hardier, but, as may be gathered from what is stated above, R. speciosum is quite hardy in this country. No doubt many of our richest coloured deciduous azaleas owe much of their vivid red and scarlet hues to this species.

R. SPERABILE, *Balfour and Farrer*

(Bot. Mag., t. 9301 ; Gardeners' Chronicle, 16th May 1925, fig. 144)

An evergreen shrub 3 to 5 ft. high of stiff habit ; young shoots clothed with loose and (at first) white wool and glandular bristles. Leaves lanceolate or narrowly elliptic, sharply pointed ; 2 to 4 ins. long, ½ to 1¼ ins. wide ; dark green and becoming glabrous above, covered beneath with a thick loose wool which is at first dull white, later reddish brown, and persists till the leaf falls ; stalk ¼ to ½ in. long, woolly and glandular like the young shoot. Flowers in a terminal hemispherical truss 3 ins. wide, opening in May. Corolla bell-shaped, clear scarlet, about 1½ ins. long and wide, five-lobed. Stamens ten, 1 to 1½ ins. long, glabrous ; ovary slender, tapered, thickly clothed like the lower part of the style with glandular hairs. Calyx small, shallowly five-lobed, glandular ; flower-stalk ⅜ in. long, woolly and glandular.

Native of S.E. Tibet ; discovered and introduced by Farrer in 1919. A good truss of it was shown at Westminster by Mr Lionel de Rothschild in May 1925, when the species was given an Award of Merit. It had been grown at Exbury, Hants, where there is a fine muster of plants succeeding admirably and giving flowers of different shades of red. It has flowered out-of-doors at Kew, but prefers a softer climate.

R. SPERABILOIDES, *Tagg and Forrest.* — Resembling the above in general appearance this differs in having no glands on the ovary, leaf-stalk and young shoots. The stamens also are hairy at the base. Flowers of various shades of crimson, borne in trusses of six to ten flowers, the corolla 1 to 1½ ins. long. Native of S.E. Tibet, up to elevations of 13,000 ft., discovered by Forrest in 1921. I saw some very handsome forms in bloom at Exbury in early April 1933. Both these species are placed in the Neriiflorum series.

R. SPINULIFERUM, *Franchet*

(Bot. Mag. t. 8408)

An evergreen shrub, 3 to 8 ft. high, the young shoots covered with pale hairs and bristles. Leaves lanceolate or oblanceolate, pointed at the apex, wedge-shaped at the base ; 1½ to 2¼ ins. long, ½ to ¾ in. wide ; somewhat hooded and puckered above, with a few hairs near the margin, scaly and hairy beneath ; stalk ¼ in. long. Flowers pale pink to bright red, in a few-flowered cluster ; corolla tubular, about 1 in. long and ½ in. wide, the five ovate lobes being erect or pressing inwards round the ten glabrous stamens which protrude about ¼ in. beyond them. Calyx very short, downy ; flower-stalks downy, ¼ in. long. Ovary and base of style downy. Flowers in April.

Native of Yunnan, China ; discovered by the Abbé Delavay, and introduced to France by Mr Maurice de Vilmorin in 1907, thence to Kew in 1910. The fears at first expressed as to its probable tenderness have not been borne out by experience. At Kew it has proved to be quite hardy. In the tubular shape of the corolla, which narrows rather than expands towards the mouth the species resembles the rare R. Keysii.

RHODODENDRON SPINULIFERUM

R. SPINULOSUM, *W. Watson*

A hybrid between R. spinuli-ferum and R. racemosum, raised at Kew in 1914. It is a pleasing evergreen bush intermediate in most respects between the two parents. Leaves oval, 1 to 1½ ins. long, dark green and speckled with dark scales above, rather glaucous and very scaly beneath. In their hard texture they take after spinuliferum, but in scaliness are nearer racemosum. Flowers arranged in clusters of about four in the axils of several of the terminal leaves. Corolla funnel-shaped, the five lobes neither reflexed nor incurved, pink at first, becoming nearly pure white, ⅝ in. long. Stamens white, ten ; anthers brown, standing out ¼ in. beyond the corolla and giving the plant a characteristic and unusual appearance when in bloom. Style slightly longer than the stamens. This hybrid is quite hardy and flowers in April. It seems to show that from R. spinuliferum a distinct race of hybrids can be raised well marked by a narrow deep corolla and conspicuous stamens.

R. STAMINEUM, *Franchet*

(Bot. Mag., t. 8601 ; R. pittosporæfolium, *Hemsley*)

An evergreen shrub 6 to 15 ft. high ; young shoots glabrous, slender, brown. Leaves clustered at the end of the twig, narrowly oval to oblanceolate, abruptly but sharply pointed, tapered at the base, of stiff texture ; 2 to 4 ins. long, 1 to 1½ ins. wide ; dark shining green above, paler beneath, quite glabrous ; stalk ¼ to ½ in. long. Flowers fragrant, produced in April or May in clusters of three or four, each cluster springing from an axil of one of the leaves which are crowded near the end of the shoot. Corolla white, stained with yellow on the three upper lobes, funnel-shaped with a slender tube, spreading into five recurved lobes, and 1 to 2 ins. wide. Stamens ten, 1½ to 2 ins. long, standing out far beyond the corolla, with some white down near the base. Ovary glabrous or slightly downy ; style rather longer than the stamens and quite glabrous. Calyx with five glabrous, narrow, bluntish lobes up to ⅛ in. long; flower-stalk ¾ in. long.

Native of W. Hupeh, Szechuen, and Yunnan, China ; discovered by Delavay in 1882 and introduced by Wilson in 1900. It is the type species of a " series," uncommon in cultivation, tender and not always easy to manage. The best plant in the country is a bush at Caerhays which, as I remember it, was some 8 or 9 ft. high and grew on a steep, unshaded slope exposed to the east. It is a well-marked species amongst the generally cultivated ones in its glabrous parts, stiff glossy foliage, and white scented flowers with long stamens and slightly longer style. Wilson, who found it 20 ft. and upwards high, observes that although widely distributed it is nowhere common and affects mostly rocky shady ravines. The clustering of several inflorescences at the end of the shoot, with a total of ten or a dozen flowers, gives a fine effect.

R. STEWARTIANUM, *Diels*

(R. aiolosalpinx, *Balfour fil. and Farrer* ; R. nipholobum, *Balfour fil. and Farrer*)

An evergreen shrub up to 7 ft. high, young shoots glabrous. Leaves obovate to oval, 2 to 4½ ins. long, more or less rounded at both ends, grey-green above and at first with a powdery yellowish indumentum beneath ; stalk about ¼ in. long. Flowers in trusses of three to seven, opening in March and April. Corolla broadly funnel-shaped, 1¾ ins. long and wide, with five rounded, notched lobes ; the colour, according to Farrer, ranging from " cream and pure white through all flushes and shades of pink to rich deep rose " ; another collector found plants with " scarlet red " flowers, and others are described as " deep crimson." Stamens ten, downy at the base ; ovary glandular ; style glabrous. Calyx glabrous, five-lobed.

Native of N.E. Burma, S.E. Tibet, and W. Yunnan ; originally discovered by Forrest in 1904. It flowered for the first time in the spring of 1930 at Exbury, Logan, and Bodnant. As it is described as inhabiting altitudes up to 14,000 ft. it should be pretty hardy. It is remarkably variable in the colour of its flowers and Farrer found, on one area, plants growing together bearing flowers of nearly all the shades mentioned above. In some plants the colour is deepest nearest the margin of the corolla, paling downwards. It belongs to the Thomsonii series and closely related to it is

R. CERASINUM, *Tagg*.—An evergreen bush up to 10 or 12 ft. high ; leaves 2 or 3 ins. long, half as much wide, rounded at both ends. Flowers pendulous, six to eight in a truss. Corolla bell-shaped, 1½ to 2 ins. long, " creamy white with a broad cherry-red band round the summit, or cherry-red, or brilliant scarlet " (Tagg). Calyx densely glandular ; stamens ten, nowhere downy ; anthers reddish brown. Native of S.E. Tibet and very distinct in its group in having a style glandular all over.

R. STRIGILLOSUM, *Franchet*
(Bot. Mag., t. 8864)

An evergreen shrub or small tree, up to 20 ft. high, the young shoots and leaf-stalks clothed thickly with stiff, pale, gland-tipped bristles, ⅙ in. long, which persist partially through the first winter. Leaves narrowly oblong-lanceolate, slender-pointed, heart-shaped at the base ; 3 to 6 ins. long, ¾ to 1½ ins. wide ; dull green and glabrous above, clothed with brown hairs beneath, especially on the midrib ; stalk ¼ to ⅜ in. long. Flowers rich red, bell-shaped, 1½ to 2 ins. long and wide ; stamens ten, perfectly glabrous. Flower-stalk, calyx, and seed-pod bristly like the branchlets.

Native of W. China and Tibet ; introduced by Wilson for Messrs Veitch in 1904. A striking plant because of the bristliness of the various parts. The rich red flowers should make it welcome if it will thrive, but whilst young at least it is rather spring tender. Wilson observes that the flowers vary from crimson to pure white. It flowers in March.

R. SUBEROSUM, *Balfour fil. and Forrest*

An evergreen shrub up to 9 ft. high; young shoots slightly scaly. Leaves narrowly lanceolate, pointed, 1½ to 3 ins. long, ¼ to ⅝ in. wide; margins decurved and edged with bristles, tapered at the base to a stalk ¼ in. or less long. Flowers in a cluster of two- or three-flowered umbels at the top of the twig, opening in May. Corolla ¾ to 1 in. long and 1 to 1¼ ins. wide, with five oblong-oval lobes; pale rose with deeper coloured markings, thinly scaly outside, downy within. Calyx small, scaly outside, the margins thickly set with long pale bristles; stamens ten, downy towards the base, style glabrous.

Native of Yunnan, China, where it was found at 12,000 to 13,000 ft. altitude by Forrest flowering in May 1919, and was afterwards introduced by him. It is one of the Triflorum-yunnanense series and quite a worthy member thereof. Its chief distinguishing features are the stiff bristles on the calyx and leaf-margins; in the latter case the bristles, with age, break or wear away and leave a rough, or erose, edge to which the specific name refers. The plant is usually very leafy.

R. SULFUREUM, *Franchet*

(Bot. Mag., t. 8946)

An evergreen shrub 2 to 4 ft. high; young shoots sprinkled with glands. Leaves leathery, oval, tapering to a short stalk at the base, abruptly pointed and with a mucro at the apex; 1½ to 3 ins. long, ¾ to 1½ ins. wide; dark dull green and glabrous above, glaucous and with numerous small scales beneath. Flowers closely packed in compact terminal clusters of four to eight, opening in April. Corolla rather flat and open but bell-shaped at the base, about 1 in. wide, bright yellow, faintly-spotted inside, scaly outside, five-lobed, the lobes roundish ovate, ⅜ in. wide. Stamens ten, ⅜ in. long, densely clad with white hairs at the base; anthers large, reddish brown. Ovary scaly; style glabrous, ¼ in. long, abruptly bent over. Calyx scaly, deeply five-lobed, the lobes ⅛ in. long, rounded at the end; flower-stalks ½ to ⅝ in. long, scaly.

Native of Yunnan, China, at altitudes of 9000 to 10,000 ft., discovered by Delavay in 1886; introduced by Forrest in 1905, who found it on " moist shady ledges of cliffs on the eastern flank of the Tali Range." It flowered at Caerhays, Cornwall, in April 1920. It has been placed in the Boothii series, notable characteristics of which are the usually yellow flowers and short, thick, curved style (leucaspis, however, has white flowers and tephropeplum rose and purple ones). It is scarcely hardy enough for our average climate.

R. SUTCHUENENSE, *Franchet*

(Bot. Mag., t. 8362)

A stout, evergreen shrub, eventually 10 ft. high; young shoots very thick (½ in. or rather more in diameter), covered with a greyish floss. Leaves 6 to 10 ins. long, 1½ to 2½ ins. wide; tapering at both ends, more gradually towards the base, dark green and glabrous above, paler and also glabrous beneath except on the midrib, which is slightly downy; stalk 1 in. long, stout, yellowish, and wrinkled. Flowers 3 ins. across, rosy lilac with purple spots on the upper side, produced in March in terminal clusters 6 or 8 ins. across. Corolla five-lobed, open bell-shaped; calyx glabrous, with five broad, abruptly pointed lobes; stamens twelve to fifteen, downy near the base; anthers very dark; flower-stalk about 1 in. long.

Native of W. Hupeh, China; introduced for Messrs Veitch by Wilson, in 1901. This species, which flowers when quite small, is one of the finest and most striking of Chinese rhododendrons. It first flowered in the Coombe Wood nursery in March 1910. This early flowering renders it liable to injury by spring frosts. Allied to R. calophytum.

R. TAGGIANUM, *Hutchinson*

(Bot. Mag., t. 9612 ; Gardeners' Chronicle, 17th May 1930, fig. 160)

An evergreen shrub 6 to 7 ft. high ; young shoots scaly. Leaves oblong-elliptical, tapered at both ends ; 3 to 6 ins. long, 1 to 2 ins. wide ; glaucous and with numerous tiny dark scales beneath ; stalk ½ to 1 in. long, not grooved. Flowers usually three or four in a cluster, very fragrant. Corolla pure glistening white except for a pale yellow blotch at the base inside, funnel-shaped, five-lobed, 3 to 4 ins. long and wide. Stamens ten, 2 ins. long, downy on the lower half. Ovary densely scaly ; style as long as the stamens, scaly on the lowest third. Calyx large, ⅝ to ¾ in. long, deeply five-lobed, the lobes oval, ⅓ to ½ in. wide ; flower-stalk ¾ in. long, very scaly. Seed-vessel 2 ins. long, glandular, the calyx persisting at the base.

Native of N.E. Burma ; discovered and introduced by Forrest in 1925-6, soon after by Kingdon Ward. It belongs to the megacalyx section of the Maddenii series which is characterised by the large calyx, and is itself distinguished by the combination of its glandular seed-vessel, its narrow leaves, its scaly but not hairy flower-stalks, with the absence of scales on the corolla except at the base. It flowered for the first time in the Edinburgh Botanic Garden in May 1930 (under glass), the plant, which had been raised from Forrest's 1925 seed, being then only 18 ins. high. As it grows at altitudes of 10,000 to 11,000 ft., it should be hardy in the maritime parts of the south and south-west. It is a valuable member of a beautiful group. A plant shown at Westminster by the Marquis of Headfort on 5th April 1932 received an Award of Merit. It had been brought into early flower under glass.

R. TALIENSE, *Franchet*

An evergreen shrub, up to 10 ft. high ; young shoots clothed with pale scurfy down. Leaves thick and leathery, oblong to oval, 2 to 4 ins. long, ¾ to 1¾ ins. wide ; rounded or slightly auricled at the base, abruptly narrowed at the apex to a short fine point ; dark green and glabrous above, clothed beneath with a close rusty-brown felt ; stalk stout, ½ in. long, scurfy-downy. Flowers six to twelve in a truss, the corolla blush-white, about 1¼ ins. wide and deep ; stamens ten, downy at the base ; ovary glabrous ; calyx small, with rounded ovate lobes.

Discovered in Yunnan, China, by the Abbé Delavay ; introduced by Wilson from Szechuen in 1903. Notable for its very densely woolly leaf-stalks and flower-stalks.

R. TANASTYLUM, *Balfour fil. and Ward*

An evergreen shrub varying from 8 to 20 ft. high in a wild state ; young shoots soon becoming glabrous. Leaves elliptic-lanceolate or oblanceolate, tapered about equally towards both ends but terminated by a short slender point ; 3 to 5½ ins. long, 1 to 1¾ ins. wide ; glabrous and green on both surfaces ; stalk ½ to ⅝ in. long. Flowers borne during May in a racemose cluster of about eight. Corolla funnel-shaped, 2 ins. long, 1½ ins. wide, deep crimson with darker spots, five-lobed, the lobes notched. Stamens ten, glabrous or slightly downy at the base ; ovary and style glabrous, the latter much longer than the stamens and standing out well beyond the corolla. Calyx small, a mere wavy rim ; flower-stalk ⅓ to ½ in. long.

Native of E. Upper Burma ; discovered by Kingdon Ward in 1914. This is one of the most richly coloured of the Irroratum series and in its narrow, hard-textured, sharply pointed leaves resembles anthosphærum, araiophyllum and irroratum. Probably only really hardy in the south and west. The combination of the long style with the narrow leaves and crimson blossom is distinctive in its own group.

R. TELMATEIUM, *Balfour fil. and W. W. Smith*

(R. vicarium, *Balfour fil.*)

An evergreen shrub of erect habit up to 3 ft. high ; young shoots very scurfy. Leaves elliptic-lanceolate, tapered about equally to both ends, ¼ to ½ in. long, 1/10 to 3/16 in. wide, dull dark green above, pale brown below, very scaly on both sides ; stalk 1/16 in. long. Flowers solitary or it may be in pairs, opening in May. Corolla widely funnel-shaped, ½ in. wide, five-lobed, rosy purple, the lobes more or less scaly up the centre outside. Stamens normally ten, sometimes less, downy towards the base. Ovary scaly ; style glabrous. Calyx very small, scaly ; flower-stalk ⅓ in. long, scaly.

Native of Yunnan, up to 12,000 ft. altitude ; discovered and introduced by Forrest in 1914. This is a dainty species belonging to the Lapponicum " series " in which it is distinct in the combination of the following characters : the small size of its leaves, the corolla being scaly outside, the calyx-lobes not being fringed, and the erect habit. It is very hardy and makes a pleasant evergreen for the rock garden.

R. TEPHROPEPLUM, *Balfour fil. and Farrer*

(Bot. Mag., t. 9343 ; R. spodopeplum, *Balfour fil. and Farrer*)

A small evergreen shrub 2 to 4 ft. high ; young shoots scaly. Leaves oblong to obovate, rounded or pointed at the mucronate apex, mostly tapered at the base ; 1¼ to 2½ ins. long, ½ to 1 in. wide ; sprinkled with tiny black glands above, glaucous and very scaly beneath ; style ⅛ to ¼ in. long. Flowers opening in May usually in a truss of three or four. Corolla funnel-shaped, 1 to 1¼ ins. long and wide, varying from pale pink to rosy crimson and crimson purple, five-lobed, the lobes roundish ovate. Stamens ten, slightly downy at the base. Ovary densely scaly, deeply grooved ; style scaly towards the base. Calyx deeply five-lobed, the lobes membranous, ¼ in. long, rounded ; flower-stalk ½ to ¾ in. long, densely scaly like the base of the calyx.

Native of S.E. Tibet and N.E. Upper Burma ; discovered in the latter country by Farrer in 1920, but apparently not introduced by him. Its existence in gardens we owe to Forrest and Kingdon Ward. It has been assigned, evidently with some doubt, to the Boothii series, in which the colour of the flowers and the long, not curved style are anomalous. It is an attractive rhododendron, of which Mr L. de Rothschild said, " my opinion of it increases with each new variety of the species I see in flower." It is surmised that it is only likely to be a success in the maritime counties from Sussex and Hampshire westwards, although the altitude (14,000 ft.) at which Forrest found his No. 20884 would seem to promise hardiness. It grows on cliffs of limestone, probably of the magnesian variety. Plants raised from seed at Exbury have flowered when two years old. There is a white-flowered form.

R. Thayerianum, *Rehder and Wilson*

(Bot. Mag., t. 8983)

An evergreen shrub up to 12 ft. high in a wild state ; young shoots sticky and downy. Leaves crowded at the end of the shoot in a cluster of as many as twelve or more ; leathery, oblanceolate, tapered abruptly to a finely pointed apex and gradually towards the stalk, which is ⅛ to ½ in. long ; they are 2½ to 8 ins. long, ⅜ to 1¼ ins. wide ; bright green and ultimately glabrous above, covered beneath with a very close yellowish-brown felt. Flowers opening pink, turning white, with bands of rosy red running lengthwise ; ten to sixteen in a terminal raceme the main-stalk of which is 1 to 1½ ins. long, glandular ; the individual flower-stalks 1½ to 2 ins. long, slender, sticky with glands. Corolla five-lobed, funnel-shaped, about 1¼ ins. long and a little more wide. Stamens normally ten, their white stalks downy on the lower half, about 1 in. long ; anthers pale brown. Ovary and style very glandular. Calyx cupped, with five glandular roundish lobes ⅛ in. long.

Native of W. Szechuen, China ; discovered and introduced by Wilson in 1910. It is quite hardy at Kew, but grows slowly and flowers reluctantly. No doubt it prefers a warmer climate ; at Caerhays, for instance, I have measured a leaf 9 ins. long. The rather loose trusses of flowers, which open in June and July, are delicately tinted and very charming. This is a very well-marked species, especially in its long narrow leaves which persist on the branches for four or five years ; in the long slender flower-stalks which give the truss its loose appearance and a diameter of 6 ins. ; and in the sticky, glandular character of the young parts. It grows wild in woodlands. The Thayer family after whom it is named is an old and well-known one whose ancestral home is at Lancaster in Massachusetts. They generously supported the earlier Chinese expeditions. (Arboreum series.)

R. Thomsoni, *Hooker fil.*

(Bot. Mag., t. 4997)

An evergreen, glabrous shrub, up to 14 ft. high and more in diameter in the Cornish gardens. Leaves roundish oval, 2 to 4 ins. long, two-thirds as wide ; round at the apex except for a short, abrupt tip, and rounded or slightly heart-shaped at the base ; dark green above, blue-white below ; stalk about ¾ in. long. Flowers rich blood-red, 2 to 3 ins. across, produced in March in loose clusters, about six or seven together ; corolla open bell-shaped, five-lobed ; calyx unusually large, cup-shaped, ½ to ¾ in. across, ½ in. deep ; stamens ten, and like the ovary, glabrous.

Native of Nepal and Sikkim at 11,000 to 13,000 ft. ; introduced in 1849. It is hardy at Kew, but needs a sheltered position, and even then its flowers and young growths are very liable to injury by late frost. In the Cornish gardens it is magnificent. It is a very distinct species ; the large blood-red corolla, the extraordinarily large calyx, and the vividly glaucous under-surface of the leaves furnish three characters not united in any other species. It has been used to some extent by hybridists, and among its progeny are Luscombei (with Fortunei), Shilsoni (with barbatum), Harrisii (with arboreum), and " Ascot Brilliant " (with some garden variety). Of these, Luscombei, with soft rosy blossoms 3 ins. across produced in loose trusses in April ; and " Ascot Brilliant," raised by the late John Standish, with flowers of almost as brilliant a red as Thomsoni itself and produced early in May, are quite hardy.

R. TOSAENSE, *Makino*

(R. Komiyamæ, *Makino*)

A semi-deciduous, twiggy azalea usually from 3 to 5 ft. high ; young shoots very slender, clothed with appressed, flattened, forward-pointing hairs, of a grey or greyish-brown colour. Leaves lanceolate to oblanceolate, $\frac{1}{3}$ to $1\frac{1}{2}$ ins. long, $\frac{1}{16}$ to $\frac{2}{5}$ in. wide ; toothless, furnished on both surfaces with appressed hairs ; stalk very short. Flowers in clusters of two to six, or solitary, lilac-purple, $1\frac{1}{4}$ ins. wide. Stamens five to ten, shorter than the corolla, downy at the base ; ovary bristly ; style glabrous. Seed-vessel egg-shaped, $\frac{1}{3}$ in. long, covered with appressed hairs, the calyx persisting at the base.

Native of Japan, in the province of Tosa, up to 3000 ft. altitude. Wilson describes it as abundant on lower mountain slopes ; the colour of the flowers he regarded as unattractive, but the leaves change to purple-crimson in autumn. He collected seeds in 1914 which were distributed from the Arnold Arboretum ; it has not proved hardy in Massachusetts. It is interesting in producing two types of leaves ; those produced in spring up to the largest dimensions given above ; the summer leaves down to the smallest. The species is closely related to R. indicum, but that has never more than five stamens, has larger flowers and leaves, the latter minutely toothed.

R. TRICHOCLADUM, *Franchet*

(Bot. Mag., t. 9073 ; R. xanthinum, *Balfour fil. and W. W. Smith* ; R. brachystylum, *Balfour fil. and Ward*)

A deciduous or partly evergreen shrub up to 4 ft. high, with usually stiff erect branchlets, clothed their first and part of their second year with long, pale bristles. Leaves oblong to obovate and oval, often rounded at the apex ; 1 to $1\frac{1}{2}$ ins. long, $\frac{1}{3}$ to $\frac{3}{4}$ in. wide ; dark dull green and glabrous except for a few bristles above ; scaly beneath with bristles on the midrib when young ; margins bristly. Flowers as many as five in a terminal compact cluster, open in May. Corolla open and flattish, 1 to $1\frac{1}{4}$ ins. wide, yellow tinged with green, woolly in the throat, slightly scaly outside, five-lobed, the lobes rounded. Stamens ten, scarcely $\frac{1}{2}$ in. long, downy towards the base, anthers brown. Ovary scaly ; style glabrous, abruptly bent over. Calyx five-lobed, the lanceolate lobes $\frac{1}{8}$ in. long, fringed with long bristles; flower-stalk $\frac{1}{2}$ to $\frac{3}{4}$ in. long, scaly and very bristly.

Native of Yunnan, China ; discovered about 1884 by the Abbé Delavay ; introduced by Forrest in 1910. It is the representative species of its series, which consists of about ten species of a deciduous or semi-evergreen character and bearing yellow flowers. R. trichocladum is no great beauty, its growth being curiously stiff ; still its soft yellow, flatly open flowers have some attractiveness. Forrest found it at 11,000 ft. altitude and upwards and it is quite hardy. Flowers frequently open in autumn. Two other species in this series may be mentioned, viz.,

R. MELINANTHUM, *Balfour fil. and Ward*, which is distinguished from trichocladum in the calyx not being as a rule fringed with hairs, and in the leaves soon becoming glabrous above.

R. RUBROLINEATUM, *Balfour fil. and Forrest*, whose flowers are " lined and flushed " with rose. Both have flowers yellow in the main. The first was found in E. Upper Burma by Ward, the second in N.W. Yunnan by Forrest.

R. TRIFLORUM, *Hooker fil.*

(Gardeners' Chronicle, 8th July 1882, fig. 9)

An evergreen shrub 6 to 10 ft. high with glabrous, red, peeling bark ; young shoots slender, glaucous, scaly. Leaves ovate-lanceolate, rounded at the base, sharply pointed ; 2 to 3 ins. long, 1 to 1¼ ins. broad, bright green and glabrous above, glaucous and thickly furnished with scales beneath ; stalk ¼ to ⅓ in. long. Flowers fragrant, opening in May and June, usually in threes, at the end of the shoot when young growths are pushing. Corolla pale yellow spotted with green, with a short funnel-shaped tube and five spreading oblong lobes giving the flower a diameter of 1½ to 2 ins., scaly outside. Stamens ten, ½ to 1 in. long, downy towards the base ; ovary scaly ; style longer than stamens. glabrous. Calyx small, shallowly undulated ; flower-stalks ½ to ⅞ in. long, Seed-vessel ⅜ to ½ in. long.

Native of the Sikkim Himalaya ; discovered and introduced by the younger Hooker about 1849. It just fails to be hardy at Kew, but twenty to fifty miles southwards, as at Leonardslee, it succeeds very well. It is not a showy plant, although the flowers are interesting in their unusual colour. The red, semi-transparent, loose bark is also attractive with sunlight behind it. It is the type species of a large group or " series," with mostly three flowers in a cluster (but occasionally four and frequently two), ten stamens downy near or at the base, and a glabrous style. A close ally is the Japanese R. Keiskei, a dwarfer quite hardy shrub whose leaf-stalks when young have bristly hairs on the margin.

R. TSARONGENSE, *Balfour fil. and Forrest*

An evergreen strongly aromatic shrub 1 to 2½ ft. high ; young shoots densely covered with scales ; leaf-bud scales soon falling. Leaves oval or inclined to oblong, tapered about equally to both ends, but with a mucro at the tip ; ½ to 1 in. long, ¼ to ⅜ in. wide ; dark, rather bright green and somewhat scaly above, thickly covered beneath with reddish scurf ; leaf-stalk ⅛ in. long. Flowers in a many-flowered, compact, hemispherical truss opening in spring. Corolla ¾ in. long, tubular and yellow below, spreading above into five rounded white lobes, downy outside, hairy in the tube. Stamens five, enclosed in the tube, finely downy at the base ; ovary scaly, dome-shaped ; style very short, stout, glabrous, with a broad flat stigma. Calyx ¼ in. long, five-lobed, the lobes unequal in length, fringed with hairs, finely downy outside ; flower-stalk ½ in. long.

Native of Tsarong, S.E. Tibet ; found by Forrest in July 1917, in open situations on cliffs and stony slopes at 14,000 ft. altitude. It is one of the small, hardy Anthopogon series in which it is distinguished by the following combination of characters : leaf-bud scales soon falling ; calyx scaly outside, densely ciliate ; corolla-tube yellow, scaly outside ; corolla-lobes white. The very short style and aromatic foliage are common to the whole group. (See also R. hypenanthum, which is the only species with persistent leaf scales.)

R. TSCHONOSKII, *Maximowicz*

(Azalea Tschonoskii, *O. Kuntze*)

A semi-evergreen azalea, 2 ft. or perhaps more high, with rather horizontal branches, the young shoots covered with appressed, dark brown, linear bristles pointing towards the end of the shoot. Leaves in a tuft at the end of the twig ; ½ to 1½ ins. long, ⅛ to ⅝ in. wide, oval, tapering and pointed ; upper surface dull, dark green, lower one pale, both covered with bristly hairs. Flowers white, ¼ in. across, produced two to six together, each on a bristly stalk so short that the flower is almost hidden in the tuft of leaves ; corolla downy inside, funnel-shaped ; stamens five ; calyx covered with bristles.

Native of Japan ; introduced by Maries in 1878. This curious little azalea is of the same group as R. indicum, but is the most insignificant of them. It is only worth cultivating for the orange-red of its fading leaves. Propagated by cuttings. Flowers in May.

R. UNGERNII, *Trautvetter*

(Bot. Mag., t. 8332)

An evergreen shrub or small tree, up to 20 ft. high in a wild state ; young shoots downy. Leaves narrow oblong, 3 to 6 ins. long, one-third as wide ; tapering at the base, the apex ending in a short, abrupt point ; glabrous above, but covered beneath with pale brownish wool ; stalk ¾ in. long. Flowers white to pale rose, 1½ to 2 ins. across, in large trusses 6 ins. through. Corolla broadly bell-shaped, with five rounded, slightly notched lobes. Calyx-lobes five, lanceolate, covered with glandular hairs ; stamens ten, with gland-tipped hairs towards the base.

Native of the Caucasus ; introduced to cultivation in 1886 by way of the St Petersburg Botanic Garden, having been discovered the previous year by Baron Ungern-Sternberg. It has not yet been much cultivated out-of-doors, but is quite hardy. I have seen it growing outside in a nursery near Berlin, where the winters are much more trying for evergreens than ours. It was discovered and introduced at the same time as R. Smirnowi, with which it is often confounded. The leaves differ only in having the mucronate tip alluded to above ; the petals, however, are not frilled as in Smirnowi, the calyx-lobes are longer and more pointed, and the flower-stalks are very glandular-hairy. Blossoms in July.

R. VACCINIOIDES, *Hooker fil.*

(Bot. Mag., t. 9407 B)

A small, compact, evergreen shrub often found wild on trees growing as an epiphyte, or on rocks and only a few inches high. Shoots thickly set with leaves and rough with wart-like glands the first year, densely furnished with stalked glands the second. Leaves obovate to oblanceolate, with a notched, mucronate apex, tapering to a stout winged stalk ; ½ to 1¼ ins. long, ¼ to ⅓ in. wide, glabrous except for a few scattered scales. Flowers solitary or in pairs, terminal ; corolla pink, tubular at the base, ⅕ in. long, spreading at the mouth into five rounded lobes each ⅕ in. long, with scattered glandular scales outside ; stamens ten, hairy on the middle part only.

Native of the E. Himalaya, S.E. Tibet, and N. Burma, discovered in Sikkim by Sir Joseph Hooker in 1849 and later by Forrest in Tibet when he collected seeds. Afterwards Kingdon Ward found it in Burma. The *Bot. Mag.* figure was made from a plant flowered by the late Marquess of Headfort, who found it too tender for out-of-doors in Co. Meath but that it grew well in a shaded cold frame.

R. VALENTINIANUM, *Forrest*

An evergreen shrub 3 or 4 ft. high ; young shoots densely bristly and scaly beneath the bristles. Leaves oval inclined to oblong, 1½ to 2 ins. long, ¾ to 1 in. wide, pale green and bristly above, nearly covered with tawny scales beneath ; margins bristly ; leaf-stalks ¼ to ⅓ in. long, bristly and scaly. Flowers two to six in a close terminal cluster. Corolla bright yellow, between funnel- and bell-shaped, about 1½ ins. long, five-lobed, densely scaly outside. Stamens ten, with white hairs at the lower part ; anthers pink. Ovary and base of style scaly. Calyx ⅓ in. long, five-lobed, the lobes oblong, scaly outside and densely woolly-hairy on the margin. (Maddenii series.)

Native of Yunnan, China, at elevations of 11,000 ft.; discovered and introduced by Forrest in 1917. It is apparently most closely akin to R. ciliatum which, apart from its rose-tinted, white flowers, differs in the leaves having bristles on the midrib beneath and in the style being free from scales. The two are described as being very much alike in habit, but ciliatum is 6 to 9 ft. high in Cornwall. Sir Isaac Bayley Balfour wrote that R. Valentinianum should be " thoroughly hardy if grown under right conditions." So far as Edinburgh was concerned these conditions appear to be those which suit R. ciliatum so well there, namely, a place high up on the rock garden " in a shallow *col* between mounds where it will get every ray of sunshine available and a blow from every wind, an absence, in fact, of any coddling." As regards ciliatum this treatment is a great success, for although the plant there grows only 1 ft. high, it is dense in growth and covers itself every spring with blossom. R. Valentinianum is certainly one of the most attractive of yellow rhododendrons. Mr E. H. M. Cox tells me it is quite hardy at Glendoick, in the Tay valley below Perth. Flowers in April.

R. Vaseyi, *A. Gray*

(Bot. Mag., t. 8081 ; Azalea Vaseyi, *Rehder*)

A deciduous azalea, attaining heights of 12 to 15 ft. in a wild state, bushy. Leaves linear-oval, very tapering at both ends ; 2 to 4 ins. long, ½ to 1½ ins.

Rhododendron Vaseyi

wide ; at first sparsely bristly, becoming glabrous ; upper surface lustrous, hairy on the midrib and at the edges ; stalk ¼ in. or less long. Flowers 1½ ins. across, clear pale pink, produced before the leaves in early May, four to eight together in a terminal cluster ; corolla lobes oblong, the three upper ones spotted with red-brown at the base; calyx very small, with minute lobes, and covered with glands like the flower-stalk, which is ⅓ in. long ; stamens normally five, glabrous ; ovary glandular.

Native of the mountains of the Carolinas ; introduced to Kew in 1891 ; first discovered in 1878 by Mr G. R. Vasey on Balsam Mountain, N. Carolina. It is remarkable that so beautiful a shrub should so long have escaped notice. It is quite hardy, and can readily be raised from seed, which it ripens in plenty. Remarkably distinct from all other American azaleas, it bears a certain resemblance in the contour of the corolla to the R. reticulatum (N. Asiatic) group. It is worthy of a place in any garden. Among the seedlings raised at Kew was one with pure white flowers. It has been called var. ALBUM. Occasionally the stamens number seven.

R. VERNICOSUM, *Franchet*

(Bot. Mag., tt. 8834, 8904 ; R. adoxum, *Balfour fil. and Forrest* ; R. lucidum, *Franchet,* not *Nuttall*)

An evergreen shrub said occasionally to be 15 to 25 ft. high in a wild state ; but considerably less at present in cultivation ; young shoots glabrous. Leaves glabrous, oval to oblong-ovate, rounded at the base and abruptly narrowed to a mucro at the apex ; 2½ to 5 ins. long, about half as much wide ; dull green above, rather glaucous beneath ; stalk ¾ to 1¼ ins. long. Flowers not fragrant, opening in May in rather loose trusses of about ten. Corolla widely funnel-shaped, 2¼ ins. wide, pale clear rose, seven-lobed. Stamens fourteen, glabrous ; ovary densely glandular, the style also densely furnished over its whole length with dark red glands. Calyx small, fleshy, being only an unequal-sided development of the flower-stalk, which is about 1 in. long and glandular.

Native of Szechuen and Yunnan, China ; discovered by Soulié in 1893 ; introduced by Wilson in 1904. It belongs to the Fortunei series and is nearly related to decorum, discolor, and Fortunei. From decorum it is distinct in its lack of fragrance, in its funnel-shaped corolla and glabrous stamens, and from all of them by the remarkable red glands on the style. The finest plant I have seen in blossom grows in Mr Balfour's garden at Dawyck, near Peebles ; this was towards the end of May 1931. In this cold region it was in perfect health, some 7 or 8 ft. high and wide, and full of flower. The long styles, covered with dark red glands, were very conspicuous. The specific name, which means " varnished," seems very unfitted for a dull-leaved plant like this. But a varnished appearance can be developed by heating the surface of the leaf, which was, probably, what had been done by the collector when drying the original specimens on which Franchet based his description. For the colder parts of Britain, R. vernicosum can be strongly recommended ; it is much more beautiful than is suggested by the earlier *Botanical Magazine* plate.

R. VERRUCOLOSUM, *Rehder and Wilson*

An evergreen shrub 2 to 3 ft. high ; young shoots rough with scales. Leaves oval, ⅕ to ¾ in. long, ⅕ to ⅓ in. wide, dark green and thickly set with shining yellow scales above, more thinly scaly beneath ; stalk ⅛ in. long. Flowers solitary, with a very short scaly stalk. Corolla about 1 in. wide, purple, five-lobed, scaly outside ; stamens seven or eight with purple stalks about ⅓ in. long, downy near but not at the base ; anthers yellowish ; ovary densely scaly ; style purple, glabrous. Calyx deeply five-lobed, the lobes oval-oblong, blunt-ended, 1/10 in. long, edged with pale hairs, scaly outside.

Native of W. Szechuen, China ; discovered by Wilson in 1908 at altitudes of 10,000 ft. and upwards. It flowers there in June, but a month earlier with us. It is one of the numerous purple-flowered, scaly rhododendrons from

W. China that are so difficult to differentiate. Some of its distinctive characters are : stamens seven or eight, leaf-scales set well apart, and corolla lobes scaly outside. It is distinct also in the curious roughness of the young shoots due to the presence of short-stalked scales. A very hardy member of the Lap-ponicum series.

R. VILLOSUM, *Hemsley and Wilson*

(Bot. Mag., t. 8880)

An evergreen shrub, up to 18 ft. high ; branchlets slender, scaly, and clothed with pale bristles ⅛ in. long. Leaves scattered on the vigorous shoots, clustered at the end of weaker ones ; ovate or oblong, pointed, rounded or tapered at the base ; 2 to 3½ ins. long, ¾ to 1¼ ins. wide ; upper surface sparsely scaly, downy about the midrib, and freely sprinkled with pale, long bristles ; lower surface more scaly but less bristly, and downy only on and about the midrib ; stalk ⅛ to ¼ in. long, bristly. Flowers light to dark purple, 1½ to 1¾ ins. across, produced in clusters of three or more. Corolla 1¾ ins. wide, with a funnel-shaped tube and deeply five-lobed, scaly and bristly outside ; calyx saucer-shaped, hidden in bristles ; stamens about ten, with a tuft of hairs near, but not at, the base ; flower-stalk ½ to ¾ in. long, hairy.

Introduced by Wilson in 1904, from Szechuen, China. A species very distinct in the bristly character of its various parts ; flowers variable in tint, the darkest purple forms rather striking ; opening in May.

R. VILMORINIANUM, *Balfour fil.*

(R. Augustinii album, *Hort.*)

An evergreen shrub of erect habit probably up to 8 ft. or more high ; young shoots slender, downy. Leaves lanceolate, slenderly pointed, 1 to 2½ ins. long, ⅓ to ¾ in. wide, dull dark green and downy on the midrib above, scaly below ; leaf-stalk ⅛ to ¼ in. long, furnished with a few long bristles. Flowers opening in May, two to four in a terminal cluster. Corolla shortly tubed, 1½ ins. wide, yellowish white with brownish spots on the upper side ; scaly outside. Stamens ten, the longest 1¼ ins. long, all with a tuft of white down near, but not at, the base of the white stalks ; anthers exposed, crimson. Ovary scaly with a fringe of white hairs at the top ; style glabrous, greenish yellow, except where it joins the ovary. Calyx very small, five-lobed, the larger lobes 1/10 in. long, scaly; flower-stalk ⅓ in. long.

Native of China, probably from E. Szechuen, and collected by Farges ; raised from seed by the late Maurice de Vilmorin at Les Barres. It is the plant distributed by Chenault of Orleans as " R. Augustinii album," but is of course easily distinguished from R. Augustinii at any time by the absence of the line of down on the midrib beneath that is so distinctive a character of that species. R. Vilmorinianum is best marked by the yellowish scales and their occurrence outside the corolla-tube, by the down on the shoots and upper surface of the midrib, and by the bristles on the leaf-stalk. (Triflorum-yunnanense series.)

R. VIRGATUM, *Hooker fil.*

(Bot. Mag., t. 5060)

An evergreen shrub, up to 3 ft. high, with slender branches, covered when young (like the under-surface and stalk of the leaves and the flower-stalks) with glistening scales. Leaves 1½ to 3 ins. long, ½ to 1 in. wide ; narrowly oval, tapering at both ends, dark green and glabrous above ; stalk ⅛ to ¼ in. long. Flowers 1¼ to 1¾ ins. across, blush-coloured, produced in April singly or in pairs from each one of several axillary buds near the apex of the twigs ; corolla with a tube ¾ in. long, and five rounded, spreading lobes ; calyx cup-shaped, with five rounded lobes ; stamens ten to twelve, hairy at the base ; flower-stalk very short.

Native of Sikkim and Bhotan ; introduced about 1849, now rare in cultivation. It is perhaps not quite hardy in our average climate, but I have seen it thriving in the late Mr Osgood Mackenzie's garden, near Poolewe, on the coast of Ross-shire, where it flowers in June and July.

R. VISCOSUM, *Torrey.* SWAMP HONEYSUCKLE

(Azalea viscosa, *Linnæus*)

A deciduous shrub of bushy habit, eventually 6 to 8 ft. high, with twiggy branches, hairy when young. Leaves thinly arranged along the shoot or in a tuft of five or six at the end ; obovate, 1 to 2 ins. long, tapering to a short stalk at the base ; dark green and glabrous above, paler and bristly along the midrib beneath ; margins bristly. Flowers white or pink, produced during June and July at the end of the previous year's shoots, six to twelve together in a cluster ; corolla 1 to 1¼ ins. long, the lower half is a narrow tube often more highly coloured, the upper half five expanded oblong lobes ¾ in. long. The whole corolla, but especially the tubular part, is covered with sticky hairs. Calyx small, and like the slender flower-stalk, glandular-hairy. Seed-vessel ¾ in. long, curved, hairy.

Native of eastern N. America ; introduced in 1734, and still one of the most delightful of garden shrubs because of its late blossoming and its exquisitely fragrant flowers. It is the reputed parent, or one of the parents of a great number of garden azaleas. Loddiges in their catalogue for 1836 gave a list of one hundred and seven varieties, which, according to Loudon, were hybrids or varieties of R. viscosum. The identity of many of these old varieties is lost, but some are still to be obtained under their old names. Comparatively few, however, show any viscosum " blood," but rather that of nudiflorum and calendulaceum. The viscosum group at the present time is, as a matter of fact, a rather limited one, but is well distinguished by the lateness in flowering, strong fragrance, and the viscous blossoms.

Var. GLAUCUM (Azalea glauca).—The swamp honeysuckle is variable in a wild state, more especially in the colour of the flowers and leaves. This is its most distinct variety, with pure white, fragrant flowers, and leaves blue-white on the lower, or sometimes on both, surfaces. A very charming shrub, flowering late like the type.

R. WARDII, *W. W. Smith.* (Plate 16)

(R. glœoblastum, *Balfour fil. and Forrest* ; R. oresterum, *Balfour fil. and Forrest*)

An evergreen shrub found in a wild state from 15 to 20 ft. high ; young shoots at first slightly glandular, afterwards glabrous. Leaves glabrous, roundish ovate to oval, mostly heart-shaped at the base, rounded at the apex ; 2 to 4 ins. long, 1½ to 2½ ins. wide ; dark green above, glaucous beneath ; stalk ½ to 1⅛ ins. long. Flowers seven or more in a truss, opening in May. Corolla clear bright yellow without markings, five-lobed, bowl-shaped 1½ ins. long, 2 to 2½ ins. wide. Stamens ten, glabrous ; ovary and style entirely covered with glands. Calyx cup-shaped, ¼ to ⅜ in. long, with five rounded, glandular lobes ; flower-stalks slightly glandular.

Native of W. Yunnan, China, where it was originally discovered by Kingdon Ward in 1913, and introduced by him ; Forrest afterwards found it in the same region. This beautiful rhododendron, so valuable an addition to the comparatively few with large yellow flowers, belongs to the Thomsonii series, more especially to the Souliei section which is characterised by a widely open corolla and an ovary and style completely covered with glands. R. Wardii, to be seen at its best, needs a climate milder than that of the London district, but succeeds very well twenty or more miles to the south. In the same group comes

R. ASTROCALYX, *Balfour and Forrest*, a smaller shrub 3 to 5 ft. high, with smaller oval leaves up to 2½ ins. long, scarcely heart-shaped at the base ; pale yellow flowers 1½ ins. wide ; and ovary and style glandular from top to bottom. Calyx with five narrowly oblong, blunt lobes, glandular like the flower-stalk, spreading in star-like fashion, as the specific name indicates. Native of N.W. Yunnan ; discovered by Forrest in 1917.

R. WASONII, *Hemsley and Wilson*

(Bot. Mag., t. 9190)

A sturdy evergreen shrub, 2 to 5 ft. high ; young shoots thick, stiff, greyish white at first. Leaves narrowly oval or ovate, pointed, mostly rounded at the base ; 2 to 3 ins. long, 1 to 1½ ins. wide ; of hard leathery texture, ultimately glabrous and dark green above, clothed beneath with a close, rusty-brown down which becomes very dark on the two-year-old leaves ; stalk ¼ to ½ in. long. Flowers produced in March and April in a terminal truss of six to ten. Corolla bell-shaped, 1¼ to 2 ins. wide, creamy white or lemon-yellow shaded with rose, or wholly rose-coloured, always spotted with crimson ; five-lobed, the lobes overlapping. Stamens ten, about ½ in. long, downy at the base ; anthers dark brown ; ovary clothed with white down ; style as long as the corolla, glabrous, pale yellow. Calyx very small ; flower-stalk ½ to 1 in. long, both white with down.

Native of W. Szechuen, China ; discovered and introduced in 1904 by Wilson, who observed that it is " a common low-growing species partial to rocks in forests." So far as I have seen, it is one of the least commendable of the W. Chinese rhododendrons, growing slowly and flowering poorly, but quite hardy. Of the forms with variously coloured flowers the one on which they are lemon-yellow flushed with rose seems to be the prettiest. The species belongs to the Taliense series and nearly related to it is

R. WELDIANUM, *Rehder and Wilson*, which has larger leaves that are more or less obovate and tapered towards the base, also covered beneath with a loose rusty-brown wool. Flowers about 1 in. long, in trusses 3 ins. across, probably creamy-white or pink, but I have not seen living ones. Found by Wilson in W. Szechuen in 1904 and by Purdom in Kansu in 1911. At Dawyck, in Peeblesshire, there was a plant 6 ft. high and wide.

R. WATSONII, *Hemsley and Wilson*

An evergreen bush, slow-growing and of low stature in cultivation ; young shoots stout, often ⅝ in. in diameter, scurfy white when young, becoming yellowish. Leaves oblanceolate to obovate, abruptly narrowed at the apex to a short point, tapered at the base to a thick, winged, yellowish stalk that is up to 1 in. long and ½ in. wide ; 6 to 9 ins. long, 2 to 4 ins. wide ; dark dull green and glabrous above, covered beneath with a pale, very close scurf ; midrib broad and yellow above. Flowers produced from February to April in trusses of twelve to eighteen blooms and about 6 ins. wide. Corolla bell-shaped, 2 ins. wide, nearly as deep, seven-lobed, white with a small purple blotch at the base. Stamens fourteen, shorter than the corolla, their white stalks downy towards the base. Ovary and style glabrous. Calyx small, $\frac{1}{12}$ in. long, with even triangular teeth ; flower-stalks 1 to 1½ ins. long, thinly downy.

Native of Szechuen, China ; discovered and introduced by Wilson in 1904. Although, according to Wilson's field notes, it is capable of growing 25 to 30 ft. high with a trunk 2 ft. in girth, it is as yet only a few feet high in this country. The description given above was made from a truss kindly sent to me by Mr J. C. Williams from Caerhays, Cornwall, in February 1920. The species is distinct in the broad yellow midrib, the curiously flat, winged leaf-stalks, and the grey metallic lustre beneath the leaves. It has been assigned to the Grande series ; named after Mr Haines-Watson of the Chinese Customs Service ; very hardy but not likely ever to acquire much importance in English gardens.

R. WEBSTERIANUM, *Rehder and Wilson*

An evergreen shrub up to 3 ft. high, with erect branches and young shoots densely covered with glistening, yellowish grey scales. Leaves ovate to elliptical, blunt-ended ; ¼ to ¾ in. long, half as wide ; dark green and scaly above, thickly covered beneath with yellowish-grey scales. Flowers usually solitary, rarely in pairs or threes. Corolla rosy-purple, about 1 in. wide, with a short tube (hairy inside) and five rounded oval lobes ⅜ in. long, not scaly. Stamens ten, ⅜ to ½ in. long, downy close to the base ; anthers yellowish. Ovary scaly, conical, $\frac{1}{12}$ in. long ; style glabrous or sometimes slightly scaly towards the bottom, slightly longer than the stamens. Calyx deeply five-lobed, the lobes about ⅛ in. long, oval, scaly down the centre, fringed with down.

Native of W. Szechuen, China, up to 15,000 ft., discovered and introduced by Wilson in 1908. This is one of the purple-flowered, small-leaved rhododendrons which have been introduced in such large numbers from W. China and are now aggregated in the Lapponicum series. It is a very hardy shrub.

R. WEYRICHII, *Maximowicz*. WEYRICH'S AZALEA

A deciduous azalea, described as often tree-like in habit in a wild state 3 to 15 ft. high (Wilson) ; young shoots clothed with forward-pointing hairs, becoming brown and nearly glabrous the second year. Leaves obovate, ovate, or diamond-shaped, usually acutely pointed ; distributed along vigorous shoots but often produced in a whorl at the end of shorter twigs ; 1½ to 3½ ins. long, 1 to 2¼ ins. wide ; pale green and soon glabrous above, greyer green and rather conspicuously veined beneath ; stalk ¼ to ½ in. long, downy only when young. Flowers produced two to four together in a terminal cluster. Corolla about 2 ins. wide, of a rather dull rich red, funnel-shaped at the base, with five spreading lobes. Stamens six to ten, usually glabrous ; ovary densely clothed with erect, pale, reddish hairs ; style usually glabrous. Calyx very small but very hairy, as is also the flower-stalk.

Native of several Japanese islands and the Korean island of Quelpaert ; introduced by Wilson in 1914 to the Arnold Arboretum. Plants raised from seed obtained from that institution in 1915 flowered in May 1921 at Kew, where the species has proved fairly hardy in a sheltered place. It is most nearly akin to R. reticulatum, but is well marked by the colour of the flowers which may be termed rich brick red and as distinct among azaleas as that of Griersonianum is among rhododendrons proper.

R. WIGHTII, *Hooker fil.*

(Bot. Mag., t. 8492)

An evergreen shrub of bushy habit, and up to 10 ft. high, with very leathery, dark green leaves, 6 to 8 ins., sometimes more, long, 2½ to 3 ins. wide ; covered beneath with a reddish brown felt. Flowers bell-shaped, pale yellow, blotched at the base with crimson; about 1½ ins. across, the five lobes shallow, notched, and reflexed. Calyx-lobes very shallow, broadly triangular, and like the flower-stalk, which is 1½ to 3 ins. long, downy; stamens ten, much shorter than the corolla, downy at the base; ovary clothed with a white felt; style glabrous, much longer than the stamens.

Native of the Himalaya up to 14,000 ft.; very rare in cultivation, but existing in the open ground in Miss A. Mangles' collection at Littleworth, near Farnham, also at Kew (under glass). It is a rhododendron of great beauty and distinctness in its pale yellow flowers, which are borne as many as twenty together in rather loose heads.

R. WILLIAMSIANUM, *Rehder and Wilson.* (Plate 17)

(Bot. Mag., t. 8935; Garden, 22nd May 1920, fig.)

An evergreen shrub up to 4 or 5 ft. high, of rounded shape and usually wider than high, keeping close to the ground, densely and intricately branched; young shoots slender, glaucous, thinly furnished with gland-tipped bristles. Leaves orbicular to ovate, usually heart-shaped at the base, 1 to 2 ins. long, at first bronzy, finally dark green above, glaucous beneath; stalk ⅓ to ⅝ in. long, purplish when young, glandular-bristly. Flowers two to (rarely) four in a loose terminal cluster, opening in April. Corolla bell-shaped, 2¼ ins. wide, soft rosy red, five- (rarely six-) lobed, the lobes notched: stamens ten, 1¼ ins. long, glabrous; style overtopping the stamens and, like the ovary, sparsely set with stalked glands. Calyx minute, glandular at the margin; flower-stalk ¾ to 1⅛ ins. long, glandular. Seed-vessel ⅔ in. long, cylindrical.

Native of W. Szechuen, China; discovered and introduced by Wilson in 1908; he describes it as very local and occurring only in isolated thickets on the cliffs of Wa-Shan. It is named in honour of the late Mr J. C. Williams of Caerhays and is one of the most distinct as well as beautiful of Chinese rhododendrons. It flowers when quite small, attracting notice then by the curiously disproportionate largeness of the flowers. It is quite hardy at Kew, but is slow-growing and dwarf. In the warmer counties it makes dense hemispherical bushes not only attractive for its delicately coloured blossom but also for bronzy young foliage. Easily increased by late summer cuttings. It must be regarded as indispensable to any collection of rhododendrons. (Thomsonii series).

R. WILSONÆ, *Hemsley and Wilson*

An evergreen shrub, up to 6 or 7 ft. high, with glabrous, slender branches. Leaves narrowly oval or oval-lanceolate; 2½ to 4½ ins. long, 1 to 1¾ ins. wide; narrowly tapered at the base, acuminate at the apex, glabrous on both surfaces, rather glossy above, pale beneath, the texture leathery or even hardish; stalk up to ½ in. long. Flowers slightly fragrant, produced singly from a scaly bud in the axil of each leaf at the end of the shoot, four or six in all; flesh-pink, about 2 ins. across; corolla funnel-shaped at the base, deeply five-lobed, the upper lobe spotted with brown. Stamens ten, hairy at the base. Style and ovary glabrous, the latter long and slender. Calyx five-lobed, the lobes curiously diverse in length, some being quite short, others linear and up to ½ in. long. Flower-stalk glabrous, ¾ to 1 in. long. Related to R. stamineum.

Native of Hupeh, China; introduced by Wilson about 1903. Although the collector spoke highly of it in a wild state, it has not yet proved ornamental in cultivation.

R. WILTONII, *Hemsley and Wilson*

(Bot. Mag., t. 9388)

An evergreen shrub, 5 to 12 ft. high; young shoots clothed with a thick, brown wool. Leaves obovate, tapered at the base, abruptly narrowed at the apex to a short tip; 2 to 4 ins. long, ¾ to 1¼ ins. wide; glossy green and deeply wrinkled above; thickly clothed beneath with brown wool; stalk about ½ in. long. Flowers pink, with a purple blotch at the base, in clusters of about ten, bell-shaped, 1¼ ins. deep, rather more wide, the five lobes almost erect. Stamens ten, shorter than the corolla, downy towards the base; flower-stalk (1 to 1½ ins. long), and ovary covered with pale brown wool; style quite glabrous; calyx very small. Seed-vessel 1 in. long, ⅕ in. wide.

Introduced by Wilson from W. China in 1904. Although found at 10,000 ft. altitude, and therefore capable of withstanding great frost, it has proved so far to be liable to injury from late frosts by starting into growth early. A very distinct species on account of its shining, deeply wrinkled leaves, and the pale brown wool that covers the various younger parts.

R. YANTHINUM, *Franchet*

(R. Benthamianum, *Hemsley*)

An evergreen shrub, 4 to 6 ft. high, with scaly young shoots. Leaves aromatic, oval or ovate; 1 to 2 ins. long, ½ to 1 in. wide; pointed, broadly tapered or rounded at the base; dark green, minutely wrinkled, and slightly scaly above, brown with scales beneath; leaf-stalk ¼ in. or less long. Flowers four to eight in a truss, pale purple, with brown blotches on the upper side of the corolla, which is broadly bell-shaped and 2 ins. across, scaly outside. Calyx with linear-lanceolate lobes, ⅛ to ¼ in. long, and like the flower-stalk, scaly. Stamens ten, about as long as the corolla, bearded with white hairs near the base; ovary scaly; style quite glabrous.

Native of Central China; introduced by Wilson in 1901. It belongs to a group of scaly, purple-flowered rhododendrons not yet clearly defined, but including R. concinnum and R. polylepis. The former has smaller paler flowers, and a shallowly round-lobed calyx; the latter has a similar calyx to R. concinnum, but protruding stamens, and its leaves are longer and narrower than in R. yanthinum. R. ambiguum is also closely akin.

R. YEDOËNSE POUKHANENSE, *Nakai*. KOREAN AZALEA

(R. poukhanense, *Léveillé*; R. coreanum, *Rehder*)

A deciduous or nearly deciduous azalea 3, 4, or occasionally up to 6 ft. high; young shoots clothed with appressed bristles. Leaves lanceolate, oval-lanceolate, or oblanceolate, pointed, tapered at the base to a stalk ⅛ to ⅙ in. long; 1½ to 3 ins. long; both surfaces bristly, especially at the margins. Flowers fragrant, produced in April and May usually two to four together in a terminal cluster. Corolla rosy purple, funnel-shaped, 1½ ins. long, rather more wide, five-lobed, freely spotted on the upper lobes. Stamens ten, about as long as the corolla, downy on the lower third; anthers purple; ovary bristly; style 1¾ ins. long, usually glabrous. Calyx five-lobed; the lobes ovate, about ¼ in. long, very bristly, especially on the margins, green. Flower-stalk ⅓ in. long, bristly.

Native of Korea; introduced to the Arnold Arboretum by Mr J. G. Jack in 1905, thence to England in 1913. It flowered at Kew in April 1914. Although now known by the above varietal name, it is a genuine wild type and according to Wilson is the common azalea of Korea from about the latitude of the capital, Seoul, southward. In gardens it is very distinct on account of the rather glaring purple of its flowers. It belongs to the indicum group of azaleas characterised by the flattened, appressed bristles on the shoots, and is best known in cultivation by Rehder's appropriate name, " coreanum," under which it was introduced. It is quite hardy.

R. YEDOËNSE, *Maximowicz* (R. Yodogawa, *Hort. Japan*), is a double-flowered form of the above, but owing to its having been previously named and described it takes specific rank, one of the illogical arrangements characteristic of modern plant nomenclature. It is looser in habit than poukhanense and has an often larger calyx. This double-flowered azalea has been confused in gardens with a rosy purple form of

RHODODENDRON YUNNANENSE

R. mucronatum, sometimes erroneously known as " narcissiflorum," a name which should be reserved for a double white form of R. mucronatum, the rosy purple one being called var. plenum.

R. mucronatum (*i.e.*, R. ledifolium of our previous editions) differs from yedoënse in most of the bristles on the young shoots being outstanding and not appressed, in their being occasionally gland-tipped, and in the narrower, lanceolately lobed, very glandular calyx.

R. YUNNANENSE, *Franchet*

(Bot. Mag., t. 7614)

A semi-evergreen or nearly deciduous shrub, ultimately 8 to 12 ft. high; stiffly and somewhat thinly branched; young wood slightly scaly. Leaves narrowly oval or obovate; 1½ to 3 ins. long, ½ to ¾ in. wide; tapering at both ends, ciliate and sometimes sparsely bristly when young, bright green above, paler beneath, slightly scaly on both sides ; stalk ¼ in. or less long. Flowers produced in one or more clusters at the end of the previous year's shoots during the latter half of May, each cluster consisting of four or five flowers ; corolla 1½ to 2 ins. across, pale blush with brown crimson spots on the upper side ; lobes five, ovate and rounded, base funnel-shaped ; calyx very small, almost evenly circular ; stamens ten, 1 to 1½ ins. long, hairy at the base, much protruded ; ovary scaly ; style glabrous ; flower-stalk ¾ to 1 in. long.

Native of W. China ; introduced about 1889 by the Abbé Delavay to Paris. thence to England. This very charming species is quite hardy and flowers profusely almost every year, but its foliage is somewhat meagre, and in hard winters most of it is lost. The colour of the flowers is one of the most delicate seen in rhododendrons. Since the first plants were introduced, others, raised either from subsequently imported seeds or from cultivated plants, have appeared, which vary considerably in the tint and spotting of the corolla. It is easily increased by cuttings.

R. ZALEUCUM, *Balfour and W. W. Smith*

(Bot. Mag., t. 8878)

An evergreen shrub found by collectors varying from 6 to 30 ft. high ; young shoots scaly. Leaves oval-lanceolate, wedge-shaped to rounded at the base, usually sharply pointed ; 1½ to 3 ins. long, ⅜ to 1¼ ins. wide ; dark green and with a few scales above, very glaucous or bluish white and scaly beneath, the scales well apart from each other ; stalk ¼ to ⅓ in. long. The margin of the leaf is fringed with hairs when young, but most of them fall away. Flowers produced in March or April from the end of the shoot and the axils of the terminal leaves in umbels of three to five, slightly fragrant. Corolla rosy white, 1 to 1⅜ ins. long, funnel-shaped at the base, expanding at the mouth into five oval rounded lobes ; scaly all over the outside. Stamens ten, slightly downy towards the base. Ovary scaly ; style glabrous. Calyx small, shallowly bowl-shaped, with a few hairs on the margin. Flower-stalk ⅖ in. long, scaly.

Native of W. Yunnan, China ; discovered and introduced by Forrest in 1912 ; also found by Kingdon Ward in Eastern Upper Burma in 1914. The most striking character of this rhododendron is the intensely glaucous white undersurface of the leaves, due to a coating of wax. It is remarkable that the same species should occur in two such widely separated localities, but the late Sir Isaac Balfour had no doubts about their identicalness. Ward found it in damp rain forest as a " tall thin tree of 20 to 30 ft." The plants of Forrest's introduction are quite hardy and are well worth cultivation for the delicate colouring of the flowers and the vividly white under surface of the leaves. (Triflorum-yunnanense group.)

RHODOSTACHYS. BROMELIACEÆ

A genus of about half a dozen species, natives of South America, closely related to the pine-apple plant and having the same rosette-like arrangement of the leaves. They are sun-loving plants, woody only at the base, and can be propagated by division. The generic name refers to the rose-coloured flower-spikes of R. andina, the species on which the genus was founded by Philippi, the Chilean botanist.

R. ANDINA, *Philippi*

(Bot. Mag., t. 7148 ; R. carneus, *Mez* ; Bromelia longifolia, *Lindley*, not *Rudge*)

A short-stemmed evergreen 1 to 1½ ft. high, the crowded leaves forming a kind of rosette 18 ins. or so wide, in the manner of the pine-apple plant. Leaves 1 to 1¾ ft. long, 1 to 1½ ins. wide at the base, tapering gradually thence to a long fine point and regularly armed on each margin with stiff incurved spines ¹⁄₁₂ in. long ; very much recurved, channelled on the upper surface ; scurfy and grey below, ultimately of a rather bright green above, and of hard, rigid texture. Flowers very numerous and densely packed in a pyramidal or globose mass 2½ to 4 ins. wide and high, proceeding from the centre of the plant on a stout main-stalk 4 to 8 ins. high. The outer bracts of this inflorescence are tinged with red, the flowers themselves bright pink ; petals three, 1 in. long, erect, of linear shape ; stamens six, anthers yellow, conspicuous.

Native of Chile ; introduced to cultivation by Hendersons, formerly nursery-men of St John's Wood, and exhibited at a meeting of the Horticultural Society on 5th August 1851, under the name " Tillandsia carnea." I have not seen it anywhere finer than in the garden at Ludgvan, near Penzance, where is a dense patch of closely packed growths several feet across. At Kew, in the most sheltered nook that can be found for it, it is quite healthy out-of-doors, although suffering somewhat in hard winters. There are many places towards, and on, the south coast where it should succeed very well if given the sunniest possible place and perfect drainage. Canon Boscawen grew it on a stony mound. It appears usually to flower in the autumn.

R. PITCAIRNIIFOLIA, *Bentham and Hooker*

(Bot. Mag., t. 8087 ; Fascicularia pitcairniifolia, *Mez* ; Bromelia pitcairniifolia, *Koch*)

An evergreen with the leaf arrangement of a pine-apple plant, having short stems and consisting mainly of rosettes, 18 ins. or more across, of hard-textured, recurved leaves. Leaves 9 to 18 ins. long, 1½ ins. wide at the base, gradually narrowing thence to a point and armed with short incurved spines on the margins ; they are scurfy on both surfaces when young, becoming ultimately almost smooth and greyish green. Flowers produced from the centre of the rosette very closely packed in an apparently stalkless, flattish round head 2 to 2½ ins. wide. Each flower is about ⅓ in. wide with three blue petals, white sepals and yellow anthers. At the time of flowering (autumn), the short inner leaves of the rosette become bright red, partially or wholly, and add greatly to the beauty of the plant.

Native of Chile ; first flowered at Paris in 1866, at Kew in 1891 and quite often since—always under glass. It succeeds very well in the open air at Tresco in the Scilly Isles and in Cornwall. There was a patch of it, 10 ft. wide, in the Rectory garden at Ludgvan, thickly packed with rosettes of leaves. At Kew it has only been grown in a cool greenhouse, but although possibly not so hardy as R. andina (it is wild in very nearly the same region, but it may be at lower elevations) it should be tried where that species succeeds. Known best under the generic name here used and much resembling R. andina in growth, it has lately been placed in a separate genus, FASCICULARIA. It is well distinguished from R. andina by that species having a pyramidal inflorescence borne on a stalk several inches long.

RHODOTHAMNUS Chamæcistus, *Reichenbach.*   ERICACEÆ

(Rhododendron Chamæcistus, *Linnæus* ; Bot. Mag., t. 488)

A low or semi-prostrate evergreen shrub, rarely more than 1 ft. high ; young shoots minutely downy, but almost hidden by the closely set leaves. Leaves almost without stalks, narrowly oval, ¼ to ½ in. long,

half or less than half as wide, tapered at both ends, edged with conspicuous bristles, otherwise glabrous and glossy green on both sides. Flowers produced during April at the end of the twigs, two to four in each cluster. Corolla pale, clear rose, spreading, 1 to 1¼ ins. diameter, the five lobes ovate, rounded half as deep as the corolla ; calyx ½ in. diameter, the five lobes linear-ovate, pointed, covered like the stalk (which is ½ in. long) with gland-tipped hairs. Stamens ten, glabrous, ½ in. long ; anthers very dark purple. Seed-vessel globose, hairy, many-seeded, with the sepals persisting at the base.

Native of the Austrian Alps ; introduced by the firm of Loddiges in 1786. Plants are usually imported from the Tyrol, where they are always found on a limestone formation, but prove difficult to establish.

RHODOTHAMNUS CHAMÆCISTUS

It is essentially a rock garden shrub, the best position for it being one exposed to full sunshine, but where its roots can spread in some pocket or crevice between the stones, always cool and moist. A healthy, well-established plant covers itself with blossom every spring. It is one of the most attractive of all alpine shrubs. The only successful method of propagation appears to be by separating pieces with roots attached from the older plants. Limestone is probably desirable in the neighbourhood of its roots, but not essential.

RHODOTYPOS Kerrioides, *Siebold and Zuccarini.*
ROSACEÆ

(Bot. Mag., t. 5805 ; R. scandens, *Makino*)

A deciduous shrub growing about 6 ft. high ; branches erect ; young shoots glabrous. Leaves opposite, ovate, long-pointed ; 2½ to 4 ins. long, half as much wide ; upper surface dark green and soon becoming glabrous, under-surface paler and hairy, prominently parallel-ribbed, the margins deeply, irregularly, and sharply toothed. Flowers solitary at the end of short twigs, 1¼ to 2 ins. across, pure white ; petals four, rounded, with a short claw ; calyx four-lobed, the lobes leaflike, hairy, toothed, persisting until the fruit is ripe. Fruits about the size of small peas, shining, black, clustered above the calyx.

Native of China, and perhaps Japan ; introduced in 1866. Nearly allied to Kerria, and often called " Kerria japonica alba " in gardens,

RHODOTYPUS KERRIOIDES

this is easily distinguished by its opposite leaves, four petals, and white flowers. It is a very hardy plant, and quite easily propagated by cuttings made of moderately soft wood and placed in brisk bottom heat. Its flowers are at their best in May and June, but they continue to expand up to the end of July. The generic name refers to the rose-like flowers. This is the only species known.

RHUS. SUMACH. ANACARDIACEÆ

A large genus of shrubs, small trees, or climbers, with simple, ternate, or pinnate leaves, found in most temperate regions of the globe, and occasionally in the tropics. About a dozen species are grown in the open air in the British Isles, but several others (such as R. succedanea) can be cultivated in Cornwall and similar places. Individually the flowers of the sumachs are small and of little beauty, being greenish, yellowish, or dull white, but in a few species the panicles are sufficiently large and the flowers white enough to give a pleasing effect. In some species the fruits are handsome, but, on the whole, their value in gardens is in th size and autumn colouring of the foliage. The leading characters of th genus are the alternate leaves and usually diœcious flowers, the five-lobe calyx (which adheres to the fruit), the five petals, the one-celled ovar with three styles, and the usually globose fruit, either glabrous or hairy containing one bony seed.

The juice of several species, notably R. Toxicodendron and R. Vernix is exceedingly acrid and poisonous to many people, but care should b taken in pruning or making cuttings of any of the species. R. verniciflu yields the famous lacquer of Japan. The leaves of R. CORIARIA, *Linnæus* a species too tender for the ordinary climate of Great Britain, contain valuable tanning and dyeing substance. Finely ground, they constitut the " sumach " of commerce. The leaves of several other species hav also an economic value either for dyeing or tanning, and the fruits of some like R. succedanea and verniciflua, give a wax used for candle-making.

The cultivation of all the sumachs is simple. They do not requir a very rich soil except when they are grown purely for size of foliag as R. typhina (*q.v.*) and R. glabra sometimes are. Where autumn colou is desired, ordinary garden soil without added manure is sufficient. Lik many other trees with soft wood and a large pith, they are subject to th attacks of the " coral-spot " fungus (*Nectria cinnabarina*). Branches s attacked should be cleanly cut off and burnt, the wound coated with tar The simple-leaved species (Cotinus and cotinoides) can be increased b ordinary cuttings, most of the others by root-cuttings, and seed is ofte available.

SIMPLE LEAVES
Cotinus, cotinoides.

TERNATE LEAVES (three leaflets)
Aromatica, Toxicodendron.

PINNATE LEAVES WITH WINGED LEAF-STALK
Copallina (entire), *chinensis* (toothed).

PINNATE LEAVES ; ENTIRE LEAFLETS
Potaninii, trichocarpa, Vernix, verniciflua.

PINNATE LEAVES ; TOOTHED LEAFLETS
Glabra, Michauxi, typhina.

R. AROMATICA, *Aiton.* FRAGRANT SUMACH

(R. canadensis, *Marshall*)

A low, spreading, deciduous shrub, 3 to 5 ft. high ; shoots downy. Leave aromatically fragrant when bruised, trifoliolate, with a common stalk ½ to ¾ in long. Leaflets not stalked, the side ones broadly ovate, the terminal one th largest, obovate, and 1½ to 3 ins. long, the side ones about half as big ; a coarsely toothed, lower surface very downy. Flowers yellowish, in dens roundish clusters ½ to ¾ in. across, produced in April at the end of short stalk on the shoots of the preceding year. Fruits red, hairy, about the size of smal red currants.

Var. TRILOBATA, *A. Gray* (R. trilobata, *Nuttall*).—Leaves smaller, th leaflets ½ to 1 in. long, the terminal one often fan-shaped, with a few com aratively large lobes. They are rather unpleasantly scented, and the shrub s sometimes known as "Skunk bush." Sometimes regarded as a distinct species.

The type is a native of the eastern United States; introduced in 1759, and still occasionally seen in shrubberies. It is rather pretty in spring, when its twigs are clothed with the abundant yellow flowers, and its scented foliage s handsome and distinct. Var. trilobata has a more western distribution, and is found in Texas, California, British Columbia, etc.

R. CHINENSIS, *Miller*

(R. javanica, *Thunberg*; R. Osbeckii, *Steudel*)

A small deciduous tree, sometimes 20 ft. or more high, with a short trunk and a rounded gauntly branched head; branchlets yellowish, downy; winter buds brown, velvety. Leaves pinnate, varying in size according to the vigour of the plant, ordinarily from 8 to 15 ins. long, and composed of seven to thirteen leaflets, between each pair of which the common leaf-stalk is winged. Leaflets stalkless, oval, usually 2½ to 4 (occasionally 6) ins. long, and about half as wide; pointed, the margins conspicuously round- or sharply toothed. The under-surface covered with velvety down. Flowers in a large, terminal panicle 8 or 10 ins. long and wide, yellowish white, produced in August. Fruit small, orange-coloured.

Native of China and Japan. This handsome tree is well marked by its winged leaf-stalks, the only other hardy species so distinguished being the American R. copallina, which has smaller, entire leaflets. As a flowering plant it is one of the handsomest of the sumachs, although it does not bloom so freely here as on the Continent. It may be cut down annually like R. glabra laciniata (*q.v.*). In some places, as at Monreith in Wigtownshire, it colours brilliantly in autumn.

R. COPALLINA, *Linnæus*. DWARF SUMACH

A deciduous shrub, rarely more than 4 ft. high in this country, but said to become a small tree 25 to 30 ft. high in the southern United States; branchlets covered with a fine reddish down. Leaves pinnate, composed of nine to fifteen (occasionally more) leaflets, the common stalk being winged on both sides between the leaflets, which are stalkless (or the basal ones shortly stalked), lanceolate, 2 to 3½ ins. long, rarely toothed; dark glossy green above, paler and downy beneath, the lower leaflets the smallest. Flowers greenish yellow, unisexual, produced in crowded pyramidal panicles 4 to 6 ins. long, 3 to 4 ins. wide, the female panicle normally the smaller. Fruit bright red, hairy.

Widely spread in eastern N. America, this species varies considerably in a wild state. The form cultivated in Britain is, no doubt, the shrubby Northern one. American writers describe it as being of singular beauty, its foliage dying off a rich reddish purple which, with the scarlet fruits of the female tree, gives a charming combination of colour. It flowers in July and August. Introduced to England and cultivated in the Fulham Palace grounds in 1688. Distinct because of its entire leaflets and winged stalk.

R. COTINOIDES, *Nuttall*. CHITTAM WOOD

(Cotinus cotinoides, *Britton*)

A deciduous shrub or small tree, as much as 30 ft. high in a wild state, its trunk 1 ft. or more in diameter; in this country usually under 15 ft. high, the young vigorous shoots and leaves often reddish purple. Leaves simple, obovate or oval, varying much in size according to the age and vigour of the plant, but ordinarily 2 to 5 ins. long, rather more than half as wide ; tapering to the stalk (which is ½ to 1½ ins. long), but broad and rounded at the apex. In the female plant the flowers are borne on a large, sparse, terminal panicle, 6 to 12 ins. long, three-fourths as wide. The larger proportion of the final ramifications of the inflorescence do not carry a flower, but are mere thread-like stalks clothed with fine hairs. Fruit ⅛ in. long, very sparsely produced. The male plant has the inflorescence better set with flowers.

This remarkable species is found in a few isolated localities in Tennessee, Alabama, and other south-eastern United States, but is nowhere common. First discovered by Nuttall in 1819, it did not reach this country until 1882, when it was sent to Kew by Prof. Sargent. In the beauty of its inflorescences it is very much inferior to R. Cotinus, but, on the other hand, it is one of the loveliest of all shrubs in autumn, its leaves turning to various shades of scarlet, claret colour, and orange before they fall. Disappointment has some-times been caused by the failure of this shrub to colour as described, but this is nearly always due, so far as I have seen, to over-generous conditions at the root. In order to bring out its best colour, it should not be grown in rich or manured soil, which renders the growth too rank and coarse. In a wild state it is said to be in danger of extinction ; many large specimens have been cut down for the dye obtained from the wood, especially during the Civil War in N. America.

R. COTINUS, *Linnæus*. VENETIAN SUMACH

(Cotinus Coggyria, *Scopoli*)

A deciduous shrub, up to 15 ft. high, of round, bushy habit, and often considerably wider than it is high ; the branchlets glabrous. Leaves simple, glabrous, orbicular or obovate, rounded or slightly notched at the apex ; 1½ to 3 ins. long, with well-marked parallel veins and a stalk about half the length of the blade. Panicles loose, terminal, much-branched, many of the thread-like, final ramifications bearing no flower but developing a large number of silky hairs. During July the whole inflorescence (6 to 8 or more inches long and wide) turns a pale flesh colour, afterwards a smoky grey. Flowers few and small ; fruit dry, prominently veined, one-seeded, ¼ in. across.

Native of Middle and S. Europe, extending eastwards to the Himalaya. In the late summer few hardy shrubs are more striking and beautiful than this. It produces its inflorescences so abundantly that the entire plant becomes covered with a filmy pinkish envelope. The leaves remain long on the plant, and turn yellow before they fall. The wood, too, is yellowish, and a good yellow dye is obtained from the twigs. Several popular names have been given to it besides the one quoted above, such as " smoke plant," " burning bush," and " wig-tree," all in allusion to the characteristic inflorescence. This shrub, like its American ally, does not require a very rich soil, as it then grows too much and gives little flower. The two following varieties are in cultivation :—

Var. PURPUREA, *Rehder*.—Leaves, young wood, and inflorescence purple.

Var. PENDULA.—Branches drooping.

A downy form—PUBESCENS, *Engler*—is also known, but I have not seen it in cultivation.

R. GLABRA, *Linnæus*. SMOOTH SUMACH

A deciduous shrub, usually from 4 to 6 (rarely 10) ft. high, with glabrous leaves and branches. Leaves pinnate, about 12 to 18 ins. long, composed usually of from fifteen to twenty-nine leaflets, which are oblong-lanceolate, shallowly to rather deeply toothed ; 2 to 4½ ins. long, ½ to ¾ in. wide, glaucous beneath. Flowers unisexual, closely packed in a dense pyramidal panicle 4 to 10 ins. long, the stalks covered with red down. Fruit the size of large shot, packed like the flowers in a dense panicle, and covered with soft crimson hairs. They remain long on the plant after the leaves have fallen. Native of the eastern United States, where in some parts it is almost a weed. It is nearly allied to R. typhina, and is very similar in its handsome fruit, but differs in the glabrous young wood and leaves, and its purely shrubby habit. The foliage turns a bright, rich red. Flowers in July and August.

Var. LACINIATA.—One of the handsomest of hardy foliage plants, the leaflets being deeply cut so as to make the leaf almost or quite doubly pinnate. Its greatest beauty is obtained by cutting it hard back every spring, and thinning down the young shoots to one or two, thus obtaining broad feathery leaves 3 ft. long, very striking in their autumn colour.

R. HYBRIDA, *Rehder*, is a hybrid between this species and R. typhina occasionally found wild in N. America.

R. MICHAUXI, *Sargent*

(Garden and Forest, 1895, fig. 55)

A low, deciduous shrub, up to 3½ ft. high, spreading by means of underground suckers ; stems erect and rather stout, covered with short hairs. Leaves pinnate, 8 to 12 ins. long, dull green ; leaflets usually nine to fifteen, ovate or oblong, 1½ to 3 ins. long, rounded and slightly oblique at the base, the terminal one the largest, with a winged stalk, the upper surface hairy, the lower one covered with a dense, yellowish down, the margins coarsely toothed. Panicle erect, terminal, hairy, 6 to 8 ins. high, half as much wide ; flowers ⅛ in. wide, densely arranged, petals greenish yellow ; calyx covered with grey down. Fruit nearly round, ⅛ in. diameter, scarlet, very downy. Native of N. Carolina ; first discovered by Michaux towards the end of the eighteenth century. For about one hundred years it was lost sight of, but was again discovered and re-introduced to cultivation. It was sent to Kew in 1901 from the Biltmore Arboretum, U.S.A., and flowered the same year. According to some authorities it is very poisonous, perhaps the most poisonous of American sumachs, but I have spoken with Americans who regard it as harmless.

R. POTANINII, *Maximowicz*

(R. Henryi, *Diels*)

A deciduous tree, up to 30 ft. high, with a rounded head of branches ; young shoots glabrous or minutely downy. Leaves from 10 to 16 ins. long, composed of seven, nine, or eleven leaflets, which are oblong to oblong-lanceolate, obliquely rounded or broadly tapered at the base, tapered at the apex to a fine point ; 2½ to 5 ins. long, 1 to 1¾ ins. wide ; margins entire or sparsely toothed, glabrous and dark green above, but with a tuft of hairs at the base of the midrib and on the short stalk. Flowers small, produced in June on terminal pyramidal downy panicles 3 to 7 ins. high, the main and secondary flower-stalks as well as the sepals covered with brown down ; the greenish white petals are also downy outside, and about ⅛ in. long. Fruit rich red, downy, about the size of peppercorns, densely packed in drooping panicles. Native of Szechuen in China ; discovered by Henry in 1888. It is a handsome small tree both in its foliage and fruit, very closely allied to the Himalayan R. punjabensis, *Stewart*.

III   F

R. SUCCEDANEA, *Linnæus*. WAX TREE

A deciduous tree up to 30 or 35 ft. high. Leaves pinnate, up to 1 ft. in length ; leaflets usually nine or eleven but sometimes as many as fifteen, ovate-oblong (often obliquely so), narrowed to a long point, not toothed ; 2 to 4½ ins. long, ⅝ to 1¼ ins. wide ; shortly stalked, glabrous on both surfaces. The midrib usually runs nearer one side of the blade than the other and from it proceed, almost at right angles, ten to twenty pairs of thin veins. The leaves have a glossy, often purplish hue. Flowers very small, yellowish, produced in slender panicles 3 to 5 ins. long that come in the crowded leaf-axils near the end of the shoot, the whole forming a thick cluster of blossom there. Fruit ⅜ in. broad, globose to rather kidney-shaped, borne in pendulous clusters, the seed and its waxy covering enclosed by a thin, smooth, yellowish brown skin.

Native of Japan, where it used to be much cultivated in the southern islands for the sake of the wax or tallow obtained from the fruits. This wax was used for making candles and was a principal source of artificial light in Japan until the importation of petroleum from America and Russia. Seeds appear to have first been introduced from Japan to France in 1862, but the species is a native also of China, Formosa, and the Himalaya. It is scarcely hardy at Kew although it may survive for several years in a sheltered place. The leaves of plants grown in pots open with a pale bronzy tint and turn a lovely soft red colour before falling, and the species will no doubt be well worth cultivation in our warmer counties for its autumnal beauty.

R. TOXICODENDRON, *Linnæus*. POISON IVY

A deciduous shrub, either climbing or loosely spreading in habit, the climbing form attaching itself to rocks, walls, trunks of trees, etc., by means of aerial roots like those of the ivy, and frequently reaching to a considerable height ; the bushy form up to 8 or 9 ft. high. Leaves always composed of three leaflets, the side ones very shortly stalked, the end one with a stalk ½ to 1¼ ins. long, the common leaf-stalk 2 to 4 ins. long. Leaflets very variable in size, shape, and toothing, broadly ovate to obovate, pointed, sometimes quite entire, often coarsely and irregularly notched at the margin, and either glabrous or slightly downy beneath. The terminal leaflet is always the largest, and from 2 to 5 ins. long, the lateral ones about two-thirds as large. Flowers dull white, ⅛ in. across, on slender panicles 1½ to 2½ ins. long, often unisexual, the sexes sometimes separated. Fruit a round, whitish berry, ¼ in. wide, smooth.

Var. RADICANS, *Torrey* (R. radicans, *Linnæus*, Bot. Mag., t. 1806).—This is the climbing form above mentioned.

The poison ivy is very abundant in the eastern United States, and a climbing form with bristly fruits and young stems is found in Japan. As a garden plant its chief value is in the beautiful red tints of its autumn foliage. It was cultivated by Compton, Bishop of London, at Fulham, in the seventeenth century. The poisonous effects of the sap—a yellowish milk-like fluid which soon turns black on exposure—have long been known. As long ago as 1623, the author of the *Historye of the Bermudaes* referred to them. On the skin of many persons, but far from all, the sap produces blisters and eczema-like eruptions, which are exceedingly painful and persistent. The supposed active principle, "toxicodendrol," is insoluble in water, and it is of no use to attempt to remove it from the skin by ordinary washing. The best-known remedy to apply is an alcoholic solution of sugar of lead (lead acetate, and the sooner it is used on the affected parts the more effective it is.

So serious are the effects of the Rhus poison on some people that the plant should never be grown where its toxic properties are not clearly made known. Cases of permanent disablement have been caused by it in western N. America, where a smoother, thicker-leaved form (var. RYDBERGII) appears to be excessively virulent ; but even in England I know of a man who had been making cuttings of it for propagation, who was kept in hospital for several months through the almost corrosive effects of the sap. It is said that the symptoms are sometimes recurrent, and that on some persons the eruptions break out annually at the same time of year, but with decreasing virulency. This phenomenon, extraordinary if true, does not appear to have been conclusively established, although the testimony of patients is on record who aver that they have had second and third attacks, although they have never been near the plant after the first. In my experience mere contiguity to the plant without touching it will not induce skin poisoning, although when in flower the escaping pollen appears to have evil effects, especially on the eyes, in N. America.

There is one other property of this remarkable plant to which attention may be drawn. This is the indelibility of its juice when applied to linen. It produces a quite ineradicable stain, and is, in fact, one of the best possible marking inks available.

A popular confusion exists between this plant and the harmless creeper (Vitis inconstans or Ampelopsis Veitchii) so much used for covering the walls of houses. The vine is easily distinguished by its mostly simple leaves, and by its tendrils, neither of which the rhus possesses (it is always trifoliolate). The confusion has been increased by the rhus being grown in nurseries and gardens under the wrong and misleading names of " Ampelopsis Hoggii " and " A. japonica."

The climbing form from Japan, mentioned above as having bristly fruits, has lately been distinguished as a species, R. ORIENTALIS, *C. K. Schneider.*

R. TRICHOCARPA, *Miquel*

A deciduous tree of slender habit, 20 to 25 ft. high. Leaves from 12 to 20 ins. long, carrying thirteen to seventeen leaflets, which are broadly ovate, entire, 1½ to 2½ ins. long, largest towards the apex of the leaf, very downy on both sides. Flowers in slender, downy, long-stalked panicles, inconspicuous. Fruits described as " large, pale, prickly drupes, ripening in August and September," and produced in pendulous clusters (Sargent).

Native of Japan, common in the forests of Yezo, and on the mountains of the main islands ; introduced to the United States by Prof. Sargent about 1892, and thence to Kew a few years later. It has proved hardy, and flowers in June. No hardy tree or shrub is more beautiful in its autumn colouring than this, the leaves turning a deep orange-scarlet.

R. TYPHINA, *Linnæus.* STAG'S-HORN SUMACH

(R. hirta, *Sudworth*)

A deciduous, small tree of gaunt, flat-topped habit, occasionally 25 or more feet high ; branchlets thick, very pithy, yielding when cut a copious, yellowish white, thick juice, soon turning black and hard on exposure ; all the young bark is covered with short, dense, reddish hairs. Leaves pinnate, 1 to 2 ft. long, consisting of from about thirteen to twice as many leaflets, which are oblong-lanceolate, 2 to 4½ ins. long, ½ to 1 in. wide ; long-pointed, toothed, covered with brownish hairs when young, nearly or quite glabrous by autumn (the stalk remaining downy). Female flowers crowded in a dense, pyramidal, very hairy panicle 4 to 8 ins. long ; male flowers (which are borne on separate plants) greenish, and on a bigger, more open panicle. Fruits closely packed in dense panicles, and covered thickly with crimson hairs.

Native of eastern N. America, and cultivated in England since the reign of James I. The female plant is one of the handsomest of sumachs, for, added to its finely coloured fruit clusters, its leaves acquire in autumn rich shades of orange, red, and purple. The male plant, which colours its leaves too, is sometimes known as " R. viridiflora." This tree succeeds remarkably well in some of the murkiest of London suburbs. It is sometimes used as a fine-foliaged summer shrub, grown in a group, and cut back every spring almost to the ground, the young shoots being afterwards reduced to one or two. Given liberal treatment at the root, erect stems 5 or 6 ft. high with leaves up to 3 ft. long will be produced, the leaflets correspondingly large.

Var. LACINIATA.—Leaflets very handsomely cut.

R. VERNICIFLUA, *Stokes*. VARNISH TREE

(R. vernicifera, *De Candolle*)

A deciduous tree, up to 60 ft. high in China, of erect, slender habit when young. Leaves pinnate, 1 to 2 ft. long, with seven to thirteen leaflets which are broadly ovate, the largest 6 or 7 ins. long, half as much wide, sometimes obliquely heart-shaped at the base, shortly stalked, velvety downy beneath, especially on the sixteen to thirty veins. Flowers yellowish white, small and inconspicuous, produced during July in a cluster of lax, branching panicles from the leaf-axils near the end of the shoots, the largest panicles 10 ins. long by 6 ins. wide. Fruits about the size of small peas, yellowish.

Native of Central and W. China, and cultivated there largely ; it is also much cultivated in Japan. This is the tree which yields by incision the famous varnish or lacquer of Japan. As a tree for the garden it is desirable for its noble foliage. The fruits also are ornamental, as I have seen them in Mr de Vilmorin's garden at Les Barres, in long lax panicles ; but they may not be so freely produced in our less sunny climate. Mr Wilson collected seeds in China from trees growing truly wild on the mountains, and the plants that have been raised from them will, he believed, be hardier than the Japanese trees which previously were the only representatives of the species in gardens ; they grow much faster at any rate. An oil is expressed from the fruit, which is used for candle-making.

R. VERNIX, *Linnæus*. POISON SUMACH

(R. venenata, *De Candolle*)

A small deciduous tree, up to 20 ft. high, with a trunk 15 to 18 ins. thick, usually much smaller in England, and often breaking near the ground into two or three stems ; branchlets glabrous and grey. Leaves pinnate, with purplish stalks, quite glabrous except when young ; leaflets nine to thirteen, 2 to 4 ins. long, one-third as much wide, ovate or obovate, entire. Flowers $\frac{1}{8}$ in. across, greenish yellow, produced on thin, slender panicles 4 to 8 ins. long from the leaf-axils of the current season's growth. Fruit the size of a pepper-corn, yellowish white, and hanging in a cluster of graceful panicles from near the end of the branchlets. Plants unisexual.

Native of the eastern United States ; cultivated in England since early in the eighteenth century. Few of the sumachs are more beautiful than this in their autumn tints, the foliage putting on brilliant shades of orange and scarlet before it falls. Yet it is not much grown in this country, and perhaps wisely so, for it is one of the most dangerous hardy trees in cultivation, owing to the toxic properties of its sap—even, it is said, of its exhalations ! The latter may be doubtful ; but all that has been said as to the need of care in dealing with R. Toxicodendron applies with equal, if not greater, force to this species. It appears with both that persons in a state of perspiration are most susceptible to their effects. It flowers in July, and the fruit often remains throughout the winter.

RIBES. CURRANTS AND GOOSEBERRIES. SAXIFRAGACEÆ

Important as this genus is in comprising the gooseberries, the black, red, and white currants of our fruit gardens, it does not, in the ornamental garden, possess anything like the importance suggested by the number of its species at present in cultivation. It is composed of two well-marked groups : the gooseberries, sometimes regarded as a distinct genus called GROSSULARIA ; and the currants, which may be termed the true RIBES. These two groups are roughly distinguished by the former having spines (often triple spines) at the joints, and articulated flower-stalks ; the latter by having no spines at the joints, and flower-stalks not articulated. In the following descriptions the words " armed " or " unarmed " will usually indicate to which group each species belongs ; but there are species of an intermediate character, such as Diacantha, lacustre, and montigenum (p. 172), which are spiny but belong in other respects to the currants.

They are all shrubs, a few of them evergreen, with usually three- or five-lobed, alternate leaves. Flowers occasionally highly coloured and red or yellow, sometimes white, oftenest green or greenish. In the gooseberries the flowers are usually few in the raceme or even solitary, but in the currants they are always in racemes, usually numerous. The fruit is a berry full of pulp in which the seeds are embedded, and is always terminated by the shrivelled remains of the flower.

The ribes present no difficulty in cultivation ; they like a loamy soil of at least average quality, and the West N. American gooseberries need as sunny a spot as possible. They are propagated by seed or by cuttings. The latter will frequently form roots when made of leafless shoots in November and placed in the open air--as common gooseberries are—but they are more certain if placed under a handlight. A second method, better adapted to the currants, is to make cuttings of leafy shoots in July and August and place them in gentle bottom heat, but most of them will strike root also in the open ground, of course much more slowly. For cultivators desirous of growing only the most ornamental, the following half a dozen may be recommended :—*alpinum, cruentum* (or *amictum*), *aureum, cereum, sanguineum* (especially var. *splendens*), and *speciosum.*

R. ALPINUM, *Linnæus.* ALPINE CURRANT

A deciduous, unarmed shrub, reaching in gardens 6 to 9 ft. in height and as much or more in diameter, of dense, close habit ; young twigs shining, and at first more or less glandular. Leaves broadly ovate or roundish, three-sometimes five-lobed, the lobes coarsely toothed ; the base straight or heart-shaped, with five radiating veins ; upper surface with scattered bristly hairs, the lower one usually shining and more or less hairy on the veins ; ¼ to 1½ ins. long and wide ; stalk glandular-downy, ¼ to ½ in. long. Flowers unisexual, the sexes nearly always on separate plants, produced in the axils of bracts longer than the flower-stalk, greenish yellow ; the males on small, erect, glandular racemes 1 to 1½ ins. long, the females fewer, and on racemes half as long. Currants red, not palatable.

Native of northern latitudes of the Old World, including England and Scotland. It is abundant in woods near Fountains Abbey, in Yorkshire. The largest specimens I know of form part of the old hedge on the east front terrace of the old hall at Troutbeck ; according to a letter at Kew they are tree-like, 15 ft. high, and not less than three hundred years old. Although this currant has no special beauty of flower or fruit it makes a very neat and pleasing shrub, admirable for shady places. Occasionally plants with perfect flowers may be found.

Var. AUREUM.—Leaves bright yellow when young.

Var. LACINIATUM.—Leaves more deeply lobed and toothed than in the type.

Var. PUMILUM, *Lindley.*—A dwarf variety with smaller leaves, 2 to 3 ft. high, but more in diameter ; a very neat bush. There is a yellow-leaved form of this (PUMILUM AUREUM).

The so-called var. " sterile " appears to be merely the normal male-flowered plant. None of the forms of R. alpinum need a rich soil. They retain the neat, compact habit which is their greatest merit, in rather poor soil. The yellow-leaved forms colour best in full sun.

R. AMERICANUM, *Miller.* AMERICAN BLACK CURRANT

(R. floridum, *L'Heritier*)

This shrub is unarmed, and closely akin to the common black currant, which it resembles in having three- or five-lobed leaves with a coarse, irregular toothing and deeply heart-shaped base, and in possessing the same heavy odour, due to yellowish glands on the lower surface. The fruit also is black. The American species, however, is quite distinct in the flowers ; these are nearly twice as long, more tapering and funnel-shaped, and yellow. Moreover, the bract from the axil of which each flower springs on the raceme is longer than the stalk. (In R. nigrum it is small and much shorter than the flower-stalk.)

Native of eastern N. America from New Brunswick to Virginia, Kentucky, etc. ; introduced in 1729. As a garden shrub the only quality which recommends this currant is that its foliage becomes suffused with brilliant hues of crimson and yellow in autumn. For this quality it is sold in nurseries, often as R. missouriense—wrongly, for the true plant of that name is a gooseberry with spiny branches (see under R. Grossularia).

R. AUREUM, *Pursh.* BUFFALO CURRANT

(Bot. Reg., t. 125 ; R. fragrans, *Loddiges*, Bot. Cat., t. 1533)

A deciduous, lax-habited, spineless shrub, 6 to 8 ft. high, producing a crowded mass of stems which branch and arch outwards at the top ; young shoots minutely downy. Leaves usually three-lobed, often broadly wedge-shaped or palmate, the lobes coarsely toothed ; ¾ to 2 ins. long, as much or more wide ; pale green on both sides, and glabrous, or soon becoming so ; stalks glabrous or downy, ½ to 2 ins. long, very variable in length compared with the blade. Flowers spicily fragrant, bright golden yellow, appearing in April in semi-pendulous racemes 1 to 2 ins. long, each flower with a tubular calyx ½ in. long, the spreading lobes ¼ to ⅜ in. long ; bract at the base of the flower-stalk longer than the latter is. Fruit black-purple, round, glabrous, ⅓ in. diameter.

Native of the western United States ; introduced in 1812. This species and R. sanguineum are by far the most attractive of the currants in their blossom, and it is very distinct among them in its long, tubular, yellow calyx. Of several forms the best is

Var. AURANTIACUM, with fragrant flowers of a deeper, more orange shade than usual, and a more compact habit.

Var. CHRYSOCOCCUM, *Rydberg*.—Fruit orange-yellow.

Var. TENUIFLORUM (R. tenuiflorum, *Lindley*, Bot. Reg., 1274), differs from the type in having smaller flowers without fragrance, and in the fruits being amber coloured and translucent, with an acid flavour. It is also a taller shrub, up to 12 ft. high. According to Dr Coville this is the true R. aureum of Pursh.

R. BRACTEOSUM, *Douglas*. CALIFORNIAN BLACK CURRANT

(Bot. Mag., t. 7419)

An unarmed, deciduous shrub, 6 to 10 ft. high ; young shoots glabrous, except for a little loose down at first. Leaves handsomely five- or seven-lobed, 3 to 7 ins. (sometimes more) wide ; the lobes palmate, reaching half or more than half-way to the midrib, sharply and irregularly toothed ; dotted with resin-glands beneath ; bright green and soon quite glabrous above ; stalk slender, often longer than the blade, glabrous except for a few bristles at the base. Racemes produced in May, erect, slender, up to 8 ins. long. Flowers numerous, greenish yellow, erect, ¼ in. across, each on a slender, slightly downy stalk about ¼ in. long. Currants erect, resin-dotted, globose, ¼ in. diameter, black with a blue-white bloom.

Native of western N. America ; discovered by Douglas in 1826. An interesting species of the black currant (nigrum) group, very distinct in its large maple-like leaves (occasionally 10 ins. across) and long, slender, erect racemes. Rarely seen, but quite hardy at Kew.

R. CEREUM, *Douglas*

(Bot. Mag., t. 3008)

A grey, deciduous, unarmed shrub, 3 to 6 ft. high, of rounded, compact habit ; young shoots downy and glandular. Leaves roundish or rather broader than long, three- or five-lobed, the lobes irregularly round-toothed, the base straight or heart-shaped, ½ to 1¼ ins. wide ; upper surface sown with white, resinous glands and slightly downy, lower one downy on the veins ; stalk downy, glandular, nearly as long as the blade. Flowers tubular, ¼ to ½ in. long, clustered two to five together at the end of a short, downy, glandular stalk, the individual flower almost stalkless, downy, white tinged with rose, produced in the axil of a comparatively large, toothed, glandular-downy, wedge-shaped bract. Style downy. Fruit bright red, ¼ in. diameter.

Native of western N. America ; introduced in 1827 by David Douglas. It is a very pleasing shrub, conspicuous in the pale grey tint of its young leaves, and pretty in the delicate colouring of its abundant blooms. These appear with the young leaves in April.

R. INEBRIANS, *Lindley* (Bot. Reg., t. 1471).—Very similar to the above, and equally pleasing, this differs in having the bract at the base of each flower not toothed and pointed, the style glabrous, and the flowers deeper in colour. Introduced from western N. America in 1827. R. SPÆTHI-ANUM, *Koehne*, is the same or a slight form.

R. cereum and R. inebrians are distinct in the arrangement of their leaves, each one of which has the eighth one above it directly superposed; the intermediate ones being set round the stem in a spiral of three circuits.

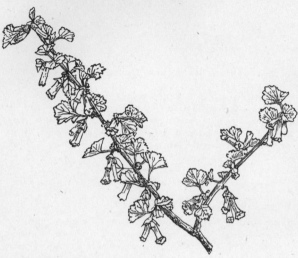

RIBES CEREUM

R. CILIATUM, *Humboldt and Bonpland*

R. jorullense, (*Humboldt*)

A deciduous unarmed shrub up to 10 ft. high, of bushy rounded shape; young shoots slender, arching, downy and furnished with stalked glands. Leaves three- or sometimes five-lobed, doubly toothed, heart-shaped at the base, 1½ to 2 ins. long and wide; dark dull green above and sprinkled with appressed bristles; downy beneath and furnished there with stalked glands, especially on the veins; margins glandular; stalk ¾ to 1¼ ins. long, glandular. Flowers nearly ½ in. long, borne six to twelve together during April in nodding, stalked racemes about 2 ins. long; greenish, downy outside, bell-shaped; ovary glabrous; main and secondary flower-stalks glandular and downy. Fruit globose, black, shining, as large as a red currant.

Native of Mexico and found in the damp canyons of the Nevada de Toluca at 12,000 to 13,000 ft. altitude. It is one of the currant section of the genus and is quite hardy at Kew, where there is a bush measuring 9 ft. by 12 ft. This flowers freely every year. The stalked glands are black and shining.

R. CRUENTUM, *Greene*

(Bot. Mag., t. 8105)

A deciduous, spiny shrub, 3 to 6 ft. high, more in diameter; young shoots minutely downy. Leaves roundish, ¾ to 1½ ins. wide, three- or five-lobed, the lobes coarsely round-toothed; nearly or quite glabrous on both surfaces; stalk minutely downy, slender, ¼ to ½ in. long. Flowers ¾ in. wide, solitary, rarely in pairs, on a slender stalk ⅓ in. long, pendent. Calyx ½ in. long, crimson, the tube narrowly bell-shaped, glabrous; the five sepals lanceolate, finally reflexed. Petals white, much shorter than the sepals; ovary covered with incipient spines. Berry red, $\frac{2}{3}$ in. across, with a hedgehog-like appearance due to its covering of numerous spines, each $\frac{1}{8}$ to $\frac{1}{4}$ in. long.

Native of California ; introduced in 1899. This interesting and remarkable gooseberry has flowers extremely pretty in their contrast of crimson and white, but they are not particularly abundant, usually one at each joint of the previous year's wood. The berries are remarkable in their prickliness. It is

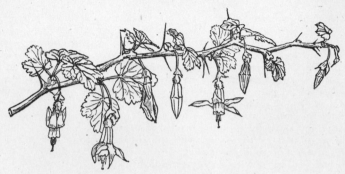

Ribes cruentum

closely allied to, and perhaps only a variety of R. Roezlii, but that species is distinctly downy on leaf and calyx. Effective grown as a standard.

R. curvatum, *Small*

A low, deciduous, bushy shrub, 3 ft. high ; the shoots glabrous, purplish, armed with slender, simple or triple spines. Leaves roundish, usually 1 in. or less in diameter, three- to five-lobed, toothed, slightly downy ; stalk slender, downy. Flowers produced singly or in pairs (rarely more) on pendent stalks, white ; calyx bell-shaped with linear, much reflexed sepals $\frac{1}{4}$ in. long ; petals very short, white ; ovary covered with resinous glands ; stamens $\frac{1}{4}$ in. long, erect, both they and the style downy. Fruits globose, glabrous, $\frac{1}{3}$ in. across, purplish-green.

Native of the south-eastern United States, hardy. I brought plants from the Arnold Arboretum to Kew in July 1910, which, so far as I am aware, were the first introduced to this country. R. curvatum is, however, no longer represented at Kew. It is closely allied to R. niveum, which it resembles in its white flowers and downy style and stamens, but the glandular ovary and often glabrous anthers are different. R. curvatum is also much dwarfer in habit, and comes from the opposite side of N. America.

R. Diacantha, *Pallas*

A deciduous shrub, 4 to 6 ft. high, armed with spines in pairs $\frac{1}{8}$ to $\frac{1}{5}$ in. long, or sometimes unarmed ; young shoots not downy. Leaves obovate or rounded, often three-lobed, the lobes coarsely toothed ; $\frac{3}{4}$ to 2 ins. wide, the base ordinarily wedge-shaped but sometimes rounded, quite glabrous ; stalk $\frac{1}{4}$ to $\frac{5}{8}$ in. long, more or less furnished with bristles. Flowers unisexual, the sexes on different plants. Males yellowish, in erect glandular racemes. Fruit roundish oval, about as big as a red currant, glabrous, scarlet-red.

Native of Siberia, Manchuria, etc. ; introduced in 1781. This shrub, which has no particular merit, resembles R. alpinum in the plants being one-sexed, but differs in having prickles, and in the markedly wedge-shaped leaves. In having spines, and flowers in racemes, it unites the characters of the currants and gooseberries, but its affinities are with the former.

R. FASCICULATUM, *Siebold and Zuccarini*

(Sargent's Trees and Shrubs, t. 38)

A deciduous, unarmed shrub, 3 to 5 ft. high ; young shoots finely downy. Leaves three- to five-lobed, the largest 2 ins. long, 2½ to 3 ins. wide ; the lobes coarsely toothed, usually more or less downy ; stalk downy and with feathered bristles near the base. Flowers unisexual, the sexes on separate plants. Males clustered four to nine together in a stalkless umbel, each flower is on its own stalk without uniting on a common one ; yellow, fragrant ; females usually in pairs, sometimes three or four. Fruits erect on a stalk ⅕ in. long, round, ⅓ to ½ in. diameter, glabrous, bright scarlet.

Native of China, Japan, and Korea, and distinct from all other species in cultivation in having the flowers clustered in fascicles.

Var. CHINENSE, *Maximowicz* (R. Billiardii, *Carrière*), is a taller shrub partially evergreen, more downy than the type. The fruits of both are ornamental, and remain long on the branches.

R. GAYANUM, *Steudel*

(R. villosum, *Gay*, Bot. Mag., t. 7611)

An unarmed evergreen shrub, 3 to 5 ft. high ; the young wood, leaf-stalks, flower-stalks, ovary, and calyx shaggy with soft hairs. Leaves stout, greyish, very broadly or roundish ovate ; 1 to 2 ins. long and broad ; the three lobes rounded and toothed, the base usually straight ; downy on both sides. Flowers bell-shaped, yellow, honey-scented, closely packed in erect, cylindrical racemes, 1 to 2 ins. long, ½ in. diameter. Berries about the size of peas, purple-black, hairy.

Native of Chile. A handsome evergreen, and distinct in the shape and colour of its inflorescence, and the hairiness of its various parts. Some forms are less downy. Flowers in early June. It has been cultivated at Kew for many years, and is quite hardy.

R. GORDONIANUM, *Lemaire*

(R. Beatonii, *Hort.*)

A hybrid between R. aureum and R. sanguineum, raised at Shrubland Park, near Ipswich, about 1837, by Donald Beaton, a famous gardener of his time. It is intermediate in most respects between its parents—in habit, in the leaves being smaller and less hairy than those of R. sanguineum, and in the colour of the flowers, which are reddish outside, yellowish within, a curious blend. It is hardier than R. sanguineum, and can be grown in parts of the New England States where that species is too tender to thrive. It is interesting and not without beauty, but is inferior to both of its parents.

R. GROSSULARIA, *Linnæus*. COMMON GOOSEBERRY

There is a group of species closely allied to this, composed of deciduous, bushy, spiny shrubs with small green or purplish flowers which have no value in gardens apart from their use as fruit-bearers. They need not be given detailed notice, but may be included here.

The common gooseberry (R. Grossularia) is found wild in Britain, but is
believed to be an escape from gardens. It is a genuine native of most parts
of mountainous Europe, and on the Mount Atlas range in N. Africa. In
a wild state it is distinguished by its bristly young wood, its downy calyx and
hairy ovary, its style downy at the base, and its yellowish or red berry, more
or less glandular-hairy. Some cultivated varieties have quite smooth berries.

R. OXYACANTHOIDES, *Linnæus*, is widely spread over N. America. It has bristly
branches, the leaves are downy, and more or less glandular, the stamens as long as the
petals ; the ovary, calyx, and berry glabrous, the last red-purple. R. HIRTELLUM,
Michaux, is very near this species, but has glabrous shoots and stamens twice as long
as the petals, which are purplish. Berry glabrous, purplish or black, $\frac{1}{2}$ in. across—
Bot. Mag., t. 6892 (as oxyacanthoides). It has borne very good fruit in the Isle of
Wight, where it is known as " currant-gooseberry."

R. ROTUNDIFOLIUM, *Michaux*, is a native of the eastern United States, from
Massachusetts to N. Carolina. Its solitary spines are small and inconspicuous ;
young wood and leaves downy, but not glandular or bristly ; flowers greenish purple ;
calyx, ovary, and berry glabrous. The fruit is purple and of good flavour.`

R. DIVARICATUM, *Douglas* (Bot. Reg., t. 1359).—A native of the coast region
of western N. America, of vigorous growth, and up to 10 ft. high. Its young wood is
armed with single or triple spines up to $\frac{2}{3}$ in. long, and is sometimes bristly, usually
glabrous. Leaves with appressed hairs above, almost or quite glabrous beneath.
Calyx downy, greenish purple, petals whitish, ovary and berry glabrous, the last
globose, $\frac{1}{4}$ in. diameter, black-purple. This species is nearly allied to R. rotundifolium,
but is found wild on the opposite side of the continent, and is a bigger bush, well-
armed with long stout spines.

R. MISSOURIENSE, *Nuttall*, may be mentioned here although I do not know that
it is in cultivation. The name occurs in nursery catalogues, but the plant so-called
is a currant—R. americanum. The true plant is a gooseberry, native of the south
central United States ; very closely allied to R. rotundifolium, perhaps a mere form of it.

R. GROSSULARIOIDES, *Maximowicz*.—A native of China and Japan, with smooth
or bristly stems armed with triple spines ; leaves glabrous or with glandular bristles.
It differs from R. Grossularia in the style not being downy and in the red berry being
glabrous. Introduced to Kew from N. China by the late Dr Bretschneider in 1881.

R. CYNOSBATI, *Linnæus*. Dogberry.—A native of eastern N. America ; introduced
in 1759. Its stems are weakly armed or not at all ; leaves and leaf-stalks downy,
calyx green, bell-shaped with reflexed sepals ; petals white ; ovary bristly, the bristles
not gland-tipped ; style downy towards the base ; fruit reddish purple, scarcely $\frac{1}{2}$ in.
in diameter, more or less covered with slender prickles. Var. INERME has its fruits
smooth, not prickly.

R. HENRYI, *Franchet*. HENRY'S CURRANT

An evergreen shrub 3 to 4 ft. high ; young shoots glandular-bristly. Leaves
obovate or diamond-shaped, tapering about equally towards both ends or more
abruptly towards the apex, sharply pointed, finely and irregularly toothed, the
teeth gland-tipped, with tiny bristles between them ; 2 to 4 ins. long, 1 to $2\frac{1}{4}$ ins.
wide ; glabrous, yellowish green above with conspicuous sunken veins in about
five pairs ; lower surface pale, with short stiff hairs on the midrib and veins,
between which the blade is thickly sprinkled with minute sticky glands ; stalk
$\frac{1}{4}$ in. or less long, glandular-bristly. Flowers greenish yellow, produced early
in the year along with new shoots in racemes 1 to 2 ins. long, surrounded at
the base by a cluster of pale green, membranous bracts ; main and secondary
flower-stalks clothed with glandular hairs, giving them a mossy appearance as
seen under the lens. Fruit narrowly oval, $\frac{1}{2}$ in. long, glandular-hairy.

Native of Szechuen, China ; introduced (apparently inadvertently) by
Wilson in 1908. A plant which came up in a sowing of seeds of Sinowilsonia
Henryi at the Edinburgh Botanic Garden proved to be this species. It is
closely akin to R. laurifolium and, like it, flowers in February and March,

but the glabrous leaf-blades of that species easily distinguish it. The moss-like down of R. Henryi is also much longer and more conspicuous. Male and female flowers are borne on separate plants. Miss Willmott flowered a male plant at Warley, Essex, in 1918. This currant is quite hardy and is succeeding well in the rock garden of the Edinburgh Botanic Garden.

R. LACUSTRE, *Poiret*

A deciduous shrub, 3 to 5 ft. high, the stems thickly covered with slender prickles or stiff bristles ; spines at the joints numerous, from three to nine arranged in a semicircle. Leaves 1 to 2¼ ins. long and wide, handsomely and deeply three- or five-lobed, the lobes often again deeply cut ; stalk and chief veins more or less bristly. Flowers from twelve to twenty in glandular-downy drooping racemes, 2 to 3 ins. long, funnel-shaped, with short, spreading sepals brownish crimson inside, creamy white or pinkish outside. Berry round, about the size of a black currant, covered with gland-tipped bristles, black.

Native of N. America on both sides of the continent, inhabiting cold damp localities ; introduced in 1812. Although the general aspect of this shrub is that of a gooseberry, especially in the shape of its leaves and in its spines, it has the long racemes and flowers of the currants. Its multiple spines are also distinct. Although it has no lively colour to recommend it, it is pretty when its branches are strung with the graceful drooping racemes.

R. MONTIGENUM, *McClatchie* (R. lentum, *Coville*), is another species which unites, as lacustre does, the two sections of the genus, but has shorter, fewer-flowered racemes (six to ten) and bright red fruits. Introduced from western N. America in 1905.

R. LAURIFOLIUM, *Janczewski*

(Bot. Mag., t. 8543)

An unarmed evergreen shrub, 4 to 6 ft. high, branchlets at first glandular, then smooth and brown. Leaves leathery, ovate to oval, pointed, the largest 5 ins. long, half as wide, coarsely toothed, each tooth terminated by a minute glandular tip, dark dull green above, paler and brighter beneath, glabrous on both surfaces ; stalk and stipules bristly. Racemes nodding, 1½ to 2½ ins. long, 1 in. wide, main-stalk glandular-downy, viscid. Flowers greenish yellow, ⅓ in. diameter ; calyx and stalk downy. Bracts oblong, inclined to obovate, ⅝ in. long, thin, greenish white. Fruit oval, reddish at first, finally purplish black, ½ in. long.

Native of W. China ; discovered and introduced in 1908 by Wilson. It is not a showy plant, but is interesting and welcome in flowering as early as February. The flowers are unisexual, the sexes separated on different plants ; the females are longer than the males, and with only abortive stamens. Mr Wilson says it is rare in a wild state. Young shoots are often red.

R. LEPTANTHUM, *A. Gray*

A deciduous, spiny shrub, 3 to 6 ft. high, with slightly downy, occasionally glandular-bristly young branches ; spines usually slender, solitary, up to ½ in. long. Leaves roundish or somewhat kidney-shaped, ¼ to ¾ in. wide, deeply three- or five-lobed, toothed, the base mostly truncate ; stalk as long as the blade, downy at the base. Flowers white tinged with pink, one to three on a short stalk ; calyx cylindrical, the sepals downy, ultimately reflexed. Fruit oval, shining, blackish red, slightly downy or glabrous.

Native of Colorado, New Mexico, etc. ; one of the prettiest and daintiest of gooseberries, the branches being slender and densely clothed with tiny leaves. Introduced in 1893.

Var. QUERCETORUM (R. quercetorum, *Greene*), has pale yellow flowers, fragrant, and produced two to four together. Native of California.

R. LOBBII, *A. Gray*

A deciduous, spiny shrub, 3 to 6 ft. high ; young shoots downy. Leaves roundish in the main, ¾ to 2 ins. wide, three- to five-lobed ; the lobes roundish toothed, downy or glabrous above, downy and glandular beneath and on the stalk. Flowers usually in pairs on a glandular-hairy stalk ; calyx purplish red, downy, the sepals twice or thrice the length of the tube, recurved ; petals white, erect, the stamens much protruded beyond them ; anthers almost as broad as long ; ovary covered with glands. Berry oblong, red brown, glandular.

Native of N. California and S. British Columbia ; introduced about 1852 by Wm. Lobb for Messrs Veitch, but not often seen now, although, like the others of this group, very pretty when flowering in April. From the allied crimson-flowered gooseberries in cultivation, viz., Menziesii, Roezlii, and cruentum, this is very well distinguished in flower by the anthers being rounded at the top (in the others they are tapered like an arrowhead).

R. LONGERACEMOSUM, *Franchet*

Mr Wilson introduced this extraordinary currant in 1908 from W. China, where it had originally been discovered by the Abbé David. The one character which distinguishes it from all its tribe is its remarkable racemes, from 12 to 18 ins. long, pendulous, thinly set with greenish flowers and afterwards with jet-black fruits which Mr Wilson told me are about the size of an ordinary black currant and of good flavour. It is a deciduous, unarmed shrub with glabrous young shoots and three- or five-lobed, glabrous leaves, 3 to 5½ ins. long and wide ; stalks up to 4½ ins. long, furnished with glandular bristles most numerous towards each end. Flowers tubular, bell-shaped, glabrous. The species appears to be quite hardy, and is worth the attention of lovers of curiosities and of fruit-growers for hybridising. The fruits, however, are very thinly disposed along the stalk.

R. MAXIMOWICZII, *Batalin*

(Gardeners' Chronicle, May 20, 1916, fig. 114)

A deciduous unarmed bush, ultimately 6 to 9 ft. high, the young shoots clothed with pale hairs, some of which are glandular. Leaves of the black currant type, three- or sometimes five-lobed ; 2 to 5 ins. wide and about as long, glossy dark green and thinly downy above, clothed beneath with soft pale down, especially on the veins ; stalk 1 to 2½ ins. long, downy. Racemes slender, erect, 2 to 4 ins. long, about ½ in. wide ; main-stalk as well as individual flower-stalks very downy and glandular. Flowers ¼ in. wide, dull lurid red ; calyx-tube funnel-shaped, glandular downy. Fruit globose, ⅜ in. wide, orange-coloured or red and covered with stalked glands.

Native of W. China, from Kansu to Szechuen ; discovered by the Russian traveller, Potanin, in 1885 ; introduced by Wilson in 1904 and again in 1908 and 1910. It is a curious and remarkable currant on account of the racemes and very glandular fruit and the lurid hue of the blossoms which open in May.

Var. FLORIBUNDUM, *Jesson* (R. Jessoniæ, *Stapf*, Bot. Mag., t. 8840). A variety discovered by Wilson in Szechuen in 1903, and introduced by him in 1908. It seems to have first flowered with Lieut.-Col. Stephenson Clarke in 1915. It differs from typical R. Maximowiczii in the longer inflorescences (4 to 6 ins. long), the more numerous flowers, and by the shorter and fewer glandular bristles on the berries. Fruits " rusty yellow " in this country. This variety was grown very successfully by the late Mrs Berkeley of Spetchley, near Worcester, and a very palatable jam made of its fruits.

R. MENZIESII, *Pursh*

A deciduous, spiny shrub, up to 6 ft. high ; young shoots downy and covered with long, slender bristles. Leaves roundish ovate in the main, 1 to 2 ins. wide, deeply three- sometimes five-lobed, the lobes toothed ; either glabrous or with gland-tipped hairs above, very downy and glandular beneath and on the stalk. Flowers in pairs or solitary on the slender, glandular, and downy stalk ; calyx red-purple with a short, bell-shaped base, the sepals ⅓ in. long ; petals white, sometimes rosy tinted. Berry globose, covered with glandular bristles, the remains of the flower persisting at the top.

Native of western N. America ; introduced in 1830. A free-growing gooseberry, which flowers freely in this country in May. From R. Lobbii, with which it is much confused in gardens, it is distinguished by its bristly stems, the stalked glands on the ovary, and the tapered anthers. The contrast of purple and white in the flowers is pretty.

R. MOGOLLONICUM, *Greene*
(Bot. Mag., t. 8120 ; R. Wolfii, *Rothrock*)

A sturdy unarmed shrub, said to become 9 to 11 ft. high ; young shoots glabrous or nearly so. Leaves three- or five-lobed, 2 to 3½ ins. long and wide ; heart-shaped at the base, glabrous above, downy only on the veins beneath, and with scattered glands which impart a somewhat disagreeable odour to the leaves when rubbed ; stalk downy and glandular. Flowers greenish white, themselves short-stalked, but closely set on erect long-stalked racemes 1 to 1½ ins. long ; the stalks and ovary covered densely with stalked glands. Currants ⅓ in. wide, roundish ovoid, glandular, purplish black.

Native of Colorado, New Mexico, etc. ; introduced to Kew in 1900, where it is very hardy and fruits freely. Its only interest for the garden is in the blue, ultimately black, glandular fruits arranged densely in more or less erect spikes. It belongs to the same group of currants as R. sanguineum, but has none of the flower beauty of that species.

R. MULTIFLORUM, *Kitaibel*
(Bot. Mag., t. 2368)

This is one of the red currant group, and, as regards its flowers, the most attractive ; they are yellowish green, crowded on slender, cylindrical, pendulous racemes, sometimes 4 to 5 ins. long. When well furnished with these the shrub is quite ornamental. For the rest, it is vigorous, up to 6 ft. high, and has stout unarmed branches—stouter perhaps than those of any other currant ; leaves of the red currant shape and size, grey with down beneath. Stamens and style exserted. Fruit roundish, red when ripe, ⅓ in. diameter in racemes 4 to 5 ins. long.

Native of S. and E. Europe ; introduced about 1818.

R. NIGRUM, *Linnæus*. BLACK CURRANT

An unarmed shrub, 5 or 6 ft. high, distinguished by its peculiar odour, due to small yellowish glands sprinkled freely over the lower surface of the leaf, which is conspicuously three-lobed, deeply notched at the base, long stalked, coarsely toothed. Flowers bell-shaped, dull white, in racemes, each flower from the axil of a minute bract ; fruits black.

Native of Europe and Siberia, possibly of Britain. Several varieties of this species—so well known as the "black currant" of fruit gardens—have been distinguished. The two first mentioned are curious and interesting, but no others are worth cultivating as ornamental shrubs :—

Var. DISSECTUM.—Leaves very curiously cut, each of the three lobes reaching back to the stalk, and again bipinnately lobed.

Var. LACINIATUM.—The three primary lobes reaching nearly or quite to the stalk, and pinnately lobed.

Var. RETICULATUM.—Leaves mottled thickly with yellow.

R. CULVERWELLII, *Macfarlane*, is a hybrid between the black currant (female) and the gooseberry, raised by Mr Culverwell, of Thorpe Perrow, Yorkshire, about 1880. It is a spineless shrub, and has flowers like the black currant, but the foliage and inflorescence are more suggestive of the gooseberry. An interesting curiosity of no value apparently either for fruit or ornament. R. SCHNEIDERI, *Maurer*, is a hybrid of the same parentage, raised in Germany, but with the sexes reversed.

R. NIVEUM, *Lindley*

(Bot. Mag., t. 8849)

An armed, deciduous shrub, up to 9 ft. high, the young shoots quite glabrous ; spines solitary or in threes, about ½ in. long. Leaves between roundish and kidney-shaped, three- to five-lobed, 1 to 1½ ins. across ; usually truncate at the base, the lobes unequally and bluntly toothed. Flowers two to four together in slender-stalked, drooping clusters ; calyx and petals glabrous, white ; sepals ultimately much reflexed, leaving the stamens exposed for ¼ in. Ovary glabrous, stamens and style downy. Berry globose, glabrous, black with a purplish bloom, about ⅓ in. diameter.

Native of western N. America ; introduced in 1826. This gooseberry is rather pretty and distinct in its wholly white flowers, which open in April.

R. ROBUSTUM, *Janczewski*, is a hybrid between R. niveum and oxyacanthoides. It is a very vigorous bush, and was received at Kew in 1890 from the late Mr Nyeland, gardener to the King of Denmark. Beyond that I know nothing of its origin.

R. ORIENTALE, *Desfontaines*

An unarmed, deciduous shrub, 5 or 6 ft. high ; young shoots and leaf-stalks covered with stiff, gland-tipped sticky hairs. Leaves of the red currant size and shape, but shining green and with bristly down on the nerves beneath ; stalk ½ to 1 in. long. Flowers unisexual, the sexes on different plants, and produced on somewhat erect racemes 1 to 2 ins. long ; they are green suffused with red and covered with viscid hairs ; berry red, downy.

Native of E. Europe and W. Asia. The R. resinosum of Pursh, until recently regarded as a native of N. America, and figured as such in Bot. Mag., t. 1583, is really this species. It has little garden value, but is distinct in its unisexual flowers, very viscid glands, and erect racemes.

R. PINETORUM, *Greene.*   PINE-WOOD GOOSEBERRY

A gooseberry growing 6 ft. high, found in the Mogollon Mountains of New Mexico and in Arizona, often in pine-woods, an association from which it derives its name ; introduced in 1902. It has the typically shaped leaf of the gooseberries, glabrous, blunt-toothed, and with long, slender stalks. The young shoots are quite glabrous ; the spines solitary, in pairs, or in threes, rich brown, stout, slightly curved. Flowers solitary, orange-yellow, hairy outside ; the sepals much reflexed, showing the erect petals. Berry black-purple, globose, ½ in. diameter, with numerous bristles. Although this species has some of the most brilliantly coloured blossoms among gooseberries, they are short-stalked and solitary (or very rarely in pairs) at each joint, and make no great display. They appear in May, when the leaves are one-third grown.

R. PROSTRATUM, *L'Heritier*
(R. glandulosum, *Weber*)

A deciduous, unarmed shrub with prostrate, rooting branches ; young shoots glabrous. Leaves deeply five- to seven-lobed, 1½ to 4 ins. wide, the lobes doubly toothed ; bright green and smooth on both sides, except for occasional hairs on the veins beneath ; stalk bristly at the base. Flowers greenish, produced eight to twelve together on erect, slender racemes, 2 to 3 ins. long, stalks and ovary with gland-tipped hairs ; sepals glabrous outside. Fruit red, glandular, ¼ in. diameter. (Syn. R. glandulosum, *Aiton.*)

Native of N. America, where it is widely spread over the cool moist regions on both east and west sides ; introduced in 1812. It is distinct in its prostrate habit, nearly or quite glabrous, evil-smelling leaves, and red, glanded fruits. Nearly allied to this is

R. LAXIFLORUM, *Pursh* (R. affine, *Douglas*, not *Kunth*), also a prostrate shrub, but with leaves more downy beneath when young, the fan-shaped petals as broad as they are long (in prostratum they are much longer than broad), the sepals downy but not glandular outside, and the fruits black or dark purple, with glandular down and a glaucous bloom. Native of western N. America, whence it was introduced by Douglas in 1818, and Japan.

R. COLORADENSE, *Coville,* is a third species belonging to the same group, being of prostrate habit ; the young shoots are finely downy. the sepals with glandular hairs outside, the purplish petals twice as broad as long, the fruit black, not glaucous with bloom. Native of Colorado and New Mexico ; introduced in 1905.

None of these three have much garden value, although their prostrate habit gives them interest.

R. ROEZLII, *Regel.*   AMICE GOOSEBERRY
(R. amictum, *Greene*)

A deciduous armed shrub, 3 to 6 ft. high ; young shoots downy. Leaves ½ to 1 in. wide, roundish or kidney-shaped in general outline, three- or five-lobed, the lobes with often sharp teeth ; more or less downy on both surfaces, especially beneath ; stalk ⅓ in. long, usually downy and sometimes glandular-hairy. Flowers solitary or in pairs on a short downy, often glandular stalk, pendent. Calyx purplish crimson, downy ; the tube cylindrical, ¼ in. long ; the sepals ⅓ in. long ; petals rosy white, erect, shorter than the sepals. Berry purple, ½ in. wide, covered with slender bristles.

Native of California. This pretty and curious gooseberry is not common in cultivation ; the plant that has been distributed for it from nurseries being as a rule either R. Lobbii or R. Menziesii. Its nearest ally is R. cruentum (*q.v.*).

The name " amictum " refers to the shape of the bract surrounding the base of each flower, which resembles the amict, or hood, worn by Roman Catholic clergy at mass.

R. SANGUINEUM, *Pursh.* FLOWERING CURRANT
(Bot. Mag., t. 3335)

A deciduous, glandular, unarmed bush, 7 or 8 ft. high, usually considerably more in diameter ; young shoots covered with a close, fine down. Leaves three- or five-lobed, palmately veined, the lobes broad and rounded, unequally toothed, the base conspicuously heart-shaped ; 2 to 4 ins. wide, less in length ; glabrous or nearly so above, soft with pale down beneath ; stalk ¾ to 2 ins. long, covered with minute down like the young shoots, but with a few bristles near the base. Flowers deep rosy red, produced during April in drooping, finally ascending, racemes 2 to 4 ins. long, 1 to 1½ ins. wide ; each flower ½ in. long and nearly as wide ; the slender flower-stalk, ovary, and tubular calyx dotted with glandular down. Currants globose, ¼ in. diameter, glandular, black covered with blue bloom.

Native of western N. America ; discovered by A. Menzies in 1793, and introduced by Douglas for the Horticultural Society in 1826. This currant is the finest of ribes and in the very front rank of all spring-flowering shrubs, being one of those that never fail to blossom well. Whilst all its forms are beautiful, some are preferable ; the following is a selection :—

Var. ALBIDUM, *Paxton.*—Flowers white, with only a slight tinge of colour. In my experience this variety is not so robust as the red ones.

Var. ATRORUBENS.—Flowers of a very deep red but smaller, and in smaller racemes than the type.

Var. BROCKLEBANKII.—Leaves a good yellow, the colour lasting well.

Var. PLENA.—Flowers double, but inferior in beauty.

Var. SPLENDENS.—Sent out by Mr Smith of Newry about the end of last century, this is, I consider, one of the finest forms of flowering currant known. It approaches the blood-red tint indicated by the specific name nearer than any other except atrorubens, and unlike that form, unites a goodly size of flower and raceme with its richness of colour.

A variety named " King Edward VII " has intense crimson flowers and is of dwarfer habit ; probably the best variety.

All the forms of R. sanguineum are easily propagated by cuttings of naked wood like the gooseberry.

Closely allied to R. sanguineum are the two following—sometimes regarded as varieties of it :—

R. GLUTINOSUM, *Bentham.*—This differs from R. sanguineum in the young shoots and leaves being furnished with glandular glutinous hairs, and in being less downy ; also in its mostly pendulous racemes. It is inferior in garden value. Native of California and Washington.

R. MALVACEUM, *Smith.*—Leaves bristly, rough, and finely wrinkled above, the lower surface and stalk covered with a grey felt with which are mixed glandular hairs. The flower-stalk, ovary, and calyx are also covered with bristly down. Flowers bright rose, smaller and not so beautiful as in R. sanguineum. From that species and R. glutinosum it is distinct in having the ovary and style covered with white hairs. Native of California.

R. SATIVUM, *Syme.* RED CURRANT
(R. rubrum of most authors, not *Linnæus* ; R. vulgare, *Janczewski*, not *Lamarck*)

Little need be said here about the red currant, so well known in its cultivated form in English fruit gardens. It is an unarmed, spreading shrub with three- or five-lobed leaves, 2 to 4 ins. across, heart-shaped at the base ;

very downy beneath, and with scattered hairs above, at least when young ; stalk from half to twice as long as the blade. Flowers saucer-shaped, flattish, greenish, produced in recurved racemes from the joints of last year's wood. Fruit juicy, red and shining ; in a cultivated variety (ALBUM) white. Native of Europe. Of little interest except in fruit gardens. The true R. RUBRUM, *Linnæus*, found wild in Britain, is sometimes met with in gardens under the name of R. Schlectendalii, *Lange*. Its racemes are horizontal or ascending, not drooping or pendent as in sativum, and the flowers are urn-shaped or broadly funnel-shaped rather than saucer-shaped. Cultivated forms of this species are grown in the gardens of Scandinavia, but in Western and Central Europe the cultivated red and white currants are exclusively R. sativum.

R. WARSCEWICZII, *Janczewski*, is near R. rubrum, but has larger, pinkish flowers and more highly coloured, more acid and larger blackish purple fruits. Flowers of the same shape, but in pendulous racemes. Siberia and Amurland ; introduced in 1903. R. TRISTE, *Pallas*, is the American form of red currant, a shrub of laxer habit than R. sativum, the leaves white with down beneath when young ; flowers purplish ; fruit red, small and hard. It is said to be pretty and graceful in blossom in the United States and Canada, where it inhabits cold bogs and woods from New Hampshire to Nova Scotia. It is a native also of N. Asia. R. PETRÆUM, *Wulfen*, is another of the red currant group, widely spread in a state of nature in Europe and N. Africa. It has no value as an ornamental shrub, its flowers being green suffused with purple, somewhat bell-shaped, in horizontal or slightly nodding racemes, 3 or 4 ins. long. The leaves are more deeply lobed than in the common red currant, the lobes pointed. Fruit roundish, flattened somewhat at the end, red, very acid.

R. SPECIOSUM, *Pursh*

(Bot. Mag., t. 3530 ; R. fuchsioides, *Mocino and Sesse*)

A deciduous, spiny shrub, 6 to 12 ft. high, the young shoots furnished with gland-tipped bristles. Leaves three- sometimes five-lobed, sparsely toothed, and from ¾ to 1¼ ins. long and wide, with smaller ones often obovate and tapered at the base ; usually quite glabrous ; stalk slender, scarcely as long as the blade, with a few glandular bristles, especially at the base. Flowers rich red, usually two to five in pendulous clusters, the main-stalk longer and less glandular than the minor ones. Calyx tubular, ½in. long, glandular ; sepals four, not reflexed ; petals four, about as long as the sepals ; stamens four, red, standing out ¾ in. beyond the calyx. Fruit glandular-bristly, red, ½ in. long, rarely seen in this country.

Native of California ; discovered by Menzies about 1793, and introduced from Monterey by a naval surgeon named Collie in 1828. As a flowering shrub it is the most beautiful of the gooseberries. Its young shoots are reddish, horizontal, or slightly dependent, and from their under-side the richly coloured, fuchsia-like blossoms hang profusely in rows during April and May. It is very distinct in the parts of the flower being in fours (not the usual fives), and in the very long highly coloured stamens. It is one of the earliest shrubs to break into leaf—often in early February. It shows to best advantage perhaps against a wall, where it will grow 10 or 12 ft. high, but is quite hardy in the open at Kew, where it has grown 6 or 7 ft. high. It can be rooted from cuttings, but does not strike readily ; layering is a more certain process.

R. TENUE, *Janczewski*

A deciduous shrub up to 6 or 8 ft. high of bushy habit and with slender unarmed, glabrous young shoots. Leaves broadly or roundish ovate in main outline, but deeply three- (sometimes five-) lobed as well as sharply and deeply toothed, each lobe pointed; the base cut straight across or slightly heart-shaped; 1 to 2¼ ins. long, scarcely so much wide; sprinkled with appressed bristles; stalk slender, ⅓ to 1 in. long, reddish. Racemes of male flowers 1½ to 2 ins. long, female ones shorter. Flowers brownish red, main flower-stalk slightly glandular. Fruit globose, red, ¼ in. wide.

Native of the Himalaya and W. China; introduced from the latter habitat by Wilson in 1900. It is closely related to our native R. alpinum, which differs in its greenish yellow flowers. Beyond its neat habit and small handsomely cut leaves, it has no particular merit. It is one of the earliest of the currants to burst into leaf in spring and flowers in April.

R. VALDIVIANUM, *Philippi*

(Bot. Mag., t. 9647; R. glandulosum, *Ruiz and Pavon*)

A deciduous shrub 6 to 12 ft. high, much branched; stems grey-hairy at first, sometimes producing sucker growths. Leaves ovate, 1 to 2½ ins. long, often nearly as wide, the base varying from cordate to slightly tapered; mostly three-lobed and coarsely toothed, apex pointed to rounded; bright green above, paler beneath and downy on the veins; stalk ½ to 1⅓ ins. long. Flowers yellow, ⅛ in. wide, ⅓ in. long, borne on downy, unisexual racemes, arching or pendulous, the males the larger and up to 3 ins. long by ½ in. wide; each raceme comes from the axil of a small, pointed bract; main and individual stalks greyish-hairy. Berry globose, ⅓ in. wide, purplish black, hairy, edible.

Native of Chile and the Argentine and grown at Kew over fifty years ago, re-introduced by H. F. Comber in 1926. It blooms in late April and May. Except for its liability to injury by late spring frosts, it is hardy. Some of its forms are described as having green flowers. The yellow-flowered ones are quite attractive.

R. VIBURNIFOLIUM, *A. Gray*

(Bot. Mag., t. 8094)

An evergreen, unarmed shrub, 7 or 8 ft. high against a wall; young shoots slightly downy at first, with numerous resin glands. Leaves ovate or oval, ¾ to 1¾ ins. long, ½ to 1¼ ins. wide; rounded at the base, blunt at the apex, coarsely toothed, glossy and glabrous above, almost or quite devoid of down beneath, but thickly sown with resin-dots which emit a very pleasant turpentine-like odour when rubbed; stalk downy, ⅛ to ⅙ in. long. Flowers ⅓ in. across, produced in April in erect racemes about 1 in. long, terminating short, densely leafy shoots; dull rose-coloured, the sepals spreading. Berry oval, red, ⅓ in. long.

Native of Lower California and Santa Catalina Island; introduced to Kew in 1897 but is no longer there. A remarkably distinct species, of little beauty, but interesting for its evergreen aromatically scented leaves. It needs wall protection when grown at Kew.

RICHEA SCOPARIA, *Hooker fil.* EPACRIDACEÆ

(Bot. Mag., t. 9632)

An evergreen shrub up to 10 ft. high, often, we are told, found wild in places up to 3500 ft. altitude as rounded very dense hummocks 2 to 3 ft. high and up to 8 ft. across. Leaves bright green, ¾ to 1½ ins. long, $\frac{1}{10}$ to ⅕ in. wide, linear-lanceolate, tapering from the base to a slender point, sheathing and completely covering the stem by the broadened base, slightly decurved, glabrous. Flowers closely packed in a terminal, stiffly erect, spike-like raceme, 2 to 4 ins. long, 1¼ ins. wide ; corolla obovate to ovoid, ¼ to ⅜ in. long, white with a flush of crimson round the tiny mucro ; it has no opening and encloses the five stamens which fall away with it.

Native of Tasmania and a remarkable ally of Epacris, conveying some suggestion of a monocotyledonous plant. It was first introduced by Mr Overall, a Tasmanian nurseryman, the plants now in cultivation were raised from seed collected by H. F. Comber in 1930. Whilst not likely to be a success in our colder localities, it is succeeding well in several gardens in the south of England. The place where I have seen it best is at Borde Hill with Col. Stephenson R. Clarke. It is evidently a sun-loving plant and Mr Comber recommends for it a moist acid soil.

ROBINIA. LEGUMINOSÆ

A genus of about twenty deciduous trees and shrubs confined to N. America, whose name commemorates Jean Robin, herbalist to Henry IV of France, and his son Vespasien. They are amongst the most ornamental of all hardy trees both in leaf and flower. The leaves are pinnate, and the pea-shaped flowers are borne in pendulous racemes. Pods flat, many-seeded. Stipules often developing into spines.

All the species thrive well in a soil of moderate quality. If given very rich or manured soil they grow so coarse and rank that the danger of damage by wind, due to the brittleness of the branches, is increased. The best method of propagation is by seed, but in the case of R. hispida and Kelseyi, and garden varieties, it is usual to graft them on roots or stems of R. Pseudacacia. This should be done in spring with leafless scions, and the union is more quickly and surely effected if the plants can be kept in a warm greenhouse. R. Pseudacacia, hispida, and Kelseyi can be increased also by suckers. The only hardy tree with which the Robinias can be confounded is Sophora japonica, whose unarmed branches and autumnal flowering readily distinguish it.

R. BOYNTONII, *Ashe*. BOYNTON ACACIA

(R. hispida rosea, *Hort.*)

A deciduous shrub up to 10 ft. high ; young shoots unarmed, glabrous or very finely downy. Leaves 6 to 10 ins. long, consisting of seven to thirteen leaflets which are oblong, blunt or pointed ; 1 to 2 ins. long, ½ to 1 in. wide, glabrous or soon becoming so. Flowers six to twelve together in loose racemes 2½ to 3½ ins. long, produced from the lower leaf-axils of the young shoots in May and June, each flower barely 1 in. long ; standard petal ¾ to 1 in. wide ; calyx ¼ in. wide, bristly. The colour is described by Ashe as " rose-purple, pink, or purple and pink on the outer portion, white or much paler at the base." Pod glandular-bristly.

Native of the E. United States from N. Carolina and Tennessee to Georgia and Alabama. It may have been introduced long ago and grown under the name " R. hispida rosea," but the plant definitely named Boyntonii by Ashe reached Kew in 1919. It is, however, not in cultivation at Kew at present. Ashe separates it from true hispida " by its greater size, more oblong leaflets, many-flowered racemes, short calyx-lobes and smoothness." The young shoots of that species are, of course, very bristly.

R. ELLIOTTII, *Ashe*. ELLIOTT ACACIA

I do not know that this species is in cultivation in this country, but it was distinguished as long ago as 1903 and has been cultivated in the United States since and before then. It would appear to be well worth introducing as one of the dwarfest of the robinias, its maximum height being given as about 6 ft. Its stems are erect wands with a few short stout branches near the top ; young shoots grey with down. There are eleven to fifteen leaflets to a leaf which are oval, ½ to 1 in. long, grey-downy beneath. Flowers " rose-purple or purple and white," nearly 1 in. long, produced in racemes five to ten together ; flower-stalks and calyx grey downy. Pod bristly. Blooms in May and June.

Native of the S.E. United States from N. Carolina to Georgia, chiefly near the coast. Like R. Boyntonii it has been grown as " hispida rosea," but that species differs in not having the grey down on the young shoots, leaves, flower-stalks, and calyx which makes R. Elliottii so distinct.

R. HARTWIGII, *Koehne*. HARTWIG ACACIA

(Gardeners' Chronicle, Nov. 21, 1931—Supplement)

A deciduous shrub up to 12 ft. high ; young shoots, leaf-stalks, flower-stalks, and calyx all downy and furnished with stalked glands. Leaves up to 6 or 7 ins. long, made up of eleven to twenty-three leaflets which are oval or inclined to ovate, ¾ to 1½ ins. long, downy on both sides but more especially underneath, which is greyish. Flowers whitish to rosy purple, nearly 1 in. long including the stalk, densely borne in June and July twenty to thirty together on racemes up to 4½ ins. long including an inch or more of bare stalk at the base. Calyx downy, ⅜ in. long, bell-shaped with triangular to awl-shaped lobes. Pod oblong, 2 to 3½ ins. long, furnished with down and glandular bristles.

Native of the S.E. United States from N. Carolina to Alabama. This is one of the charming dwarf section of the robinias, its distinctive mark being the mixture of down and stalked glands on the young shoots and leaf-stalks. It was first named in 1913 but had been known in cultivation since 1904 at least. A bush originally obtained from the Arnold Arboretum flowered beautifully at Kew in July 1931. The species is worthy of wide cultivation.

R. HISPIDA, *Linnæus*. ROSE ACACIA

(Bot. Mag., t. 311)

A deciduous, unarmed shrub, 6 to 8 ft. high, of lax, rather gaunt habit, spreading by means of underground suckers, the branches covered with gland-tipped bristles ⅛ in. long. Leaves pinnate, 6 to 10 ins. long ; leaflets seven to thirteen, each 1½ to 2½ ins. long, and from ¾ to 1½ ins. wide, oval or ovate with a short bristle-like tip, very dark green ; stalk hairy. Racemes 2 or 3 ins. long, nearly as much wide, carrying five to ten flowers. The flowers are the largest and most showy among robinias, each about 1¼ ins. long, with the rounded standard petal as much across, of a lovely deep rose ; calyx ½ to ⅔ in. long, with long, slender, awl-shaped teeth, and bristly like the flower-stalk. Pod 1½ to 2½ ins. long, ⅓ in. wide, thickly covered with gland-tipped bristles. Blossoms in May and June.

Var. MACROPHYLLA, *De Candolle* (var. inermis, *Carrière* ; R. macrophylla, *Hort.*).—Distinguished chiefly by the branches and leaf-stalks being nearly or quite free from bristles. The stalks of the racemes and flowers are hairy, but by no means so markedly so as in the type. The flowers are even larger and more brightly coloured, the leaves rounder.

Native of the south-eastern United States ; introduced in 1743. In a state of nature it spreads and renews itself by means of sucker-growths extending several feet in a single season, but in cultivation it is usually grafted as a standard on R. Pseudacacia so as to form a low, bushy-headed tree. Undoubtedly one of the loveliest of all trees of that character, it is, unfortunately, very liable to lose its branches during storms, owing to the brittle nature of its wood. For this reason a secluded spot is desirable for it. A remarkable fact in connection with this tree is the rarity with which it produces seed. It has probably never borne pods in this country, and even in a state of nature they are very seldom seen. The pods in the Kew Herbarium are three contributed by the late Mr T. Meehan of Philadelphia, to whom they had been sent in response to inquiries made in a public journal. He himself had made diligent search for seed-pods on the mountains of Tennessee, where the shrub grows in great abundance, but never found any. The defect seems to be in the male part of the flower, and due to the absence of pollen. Still, fertile plants do exist in N. America, and from them no doubt a seed-bearing race could be established.

R. KELSEYI, *Hutchinson*

(Bot. Mag., t. 8213)

A lax-habited, deciduous shrub or small tree, with glabrous, slender branches. Leaves pinnate, 4 to 6 ins. long ; leaflets nine or eleven, oblong to ovate, 1 to 2 ins. long, $\frac{1}{3}$ to $\frac{5}{8}$ in. wide, pointed, glabrous. Flowers brightly rose-coloured, in small clusters at the base of the young twigs ; these clusters are sometimes simple racemes of three to eight flowers, but they are frequently forked or triplicate, the stalks always covered with glandular hairs. Each flower is $\frac{3}{4}$ to 1 in. long, with a rounded standard petal $\frac{3}{4}$ in. across ; calyx $\frac{1}{4}$ in. long, glandular-hairy, teeth narrow, awl-shaped. Pod 2 ins. long, $\frac{1}{3}$ in. wide, covered with reddish gland-tipped bristles $\frac{1}{8}$ in. long.

The origin of this beautiful robinia is not definitely known. It was put into commerce about 1901, by Mr Harlan P. Kelsey, of Boston, U.S.A., who informs me in a letter that it was " discovered in our nursery apparently growing spontaneously. We thought at first it was a cross between R. hispida and R. Pseudacacia, but now we think it is a true species that has crept into the collections from the southern Allegheny Mountains." It was introduced to Kew in 1903, and is certainly one of the most beautiful shrubs added to gardens in recent years. The flowers appear in great profusion in June, and they are followed by handsome red pods. Its affinity with R. hispida, especially the smooth-branched form, is apparent, but it is abundantly distinct. Judging by its behaviour at Kew it can be made into a small tree, but it is very brittle. Increase is easily effected by grafting on roots of R. Pseudacacia in spring.

A new hybrid called R. SLAVINII, *Rehder*, was introduced to Kew in 1922. It originated from seed of R. Kelseyi collected by Mr Slavin, in 1914, in the Durand-Eastman Park, Rochester, N.Y., the pollen parent being R. pseudacacia. The flowers are rosy pink, more numerous on the raceme than those of R. Kelseyi and the pod is warty. It is of more vigorous, tree-like habit than R. Kelseyi.

R. LUXURIANS, *C. K. Schneider*

(Bot. Mag., t. 7726 and in former editions as R. neomexicana)

A deciduous shrub or small tree, 20 to 40 ft. high, with a trunk 12 ins. or more thick; branchlets downy. Leaves pinnate, 6 to 12 ins. long, with downy stalks; leaflets fifteen to twenty-five, oval to slightly ovate, 1 to 1¾ ins. long, ½ to ⅔ in. wide; with a bristle-like tip; stipules spiny, ultimately 1 in. long. Racemes 2 to 3 ins. long, 2 ins. wide, the stalk covered with brown shaggy hairs. Flowers ¾ to 1 in. long pale rose, each on a hairy stalk ¼ in.

ROBINIA KELSEYI (see p. 182)

long; the standard petal large, the calyx glandular, shaggy, with slender teeth. Pods 3 or 4 ins. long, ⅓ in. wide, covered with gland-tipped bristles ⅛ in. or more long.

Native of Colorado, New Mexico, Arizona, and S. Utah, in places at 7000 ft. above sea-level. First discovered by Dr Thurber in 1851; introduced to Kew in 1887, where the original tree is now 30 ft. high, with a trunk 12 ins. in diameter. It flowers very prettily every year in June, and frequently a second time in August. It differs from R. Pseudacacia in its bristly pods, and from R. viscosa in the young twigs not being viscid. It is said to be found more often as a shrub than as a tree in a wild state.

R. HOLDTII, *Beissner.*—A hybrid between R. luxurians and R. Pseudacacia whose racemes are looser and longer than in R. luxurians and the flowers of a paler colour. The keel and wing-petals are almost white, the standard pale red with white markings. Habit and vigour of growth similar to those of R. Pseudacacia. Pod rather glandular. Obtained by Mr Von Holdt, Alcott, Colorado, and put into commerce about 1902.

R. Pseudacacia, *Linnæus*. Locust, Acacia

A deciduous tree, 70 to 80 ft. high, with a large, rounded head of branches, and a trunk 2 to 4 ft. in diameter, covered with a rugged, deeply furrowed bark. Leaves pinnate, 6 to 12 ins. long; leaflets in five and a half to eleven and a half pairs, oval or ovate, 1 to 2 ins. (sometimes 2½) ins. long in the typical form, covered with silvery hairs when quite young, eventually nearly glabrous. Stipules at first ½ in. long, downy, becoming stout, persistent spines 1 in. long; most conspicuous on young trees and suckers. Racemes 3 to 7 ins. long, 1½ to 2 ins. wide, pendulous. Flowers ¾ in. long; white, fragrant; each on a slender stalk, ⅓ in. long; standard petal blotched with yellow at the base; calyx ⅓ in. long, downy. Pod 2½ to 3½ ins. long, ½ in. wide, upper seam winged, lower one thickened, containing four to ten seeds, glabrous.

Native of the eastern United States; introduced to France about 1601 and to England soon after. The first plant sent to France was planted by Vespasien Robin in the Jardin des Plantes at Paris, where the ancient stump still remains. As an ornamental tree the robinia has much to recommend it. Its graceful feathery foliage is singularly effective in healthy trees, and when the tree is loaded with its white racemes in June the contrast of white and green is very effective. It grows with great rapidity when young, and its branches are apt to be broken off by wind in consequence. A judicious shortening back of the shoots in winter is helpful in inducing a sturdier growth. When old, the tree is apt to lose its large branches by their splitting off from the main trunk, or if the tree has been allowed to "fork," nearly half of it may be lost at a time. The best way to prevent this is to keep the tree to a single leader until it is at least 25 ft. high, so that one strong straight trunk is formed, and no branch allowed to develop sufficiently to rival it. It is propagated by seeds or by the suckers the roots produce so plentifully, especially after the parent tree is felled.

Perhaps no American tree has made itself so thoroughly at home in Europe as this. The railway cuttings south of Paris are in places completely overrun with it, and I have noticed it thoroughly established in the Rhone Valley above Geneva, and on the hillsides between Trieste and the Chateau of Miramar.

The locust produces a timber valuable on account of its peculiar quality of resisting decay in contact with the soil. On this account it is highly valued for making gate-posts and similar articles. Owing to the representations of William Cobbett, the famous Radical, who about 1825 to 1828 extolled the tree and its uses in his own peculiarly vigorous fashion, quite a mania for the tree was established. He himself set up as a dealer in seeds and plants, and to such purpose had he written up the tree and its virtues that he was, for a time, unable to meet the demand, although it is recorded that he imported seeds from America in tons. It did not prove a success as a forest tree, and is now rarely planted except for ornament. But every few years a controversy is started as to its value as a timber tree in Britain. There is no doubt about the value of the timber for certain minor purposes—it was once, and may be now, largely used for pins ("tree-nails") to fasten timbers together in shipbuilding—but it is not produced in sufficient bulk, nor is it of a quality to render it of great value for constructive purposes.

An extraordinary number of seminal varieties of the locust have been raised in Europe. Between three and four dozen of them are cultivated at Kew, but many are not sufficiently distinct to require mention here. The following may be regarded as the most important :—

Var. Angustifolia (myrtifolia).—Leaflets small and narrow, about 1 in. long, ¼ in. wide.

Var. AUREA.—Leaves golden yellow in early summer, turning green later.

Var. BELLA-ROSEA.—Flowers rose-coloured ; leaflets small ; elegant.

Var. BESSONIANA LATIFOLIA.—Leaflets few (usually five) and large, each
2 to 4 ins. long. Var. COLUTEOIDES. Flowers and racemes small, very
abundant.

Var. CRISPA.—Leaflets twisted and wavy ; branches unarmed.

Var. DECAISNEANA.—A fine strong grower, with large racemes of rose-
coloured flowers. It appeared in France about 1862. Very handsome.

Var. FASTIGIATA.—A slender columnar tree, narrower even in proportion
o its height than the Lombardy poplar. Also known as " pyramidalis."

Var. HETEROPHYLLA.—Leaflets strangely diverse in shape, varying from
1 to 3 ins. long and from $\frac{1}{8}$ to $\frac{3}{4}$ in. wide.

Var. INERMIS.—A mop-headed, unarmed small tree which rarely or never
flowers. Very frequent in villa gardens in the London suburbs ; UMBRA-
CULIFERA is somewhat similar. There is a variegated form—INERMIS
VARIEGATA.

Var. MICROPHYLLA.—Leaflets $\frac{1}{2}$ in. long, $\frac{1}{8}$ in. wide.

Var. MONOPHYLLA (unifoliolata).—Leaflets reduced in number to one, two,
or three, being either the terminal leaflet alone (always much larger than
n the type and often 4 ins. long by $1\frac{1}{2}$ ins. wide), or accompanied by one or
two others about the normal size. This remarkable variety, which flowers
freely, is also represented by a fastigiate form (MONOPHYLLA FASTIGIATA),
and one with slender semi-pendulous branches (MONOPHYLLA PENDULA).

Var. REHDERI.—A dwarf bushy tree, unarmed, with rather erect branches.

Var. ROSYNSKIANA.—Leaves up to 15 ins. long and pendulous ; leaflets
large. A curiosity.

Var. TORTUOSA.—Branches curiously twisted. Racemes small and thinly
set with bloom.

Var. SEMPERFLORENS.—In fine sunny summers this continues to flower
more or less throughout the growing season.

Var. VARIEGATA has the leaflets mottled with white.

Loudon mentions a yellow-flowered variety—" flore luteo "—but if ever
such a plant existed, which is doubtful, it has disappeared. Such a variety
would be a great acquisition.

R. VISCOSA, *Ventenat*. CLAMMY LOCUST

(R. glutinosa, *Sims*, Bot. Mag., t. 560)

A deciduous tree, 30 to 40 ft. high, with a trunk 12 to 18 ins. thick, and
often furnished with large burrs ; young branches covered with glands which
exude a sticky substance that adheres to the fingers when touched. Leaves
pinnate, 3 to 10 ins. long, the main-stalk hairy and viscid like the young twigs.
Leaflets eleven to twenty-one, oval or ovate, 1 to 2 ins. long, $\frac{1}{3}$ to $\frac{3}{4}$ in. wide ;
dark green above, paler and at first slightly downy beneath, ultimately glabrous.
Stipules at first $\frac{1}{4}$ in. long, becoming longer and spiny with age. Racemes
2 to $2\frac{1}{2}$ ins. long, almost as wide, with a naked stalk half as long. Flowers
$\frac{3}{4}$ in. long, ten to fifteen in a raceme, without fragrance ; petals pale rose with
a yellow blotch on the standard ; calyx dark red, hairy. Pod 2 to $3\frac{1}{2}$ ins. long,
covered with viscid glands.

Native of the mountains of North Carolina, where it was originally discovered by Wm. Bartram in 1776. It was introduced to France by Michaux in
1791, and six years later to England. It is a smaller tree than R. Pseudacacia
and of more stunted growth, but it flowers very freely and makes a bright
picture towards the end of June. The viscid substance on the branches renders

it easily distinguishable, although this appears to vary in amount, and is sometimes not very discernible. According to Sargent it is one of the rarest of American trees, and from the time of Michaux to 1882 was never found in a genuinely wild state. But it is now naturalised in many parts of the eastern United States. It is not common in English gardens, but there are several old trees at Kew, the largest of which has a trunk 5 ft. 3 ins. in girth at 5 ft. from the ground, which is considerably more than the dimensions recorded of wild specimens. These old trees are almost unarmed, the spines only occurring on exceptionally vigorous shoots. A handsome tree in bloom.

The robinia called "bella-rosea" is a form of a hybrid raised early in the

ROBINIA VISCOSA

nineteenth century between R. viscosa and Pseudacacia and now known as R. AMBIGUA, *Poiret* (syns. R. dubia, *Foucault* ; R. intermedia, *Bodin*). I do not know if the original hybrid is still in cultivation but the variety, which Dr Rehder calls R. AMBIGUA BELLA-ROSEA, has been cultivated at Kew for at least fifty years. This variety is marked by its small leaflets, the soft luxuriant foliage and elegant habit ; flowers pale rose-coloured. A slight stickiness of the young shoots indicates its descent from R. viscosa.

ROMNEYA. PAPAVERACEÆ

A genus of two semi-herbaceous shrubs, both Californian, and known generally as "tree poppies." The name commemorates Dr F. Romney Robinson, an astronomer at Armagh in 1844, when the genus was founded. There is a hybrid between the two following species.

R. Coulteri, *Harvey*

(The Garden, Nov. 8, 1884)

A semi-shrubby plant, with succulent herbaceous stems 4 to 8 ft. high, according to the mildness of the climate in which it grows. Leaves varying much in size according to the strength of the shoot which bears them, but averaging from 3 to 5 ins. long, and of a very glaucous colour ; they are obovate to pinnately lobed, the end lobe usually much the largest and itself more or less lobed, glabrous except for a few spine-like bristles on the stalk and midrib. Flowers solitary or in pairs, terminating short twigs near the end of the stem, each one 4 to 5 ins. across, with five or six overlapping, satiny-white, delicately textured petals surrounding a mass of golden yellow stamens 1 to 1½ ins. across. Calyx glabrous.

This beautiful plant, discovered in California by Dr Coulter in 1844, is not hardy in all situations, but is well worth the protection it requires. Perhaps in localities where it is not absolutely hardy the best place for it is in front of a south or west wall, where the shelter of a glass light or something of the kind can be given in winter. Treated in this way I have seen it thriving splendidly as far north as Chester. It should have a warm, well-drained loamy soil, and abundant moisture during the growing season. It is not easily increased by cuttings of the stems, but its thick fleshy roots afford a ready means. They should be cut up into lengths of about 2 ins., placed in pots, and just covered with sandy soil. A mild heat is desirable. The roots of old plants send up young shoots, and these also may be removed, potted, and given warmth. So sensitive to injury is this plant at the root that young plants should be kept in pots until put out in permanent quarters. It flowers from July to October, the blossoms delightfully fragrant.

R. Trichocalyx, *Eastwood*

(Bot. Mag., t. 8002)

A shrub not distinguishable in stem and leaf characters from the preceding, but at once recognised when in flower by the bristly hairs on the calyx. The flowers are the same in size and colour. Until 1898, this species was confused with R. Coulteri, and no doubt the two are very closely related. It is a better plant for colder situated gardens, being of hardier constitution, not so gross in habit, and cultivated with less trouble. At Kew it thrives very well in a border on the south side of a glasshouse, without other protection than that gives. It can be increased by cuttings of the stem taken from ripe shoots and put in gentle heat. It appears to have been first noticed in flower in the garden of the late Mr Hiatt C. Baker, of Almondsbury, near Bristol, in 1902.

ROSA. Rose. ROSACEÆ

In the great natural order of Rosaceæ, which gives to gardens more beautiful hardy deciduous trees and shrubs than any other, no genus stands out with greater distinctness than the one from which it derives its name. The leading characters of Rosa are its usually very thorny stems, the alternate pinnate leaves, the stipules (except in a few species) joined to the base of the leaf-stalk, the numerous stamens and carpels, and the rounded or elongated fruit, which is really a fleshy development

of the calyx-tube, containing, when ripe, a large number of dry, har᷈
seeds. The species are spread over all the temperate parts of the norther᷈
hemisphere, but three or four only of them occur south of the Tropic c
Cancer.

There is an extraordinary diversity in the number of species of ros
as estimated by different authors. The late Mr J. G. Baker, the leadin᷈
British authority, some years ago estimated them at about seventy. A
the present time new species from China and elsewhere have brough᷈
the number up over a hundred. Other writers have made over thre᷈
hundred species. No group of plants, in fact, unless it be Rubus, ha᷈
suffered more at the hands of injudicious and incompetent species maker
than this. One gentleman is known to have cut his species so fine tha᷈
two of them could be found on the same bush.

The wild roses suffer somewhat in the estimation of planters becaus
they have to bear comparison with those innumerable garden types
evolved by ages of cultivation and selection, which include what are
by common consent, the loveliest products of the garden. Few of them
remain in bloom more than a month, where again a comparison is mad
to their disadvantage when the hybrid perpetual, teas, and other long
blossoming races are considered. Still, when the wild roses are regarded
as in justice they should be, from the standpoint of their own merits
there are few hardy shrubs which surpass the best of them in beauty
grace, and fragrance. Take the humblest of them all, the dog-rose anᴄ
the sweet-briar of our hedgerows, is either of them excelled in thei᷈
sweetness and charm on a fresh June morning? And many have iᴦ
their often large, abundant, and handsomely coloured fruits a beautᴟ
in autumn the garden races do not possess.

Cultivation.—These roses are of the simplest cultivation. Theᴟ
all do well in a good loamy soil such as suits the garden types, althougᴉ
it need not be quite so rich. Many of the stronger, more or less ramblinᴦ
growers, like multiflora, moschata, arvensis, and Wichuraiana, are verᴟ
well adapted for planting in big shrubberies, on rough slopes, agains᷈
unsightly fences, or on the outskirts of woodland. The smaller anᴄ
daintier ones like sicula, Ecæ, Webbiana, lutea, horrida, etc., will neeᴄ
a front place in the ordinary shrubbery; some may even be planteᴄ
in the rock garden. The common bushy type, such as sericea, rugosa
Roxburghii, are pleasing as isolated shrubs on lawns. Whilst all thosᴇ
strong enough and bushy enough to kill the grass beneath their branchᴇ
are admirable for the wild garden.

Most of the species can be propagated by cuttings made of firm wooᴅ
in July and August, and placed in gentle heat. Cuttings should be madᴇ
of short twigs with a " heel " of older wood attached. Many of thᴇ
robuster sorts can be increased by cuttings put under hand-glasses out-of-
doors, or even in the open ground, but this is not so quick and certaiᴎ
as where a gentle bottom heat is given. But some do not root at alᴌ
freely, such as Webbiana, lutea, the Scotch rose group, and generallᴟ
those with very prickly stems and small leaves. For such of those aᴤ
have spreading roots and sucker freely, like the Scotch roses, it is besᴛ
to break them up into small pieces and replant them; pieces with a littlᴇ

root attached may be potted and placed in a close frame for a short time. For the remainder it is best to adopt the layering method described in the introductory chapters, which may, indeed, be advantageously adopted for all the non-suckering species where a few plants only are wanted. Seeds may, of course, be used, but so freely do the wild roses intercross through insect agency, that they can never be relied on to come true unless the plants are isolated. At Kew, where the species of Rosa are grown together for purposes of study and comparison, it has long been ascertained that it is a waste of time raising seedlings from them ; and seeds of other than isolated plants are no longer offered in exchange. Most of these mongrels are worthless for garden purposes, and so common are they that they have ceased to have any scientific interest.

The principles explained in an early chapter govern the pruning of roses as of other shrubs. Most of them produce flowers on short twigs issuing from the previous year's growth ; the shoots cannot therefore be shortened back without reducing the crop of flowers. Such pruning as is necessary for these is chiefly a matter of removing the older wornout stems. Those of the gallica and indica types, which flower on the growths of the current year, may be pruned back in the same way as hybrid perpetuals and tea roses are.

The flowering of these wild types commences soon after the middle of May with sericea, hispida, and the Scotch roses ; and it ends in August with setigera and Wichuraiana ; the great majority blossom in June and July.

R. ACICULARIS, *Lindley*

A vigorous bush up to 4 ft. high, abundantly furnished with bristle-like prickles on the young stems. Leaves 3 to 5 ins. long, consisting of five to nine leaflets, which are $\frac{3}{4}$ to $1\frac{1}{2}$ ins. long, $\frac{3}{8}$ to $\frac{5}{8}$ in. wide, oval or obovate, bluish green, toothed, usually downy beneath ; stipules $\frac{1}{2}$ to 1 in. long, narrow, pointed, toothed. Flowers solitary, in pairs or threes, bright rosy pink, $2\frac{1}{4}$ ins. across ; the stalk 1 to $1\frac{1}{2}$ ins. long, more or less glandular-bristly ; sepals 1 to $1\frac{1}{4}$ ins. long, expanded at the end into a leaflike tip. Fruit 1 in. long, half as wide, more or less pear-shaped, bright rose, crowned with erect, persistent sepals.

A species very widely spread in nature, extending across the northern part of the Old World from Finland to Japan, and through Siberia across Behring Straits to N. Alaska. It is worth cultivating in semi-wild spots for its large pink flowers and abundant red hips.

R. SAYI, *Schweinitz*, is a N. American ally, perhaps a form of acicularis. It, too, has densely prickly or bristly stems, and sepals erect on the fruit, but the leaflets are often doubly-toothed, the flower-stalk is not so glandular-bristly, and the fruit is rounder.

R. acicularis differs from blanda in its densely bristly stems, and from arkansana in the erect (not spreading) sepals on the fruit. (See also Englemannii and nipponensis.)

R. ALBA, *Linnæus*

(Andrews' Roses, t. 10)

A bush 6 to 8 ft. high, of strong growth, armed with prickles of various shapes and sizes, but usually more or less hooked. Leaflets five or seven, greyish, wrinkled, oblong, broadly oval or ovate, simply toothed, 1 to $2\frac{1}{2}$ ins.

long, downy beneath. Flowers 3 ins. across, single, white or blush-coloured produced in clusters ; stalk, sepals, and lower part of calyx-tube bristly Fruit bright red, oblong, ¾ in. long, with the sepals fallen away.

This beautiful rose—the type of a pleasing group of garden varieties characterised by soft pink, often double flowers, and a charming fragrance— is generally considered to be a natural hybrid between R. gallica and R. canina dumetorum. It is found wild in several parts of Europe, and ha also been found in England, but always in places which show it to have beer an escape from gardens.

Var. SUAVEOLENS, *Dieck*, is one of the chief roses from whose flower attar is obtained. It is largely grown in Roumelia and Bulgaria.

R. MACRANTHA, *Desportes.*—A hybrid of similar origin to that of R. alba. Thi beautiful rose appears first to have been found wild in N.W. France in 1823. It is a erect bush, ultimately 6 ft. or more high, whose leaves have five or seven divisions The flowers are in clusters of three to five, each blossom 3 to 4 ins. across, single, flushee with rose on first opening, then becoming almost pure white. Its large blossoms produced in great profusion, make it one of the loveliest of the wild or semi-wild types It may be mentioned that R. Dupontii—a beautiful rose, but not so free and hardy a this—is sometimes sold as R. macrantha.

R. ALBERTII, *Regel*

A shrub 2 to 4 ft. high, the stems armed with numerous, straight, needle like prickles. Leaves 1 to 3 ins. long, composed of five to nine leaflets, whic are ovate, obovate, or roundish, ¼ to 1¼ ins. long, sharply and often doubl toothed on the terminal part, glabrous above, minutely downy beneath, ofte glandular on the margins ; common stalk downy and glandular. Flower white, 1½ ins. across, solitary ; flower-stalk glandular, calyx and outside o sepals glabrous, the last lanceolate, woolly at the edges and inside. Frui ¾ in. long, slenderly pear-shaped, the sepals falling away when ripe.

Discovered in 1877 in the Thianschan Mountains of Turkestan, an introduced to cultivation in the St Petersburg Botanic Garden by Dr Alber Regel. It is allied to R. spinosissima, but is distinguished by the down under-surface of the leaves. The plant generally grown under the name ha yellow flowers, and appears to be nearer R. Ecæ.

R. ANEMONEFLORA, *Fortune*

(R. triphylla, *Roxburgh*)

A bush with spreading branches armed with scattered slender prickle and three- or five-foliolate leaves—the latter on the young barren shoots o the first year. Leaflets ovate or ovate-lanceolate, 1½ to 3 ins. long, very finel and simply toothed, glabrous on both surfaces, dark green above, pale below Flowers blush-white, 1 to 1½ ins. across, in loose corymbs, double ; the inne petals narrow and ragged ; stalks slender, naked, or with a few glandula bristles. This rose was introduced from China in 1844, by Fortune, wh found it in a garden at Shanghai. It has not been found wild, and is nov believed to be a hybrid between lævigata and multiflora. It is a curious an rather pretty rose, but not very hardy.

R. ARKANSANA, *Porter*. ARKANSAS ROSE

(R. blanda arkansana, *Best*)

A small bush, under 3 ft. high, whose stems are densely covered with fin straight prickles. Leaflets five to eleven, oval or obovate, tapering at th base, ½ to 1 in. long simply and sharply toothed, glabrous or very slightl owny. Flowers in clusters or solitary, 1½ ins. wide, pink ; sepals glabrous or lightly downy, with long narrow points. Fruit ½ in. in diameter, glabrous, globose, red, crowned with the spreading sepals.

Native of the central United States. It has been placed as a variety of R. blanda, but its weaker habit, its densely prickly stems, and spreading (not erect) sepals on the fruit distinguish it.

R. ARVENSIS, *Hudson*. AYRSHIRE ROSE

A deciduous trailing or climbing shrub, with long slender branches no thicker than stout string, and armed with scattered, hooked prickles ⅓ in. long. Leaflets usually five, or seven, ovate, oval or obovate, ¾ to 2 ins. long, simply toothed, glabrous and shining green above, a little paler or glaucous below. Flowers white, with little or no fragrance, 1½ to 2 ins. across, one to several in a cluster ; stalks glandular ; calyx-tube glabrous, sepals entire, glandular outside, downy within, ½ in. long, deciduous. Fruit dark red, round or oval.

This rose, the type of the Ayrshire group of roses in gardens, is widely spread over Europe, and is abundant in hedgerows, etc., in England and Ireland, but (in spite of its name) much scarcer in Scotland. It is very easily distinguished among British roses by its thin shoots, which often grow several yards long in a season, and by the styles being united in a column. (The only other British species with joined styles is R. STYLOSA, *Desvois*—a sturdy bush with the dog-rose habit.) The name " Ayrshire rose " appears to have arisen from a plant growing at Loudon Castle, in the county of Ayr, and now known as

Var. CAPREOLATA, Bot. Mag., t. 2054 (R. capreolata, *Neill*).—This differs from ordinary R. arvensis in having the leaves quite green on both sides and retaining them on the branches longer.

Var. PLENA has double white flowers and is a very pretty rambling rose, useful for quickly covering unsightly banks, etc.

R. BANKSIÆ, *R. Brown*. BANKSIAN ROSE

A climbing shrub, up to 40 ft. high, with slender, glabrous, unarmed shoots. Leaves with three or five leaflets, which are 1 to 2½ ins. long, one-third to half as wide ; oblong-lanceolate, pointed, simply toothed, glabrous on both surfaces except that the midrib beneath and common stalk are sometimes lightly downy ; stipules narrow, and soon falling away. Flowers white or yellow, 1¼ ins. diameter, numerous in an umbel, each flower on a stalk about 1 in. long, slightly fragrant ; sepals ⅓ in. long, ovate, entire, downy within. Fruit globose, about the size of a pea, with the sepals fallen away.

Native of China, where it has long been cultivated. It was a garden form, one with double white flowers (ALBA PLENA, Bot. Mag., t. 1954), that was first introduced to Kew in 1807 by Wm. Kerr when collecting for that institution in China. In 1824 the yellow double-flowered variety was introduced by Mr Parks for the Horticultural Society. The single yellow form (LUTEA) appeared about 1870 (see Bot. Mag., t. 7171). All this time what ought perhaps to be regarded as the type—the form with single white flowers—was unknown. From the following note, contributed to the Royal Horticultural Society's *Journal*, 1909, p. 218, it would appear, however, to have existed in the British Isles some years previous to Kerr's introduction of the double white form in 1807 :—

" Four years ago I found a rose growing on the wall of Megginch Castle, Strathtay, Scotland, which seemed to be a very slender-growing form of R. Banksiæ. Capt.

Drummond of Megginch told me it was a rose that his ancestor, Robt. Drummond, had brought with other plants from China in 1796. This old rose had been repeatedly cut to the ground by severe winters, and had rarely, if ever, flowered. The impression however, was that it was white and very small. Cuttings which I took to Nice flowered this year, proving themselves to be the typical single white Banksian rose, so long sought for and hidden away in this nook of Scotland for more than one hundred years."

The Banksian rose in all its forms is one of the most lovely of all, but unfortunately it is too tender and too fond of the sun to thrive in any but the more favoured parts of the British Isles. The yellow-flowered forms are considered the hardier, and will succeed on a warm wall in the south of England. But they find their most congenial conditions in the heat and brilliant sunlight of S. France, Italy, Dalmatia, etc., where these roses, but especially the double yellow, make one of the chief glories of the gardens in spring.

R. BEGGERIANA, *Schrenk*

A shrub 6 to 10 ft. high ; stems and branches armed with light-coloured hooked spines, $\frac{1}{4}$ to $\frac{1}{3}$ in. long, often arranged in pairs at the base of each leaf-stalk, and with numerous others scattered near the base of the stems Leaflets five to nine, $\frac{1}{3}$ to 1 in. long, oval or slightly obovate, simply toothed except near the base, glabrous on both surfaces or downy beneath and on the common stalk, grey-green. Flowers white, 1 to $1\frac{1}{2}$ ins. across, produced in clusters up to nine or more. Fruit globose, glabrous, red at first, finally purplish, $\frac{1}{4}$ to $\frac{1}{3}$ in. across, sepals ultimately falling away.

Native of Central Asia, the leaves having a sweet-briar scent ; flowers unpleasantly scented ; introduced about 1881. A rose nearly allied to the above is R. ANSERINIFOLIA, *Boissier*, found in Afghanistan, Beluchistan, etc., which appears to differ only in the leaves being downy on both sides.

R. BLANDA, *Aiton*. SMOOTH or MEADOW ROSE

A shrub 4 to 6 ft. high, whose stems are quite unarmed or furnished with a few slender, scattered, straight prickles. Leaves 2 to 5 ins. long, with smooth broad stipules and a glabrous or slightly downy stalk ; leaflets usually five or seven, obovate, narrowed towards the base, $\frac{3}{4}$ to $2\frac{1}{2}$ ins. long, shortly stalked, commonly quite glabrous, sometimes downy, simply toothed Flowers in clusters of three to seven or often solitary, $2\frac{1}{2}$ to 3 ins. across, rosy pink ; sepals 1 in. long, lanceolate, entire, with narrowly expanded tips, downy and sometimes bristly. Fruit globose or pear-shaped, red, $\frac{1}{3}$ to $\frac{1}{2}$ in. wide, crowned with erect and persistent sepals.

Widely spread in N. America from Canada and the eastern United States to the western States ; introduced in 1773. A handsome rose and one of the largest flowered of the purely wild types. It bears a close general resemblance to R. nutkana, but the often stout and hooked spines of the latter set in pairs at the base of each leaf-stalk afford a ready distinction.

R. BRACTEATA, *Wendland*. MACARTNEY ROSE

(Bot. Mag., t. 1377)

An evergreen shrub of rambling habit, reaching on walls in favoured places a height of 20 ft. Branches very thick and sturdy, covered with brownish down, and armed with pairs of stout, hooked prickles and numerous scattered bristly ones. Leaflets five to eleven, obovate, often widely truncate

at the end and finely toothed, ¾ in. to (in vigorous plants) 2 ins. long, ½ to
1 in. wide ; of a very deep green and highly polished above, either glabrous or
downy on the midrib beneath ; common stalk glandular-downy ; stipules
laciniated. Flowers 3 to 4 ins. across, white, borne singly on a very short
stalk which is surrounded by several large, laciniated, downy bracts. Calyx-
tube and sepals (the latter ¾ in. long) covered with a pale brown wool. Fruit
globose, orange-red, woolly, about 1½ ins. wide.

Native of China ; introduced in 1793 by Lord Macartney. This distinct
and remarkable rose is, unfortunately, not very hardy except in the south-west
counties and similar places, where its rich evergreen foliage and large flowers
make it one of the most striking of all the wild types. Near London, even
grown on a wall, it is occasionally damaged badly by frost. Its flowers appear
from June until late autumn, and have a delicate fruity perfume. The
" Marie Leonida " rose (or R. alba odorata of gardens), with creamy white
double flowers, is a cross between bracteata and lævigata.

R. CALIFORNICA, *Chamisso and Schlectendal*

A shrub 5 to 8 ft. high, the stems armed with stout, hooked prickles.
Leaves 3 to 5 ins. long, common stalk downy ; leaflets usually five or seven,
oval or ovate, 1 to 1½ ins. long, smooth or slightly downy above, downy
beneath, especially on the midrib and nerves, simply toothed. Flowers about
1½ ins. across, pink, frequently over a dozen in a cluster ; stalk and calyx-tube
glabrous ; sepals ½ in. or more long with expanded tips, sometimes glabrous,
sometimes downy. Fruit globose or slightly elongated, ⅓ to ½ in. wide, contracted into a well-defined neck below the persisting erect sepals.

Native of western N. America from British Columbia to California. It
differs from R. pisocarpa in the hooked spines, more numerous flowers in a
cluster, and larger fruit. It is represented in gardens by a very pretty double-
flowered variety—PLENA, and a dwarf one—NANA.

R. CANINA, *Linnæus.* DOG ROSE

A strong-growing shrub, from 6 to 12 ft. high ; stems armed with scattered
prickles which are uniform, hooked, with no mixture of smaller bristle-like
ones. Leaflets five or seven, ovate, oval, usually simply toothed and glabrous,
sometimes downy and doubly toothed. Flowers fragrant, white or pinkish,
in clusters ; two of the sepals are usually entire, two pinnately lobed on both
margins, and one similarly lobed on one margin only. Fruit egg-shaped or
roundish, bright red, with the sepals fallen away or remaining until the fruit
changes colour.

The dog rose in one or other of its forms is spread over most of the cooler
parts of Europe and W. Asia. It is naturalised in N. America. In the British
Isles it is one of the commonest and most beautiful of wild shrubs, giving to
English country lanes one of their sweetest and most characteristic charms.
For this reason the dog rose is out of place in the trim garden where so many
other roses with a richer beauty compete for room. The curiously diverse
form of the sepals furnishes the answer to an old-time Latin riddle translated
thus :—

> Five brothers of one house are we,
> All in one little family,
> Two have beards and two have none,
> And only half a beard has one.

Of all roses the dog rose is the most diverse and varied in its characters It may be taken as the type of a group of numerous forms ranging in importance from sub-species to minor varieties. Most of these are not of sufficient importance in a garden sense to need mention here, but the following more striking ones may be alluded to :—

Var. ANDEGAVENSIS, *Baker.*—Leaflets glabrous on both surfaces and without glands ; flower-stalks and base of calyx-tube with numerous glandular bristles.

Var. ARVATICA, *Baker.*— Leaflets glabrous above, paler, hairy, and glandular on the veins beneath ; doubly toothed ; flower-stalk glabrous.

Var. BAKERI.—Leaflets slightly hairy above, very downy and more or less glandular beneath ; flower-stalks short, glabrous or slightly bristly Closely allied to this is var. TOMENTELLA, *Baker.*

Var. CÆSIA.—A glaucous variety ; leaflets glabrous above, downy beneath ; flower-stalks with numerous bristles.

Var. CORIFOLIA, *Baker.*—Leaflets broadly ovate, stout, very downy but not glandular beneath, dull and slightly hairy above ; flower-stalks very short

Var. DUMETORUM, *Baker* (R. dumetorum, *Thuillier*).—Chiefly distinguished from ordinary canina by the dull grey hue and the downy character of its leaflets, without glands beneath ; flower-stalks glabrous. Often regarded as a distinct species. (Syn. R. corymbifera, *Borkhausen.*)

Var. LUTETIANA, *Baker.*—Leaflets glabrous on both sides ; flower-stalks short and glabrous.

Var. SUBCRISTATA, *Baker.*—Fruit with erect sepals adhering until the fruit is ripe ; leaflets glaucous green and smooth ; flower-stalk glabrous.

R. CANTABRIGENSIS, *Preston.* CAMBRIDGE ROSE

A very attractive hybrid raised in the Cambridge Botanic Garden from R. Hugonis crossed with R. sericea. Its flowers are yellow, but rather larger than in R. Hugonis and they are described as having only forty stamens, whereas R. Hugonis has twice as many. The leaves are fragrant, an inheritance from R. sericea. The hybrid received an Award of Merit at Vincent Square on 2nd June 1931, also later the Cory Cup as the best hybrid hardy shrub exhibited that year.

R. CAROLINA, *Linnæus*

A shrub 4 to 6 ft. high, with crowded, erect stems forming dense thickets ; prickles hooked or straight, usually in pairs at the base of the leaf. Leaves 3 or 4 ins. long, with generally five or seven leaflets, which are full green above, grey beneath, narrowly oval, ovate or obovate, 1 to 1½ ins. long, one-third as wide, finely and simply toothed, more or less downy beneath. Flowers 2 to 2½ ins. across, deep purplish rose, fragrant, produced in clusters on glandular stalks ; sepals 1 to 1¼ ins. long, long-pointed, glandular and downy. Fruit red, globose, or orange-shaped, ⅓ in. wide, glandular-hairy, with the sepals fallen away.

Native of eastern N. America ; introduced in 1726. This pretty rose is useful for forming close thickets in the wilder parts of the garden or in thin woodland, flowering from June to August. In good ground it spreads rapidly by underground suckers. It is similar in habit to R. virginiana (lucida) but is easily distinguished from both by its finely toothed leaflets, the absence of any bristly spines on the stems, and from virginiana especially by the dull green of its leaves.

Var. NUTTALLIANA.—Flowers larger, and produced up to September—some weeks later than the type. Put in commerce by Messrs Paul of Cheshunt about 1893.

R. CAUDATA, *Baker*

(Willmott, Genus Rosa, vol. ii., fig. 163)

A deciduous shrub up to 12 ft. high ; spines scattered, dilated at the base, stout, ⅓ in. long. Leaves 4 to 7 ins. long, consisting usually of seven or nine leaflets, the main-stalk with a few scattered glands and prickles. Leaflets oval to ovate, 1 to 2 ins. long, simply toothed, glabrous, rather glaucous beneath. Flowers 1½ to 2 ins. wide, bright red, produced in June a few together in corymbs, each on a glandular-bristly stalk 1 to 1¼ ins. long. Calyx-tube narrowly oblong, glandular-bristly ; the sepals developing a long tail-like apex from an ovate base, glabrous or nearly so. Fruit oblong, coral or orange-red, ¾ to 1 in. long, surmounted by the erect persisting sepals, beneath which it is narrowed to a long neck.

Native of W. Hupeh, China ; introduced by Wilson in 1907. Miss Willmott first flowered it in this country in June 1911, at Warley, where it proved a vigorous and beautiful rose. The tail-like sepals to which the specific name refers constitute perhaps its most distinctive character, although I have not seen them quite the maximum length (2 ins.) described by Baker. Nearly akin to it is

R. BANKSIOPSIS, *Baker*, which has rose-red flowers and coral-red or orange-red, globose fruits crowned with long, erect, persistent sepals, but the leaves are usually downy beneath and the flower-stalks and calyx-tube devoid of the glandular bristles so marked in R. caudata. Native of Hupeh and Szechuen ; introduced by Wilson in 1907 ; flowered at Warley in 1911. Miss Willmott commended it " not only for its flowers but also for its brilliant and striking masses of fruit in autumn."

R. CENTIFOLIA, *Linnæus*. CABBAGE ROSE

(R. gallica centifolia *Regel*)

A shrub up to 6 ft. in height, whose erect stems are armed with numerous prickles, the larger ones hooked. Leaflets five, of firm, even leathery texture, broadly oval, sometimes coarsely toothed, and markedly glandular on the margins and on the common stalk. Flowers very fragrant, borne in clusters, nearly always double, the numerous petals erect and overlapping like the leaves of a cabbage, red ; sepals 1 to 1¼ ins. long, pinnately lobed and, like the calyx-tube and flower-stalk, covered with sticky glands. Fruit rounded or oblong, never pear-shaped.

The origin of the cabbage rose is not definitely known. It is one of the most ancient of garden roses, and one of those mentioned by Pliny. From damascena it is best distinguished by its glandular-toothed leaflets, the erect, very glandular, never reflexed sepals, and roundish or oblong fruit. It is, no doubt, closely related to R. gallica, which differs from it by its erect, stiff flower-stalks, its usually lower habit, and smaller prickles.

Var. MUSCOSA (R. muscosa, *Miller*). Moss Rose.—The mossy character of the flowers of this loveliest of roses is due to the excessively glandular, much-divided sepals and flower-stalk. The leaf-stalk also is of a similar character.

Var. PROVINCIALIS (R. provincialis, *Miller*). Provence Rose.—This is usually regarded as a form of centifolia, but its origin is probably not quite the same. It differs in the more open and not so many-petalled flowers with less glandular sepals.

R. CERASOCARPA, *Rolfe*

(Bot. Mag., t. 8688)

A deciduous climbing or semi-climbing shrub up to 15 ft. high ; young shoots somewhat glaucous, armed with a few scattered recurved spines. Leaves up to 7 or 8 ins. long, consisting of three or (usually) five leaflets ; main-stalk glandular, slightly prickly. Leaflets narrowly ovate or oval, long-pointed, sharply and conspicuously toothed ; 2 to 4 ins. long, half as much wide ; glabrous or nearly so, rather glaucous beneath. Flowers white, produced in June in fine corymbose clusters 6 ins. wide ; each flower 1½ ins. across, borne on a glandular stalk ¾ to 1½ ins. long. Calyx-tube obovoid, downy and glandular ; sepals linear, sometimes pinnately lobed, ½ in. long, downy and glandular. Fruit globose, downy, deep red, ½ in. wide, with the sepals fallen away.

Native of Central China. The plant figured in the *Botanical Magazine* flowered with the late Sir Wm. Thiselton-Dyer in his garden in Gloucestershire in June 1914 ; it had been obtained by him from Sir Thomas Hanbury of La Mortola, Italy, who had received seeds from China. It is one of the moschata group of roses, which is distinguished by the styles being united in one column. It is a very handsome rose both in flower and in fruit and seems to have been found wild near Ichang. Rehder and Wilson have united it with R. Gentiliana, *Léveillé*, but Rolfe considered the latter distinct on account of its shorter, less acuminate leaflets, wider, more fringed stipules, and less densely glandular flower-stalks.

R. CINNAMOMEA, *Linnæus*

A strong-growing bush, 6 to 9 ft. high, stems erect, much branched near the top, with usually a pair of hooked prickles at the base of the leaf-stalks, and numerous others scattered on the stems, especially near the ground. Leaflets usually five or seven, oblong or slightly obovate, 1 to 1½ ins. long ; simply toothed except towards the base, greyish and glabrous or slightly hairy above, downy and glaucous beneath. Flowers produced on often quite unarmed shoots, either singly or few in a cluster, of varying shades of red, 2 ins. across ; stalks short and, like the calyx-tube, glabrous ; sepals entire, woolly at the edges. Fruit globose, or slightly elongated, red, ½ in. wide, crowned by erect sepals.

Native of Europe, Siberia, and N. China ; cultivated in England for over three hundred years, but not, as was once believed, a native. The flowers have a somewhat spicy odour, from which the species derives its name. It is regarded as the type of a large group of roses whose leading distinctions are : prickles often in pairs just below the leaf-stalks ; fruit red, glabrous, with a thin skin.

R. CORYMBULOSA, *Rolfe*

(Bot. Mag., t. 8566)

A deciduous shrub up to 6 ft. high ; young shoots not downy, becoming brown with age, usually unarmed or sometimes with a few scattered, mostly solitary prickles which are straight, slender, and ¼ in. or less long. Leaves 2 to 5 ins. long, consisting of three or five leaflets ; main-stalk downy, glandular, furnished with a few tiny prickles. Leaflets ovate-oblong (the side ones stalkless) pointed, often doubly toothed ; ½ to 2 ins. long, ¼ to 1 in. wide ; dark green above, glaucous and downy beneath ; stipules edged with tiny glands. Flowers produced during July in corymbs of up to a dozen blossoms, each ¾ to 1 in. across and borne on a slender glandular stalk ¾ to 1½ ins. long. Petals inversely heart-shaped, deep rose-pink, paling towards the base ; anthers golden yellow. Calyx-tube obovoid, glandular ; sepals ⅓ to ¾ in. long, downy, often widening at the apex. Fruits globose, ¼ to ⅓ in. wide, coral-red, crowned by the persistent sepals.

Native of China, in the province of Szechuen, where it was discovered by Henry, and of Hupeh, whence it was introduced to cultivation by Wilson in 1907. It belongs to the large macrophylla group of roses and is nearly related to R. Davidii which differs in having five to eleven leaflets and in their being simply toothed. R. corymbulosa is a pretty rose both in flower and in fruit, distinct in its almost spineless branchlets and small flowers. The leaves turn purplish red beneath in autumn.

R. DAMASCENA, *Miller*. DAMASK ROSE

A bush up to 8 ft. high, the upright stems armed with stout, hooked spines from ⅓ in. long, down to mere prickly bristles. Leaflets usually five, oval or ovate, simply toothed, ¾ to 2 ins. long ; glabrous above, pale green and downy beneath. Flowers very fragrant, borne in large clusters of sometimes a dozen, blush-white to red, each on a long stalk, densely covered with glandular bristles and small prickles. Sepals 1 in. or more long, slightly expanded at the tip, very much reflexed, and like the calyx-tube more or less glandular-bristly on the back. Fruit elongated, somewhat pear-shaped, 1 in. long, red, bristly, with the sepals fallen away.

A rose cultivated from time immemorial in E. Europe and the Orient generally. It has been suggested that it is a hybrid between R. gallica and moschata, which is doubtful. To R. gallica it is no doubt allied, but is to be distinguished by the following characters : taller and robuster habit, thinner leaflets with sharper and more open teeth, larger clusters of flowers, and longer more reflexed sepals. From both gallica and centifolia it is distinct in the more elongated fruit and in the absence of glands from the leaflet margins. Crossed with forms of R. indica the damask rose gave birth to the race of " hybrid perpetual " roses which for so long held pride of place in the family.

Var. VARIEGATA, *Keller*. The York and Lancaster Rose.—A vigorous bush with rounded blossoms, the petals of which are striped in pink and white.

Var. TRIGINTIPETALA is one of the most important attar roses of the East.

R. DAVIDII, *Crépin*. DAVID'S ROSE

(Bot. Mag., t. 8679)

A deciduous shrub of loose, spreading habit 6 to 12 ft. high ; young shoots glabrous armed (often very strongly) with scattered, straight, or slightly curved spines. Leaves up to 6 ins. or more long, composed of five to eleven (usually seven or nine) leaflets which are oval or ovate, pointed, simply toothed ; ⅓ to 2 ins. long, ¼ to 1 in. wide, each pair increasing in size towards the end ; dark green and glabrous above, rather glaucous and downy beneath, especially on the midrib and veins ; main-stalk downy, sparsely spiny. Flowers bright rose-pink, 1½ to 2 ins. wide, produced during June and July in loose corymbs, each flower on a slender, downy, more or less glandular stalk 1 to 1½ ins. long. Sepals ½ to ¾ in. long, downy, often glandular, ovate at the base but prolonged into an enlarged often spoon-shaped apex ; calyx-tube glandular and more or less downy. Fruits pendulous, scarlet-red, bottle-shaped, ¾ in. long, narrowed at the top to a slender neck, above which are the persistent sepals.

Native of W. Szechuen, China; introduced by Wilson in 1903 and again in 1908. This rose is closely related to R. macrophylla, but the flowers and fruits are smaller. It is handsomest in autumn when laden with its pendulous clusters of bright red fruits which are often very abundant. As a vigorous shrub of spreading habit it is suitable for the semi-wild part of the garden.

Var. ELONGATA, *Rehder and Wilson.*—A form with larger leaflets (the largest up to 3 ins. long) and fewer flowers (three to seven) in the corymb.

R. DUPONTII, *Déséglise*

(R. nivea, *Dupont*; R. moschata nivea, Bot. Reg., t. 861)

A robust shrub of loose but not climbing habit, 6 to 8 ft. high; leaflets usually five to each leaf, sometimes three or seven, bright green, 1½ to 3 ins. long, ovate or oval, finely toothed, downy beneath; the common stalk and stipules glandular and downy. Flowers white, shaded with pink, 2½ to 3 ins. across, single, produced in clusters; stalk and calyx downy.

This beautiful rose is closely allied to R. moschata, and is believed to be a hybrid between that species and damascena or gallica. It flowers in July, and is one of the most noteworthy of the semi-wild types at that season, in its large white blossoms. It was raised early in the nineteenth century by a French grower of roses—a Mr Dupont.

R. ECÆ, *Aitchison*

(R. xanthina, *Hooker fil.*, not *Lindley*; Bot. Mag., t. 7666)

A shrub 3 to 4 ft. high, erect and rigid in a wild state, but with slender, spreading branches under cultivation; bristles none; prickles crowded, up to ½ in. long, broad at the base. Leaves 1 in. or less long, with usually seven (occasionally five or nine) leaflets, which are oval or nearly round, ¼ in. or so long, with proportionately large teeth, glandular beneath. Flowers solitary, 1 in. across, rich buttercup yellow; stalk and calyx glabrous; fruit globose, ⅓ in. wide, crowned with the deflexed persistent sepals.

Native of Afghanistan; introduced to Kew in 1880 by the late Dr Aitchison, who found it during the survey of the Kurrum Valley. It is certainly not the R. xanthina of Lindley, as has been suggested, a name that rests merely on a two-line description made by Lindley, in 1820, of a drawing in the library of Mr A. B. Lambert. This is to the effect that it has " all the appearance of R. spinosissima, except having no setæ, and double flowers the colour of R. sulphurea. Hab. in China." It has, nevertheless, been figured as R. xanthina in the *Botanical Magazine* and in Miss Willmott's great work *The Genus Rosa*. R. Ecæ is an interesting and dainty rose, but not free-growing or easy to propagate. It should have a sunny position. The name is an adaptation of Mrs Aitchison's initials—" E. C. A."

R. ELEGANTULA, *Rolfe*

A deciduous shrub a few feet high, the young sucker shoots copiously armed with short, slender prickles 1/16 to ⅙ in. long; young shoots of the branches sparingly armed with prickles of a larger size only. Leaves 2 to 4 ins. long, composed of seven to eleven leaflets; main-stalk glabrous or sparsely glandular and prickly. Leaflets oval to ovate, ⅓ to 1 in. long, abruptly pointed or blunt, finely and mostly simply toothed, glaucous (especially beneath), downy on the midrib. Flowers solitary or a few together, 1 to 1½ ins. wide, rich rose, opening in June. Calyx-tube glabrous; sepals ¾ in. long, ovate at the base, narrowed to a slender tail, woolly at the margins and inside. Styles downy, cohering in a column $\frac{1}{12}$ in. long. Flower-stalks slender, glabrous. Fruit bright red, top-shaped, ⅓ to ½ in. long, the sepals persisting at the top.

Native of China; cultivated in 1900 at Les Barres, by Maurice de Vilmorin who had raised it from Chinese seed; afterwards introduced for Messrs Veitch by Wilson. It is a pretty little rose related to R. sertata, from which it differs in the copiously prickly sucker shoots and branches that are markedly in contrast with the almost unarmed branchlets. In the same group and very near elegantula is

R. PERSETOSA, *Rolfe*, which has its stem covered more densely than elegantula with needle-like prickles, not only on the branches but even on the flowering twigs. Flowers 1 in. wide, deep rose, opening in June numerously in lax clusters. Introduced by Vilmorin; flowered in Paul & Son's nursery at Cheshunt, 1912.

R. ELYMAITICA, *Boissier*

A low, compact bush, whose stems are armed with stout, pale-coloured, very hooked prickles, ¼ to ⅓ in. long, some of which are arranged in pairs at the base of the leaf-stalks, some scattered. Leaves 1 to 2 ins. long; leaflets mostly five, ⅓ to ½ in. long, oval or roundish, simply and coarsely toothed, downy above, felted beneath, of firm texture. Flowers rosy white, about 1 in. across, usually solitary on short, bristly stalks; calyx-tube and sepals bristly. Fruit globose, ⅓ in. wide, dark red, glandular-bristly, crowned with the spreading sepals.

A little-known species from the mountains of Persia and Kurdistan, where it reaches up to 8000 ft. It is marked by the conspicuous, light-coloured, very hooked prickles, often in pairs, and by the hairy leaves. Introduced in 1900 to Kew, where it has proved hardy.

R. ENGELMANNII, *S. Watson*

(Garden and Forest, 1899, fig. 121)

A shrub 3 to 4 ft. high, with erect stems sometimes densely covered with straight, slender prickles, sometimes unarmed. Leaves composed of usually five or seven leaflets which are oval or ovate, ¾ to 1¼ ins. long, about half as wide, the coarse teeth gland-tipped and often again toothed; upper surface glabrous, lower one downy, especially on the midrib and veins; stipules dilated and edged with resinous, glandular teeth. Flowers usually solitary, rarely two or three together, 1½ to 2¼ ins. across, bright rose; the stalk and calyx-tube glabrous. Sepals entire, ¾ to 1 in. long, sometimes dilated at the tip, becoming erect after the petals fall, and persisting on the fruit. Fruit bright red, egg-shaped, up to 1 in. long.

Native of central and western N. America; introduced in 1891. This rose is very nearly allied to R. acicularis, and is now generally regarded as a geographical form of that species, which belongs essentially to the Old World. Engelmann's rose differs from acicularis in the frequent occurrence of a pair of slender spines below the stipules, and in the double, glandular teeth. The fruit also is more tapered at the base and the young shoots less bristly.

R. ERNESTII, *Stapf*

(R. Rubus, *Rehder and Wilson*, not of *Léveillé*)

A deciduous shrub of spreading or semi-scandent habit, 8 to 15 ft. high young shoots armed with hooked spines, often purplish. Leaves 4 to 9 ins long, composed usually of five leaflets; main-stalk prickly, slightly downy-glandular. Leaflets ovate to oblong-ovate, slenderly pointed, coarsely simple-toothed; 1½ to 4½ ins. long, half as much wide on the virgin shoots, pro-portionately smaller on the flowering ones; glabrous above, glaucous or purplish and downy or glabrous beneath; except for the terminal one they are very shortly stalked. Flowers 1½ ins. across, white, produced from June to August, thirty to forty together in corymbose panicles; pleasingly fragrant. Calyx-tube, sepals, and flower-stalks glandular downy. Styles united in a short column, hairy. Fruit globose, dark red (yellowish unripe), ¼ to ⅓ in. wide.

Native of W. China; discovered by Henry about 1886; introduced by Wilson in 1907 and by Farrer later. This is a fine rose of the moschata group, very vigorous, large, free-flowering and hardy. The purple under surface of the young leaves is also attractive. Since its introduction it has been grown under the name " R. Rubus," but it is distinct from Léveillé's type of that species. Dr Stapf has in consequence named it after E. H. Wilson by way of his first baptismal name. Farrer's characteristic description of it is as follows : " A most glorious bush making shoots 12 ft. long in a season . . . the blossom of such a fragrance that all the air is drunk with its sweetness." He notes that the fragrance is only noticeable after mid-day.

R. FARRERI, *Stapf*. THREEPENNY-BIT ROSE

(Gardeners' Chronicle, 26th Feb. 1927, fig. 70)

A deciduous bush up to 6 ft. high, of spreading habit and greater width ; young shoots not downy but furnished densely at the lower part with bristle-like spines $\frac{1}{12}$ to ⅛ in. long ; the upper twigs may be similar or have a pair of spines at each joint or be unarmed. Leaves up to 2½ ins. long, made up of seven or nine leaflets ; main-stalk downy, with a few glands and small spines. Leaflets oval or ovate, sharply toothed, ¼ to ⅜ in. long, glabrous or very nearly so. Flowers coral-red in bud, ¾ to 1 in. wide, solitary on short, usually leafy twigs, of a soft warm pink, each on a very slender, quite glabrous stalk ½ to 1 in. long ; anthers golden yellow. Calyx-tube oblong, ¼ in. long, glabrous. Sepals ½ in. long, downy inside, lanceolate at the base, then narrowing to a tail, ending in a broadened, spoon-like tip. Fruit ⅓ in. long, ovoid, coral-red, bearing the mostly spreading sepals at the top.

Native of S. Kansu, China ; introduced by Farrer in 1915. A very charm-ing, dainty rose beautiful when the flowers are in bud, when they are fully open, and again in autumn when the bush is hung with the brilliantly coloured fruits and specked with the purple and crimson of the changing leaves. Next to Farrer himself, we owe the existence of this rose in our gardens to Mr E. A. Bowles, who noticed a single plant among some seedlings he had raised in his garden at Waltham Cross of Farrer's No. 774. He has found it perfectly hardy and easily increased by cuttings. Mr Bowles' plant, which is evidently superior to typical R. Farreri, has been distinguished by Dr Stapf and figured in Bot. Mag., t. 8877 as forma PERSETOSA. Ordinary R. Farreri has larger leaves and leaflets and larger, pale pink, or white flowers. Both flower in June.

R. FEDTSCHENKOANA, *Regel*

(Bot. Mag., t. 7770)

A shrub about 8 ft. high, armed with rather slender or straight prickles, sometimes ½ in. long, often reduced to bristles ; year-old wood very dark. Leaves glaucous green, 2½ to 5 ins. long, oval or obovate, rather coarsely toothed, glabrous above, downy beneath. Flowers white, 2 ins. across, produced singly or up to four on the stalk, which is furnished with a downy, leaf-like, glandular-margined bract ; calyx-tube conspicuously covered with glandular bristles ; sepals entire, long-pointed, glanded like the tube, inner surface and margins downy. Fruit red, ¾ in. long, rather pear-shaped, with sepals attached.

Native of Turkestan ; discovered by the Russian traveller Fedtschenko (1868-1871). In a border of wild roses it is at once marked by its pale glaucous foliage, a character which distinguishes it from R. acicularis (to which it is allied), as do also the white flowers and very glandular calyx-tube.

R. FILIPES, *Rehder and Wilson*

(Bot. Mag., t. 8894)

A very large, deciduous, rambling shrub ; shoots arching, glabrous, armed with hooked spines ⅓ in. long. Leaves usually of five but sometimes seven leaflets which are oval to oval-lanceolate, 1½ to 3½ ins. long, ¾ to 2 ins. wide, dark green and glabrous above, glabrous or with a few spines on the midrib and glands beneath, shallowly toothed, main-stalk sparsely spiny. Flowers cream coloured in bud, white or tinged with pink when fully open ; fragrant, ⅓ in. wide, very numerously produced in several corymbose panicles near the end of the shoots, giving a terminal mass of blossom 6 to 12 ins. wide ; petals obovate ; stamens very numerous with golden-yellow anthers. Fruit globose, ⅓ in. wide, orange to crimson-scarlet.

Native of W. China ; found by Wilson in 1908 and 1910. It is one of the magnificent group of Western Chinese roses of very vigorous growth belonging to the moschata group, making shoots 12 ft. long in a season.

R. FOLIOLOSA, *Nuttall*

(Bot. Mag., t. 8513)

A shrub usually under 3 ft. in height, spreading by means of underground suckers ; stems clustered, erect, either unarmed or with a few straight, slender prickles. Leaflets seven to eleven, narrowly oblong, ¾ to 2 ins. long, glabrous and glossy above, downy on the midrib beneath, toothed. Flowers bright pink, 2 to 2½ ins. across, fragrant, solitary or few on short stalks ; sepals ¾ to ⅓ in. long, bristly outside. Fruit red, bristly, orange-shaped, ⅓ to ½ in. wide, sepals spreading.

Native of the south-western United States, and distinct among American roses by reason of its oblong, rather narrow, forward-pointing leaflets, closely set on a common stalk. It is allied to virginiana, but is altogether smaller.

R. FORTUNEANA, *Lindley*. FORTUNE'S ROSE

A climbing shrub, up to 30 or 40 ft. high ; introduced from China by Fortune about 1845. It has much the general character of the Banksian rose, having three or five leaflets to each leaf, glabrous and simply toothed. It is considered to be a hybrid between that species and R. lævigata. The flowers are white, double as in the forms of R. Banksiæ, but larger, and with the bristly stalk and calyx-tube of lævigata, whose influence is further shown in the large leaflets, which are downy only at the base of the midrib. A handsome and vigorous climber which thrives on sheltered, sunny walls near London. The flowers, like those of R. lævigata, are solitary.

There is a form of R. indica (var. PSEUDO-INDICA, *Lindley*) which has also been called " Fortuneana," but with which the above must not be confounded. It has large, double yellow flowers tinged with red, and sweetly scented.

R. GALLICA, *Linnæus*. FRENCH ROSE

A bush 3 to 5 ft. high, with creeping roots and erect stems, armed with small, slender prickles, mostly $\frac{1}{16}$ to $\frac{1}{8}$ in. long, the larger ones slightly decurved. Leaves of firm texture, composed of three, five or seven leaflets, which are oval or ovate, rounded or blunt-pointed at the end ; 1 to 3 ins. long, $\frac{1}{2}$ to $1\frac{1}{2}$ ins. wide ; simply toothed and glandular on the margins ; glabrous, dark green above, paler and downy beneath. Flowers usually solitary, sometimes in pairs or threes, dark red, 2 to $2\frac{1}{2}$ ins. across, each on an erect, stiff stalk, densely covered with small prickles and glandular bristles. Sepals spreading, ovate-lanceolate, pinnately lobed, very glandular on the back and margins. Fruit roundish or pear-shaped, $\frac{1}{3}$ to $\frac{1}{2}$ in. wide, dark dull red, with the sepals fallen away.

Native of Central and S.E. Europe ; cultivated from time immemorial. This species is the chief source of the most cherished of garden roses, and through the damask rose—of which it is supposed to be a parent—is one of the chief sources from which the " hybrid perpetual " roses have been derived. It has hybridised with numerous other species and varieties of rose, but a discussion of the progeny belongs rather to a work on roses alone than to the present one. The cabbage rose, R. centifolia (*q.v.*) is sometimes reduced to a variety of gallica. The following are a few of the more important crosses :—

Gallica	× moschata	= R. Dupontii (*q.v.*) (p. 198)
,,	× setigera	= Prairie roses.
,,	× arvensis	= R. geminata.
,,	× indica	= Bourbon roses.
,,	× canina	= R. macrantha (*q.v.*) (p. 190)

R. GIGANTEA, *Collet*

(Bot. Mag., t. 7972 ; Willmott Genus, Rosa, vol. i., t. 34)

A very vigorous deciduous or semi-evergreen climber attaining 40 ft., o in warm climates, 60 to 80 ft. in height ; young shoots growing 15 to 20 ft. i length and as much as 1 in. in diameter in one season, armed with stout uniform, hooked spines. Leaves usually composed of seven leaflets which ar oval, oblong, or ovate, rounded or tapered at the base, pointed, finely an mostly simply toothed ; $1\frac{1}{2}$ to $3\frac{1}{2}$ ins. long, $\frac{1}{2}$ to $1\frac{1}{4}$ ins. wide, glabrous ; main stalk spiny. Flowers solitary on glabrous stalks, 4 to 6 ins. across, fragrant white in cultivated plants, but said to be also pink and shades of yellow Calyx-tube glabrous ; sepals lance-shaped, 1 to $1\frac{1}{2}$ ins. long, not toothed o lobed, downy inside and at the margins. Petals broadly wedge-shaped stamens white with yellow anthers ; styles very downy. Fruit globose, glabrous bright red, with the sepals fallen away when ripe.

Native of the Shan Hills, Upper Burma, whence it was introduced t Europe by Sir Henry Collet in 1889 ; also of Manipur, where it was discovere in 1882 by Sir Geo. Watt ; and of Yunnan. The largest flowered of all wil roses and one of the most rampant growers, this remarkable species has not proved very free-flowering. It first flowered with Lord Brougham at Cannes in 1898, and in England five years later at Albury, near Guildford. It now flowers annually in the Temperate House at Kew. It is not hardy outside there, even against a wall, but in June 1915 I had flowers from Capt. Salmon's garden near Bristol, where it is grown in the open air, and it has flowered on a south wall in Suffolk gardens. There is no doubt it likes a very sunny climate to bring it to perfection in flower ; it is admirable in such places as Madeira. Rehder and Wilson make it a variety of Tea rose and call it " R. odorata gigantea," which seems to be stretching the conception of a species somewhat unduly.

R. GLUTINOSA, *Sibthorp and Smith*

A shrub of dwarf, compact, bushy habit, whose stems are copiously furnished with stiff, whitish, straight or decurved spines up to ⅓ in. long, intermixed with which are numerous small needle-like prickles and glandular bristles. Leaves 1½ to 3 ins. long, composed of from five to nine leaflets, which are oval or obovate to roundish, ¼ to 1 in. long, doubly toothed except at the base, hairy and glandular on both surfaces ; stipules with unattached triangular points, very glandular, as is the common stalk. Flowers white, 1 to 1½ ins. across, usually in pairs or solitary ; stalk ½ to 1 in. long and, like the calyx-tube and outside the sepals, densely glandular-bristly ; sepals ½ to ¾ in. long, the larger ones pinnately lobed, woolly within. Fruit roundish ½ in. wide, very bristly, dark red, crowned with persistent sepals. Var. DALMATICA differs in its egg-shaped, larger fruits. (Bot. Mag., t. 8826.)

Native of S.E. Europe, Persia, and Asia Minor. It is remarkable for its excessive covering of glandular hairs or bristles, more marked even than in its near ally, R. horrida, from which it differs also in having downy styles and persistent sepals on the fruit. From R. sicula, another ally (which has persistent sepals), it is easily distinguished by its glandular-bristly young wood and fruits.

R. GYMNOCARPA, *Nuttall*

A shrub said to become occasionally 10 ft. high in a wild state, but scarcely half that height as represented by plants in cultivation ; stems slender, with straight, scattered, slender prickles, or sometimes nearly or quite unarmed. Leaves 1½ to 3 ins. long ; stipules edged with glands ; stalk glandular and slightly prickly. Leaflets five to nine (mostly seven), usually from ⅓ to ¾ in. long, narrowly oval and pointed to almost round, doubly-toothed, glabrous. Flowers rosy, 1 to 1½ ins. across, usually one to three in a cluster ; stalks glandular ; sepals entire, short, triangular, downy inside and on the margins. Fruit rather pear-shaped or globose, red, ⅓ in. diameter, glabrous, with the sepals fallen away.

Native of western N. America from British Columbia to California and Montana. It has been associated with R. pisocarpa, from which, however, it is readily distinguished by the presence of glands on the younger parts of the plant, the double-toothing of the leaves, and the deciduous sepals. A pretty, graceful plant, introduced to cultivation about 1893.

R. HELENÆ, *Rehder and Wilson*

(Gardeners' Chronicle, 2nd Oct. 1915, fig. 70—as R. floribunda)

A deciduous rambling shrub up to 18 ft. high ; young shoots armed with short hooked spines, becoming purplish brown. Leaves 3 to 7 ins. long ; main-stalk downy, armed with small hooked prickles. Leaflets three to nine,

very shortly stalked, ovate, ovate-oblong or occasionally oval or obovate, sharply
pointed, finely simple-toothed ; ¾ to 2½ ins. long, ⅛ to 1¼ ins. wide ; glabrous
above, greyish and downy on the midrib beneath. Flowers white, fragrant,
1½ ins. wide, produced during June in many-flowered terminal corymbs 4 to
6 ins. wide. Calyx-tube obovoid and, like the flower-stalks, very glandular ;
sepals awl-shaped, ¼ to ½ in. long, glandular outside, downy inside. Styles
united in one downy column. Fruits roundish egg-shaped, orange red or
scarlet, ½ in. long, the sepals fallen away.

Native of Hupeh and Szechuen, China ; discovered by Wilson in 1900 and
introduced by him in 1907. It is a fine rose, producing great masses of white
flowers and needs abundant space to show its full beauty. Wilson found it
spreading 18 ft. in diameter. Belonging to the moschata group of roses, it is
most nearly akin to the cultivated R. moschata, which has more globose fruits,
and to R. moschata nepaulensis, in which the young shoots and other parts,
especially the under surface of the leaves, are downy. The species is named
after Helen, the wife of E. H. Wilson, who was killed in the motor accident
in which he also lost his life on 15th October 1930.

Two other related, similarly strong-growing roses, of the same type as R. Helenæ
are R. FILIPES and R. GENTILIANA, both of which Wilson found 20 ft. high. They
have clusters up to 1 ft. wide carrying scores of fragrant white flowers, each 1 in. across.
R. filipes differs from R. Gentiliana in having glands on the leaflets beneath.

R. HEMISPHÆRICA, *Hermann*
(R. sulphurea, *Aiton* ; Bot. Reg., t. 46)

Growing on a wall, as this rose usually is in the British Isles, it will attain
a height of 10 ft. or more ; branches slender, furnished with scattered, slender
decurved prickles. Leaflets 5 to 9, obovate, ½ to 1½ ins. long, rounded and
coarsely toothed at the apex ; glabrous and of a glaucous hue above, more
glaucous beneath. Flowers solitary, drooping, delicate sulphur-yellow, 2 ins.
across, with numerous petals ; flower-stalks and calyx-tube glabrous or with
glands ; sepals 1 in. long, the tips coarsely toothed, leaflike.

This beautiful yellow rose is known to have been in cultivation early in
the seventh century, but owing to its difficult cultivation has always been
very rare. Near London especially it refuses to thrive, and in many places
where it grows fairly well, its flowers do not expand properly. It is found in
the gardens of Asia Minor, Persia, Armenia, etc. The English climate is too
dull and damp to suit it, but one occasionally sees it doing well. In the garden
of Bitton Vicarage, near Bath, Canon Ellacombe had it in splendid health
for many years ; and I remember, many years ago, seeing it there laden with
scores of its drooping blossoms. The flowers do not open well in cold, wet
summers.

R. RAPINII, *Boissier*, is generally considered to be the wild type from which
R. hemisphærica was derived centuries ago, probably in the gardens of the East. It
has fine flowers 2½ ins. across, the five petals yellow. Fruit globose, ½ in. diameter
crowned with spreading, downy sepals.

R. HIBERNICA, *Smith*. IRISH ROSE

A shrub 6 to 9 ft. high in gardens, with erect stems and arching branches
armed with scattered prickles, the sucker shoots usually very freely furnished
with prickles and bristles. Leaflets five to nine, oval or ovate, simply toothed
¾ to 1 in. long, downy beneath, especially on the midrib. Flowers pink
usually one to three in a cluster (sometimes more), each on a glabrous stalk
and 1½ ins. across ; sepals with an expanded leaflike tip, more or less pinnately
lobed. Fruit globose, ½ in. diameter, red, crowned with the persisting sepals.

This interesting rose is thought to be a hybrid between R. canina and R. spinosissima. It is, at any rate, fairly intermediate between them. First discovered near Belfast, in 1802, by Mr John Templeton (who thereby won a prize of five guineas for the discovery of a new Irish plant), this rose has been found nowhere else up to the present, although in England two slightly different forms of it have been discovered.

Var. GLABRA, *Baker.*—Leaves and leaf-stalks without down.

R. HISPIDA, *Sims*

(Bot. Mag., t. 1570 ; R. lutescens, *Pursh* ; R. spinosissima hispida, *Koehne*)

A shrub up to 6 ft. high, with sturdy, quite erect stems covered with slender, bristle-like prickles. Leaflets five to eleven, oval or obovate, ¾ to 1¼ ins. long, ⅜ to ½ in. wide ; simply toothed, quite free from down. Flowers solitary at the end of short lateral branches, yellow at first, changing to creamy white, 2 to 3 ins. across, opening the third or fourth week in May. Calyx and flower-stalk smooth. Fruit globose, ⅝ in. diameter, nearly black when ripe, and crowned with the sepals.

There is some doubt as to the origin of this rose. It was at one time called " yellow American rose," and Pursh included it in his *Flora of N. America.* It has never been found wild in America, and all the later authorities discard it. But its real native country is still not definitely known, although it is generally believed to come from Siberia. It has been raised from seed at Kew and come quite true, which would appear to show that it is not of hybrid origin. Some authors regard it as a variety of R. spinosissima, and it is, no doubt, closely allied to that species, but is still so distinct in habit and general appearance that it seems preferable to give it a separate standing. It is one of the most lovely of single roses.

R. HORRIDA, *Fischer*

(R. ferox, *Bieberstein*, not *Lawrance*)

A dwarf, compact, little bush, 1 to 2 ft. high, of rounded form, armed with numerous decurved prickles, ¼ in. or less long ; young shoots furnished with numerous glandular bristles. Leaves 1 to 2 ins. long, with five or seven leaflets, which are oval or roundish, ¼ to ¾ in. long, coarsely but evenly and doubly toothed ; the teeth, common stalk, stipules and under-surface copiously glandular. Flowers 1 to 1¼ ins. across, white, solitary or two or three together ; sepals pinnately lobed, glandular-toothed, and ciliate ; flower-stalk glandular. Fruit roundish, red, with the sepals fallen away.

Native of the Crimea and Caucasus. This interesting and pretty little rose forms a dense mass of interlacing, very spiny twigs. It is allied to the more western R. sicula, but is easily recognised by the glandular young shoots, flower-stalk, and calyx-tube ; and by the pinnately lobed sepals, which do not persist on the fruit (see also R. glutinosa). It must not be confounded with the R. ferox of Lawrance—an obsolete name for R. rugosa (Bot. Reg., t. 420).

R. HUGONIS, *Hemsley*

(Bot. Mag., t. 8004)

A bush of rounded habit, 8 ft. high, and more in diameter ; branches slender, sometimes gracefully arching, armed with straight, flattened spines of varying length, which are associated on the barren shoots with numerous bristles. Leaves 1 to 4 ins. long, quite glabrous. Leaflets five to eleven, oval or obovate, ¼ to ¾ in. long; finely toothed, deep grass green. Flowers 2 ins. across, bright yellow, solitary on short lateral twigs; flower-stalk glabrous, slender, ¾ in. or less in length; calyx-tube glabrous, sepals ½ in. long, entire, downy inside. Fruit glabrous, globose, ½ to ⅝ in. wide, blackish red when ripe, the calyx persisting at the top.

Native of W. China; first raised at Kew in 1899, from seed sent to England by Father Hugh Scallan (Patér Hugo), a missionary in its native country. It is a most charming rose and the most vigorous of the yellow-flowered species, beautiful even when not in flower, for its luxuriant, féathery masses of foliage. It shares with R. sericea the distinction of being the earliest of roses to flower— usually by mid-May. It is allied to the Scotch rose, but differs markedly in

ROSA HUGONIS

habit. It is perfectly hardy, free, but neat and not rampant in growth. The spines vary much in character and are often altogether absent from some portions of the shoots; the largest are thin, flattened, triangular, ½ in. long, reddish and translucent.

R. INDICA, *Lindley*. CHINA or MONTHLY ROSE

(R. chinensis, *Jacquin*)

What the wild plant really was from which were derived the China roses imported to this country from near Canton in 1789, was for long not definitely known. In 1864, Richard Oldham found a rose in Formosa which was of the indica breed, but it was doubtfully wild. It was not until more than twenty years later that Prof. A. Henry found in the glens near Ichang, Central China, a rose with single flowers, apparently truly wild, which is R. indica. Henry describes this rose as a large shrub climbing over rocks, and as having generally deep red but occasionally pink flowers. This plant does not appear to be at present in cultivation; the following description represents the plant introduced from Canton, and known as the "monthly rose." It is probably R. indica, with a slight admixture of some other rose. Stems green, armed with stout, scattered, flattened, hooked prickles. Leaflets three or five, shining above, glabrous on both surfaces, glaucous beneath, 1½ to 3 ins. long, ovate or oval, pointed, simply or occasionally doubly toothed ; common stalk glandular and prickly. Flowers faintly perfumed, borne in clusters, more or less double, red ; stalks long, erect, with a few glandular bristles ; calyx-tube glabrous ; sepals ovate, slightly or not at all lobed. Fruit scarlet, ¾ in. long, top-shaped. The true wild R. indica differs from the above in having solitary flowers with five petals and shorter stalks, and the glaucous colour of the leaves beneath is more pronounced.

Var. FRAGRANS (R. fragrans, *Thory*). Tea-scented Rose.—Introduced in 1810. A rose with a delightful fragrance like that of tea. This is the chief source of the great race of " tea roses." The yellow tea-scented rose was introduced from China in 1824, and is probably a parent of the roses typified in " Marechal Niel " and " Gloire de Dijon."

Var. MINIMA. Fairy Rose.—A dwarf form first introduced from Mauritius by Sweet in 1810, but no doubt originally from China. The " fairy " roses of gardens have been mostly derived from this. The original had pale pink flowers, single or slightly double, 1 to 1½ ins. diameter. (Figured in Bot. Reg., t. 538, as R. Lawranceana, *Sweet*.)

Var. MONSTROSA (R. viridiflora). Green Rose.—A monstrous form, in which the numerous petals have reverted to a green, leaf-like condition. It has no beauty, but is of considerable interest to morphologists. First noticed in Paris in 1855, in the garden of a Mr Verdier, who is said to have received it from Augusta, Georgia, U.S.A.

Var. SEMPERFLORENS (R. semperflorens, *Curtis*, Bot. Mag., t. 284). Crimson China Rose.—Introduced from China to England by Mr Gilbert Slater in 1789. Flowers all the summer and autumn. It has much more slender stems than the " monthly " rose, the leaves are purplish red, and the flowers of a rich blood red, on very long, slender stalks.

All the roses of the " indica " type are notable for their long-continued flowering. They commence in June and continue until the winter, frequently well into November. Numerous hybrids have arisen from them, amongst which may be mentioned :—

Boursault Roses (indica × pendulina).
Bourbon Roses (indica × gallica). Originated in the Isle of Bourbon about 1817.
Noisette Roses (indica ? × moschata).
R. ruga, Lindley, Bot. Reg., t. 1389 (indica × arvensis).

R. INVOLUTA, *Smith*

A shrub 5 to 9 ft. high, the stems armed with slender, straight prickles varying in length from ⅓ in. to mere stiff bristles. Leaflets five to nine, oval, simply or occasionally doubly toothed, glabrous above, rather downy below ; common stalk prickly and downy. Flowers pink, solitary on short, bristly stalks. Fruit globose, red, with persistent sepals. Found originally in the Scottish Highlands in the early part of the nineteenth century, this rose is believed to be a natural hybrid between R. spinosissima and one of the VILLOSÆ group—probably tomentosa or mollis. Several forms are associated with it as varieties, some no doubt of independent origin. The most distinct of them is

Var. SABINII, *Baker*.—A more robust shrub up to 10 ft. high, leaflets oval to ovate, doubly toothed, slightly hairy above, and very downy and glandular beneath. Fruit prickly.

R. JUNDZILLII, *Besser*. JUNDZIL'S ROSE

(R. marginata, *Wallroth*)

A bush 6 ft. or so high, the stems armed with scattered, uniform, slightly decurved prickles, not bristly or needle-like. Leaflets five or seven, oval, rounded at the base, pointed, from 1 to 1¾ ins. long, doubly-toothed, smooth or nearly so above, but downy beneath, especially on the midrib and veins ; common stalk downy, and furnished abundantly with sticky glands, as are also the teeth and under-surface of the leaflets. Flowers 3 ins. across, pink, produced singly or in threes ; stalk glandular-bristly ; sepals edged with numerous glands, the larger ones pinnately lobed. Fruit globose or slightly egg-shaped, bright red, with the sepals fallen away.

Native of Central Europe, and one of the most distinct and handsome of the wild European roses. It is remarkable for its copious furnishing of glands. It belongs to the sweet-briar group (RUBIGINOSÆ). An identical or very similar rose has been found in England, but it is not thought to be a true native. From its nearest allies—rubiginosa and micrantha—it is readily distinguished by the absence of the fine bristles on the stem.

R. LÆVIGATA, *Michaux*. CHEROKEE ROSE

(R. sinica, *Aiton*, Bot. Mag., t. 2847 ; R. ternata, *Poiret*)

A climbing shrub, growing over the branches of trees in a wild state ; its stems armed with hooked spines. Leaves three-foliolate, brilliantly glossy green, and quite glabrous ; leaflets shortly stalked, oval or ovate, simply toothed, 1½ to 4 ins. long, half as wide, of thick, firm texture. Flowers 3 to 4 ins. across, pure white, fragrant, solitary, and borne on a very bristly stalk ; sepals stout, 1 in. or more long, with leafy tips and more or less bristly. Fruit red, ¾ in. wide, somewhat longer, thickly set with bristles ⅛ in. long, the sepals persisting at the top for a long time.

Native of China, but long naturalised in the southern United States, and first named in 1803 from specimens collected in Georgia by Pursh, the American botanist. How it reached America from China does not appear to be known, but it was in cultivation in Georgia in 1780. Afterwards it received a multitude of names, the best known of which was " sinica." One of the most beautiful of all single wild roses when seen at its best, it is, unfortunately, too tender for the open air, except in such places as Cornwall. Elsewhere it can only succeed in exceptionally sheltered sunny corners. A cross between this species and some other rose (perhaps a form of indica) is called " Anemone." This is hardy on a wall, and bears several large, lovely, blush-coloured flowers in a cluster.

R. LONGICUSPIS, *Bertoloni*

(R. sinowilsonii, *Hemsley*)

A rambling, more or less evergreen, scrambling shrub up to 18 ft. high in a wild state, with glabrous, shining, deep brownish red young shoots that are armed with stout, hooked, decurved, flattened spines ⅛ to ¼ in. long. Leaves 5 to 11 ins. long, composed of five, seven, sometimes nine leaflets ; main-stalk with short decurved prickles underneath. Leaflets ovate-oblong, simply or doubly toothed, rounded at the base, slenderly pointed ; 1 to 4 ins. long, ½ to 2 ins. wide ; dark glittering green above and glabrous on both surfaces. Flowers white, 2 ins. wide, produced in June up to eight or ten together in

a terminal corymbose panicle. Calyx-tube globose, usually more or less
glandular; sepals up to 1 in. long, ovate at the base, drawn out into a slender
tail varying from glabrous to very glandular; petals downy at the back.
Flower-stalks up to 2 ins. long, glandular to nearly glabrous. Fruit globose,
ovoid, red, ½ to ⅝ in. long, sepals ultimately falling.

Native of W. China and India. The plant originally named " R. sinowilsonii " by Hemsley (*Kew Bulletin*, 1906, p. 158) seems to be a distinct form
in the large size of its leaves and leaflets, the great length of the flower-stalks
which, like the calyx-tube, are free from glands. The petals are, however,
downy outside—a strong characteristic of R. longicuspis. It is not very hardy
at Kew except against a wall, but in the milder counties is a very striking rose
because of its large shining green leaves and dark, glittering, reddish young
shoots and spines. It belongs to the moschata group.

R. LUCENS, *Rolfe*

A rambling, semi-evergreen shrub ultimately 6 to 9 ft. high, with glabrous,
very lustrous, brownish red young shoots armed with similarly coloured,
recurved spines up to ⅔ in. long. Leaves 3 to 6 ins. long, with five to nine
leaflets, main-stalk glabrous, spiny. Leaflets oval-oblong or ovate, slenderly
pointed, mostly rounded at the base, finely and sharply toothed; ¾ to 2½ ins.
long, ½ to 1¾ ins. wide; glabrous, dark, very lustrous green. Flowers white,
1½ ins. wide; produced during June in lax corymbs of ten or more blossoms;
calyx-tube, sepals, and flower-stalks glandular; petals not downy. Fruit dark
red, globose, ⅓ to ½ in. wide, ripening late, the sepals late-falling but ultimately
deciduous.

Native of W. China; originally introduced to Kew in 1899 and later by
Wilson (Nos. 1334, 4127) but is no longer there. It has by Rehder and
Wilson been united, along with R. sinowilsonii, to R. longicuspis, but seems
distinct enough to deserve the separate name given to it by Rolfe (see *Kew
Bulletin*, 1916, p. 34). From typical R. longicuspis it differs in its glabrous
petals and from R. sinowilsonii (see note on preceding species) in its very
glandular calyx-tube, sepals, and flower-stalks. Although injured in severe
winters it is definitely hardier than he latter.

R. LUTEA, *Miller*. AUSTRIAN BRIAR

(Bot. Mag., t. 363; R. Eglanteria, *Miller*; R. fœtida, *Hermann*)

A shrub 3 to 8 ft. high, with erect or arching stems, not bristly, but
furnished with many slender straight prickles, up to ¼ in. long. Leaflets five,
seven, or nine, oval or obovate, ¾ to 1½ ins. long, half or more than half as
wide; doubly toothed; dark green and glabrous, or with scattered hairs
above; more or less downy and glandular beneath, like the common stalk
and stipules. Flowers deep yellow, 2 to 3 ins. across, usually solitary; calyx
and flower-stalk glabrous; sepals ¾ to 1 in. long, downy inside, lanceolate,
with expanded leaf-like tips, which are sometimes coarsely toothed. Fruit
rarely seen, but described as globose, red, and ½ in. diameter.

The " Austrian " briar has been known in gardens for between three
hundred and four hundred years, and differs from the Scotch rose in having
no bristles (as distinct from spines) on the stems. It does not appear to be
a genuine native of any part of Europe, but occurs wild from Asia Minor
eastwards through Persia to Afghanistan, also in the dry N.W. Himalaya
and in Turkestan. It is essentially a sun-loving plant, inhabiting regions
with a hot, often arid summer. It thrives, nevertheless, in many parts of

S. England, but not in or near London. I believe it is a lime-loving rose, and in places where it is found not to succeed, would advise the addition of lime to the soil if it be not naturally present. The most striking of its varieties is Var. PUNICEA, *Keller* (R. punicea, *Miller* ; R. lutea bicolor, Bot. Mag., t. 1077). Austrian Copper Rose.—This singularly and beautifully coloured rose has petals of a coppery red. In other respects it is similar to lutea ; in fact, yellow flowers frequently appear on some of its branches. It appears to be even less amenable to the London atmosphere than R. lutea. All the forms of R. lutea are frequently deficient in good pollen, but have nevertheless been used for hybridising. The " Persian yellow rose " is a double-flowered variety of R. lutea.

Harisson's double yellow rose first appeared in the garden of the Rev. Mr Harisson, of Trinity Church, New York City, about 1825. Judging by seedlings raised from it by Mr Allard of Angers, which showed by their prickles and black-purple fruits certain characteristics of R. spinosissima, it is probably a hybrid between some form of that species and R. lutea. Its flowers are deep yellow, double ; the leaves, leaf-stalks, and sepals very glandular ; leaflets double-toothed.

R. MACROPHYLLA, *Lindley*

A shrub 8 ft. or more high, with erect stems and arching branches, sometimes unarmed, but usually furnished with straight prickles ⅓ to ½ in. long, more or less pointed upwards. Leaves up to 8 ins. long, consisting of from five to eleven leaflets which are 1 to 2½ ins. long, oval, toothed except near the base, glabrous above, downy beneath ; common stalk downy. Flowers 2 to 3 ins. in diameter, deep blush-red, produced in clusters of varying number down to solitary blossoms ; sepals 1 to 1½ ins. long, expanding into a leafy tip, glandular and downy like the calyx-tube and flower-stalk. Fruit elongated, pear-shaped, ¾ to 1½ ins. long, bright red, crowned with erect, persistent sepals.

Native of the Himalaya and W. China. This fine rose was introduced about 1818, and is among the handsomest in the genus in regard to its fruits, which often hang in numerous clusters. Their elongated, bottle-like shape and crown of large sepals make them very distinct. The species is an extremely variable one, and Mr Wilson found and introduced many allies or forms of this rose from W. China, where he found it up to 11,000 ft. Some of them have already received distinctive names, and others when fully developed will no doubt need them. Mr de Vilmorin also for several years cultivated several distinct forms of this species. R. macrophylla in any of its forms is worth growing, being marked by grace and distinction.

Var. KOROLKOWII.—Stems erect, stout, almost thornless, purplish red. Leaves mostly of nine stalked leaflets up to 2½ ins. long, half as wide, glandular and silky-hairy on the veins beneath. Flowers pink, 2½ ins. wide ; ovary very glandular ; fruits vermilion, 1½ to 2 ins. long, tapering to the base.

R. MALYI, *Kerner*

A compact bush, 3 to 6 ft. high, the stems armed towards the base with short spines and bristle-like prickles, the flowering branches unarmed. Leaflets usually seven or nine, oval or roundish, ½ to 1¼ ins. long, mostly doubly toothed, glabrous on both surfaces ; common stalk slightly glandular. Flowers deep red, 1½ ins. diameter, usually solitary, occasionally in threes ; stalk glandular, like the calyx-tube and narrowly lanceolate sepals. Fruit ¾ to 1 in. long, bottle-shaped, red, crowned with sepals.

This pleasing rose is a native of Dalmatia, and is considered to have an origin similar to that of R. reversa—a natural hybrid between pendulina and spinosissima. In most respects it resembles pendulina, especially in its flowers and pendulous red fruits ; but the smaller, often orbicular leaflets with rounded bases suggest the Scotch rose. It was first distinguished in 1869.

R. MAXIMOWICZIANA, *Regel*

I do not know that the typical rose of this name is in cultivation, but it is represented in gardens by a rose found by Mr J. G. Jack in Korea during 1905 which was originally named " R. Jackii " by Rehder. Since then he has placed it under R. Maximowicziana as var. JACKII. It belongs to the multiflora group of roses and at the Arnold Arboretum is regarded as a beautiful wild rose and a good garden plant.

A deciduous shrub with long, prostrate or semi-prostrate stems, the younger shoots armed with small, pale, uniform, hooked prickles. Leaves 1½ to 4 ins. long, composed of five to nine leaflets ; main-stalk prickly underneath. Leaflets narrowly oval to lanceolate, pointed, tapered at the base, simply toothed ; ¾ to 2½ ins. long, ¼ to ¾ in. wide ; smooth glossy green above, downy on the midrib beneath ; stalk very short. Flowers pure white, each 1½ to 2 ins. wide, produced in July in many flowered clusters, fragrant. Calyx-tube egg-shaped, glabrous ; sepals ⅜ in. long, ovate with a short, slender apex, glandular (like the flower-stalks) outside, downy inside. Fruit egg-shaped, red, ¼ in. long, the sepals fallen away.

Introduced to Kew in 1910 but is not cultivated there at present. It differs from R. multiflora in having merely simply toothed, not fringed stipules and larger flowers. It is described as R. Kelleri, *Baker*, in Willmott's *The Genus Rose*. R. Maximowicziana (type) according to Rehder differs from this variety in having bristles as well as prickles on the young shoots.

R. MIRIFICA, *Greene*. SACRAMENTO ROSE

(Bot. Mag., t. 9070 ; R. stellata mirifica, *Cockerell*)

A deciduous, suckering shrub 4 to 6 ft. high, with slender, pendulous branches ; young shoots furnished with stalked glands and a pair of pale slender spines about ¼ in. long at the base of each leaf, often also with numerous prickles. Leaves ¾ to 1½ ins. long, composed of three or five leaflets which are obovate, tapered at the base, coarsely and bluntly toothed, ¼ to ⅜ in. long, side ones stalkless ; they are glabrous except for minute down and some glands on the main-stalk. Stipules triangular, spreading. Flowers solitary, terminal, 2 ins. wide, fragrant ; petals widely obovate, ¾ in. wide, clear rose. Calyx of five sepals, two of which are entire, two pinnately lobed, the fifth lobed on one side only, ⅜ to ¾ in. long, lanceolate to slenderly triangular, broadened at the end or pointed, more or less prickly beneath, whitish and downy at the margins. Fruit ovoid, ½ in. wide, dull deep red, prickly, crowned by the persisting erect sepals. Blossoms in July and August.

Native of the Sacramento Mountains of New Mexico at 6000 ft. altitude, where it is said to form large patches, acres in extent. It was introduced to Kew in 1917 by means of seed collected the previous autumn for the Arnold Arboretum by Dr Rehder in its native haunts. It is quite at home in this country, spreads by means of underground suckers, which afford a simple means of propagation. It is a very distinct rose in its slender branches, pale thin spines, small coarsely toothed leaflets and prickly calyx-tube. The sepals, in the variableness of their margins resemble our native dog-rose. It is closely

related to R. stellata (*q.v.*), which has rarely other than three leaflets to
leaf and its young shoots are covered with pale grey stellate down. The
particular shade of clear rose in the petals of R. mirifica is almost uniqu
amongst wild roses.

R. MOLLIS, *Smith*

An erect bush, 3 to 6 ft. high, armed with scattered, slender prickles
Leaves 2 to 4 ins. long, with a downy common stalk and stipules. Leaflet
five or seven, oblong or ovate, ½ to 1½ ins. long, doubly toothed, downy on
both sides, especially beneath. Flowers rosy red, 2 ins. across, produce
usually two to four together ; stalk and calyx-tube usually bristly, sometime
bare ; sepals ¾ in. long, narrow, with expanded tips, very glandular an
downy, usually undivided, but occasionally lobed. Fruit globose, ½ in. or
more in diameter, red, surmounted by erect sepals.

Native of Europe and the Caucasus, and wild over most of Britain. I
is allied to pomifera and to tomentosa, differing from the former in its smalle
parts—especially leaves and fruits, its less bristly character, and the undivide
sepals ; and from tomentosa by the softer, more downy leaves and narrowe
persistent sepals.

R. MOSCHATA, *Herrman*. MUSK ROSE
(R. Brunonii, *Lindley* ; Bot. Mag., t. 4030)

A tall, climbing species reaching to the tops of lofty trees ; the stems an
branches armed with short, scattered, stout, hooked prickles. Leaves up t
7 or 8 ins. long ; leaflets five to nine, oval-lanceolate, from 1 to 3 ins. long
about one-third as wide, simply and regularly toothed, glabrous above, mor
or less downy beneath ; common stalk prickly and glandular. Flowers a
first pale yellow, changing to almost pure white, about 1½ ins. across, pro
duced in corymbose clusters—or rather a cluster of corymbs—often forming
an inflorescence over 1 foot across. Calyx-tube, sepals, and flower-stall
downy, the sepals deflexed ; styles united in a column. Fruit red, ⅓ in. wide
obovoid, with the sepals fallen away.

Widely spread in the East from S. Europe to N. India and China
cultivated in England for over three hundred years. This rose is remarkabl
for its enormous clusters of blossom, which, with the white petals and grea
clusters of yellow stamens, make a fine show. It is not one of the hardiest
and the long succulent shoots it makes during summer when young (often
8 to 12 ft. long) are frequently killed back in winter. There are two form:
in cultivation, one with dull green foliage, the other with pale glaucous foliage.
The former is the hardier, and near the London district when once established
is rarely severely cut. The most suitable place for this rose is in a rough
shrubbery, where it can grow over, and be supported by, other shrubs. At
Kew a plant has spread through and over a holly 30 ft. high, and when in
blossom the flowers are particularly effective against the dark glossy green
leaves of its companion. The musky odour of the flowers is very faint.

Var. PLENA has double flowers, and shorter, broader leaves. It is not so
vigorous a plant as the type.

Var. NEPAULENSIS (R. nepaulensis, Andrews' Roses, t. 82) has pale yellow
flowers, and dull green, downy foliage.

Var. PISSARDII (R. Pissardii, *Carrière*).—A variety or ally of moschata
with pink-tinged flowers, and with leaflets not downy beneath. Introduced
from Persia about 1879.

R. MOYESII, *Hemsley and Wilson*

(Bot. Mag., t. 8338)

A shrub 6 to 10 ft. high, of sturdy habit ; stems erect, armed with stout, pale, scattered, broad-based spines, very abundant on the barren shoots, the lower part of which is also abundantly furnished with fine needle-like prickles. Flowering shoots much less prickly. Leaves 3 to 6 ins. long, with from seven to thirteen leaflets, which are ovate to roundish oval, ¾ to 1½ ins. long, simply or doubly toothed, glabrous except on the midrib beneath, which is downy and sometimes prickly, dark green above, pale or somewhat glaucous beneath ; common stalk glandular and prickly. Flowers a lurid dark red, 2 to 2½ ins. across, mostly solitary or in pairs ; stalk and calyx-tube

ROSA MOYESII

glandular-bristly ; sepals 1 in. or more long, with expanded tips and a few glands outside, downy inside. Fruits red, bottle-shaped, 1½ ins. or more long, crowned by the erect, persisting sepals, between which and the body of the fruit is a distinct neck ; glandular-hairy towards the base.

Native of W. China ; first found about 1890 by Mr A. E. Pratt on the Tibetan frontier, at 9000 ft. and over, and in 1903 by Wilson, who introduced it to cultivation. It was first exhibited in flower by Messrs Veitch in June 1908. It is perfectly hardy, and promises to be one of the most attractive of wild roses, especially in the unique colour of its petals, although undoubtedly closely allied to R. macrophylla. It is named after the Rev. J. Moyes, a missionary in W. China.

R. MULTIBRACTEATA, *Hemsley and Wilson*

(R. reducta, *Baker*, Willmott's Genus Rosa, vol. ii., fig. 158)

A deciduous bush up to 6 ft. high ; young shoots slender, glabrous, armed with slender, straight, pale spines usually in pairs, ¼ to ½ in. long. Leaves 1½ to 2½ ins. long, composed of five to nine leaflets ; main-stalk slightly prickly and glandular. Leaflets obovate or oval to almost quite round, simply or doubly toothed, dark green and glabrous above, greyish beneath and downy on the midrib ; ¼ to ⅜ in. long, from two-thirds to quite as much wide. Flowers sometimes numerous in terminal clusters, sometimes few or even solitary, subtended by a group of leaf-like bracts, each flower being 1 to 1½ ins. wide bright pink. Individual flower-stalks ¼ to ¾ in. long, downy and glandular. Calyx-tube ¼ in. long, slender, covered with gland-tipped bristles ; sepals ⅓ in. long, ovate, drawn out into slender tips, downy inside, glandular outside ; styles free, very downy. Fruit globose, ⅓ in. wide, orange-red with the sepals at the top and a few glandular bristles persisting.

Native of W. Szechuen, China ; discovered in the valley of the Min River and introduced by Wilson in 1908. It belongs to the very attractive group of small-leaved roses which includes R. Webbiana and R. Willmottiæ, both of which have only solitary flowers. The crowded bracts on the inflorescence are distinctive. It flowers in June.

R. MULTIFLORA, *Thunberg*

(Bot. Mag., t. 7119 ; R. polyantha, *Siebold and Zuccarini*)

A wide-spreading bush, ultimately 10 to 15 ft. high, sending out every year from the main body of the plant long arching stems which are clothed with blossom the following June. Branches glabrous, armed with small decurved prickles. Leaves 3 to 6 ins. long, more on exceptionally vigorous shoots, composed of seven or nine leaflets ; stipules deeply laciniated, and with glandular teeth. Leaflets 1 to 2 ins. long, obovate or oval, simply toothed, slightly downy above when young, more so beneath. Flowers white, 1 in. across, very numerously borne in branching panicles, 4 to 6 ins. across, and as much high ; stamens golden yellow. Calyx-tube and flower-stalk hairy ; sepals reflexed, white-woolly and glandular. Fruit oval to round, ¼ in. long, red, with the sepals fallen away.

Native of N. China, Korea, and Japan ; long known in gardens by its double and variously coloured forms ; the single-flowered type was not introduced until 1875. This is the parent species (or in the case of hybrids, the dominating species) of the great and valuable group of roses classed as "polyantha," characterised by small, but numerous flowers in large trusses, and usually a rambling habit. A discussion of these is outside the province of this work. The distinctive mark of R. multiflora, which is more or less evident also in its progeny, is the conspicuously laciniated stipules. It is one of the most beautiful of wild roses ; of a robust and very graceful habit, a single bush growing 10 ft. or more high, and still more in diameter, every branch wreathed with blossom during June. The lower branches take root if resting on loose soil, and for ordinary purposes afford a sufficient means of increase. When more are needed they can be obtained from cuttings with the greatest ease. R. multiflora is useful for clothing high fencing, for planting on banks, and in any place where its vigorous growths can have ample space to develop.

Var. PLENA. Bramble-flowered Rose.—Introduced to Kew in 1804, this has flowers similar in size and arrangement to the type, but with numerous petals.

Var. PLATYPHYLLA. Seven Sisters Rose.—A beautiful rose with large leaves, twice as big as those of the type ; flowers very double, varying pale rose to crimson.

R. NIPPONENSIS, *Crépin*. FUJIYAMA ROSE

(R. acicularis nipponensis, *Hooker fil.* ; Bot. Mag., t. 7646)

A bush 3 to 7 ft. high, with erect stems, sometimes naked, sometimes furnished with bristle-like spines, ⅛ to ¼ in. long. Leaves 2 to 4 ins. long, composed of usually seven or nine leaflets (sometimes five or eleven), which are ⅓ to 1 in. or more long, pointed or rounded at the apex, simply toothed, glabrous on both surfaces; common stalk more or less bristly. Flowers almost always solitary, 1½ to 1¾ ins. across, of a beautiful deep purplish red; stalk glandular-bristly; sepals extending slightly beyond the petals, very downy on the lower half. Fruit bright red, ¾ in. long, ovoid, crowned by the erect, persistent sepals.

Native of Japan, on Fujiyama Mountain. This rose is closely allied to acicularis, but differs in its more deeply coloured flowers and smooth leaves. It is, perhaps, the most pleasing of the acicularis group, distinguished by their erect sepals on red fruits. Introduced to Kew in 1894.

R. NITIDA, *Willdenow*

A low bush, rarely more than 2 ft. high, with erect, often reddish stems, densely furnished with prickly bristles. Leaves 2 to 3 ins. long, very shining green, becoming purplish red in autumn; stipules with glandular-toothed margins; leaflets five to nine, narrow oblong, tapering at both ends; from ½ in. to 1¼ ins. long, one-quarter to one-third as wide; finely and sharply toothed, glabrous all over, and of firm texture. Flowers bright rosy red, 2 to 2½ ins. across, usually solitary, occasionally two to three together; flower-stalks and sepals bristly or glandular, the latter entire, lanceolate, and reflexed. Fruit globose, ⅓ in. wide, scarlet, bristly, with the sepals fallen away.

Native of eastern N. America; introduced in 1807. A charming little rose, very distinct among dwarf kinds by its shining, narrow leaflets, its very prickly stems, and highly coloured flowers. The leaves often turn bright red in autumn.

R. NOISETTIANA, *Thory*. NOISETTE ROSE

A vigorous bush, with arching branches, forming a rounded mass 8 or 10 ft. through and nearly as much high, the stems armed with scattered, hooked prickles. Leaflets three to seven, oblong, with a short, fine point, 1½ to 3 ins. long, more than half as wide, glabrous, finely toothed. Flowers 2 ins. across, white, produced up to twenty or more together in large terminal clusters in July and August.

This rose is considered to be a hybrid between R. moschata and some form of R. indica raised (accidentally it is said) in N. America by Mr Philippe Noisette, early in the nineteenth century, and by him sent to Paris in 1817. It is the type of a considerable group of garden roses, known as the "noisettes," many of which, being crossed with the gallica and indica types, depart widely from the original form, which is itself rare. Wm. Paul in his last edition of *The Rose Garden* gave a list of thirty-five varieties. A fine plant on one of the lawns at Kew makes a beautiful display every summer; a small spray from it is here figured. It is difficult, however, to see any indication of R. indica.

R. NUTKANA, *Presl*. NOOTKA ROSE

A robust shrub, 6 to 10 ft. high, spines stout, hooked or straight, sometimes ½ in. or more long on the young barren stems, often absent from the flowering shoots. Leaves 3 to 5 ins. long, stipules edged with glands; leaflets five to nine, broadly oval to ovate, ¾ to 2 ins. long, simply or doubly toothed, downy beneath (sometimes glabrous). Flowers solitary, or in twos or threes, bright red, 2 to 2½ ins. across; calyx-tube and flower-stalk glabrous; sepals 1 to

1½ ins. long, narrow, with an expanded leaf-like apex, glandular and more or less downy. Fruit globose or orange-shaped, bright red, ½ to ⅝ in. wide, crowned with the long, erect sepals.

Native of western N. America, common along the Pacific coast ; discovered by Archibald Menzies on Vancouver Island in 1793. It is a handsome

ROSA NOISETTIANA (see p. 215)

wild rose, perhaps the handsomest of W. American species, and flowers and fruits well in this country.

Var. HISPIDA, *Fernald.*—Leaves coarsely toothed ; flower-head glandular bristly (R. MacDougalii).

R. OMEIENSIS, *Rolfe.*   MT. OMI ROSE
(Bot. Mag., t. 8471)

A shrub up to 10 or 12 ft. high, with the habit and general aspect of R. sericea ; stems and branches variable in their armature, some being smooth, some having a pair of spines at the base of the leaf-stalk, and some very densely set with bristles and spines, the latter compressed and flat, awl-shaped, up to ⅓ in. long. Leaves 1½ to 4 ins. long, consisting of usually eleven or thirteen (but sometimes seventeen or nineteen) leaflets, which are oblong or obovate ; ¼ to 1¼ ins. long, ⅛ to ½ in. wide ; dark dull green and

glabrous above, downy and often spiny on the midrib beneath ; the teeth
slender, incurved, simple ; common stalk downy and spiny.   Flowers solitary,
white, 1 to 1½ ins. wide ; petals four.   Fruit pear-shaped, ½ to 1 in. long,
bright red, with a thickened stalk of bright yellow, the sepals persisting.
Discovered on Mount Omi, in Szechuen, China, by the Rev. E. Faber
about 1886, and later by Henry ; introduced by Wilson in 1901.   Although
palpably a close ally of R. sericea (*q.v.*), it is distinct from that and all other
species known to me in the colouring of the fruit.   It differs also in the greater
number of leaflets and in the thick, fleshy footstalk of the fruit.

Var. PTERACANTHA, *Rehder and Wilson* (Bot. Mag., t. 8218—as R. sericea
pteracantha).—A shrub of open, slender habit, eventually as large as the
type.   Stems covered when young with blood red, translucent spines which
are sometimes 1½ ins. wide at the base, ½ to ¾ in. deep, flat and thin, contracting
abruptly to a sharp point.   The second year they become grey and woody.
This remarkable plant is a native of W. China, but a very similar one has been
collected by Sir Geo. Watt in Manipur.   These richly coloured, enormous
spines, add a new attraction to wild roses.   The flowers, perhaps, are smaller,
and the leaflets are nine to thirteen on each leaf.

In *Plantæ Wilsonianæ*, Vol. ii., p. 331, Messrs Rehder and Wilson place
all those roses which were previously considered Chinese forms of R. sericea
by Franchet and Focke under R. omeiensis.   They do not consider that the
true R. sericea reaches China, although they seem somewhat doubtful about
the standing of certain forms found in Yunnan, which, in number of leaflets
at least, resemble the Himalayan R. sericea.   Variable as the Chinese forms
of this rose are, they recognise only two by name, viz., typical R. omeiensis and
the var. pteracantha above noted.   R. omeiensis differs from R. sericea in the
greater number of leaflets and in the thickened, fleshy footstalk of the fruit.

R. PENDULINA, *Linnæus*

(R. alpina, *Linnæus*)

A robust shrub, ultimately 2 to 4 ft. high, with branches almost or quite
devoid of prickles.   Leaves 2 to 6 ins. long, with five to nine leaflets, the
common stalk of which is glandular and sometimes downy ; stipules with
large leafy tips edged with glands.   Leaflets oval or ovate, 1 to 2 ins. long,
usually double-toothed ; midrib minutely prickly, otherwise glabrous on both
sides.   Flower often solitary, deep pink, 1½ ins. across, produced on a
glandular-bristly (sometimes naked) stalk, 1 to 1½ ins. long.   Sepals ¾ in.
long, entire, expanded at the tips, glandular or smooth outside, downy within.
Fruit bright red, ¾ to 1 in. long, narrowly pear-shaped, with a neck surmounted
by erect, persistent sepals.

Native of the mountains of Central and S. Europe ; cultivated in England
since late in the seventeenth century.   It is a rose of great interest to many
because of its unarmed condition, and is sometimes known as the " rose
without a thorn."   Often the only prickles are a few weak ones at the base
of the branches.   It has fine foliage and is also very handsome in fruit, the
long, pendulous hips of a curious bottle shape, being of large size and highly
coloured.   Whilst the form described above may be regarded as the type,
the species as a whole is variable.   One of the most distinct forms is

Var. PYRENAICA (R. pyrenaica, *Gouan*), Bot. Mag., t. 6724.—This has
more or less glaucous branches, and is especially distinguished by glandular
bristles on the flower-stalk and calyx-tube.   These glands often persist on
the fruit and give off, when rubbed, a distinct turpentine-like odour.

R. PERSICA, *Michaux*

(R. berberifolia, *Pallas* ; Bot. Mag., t. 7096 ; R. simplicifolia, *Salisbury*)

A thin, straggling bush, 2 or 3 ft. high, with slender, wiry, downy stem furnished with hooked spines and slender prickles, spreading by means of underground suckers. Leaves glaucous, simple (consisting of one leaflet) stalkless, obovate or oval, ½ to 1¼ ins. long, toothed towards the apex, covered with fine down. Flowers about 1 in. across, solitary at the end of the shoot on a slender, spiny stalk, the petals deep yellow with a crimson spot at the base ; calyx-tube thickly covered with pale prickles ⅛ in. long ; sepals lanceolate downy, more or less prickly. Fruit not seen in this country, but, according to Pallas, globose, very prickly, and crowned with the persisting sepals.

Native of the Orient, Afghanistan, etc., inhabiting dry, hot regions ; introduced in 1790. This remarkable rose, distinguished from all others by the undivided leaf and absence of stipules, is exceedingly rare in cultivation. It is not really hardy perhaps in any part of the country, and never appears to have been kept more than a few years in the open air, even in such places as the Isle of Wight. Perhaps it might thrive on some sunny bank in the Isles of Scilly. A plant in a cool unshaded house at Kew, which has been growing there for over twenty years, is planted near the glass in loam mixed with lime rubble. Out-of-doors it would be most likely to succeed in some " sun-trap " on a mound of loam and rubble, and covered with a glass light in winter. Of various modes of propagation tried with this rose, the only one that has succeeded is to sever the suckers from the main plant, and then allow them to remain undisturbed for several months, to form roots of their own before taking them from the soil. So distinct is this from all other roses, that it was, in 1829, made into a separate genus by Lindley under the name of Lowea berberifolia.

R. HARDII, *Cels*, is a hybrid between R. persica and some other species, probably R. clinophylla. It first appeared in the Jardin de Luxembourg, Paris, in 1836. Leaves composed of from one to seven narrowly obovate leaflets, toothed, glabrous on both surfaces, stipular. Flowers 2 ins. across, petals yellow with an orange spot at the base of each ; calyx-tube downy, but with few prickles. It wants much the same treatment as R. persica in regard to warmth and sunshine and perfect root-drainage, but is hardier and more amenable to cultivation.

R. PISOCARPA, *A. Gray*

(Bot. Mag., t. 6857)

A small shrub, usually not more than 3 to 4 ft. high, of rather straggling habit ; branches slender, unarmed, or with a few small prickles, either straight or pointing upwards. Leaves 2 to 3 ins. long, with five or seven leaflets, which are ½ to 1 in. long, oval or ovate, simply toothed, and, like the common stalk, downy beneath. Flowers 1 in. or rather more across, with rounded, overlapping, bright rosy petals ; they occur in clusters of as many as four or five, but are sometimes solitary ; stalk glabrous ; sepals ½ in. or more long with expanded tips, very downy within. Fruit about the size of a pea, globose, bright red, surmounted by the erect sepals.

Native of western N. America. An interesting and brightly coloured rose, distinct in the tiny fruits.

R. POMIFERA, *Hermann.* APPLE ROSE

(Bot. Mag., t. 7241 ; R. villosa, *Linnæus* in part)

A bush 4 to 6 ft. high, of sturdy habit ; branches glabrous or slightly hairy, armed with scattered, slender, but broad-based prickles up to ½ in. long.

,eaves 4 to 7 ins. long, with common stalks and stipules glandular and .owny. Leaflets five or seven, oblong or ovate, 1 to 2½ ins. long ¾ to 1½ ins. ⁄ide ; doubly toothed, downy on both surfaces, especially beneath. Flowers ½ to 2½ ins. across, deep rosy pink, produced in clusters of three or rarely ₁ore, each on a stalk covered thickly with glandular bristles like the calyx-₁ube. Sepals 1 in. long, with long-tailed, pinnate lobes, very glandular-hairy. ⁝ruit pear-shaped or rounded, rich red, 1 to 1½ ins. long, and about 1 in. wide, ⁝ristly and surmounted by the erect sepals.

Native of Central Europe and occasionally found wild in Britain, but not true native. It is a remarkable rose, and, when well cultivated, one of the ₁ost striking, especially in the fruit, which is larger than that of any other ₁ardy rose. It appears to thrive exceptionally well in Gloucestershire, where have seen it in splendid condition in Lord Redesdale's garden at Batsford, ₁nd with Canon Ellacombe. Its nearest allies are mollis and tomentosa (*q.v.*).

[The R. villosa of Linnæus included three species which probably are connected by ₁ntermediate forms : R. pomifera, chiefly marked by its large leaflets and fruits, and ⁝ristly character ; R. mollis, by its soft leaves and almost entire sepals erect in fruit ; ₹. tomentosa, by its late ripening fruit and reflexed sepals falling when the fruit is ripe.]

R. RICHARDII, *Rehder*. ABYSSINIAN ROSE

(R. sancta, *A. Richard*)

As seen in cultivation this rose is a low, rather open bush, whose weakish tems have a few hooked, scattered prickles of unequal size. Leaflets three ⁝r five, ovate or oblong, 1 to 2 ins. long, often blunt-pointed, simply toothed, ⁝ough but not downy above, hairy beneath ; common stalk downy and more ⁝r less prickly ; stipules edged with glands. Flowers 2 to 3 ins. across, pale ⁝ose, produced several together in a loose cluster, each flower on a slender, ⁝labrous stalk, 1 to 2 ins. long. Sepals downy and glandular, very large and ⁝innately lobed, the largest being 1½ ins. long, and ⅝ in. wide at the base, ⁝ith broad, leafy points.

Native of Abyssinia, and a close ally of R. gallica, but very distinct in the ₁arge deeply lobed sepals. It was introduced to cultivation by Messrs Paul ⁝f Cheshunt, who informed me that it is quite hardy. The synonym refers to ⁝ts being cultivated in the vicinity of churches in Abyssinia.

R. ROULETTII, *Correvon*. PYGMY ROSE

An evergreen or semi-deciduous shrub from 4 to 9 ins. high, of compact, ⁝ushy shape ; young shoots not downy but armed irregularly with spines $\frac{1}{16}$ to $\frac{1}{12}$ in. long. Leaflets three or five to each leaf, oval-lanceolate, slenderly ⁝ointed, rounded at the base, finely and sharply toothed, ¼ to ¾ in. long, about ₁alf as wide, purplish, quite glabrous, the main-stalk furnished with a few ⁝pines and glands. Flowers ¾ to 1 in. wide, very double, rosy pink, produced ⁝n erect clusters.

This pretty little rose, the smallest of them all, was first brought into ₁otice by Mr H. Correvon of Geneva in 1922. He states that a friend of his, Dr Roulet, after whom he named it, found it a few years previous to that date ⁝rown in pots as a window plant at Mauborget, near Grandson, in Switzerland. This village was afterwards completely destroyed by fire and the rose with it, ⁝ut a single plant was subsequently found in a neighbouring village. From ⁝his all the plants now in cultivation have been raised. It was believed to have been grown at Mauborget for centuries, but nothing really is known of its origin. It is no doubt a pygmy form of the China or Monthly rose (R. indica), of which the dwarf variety *minima*, or "Fairy rose," has long been known. R. Roulettii is much smaller in stature, leaf, and flower. It appears to be quite hardy in the open ground and, as regards size at any rate, is well adapted for the rock garden. Grown in pots, it seems to flower more or less continuously. In the Swiss villages its height as a window plant was apparently only 2 ins. or so, but it grows 6 to 9 ins. high planted in the open ground with us.

R. ROXBURGHII, *Trattinick*. BURR ROSE

(R. microphylla, *Roxburgh* ; Bot. Mag., t. 6548)

A sturdy bush, as much in width as it is in height, which is 6 or 8 ft. ; bark grey, peeling ; branches stiff, armed with a few stiff, straight prickles in pairs. Leaves 2 to 4 ins. long, consisting of nine to fifteen leaflets, which are oval, tapering at both ends, ⅓ to ¾ in. long, firm in texture, with fine, slender teeth ; glabrous above, rather downy beneath, especially on the midrib when young ; common stalk downy. Flowers usually solitary, delicate rose, 2 to 2½ ins. across, extremely fragrant ; calyx-tube and flower-stalk prickly ; sepals broadly ovate, lobed, downy. Fruit flattened, tomato-shaped, 1½ ins. diameter, very spiny, yellowish green, fragrant.

Native of China ; the double-flowered variety was introduced about 1820, by way of the Calcutta Botanic Garden, where it had long been cultivated. It is a most distinct rose by reason of its peeling bark, its small numerous leaflets, and especially by its large, spiny, apple-like fruit. In the leafless state its open habit, stiff branches, and peeling bark scarcely suggest a rose. When in bloom it appears to be preferred by bees to any other rose. It is a favourite in the south United States.

Var. PLENA.—Flowers double and rather lumpy. Bot. Mag., t. 3490.

R. RUBELLA, *Smith*

A hybrid of natural origin between R. spinosissima and R. pendulina, and intermediate between them. It does not often exceed 4 or 5 ft. in height, the erect stems covered with bristly prickles intermixed with which are a few straight, slender spines. Leaflets five to nine, oval, ¼ to ¾ in. long. Flowers solitary, 1½ to 2 ins. across, flushed more or less deeply with red ; stalk glandular-bristly. Fruit pendulous, egg-shaped, red, ¾ in. long, crowned with the sepals.

Native of the Alps of Europe. It resembles the Scotch rose in the armature of its stems and small leaves, but differs markedly in the drooping, red, rather elongated fruit. It has been included in the English flora on the strength of a supposed find on the coast of Durham. But as R. pendulina is not a native, this plant must have been introduced, or be an escape from gardens. There is a series of hybrids between the Scotch and Alpine roses in which R. rubella is about intermediate. Others are almost unarmed, like pendulina ; others are as prickly and bristly as spinosissima.

R. RUBIGINOSA, *Linnæus*. SWEET-BRIAR, EGLANTINE

(R. Eglanteria, *Linnæus*)

An erect bush with arching branches, 6 to 8 ft. high in gardens ; stems and branches armed with numerous, scattered, hooked prickles. Leaflets five, seven, or nine, ovate or roundish, doubly toothed, nearly or quite without

wn above, but covered beneath with sweet-smelling glands. Flowers pale
nk, 1½ ins. in diameter, produced singly, in threes or sevens or more together ;
ower-stalk and sepals bristly. Fruit bright red, egg-shaped, crowned with
ıe spreading sepals.

Native of Europe, and with the dog rose one of the summer delights of
nglish hedgerows. It is not so strong a grower as R. canina, has smaller
aves, and is always distinguished by the sweet fragrance of its leaves. On
ıis account, and unlike the dog rose, it may well be grown in gardens. It
ıakes a charming low hedge clipped back annually before growth recom-
ıences in spring. The fragrance is most perceptible after a shower, and
henever the atmosphere is fresh and moist.

Var. MAJOR has leaves about twice the size of ordinary rubiginosa, and
ıore coarsely toothed.

Var. PLENA.—Flowers double.

The sweet-briar is one of the parents of a beautiful group of garden roses
ınown as " Penzance " briars, which were raised by the late Lord Penzance
om 1884 onwards, by fertilising the flowers of this species with various other
)ecies and garden varieties. The most distinct and pleasing of these are the
ıes issuing from rubiginosa crossed with the yellow and copper-coloured
ɔrms of R. lutea.

R. MICRANTHA, *Smith.*—A British rose common in the south of England ; it
iffers from R. rubiginosa in the following respects : A somewhat stronger shrub
hose stems are not so well furnished with spines ; leaves not so strongly scented,
owers smaller ; the style, downy in rubiginosa, is glabrous ; sepals falling away
ʻom the fruit sooner. Of little value in gardens.

R. RUBRIFOLIA, *Villars*

(Bot. Reg., t. 430 ; R. ferruginea, *Déséglise*)

A shrub of erect habit, 5 to 7 ft. high, whose stems are covered with a
urplish bloom, and armed with small decurved prickles. Leaflets five or
even, ovate or oval, 1 to 1½ ins. long, simply toothed, quite glabrous on both
urfaces, of a beautiful purplish red, glaucous hue. Flowers deep red, 1½ ins.
cross, few in a cluster ; stalk naked or with a few bristles ; sepals narrow,
lowny inside, entire or occcasionally lobed, 1 in. or more long, standing out
ıeyond the petals. Fruit red, globose or nearly so, ½ in. or rather more long,
ɣlabrous, and with the sepals fallen away.

Native of Central Europe, especially the Alps and Pyrenees and other
ıountainous regions. It is nearly allied to R. canina, but is easily distinguished
ɪy the beautiful reddish colour of leaf and young stem, and by the longer
epals. Its colour makes it not only one of the most distinct of roses, but also
he most ornamental in vegetative (as distinct from floral) characters. Planted
ı groups it makes a telling feature in the landscape the summer through.
Ƭhe name must not be confounded with " rubifolia," a disused one for the
ʃorth American R. setigera.

R. RUGOSA, *Thunberg.* RAMANAS ROSE

(R. ferox, *Lawrance* (not *Bieberstein*) ; Bot. Reg., t. 420)

A shrub 4 to 6 ft. high, and one of the sturdiest of roses. Stems stout,
lensely covered with prickles of unequal size, the largest ⅓ to ½ in. long ;
hey, as well as the stem itself, downy. Leaves 3 to 7 ins. long, with large
lowny stipules ; leaflets five to nine, oblong, 1 to 2 ins. long, shallowly toothed

except towards the base, downy beneath, the very conspicuous veins giving
them the wrinkled appearance to which the specific name refers ; common
stalk downy and armed with hooked spines. Flowers very fragrant, 3½ ins
across, purplish rose, produced singly, or a few in a cluster ; petals overlapping
the calyx-tube is glabrous, but the flower-stalk and sepals are downy, the latter
1 to 1¼ ins. long. Fruit rich bright red, tomato-shaped, 1 in. or more in diameter
crowned with the sepals.

Native of China, Japan, and Korea ; introduced by Siebold about 1845
It is said to have been cultivated since A.D. 1100 in China, where the ladies of
the Court long prepared a kind of pot-pourri from its petals mixed with
camphor and musk. No rose hybridises more readily with others, and if seed
be sown from plants growing with or near other roses, little of the progeny
comes true. The consequence is that a worthless lot of mongrels have
appeared, some of which have been named, but ought never to have been
allowed to survive their first flowering. At the same time a group of
beautiful roses has been derived from it, noteworthy for their vigorous habit
fragrant flowers, and very handsome fruits.

Var. ALBA.—Flowers white. ALBO-PLENA, *Rehder*. Flowers double white

Var. PLENA.—Flowers purplish red, double ; leaflets smaller and narrower
than in the type.

Var. KAMTCHATICA (R. kamtchatica, *Ventenat* ; Bot. Reg., t. 419).—A
distinct geographical variety sometimes regarded as a species. It differs from
rugosa in having the stipular prickles distinct from the more bristly scattered
ones, in the leaves being more obovate and rounded at the apex, and in the
smaller fruits. Introduced about 1770.

A discussion of the numerous hybrids now in gardens, of the type of
" Blanc de Coubert," " Mrs A. Waterer," etc., is outside the limits of this
book ; only a few of the more noteworthy primary ones can be noticed.

R. CALOCARPA (rugosa × indica).—Sent out by Bruant of Poitiers about 1891
A handsome plant, with branches less thick than rugosa, clusters of bright red fragrant
flowers, followed by globose, scarlet fruits, ¾ in. wide, and crowned with the sepals
In a sunny season it bears fruits in remarkable abundance.

R. HETEROPHYLLA, *Cochet* (rugosa alba × lutea).—Raised by Mr Cochet of Coubert
in France, about 1894. A curious rose of little beauty. Flowers white, 1 to 1½ ins.
across ; leaves and leaflets diverse, the later ones of the season very narrow.

R. IWARA, *Siebold* (rugosa × multiflora).—Introduced from Japan. Of spreading
habit, intermediate between the parents ; flowers small, white. This hybrid may be
described as two beautiful species spoilt.

R. VILMORINII (rugosa × microphylla).—One of the best primary crosses, being
intermediate in habit and foliage, and having large, single, pale pink flowers, 4 or 5 ins.
across. Raised by the late Henri de Vilmorin.

The " Lady Duncan " rose (rugosa × Wichuraiana) was raised in the Arnold
Arboretum. It is a rambling plant, making shoots 6 or 8 ft. long in a year. Leaves
glossy green ; flowers soft rose. One of the most beautiful of these hybrids.

R. SERICEA, *Lindley*

(Bot. Mag., t. 5200)

A large spreading bush, 10 to 12 ft. high and more in diameter, with
gracefully arching branches and abundant leafage. The species shows great
variation in the armature of its stems and in the downiness or otherwise of its
leaves, but in the typical form the stems are armed with a pair of upwardly
curved prickles at the base of each leaf-stalk, and they are further furnished
with numerous glandular bristles. Leaves from 2 to 4 ins. long, composed
of from seven to eleven leaflets, downy beneath ; leaflets ¼ to 1 in. long,

bovate, rounded and toothed towards the apex, tapering and entire towards
ne base. Flowers creamy white, $1\frac{1}{2}$ to 2 ins. across, with nearly always four
etals arranged like a Maltese cross ; sepals $\frac{3}{4}$ in. long, downy. Fruit pear-
haped or roundish, $\frac{1}{2}$ in. wide, bright red, with persistent sepals.
Native of N. India, and first observed on Gossan Than, a mountain in
Jepal. In later years it has been found to extend many hundreds of miles
long the Himalaya, reaching Bhotan and Upper Burma in the east. The
reat distinctive character of R. sericea is the number of the petals, but this
s not invariably four ; towards the end of the flowering season odd flowers
nay frequently be seen with five. It is one of the earliest roses to blossom
ut-of-doors. I have noted them as early as 12th May.

In the de Vilmorin collection at Les Barres, in France, there is a great
ssemblage of roses of the sericea group. The points of variation are to be
ound in the armature and colour of the stems, the degree of pubescence on
he leaves, the number and shape of the leaflets, the colour and size of the
pines and fruits. The colour of the young wood and spines is sometimes
ich red, and the fruits, normally bright red, are, as I have been informed
y Mr de Vilmorin, yellow in the forms from Szechuen. In one of Wilson's
ntroductions the leaves have as many as seventeen leaflets, of a size and shape
uggesting those of the mountain ash.

A variety named by the late Mr Franchet is :—
Var. DENUDATA.—Stems unarmed ; leaves quite glabrous.

R. SERTATA, *Rolfe*

(Bot. Mag., t. 8473)

A shrub of elegant habit, up to 6 ft. ; branches glaucous, graceful and
lender, armed with spines up to $\frac{1}{2}$ in. long, in pairs or scattered. Leaves 2 to
 ins. long, composed of seven to eleven leaflets, which are stalkless, oval to
blong, sharply toothed ; $\frac{1}{3}$ to $\frac{3}{4}$ in. long, $\frac{3}{16}$ to $\frac{3}{8}$ in. wide ; grey-green above,
laucous beneath ; stipules edged with glandular hairs. Flowers few or
olitary on short twigs, 2 to $2\frac{1}{2}$ ins. across ; flower-stalk $\frac{2}{3}$ to $1\frac{1}{4}$ ins. long,
landular-hairy or glabrous ; petals broadly obcordate, delicate purplish
ose ; calyx-lobes ovate-lanceolate, tapering to a long, narrow point, minutely
lowny, sometimes glandular-downy, sometimes glabrous ; anthers deep
yellow. Fruit deep red, egg-shaped, $\frac{3}{4}$ in. long, the sepals persisting at the top.

Native of Central China ; introduced by Wilson in 1907, and flowered at
Kew in June 1910. It is an extremely elegant and pretty rose, allied to
R. Webbiana and R. Willmottiæ. From the former of these it differs " in its
axer habit, its few, slender, straight, stipulary thorns, and its more slender,
beaked fruit." R. Willmottiæ has smaller leaves and short-stalked flowers.

R. SETIGERA, *Michaux*. PRAIRIE ROSE

(R. rubifolia, *R. Brown*)

A rambling shrub making slender stems several yards long in a season,
armed with short, hooked prickles, not downy. Leaves trifoliolate, with a
lowny, glandular stalk and narrow stipules edged with glands. Leaflets
among the largest in the genus, up to 3 ins. long by over 2 ins. wide ; ovate,
coarsely toothed, deep green and glabrous above, pale and downy beneath.
Flowers 2 to $2\frac{1}{2}$ ins. across, deep rose, several in corymbs ; the stalk glandular.
Sepals ovate, pointed, $\frac{1}{2}$ in. long, very downy. Fruit globose, about $\frac{1}{3}$ in.
diameter, with the sepals fallen away.

Native of E. and Central North America, from Ontario to Florida, an
west to Kansas and Texas. Introduced in 1800. This is the most distin
and, in its flowers, perhaps the most beautiful of N. American roses. It
the only one from that region belonging to the group whose styles are unite
in a column (Synstylæ); the only one with normally three leaflets, and th
only climbing species. It is an attractive plant, producing its large, ric
rosy blossoms in clusters 6 ins. or more across, but they have little or
fragrance. Flowering in July and August when few wild roses or shrubs
any kind are in flower, its value is increased. It may be trained up roug
branches of oak, then left to form a tangle. Several garden varieties hav
been raised from it.

R. SETIPODA, *Hemsley and Wilson*

A bushy shrub 6 to 10 ft. high; stems sometimes unarmed, sometime
furnished with few to many straight, stout spines. Leaves 4 to 7 ins. long
composed of five to nine leaflets, which are oval, obovate, or ovate; ¾ to 2½ in
long, half or more than half as wide; tapering towards both ends, simply
very frequently doubly toothed; dark green and glabrous above, pale, rath
glaucous, usually covered with glands beneath, and downy on the midrib
common stalk usually more or less glandular and prickly. Flowers purplis
rose, 2 to 2½ ins. across, produced in loose terminal corymbs of from over thirt
down to half a dozen blossoms. Each flower is borne on a slender stalk 1 t
1½ ins. long, conspicuously furnished with numerous, spreading, glandula
bristles. Calyx-tube and sepals more or less glandular bristly, the latte
felted within, 1 in. or more long, with expanded tips. Fruit red, 1 in. long
glandular-downy, bottle-shaped, the distinct neck crowned with erect persistin
sepals.

Native of Central China (Hupeh); introduced by Wilson to the Coomb
Wood nursery, where it first flowered in June 1909. It is allied to macrophylla
and like all of that group is an interesting and pretty rose. The most dis
tinctive features are the large leafy bracts on the corymb, and the very cor
spicuous bristles on the flower-stalks.

R. SICULA, *Trattinick*

(Bot. Mag., t. 7761, as R. Seraphinii)

A close-habited, densely branched bush of rounded habit, 2 to 5 ft. high
young wood not downy, but thickly furnished with stiff, flattened, decurve
spines of unequal length, the largest about ¼ in. long. Leaves 1½ to 2 in
long, composed of five or seven leaflets which are broadly ovate or round
¼ to ¾ in. long, doubly toothed, and with glands on the teeth, lower surface
common stalk, and stipules. Flowers 1 to 1¼ ins. across, bright rose, usuall
solitary, sometimes two or three together; stalk glabrous or glandular-bristly
calyx-tube quite glabrous; sepals lanceolate or two- or three-lobed, wit
glandular and ciliated margins; styles downy. Fruit about the size of
large pea, red, glabrous, finally black, crowned with persistent sepals.

Native of Italy (Sardinia, Sicily, etc.) and Corsica. A neat and pleasin
little rose, seldom seen in gardens, but quite hardy. It resembles R. horrida i
its dwarf habit, small leaves, and abundant spines, but differs in the particular
pointed out under that species. It is very similar to and confused wit
R. SERAPHINII, *Viviani*, the true plant of which is not in cultivation; th
differs from R. sicula in having glabrous styles.

R. Soulieana, *Crépin.*   Père Soulie's Rose

(Bot. Mag., t. 8158)

A very robust shrub, up to 10 or 12 ft. high, forming an impenetrable angle of branches wider than it is high. Shoots 10 to 12 ft. long are made n a year on young vigorous plants ; formidably armed with pale spines, which re compressed, decurved, scattered irregularly on the shoots. Leaves 2½ to . ins. long, grey-green, composed of seven or nine leaflets, which are oval or bovate, ½ to 1 in. long, finely and simply toothed, perfectly glabrous on both urfaces except on the midrib, which, like the common stalk, is more or less owny. Flowers yellowish white, 1½ ins. diameter, produced abundantly in uly on branching corymbs 4 to 6 ins. across ; stalk slender, and, like the alyx-tube, glandular ; styles united ; sepals attenuated, downy. Fruit range-red, egg-shaped, ½ in. long, ⅓ in. wide, with the sepals fallen away. Native of W. China ; sent to Kew in 1899 by Mr Maurice de Vilmorin, who ad raised it from Chinese seed three years before. It is one of the most obust of all roses, and well adapted for the wild garden, where it can have nlimited room, and never be touched with the knife. In such a spot it is triking all the summer because of its luxuriant grey-green foliage, but specially in July when in flower, and in autumn when the fruits have coloured.

R. spinosissima, *Linnæus.*   Scotch or Burnet Rose

(R. pimpinellifolia, *Linnæus* ; R. scotica, *Miller*)

A dwarf bush with creeping roots, rarely more than 3 or 4 ft. high in the ypical state, with erect, short-branched stems covered with slender spines nd stout bristles intermixed. Leaves closely set on the branches, 1 to 2½ ins. ong, composed of five, seven, or nine leaflets, which are round or oval, or roadly obovate ; ¼ to ½ in. long, simply toothed, deep green, and quite glabrous. Flowers 1½ to 2 ins. across, white or pale pink, solitary ; stalk and alyx-tube glabrous, sometimes bristly. Fruit dark brown, finally blackish, globose, ½ to ¾ in. wide, crowned with the sepals.   .

Very widely spread in Europe and N. Asia ; found also in Britain, frequently on dry hills, often near the sea. It is the parent of the group of garden roses known as "Scotch," as well as the type of a botanical group of species—the PIMPINELLIFOLIÆ—characterised chiefly by the numerous slender straight prickles of unequal size on the stems. In gardens the species gives place as a rule to its numerous and variable progeny, some of which are very beautiful in their single or double deep rose, white striped with rose, or yellow flowers. Of their abundance an estimate can be made from the fact that a collection of ninety varieties was got together in the gardens of Dalkeith Palace early in the nineteenth century. A consideration of these is outside the province of this work, but several natural varieties remain to be noticed.

Var. ALTAICA (R. altaica, *Willdenow* ; R. grandiflora, *Lindley*).—A shrub up to 6 ft. high, chiefly distinguished from spinosissima by its large size, and the absence or comparative scarcity of bristles among the prickles of the stems. The flowers are 3 ins. across, creamy white, and the leaflets up to 1 in. long. A group of this rose when in full bloom at the end of May makes a very beautiful picture. Native of Siberia.

Var. FULGENS.—Flowers bright rose-coloured, habit like the type.

Var. LUTEA.—A vigorous bush a yard high, increasing rapidly by root-suckers. Leaflets broadly oval, the largest 1 in. long, by ¾ in. wide, downy beneath. Flowers bright buttercup-yellow, 2 ins. across. This variety has

III   H

much of the beauty of the Persian yellow rose but is more amenable to
cultivation—thrives as well, indeed, as the ordinary Scotch rose.

Var. MACRACANTHA.—This variety has been found near Gap, in the Alpine
region of S.E. France. It is very remarkable for its spines, which are flat,
rigid, ⅝ in. long, ¼ in. wide at the base.

Var. MYRIACANTHA (R. myriacantha, *De Candolle*).—A very distinct
variety (probably a good species) with the habit and flowers of ordinary
spinosissima, but with longer and more numerous spines. The best distinction, however, is furnished by the numerous glands on the leaves beneath,
on the leaf-stalks, stipules, flower-stalks, and sepals, and by the double toothing
of the leaflets. Native of S. France.

R. STELLATA, *Wooton*

(Willmott's Genus Rosa, vol. ii., p. 305, with plate)

A deciduous shrub up to 2 ft. high, with slender leafy shoots and of lax
habit ; young shoots thickly covered with starry down and armed with straight,
pale, yellowish white, slender spines ¼ to ⅓ in. long, mixed with which are tiny
prickles and stalked glands. Leaves ¾ to 1½ ins. long, composed of usually
three, sometimes five leaflets ; main-stalk glandular-downy. Leaflets wedge-
shaped or triangular, toothed mainly or only at the broad end ; teeth
comparatively large, blunt ; ¼ to ½ in. long, glabrous and dullish green above,
greyish and slightly downy beneath. Flowers solitary, 2 to 2½ ins. wide, of
a beautiful soft rose ; petals inversely heart-shaped, deeply notched ; anthers
yellow. Calyx-tube globose, covered with pale spines ; sepals ½ in. long,
lance-shaped, two of them pinnately lobed, with a spoon-like tip, glandular
and spiny outside, woolly on the margins. Fruit hemispherical, flat-topped,
prickly, red, ½ in. wide, the sepals persisting at the top.

Native of W. North America from W. Texas to Arizona ; discovered by
Mr E. O. Wooton in 1895 ; introduced to cultivation in 1902. This very
distinct and beautifully coloured rose is not easy to grow in this country.
Its native places are described as dry and very sunny, and no doubt it misses
these conditions here sufficiently to explain our ill success with it. The late
Dr A. R. Wallace got it to flower in his garden at Broadstone, Dorset, in 1912.
It is distinguished from R. mirifica by the stellate down on the young shoots
and by the usually trifoliolate (rarely quinquefoliolate) leaves.

R. MINUTIFOLIA, *Engelmann*, is the third species constituting this group, native of
Lower California, discovered in 1882. It was introduced to Kew in 1888 but did not
long survive and is scarcely likely to be hardy. Leaves ¾ to 1½ ins. long, made up of
three, five, sometimes seven leaflets which are ⅛ to ¼ in. long, oval or obovate, deeply
toothed, very downy beneath, and borne on a pale, downy, thread-like stalk. Young
shoots downy, with numerous slender spines up to ⅜ in. long. Flowers 1 in. wide, pink
or nearly white. Fruit globose, very spiny, ⅓ in. wide. Probably better suited for the
Riviera than any part of the British Isles.

R. TOMENTOSA, *Smith*

A vigorous shrub 6 to 8 ft., or even more high, with arching branches,
closely allied to R. mollis (*q.v.*). Besides its more robust habit, it differs also
in its leaves being much less soft to the touch ; by its longer flower-stalks,
and its wider, more distinctly pinnately lobed sepals. The flower is about the
same as in mollis, being about 2 ins. across, and produced either singly, or
in clusters up to four ; petals rosy-red (rarely white). Fruit bright red, oval
or rather top-shaped, slightly bristly, crowned at first with the reflexed sepals,
which fall away by the time it is ripe.

Native of Britain, and spreading across Europe to the Caucasus. It has a considerable resemblance to the common dog rose, and may be grown in the wilder parts of the garden where it can take care of itself. It produces very pleasing effects when laden with bright red fruits in autumn. (See R. pomifera.)

R. VIRGINIANA, *Miller*

(R. humilis, *Marshall*; R. lucida, *Ehrhart*)

A shrub 3 to 6 ft. high, forming a dense mass of erect stems, armed usually at the base of the leaves with straight or slightly hooked spines, and with scattered bristly prickles on the young sucker stems. Leaves glossy green above, 3 to 5 ins. long, composed of usually seven, sometimes nine leaflets, which are ovate or narrowly oval, 1 to 2 ins. long ; rather coarsely toothed except towards the base ; quite glabrous above, often the same below, but occasionally downy on the midrib as well as on the common stalk. Flowers in clusters of often three, sometimes solitary ; each 2 to 2½ ins. across, pink ; stalk and calyx-tube smooth or glandular ; sepals 1 in. long, with long, slender points, glandular and downy. Fruit orange-shaped, ½ in. wide, red, crowned at first with spreading sepals which fall away when the fruit is ripe.

Native of eastern N. America, and probably the first of American roses introduced to Britain. It is a useful plant for forming thickets in the wild garden, and its glossy green leaves are always pleasing. In habit it resembles R. carolina, but is easily distinguished by its glossy leaves and bristly stems. Many of the flowering portions of R. virginiana are quite unarmed.

Var. ALBA has white flowers, and differs also from the type in the more numerous flowers and more glandular flower-stalks and calyx ; leaflets paler green, with leaflets and midribs downy. Said to have been discovered in the United States about 1868, but believed by Prof. Sargent to be an escape from cultivation and a hybrid of garden origin.

Var. PLENA.—The plant grown under this name may be a hybrid between virginiana and some other rose. The flowers are double and very pretty in the bud state, and the plant differs from the type in the frequently double-toothing of its leaflets and its pinnately lobed sepals.

Var. GRANDIFLORA.—A very pretty variety, the petals being 1¼ ins. long and wide, and of a deep rose ; the sepals even longer, with expanded leafy tips. Rehder regards this as a variety of R. carolina.

R. WATSONIANA, *Crépin*

(Garden and Forest, 1890, fig. 59)

A trailing shrub whose glabrous, slender stems are armed with small hooked prickles. Leaflets three or five, linear, 1 to 2½ ins. long, ⅛ to ¼ in. wide ; margins wavy, not toothed ; downy beneath, usually mottled with yellow down the centre above ; common stalk downy, glandular, spiny. Flowers pale rose, ½ in. diameter, crowded on short broad panicles, 3 or 4 ins. wide ; sepals entire, lanceolate, very downy inside. Fruit globose, red, ¼ in. wide.

Introduced from Japan to the United States over seventy years ago, and thence to England. The styles are united in a column, and in this as well as in its crowded small blossoms it shows affinity with R. multiflora. But its long, narrow leaflets distinguish it at once from all other roses. It may not be a genuinely wild species, but a variety of Japanese garden origin.

It is a rose of delicate constitution, although it thrives very well with Mr. Chambers, near Haslemere. The best plants I have seen are at La Mortola and on Isola Madre, Lake Maggiore. But anywhere it must be regarded more as a curiosity than anything else.

R. WEBBIANA, *Wallich*

A graceful shrub of thin habit, 4 to 6 ft. high, whose long, slender branches are armed with straight spines ⅛ to ½ in. long, often in pairs ; stems often blue-white when young. Leaves 1 to 3 ins. long, usually glabrous, sometimes downy, composed of five to nine leaflets ; common stalk with tiny prickles beneath. Leaflets obovate, broadly oval, or almost round, ¼ to ¾ in. long toothed towards the end. Flowers 1½ to 2 ins. across, pale pink, produced singly on short lateral twigs ; flower-stalk ⅛ to ½ in. long, glabrous or slightly glandular ; sepals about ½ in. long, lanceolate, terminating in a short tail. ciliate ; calyx-tube more or less glandular. Fruit pitcher-shaped, bright red, ¾ in. long, apart from the persisting sepals with which it is crowned.

Native of the Himalaya, at from 6000 to 18,000 ft. elevation. This delightful rose, so distinct in its thin, graceful habit, its pale yellowish prickles, its tiny leaves and glaucous young stems, is also very pretty in June when covered with its blush-tinted flowers, and in autumn when carrying its bright red fruits. It can best be propagated by layering, also by seeds, when the plant is sufficiently isolated to be safe against cross-fertilisation, but is still very rare in cultivation. It has a recently introduced ally in R. Willmottiæ, from W. China.

R. WICHURAIANA, *Crépin*

(Bot. Mag., t. 7421 (as R. Luciæ))

A procumbent shrub rising a few inches only above the ground, and making shoots 10 or 12 ft. long in a season. Barren shoots unbranched, quite glabrous, but armed at irregular intervals with solitary curved prickles ¼ in. long. Flowering shoots branching and more slender. Leaves 2 to 4 ins. long, quite glabrous, consisting of five, seven, or nine leaflets, the common stalk of which is armed beneath with small, hooked spines. Leaflets oval, broadly ovate, or almost orbicular, from ¼ to 1 in. long, coarsely toothed and deep polished green on both surfaces ; stipules with jagged margins. Flowers nearly 2 ins. across, pure white, produced in July and August in panicles of six to ten blossoms rising out of the dense carpet of foliage ; petals often more than the normal five ; sepals ⅓ in. long, entire, downy. Fruit globose, ⅓ in. long, not crowned by the sepals.

Native of Japan ; introduced to Kew from N. America in 1891. A very distinct and beautiful rose, marked by its prostrate habit and exceedingly glossy foliage. It belongs to the same group as, and is allied to, R. multi-flora and R. Luciæ. Although somewhat eclipsed now by the large number of exquisite hybrids raised from it, it is well worth growing for its own sake. It flowers when nearly all other wild roses are past, and for making a low covering for a sunny bank few plants are better suited. Among its numerous progeny are—Dorothy Perkins, Lady Gay, excelsa, Alberic Barbier, Elise Robichon, Jersey Beauty, Pink Roamer, etc.

Var. RUBRA is said to be a hybrid between this species and Crimson Rambler. Flowers single, 1½ to 2 ins. across ; petals bright red, white at the base.

R. Willmottiæ, *Hemsley*

(Bot. Mag., t. 8186)

A densely branched shrub, 5 to 10 ft. high, stems glaucous when young; branches slender, red-brown, armed with straight prickles ¼ to ⅜ in. long and in pairs. Leaves ¾ to 2 ins. long, glabrous (except for the stipules, which are fringed with glandular hairs), and composed of usually nine leaflets. Leaflets oblong, obovate, or nearly round, ¼ to ½ in. long, toothed except towards the base. Flowers 1 to 1½ ins. across, bright purplish rose, produced singly on short lateral twigs; stalk ¼ to ½ in. long, glabrous. Sepals lanceolate, ½ in. long, entire, glabrous outside, white-felted within. Fruit roundish, orange-red. Native of W. China, near the Tibetan frontier; found by Wilson when collecting for Messrs Veitch in the Sangpan Mountains, at 9500 to 11,000 ft. elevation. It is closely allied to the Himalayan R. Webbiana, differing chiefly in the absence of glands on the calyx, and is an equally charming rose with the same finely bred appearance.

R. xanthina, *Lindley*

Under the notice of R. Ecæ in previous editions I pointed out that although that species had been figured, both in the *Botanical Magazine*, t. 7666, and by Miss Willmott in her *Genus Rosa* as R. xanthina, the two were quite different species. The name xanthina was based by Lindley on a drawing of a Chinese rose with double yellow flowers in A. B. Lambert's library. At the time I was preparing the notes on Rosa for the original edition, I endeavoured to trace this drawing at the British Museum and elsewhere, but failed to do so. It may be no longer in existence, for it was as long ago as 1820 that Lindley used it. In 1907 the late Mr F. N. Meyer sent to the Arnold Arboretum a double yellow rose which would appear undoubtedly to be R. xanthina, inasmuch as of the two or three roses with yellow flowers in China it is the one that fits Lindley's description. It flowered in the Arnold Arboretum in 1915, having remained practically unknown for ninety-five years.

A deciduous shrub 8 to 12 ft. high, with arching graceful branches; young shoots brown, armed with stout prickles but not bristly. Leaves 1½ to 3 ins. long made up of seven to thirteen leaflets, which are oval to nearly circular, ¼ to ¾ in. long, toothed, mostly rounded at the apex, glabrous above, downy beneath. Flowers solitary, yellow, 1½ ins. wide, more or less double, borne on a stalk about 1 in. long in June.

Var. spontanea, *Rehder*, considered to be the wild form, has single flowers 1½ ins. across, yellow; fruits globose, ½ in. wide, dark dull red, with the narrow linear reflexed sepals adhering at the top. It flowered in Paul & Son's nursery at Cheshunt in June 1915, and has done so annually in June for a good many years past at Kew. A very charming rose. Its closest ally is R. Hugonis, which differs in its quite glabrous leaves and in having bristles as well as spines on the shoots. The leaves of R. Ecæ differ in being glandular beneath.

ROSMARINUS officinalis, *Linnæus*. Rosemary. Labiatæ

An evergreen shrub of dense, leafy habit, forming a bush 6 or 7 ft. high and as much wide; young stems slender, downy. Leaves opposite, linear, ¾ to 2 ins. long, 1/16 to ⅛ in. wide; not stalked, blunt at the apex; margins recurved; dark rather glossy green above, white-felted beneath, aromatically fragrant when crushed. Flowers produced during May in clusters of two or three in the leaf-axils of the previous year's shoots.

Corolla two-lipped, pale violet-blue and white; calyx darker and purplish, very downy.

Native of Europe and Asia Minor; cultivated in Britain for four hundred years, probably much longer. It is the only species of the genus, but there are some distinct forms. Nearly related to the lavender, this shrub is also much associated with it in gardens. Its aromatic odour suggests nutmeg. A fragrant oil is extracted from the plant. The rosemary, which likes a sunny spot and not too heavy a soil, is scarcely so hardy as the lavender, although it is rarely injured. During the peculiarly trying winter of 1908-9, however, most of the old plants at Kew were killed, whilst two-year-old plants were not injured. It is readily increased by cuttings placed in a cold frame. Old specimens form short, rugged trunks, and are very picturesque.

ROSMARINUS OFFICINALIS. ROSEMARY

Both in S. Europe and in Britain the rosemary fills a notable place in folk-lore. At one time it was believed to possess a stimulating influence on the memory, and was even known as " herb of memory." The well-known line of Ophelia, " There's rosemary that's for remembrance," gave the text and the title for a delightful play performed many times in London by Sir Charles Wyndham and Miss Mary Moore some years ago. The same idea has also given it a significance in association with the dead. In the old *Chanson de Malbrouk* we find the lines :

" A l'entour de sa tombe, romarin l'on planta,
    Sur la plus haute branche, le rossignol chanta."

Var. ANGUSTISSIMUS (" Benenden Blue ").—Introduced from Corsica by
Mr Collingwood Ingram. Leaves narrower than in the type ; flowers sky-blue.
Given an Award of Merit at Vincent Square, 9th May 1933.
Var. AUREUS.—Leaves marked with yellow ; of little value.
Var. FASTIGIATUS.—Of erect growth and compact habit.
Var. PROSTRATUS.—A low-growing plant introduced some years ago
from the Isle of Capri, but it is much more tender than common rosemary
and will survive only the mildest winters at Kew. Probably a distinct species.

RUBUS. RASPBERRIES AND BRAMBLES. ROSACEÆ

It is difficult to estimate the number of species of which this genus
of herbs and shrubs is composed. Specific names have been given to
scores of European brambles which have no claim to rank as species,
some of them scarcely as varieties. It is probable that there are at least
three hundred genuine species, which are spread more or less over all the
temperate and tropical parts of the globe. Of those that can be grown
in the open air in the British Isles, the majority come from N.E. Asia,
the rest from N. America, Europe, and (one species) from New Zealand.
The most distinctive character of the genus is the fruit, which is
typically represented in the bramble and the raspberry. In both the
seeds are embedded singly in juicy drupes, which are united so as to form
a rounded or hemispherical cap fitted on a cone-shaped receptacle. In
the raspberries the fruit can be easily pulled off the receptacle, but in the
brambles the two adhere.
In the garden of ornamental shrubs the Rubi do not occupy anything like so important a place as their number would seem to justify.
Comparatively few of them are worth growing for beauty of flower, but
a considerable number are elegant in habit or handsome in foliage.
Many species have their stems more or less covered with blue-white or
purple bloom, and a few of the most striking are cultivated on that
account. Others are grown for the beauty or edible value of their fruits.
Besides the form of the fruit, which has already been adverted to,
the leading characteristics of the genus are its usually spiny stems ; its
alternate leaves, either pinnate, digitate, deeply lobed, or simple ; and
the five-lobed persistent calyx.
The cultivation of the hardy Rubi presents no problems. They all
like a loamy soil of good quality, and those of semi-scandent habit need
some sort of support. This may be a stout post, up which the main
shoots may be loosely tied, leaving the lateral branches free ; it may be
three or more rough oak branches set up to form a sort of pyramid ; or
the longer-stemmed ones may be used for covering pergolas or other
structures of a similar nature.
In the case of the biennial-stemmed species, it is necessary to cut
away the two-year-old stems which flower, bear fruit, and then die. With
those whose stems are of longer duration, it is also advisable to cut away
the older, worn-out stems occasionally. Some of the Rubi, especially
these with biennial stems, have a tendency to decrease in vigour after
a few years. The base in time forms a large woody root-stock which

does not send up such vigorous stems as younger ones. The remedy is, of course, to renew the stock by seed or other means.

PROPAGATION.—The mode of propagation depends largely on the character of the individual species. Those that form thickets (like odoratus and parviflorus) can be divided up into comparatively small pieces ; this is best done in autumn just before the leaves fall, or in spring. Apart from any desire to increase the stock, the plants are benefited by undergoing this process occasionally. For many of the pure species, especially those with white stems like biflorus, seeds when obtainable give the best new stock. Where neither division nor seeds afford means of increase, recourse must be had to either cuttings or layers. R. deliciosus is best increased by layering ; the double-flowered brambles strike root quite well from cuttings.

In the following descriptive notes the scores of so-called species native of Britain and Europe are ignored, with the exception of a few leading types. The late Mr Bentham reduced the shrubby species of Great Britain to three, viz., R. Idæus (the wild raspberry), R. cæsius (the dewberry), and R. fruticosus (the blackberry). The inclusion of all the blackberries under one species had the merit of simplicity, although it was perhaps taking too broad a view. It is, at any rate, preferable to the making of an endless number of supposed species which differ from each other only in particulars so obscure and unimportant that no two authorities agree about them. The advanced study of British Rubi as carried on in recent times is only suited to persons with abundant leisure. The best and most authoritative work on the subject is the *Handbook of the British Rubi*, published in 1900 by the Rev. W. Moyle Rogers. In this work the author describes one hundred and three species, besides which there are numerous sub-species and varieties. The descriptions of the few British blackberries here included are based on those given in this work.

The wild brambles of the British Isles have little or no garden value, but they are useful in woodland not only for their fruits, but because they furnish one of the best of all ground covers for shady places—a cover, too, that is nearly evergreen, and entails no trouble to maintain.

The following selections of a score of species may be of use :—

1. *For flower beauty.*—Deliciosus, nigrobaccus fl. pl., parviflorus, odoratus, spectabilis, thyrsoideus fl. pl., ulmifolius fl. pl.

2. *For white stems.*—Biflorus, Giraldianus, lasiostylus, thibetanus.

3. *For beauty of leaf and habit.*—Bambusarum, coreanus, flagelliflorus, irenæus, trifidus.

4. *For ground covering.*—Hispidus, nutans, tricolor.

5. *For fruit.*—Laciniatus, phœnicolasius.

Remarkable as many of the new Chinese species are in introducing new types of foliage to our gardens, they are curiously and almost invariably devoid of any floral beauty.

A species of Rubus has lately come into notice because of its remarkable strawberry-like, red fruits and has been called " strawberry-raspberry." It is R. ILLECEBROSUS, *Focke*, a native of Mount Fuji-yama, Japan. It is not, however, shrubby, its stems dying to the ground in winter.

A few of the more important British types of Rubi are here briefly described as representing the main groups in Mr Moyle Rogers' monograph :—

R. CARPINIFOLIUS, *Weihe and Nees.*—A spreading shrub of vigorous habit, its long stems strongly angled, and armed with numerous strong, yellowish, decurved or straight prickles. Leaves with normally five leaflets, soft with greyish down beneath. Terminal leaflets oval, with a tapered point, the blade about three times longer than the prickly stalk. Flowers with pure white petals, produced in large, very prickly panicles. Fruit of good quality, large, with the sepals spreading. Widely spread in Britain, and frequent in the wild parts of Kew and other parts south-west of London. Belonging to the same group is

R. RHAMNIFOLIUS, *Weihe and Nees.*—This differs in having the blade of the terminal leaflet only twice the length of the stalk. This and the other leaflets are of thick, leathery texture, covered beneath with a felt of grey-white down. Flowers white or pale pink, cup-shaped, borne in slender panicles. Sepals whitish with down, reflexed. Widely spread in South Britain. (RHAMNIFOLII group.)

R. CORYLIFOLIUS, *Smith.*—A shrub with roundish glaucous stems that are free, or nearly free from down or hairs, but armed with irregularly scattered, awl-shaped prickles. Leaflets usually five, sometimes six or seven, broad or overlapping, leathery, covered beneath with a grey or greenish felt. Flowers white or pinkish (the petals broadly ovate), produced on an irregular panicle, the stalks of which are felted and often glandular. Fruit of no edible value ; the sepals felted and reflexed. A very common bramble in Great Britain and Ireland, allied to the dewberry (R. cæsius), and one of the connecting links between that species and the other groups, as shown by the glaucous, nearly or quite glabrous stems. (CÆSII group.)

R. HIRTUS, *Waldstein.*—A prostrate, sometimes climbing shrub, with the stems covered with stalked glands and hairs, and furnished with straight, bristle-like prickles. Leaflets usually three, occasionally five on vigorous stems, broadly oval, rounded at the base, shortly pointed, coarsely toothed, dark green and bristly above, very hairy on the veins beneath. Flowers white, produced in large panicles, the main stalk furnished with violet-coloured or purple gland-tipped hairs and bristles. Fruit globular; the sepals erect. A common species in Great Britain, very characteristic of the group with glandular hairs and bristles on the inflorescence. (GLANDULOSI group.)

R. LEUCOSTACHYS *Schleich* (R. vestitus, *Weihe*).—A shrub with prostrate or climbing stems, angular hairy, and clothed with felt ; armed with long, straight prickles. Leaflets five, rather small, but broad in proportion to their length ; the margins wavy, shallowly and evenly toothed ; upper surface bristly and glossy, lower one covered beneath with a soft yellowish or grey felt. Flowers (with rounded bright pink or white petals) produced in long cylindrical panicles, the stalks felted like the stems and leaves. Sepals reflexed. Fruit sweet, insipid. A common species in Great Britain, distinguished by its round petals and densely felted parts. (VESTITI group.)

R. MUCRONATUS, *Bloxam.*—A shrub with low, arching, or prostrate stems, which are hairy, glandular, bristly, and armed with small, needle-like prickles. Leaflets five, overlapping, very bristly above, thinly hairy beneath, evenly and shallowly toothed, the terminal one being very broadly obovate, heart-shaped at the base ; the broad flat apex relieved by a short abrupt point. Flowers pinkish, produced on a long, rather cylindrical panicle ; the main and subsidiary flower-stalks covered with dense felt and hairs, and furnished also with a few slender deflexed prickles and stalked glands. Sepals of fruit more or less reflexed. Widely spread through the British Isles, and especially abundant in Scotland. (EGREGII group.)

R. PULCHERRIMUS, *Neumann.*—A shrub with arching or prostrate stems, often of a reddish hue and hairy, armed with numerous straight or deflexed prickles. Leaflets five or six, rarely seven, rather leathery, finely toothed, bristly and grey-green above, covered beneath with a pale felt. Flowers bright pink or pinkish, produced on a long, slenderly pyramidal panicle, the main and secondary flower-stalks prickly and with stalked glands. Sepals reflexed ; stamens longer than the style. Fruit of very good quality. This bramble is one of the commonest and most generally distributed in Great Britain. It is also one of the handsomest. (RHAMNIFOLII group.)

R. RUDIS, *Wiehe and Nees.*—A shrub with sub-prostrate or low arching stems of dark purplish colour, armed with short decurved prickles, and furnished with numerous stalked glands. Leaves large among brambles, and composed of three or five leaflets. Leaflets whitish downy beneath, becoming greenish, the terminal one oval or obovate with a slenderly tapered point, doubly toothed. Flowers pink, borne on a loose, wide panicle, the stalks downy and thickly furnished with shortly stalked glands. Fruit small. Common in the south of England, and wild in the neighbourhood of Kew. Distinguished by its thickly glanded stems and inflorescence. Nearly allied to and sometimes confused with it, but more widely spread northwards, is

R. ECHINATUS, *Lindley*.—This also has glandular stems and panicles, but the latter are cylindrical. Flowers pink, with much-reflexed sepals. It occurs as far north as Elgin. (RADULÆ group.)

R. SILVATICUS, *Wiehe and Nees*.—A shrub with low arching or prostrate stems angular on the upper side, more or less furnished with pale hairs, and armed with stout deflexed prickles. Leaflets five, hairy on both sides, narrowly obovate or oval long-pointed, coarsely and irregularly toothed. Flowers white, sometimes pinkish produced on a long panicle which is furnished with small, needle-like prickles and coarse hairs on the flower-stalks. Sepals beneath the fruit reflexed. Found chiefly in the West of England and in Wales. (SILVATICI group.)

R. SUBERECTUS, *Andersson*.—A strong-growing tall shrub, with sub-erect distinctly angular stems, sparsely armed with short conical prickles set upon the angles. Leaves with from three to seven leaflets, which are thin, glossy, rather evenly toothed, lowest pair scarcely stalked. Flowers red in the bud state, afterwards white produced in large racemes. Stamens longer than the style. Fruit dark red, sometimes almost black. Widely spread in North and Central Europe. It does not naturally root at the tips of the shoots. (SUBERECTI group.)

R. VILLICAULIS, *Koehler*.—Stems prominently angled, arching, clothed with brown hairs, and armed with numerous long, mostly straight prickles. Leaflets three or five, borne on a very long main-stalk; they are of thick texture, covered beneath with long silky hairs or felt. Flowers pale pink or white (the petals obovate the sepals reflexed), borne in a large panicle, the stalks of which are felted with down and abundantly armed with hooked prickles. Fruit of very good quality. A common bramble in Scotland, less so in the West of England. (VILLICAULES group.)

The following British species will be found described in their order :— cæsius, Idæus, laciniatus, thyrsoideus, ulmifolius.

R. ADENOPHORUS, *Rolfe*

(R. sagatus, *Focke*)

A robust bramble, deciduous, 8 ft. or more high; stems erect or arching towards the top, stout, armed with stiff, short, broad-based spines, densely clothed with bristles, and with stalked glands. Leaves of the first-year (or barren) shoots mostly pinnate, 8 to 12 ins. long, with five leaflets; those of the flowering shoots shorter, with three leaflets or sometimes simple. Leaflets obliquely obovate or ovate; 2 to 5 ins. long, $1\frac{1}{4}$ to $3\frac{1}{2}$ ins. wide; tapered rounded, or heart-shaped at the base; slender-pointed, sharply and doubly toothed, dull and hairy on both sides; main-stalk bristly and furnished with stalked glands like the shoots. Flowers produced in July in terminal cylindrical panicles 4 or 5 ins. long, the petals pink, toothed, the flower-stalk and calyx densely clothed with bristles and stalked glands. Fruit black, about $\frac{1}{2}$ in. wide, edible.

Native of W. Hupeh; introduced by Wilson in 1907. The most remarkable feature of this bramble are the conspicuous dark glands, resembling minute black-headed pins, stuck among the bristles on the stems and leaf stalks, but extraordinarily abundant on the sepals and flower-stalks. The leaf next to the panicle is often simple.

R. AMABILIS, *Focke*

A deciduous shrub up to 6 or 7 ft. high ; young shoots slightly downy and
armed with small prickles. Leaves pinnate, 4 to 8 ins. long, composed of seven
to eleven leaflets ; main-stalk prickly. Leaflets very shortly stalked, ovate,
pointed, sharply and doubly toothed ; ¾ to 2 ins. long, ½ to 1 in. wide (terminal
one larger) ; usually downy on the veins and armed with a few prickles on the
midrib. Flowers white, 1½ to 2 ins. wide, solitary at the end of short leafy
twigs, petals overlapping. Fruit conical, red, edible, ⅝ in. long.
   Native of W. Szechuen, China ; discovered and introduced by Wilson in
1908. This rubus is distinct in its graceful habit, its handsome, much laciniated
leaves, and its large solitary flowers which open in June and July.

R. AUSTRALIS, *Forster*.   LAWYER VINE

A climbing evergreen shrub reaching sometimes in its native state the
summits of lofty trees. It has slender zigzagged stems, not downy but
armed more or less with small, hooked prickles. Leaves usually trifoliolate,
but extraordinarily variable in the size and shape of the leaflet blades. In
one form (typical) they are ovate with a heart-shaped base, 2 to 5 ins. long
by 1 to 2 ins. wide ; in another, known as cissoides, they are linear, 2 ins.
long by ¼ in. wide, and so on, the most remarkable being a skeletonised
one in which the blade of the leaflet almost disappears, being reduced to
¼ or ½ in. long and from 1/16 to ⅛ in. wide, the leaf consisting of a long slender
leaf-stalk branching into three, and thickly furnished with stiff, sharp, hooked
spines. This is called pauperatus. Flowers unisexual, about ½ in. across,
white, pinkish, or yellowish, fragrant, produced in panicles ; the males the
largest, and distinguished by a conspicuous ring of stamens. Fruit ¼ in.
diameter, reddish orange.
   Native of New Zealand, commonest on the borders of forests. Some
authorities regard some of the forms of this rubus as distinct species, but
none of them can be confused with any other Rubi grown in Britain. Those
with the smaller leaf-blades appear to be hardiest, and will thrive in the
warmer parts of the British Isles. There is a fine plant at Fota. In Canon
Ellacombe's garden at Bitton a fairly large-bladed form grew well against a
wall. But on the whole the plant must be regarded as tender.

R. BAMBUSARUM, *Focke*

(R. Henryi bambusarum, *Rehder*)

An evergreen climbing shrub, with very slender, cord-like stems, covered
when young with a whitish, cobweb-like substance, becoming dark green
later ; spines small, stiff, sharp, irregularly arranged. Leaves usually
composed of three leaflets, but sometimes four or five ; leaflets 2½ to 5 ins.
long ; ⅛ to ¾ in. wide ; pointed, narrowly lance-shaped, dark green, and
glabrous above, covered beneath with a thick, dull white, or pale brown felt ;
the margins shallowly saw-toothed, stalks ⅛ in. or less long ; main leaf-stalk
1 in. long. Flowers in terminal panicles, pink, but insignificant. Fruits black,
roundish, ½ in. wide, and of good flavour.
   Native of Central and W. China, where it is common in thickets and open
woodland up to 7000 ft. elevation. Originally discovered by Henry in Hupeh,
it was first introduced by Wilson for Messrs Veitch in 1900. It is notable for
its elegant and rapid growth. When trained up a pillar or similar support,

its slender branches arch outwards in all directions. Growths 10 to 12 ft. long are made in one season. The panicles of black fruits, 3 to 5 ins. long, are also handsome. (See also R. Henryi.)

R. BIFLORUS, *Buchanan-Hamilton*

(Bot. Mag., t. 4678)

A deciduous shrub, with erect stems up to 10 ft. high, and 1 in. thick at the base, covered with a thick, white, waxy coating, and armed with straight broad-based spines. Towards the top the stems branch freely, the branches also being white, and, like the leaf-stalks and often the midrib, spiny. Leaves 4 to 10 ins. long, composed of three or five leaflets, which are dark green above, covered beneath with a close white felt, ovate, pointed, sharply and irregularly toothed, and from 1½ to 4 ins. long. Flowers terminal and axillary, white, ¾ in. across ; fruits yellow, roundish, ¾ in. diameter, edible.

Native of the Himalaya up to 10,000 ft. ; introduced in 1818. Among the longer cultivated, white-stemmed raspberries this is by far the most effective, although it is no doubt equalled by some of the newer Chinese species (see Giraldianus and lasiostylus). Its flowers are of little consequence, being small and of little beauty. It should be raised from seed (which ripens here), and planted in groups of not less than half a dozen. The soil should be a good loam, the aim being to produce stout thick stems, for the stouter they are, the whiter and more persistent is their waxy covering. After the previous year's stems have flowered and borne fruit, they should be cut away (usually about August) leaving only the virgin growths of the year. During autumn and winter a group of this rubus makes one of the most notable plant pictures in the open air.

Var. QUINQUEFLORUS.—A vigorous Chinese form introduced by Wilson in 1908, with the terminal inflorescence composed most frequently of five (sometimes up to eight) flowers. In the type they are usually two or three.

R. CÆSIUS, *Linnæus*. DEWBERRY

A deciduous shrub, with slender creeping stems, prickly, and covered with a whitish bloom when young. Leaves usually composed of three leaflets which are green and slightly hairy on both sides. Flowers white, in small clusters. Fruit composed of a few large carpels, covered with a blue-white bloom when ripe.

This is one of the British brambles easily distinguished from all the forms of common blackberry by the few but large " pips " composing the fruit, and by their being covered, like the young stems, with a white or bluish bloom. It is common in Britain and over Europe, extending into N. Asia. Of no value for gardens.

R. CALYCINOIDES, *Hayata*

(Bot. Mag., t. 9644)

An evergreen, prostrate, spreading shrub, self-rooting freely from branches on the ground ; young shoots, leaf-stalks, underside of leaves and flower-stalks all covered densely with pale down. Leaves ½ to 1½ ins. long, broadly ovate to cordate, three-lobed, the lobes rounded, toothed, very much wrinkled, the dense network of veins sunken above, prominent beneath ; stalks ¼ to 1¼ ins. long, sparsely prickly. Flowers ⅝ in. across, solitary or in pairs, terminal mostly on short, leafy, lateral shoots ; petals white, roundish, minutely ciliate ; sepals large, downy, its lobes toothed. Fruit scarlet, $\frac{2}{3}$ in. long, style and ring of stamens persisting.

Native of Formosa ; introduced by the late Lord Headfort from seed collected by a Japanese. He found it quite hardy in Co. Meath and without being in any way showy it flowers and develops fruits every year and makes an interesting ground-cover several feet across.

R. CANADENSIS, *Linnæus*. LOW BLACKBERRY

(Bot. Mag., t. 8264 ; R. Millspaughii, *Britton*)

A deciduous shrub, with erect or arching stems 6 to 8 ft. high, glabrous, unarmed, or furnished with a few short prickles. Leaves long-stalked, composed of five leaflets arranged as in the horse-chestnut, soon nearly or quite glabrous on both surfaces except for inconspicuous tufts of down in the vein-axils beneath ; leaflets lanceolate, $2\frac{1}{2}$ to 6 ins. long, $1\frac{1}{4}$ to 2 ins. wide, long-pointed, rounded or slightly heart-shaped at the base. The terminal leaflet has a stalk 1 to $1\frac{1}{2}$ ins. long, the middle pair have stalks about half as long, whilst the basal pair are scarcely stalked at all. The leaflets are occasionally reduced to three. Flowers white, 1 in. across, borne in downy racemes which terminate short shoots from the previous year's wood ; each flower has a slender, downy stalk 1 in. long. Fruit black, juicy but sour.

Native of eastern N. America. This blackberry flowers in June and is then very pretty, the upper part of the previous year's stems being crowded with racemes of white flowers.

R. CHROÖSEPALUS, *Focke*

A large, semi-evergreen, straggling shrub, with round, slender, glabrous stems armed with short, decurved prickles. Leaves simple, heart-shaped, with a long tapering apex, 3 to 7 ins. long, more than half as wide ; the margins very finely and sharply toothed, and often scalloped into a few broad, very shallow lobes ; of firm texture ; glabrous above, but conspicuously silvery beneath with a close felt ; stalks glabrous, 1 to $2\frac{1}{2}$ ins. long, with one or two spines. Flowers borne in a terminal panicle, 6 to 9 ins. long ; each flower $\frac{1}{2}$ in. across with no petals, but a coloured, downy calyx. Fruit black, small, and of poor flavour.

Native of Central China ; originally discovered by Henry ; introduced to cultivation by Wilson about 1900. Its leaves bear a striking resemblance to those of Tilia tomentosa. A remarkably distinct as well as rather handsome and effective shrub.

R. CORCHORIFOLIUS, *Linnæus fil.*

A deciduous shrub of vigorous growth, spreading by underground suckers ; stems erect, 6 to 8 ft. high, branching towards the top, round, covered with an excedingly fine down when young, and furnished with rather broad-based prickles. Leaves simple, ovate, with a heart-shaped base ; 3 to 7 ins. long, two-thirds as wide ; those of the sterile sucker stems very deeply three-lobed, purplish when young ; margins irregularly toothed ; upper surface dull dark green, nearly glabrous ; the lower one paler and downy about the veins ; midrib spiny ; leaf-stalk 1 to $1\frac{1}{2}$ ins. long, spiny. Flowers white, borne singly or a few together on short lateral twigs. Fruit large, bright red, and, Mr Wilson informed me, of " delicious, vinous flavour."

Introduced by Wilson in 1907 from Central China, but described and named by the younger Linnæus as long ago as 1781 from Japanese specimens. It appears to be widely spread in China and Japan. It may prove useful in the wild garden, judging by the way it spreads in borders.

R. COREANUS, *Miquel*

A deciduous shrub, 8 to 10 ft. high (it has been found 15 ft. high in a wild state), with erect or arching, stout, biennial stems, branching towards the top ; glabrous, but covered with a blue-white bloom, and armed with stiff, broad-based spines, up to ½ in. long. Leaves pinnate, 6 to 10 ins. long, composed usually of seven leaflets, which are ovate or broadly oval, from 1½ to 3 ins. long, 1 to 2 ins. wide ; the lateral ones stalkless or nearly so, tapering at the base and smaller than the terminal one, which is broader, rounded or heart-shaped at the base, and stalked ; all are parallel-veined, dark lustrous green, coarsely toothed, except towards the base, and have silky hairs on the veins when young. Flowers borne in flattish clusters 1 to 3 ins. across, terminating short shoots from the wood of the previous year. Fruit of various colours from red to nearly black, edible but small, and of poor flavour.

Native of Korea and China ; introduced from the latter country in 1907 by Wilson, who found it at altitudes up to 6000 ft. It is one of the handsomest of all Rubi in its vigorous blue-white stems and beautiful pinnate foliage, and may prove a valuable acquisition in gardens should it be quite hardy.

R. CRATÆGIFOLIUS, *Bunge*

An erect, deciduous shrub of stiff habit, 6 to 8 ft. high, with stout biennial stems branched towards the top, grooved and armed with small scattered prickles. Leaves on the barren shoots of the year, large, palmately three- or five-lobed, 5 to 8 ins. across ; heart-shaped at the base, sharply and often doubly toothed, downy beneath ; stalks and midrib prickly ; leaves of the flowering twigs much smaller, usually three-lobed. Flowers ¾ to 1 in. across ; produced in clusters terminating short twigs ; petals white, prettily crimped at the margins ; calyx segments lanceolate, much decurved. Fruit the size of a small raspberry, red.

Native of China, Korea, and Japan. The name cratægifolius is only appropriate to the small leaves of the flowering twigs ; on the barren, first-year stems they are more like those of a vine or maple, and in good soil are sometimes of very large size—8 to 12 ins. across.

R. DELICIOSUS, *Torrey*
(Bot. Mag., t. 6062)

A deciduous shrub of sturdy habit, reaching 6 to 10 ft. in height, bark peeling ; branches often arching or pendulous, quite unarmed, downy when young. Leaves like those of a black currant in shape and size, being three- or five-lobed, with jagged edges, the base truncate or heart-shaped ; 1½ to 3 ins. long, rather more wide, downy on both sides when young, especially beneath ; stalk 1 to 1½ ins. long. Flowers mostly solitary, pure white, 2 ins. across, borne in May on short twigs from the previous year's branches ; sepals downy, ovate, ½ in. long. Fruit ½ in. across, dry, and of no flavour.

Native of the Rocky Mountains, where it was discovered in 1820 by Dr James. The fruit is not delicious but no doubt the name refers to the delight the flowers gave to the eye, for in this respect it is the most lovely of all Rubi, the blossoms being as beautiful as single roses, and as profusely borne. It was introduced in 1870. It is not very easily increased by cuttings (especially the better of two forms in cultivation), but can be layered, although the layers will sometimes take a twelvemonth before they become sufficiently rooted to be

RUBUS DELICIOSUS

removable. A good loamy soil, a sunny position, and an occasional pruning out of the old wood complete its requirements. It is one of the élite of hardy shrubs.

R. FLAGELLIFLORUS, *Focke*

A climbing evergreen shrub, with slender, graceful stems growing 5 or 6 ft. in length in one season ; when young they are covered with a whitish felt, sprinkled amongst which are tiny decurved prickles. Leaves broadly ovate, long-pointed, the base heart-shaped ; the largest are 6 or 7 ins. long, and about two-thirds as wide, shallowly lobed on the margins as well as finely and sharply toothed ; the upper surface has appressed hairs between the veins, the lower one is covered with a thick, yellowish felt ; stalk 1½ to 2½ ins. long, slightly spiny. Flowers white, borne in axillary clusters. Fruits shining black, ½ in. wide, edible.

Native of Central and W. China, up to 6000 ft. ; introduced for Messrs Veitch by Wilson about 1901. In habit this is one of the most elegant of the new Chinese Rubi, and one of the handsomest in its foliage. When trained up a post or other support, the slender, whip-like shoots push out in all directions. The leaves often put on a marbled appearance in the shade. The appropriate name of "flagelliformis" is rather commonly applied to this plant, but the one given above is correct.

R. FLOSCULOSUS, *Focke*

A deciduous shrub up to 10 or 12 ft. high ; the stout stems erect, arching at the much-branched top, biennial, glabrous except for a few spines. Leaves pinnate, 4 to 7 ins. long, composed of five or seven leaflets which are ovate ¾ to 1½ ins. long ; the terminal one larger, often three-lobed, and 3 ins. long , glabrous above or becoming so, covered beneath with a close white felt ; coarsely, often doubly toothed. Flowers small, pink, ¼ in. wide, produced in narrow, cylindrical racemes 2 to 4 ins. long, terminating the shoot, and in shorter ones from the axils of the terminal leaves. Fruit small, very dark red, or black.

Native of Central and W. China ; introduced by Wilson in 1907. A very vigorous, pinnate-leaved bramble, allied to R. Giraldianus, but with dark purplish brown stems.

R. GIRALDIANUS, *Focke*
(Kew Bulletin, 1914)

A vigorous deciduous shrub up to 8 or 10 ft. high ; its biennial stems much branched towards the summit, pendulous at the ends, covered with a vividly white, waxy covering, not downy, armed rather sparely with broad-based spines. Leaves pinnate, consisting of usually nine leaflets, and from 5 to 8 ins. long ; the main-stalk downy, and armed with hooked spines. Leaflets 1½ to 2½ ins. long, ¾ to 1¼ ins. wide, the terminal one the largest ; ovate or rather diamond-shaped ; lateral ones oval-lanceolate ; all unequally and rather coarsely toothed, slender-pointed, glabrous above, white beneath with a close felt. Inflorescence a terminal panicle ; the flowers small and of little beauty, purple. Fruit black.

Native of China ; first found in the province of Shensi by Giraldi, later in Szechuen by Wilson, who introduced it in 1907. Its claims to recognition in the garden are its remarkably white stems, which are as notable in this respect as those of R. biflorus, and its arching, pendulous branches, which give a remarkable fountain-like aspect to the shrub.

R. GRACILIS, *Roxburgh*
(R. niveus, *Wallich*)

A deciduous shrub, with very stout, erect, biennial stems, 1 to 1½ ins. thick and in vigorous plants 4 to 6 yards high, covered with a soft, thick, velvety down, and sprinkled over with minute prickles. Leaves 6 to over 12 ins. long, composed of three or five leaflets. Side leaflets about half the size of the terminal one, stalkless or nearly so, obliquely ovate, coarsely and doubly toothed, slightly hairy above, covered with a close white felt beneath, and with silvery hairs on the veins ; terminal leaflets ovate to roundish heart-shaped, long-stalked, from 3 to 5 ins. long and wide, in other respects the same as the side ones. Flowers white or pale pink, ½ in. across, the petals shorter than the sepals. Fruits blue-black, small.

Native of W. and Central China, whence it was introduced about 1901 ; the species had, however, been known to botanists as far back as 1825 from plants growing on the Himalaya. The Chinese plants are chiefly remarkable for their vigour ; Mr Wilson stated that it is occasionally 20 ft. high. It is the most robust of all Rubi ; hardy in Britain.

R. HENRYI, *Hemsley*

An evergreen, elegant, scandent shrub, growing 20 ft. high where support is available ; stems slender, cord-like, armed with a few spines. Leaves three-lobed, 4 to 6 ins. long, glabrous above, covered beneath with a close white felt ; stalk 1 to 1½ ins. long ; lobes of varying depth but usually reaching about three-fourths down the blade, narrow (from ¾ to 1 in. wide at the base), tapering to a long fine point, finely toothed. Flowers pink, of little beauty, ¾ in. across, borne six to ten together in terminal and axillary racemes 3 ins. or so long ; petals and sepals of about equal length, the latter covered with glandular hairs, and ending in a tail-like point. Fruit shining black, ½ in. wide, shining.

Native of Central and W. China ; first discovered near Ichang by Henry, in whose honour it is named. Introduced by Wilson in 1900. The only rubus with which it can be confused is R. bambusarum—the two, probably, are forms of one species—but that is well marked by its leaves being composed of three distinct leaflets. In other respects they are very similar.

R. HISPIDUS, *Linnæus*

A low semi-evergreen shrub, with mostly prostrate, very slender, wiry stems, armed with tiny decurved spines and more or less covered with bristles. Leaves trifoliolate, the common stalk longer than the leaflets, which are short-stalked, obovate, tapering to the base, sharply and coarsely toothed towards the apex, 1 to 1¾ ins. long, ½ to 1 in. wide ; glabrous or nearly so on both surfaces. Flowers white, ½ to ¾ in. across, produced in few-flowered corymbs from the leaf-axils and the ends of erect shoots 6 to 12 ins. high. Fruit at first turning red, nearly black when ripe, less than ½ in. long, and composed of few carpels, sour.

Native of eastern N. America ; introduced in 1768, but rarely seen nowadays. It flowers in June and July. Growing very quickly, it soon forms a low, dense tangle, and makes a pretty almost evergreen ground cover.

Very nearly allied to this is R. TRIVIALIS, *Michaux*, which has a more southern distribution in the United States. It differs in having larger flowers up to 1½ ins. across, and more cylindrical fruits 1 in. long, composed of numerous carpels. Rare in cultivation, probably not so hardy as hispidus.

R. HUPEHENSIS, *Oliver*

(R. Swinhoei of previous editions, not of *Hance*)

A prostrate or climbing evergreen shrub, with round, slender, dark-coloured stems, thinly furnished with a cobweb-like down when young, and armed with a few small decurved spines. Leaves simple, oblong-lanceolate ; 3 to 4½ ins. long, by about 1½ ins. wide ; the base rounded, the apex long-pointed, margins finely toothed ; veins in nine to twelve pairs ; upper surface smooth except for tiny bristles along the veins, lower one covered with a close grey felt ; leaf-stalk ¼ to ½ in. long. Flowers usually three to seven in

short, terminal, very glandular racemes, of little or no beauty ; calyx covered
with grey felt like the leaves ; petals soon falling. Fruit described as at first
red, then black-purple, austere.

Native of Central China ; originally described in 1899, but introduced
to gardens by Wilson from Hupeh in 1907. The foliage is handsome, and
distinct from that of any other cultivated species except R. malifolius ; the
inflorescence also is conspicuous in its glandular hairiness.

R. ICHANGENSIS, *Hemsley and Kuntze*

A deciduous shrub, with long, slender stems armed with small hooked
spines, and furnished with numerous dark, glandular bristles. Leaves
narrowly ovate-cordate (often with angular lobes towards the base), the sinus
open and rounded ; 3½ to 7 ins. long, 1 to 2½ ins. wide ; glabrous on both
surfaces, margins sparsely toothed. Flowers white, ¼ in. wide, produced in
an elongated terminal panicle, supplemented below by short racemes in the
axils of the uppermost leaves, the whole measuring 8 to 12 ins. or even more
in length ; flower-stalks glandular-hairy, sepals erect, enclosing the small
white petals. Fruit bright red, small, but of good flavour.

Native of Central and W. China ; discovered by Henry, and introduced
in 1900 by Wilson, who informed me that it occurs up to 7000 ft. elevation
He also stated that it is one of the finest of Chinese Rubi in regard to its fruits—
panicles of which he had often found over 2 ft. in length.

R. IDÆUS, *Linnæus*. WILD RASPBERRY

A deciduous shrub, with erect biennial stems, 3 to 6 ft. high, more or less
downy ; sometimes without prickles, but usually armed with weak ones
Leaves pinnate and composed of five leaflets on the lower part of the sterile
(first year) stems ; mostly of three leaflets at the upper part of the same, and
on the flowering branches. Leaflets ovate, 1½ to 4 ins. long, coarsely toothed,
green and soon quite glabrous above, covered with a white felt beneath ; the
terminal one is the largest and broadest, and sometimes heart-shaped at the
base. Flowers produced in a panicle at the end of short twigs springing from
the year-old stems, small, pinkish. Fruit red and juicy.

This shrub, the source of the common raspberry of the fruit garden (where
varieties with yellow and whitish fruits are grown), is found wild in British
woods, and all through Europe and N. Asia to Japan. It is only of interest
on this account, being of little value as an ornament.

Var. LEESII, *Babington*, differs in having much rounder leaflets than
common R. Idæus, the central one being rarely stalked. Found wild in
Devon and Somerset.

THE LOGANBERRY.—This hybrid, between a garden variety of R. Idæus
called " Red Antwerp," and the " Aughenbaugh " blackberry, was raised in
California in 1881 by Judge J. H. Logan. In habit it partakes more of the
blackberry than the raspberry character, making long rambling growths
12 ft. or more long in a season. It was introduced to England in 1896, and
has proved in many places a hardy and useful fruit-bearing bush. The fruit
is like a raspberry in shape, but longer and darker in colour, and of an acid
flavour.

R. IRENÆUS, *Focke*

An evergreen prostrate shrub ; stems round, slender, covered with a dense
grey down, amidst which are set numerous small decurved prickles. Leaves
roundish with a heart-shaped base, and an abrupt, pointed apex ; 6 ins. or

more across, margins toothed and bristly, sometimes obscurely lobed ; upper surface glabrous, dark green, lower one covered with a pale brown felt, and more or less hairy on the yellow veins ; stalks 1½ to 3 ins. long. Flowers white, ¾ in. wide, produced singly or in pairs in the leaf-axils, and in a small terminal cluster. Fruit large, red.

Native of Central and W. China ; introduced about 1900 by Wilson for Messrs Veitch. It is one of the most striking and remarkable of simple-leaved Rubi, the foliage being of a shape and size suggestive of a coltsfoot leaf, but having on the upper surface a curious metallic lustre. Mr Wilson informed me that it is common in woods up to 8000 ft. elevation, and will probably thrive best in partially shaded situations. It may prove of value as a handsome covering for semi-shaded slopes, or wherever a low evergreen vegetation is desired.

R. Koehneanus, *Focke*

(Bot. Mag., t. 8246)

A deciduous shrub of bushy, rounded habit, a few feet high ; the erect, or nearly erect, biennial stems covered with purplish bloom, but with few or no prickles. Leaves simple, three- or five-lobed, or sometimes scarcely lobed at all, heart-shaped at the base, 1½ to 5 ins. long, about the same wide ; glabrous and green above, white but not downy beneath ; margins sharply toothed ; leaf-stalk often as long as the blade. Flowers ¾ in. across, produced usually three together ; stalks glabrous, ¾ in. long ; petals white, oblong, calyx downy within, the triangular lobes shorter than the petals. Fruits orange red, composed of comparatively few large carpels.

Native of Japan ; introduced by Späth of Berlin, and originally distributed as " R. morifolius." It is also grown sometimes under the erroneous name of ' R. incisus." It is rather pretty in blossom, the flowers being abundant, and the purple-red anthers contrasting well with the white petals.

R. Kuntzeanus, *Hemsley*

A deciduous shrub, with erect, sturdy biennial stems, 6 to 10 ft. high, branching towards the top, covered with soft, grey, velvety down, and armed with short broad-based, scattered prickles. Leaves from 6 to 12 ins. long, composed of three or five (pinnately arranged) leaflets, the side ones of which are obliquely ovate, 2 to 4 ins. long, 1 to 2½ ins. wide ; fine-pointed, rounded at the base, irregularly toothed and very shortly stalked ; slightly hairy and dark glossy green above, covered beneath with a close white felt, interspersed with hairs on the veins ; terminal leaflet larger, broader, longer-stalked, often three-lobed, and heart-shaped at the base. The main-stalk has hooked prickles and is covered with the same velvety down as the stem. Flowers small ⅓ to ½ in. wide), produced in large terminal panicles, 1 to 1½ ft. long ; petals pink and soon falling. Fruit orange-red, rounded, ½ to ¾ in. wide, of good flavour.

Native of Central and W. China ; first introduced to Kew by Henry from Ichang in 1886, but most of the plants now in cultivation were introduced by Wilson between 1900 and 1907. The species is of some promise as a fruit-bearer, but has little to recommend it for ornament. It has been confused with R. innominatus, S. *Moore*, a species very closely allied, but distinct in its glandular stems, leaf-stalks, inflorescence, and calyx. Central China.

R. LACINIATUS, *Willdenow*. CUT-LEAVED BRAMBLE

A deciduous shrub of rambling or scandent habit, the angled stems well armed with stout, recurved spines, and hairy. Leaves composed of five (sometimes three) leaflets, radially arranged ; the common stalk 2 to 3 ins. long, beset with hooked spines. Leaflets stalked, and either pinnate, or deeply and pinnately lobed ; final subdivisions of leaf coarsely and angularly toothed ; spiny on the stalk and midrib ; downy especially beneath. The leaves vary much in size, and on vigorous shoots will, including the stalk, reach 8 to 12 ins. in length. Flowers in large terminal panicles ; flower-stalk hairy and spiny ; petals pinkish white ; calyx with narrow, downy, reflexed segments spiny at the back, ½ to ¾ ins. long, ending in a tail-like point. Fruit black, and both in size and flavour one of the finest of blackberries.

The origin of this handsome and useful bramble is not known. It was first distinguished by Willdenow in the old botanic garden of Berlin in 1909. Mr Baker believed it to be a cut-leaved form of a common British bramble called R. Selmeri ; but it comes true from seed and wild plants, sprung no doubt from seed dropped by birds, and may nearly always be found in the vicinity of cultivated plants. It is now extensively cultivated for its fruits in gardens, being perhaps the best of all blackberries for that purpose. The foliage is very handsomely divided, and the plant is sometimes grown on pergolas and trellises for its sake as well as for the fruit. It is useful also for growing on the boundary fences of suburban villas, fruiting freely there.

Var. ELEGANS.—In this bramble (which I am not sure is really a form of laciniatus) the leaves are much smaller, and more hairy on the upper surface. It is known also as " laciniatus minor " and " R. Quintlandii." It does not flower freely and I have never seen the fruit. Grown by lovers of curiosities.

R. LAMBERTIANUS, *Seringe*

A straggling sub-evergreen shrub, with slender, four-angled stems viscous when young, and armed with short decurved spines. Leaves glossy green on both surfaces, simple, sometimes three-, or obscurely five-lobed, sometimes merely wavy ; broadly ovate or triangular, 3 to 5 ins. long, nearly as much wide at the heart-shaped base, toothed, slightly downy on the veins above, more so beneath ; stalk 1 to 2 ins. long ; stipules ⅓ in. long, with usually five linear lobes. Flowers white, ⅓ in. across, produced in a terminal panicle 3 to 5 ins. long, calyx segments downy, ovate-lanceolate. Fruit red, small.

Native of Central China ; introduced by Wilson in 1907. It is a luxuriant, very leafy, scandent shrub, suitable for planting as a rough group in thin woodland.

Var. HAKONENSIS, *Franchet*.—Similar in habit to the above, stems round and like the leaves glabrous or nearly so. Fruits yellow. Native of Japan as well as China ; introduced from the latter country by Wilson in 1907.

R. LASIOSTYLUS, *Focke*

(Bot. Mag., t. 7426)

An erect-growing deciduous shrub, with biennial stems, 4 to 6 ft. high, covered with a blue-white, waxy bloom, and closely set with bristle-like spines, ¼ in. or less in length, not downy. Leaves composed of three or five leaflets, and on young vigorous plants as much as 14 ins. long, but usually some 6 or 8 ins. long. Side leaflets ovate, 2 to 4 ins. long, coarsely and unevenly toothed, very sparsely hairy above, covered with a close white felt beneath ;

:erminal leaflet much larger especially in the trifoliolate leaves, often lobed, heart-shaped at the base. Flowers small, with reddish purple petals which are shorter than the calyx segments, and soon fall. Fruit 1 in. across, roundish, red, and downy, with an agreeable acid taste.

Native of Central China ; originally discovered in Hupeh by Henry, who sent seeds to Kew in 1889, from which plants were raised that flowered in 1894. This is one of the most effective of the white-stemmed brambles. It has lately been reintroduced in quantity by Wilson from Hupeh.

R. LEUCODERMIS, *Torrey and Gray*

A deciduous shrub, 4 to 8 ft. high, with blue-white, erect, biennial stems, armed with stout prickles. Leaves composed of usually three, or five, leaflets, which are ovate or lanceolate, 1½ to 4 ins. long, pointed, doubly toothed glabrous above, covered with a close, white felt beneath. Flowers white, produced during June in terminal clusters. Fruit purplish black, sweet and agreeably flavoured.

Native of western N. America, where it takes the place of R. occidentalis of the eastern side ; to this species it is closely akin. It was introduced to Britain by Douglas, about 1829, and has been sometimes grown in gardens for its blue-white stems. The name, however, is better known than the plant, for what is often grown as " leucodermis " is the Himalayan R. biflorus, a species with much whiter (less blue) stems than this and, indeed, preferable to it.

R. LINEATUS, *Reinwardt*

A deciduous or semi-evergreen rambling shrub up to 10 ft. high ; stems slender, downy, furnished with a few tiny prickles. Leaves made up of usually five, sometimes three leaflets radiating from the end of a downy main-stalk that is 1½ to 3 ins. long. Leaflets oblanceolate to oblong, shortly and slenderly pointed, tapered at the base, scarcely stalked, evenly set all round with sharp triangular teeth ; middle leaflet the largest and from 4 to 9 ins. long by 1 to 2½ ins. wide, lowest pair often about half the size ; upper surface dark green with a line of white down on the midrib ; under surface covered completely with shining silky down ; veins parallel in thirty to fifty pairs. Flowers in short axillary clusters, white, sepals longer than the petals, downy ; fruit small, red or yellow.

Native of the Sikkim Himalaya, S.W. China, and Malaya. I first saw it cultivated out-of-doors at Caerhays, Cornwall, in 1916 ; it was then 10 ft. high. It was also grown at that time by Mr H. White at the Sunningdale Nurseries. Amongst the Rubi it is remarkably distinct in its five-foliolate leaves with the leaflets arranged as in the horse chestnut, in the singularly beautiful silvery sheen beneath them, and in their very numerous parallel veins, of which I have counted as many as fifty pairs on one leaflet. It is not hardy at Kew, but Messrs Hillier report that at Winchester it is injured only in hard winters. The plants in cultivation were raised from seed collected by Forrest, who found it in Yunnan as long ago as 1905. Henry had previously found it in the same province.

R. MALIFOLIUS, *Focke*

A deciduous shrub whose prostrate or climbing stems are sparingly armed with short recurved spines, otherwise glabrous. Leaves oval or ovate, 2 to 5 ins. long, 1 to 2 ins. wide, rounded at the base, glabrous above, downy on the veins beneath, the margins set with broad, shallow teeth, each tooth ending in a small abrupt point ; veins in seven to ten pairs, parallel ; stalk ¼ to ⅝ in. long. Flowers in terminal racemes, 2 to 4 ins. long, each flower 1 in. across, the petals white, roundish, overlapping ; anthers downy ; sepals ovate, downy like the short flower-stalk. Fruits of goodly size, black.

Native of W. China, where it is common in thickets at 2000 to 4000 ft. ; also of Central China, but rare. It is an elegant species, and in regard to its flowers is one of the handsomest of Chinese Rubi, but Mr Wilson told me that the fruit has an unpleasant flavour. It differs from R. hupehensis in the inflorescence being without glands. The specific name refers to the apple-like foliage.

R. MESOGÆUS, *Focke*

A strong-growing deciduous shrub with erect stems unbranched the first year, springing from the ground like raspberry canes and growing 10 ft. long in a season, arched at the top ; they are quite velvety with down which persists through the winter ; prickles ⅛ in. or less long, curved. Leaves trifoliolate, with a velvety, prickly main-stalk, the side leaflets very shortly stalked. The leaflets vary much in size and are from 2 to 7 ins. long and from half to nearly as much wide ; they are ovate to roundish ovate, coarsely toothed, the terminal one the largest and more or less lobed, mostly slenderly pointed, rounded or slightly heart-shaped at the base, slightly downy above, grey-velvety beneath. Flowers small, pinkish white, borne in short axillary clusters ; sepals ultimately reflexed ; fruits black, round, ⅓ in. wide with a few hairs at the summit of each pip. Blossoms in June.

Native of Central and W. China, where it is widely spread ; introduced by Wilson in 1907. It is related to the common raspberry in the stems being biennial and flowering in their second year. Notable chiefly for its strong growth and large leaves. It has been confused in gardens with R. gracilis, *Roxburgh* (R. niveus, *Wallich*), which has wholly downy fruits.

R. NIGROBACCUS, *Bailey*. HIGH BLACKBERRY

(R. villosus, *Gray*, not of *Aiton*)

A deciduous shrub, with erect or arching, angled stems, 4 to 7 ft. high, armed with stout prickles and covered with pale down. Leaves mostly trifoliolate ; leaflets ovate or oblong, coarsely, irregularly, often doubly toothed ; 2 to 4 ins. long, half as much wide ; with scattered hairs above, very downy beneath. Flowers 1 in. wide, pure white, produced in fine terminal racemes augmented by solitary flowers from the axils of the uppermost leaves ; the entire inflorescence will measure 8 to 12 ins. long. Each flower is borne on a shaggy stalk 1 to 1½ ins. long. Fruit black, ¾ to 1 in. long, very juicy.

Native of eastern N. America, long cultivated in this country and in America under the erroneous name of R. villosus. [The real R. VILLOSUS, *Aiton*, is a procumbent plant with the usually solitary flowers produced in leaf-axils.] Our present species is the parent of a well-known and valuable race of cultivated American blackberries, to which " Kittatiny," " Newman's Thornless," and other varieties belong. Over sixty years ago several of these garden varieties were imported from America and tried as fruit-bearers in this country, but none of them ever succeeded. As flowering shrubs, however, both they and the type have considerable beauty, the large terminal clusters of flowers being amongst the most effective in the genus. They expand in early June.

Var. PLENA.—Handsome, double-flowered, and more lasting in blossom. The best form to grow in English gardens.

R. NOBILIS, *Regel*

A hybrid between R. odoratus and R. Idæus, raised by Mr C. de Vos, at Hazerswoude, near Boskoop, in Holland, about 1855. It is intermediate between the parents, having erect, sturdy stems peeling like those of R. odoratus, but less glandular-hairy and not so tall. Leaves trifoliolate, large, hairy on both surfaces. Flowers purplish red, produced in terminal corymbs in June and July. A handsome, vigorous shrub of about the same value for ornament as R. odoratus—the mother plant. The leaves resemble R. Idæus in being trifoliolate, but the flowers owe their colour and size largely to R. odoratus.

R. NUTANS, *Wallich*

(Bot. Mag., t. 5023)

An evergreen, prostrate shrub, rising only a few inches above the ground ; the stems creeping, unarmed, but thickly covered with soft purplish bristles and rooting at almost every joint. Leaves trifoliolate, with bristly stalks 1½ to 2 ins. long ; leaflets glossy green above, bristly on the veins beneath, sharply toothed, the terminal one the largest and from 1 to 2½ ins. long, rhomboidal, often rounded at the apex ; the side ones half to two-thirds as large, all three very shortly stalked. Flowers pure white, 1½ ins. across, borne in the leaf-axils and at the top of erect, leafy shoots 6 or 8 ins. high, each flower on a slender stalk 1½ to 2½ ins. long, bristly like the reddish calyx.

Native of the Himalaya ; cultivated at Kew for the last sixty years. The cheerful leaves and large flowers render this one of the most pleasing of dwarf Rubi. In the Bamboo Garden at Kew, on a shady slope and growing in ordinary loam, it thrives perfectly, sending out its runner-like shoots in all directions. The plant is rare in gardens, but may be recommended as a low covering for sheltered semi-shaded slopes, etc.

R. OCCIDENTALIS, *Linnæus*.   BLACK RASPBERRY

A deciduous shrub, with arching, biennial stems, 6 to 10 ft. long, very glaucous, and armed with scattered short spines. Leaves composed of mostly three (sometimes five, pinnately arranged) leaflets, which are ovate, 1½ to 4 ins. long, pointed, coarsely and unequally toothed, covered with a close white felt beneath. Flowers white, ½ in. across, produced in terminal few-flowered corymbs during June. Fruit purple-black, flattish, hemispherical.

Native of eastern N. America, and the parent species of several races of garden raspberries largely grown in America, the best known of which are the " Gregg," " Hillborn," and " Ohio." In this country it is only worth growing for the long, arching, blue-white stems, and even in this respect it is not equal to R. biflorus or R. lasiostylus. The tips of the arching shoots often reach the ground and there take root. Allied to R. strigosus, it differs in its black fruits and glaucous stems.

Intermediate between occidentalis and strigosus is R. NEGLECTUS, *Peck.* It is thought to be a natural hybrid from them, having dark red fruits and prickly blue-white stems. Introduced to Kew in 1893.

R. ODORATUS, *Linnæus*

(Bot. Mag., t. 323)

A vigorous, deciduous shrub, with stout, erect, very pale brown stems up to 8 ft. high, bark peeling ; young stems covered with glandular hairs. Leaves simple, amongst the largest of hardy Rubi, five-lobed, vine-like, 4 to 10 (or even 12) ins. across ; lobes pointed, sharply and irregularly toothed, hairy on both sides, but especially beneath, soft and velvety to the touch. Flowers fragrant, bright purple, 1½ to 2 ins. across, borne in large, branching, corymbose clusters at the ends of the shoots ; the stalks conspicuously furnished with dense glandular hairs, the calyx similarly covered, each of its five divisions narrowed to a tail-like point. Fruits flat and broad, red when ripe, but rarely seen in this country.

Native of eastern N. America ; introduced in 1770. Next to R. deliciosus, this is perhaps the most ornamental of Rubi, in regard to blossom. It flowers from July to September, and few shrubs at that time equal it in beauty and fragrance. It loves a semi-shaded spot, where its flowers are protected from the fierce mid-day and early afternoon sun ; in such a place the blossoms last longer. It is a rampant grower, and soon forms a thicket ; good soil should be provided and the plants are all the better if pulled apart every few years, and planted more thinly. The old stems should be removed every winter. It is very similar in growth to R. parviflorus (q.v.), but commences to flower a month later.

R. OMEIENSIS, *Rolfe*

(R. clemens, *Focke*)

A large straggling shrub, with round stems, unarmed, but furnished with small, stellate hairs. Leaves of maple-like form, five-, or obscurely seven-lobed, with a heart-shaped base ; 3 to 7 ins. long and as much wide ; irregularly toothed, stellately downy beneath, less so above ; stalk 2 to 3 ins. long ; stipules ½ to ¾ in. long, cut up into deep, narrow segments. Panicles many-flowered, terminal ; flowers ½ in. across, with downy stalks ; calyx downy, the lobes pointed, triangular ; petals purple. Fruit black, well-flavoured, ripening late.

Native of W. China, and found on Mt. Omi by Wilson, who introduced it for Messrs Veitch, with whom it flowered in August 1908. It grows up to 6000 ft. elevation, and will be perfectly hardy. It makes growths 10 or 12 ft. long in a season. The stipules are rather remarkable.

R. PALMATUS, *Thunberg*

(Bot. Mag., t. 7801)

A deciduous shrub, 5 or 6 ft. high in the open (thrice as much in a cool greenhouse) ; stems not downy, but armed with small, flattened prickles. Leaves usually palmately five-lobed, sometimes three-lobed, sometimes seven- or nine-lobed ; 1 to 3 ins. long, margins doubly toothed ; green on both surfaces with silky hairs along the midrib and veins ; stalk ¾ to 1½ ins. long, with hooked spines. Flowers white, 1½ ins. across, solitary, produced from the axils of terminal leaves on short shoots that spring from the previous year's growths. Petals of narrowly oval outline, their ends rounded ; calyx downy outside, glabrous within, the lobes narrow, long-pointed, and toothed ; stalk slender, ½ to ¾ in. long. Fruit roundish, yellow and juicy, ¾ in. across.

Native of China and Japan. In the Temperate House at Kew, trained on a pillar, this shrub is 20 ft. or more high, but in the open and unprotected it is rather a low shrub. Although hardy enough, it apparently needs somewhat warmer conditions than the open air affords near London to bring out its best qualities.

R. Parkeri, *Hance*

A deciduous shrub of climbing habit ; stems biennial, round, slender, armed with short, scattered, decurved spines, and thickly covered with greyish hairs, many of them gland-tipped. Leaves simple, broadly lanceolate, long-pointed, heart-shaped at the base ; 4 to 7 ins. long, about half as wide; the margins wavy, and sharply and finely toothed ; upper surface bristly, especially along the midrib and veins, the lower one covered with a dense brownish red down ; leaf-stalk up to 1 in. long, hairy and prickly. Flowers borne on an elongated, lax panicle, the calyx being remarkable for its dense covering of reddish glandular hairs. Fruit black, ripening early.

Native of China, where it was originally discovered in the province of Szechuen by E. H. Parker, in 1881 ; introduced in 1907 by Wilson, who found it near Ichang. This bramble has distinct and striking foliage, and its habit promises to be elegant.

R. Parviflorus, *Nuttall*. Salmon Berry

(R. nutkanus, *Moçino* ; Bot. Mag., t. 3453)

A vigorous deciduous shrub, up to 8 ft. high, with erect, unarmed stems, and peeling bark ; young shoots downy and slightly glandular. Leaves simple, five-lobed, vine-like, 4 to 8 (or more) ins. across, irregularly toothed, downy on both sides especially beneath ; leaf-stalk 2 to 5 ins. long, set with glandular hairs. Flowers pure white, 1½ to 2 ins. across, borne three to ten in terminal clusters during June, and continuing for several weeks ; the flower-stalk is glandular-hairy and the calyx is very downy, each lobe contracted at the apex into a short tail. Fruit large, hemispherical and flattened, red ; said to be sometimes pleasantly flavoured in a wild state.

Native of western N. America ; introduced by Douglas in 1827. Very similar in its growth and foliage to R. odoratus, but easily distinguished by its white flowers in smaller clusters ; the shoots, too, are not so conspicuously downy and glandular, and are darker coloured. Like that species it forms, when left to itself in good soil, dense thickets, which should be overhauled every winter and the worn-out stems cut out. Easily increased by pulling old plants to pieces. Fruits ripen most seasons from the earliest flowers, but are insipid and worthless in this country.

R. Parvifolius, *Linnæus*

(Bot. Reg., t. 496 ; R. triphyllus, *Thunberg*)

A low, deciduous bramble, forming a tangle of slender, downy, prickly stems a few feet high. Leaves composed of usually three, but sometimes five, leaflets, borne on a common stalk 1½ to 2 ins. long, downy, and covered with prickles. Leaflets of various shapes and sizes, usually roundish or widely obovate, ¾ to 2 ins. long, coarsely toothed, dark green and glabrous above, clothed with a close white felt beneath, the terminal one the largest and longest stalked. Flowers produced from the leaf-axils near the end of the shoot in few-flowered corymbs on downy, prickly stalks ; petals bright rose-coloured, erect. Fruit roundish, red, edible.

Native of Japan and China ; according to Bentham some of its forms are also native of Australia. It was originally imported by the Horticultural Society in 1818. It is rather pretty in blossom, but not more so than many of our native brambles.

R. PARVUS, *Buchanan*

An evergreen, unifoliolate prostrate shrub, the slender stems often partially buried in the soil and rooting from the joints ; prickles few and small. The whole plant except the flower-stalks is glabrous. Leaves 1 to 3 ins. long, ¼ to ⅜ in. wide, linear to linear-lanceolate, more or less cordate, pointed, the margins densely and regularly set with small, sharp teeth ; stalk ½ to 1 in. long, midrib sparsely spiny beneath. Flowers solitary or in twos or threes, axillary or terminal, white, about 1 in. wide, petals ovate, spreading.

Native of the South Island, New Zealand, up to 3000 ft., cultivated by the late Sir Edmund G. Loder at Leonardslea in 1916 and very successfully by the late Mr Fred Stoker, in whose rock garden at Golding's Hill in Essex it formed a dense, low patch several feet across, flowering in May and June. The fruit is described by Cheeseman as ½ to 1 in. long, juicy, and the plant itself as unisexual.

R. PHŒNICOLASIUS, *Maximowicz.* WINEBERRY

(Bot. Mag., t. 6479)

A deciduous shrub making spreading stems 8 to 10 ft. long in favourable situations ; the stems are biennial, round, and together with the branches and leaf-stalks are covered densely with reddish, gland-tipped bristles mixed with which are a few slender prickles. Leaves 5 to 7 ins. long, composed of three leaflets. The terminal leaflet is stalked, 2 to 4 ins. long, roundish or broadly ovate, the base rounded or heart-shaped, the margins coarsely toothed and lobed ; the side leaflets differ only in being obliquely ovate, stalkless, and much smaller ; all are sparsely hairy above, white-felted beneath. Flowers in terminal racemes, the chief feature being the calyx, which is covered with glandular hairs, and measures 1½ ins. across, the five segments being very narrow and pointed ; petals ¼ in. or less in length, pink. Fruit conical, ¾ in. long, bright red, sweet and juicy, but of insipid flavour.

Native of Japan, and the province of Kansu, China ; introduced about 1876. This raspberry is hardy at Kew, bearing fruit regularly in the open, but it would probably succeed better against a wall. In a cool house, trained up a post, it bears large crops of its very handsome, brightly coloured fruits. The species is noteworthy, not only for its fruits, but also for its excessively bristly stems, its tiny petals, and large star-shaped calyx which persists and spreads out beneath the fruit. It flowers in June under glass, a few weeks later out-of-doors.

R. PLAYFAIRIANUS, *Focke*

A rambling evergreen or semi-evergreen shrub ; young stems dark coloured, round, very slender, string-like, armed with tiny hooked prickles, and covered with web-like down when young. Leaves composed of three or five leaflets radiating from the end of the stalk, which is 1½ to 2½ ins. long, and prickly ; leaflets lanceolate, sharply toothed, the terminal one the largest, and sometimes 6 ins. long, the basal pair 1 to 3 ins. long, dark glossy green above, covered beneath with a pale grey felt. Flowers about ⅓ in. across, produced in small terminal panicles, and in the leaf-axils near. Fruit resembling a raspberry, but black ; ripe in July and August.

Native of Central and W. China ; introduced in 1907 by Wilson, who states that it is found in thickets at 3000 to 6000 ft. It is a very graceful plant when trained up a support, and the shape of its leaves is very uncommon among hardy Rubi, being more suggestive of an Ampelopsis.

R. SPECTABILIS, *Pursh*

(Bot. Reg., t. 1424)

A deciduous shrub with erect stems, 4 to 6 ft. high, glabrous, but armed with fine prickles. Leaves 4 to 6 ins. long, composed of three leaflets which are ovate, from 1½ to 4 ins. long, doubly toothed, almost or quite glabrous on both surfaces, the terminal one the largest and broadest. Flowers produced singly or a few together on short shoots springing from the older wood ; purplish red, 1 in. or so across, fragrant ; calyx downy, with broad pointed lobes not so long as the petals. Fruit orange-yellow, large, somewhat egg-shaped.

Native of western N. America ; introduced by Douglas in 1827. It flowers freely towards the end of April, and is very pretty then. To some of the native tribes of N. America the fruit is valuable as food, but in this country it does not ripen freely. The plant spreads rapidly by means of sucker growths from the base, and soon forms a dense thicket. Plants should be overhauled annually, and the worn-out stems removed. Propagation is easily effected by dividing up the plants or removing offsets.

R. STRIGOSUS, *Michaux*. AMERICAN RED RASPBERRY

(R. Idæus strigosus, *Maximowicz*)

A deciduous shrub with biennial stems, 3 to 6 ft. high, and densely clothed with bristles which are frequently gland-tipped. Leaves with hairy stalks, composed of three (or five pinnately arranged) leaflets, which are ovate or oblong, 1½ to 3 ins. long, pointed, coarsely and irregularly toothed, the terminal one stalked, the side ones stalkless, all glabrous above, covered with a grey felt beneath. Flowers white, ¾ in. across, produced in the leaf-axils and at the end of the short side shoots on bristly slender stalks. Fruit red, conical.

Native of N. America from Labrador south to the Carolinas, and westward to British Columbia and New Mexico. It fills in the New World the place of R. Idæus in the Old. The two species are closely akin, but this American one is easily distinguished by its bristly stems and flower-stalks. It is the parent species of garden races grown largely in N. America, such as the " Cuthbert " and " Hansall " raspberries. This is its chief interest ; it is not worth cultivation except where collections are maintained.

R. THIBETANUS, *Franchet*

(R. Veitchii, *Rolfe*)

An erect deciduous shrub, 6 ft. or more high ; stems biennial, glabrous, round, covered with a purplish bloom, and set irregularly with straight, slender prickles. Leaves pinnate, 4 to 9 ins. long, composed of seven to thirteen leaflets, the main-stalk prickly ; leaflets oval or ovate, more or less oblique, stalkless, coarsely and angularly toothed, dark lustrous green, and with minutely silky hairs above, whitish felted beneath ; the lowest leaflets are 1 to 2 ins. long, each successive pair diminishing in size towards the apex of the leaf which is terminated by a long, deep-lobed leaflet. Flowers ½ in. across, slender-stalked, solitary in the leaf-axils, or a few together in terminal flattish panicles ; the calyx very downy, with triangular lobes ; petals purple. Fruit roundish, ⅝ in. across, black with a bluish bloom.

Native of W. China ; discovered and introduced by Wilson for Messrs Veitch, with whom it flowered in August 1908. Mr Wilson told me he found

it in the Min River Valley at elevations of 4000 to 6000 ft., where it is rare. O
the newer Chinese Rubi it is one of the most distinct and attractive-looking
both for its blue-purple stems and very handsomely cut foliage.

R. THYRSOIDEUS, *Wimmer*

A strong-growing shrub, with arching, ribbed stems becoming nearly o
quite free from down, but armed with straight or slightly hooked prickles
Leaves composed of five leaflets, the terminal one of which is ovate, ofte
broadly so, and rounded at the base, its stalk about half the length of the
blade and very prickly. All the leaflets are almost or quite glabrous above
covered beneath with a dull white felt; margins doubly toothed. Flower
white or pinkish, produced in a tall, erect panicle. This, one of the
handsomest of common brambles, has a double-flowered white variety callec
PLENA, which is well worth cultivation in the garden on account of its beauty
its flowering in July and August, and because it thrives in semi-shady places
The panicles are erect, pyramidal, 6 to 8 ins. high. The type is widely spreac
over England, Wales, and on the Continent.

R. TRIANTHUS, *Focke*

(R. conduplicatus, *Rolfe*)

A deciduous shrub of wide-spreading habit, the biennial stems erect
much branched, spiny, blue-white, 4 to 6 ft. high. Leaves simple, 3 to 6 ins
long, 1½ to 4½ ins. wide; ovate to triangular, distinctly three-lobed on the
barren stems, less markedly lobed on the flowering shoots; middle lobe long
taper-pointed, irregularly toothed, quite glabrous on both sides, whitisl
beneath, dark green above; there are hooked spines on the midrib anc
veins beneath; stalk ½ to 1½ ins. long, similarly armed. Flowers pinkisl
white, insignificant, produced a few together on cymes that are terminal or
short lateral twigs. Fruit dark red.

Native of Central China up to 4000 ft.; introduced for Messrs Veitch by
Wilson in 1900. It is distinct from most Rubi in the absence of down or hairs
but has not much garden value.

R. TRICOLOR, *Franchet*

(Bot. Mag., t. 9534; R. polytrichus, *Franchet*)

A quite prostrate, semi-evergreen shrub with round stems, devoid of prickles
and spines, but densely clothed with yellow-brown bristles about ⅛ in. long.
Leaves simple, heart-shaped, 3 or 4 ins. long by two-thirds as much wide,
irregularly toothed, pointed, dark green above, covered with a close whitish
felt beneath; there are about seven pairs of parallel veins, which on the
under-surface are furnished with bristles, but on the upper surface the bristles
are confined in rows between the veins. Leaf-stalk 1 to 1½ ins. long, bristly
like the stems. Flowers white, 1 in. across, produced singly in the leaf-axils
near the end of the shoot, and in a small terminal panicle. Fruit bright red,
and of good size and flavour.

Native of W. China; first discovered by the French missionary Delavay,
but introduced to cultivation by Wilson in 1908. It is remarkably distinct on
account of the very bristly stems and leaf-stalks. Coming from elevations up
to 10,000 ft. it ought to prove hardy.

R. TRIFIDUS, *Thunberg*

An evergreen or sub-evergreen shrub, with erect stems, 4 to 7 ft. high, igzagged towards the top, not (or but little) branched the first year, beset with glandular hairs at first, but soon becoming glabrous. Leaves dark lustrous green, usually five- or seven-lobed, 4 to 10 ins. across ; the lobes each half or two-thirds of the way to the stalk, are ovate, pointed, doubly toothed, slightly hairy on the chief veins above and below ; stalks 1 to 2½ ins. long. Flowers 1 to 1¼ ins. wide, rosy-white, produced singly in the terminal leaf-axils and in a few-flowered, terminal corymb, each on a downy stalk ¾ to ½ ins. long. Calyx very downy outside. Fruit described as red and edible.

Native of Japan ; introduced about 1888. This rubus is distinct from all other cultivated species in its large, handsome, deeply lobed leaves, which bear a great resemblance to those of Fatsia japonica, except that they are not so large. It is worth growing for their sake. The flowers, which appear in May are not freely borne, and I have never seen the fruit. The leaves of the flowering shoots are frequently three-lobed, and it is to them that the specific name refers.

R. ULMIFOLIUS, *Schott*

(R. rusticanus, *Mercier*)

A vigorous shrub whose more or less plum-coloured, arching stems are clothed with starry down and armed with long, broad-based prickles ; they root freely at the tips. Leaves composed of three or five leaflets radially arranged, which are slightly downy above but white-felted beneath, rather finely toothed. Flowers bright rosy red, and produced in showy, cylindrical panicles. This well-marked species is of little value as a fruiting bramble, its berries being small and dryish, but from it several ornamental garden varieties have been obtained. It is widely spread over the United Kingdom (except Scotland) and Europe generally.

Var. BELLIDIFLORUS, *Focke* (var. plenus, *Hort.* ; R. bellidiflorus, *Koch*).— This is the very handsome, well-known, double-flowered pink bramble, which is so useful in making a gay display in July and August. Each flower produces an extraordinary number of narrow petals. For semi-shady spots in the woodland, this bramble may be strongly recommended as a companion plant to R. thyrsoideus plenus, with white, double flowers.

Var. VARIEGATUS.—A handsome variegated form, the main part of the leaf being green, the midrib and veins picked out in bright yellow. This variety needs a more sunny spot than the others.

Var. INERMIS.—A remarkable form absolutely devoid of spines and prickles. It was received at Kew from the firm of Richard Smith & Co., of Worcester, in 1877, but beyond that I know nothing of its history. One may thrust one's hand into the middle of the bush without getting a scratch.

RUSCUS. LILIACEÆ

Strictly speaking, the three species of Ruscus described below should be regarded as shrub-like, rather than as true shrubs, none having really woody stems. They belong to the Asparagus group of the lily family, renewing themselves by stems from the base as asparagus does ; the tender young stems also are eaten in some parts of Europe. They

are evergreen, the " leaves " mostly alternate, sometimes in whorls.
has to be observed that the so-called leaves are really modified branche
flattened and resembling leaves, and performing the same function
They should, properly, be termed *cladodes*. Flowers with a perianth o
six segments, small, inconspicuous, borne in the centre of the cladode
mostly unisexual, with the sexes often on different plants. Henc
probably the rarity of the fruits of the two species common in gardens
they are propagated by division, and thus perpetuate the sex only of th
original plant obtained. They thrive in almost any soil, and are admirab
in very shady places. The best time to break up the plants for propaga
tion is spring. (See also Danaë.)

R. ACULEATUS, *Linnæus*. BUTCHER'S BROOM

An evergreen, well-armed shrub, spreading and renewing itself by mear
of sucker growths springing from the base; 1½ to 3 ft. high, the crowde
erect stems having many rigid branches near the top; stems groove
" Leaves " ovate, stalkless, ¾ to 1½ ins. long, ¼ to ¾ in. wide; slightly gloss
on both sides, tapering at the apex to a slender, stiff spine. Flowers ¼ in
across, dull white, borne singly or in pairs (apparently stalkless) in the cent
of the " leaf," but really produced in the leaf-axil, the stalk being united to th
midrib of the " leaf." The flower-bud forms early in the year, and opens i
spring. Fruit a globose or oblong, bright red berry, ¼ to ⅝ in. diameter, born
like the flower of course, in the " leaf "-centre.
   Native of Europe, including the south of England. The butcher's broo
is remarkable in being the only shrubby plant of the monocotyledonous typ
native of the British Isles. It is not, ordinarily, a showy plant, but is alwa
interesting for the curious position of its flowers and fruit. When laden wi
the latter it is very ornamental indeed; but the plants are mostly unisexua
and the fruits are not commonly seen in gardens, because one of the sexe
but more especially the female, is wanting. It is especially useful for plantin
in dense shade where very few evergreens will thrive. It is said to hav
obtained its common name through being used in the shape of brooms b
butchers to clean their blocks. In S. Italy I have seen it used as a garde
besom, the same as birch and ling are used in this country.
   Var. ANGUSTIFOLIUS, *Boissier*, has narrower " leaves " than the type.
   Var. LATIFOLIUS has " leaves " up to 2 ins. long and ¾ to 1 in. wide, gloss

R. HYPOGLOSSUM, *Linnæus*

An evergreen shrub, 8 to 18 ins. high, forming compact tufts, and increasin
by new sucker growths from the sides; stem somewhat arching, as thick as
lead pencil, scarcely woody, unbranched, green. " Leaves " not spiny, th
lower ones narrow-oval, the upper ones oblanceolate, tapered at both ends
glabrous and glossy on both sides, with prominent longitudinal veins; 3 t
4½ ins. long, 1 to 1½ ins. wide. On the upper side is borne a leaf-like brac
lanceolate, 1 to 1½ ins. long, ¼ to ⅓ in. wide, in the axil of which a few sma
yellowish flowers appear in April and May. Berry red, globose, ¼ to ½ in. wid
   Native of S. Europe; cultivated in England since the sixteenth centur
No evergreen shrub thrives better than this in shade and in competition wi
the roots of greedy trees; in this is its chief value for gardens. It flowers i
cultivation, but in my experience rarely bears fruit.

R. Hypophyllum, *Linnæus*

(Bot. Mag., t. 2049)

A small evergreen plant, 6 to 12 ins. high, similar in habit to, but in this ountry dwarfer than, R. Hypoglossum. " Leaves " oval, sometimes slightly vate; 1½ to 3 ins. long, ¾ to 1½ ins. wide; shortly stalked; the point short nd abrupt. Flowers small, white, produced in a cluster from the centre of ne under-surface of the " leaf," each flower on a slender stalk ¼ in. long; ney are borne in the axil of a small bract ¼ in. long. Berry globose, red, in. wide.

Native of S. Europe and N. Africa; introduced early in the seventeenth entury. Whilst this species has a general resemblance to R. Hypoglossum, is readily distinguished by the shorter, broader " leaves " or cladodes; the ny bract; and in the flowers coming from underneath. It is too tender to ave much value in gardens near London, but is interesting for more southern nd western localities.

RUTA graveolens, *Linnæus*. RUE. RUTACEÆ

An evergreen shrub, with erect, half-woody branches, rarely seen ore than 3 ft. high. Leaves of a markedly glaucous hue, alternate, ariable in length, but usually 3 to 5 ins. long, pinnately decompound, ne leaflets usually confined to the upper half, the ultimate subdivisions oovate, ⅛ to ½ in. long. Flowers ¾ in. wide, arranged in terminal orymbs, rather dull yellow; the sepals and petals usually four, some-mes five; the stamens twice as many. Petals scoop-shaped with jagged lges. Fruit a usually four-celled capsule.

Rue is known best, of course, as a garden herb with an acrid taste, sed in domestic and especially rustic medicine for colic, hysteria, romoting perspiration, etc. Applied locally it is a powerful irritant. hese properties are due to a volatile oil which permeates the leaves and ounger parts of the plant. Given in too large doses it is dangerous, and roduces symptoms of acrid narcotic poisoning. The species is a native S. Europe, and owing no doubt to its medicinal properties has been rown in English gardens from time immemorial. It finds frequent .ention in Shakespeare as " herb of grace " :

> " I'll set a bank of rue, sour herb of grace."
> —The gardener, in *King Richard II*.

should find a place in all extensive shrub collections not only for its sociations, but for its beauty also. When fully in flower the dark ellow blossoms contrast prettily with the glaucous foliage, and they ntinue to open from June onwards for some months. It is quite easily creased by cuttings, and will thrive all the better if lime or chalk be ixed with the soil where it is naturally absent. There is a var. ariegata in cultivation, its leaflets bordered with white.

SABIA. SABIACEÆ

An Asiatic genus of some twenty species of climbing shrubs with ndivided, untoothed, alternate leaves and small flowers produced in the af-axils. The parts of the flowers are usually in fives. The only ally near to this genus amongst hardy trees and shrubs is Meliosma, whose species are very different in their tree or bush form, their toothed or pinnate leaves, and their usually terminal panicles of flowers.

S. LATIFOLIA, *Rehder and Wilson*

(Bot. Mag., t. 8859)

A deciduous scandent shrub up to 10 ft. high ; young shoots soon glabrous yellowish green or purplish. Leaves alternate, oval, oval-oblong or slightly obovate, base rounded to tapered, often abruptly pointed, toothless ; $1\frac{1}{4}$ to $5\frac{1}{2}$ ins. long, $\frac{3}{4}$ to 3 ins. wide ; at first furnished with short hairs on both surfaces eventually becoming glabrous except on the midrib and veins beneath stalk $\frac{1}{4}$ to $\frac{3}{5}$ in. long, hairy. Flowers borne during May usually three together in axillary cymes $\frac{1}{4}$ to $\frac{1}{2}$ in. long, the stalks downy. Each flower is $\frac{1}{4}$ in. wide somewhat globose through the incurving of the five oval petals which are greenish yellow at first, changing to reddish brown, and edged with minute hairs. Sepals five, minute, roundish ovate, minutely ciliate ; stamens rather longer than the petals. Fruits bright blue, consisting of two compressed kidney-shaped parts attached to a slender stalk $\frac{3}{4}$ to 1 in. long ; each part of the fruit is $\frac{1}{8}$ in. long.

Native of W. China ; discovered by Pratt about 1888 ; introduced by Wilson in 1908. It was cultivated by Miss Willmott at Warley Place, Essex where it became 10 ft. high growing against a north wall. Here it flowered and ripened fruit in 1919. At Kew it is succeeding well in the open air in a sheltered site but otherwise unprotected. It appears to be very rare, but can be propagated by cuttings.

S. SCHUMANNIANA, *Diels*

A deciduous climber up to 10 ft. high, with glabrous, slender young shoots Leaves toothless, narrowly oblong to oval-lanceolate, slenderly pointed shortly tapered to rounded at the base : 1 to 4 ins. long, $\frac{1}{3}$ to $1\frac{1}{2}$ ins. wide glabrous ; stalk slender, $\frac{1}{8}$ to $\frac{1}{3}$ in. long. Flowers $\frac{1}{4}$ in. long, cup-shaped, three to six in axillary cymes, with a slender main-stalk up to $1\frac{1}{2}$ ins. long. Sepal small, rounded-triangular ; petals greenish or dull purple, oval, blunt, $\frac{1}{8}$ in long ; stamens about as long as the petals. Fruit kidney-shaped, $\frac{1}{4}$ in. wide blue-black, ripe in October, the sepals persisting at the base.

Native of W. China ; introduced by Wilson in 1908. It differs from S. latifolia in its narrower, smaller, glabrous leaves and longer, more slender flower-stalks. It was introduced to Kew from the Arnold Arboretum in 1912 and has ripened fruit there. Quite hardy but of no great garden value. Flowers in May.

SAGERETIA PAUCICOSTATA, *Maximowicz*. RHAMNACEÆ

A freely branching deciduous shrub up to 10 ft. high ; young shoots long and slender, glabrous, grooved, pale grey, armed with short, stiff spine-tipped, axillary,leafy branches. Leaves alternate, elliptical to ovate pointed, tapered at the base, minutely toothed, $\frac{1}{2}$ to 2 ins. long, $\frac{1}{4}$ to $\frac{3}{4}$ in wide, glabrous, veins prominent beneath, one to three each side the midrib ; stalk $\frac{1}{8}$ to $\frac{1}{4}$ in. long, very slender. Flowers stalkless, very small and white, ranging from solitary to forming terminal leafy panicle to 3 ins. long, and opening in May. Fruit a subglobose, black drupe, in. wide.

Native of N. China and in cultivation at Kew since before 1919. t is very hardy. The specific name refers to the few veins of the leaf s compared with those of other species. The generic name comnemorates Auguste Sageret, a French botanist (1763-1851). The genus s represented in N. America as well as China and contains some fifteen pecies, but has no particular garden merit.

SALIX. WILLOW. SALICACEÆ

About two hundred years ago Linnæus remarked on the difficulties nd obscurities that encumber the student in his investigation of the villows. To-day when the number of known species and varieties has astly increased, these difficulties have intensified rather than diminished. Yet most of the leading types or genuine species are not difficult to dentify. The greatest of all the troubles of the systematic botanist rise from the fact that Nature has not differentiated her species clearly. f every one stood out well apart from its fellows, half his work would >e done. In no large genus of trees and shrubs do the types merge one nto the other, and blur the dividing lines so completely as they do in Salix. In Britain there are some seventeen or eighteen native species, very one of which is considered to have hybridised with two or more >f its fellows, some with as many as nine. But whether, as is usually ssumed, the intermediates are always hybrids is doubtful. Willows generally do not, in gardens at least, produce fertile seed so freely as to upport the theory of such multiple cross-breeding. It has to be said, 1owever, that some of these natural hybrids have been duplicated under ultivation by artificial cross-fertilisation.

Salix is a large genus of perhaps three hundred species of trees and hrubs, all those hardy in Britain being deciduous or practically so. They ary from stately timber trees of the type of S. alba and S. fragilis (80 ft. or more high) to tiny shrubs like S. herbacea, creeping along the ground, nd only rising an inch or two above it. The twigs of many species are very tough, and the genus supplies vastly the greater part of the material rom which the baskets and wickerwork of the world are made. Although the twigs of several species have the ordinary toughness of he genus, they are easily snapped off in their entirety at the point of heir union with the older branchlet. This curious characteristic is best nown in, and gives the popular name to, the crack willow (S. fragilis), out there are several more that have it equally marked. The leaves of willows are very variable : the typical shape is long and narrow, slenderointed, and toothed, but from that shape to an almost circular one here is every gradation. In the remarkable S. magnifica, introduced from W. China, the leaves are over 8 ins. long by over 5 ins. wide. Normally they are alternate, although in S. purpurea it is quite usual o find opposite ones as well. Stipules produced by willows are curiously ariable both in their size and persistence. They occur most markedly on the strongest shoots, and are frequently entirely absent from weaker ones.

III   I

It is the general rule for the sexes to be kept apart on separate plants, a character which adds to the difficulty of distinguishing willows for the foliage and habit of male and female specimens of the same species are not always identical. But this rule has occasional exceptions some trees produce both sexes, sometimes on the same branch. There is an example of S. MEDEMII, *Boissier*, at Kew, which frequently has male and female flowers on the same catkin. Willow catkins vary in shape from cylindrical to egg-shaped, and are usually very silky-hairy. The flowers, which are densely packed, have no sepals or petals ; the male consists of a scale carrying two to five (sometimes eight or nine) stamens ; the female consists of a scale bearing a single ovary. On the opposite side of the stamens and ovary from the large scale, or sometimes on both sides, is a small glandular scale, often called the " nectary." This organ is relied on to afford distinctions in botanical books, but being too minute for investigation by ordinary cultivators I have omitted consideration of it in the following notes on the species. The fruit or seed-vessel is a conical body splitting in two at the top, each half recurving when ripe. Seeds minute, furnished at one end with a tuft of pale hairs.

The flowers of willows are wind-fertilised, and appear usually in spring on the naked shoots of the previous summer. They are not devoid of beauty, the males especially ; but willows as a rule are cultivated for the beauty of their foliage and habit, or on account of their fondness for moisture at the roots, which renders them valuable for planting in wet places where the choice of trees and shrubs that will thrive is limited. A selection of some of the more desirable species is given below.

Willows are propagated extremely easily by means of leafless cuttings which may be put in the open ground at any time between November and early March. Pieces one to several years old may be used ; and of the tree sorts like alba, viridis, and fragilis, it is usual to put in " sets," *i.e.* naked rods, 8 to 12 ft. long, and as thick as, or thicker than a broom stick. Plants raised from cuttings in the nursery should be put in their permanent places at not more than two years old and should be planted a few inches deeper than before ; the best results will, indeed, be obtained by putting the cutting into its destined place at the commencement if due protection and care can be given. This is always done with the big " sets " just mentioned. The majority of willows abhor dryness at the root, but will thrive in ordinary situations if the soil be deep and rather heavy. A few sorts of Alpine origin or from northern latitude are suitable for the rock garden. Whilst most of the great osier-beds are along river sides, often in places so damp or so subject to inundation as to be unavailable for ordinary crops, some of the finest quality wicker work is made from willows grown on ordinary farm land. Often several forms of osiers used in basket-making are derived from a single species (see triandra, viminalis, purpurea, etc.), which, although they vary much in quality for their particular purpose, show no botanical differences They are known in the osier trade by colloquial names.

The value of several sorts of willow trees for producing wood from which cricket-bats are made is alluded to under S. cœrulea, viridis, and fragilis, but these species as well as alba yield timber useful also for other

urposes, especially where a non-splintering wood is required, and
where it is subject to rough friction like cart or wheelbarrow bottoms.
For wattling the wasting banks of rivers or other pieces of water nothing
equals the branches of willows.

In gardens willows are undoubtedly seen to best advantage near
water. Throughout the whole range of hardy trees and shrubs there is
nothing that can give quite the same effect as S. babylonica, S. alba,
vitellina, or S. Salamoni, planted by the margin of a lake or stream.

The following is a select list of species and hybrids that may be recommended for
various purposes in the garden :—

ORNAMENTAL LARGE TREES.—S. alba and S. a. argentea, babylonica, cœrulea,
fragilis, pentandra, Salamoni, viridis.

ORNAMENTAL SHRUBS.—S. Bockii, incana, magnifica, Pierotii, purpurea, repens
var. argentea.

COLOUR OF BARK IN WINTER.—S. vitellina, yellow ; S. vitellina var. britzensis,
red ; acutifolia and daphnoides, purple.

FLOWER.—S. Bockii, gracilistyla, Caprea, Smithiana.

ROCK GARDEN.—S. Arbuscula, herbacea, myrtilloides, reticulata, retusa.

S. purpurea pendula, cæsia, repens, and others are sometimes grafted on standards,
and are in that way transformed into small weeping trees, but the practice has little
o recommend it and has much against it.

S. ADENOPHYLLA, *Hooker*. FURRY WILLOW

A shrub up to 8 ft. high, of loose habit, sparsely branched ; twigs covered
with a thick silky coat of hairs. Leaves arranged very closely on the
branchlet (about four to the inch), ovate with a heart-shaped base, rather
abruptly pointed, very finely, closely, and regularly toothed, many of the
teeth glandular, especially at the base ; 1½ to 2 ins. long, ¾ to 1¼ ins. wide ;
covered with long, whitish, silky hairs on both surfaces, not so thickly as on
the twigs ; stalk from ⅕ to ⅓ in. long ; stipules persistent, obliquely heart-
shaped, glandular-toothed, ⅓ in. diameter. The female plant only appears to
be in cultivation ; this has catkins 1½ to 3 ins. long, borne on short leafy shoots.

Native of N. America, and one of the most distinct of cultivated willows,
especially in the extreme downiness of the younger parts, in the broad, closely
set leaves, and large persisting stipules.

S. ALBA, *Linnæus*. WHITE WILLOW

A tree 70 to 80 ft. high, of elegant form, branches pendulous at the ends ;
young shoots grey with silky down, growing at angles usually of 30° to 45°
to the older branchlet from which they spring. Leaves lanceolate, 1½ to
3½ ins. long, ¼ to ⅝ in. wide ; very finely toothed, much tapered at both ends,
permanently covered beneath with silky down, less so above ; stalk ⅛ to ¼ in.
long. Catkins 1½ to 2 ins. long, opening in early May. Stamens two, silky
at the base ; ovary not stalked.

Native of Europe (including Britain) and N. Asia. One of the most
beautiful of native trees. It varies considerably in the colour of the leaves
and young shoots, some being much more silvery than others. It yields a
useful timber although scarcely so valuable as that of the blue-willow
S. cœrulea). For cricket bats it is of second-rate quality.

Var. ARGENTEA, *Wimmer* (S. regalis, *Hort*. ; S. splendens, *Bray*). Silver
Willow.—This is the most striking of all the forms of S. alba in the intense
silvery hue of its leaves, conspicuous in their shining whiteness at long
distances. Not so robust as the type. (See also S. cœrulea.)

S. ANGUSTIFOLIA. *Willdenow*

(S. Wilhelmsiana, *Bieberstein*)

A shrub up to 10 or 15 ft. high ; young twigs silky, slender. Leaves linea:
often bent or sickle-shaped, pointed ; 1 to 2 ins. long, $\frac{1}{12}$ to $\frac{1}{4}$ in. wide ; distant]
and finely toothed ; silky on both sides when young, becoming nearly or quit
glabrous later, scarcely or very shortly stalked. Catkins slender, about $\frac{3}{4}$ ir
long, produced in May on short leafy twigs ; stamens solitary (or rather tw
with their stalks united) ; ovary and scales slightly silky.

Native of the Caucasus and N. Asia, and very distinct in the extrem
narrowness of the leaves. The type is not common in cultivation, but nursery
men for several years past have offered a form of it under the name c
S. MICROSTACHYA, *Turczaninow* (S. angustifolia microstachya, *Andersson*).—
This has leaves not more than 1½ ins. long, or $\frac{1}{8}$ in. wide.

S. ARBUSCULA, *Linnæus*

(S. formosa, *Willdenow*)

A shrub sometimes only 1 ft. high and spreading, sometimes shaped lik
a miniature, bushy, very leafy tree thrice as high ; young shoots either glabrou
or (more rarely) silky. Leaves oval, obovate, or sometimes approachin
lanceolate, tapered at both ends, toothed or entire ; ½ to 2 ins. long, $\frac{1}{4}$ to $\frac{3}{4}$ ir
wide ; deep green above, usually glaucous or grey beneath ; stalk $\frac{1}{12}$ to $\frac{1}{4}$ in
long. Catkins slender, produced in May at the end of short leafy shoots
males about 1 in. long, females rather longer ; stamens two.

Native of Europe and Siberia, inhabiting high latitudes and mountains
including those of Scotland. It is a very variable shrub, most nearly allied t
phylicifolia, but differs in all its forms from that species in having the stal:
of the ovary much shorter than the gland or nectary (in phylicifolia the ovar
stalk is always the longer). Two chief varieties of S. Arbuscula have bee
distinguished, viz.—var. ERECTA, *Andersson*, the erect-growing dense-habite
shrub ; and var. HUMILIS, *Andersson*, the low spreading one. In genera
aspect it resembles S. Myrsinites, but that species has the leaves bright gree
on both sides. Of little garden value.

S. AURITA, *Linnæus*. ROUND-EARED WILLOW

A shrub varying in height from 1 to 6 or 7 ft., according to soil anc
situation ; young twigs slender, at first very downy, becoming glabrous th
second year. Leaves obovate, blunt or pointed at the apex, tapered at th
base ; 1 to 3 ins. long. ½ to 1¼ ins. wide ; rather indefinitely toothed ; th
upper surface dull dark green, wrinkled, and more or less woolly ; lowe
surface covered with a permanent dull grey wool ; stalk $\frac{1}{4}$ to $\frac{1}{8}$ in. long
stipules conspicuous on vigorous shoots, and mostly persisting till the fal
of the leaf. Catkins produced on the naked shoots in April ; male catkin:
stalkless, ½ to $\frac{3}{4}$ in. long ; stamens two, hairy towards the base.

Native of Europe (including Britain) and N. Asia. It belongs to th
same group as S. Caprea and cinerea, from the former of which it differs ir
being a more bushy plant with smaller, more wrinkled leaves and smalle
catkins. It is not so easily distinguished from S. cinerea, but has the year-olc
twigs glabrous (in cinerea they remain downy). S. aurita has hybridised witl
numerous other species.

S. BABYLONICA, *Linnæus*. WEEPING WILLOW (Plate 18)

(S. pendula, *Moench* ; S. Napoleonis, *Schultz*)

A tree usually 30 to 50 ft. high, the rugged trunk branching low and supporting a wide-spreading head of branches, the very slender, glabrous, terminal twigs of which hang down perpendicularly. Leaves lance-shaped, with long, slender points, finely toothed ; 3 to 4 ins. long, about ½ in. wide ; dark green above, blue-grey beneath, glabrous on both surfaces except when quite young ; stalk about ¼ in. long minutely downy. Catkins slender, the females 2 ins. long, males rather shorter, produced in April along with the young leaves. Stamens two.

Native of China, in the western provinces of which it was seen abundant in a wild state by Mr Wilson. It is not native of the region of the Euphrates, as the name babylonica would imply, but has no doubt been cultivated in E. Europe, N. Africa, and W. Asia from an early period. The words of the Psalmist (cxxxvii. 1, 2) : " By the rivers of Babylon, there we sat down, yea, we wept, when we remembered Zion. We hanged our harps upon the willows in the midst thereof," do not, as is generally believed, refer to Salix babylonica, but to a poplar—POPULUS EUPHRATICA, *Olivier*.

The weeping willow was probably first introduced to W. Europe by the French traveller Tournefort, towards the end of the seventeenth century. Peter Collinson says the original weeping willow was brought to England about 1730 by " Mr Vernon, Turkey Merchant at Aleppo, from the river Euphrates, and planted at his seat at Twickenham Park, where I saw it in 1748." There is also a story that Alexander Pope was one day in the company of Lady Suffolk, when she received a parcel from Spain tied up by willow twigs, and that, noticing one of the twigs was alive, he begged it, and planted it at Twickenham, where it grew into the celebrated weeping willow of his villa garden. This has been said to be the first Salix babylonica introduced to England, but no doubt Mr Vernon has the prior claim. For a long time only the female tree was known, and even now it is much the more common.

·S. babylonica is a popular waterside tree, and its beauty is nowhere so telling as by the side of a stream or lake. The banks of the Thames above Richmond owe much of their charm to it. An impetus to its cultivation was given about 1823 through the introduction from St Helena of weeping willows raised from a tree in that island which Napoleon had loved and under which he was buried. Numerous descendants of this tree are still scattered over the country.

Var. ANNULARIS, *Ascherson* (S. crispa, *Hort.*).—A curious form whose leaves are twisted into rings or spirally curled. It has little beauty.

S. BEBBIANA, *Sargent*. BEAK WILLOW

(S. rostrata, *Richards*, not of *Thuillier*)

A shrub, rarely a small tree, up to 25 ft. high, young shoots covered at first with grey down, becoming glabrous and dark brown. Leaves usually more or less obovate, sometimes oval or lance-shaped ; mostly tapered but sometimes rounded at the base, short-pointed ; 1 to 4 ins. long, ½ to 1 in. wide ; distantly toothed or almost entire ; dull green above, blue white and more or less downy beneath ; stalk ¼ to ½ in. long. It is a native of high latitudes in N. America, stretching right across the continent. A male plant introduced to Kew from the Arnold Arboretum has cylindrical catkins about 1 in. long ; stamens two, with glabrous stalks. It belongs to the Caprea group.

S. Bockii, *Seemen*

(Bot. Mag., t. 9079)

A dwarf shrub of neat habit, 3 to 10 ft. high; young shoots slender, covered with a dense grey down. Leaves oblong or obovate, tapered to a short stalk at the base, either rounded or pointed at the apex; margins entire or occasionally sparsely toothed, recurved; ¼ to ⅝ in. long, ⅛ to ¼ in. wide; dark bright green above, blue-white beneath and covered with silky hairs. Catkins produced in late summer and autumn from the leaf-axils of the current year's growth; females 1½ ins. long, ½ in. broad; males shorter. Stamens two, but with their stalks united to the summit (as in S. purpurea); bracts of catkins narrowly lanceolate and pointed.

A native of Western Szechuen, China, and abundant in river-beds up to 9000 ft. It was introduced to the Arnold Arboretum by Wilson by means of cuttings in 1908-9, and I saw it there in 1910. A plant then obtained for Kew was the first introduced to this country. It has flowered each October since. It is a pretty bush, the male, Mr Wilson told me, one of the most ornamental of willows in its flowers. Altogether it promises to be one of the most attractive of shrubby species. It has been confused with S. VARIEGATA, *Franchet*, a nearly allied species, which has its leaves quite glabrous by the end of the season, and whose catkin bracts are obtuse. In habit, too, it differs from S. Bockii in being prostrate or decumbent, and in a wild state is confined to the gorges of the Yangtse Kiang.

S. Boydii, *Linton*

A deciduous shrub of erect, rigid growth, up to 3 ft. high; shoots thinly downy at first. Leaves nearly orbicular to broadly obovate, up to 1 in. long and ¾ in. wide, usually more or less heart-shaped at the base, toothless, dark green, rugose and at first downy above, covered with a fine whitish wool beneath; midrib and veins prominent. Catkins ½ to ¾ in. long, ovoid; bracts obovate, silky hairy.

A hybrid between S. reticulata and probably S. lapponum, found by Dr Wm. Boyd, near Clova in the Braes of Angus, Forfarshire. The original plant, now over fifty years old, grows in Miss Boyd's garden near Melrose, and is about 3 ft. high.

S. CÆSIA, *Villars*. ALPINE GREY WILLOW

(S. myrtilloides, *Willdenow*, not of *Linnæus*)

A shrub of low straggling habit, 2 to 4 ft. high, very leafy, with glabrous dark brown young branches; buds glabrous, yellow. Leaves oval or obovate, tapered at the base, pointed (often abruptly) at the apex, sometimes wavy but not toothed at the margin; ¾ to 1⅓ ins. long, ⅛ to ¾ in. wide; perfectly glabrous on both surfaces, bluish beneath; stalks ⅛ in. or less long. Catkins produced in April and May at the end of short leafy shoots, each ½ to ¾ in. long. Stamens two, their stalks united by about half their length. Ovary stalkless, downy.

Native of the Alps of Central Europe; introduced in 1824. It is met with in gardens usually as "S. Zabelii pendula," being grafted on standards, and in that way transformed into a small weeping tree—pretty, but, as treated in this way, usually short-lived. It is allied to S. purpurea, especially in the connected stamens.

S. CANDIDA, *Fluegge*. SAGE WILLOW

A shrub up to 4 or 5 ft. high, the young shoots covered with a close white
wool. Leaves linear to narrow-oblong, tapered at both ends ; $1\frac{1}{2}$ to $4\frac{1}{2}$ ins.
long, $\frac{1}{8}$ to $\frac{7}{8}$ in. wide ; upper surface wrinkled, at first white with down which
afterwards falls away, leaving it dull
green ; lower surface permanently
covered with a thick white wool ;
margins decurved, obscurely toothed
or entire ; stalk $\frac{1}{8}$ to $\frac{1}{2}$ in. long ; stipules
about as long. Catkins produced in
April, leafy or naked at the base ; males
about 1 in. long ; stamens in pairs,
their stalks glabrous, white, anthers red ;
females longer ; seed-vessels densely
covered with white wool.

Native of N. America, inhabiting
cold damp regions from Newfoundland
and Athabasca south to the United
States ; introduced in 1811. This
distinct and hardy species is worth
growing for the vivid whiteness of its
young leaves. It is the American
representative of our native S. viminalis,
from which it is easily distinguished by
the leaves being dull, not glistening and
satiny, beneath.

S. CAPREA, *Linnæus*. GOAT WILLOW, SALLOW

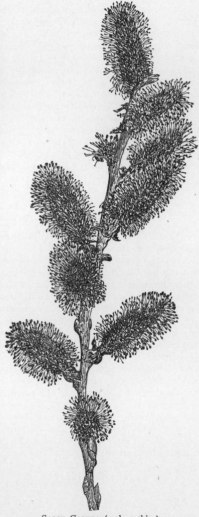

A shrub or low tree of bushy habit ;
young shoots at first grey with down,
becoming smoother. Leaves varying
in shape from roundish oval or oval
lance-shaped to obovate ; tapered,
rounded, or heart-shaped at the base ;
pointed, sometimes blunt at the apex,
toothed or entire ; $2\frac{1}{2}$ to 4 ins. long,
1 to $2\frac{1}{4}$ ins. wide ; grey-green, wrinkled
and slightly downy above ; covered
with a soft grey wool beneath ; stalk $\frac{1}{8}$ to
$\frac{3}{4}$ in. long, woolly. Catkins produced
on the naked shoots in March and
April, stalkless ; the males very silky, a
little over 1 in. long, half as thick ;
stamens two, yellow. Female catkins
ultimately 2 ins. or more long ; the seed-
vessels white with down, and stalked.

SALIX CAPREA (male catkins)

Native of Europe and N.W. Asia, and common in Britain. Flowering
branches of the male are often known in country places as " palm," and are
gathered by children the Sunday before Easter, when that day coincides
with the opening of the flowers. This willow is one of those which bear seeds

fairly freely in this country. It is often seen in hedgerows, where its yellow catkins make a cheerful display in early spring.

Var. PENDULA. Kilmarnock Willow.—Has stiffly pendulous branches.

S. CINEREA, *Linnæus*. GREY WILLOW

A willow of the Caprea or goat willow group, usually 6 to 10 ft. high, mostly shrubby, but occasionally larger and assuming the character of a small tree; the whole plant is covered with a grey down, which usually persists on the twigs through the second season. Leaves obovate or oval, tapered at the base, pointed; 2 to 3½ ins. long, ¾ to 1¾ ins. wide; entire or inconspicuously toothed; stalk up to ½ in. in length; stipules usually large. Catkins very silky, ¾ to 1¼ ins. long, ½ to ¾ in. wide; produced on the naked shoots in March and April. Stamens two, about twice as long as the silky scale; ovary silky.

Native of Europe, including Britain. This willow has much affinity with S. Caprea, but differs in its smaller, usually narrower leaves and catkins. It flowers at the same season, and its flowering twigs are gathered like those of the goat willow on Palm Sunday. Otherwise of little interest.

Var. TRICOLOR, *Dippel*.—Leaves blotched and dotted with yellow and white. Of little beauty so far as I have observed.

S. CŒRULEA, *Smith*. CRICKET-BAT WILLOW (Plate 19)

(S. alba cœrulea, *Syme*)

This fine tree, sometimes called the " blue willow," occasionally reaches a height of 100 ft., and 15 to 18 ft. in girth. It differs from the white willow in its pyramidal growth and erect branching, and by the leaves losing their silky down and becoming glabrous late in the summer, and blue-grey beneath. Only the female tree is known, and its ovaries, according to Henry, are slightly stalked, thus differing from the stalkless ones of S. alba. It is best distinguished from that species by its habit of growth, but the veins are more transparent.

The origin of this valuable willow is uncertain. It appears to be confined in a wild state to the eastern counties of England, especially Hertford, Essex, Suffolk, and Norfolk, where it has been known for over a century. Its timber is more prized by cricket-bat makers than any other, and having now become somewhat scarce, fetches seven to twelve shillings (sometimes more) per cubic foot. It grows with extraordinary rapidity in good situations (it likes a stiff, moist, but not waterlogged soil), and, raised from a cutting will, in twelve or fourteen years, attain a girth of 4 to 5 ft. Henry suggested that this willow may be a hybrid between alba and fragilis, a theory supported by the leaves becoming glabrous with age, by the slightly stalked ovary, and by the fact that, on vigorous shoots of newly rooted cuttings, the leaves are almost identical with those of fragilis.

S. CORDATA, *Muehlenberg*

A vigorous, richly leafy shrub or small tree, making long stiff shoots annually, and reaching 10 to 15 ft. high; young shoots downy at first, getting glabrous by late summer. Leaves closely set on the branch, often furnished with a pair of large ear-shaped stipules; ovate-lanceolate, rounded or heart-shaped at the base, slender pointed, finely toothed; 3 to 6 ins. long, ¾ to 1½ ins. wide; green and glabrous on both sides except the midrib, which is slightly downy above; stalk ½ to 1 in. long. Catkins up to 2 ins. long, produced on the naked wood in April, with one or a few tiny leaflike bracts at the base of each. Stamens two.

Native of N. America from New Brunswick to British Columbia and southwards; introduced in 1812. A very well-marked willow by reason of the large, long-stalked leaves with a heart-shaped base, and the conspicuous persistent stipules. Very common in its native country in different forms that vary in the comparative length and width of the leaves.

S. NICHOLSONI, *Dieck*, does not differ at all from S. cordata so far as I can see, except that the young leaves are reddish purple when young.

S. DAPHNOIDES, *Villars*. VIOLET WILLOW

A tree of erect, vigorous habit up to 40 ft. high; young shoots at first downy, becoming glabrous, and covered with a conspicuous plum-coloured bloom; twigs brittle. Leaves oval-lanceolate, tapered at both ends, but more gradually at the point, finely toothed (the teeth glandular); 1½ to 4½ ins. long, ⅜ to 1 in. wide; somewhat leathery; glabrous, dark green and glossy above, blue beneath; stalk ⅛ to ½ in. long. Catkins produced in March; males 1 to 2 ins. long, ½ to ¾ in. wide, rather striking, and resembling those of the goat willow; females more slender.

Native of Europe, eastwards to Siberia and the Himalaya. It has been found naturalised in Cleveland, Yorkshire, but is not truly British. As a willow for gardens it is worth growing for the beautiful purple or violet-coloured waxy bloom on the shoots. If the plants are cut back about every second spring the crop of young wands makes a pleasing winter effect. In the osier basket trade it is known as " Violets."

S. ACUTIFOLIA, *Willdenow* (S. violacea, *Andrews*; S. pruinosa, *Wendland*).—
Sometimes regarded as a variety only of S. daphnoides, this differs from that species chiefly in its more slender shoots, and in the narrower leaves and lance-shaped (rather than semi-cordate) stipules. The shoots are similarly covered with a fine plum-coloured bloom, and the leaves are white beneath. A native of Russia and Turkestan, not quite so striking in its pruinose young wood as S. daphnoides.

Between S. daphnoides and S. Caprea there is a hybrid—S. ERDINGERI, *Kerner*.—
It is a handsome willow with dark purplish brown shoots, and oblong-obovate leaves, up to 4 ins. long and 1 in. wide; silky when young, soon becoming nearly glabrous. It is a female, and the catkins are cylindrical, 1¼ to 1¾ ins. long, ½ in. wide, and rather effective when they appear in March.

S. DISCOLOR, *Muehlenberg*. PUSSY WILLOW

A shrub or low tree not more than 25 ft. high; young shoots purplish brown, at first downy. Leaves oblong, oval, or obovate, tapered at both ends, toothed except towards the base; 2 to 5 ins. long, ⅝ to 1¼ ins. wide; at first somewhat downy, soon becoming glabrous, bright green above, and blue-white beneath; stalk ¼ to 1 in. long. Catkins opening in March and April on the leafless shoots; males up to 1½ ins. long, cylindrical; stamens two, with glabrous stalks; female catkins up to 3 ins. long in fruit.

Native of the eastern United States and Canada; introduced in 1811. It is rather striking in its deep brown branchlets and very glaucous under-surface of the leaves.

S. FARGESII, *Burkill*. FARGES' WILLOW

A deciduous shrub, apparently 6 to 8 ft. high, of wide-spreading habit; young shoots stout, quite glabrous, brownish green, changing by the second year to a dark shining brown; winter buds bright red. Leaves elliptic to elliptic-lanceolate, pointed, tapered at the base, finely toothed ; 3 to 7 ins. long, 1¼ to 3 ins. wide ; shining dark green above, wrinkled, and at first dull green beneath and silky hairy, especially on the midrib and veins ; veins in fifteen to twenty-five pairs, deeply impressed above ; stalk ½ to ¾ in. long and of the same colour as the young shoots. Catkins erect on short, leafy, silky stalks ; the females cylindric, up to 6½ ins. long, ¼ in. in diameter, the males up to 4½ ins. long. Ovary glabrous, ovoid-cylindric ; stigmas two, bilobed ; bract oblong, rounded at the end, silky at the margin. Flowers in spring.

Native of Central China ; introduced by Wilson to the Arnold Arboretum and to Kew in 1911. This fine, handsome willow has become spread through the country under the name " hypoleuca," but the true plant to which that name belongs is a quite different shrub, by no means so striking or so distinct from willows in general as this is. S. Fargesii is remarkable for its brightly coloured winter-buds, the dark glossiness of its younger bark, the large many-veined leaves, and slender erect catkins. It is probably quite hardy in all but the most inclement parts and grows very well in Co. Meath. Good examples are in the gardens at Burford, near Dorking, and at Exbury in Hants ; there is also a very fine one in the Rectory garden at Ludgvan, near Penzance. It is well worth general cultivation. So far as I know the female plant only is in cultivation.

S. FRAGILIS, *Linnæus.* CRACK WILLOW

(S. Russelliana, *Smith* ; S. monspeliensis, *Forbes*)

A tree 80 to 90 ft. high, with a rough corrugated trunk ; branchlets growing at an angle of 60° to 90° to those from which they spring ; young shoots glabrous. Leaves narrowly lanceolate to narrowly oblong, 2 to 7 ins. long, ⅜ to 1¼ ins. wide ; tapered at the base, the apex drawn out into a long, slender point ; distinctly and regularly toothed (more coarsely in the male) ; usually somewhat silky at first, soon becoming glabrous ; stalk ¼ to ¾ ins. long. Catkins 2 to 2½ ins. long, produced in April and May on short leafy shoots. Stamens two, hairy at the extreme base only. Ovary much tapered ; fruit stalked.

Native of Europe, including Britain, and parts of N. Asia. It obtains its common name from the readiness with which the twigs snap off in their entirety at the joint when bent. It is allied to and connected by intermediate forms with S. alba, differing chiefly in the wider angle of its branching, its larger, glabrous, greener leaves, and its stalked, more elongated ovaries. It produces a useful reddish timber, used for various purposes where a wood that is tough and capable of withstanding much friction is needed. It has been used for wheelbarrows and cart bottoms. Cheap cricket-bats are also made from it ; manufacturers know it as the " open-bark " willow.

Var. BASFORDIANA (S. basfordiana, *Salter* ; S. sanguinea, *Scaling*).—A variety found by Mr Scaling of Basford, Notts, in the Ardennes about 1863. Its most distinctive character is the " brilliant orange, passing to red," of the shining bark of the twigs.

The crack willow and all the forms that belong to it make handsome bushy-headed trees.

S. DECIPIENS, *Hoffmann,* is now generally regarded as a hybrid between S. fragilis and S. triandra, although many authorities have considered it a variety of S. fragilis merely. From that species it differs in being a bush or small tree only ; it branches at a narrower angle, the twigs are not so brittle, and have a very polished, even varnished appearance the second year. Leaves smaller and broader in proportion, duller green. From the rich red bark of its branchlets it is sometimes known as " Cardinal willow " (S. cardinalis). The basket-makers know it as " Belgian Red Willow."

S. GRACILISTYLA, *Miquel*

(Bot. Mag., t. 9122 ; S. mutabilis, *Hort.*)

A bush of a spreading habit, probably not more than 6 to 10 ft. high ; young shoots covered with grey down. Leaves oblong, oval, or narrowly ovate, tapered somewhat abruptly at both ends ; 2 to 4 ins. long, $\frac{1}{2}$ to $1\frac{1}{4}$ ins. wide ; indistinctly toothed except towards the base ; grey-green above, and at first covered with appressed silky hairs which afterwards fall away except on the midrib ; rather glaucous and persistently silky beneath ; veins numerous, conspicuous, parallel ; stalk $\frac{1}{8}$ to $\frac{1}{4}$ in. long ; stipules up to $\frac{1}{3}$ in. long, persisting. Catkins produced on naked shoots in March and April ; males grey suffused with red, 1 to $1\frac{1}{2}$ ins. long ; stamens in pairs, much longer than the scale. I have not seen the female plant, but the style is long and slender.

Native of Japan and Manchuria ; introduced about 1895. It is an interesting willow, very leafy, and pretty in flower. It is distinct on account of the many-veined, characteristic leaves.

S. HASTATA, *Linnæus*. HALBERD-LEAVED WILLOW

A shrub up to 5 ft. in height ; young shoots hairy, purplish the second year. Leaves of hard texture ; ovate, oval, or obovate ; tapering, rounded or sometimes (on vigorous shoots) heart-shaped at the base ; always more or less acutely pointed, toothed ; 1 to 4 ins. long, $\frac{1}{2}$ to $2\frac{1}{4}$ ins. wide ; ordinarily quite glabrous on both surfaces ; dull green above, glaucous beneath ; veins in seven to ten pairs ; stalk $\frac{1}{8}$ to $\frac{1}{3}$ in. long ; stipules usually present, often large and conspicuous, obliquely heart-shaped. Catkins produced at the end of short leafy shoots in May ; males $1\frac{1}{2}$ ins. long, stamens two, with glabrous stalks ; females longer.

Native of the mountains of Europe and N. Asia ; introduced in 1780.

S. HERBACEA, *Linnæus*. DWARF WILLOW

A tiny shrub (the smallest of all British ones), reaching rarely more than 2 ins. above the ground (3 or 4 ins. in gardens) ; stems glabrous, or slightly silky when young, creeping and taking root and often buried in the soil. Leaves usually only two or three at the end of the twig ; round, broadly oval or obovate ; $\frac{1}{4}$ to $\frac{3}{4}$ in. long, finely round-toothed, often notched at the apex and indented at the base, glossy green on both sides and usually glabrous, sometimes slightly silky when young, prominently net-veined ; shortly but distinctly stalked. Catkins $\frac{1}{4}$ to $\frac{3}{4}$ in. long, appearing in April on short stalks. Stamens two ; seed-vessel glabrous or nearly so.

Native of the mountains of the N. Temperate zone, including those of Great Britain and Ireland. In spite of its name it is a true shrub, and makes an interesting tuft for a damp spot in the Alpine garden.

S. POLARIS, *Wahlenberg*. Polar Willow.—Very similar to S. herbacea in habit and shape of leaf ; but distinguished by the leaves being almost invariably entire and smaller on the average. The seed-vessel is also very hairy. Native of Polar regions.

S. GRAHAMII, *Borrer*, is regarded as a hybrid between herbacea and probably phylicifolia. Its leaves are oval or obovate, tapered at the base, rounded or tapered at the apex, $\frac{1}{2}$ to 1 in. long, bright green. Native of Sutherlandshire. A low, spreading shrub up to about 1 ft. in height.

S. INCANA, *Schrank*. HOARY WILLOW

(S. Elæagnos, *Scopoli*)

A shrub of dense, very leafy habit, bushy, up to 8 or 12 ft. high, half as much more in diameter ; rarely a small tree ; young shoots clothed with a fine grey felt at first, becoming glabrous later ; buds yellowish. Leaves linear, tapered at both ends ; 2 to 5 ins. long, $\frac{1}{8}$ to $\frac{3}{16}$ in. wide ; made narrower by the decurved margins ; dark green and glabrous above, covered with a blue-white felt beneath. Catkins erect, slender ; females 1 to $1\frac{1}{2}$ ins. long ; males shorter, appearing with the young leaves in April and May ; stamens two.

Native of Europe and Asia Minor ; introduced about 1820. It is one of the prettiest and most effective of bush willows in foliage. Its leaves resemble those of viminalis only they are not so coarse, or so glistening beneath. Very desirable for the banks of ponds, etc.

S. LANATA, *Linnæus*. WOOLLY WILLOW

A low, sturdy bush, 2 to 4 ft. high ; branchlets stout, furnished when young with thick, soft, grey wool. Leaves silvery on both sides, with a rich coat of silky hairs, especially at first ; oval to roundish or obovate, mostly abruptly pointed at the apex and tapered at the base, but sometimes rounded or heart-shaped ; 1 to $2\frac{1}{2}$ ins. long, $\frac{3}{4}$ to $1\frac{1}{2}$ ins. wide, nearly always entire ; stalk $\frac{1}{8}$ to $\frac{1}{4}$ in. long ; stipules up to $\frac{1}{2}$ in. long, ovate, entire, prominently veined. Catkins produced in May, often solitary at the end of the previous season's growth, of a bright golden colour ; males 1 to 2 ins. long, $\frac{1}{2}$ in. thick ; females up to 3 ins. long at the seeding stage.

Native of high latitudes in Europe and Asia ; found in Scotland in the East Grampians. It is one of the handsomest of dwarf willows, especially in spring, when the silver foliage and golden catkins are in admirable contrast. It is allied to S. Lapponum, but has broader, rounder leaves, whilst the catkins of S. Lapponum are silky white.

S. SADLERI, *Syme*, is a very distinct form of lanata, or a hybrid between that species and perhaps herbacea. It was discovered in Aberdeenshire, in August 1874, by Mr John Sadler, then of the Edinburgh Botanic Garden.

S. LAPPONUM, *Linnæus*. LAPLAND WILLOW

A shrub of spreading, much-branched habit, 2 to 4 ft. high ; young shoots dark brown, more or less downy. Leaves oval or somewhat obovate, occasionally lanceolate, tapered at both ends or sometimes rounded at the base, toothed only rarely ; 1 to 3 ins. long, $\frac{1}{8}$ to $1\frac{1}{4}$ ins. wide ; cottony above, becoming nearly or quite glabrous with age ; lower surface permanently woolly beneath, silvery white at first, ultimately grey ; stalk $\frac{1}{8}$ to $\frac{1}{3}$ in. long ; stipules inconspicuous or absent. Catkins produced on the naked shoots in April and May, very silky ; males about 1 in. long, stalkless ; females longer, shortly stalked.

Native of the high latitudes and altitudes of Europe and Siberia ; not uncommon on the Perthshire mountains, and has also been found on Helvellyn. It varies much in width of leaf, some forms found in Scotland being almost linear.

S. LASIANDRA, *Bentham*

This fine willow belongs to the same group as S. pentandra, our native bay willow, and S. lucida, and is, according to Sargent, often a tree 60 ft. high in western N. America, where it is native. It has the same dark green,

shining leaves as its allies, the glandular teeth, the conspicuous stipules on strong shoots, the glandular leaf-stalks, yellow midrib, and the five or more stamens ; but the leaf is, at first at any rate, pale or glaucous beneath and downy. In flower it is also distinguished by the scale, at the base of which the group of stamens or the ovary is attached, being toothed at the apex ; it is entire in the other two. The leaves are 4 to 5 (sometimes 6 to 7) ins. long, ½ to 1 (sometimes 1½) ins. wide.
This willow is occasionally offered by nurserymen.

S. LUCIDA, *Muehlenberg.* SHINING WILLOW

Usually a shrub, sometimes a tree up to 25 ft. in height ; young shoots glabrous, glossy ; flowering twigs downy. Leaves lance-shaped, broadly wedge-shaped or rounded at the base, with long, slender, sometimes tail-like points ; finely glandular-toothed ; 3 to 5 ins. long, ¾ to 1¼ ins. wide ; dark glossy green above, paler beneath ; stalk ¼ to ½ in. long, with several glands near the blade, downy in the groove on the upper side, and partially so up the midrib. Stipules large, roundish heart-shaped, glandular-toothed, often persistent. Catkins produced very abundantly on short, leafy twigs in April and May ; males erect, 1½ to 2½ ins. long, stamens five (sometimes three or four) ; females more slender, 2 to 3 ins. long.

Native of N. America from Newfoundland to the eastern base of the Rocky Mountains. It is a handsome-leaved willow, and the only other with which it is likely to be confused is S. pentandra—its Old World representative. S. lucida differs in having a long drawn-out point to the narrower leaf, and the net-veining is not so prominent as in S. pentandra. (See also S. lasiandra.)

S. MAGNIFICA, *Hemsley*

A small tree or shrub, from 6 to 20 ft. high, quite devoid of down in all its parts, the young shoots and conical buds purple, the former changing to red. Leaves oval or slightly obovate, entire, rounded or slightly heart-shaped at the base, the apex terminated by a short, abrupt, bluntish tip ; 4 to 8 ins. long, 3 to 5¼ ins. wide ; dull grey-green (with a bloom) above, pale and slightly glaucous beneath ; stalk ½ to 1½ ins. long, purplish. Male catkins 4 to 7 ins. long ; stamens two, four times as long as the scale ; female catkins longer, sometimes as much as 11 ins.

Native of W. China ; discovered in 1903 by Wilson in the mountains of Szechuen, at 9000 ft. altitude. It was not introduced at the time, and Mr Wilson saw only two bushes then. In 1909 he found it again, and in abundance, 20 ft. high. He sent cuttings to the Arnold Arboretum, where I saw it in 1910, and obtained it for Kew. This, I believe, was its first introduction to Europe. It is the most remarkable of all willows, and its leaves, in shape and colour, are more like those of Arbutus Menziesii than a typical willow. Leaves have been borne on cultivated plants that measure 10 ins. long, by 5¼ ins. wide ; the stalk 2 ins. long. There is every likelihood, from the altitude at which it was found, of its proving hardy. Mr Wilson informed me that in a wild state the shoots change to red the first winter, and remain that colour for several years ; also that the leaves die off a golden yellow.

S. MATSUDANA, *Koidzumi.* PEKIN WILLOW (Plate 20)

(Gardeners' Chronicle, 19th Oct. 1929, fig. 147)

A deciduous tree 40 to 50 ft. high ; young shoots at first minutely downy, slender, yellowish, changing later to brownish grey and becoming glabrous.

Leaves linear-lanceolate, slender-pointed, tapered at the base to a stalk $\frac{1}{12}$ to $\frac{1}{4}$ in. long, finely and regularly toothed (except those at the base of the shoot which are entire) ; 2 to 4 ins. long, $\frac{1}{8}$ to $\frac{2}{8}$ in. wide ; bright green above glaucous beneath and soon quite glabrous. Female flowers in cylindrical spikes about 1 in. long with a few small entire leaves at the base, main-stalk downy. The flower is stalkless in the axil of an ovate bract two-thirds as long as the ovary which is glabrous, $\frac{1}{8}$ in. long, topped by a dark stigma. Male flowers described as appearing on short cylindrical catkins about $\frac{2}{3}$ in. long main-stalk villose ; stamens two.

Native of the provinces of Chili and Kansu, China, but very generally cultivated in N. China. According to Wilson it is " planted everywhere between Pekin and Tientsin." It is said by F. N. Meyer to grow excellently everywhere on the dry lands in Northern China, where it needs no water supply beyond the scanty summer rainfall. Two female trees are growing at Kew, received from the Arnold Arboretum in 1913, to which institution it had been introduced by J. G. Jack from Korea in 1905. These trees are now over 50 ft. in height, of shapely pyramidal form and gracefully branched It is very closely akin to S. babylonica but differs botanically in the female flowers having two glands (one only in babylonica). The erect, slenderly pyramidal growth of the typical tree is also very distinct, but Schneider describes a pendulous variety (PENDULA) which is cultivated by Messrs Hillier. It is apparently the same willow as is called " S. babylonica pekinensis " by Henry The type ranks very high amongst the ornamental tree willows, and is perfectly hardy. Messrs Hillier also grow a curious variety of erect shabit, whose slender young shoots are contorted and twisted. It is called var. TORTUOSA.

S. Meyeriana, *Rostkov*

(S. cuspidata, *Schultz*)

This handsome willow is a hybrid between S. pentandra and S. fragilis, and has been found wild in Shropshire, as well as on the Continent in places inhabited by the parent species. In general appearance it very much resembles S. pentandra. The following distinctions, however, exist : the leaf is thinner, more slender, pointed, and sometimes glaucous beneath, and the tree is usually of larger size ; the male flowers have fewer (three or four) stamens, and the scale is more hairy ; the female catkins are more slender and more tapering, and the seed-vessels longer-stalked and more cylindrical. It is worth growing for its vigorous habit and its fine glossy foliage. Its leaves are oval inclined to ovate, or obovate, $1\frac{1}{2}$ to $4\frac{1}{2}$ ins. long and $\frac{1}{2}$ to $1\frac{1}{2}$ ins. wide, quite glabrous ; the marginal teeth fine, regular, glandular.

S. MOUPINENSIS, *Franchet*. MUPIN WILLOW

A deciduous shrub or small tree which Wilson found 10 to 20 ft. high ; young shoots glabrous, becoming yellowish or reddish brown ; winter buds slender, $\frac{1}{4}$ to $\frac{1}{2}$ in. long and of a similar colour. Leaves oval or obovate, broadly tapered or almost rounded at the base, abruptly pointed at the apex, finely and regularly toothed, each tooth tipped with a gland ; 2 to 5 ins. long, 1 to $2\frac{1}{4}$ ins. wide ; upper surface bright green, glabrous, with a yellowish midrib ; lower surface yellowish green, wrinkled with veins, usually more or less silky on the midrib if only when young ; stalk $\frac{1}{4}$ to $\frac{5}{8}$ in. long, glabrous or silky. Catkins very slender, the female up to 5 ins. long ; styles two bifid ; males shorter.

Native of W. Szechuen, China ; discovered by the Abbé David in 1869, later by Henry ; introduced by Wilson to the Arnold Arboretum in 1910 and thence to Kew in 1912. This willow is closely related to S Fargesii, from which Schneider chiefly distinguishes it by the style ; in Fargesii this is gradually attentuated above the ovary but in moupinensis suddenly contracts above it. The leaves of Fargesii are more silky beneath ; in moupinensis they are often quite glabrous. The young shoots of Fargesii are stouter and the winter buds larger, and, on the whole, the marginal toothing of the leaves is finer than in moupinensis. The Mupin willow is hardy and handsome as willows go, but it is not so outstanding as Farges' willow.

S. MYRSINITES, *Linnæus*. WHORTLE WILLOW

A dwarf shrub, 1 to 1½ ft. high, of bushy habit, sometimes procumbent ; young shoots slender, at first silky-hairy. Leaves roundish to narrowly oval, finely toothed, tapered at both ends, ⅓ to 1½ ins. long, ⅛ to ½ in. wide ; bright green on both sides, silky beneath when young, becoming glabrous ; veins in six to ten pairs ; stalk ⅛ in. or less long. Catkins erect, borne on short leafy shoots in May ; males cylindrical, up to 1¼ ins. long ; stamens two ; female catkins rather longer in fruit ; seed-vessels hairy.

Native of the mountains of the northern hemisphere, including the Scottish Highlands and the mountains of Sligo in Ireland. It blossoms with great freedom, and is then pretty. Among willows it has perhaps most resemblance to S. retusa, but that species has always glabrous leaves and shoots, and the parallel veins of the leaves are fewer. It much resembles Vaccinium Myrtillus in appearance, and is suitable for rock garden cultivation.

Var. JACQUINIANA, *Koch* (S. Jacquinii, *Host*), is found in the Tyrol, etc., and differs from the type in its quite entire leaves.

S. MYRTILLOIDES, *Linnæus*

A shrub from a few inches to 3 ft. high, of bushy or spreading habit ; young shoots and leaves glabrous. Leaves obovate, oblong, or sometimes ovate, rounded or tapered at the base, pointed, not toothed, but more or less decurved at the margin ; ⅓ to 1½ ins. (sometimes 2) ins. long, ⅛ to ⅞ in. wide ; dark dull green above, blue-green or purplish beneath. Catkins borne on short leafy twigs in April and May ; males ½ to ¾ in. long, narrowly cylindrical, scarcely stalked ; stamens two ; females stalked, with flowers loosely arranged ; ovary glabrous.

Native of high latitudes or altitudes in the northern hemisphere, not of Britain, but introduced in 1772. In general appearance it much resembles S. myrsinites, both strongly recalling in their foliage the common whortle-berry. S. myrsinites, however, has the young leaves quite silky beneath, and the ovary is also downy. S. cæsia is another species much resembling it in foliage, but it also is distinct in its silky ovary, and especially in its united stamens.

Var. PEDICELLARIS, *Andersson* (S. pedicellaris, *Pursh*) has narrower, longer leaves (up to 2½ ins. long), often blunt or rounded at the apex. Introduced in 1811 from eastern N. America.

S. NIGRA, *Marshall*. BLACK WILLOW

An elegant tree, 30 to 40 ft. high, occasionally much more in a wild state ; shoots yellowish, glabrous except when quite young. Leaves lanceolate or linear lanceolate, tapered or rounded at the base, narrowing gradually to a long fine point, finely and regularly toothed ; 3 to 5 ins. long, ¼ to ¾ in. wide palish green, and almost or quite glabrous on both sides except on the midrib stalk ⅛ to ¼ in. long, downy ; stipules often large, semi-heartshaped and persistent. Catkins produced on short downy shoots, furnished with small leaves in April ; 1 to 3 ins. long, slender ; stamens three to five.

Native of N. America, where it is widely spread ; introduced in 1811. It is the largest of the East American willows, but is there rather a huge bush than a tree. Sargent says it is occasionally 120 ft. high in S. Indiana and Texas. It is not so elegant a tree in this country as in the United States, although quite hardy. It has rather the aspect of a small, densely branched S. alba.

Var. FALCATA (S. falcata, *Pursh*) has curved or somewhat sickle-shaped leaves only ⅛ to ¼ in. long, green on both sides.

S. NIGRICANS, *Smith*

(S. myrsinifolia, *Salisbury* ; S. phylicifolia nigricans, *F. B. White*)

A bushy shrub, 10 to 12 ft., occasionally more high ; young shoots and buds more or less downy. Leaves extremely variable in outline (roundish, oval, ovate, obovate, or oblanceolate), pointed at the apex, rounded or tapered at the base, toothed ; 1½ to 4 ins. long, ½ to 2 ins. wide ; more or less downy, dark dull green above, bluish beneath ; stalk ¼ to ¾ in. long. Male catkins ¾ to 1¼ ins. long, ⅓ to ½ in. wide, produced in April on a short stalk furnished with a few small bracts ; stamens two, more than twice as long as the silky scale ; female catkins more slender ; ovary downy.

Native of Europe, including Britain, represented in gardens at different times by an extraordinary number of forms, varying in the shape and size of the leaves. Many of these were figured by Forbes in the *Salictum Woburnense*, but have little interest. The species is, indeed, one of the dullest and most uninteresting of hardy shrubs, and is not worth a place in the garden proper. It is seen in the seedling state oftener than most willows. Some botanists do not consider S. nigricans and S. phylicifolia as specifically distinct from each other ; S. nigricans can usually be distinguished by its thinner, larger, duller green, more downy leaves, which mostly turn black in drying.

S. PENTANDRA, *Linnæus*. BAY WILLOW

A tree 29 to 60 ft. high in gardens, often a shrub in a wild state ; twigs shining, brownish green, glabrous ; buds yellow. Leaves ovate to oval, rounded or slightly heart-shaped at the base, rather abruptly narrowed at the apex to a slender point, finely glandular toothed ; 1½ to 4½ ins. long, ¾ to 2 ins. wide ; glabrous, dark polished green above, dull and paler beneath ; midrib yellow ; stalk ¼ to ⅜ in. long, glandular near the blade. Male catkins cylindrical, about 1½ ins. long ; female catkins rather longer, both produced on leafy shoots in late May. Stamens five or more ; seed-vessels glabrous, slightly stalked.

Native of Europe (including Britain) and N. Asia. One of the handsomest of all willows in the brilliant green of its large, broad leaves, resembling those of a bay laurel. In high latitudes it is a shrub, but in moist good soil it becomes a goodly sized tree. There was one at Kew 50 ft. high and 7 ft. 8 ins. in girth but it was destroyed by the great gale of 28th March 1916.

S. PETIOLARIS, *Smith*

A shrub 6 ft. or more high, with slender twigs which are slightly silky when young, soon becoming glabrous and, later on, deep purple. Leaves narrowly lanceolate, tapered at both ends, finely and regularly toothed; 1½ to 4 ins. long, ¼ to ⅜ in. wide; silky only when quite young, soon quite glabrous, bluish beneath; stalk ¼ to ⅓ in. long. Catkins downy, produced on the naked shoots in April; males about ¾ in. long, cylindrical, stamens two; females 1 to 1½ ins. long in fruit, ¾ in. broad, the seed-vessel slenderly stalked.

Native of N. America from New Brunswick to Tennessee, inhabiting damp places. It has been cultivated in Britain since early in the nineteenth century. Used for basket making.

S. SERICEA, *Marshall*. Silky Willow.—This is sometimes made a variety of petiolaris (S. p. sericea, *Andersson*), but is no doubt distinct enough to rank as a species. It is easily distinguished by the twigs being downy, and the leaves very silky and lustrous beneath, and remaining more or less so until autumn. The leaves also are generally broader, and the seed-vessel blunter at the apex. Native of the same region.

S. PHYLICIFOLIA, *Linnæus*. TEA-LEAVED WILLOW

(S. bicolor, *Ehrhart*)

A bushy shrub, 6 to 10 ft. high; young shoots glabrous or slightly downy, shining, yellowish or brown. Leaves orbicular, oval, ovate, or obovate; slightly toothed or almost entire; ¾ to 3 ins. long, ½ to 2 ins. wide; shining green above, and either green or glaucous beneath; sometimes downy, sometimes glabrous; stalk ⅛ to ½ in. long. Catkins ¾ to 1¼ ins. long. Stamens two, thrice as long as the scale.

Native of Europe, where it is very generally spread, including Britain. Its close affinity with S. nigricans has been referred to under that species, but it is a brighter-looking, neater shrub, distinguished by the greater glossiness and smoothness of its young parts. It is not worth a place in the garden.

S. PIEROTII, *Miquel*. PIEROT'S WILLOW

(S. japonica, *Dippel*, not of *Thunberg*)

A compact, much-branched shrub, up to 6 or 8 ft. high; young shoots glabrous, or only slightly downy at first, brown and glossy; buds downy at the apex. Leaves closely set on the branch, lance-shaped, tapering at the base, slender-pointed at the apex, finely and regularly toothed; 2 to 5 ins. long, ½ to 1⅛ ins. wide; brilliant deep green and soon quite glabrous above; vivid blue-white beneath and at first somewhat silky, later glabrous; stalk ⅛ to ¼ in. long, hairy above. Catkins leafy at base, 1 to 2 ins. long; stamens solitary (really two with the stalks united right up to the anthers); ovary hairy.

Native of Japan; introduced about 1903. It is a handsome bush willow, allied to S. gracilistyla, but that species has leaves silky beneath, dull green above.

S. PURPUREA, *Linnæus*. PURPLE WILLOW

A shrub with thin, graceful branches forming a loose-habited, spreading bush, 10 to 18 ft. high under cultivation; rarely a small tree; young shoots glabrous, glossy, usually purplish where exposed to the sun, but often yellowish. Leaves linear, or narrowly oblong, mostly broadening somewhat above the middle, pointed at the apex, rounded or abruptly tapered at the base, minutely toothed towards the apex ; glabrous except when quite young, dark glossy green above, more or less blue or glaucous beneath ; $1\frac{1}{2}$ to 3 ins. long, $\frac{1}{8}$ to $\frac{1}{3}$ in. wide ; stalk about $\frac{1}{4}$ in. long. Catkins produced on the naked shoots in April, $\frac{1}{2}$ to 1 in. long, slender ; stamens solitary, but with two anthers.

Native of Britain, and reaching eastwards through Europe to Central Asia. It is a variable species, and is remarkable in having many of its leaves opposite as well as alternate. The bark is as bitter as quinine, and very rich in salicine. The twigs are very supple and tough, and much used in the manufacture of fine basketwork. The osiers known as " Red-bud," " Dicks," " Kecks," and " Welch " belong to this species. As a garden shrub it is worth growing for the sake of its loose, elegant growth and the vivid blue-white of the under-surface of the leaves. It thrives in dryish ground better than most willows.

Var. LAMBERTIANA, *Andersson*. Boyton Willow.—A variety distinguished by its larger leaves (up to 4 ins. long and $\frac{3}{4}$ in. broad) ; distinctly wider above the middle. Catkins also larger.

Var. PENDULA, *Dippel*. Weeping Purple Willow.—Grafted on standards 8 or 10 ft. high, this makes a wide-spreading head with a tangle of more or less pendulous branches. Erroneously known as " American " weeping willow. Var. scharfenbergensis, *Bolle*, does not seem to differ from pendula.

S. REPENS, *Linnæus*. CREEPING WILLOW

A low shrub of variable habit, often only 1 to $1\frac{1}{2}$ ft. high in a wild state or in poor soil, but 6 or 8 ft. high in gardens ; spreading by means of creeping or underground stems from which spring upright branches ; young shoots silky. Leaves oblong or oval to lanceolate ; normally $\frac{1}{4}$ to $\frac{3}{4}$ in. long and $\frac{1}{8}$ to $\frac{1}{3}$ in. wide, but in cultivation twice those dimensions ; tapered about equally at both ends or more gradually towards the apex ; glistening and silvery beneath, with a dense covering of silky hairs ; dull or greyish green and more or less silky above, but sometimes glabrous, especially late in the season ; stalk $\frac{1}{12}$ to $\frac{1}{6}$ in. long. Catkins produced on the naked shoots in April and May ; males $\frac{1}{2}$ to $\frac{3}{4}$ in. long, roundish oval ; stamens two.

Native of Europe (including Britain) and N. Asia. It is easily distinguished among the smaller-leaved willows by its creeping root-stock and the silvery under-surface of its leaves. Of numerous forms the best is perhaps var. ARGENTEA, *Koch*, which has both sides silvery grey. There is also a dense-habited sturdy form with leaves about $\frac{1}{3}$ in. long by $\frac{1}{8}$ in. broad, glabrous and rather glossy on the upper surface, very glaucous beneath, that makes a neat bush for the rock garden. But Salix repens is a shrub that is apt to overgrow itself, and lose much of its beauty under cultivation. It wants a moist but poor soil. It is sometimes grafted on stems of a stronger-growing willow, and made into a small weeping tree ; the var. argentea is very pretty treated this way, but short-lived.

S. RETICULATA, *Linnæus*

A low or prostrate shrub, forming large patches on the ground, but only rising from it as a rule 5 or 6 ins., rarely 12 ins. ; young branches somewhat angled, shining brown, and glabrous except at first, when they are more or less silky-hairy. Leaves mostly two to four on each twig, $\frac{1}{2}$ to $1\frac{1}{2}$ ins. long ; round, roundish oval or broadly obovate, not toothed ; slightly indented, rounded, or sometimes tapered at the apex ; deep green and much wrinkled above ; glaucous white, prominently net-veined and sometimes silky beneath ; stalk $\frac{1}{4}$ to $\frac{3}{4}$ in. long. Catkins cylindrical, $\frac{1}{2}$ to 1 in. long, produced in May and June on slender stalks 1 in. long, at the end of the twig opposite the terminal leaf. Stamens two.

Native of the mountains of Europe (including the Scottish Highlands) and Labrador. A very distinct and interesting dwarf willow, with comparatively longer leaf-stalks than any other species. Suitable for the Alpine garden.

S. RETUSA, *Linnæus*

A low, prostrate shrub, reaching only a few inches above the ground, the branches creeping and taking root ; young shoots glabrous. Leaves obovate or lozenge-shaped, $\frac{1}{3}$ to $\frac{3}{4}$ in. long, $\frac{1}{10}$ to $\frac{1}{4}$ in. wide ; tapered at the base, blunt or rounded at the apex, not toothed, quite glabrous and green on both sides ; stalk $\frac{1}{6}$ in. or less long ; nerves in three to six pairs. Catkins erect, stalked, cylindrical, about $\frac{2}{3}$ in. long, produced at the end of short, leafy shoots in May and June.

Native of the mountains of Central and E. Europe ; introduced in 1763. A neat little Alpine shrub, forming close tufts in exposed places, but spreading more freely when planted in gardens. Suitable for the rock garden.

S. SERPYLLIFOLIA, *Scopoli*, is closely allied to S. retusa, and is sometimes regarded as a variety of it. It differs chiefly in the smaller leaves, which in nature are only $\frac{1}{4}$ to $\frac{1}{3}$ in. long, forming with its stunted branches a close dense tuft. Under cultivation the plant becomes more creeping, and the leaves up to $\frac{5}{8}$ in. long. They are obovate, notched, rounded or pointed at the apex ; nerves two to four each side. Native of the Alps of Europe.

S. ROSMARINIFOLIA, *Linnæus*. ROSEMARY WILLOW

(S. Friesiana, *Andersson*)

This is a well-known name in gardens, but is usually misapplied to S. incana. The true rosmarinifolia of Linnæus appears to be a hybrid between repens and viminalis, a bushy shrub with brown, slightly downy young twigs and linear leaves, $1\frac{1}{2}$ to 3 ins. long, $\frac{1}{8}$ to $\frac{1}{4}$ in. wide, green and slightly downy above, and of a glistening silvery white beneath—very much resembling S. viminalis in this respect. S. incana differs from it in the lower surface being dull, not glistening.

There is some confusion also between rosmarinifolia and angustifolia ; the true plant of the latter name (a native of the Caucasus) is another very narrow-leaved willow, but the leaves are grey-green beneath, and almost glabrous by autumn.

Finally, a variety of S. repens (S. r. angustifolia) has also been called " rosmarinifolia." This has shorter more lance-shaped leaves than the hybrid between repens and viminalis, but in the opinion of some it is the true rosmarinifolia of Linnæus. In view of the confusion in which the name is involved, it would seem simplest to drop it altogether, and give the hybrid Andersson's name of S. FRIESIANA (see Dr F. B. White in *Journ. Linn. Soc.*, vol. xxvii., p. 391).

S. RUBRA, *Hudson*

A hybrid between S. purpurea and S. viminalis, forming a shrub or small tree ; young twigs slightly downy at first. Leaves linear-lanceolate, with long, tapered points, the base more abruptly tapered ; distantly toothed except towards the base ; 2 to $5\frac{1}{2}$ ins. long, $\frac{1}{4}$ to $\frac{2}{3}$ in. wide ; green and glabrous on both sides when mature, but grey and slightly downy beneath when young ; stalk $\frac{1}{4}$ to $\frac{1}{2}$ in. long. Catkins produced on the naked shoots in April, 1 to $1\frac{1}{2}$ ins.

long. Stamens two, but with stalks united towards the base, or sometimes nearly to the anthers.

Native of Britain and Europe, and highly valued by basket-makers. The osiers known in the trade as " Mawdesley's Long Skein " and " Tulip Willow " belong to it.

Var. FORBYANA, *Smith*.—A form of rubra (one of whose parents is probably S. purpurea Lambertiana), with wider leaves than ordinary S. rubra ; it is known in the osier trade as " Fine Basket Osier."

S. SALAMONI, *Carrière* (Plate 21)

(S. babylonica Salamoni, *Hort*.)

A hybrid between S. alba and S. babylonica, and one of the handsomest and most vigorous of all willows. It is not so weeping as babylonica, having inherited some of the firmer outlines of S. alba, but is still extremely graceful. It grows at least 60 ft. high, forming a broad shapely head of luxuriantly leafy branches ; twigs silky when young. Leaves $2\frac{1}{2}$ to 5 ins. long, $\frac{1}{2}$ to $\frac{7}{8}$ in. wide ; green above, blue-white beneath ; silky beneath on first expanding and slightly so above, but not so much so as S. alba, and soon becoming as glabrous as those of S. babylonica. It is a female tree, its flowers opening in April. The tree has been cultivated at Kew for over seventy years, and several fine specimens grow on the margins of the lake there. It first appeared on the property of Baron de Salamon at Manosque, Basses-Alpes, about ninety years ago. It deserves to be planted extensively, especially in localities too cold for S. babylonica. It retains most of its leaves until December.

The three Willows named S. ELEGANTISSIMA, *K. Koch*, S. BLANDA, *Andersson*, and S. PENDULINA, *Wender*, are hybrids between fragilis and babylonica. They are all intermediate in various degrees between the parents, having broader, usually deeper more glossy green leaves than babylonica. S. elegantissima is the tree often grown as S. babylonica on the Continent, in places where the real tree is not hardy. They are all beautiful trees, worthy, along with S. Salamoni, of attention—especially in the more inclement parts of Britain.

A few words may here be given to the various willows that have been called " S. japonica." The true S. JAPONICA, *Thunberg*, is a willow with leaves that are oval-lanceolate, often rounded at the base, very coarsely toothed except at the long, slender point, 1 to 3 ins. long, $\frac{1}{3}$ to 1 in. wide. The toothing I think would distinguish it from all the other willows in cultivation, but it does not appear to exist in this country. What is grown under the name, also as " S. japonica Lavallei," appears to be a hybrid between S. babylonica and S. alba, and has thus the same origin as S. Salamoni, but it is a male and its branching is more slender. S. japonica of *Dippel* is the same as S. Pierotii (*q.v.*).

S. SILESIACA, *Willdenow*. SILESIAN WILLOW

One of the same group as cinerea, Caprea, and aurita, to the two former of which especially it has much affinity. It is a shrub up to 6 ft. or so high, the young shoots loosely downy at first, becoming glabrous by the end of the season, thus differing from cinerea, which retains its down through the second year. Leaves obovate or oval, $1\frac{1}{2}$ to 4 ins. long, about half as wide ; downy when young, becoming glabrous above and nearly so below ; stalk $\frac{1}{4}$ to $\frac{1}{2}$ in. long. From both cinerea and Caprea it differs in its glabrous ovary. Flowers in April. Native of Europe. Of little garden interest.

S. Smithiana, *Willdenow*

A hybrid between S. viminalis and S. Caprea, or one of its group. Several slightly differing willows, probably of not identical parentage, have been included under this name, but the following description applies to the commonest in gardens. A vigorous tree up to 20 ft. with erect branches, the young ones covered with soft down. Leaves oblong-lanceolate, 3 to 6 ins. long, $\frac{5}{8}$ to $1\frac{1}{2}$ ins. wide ; sharply pointed, broadly tapered at the base, indistinctly toothed ; dark green above, glaucous and downy beneath ; stalk $\frac{1}{4}$ to $\frac{1}{2}$ in. long. Male catkins produced in March and April so abundantly as to make the male one of the handsomest of flowering willows ; they are 1 to 2 ins. long and about 1 in. wide. Stamens in pairs. Female catkins more slender. Native of Europe, including Britain.

S. sordida, *Kerner*

S. Pontederana, *Schleich*)

A hybrid between S. purpurea and cinerea, found wild on the Continent. It is a rather neat willow with downy twigs (often becoming soon glabrous.) Leaves narrowly obovate, oblong, or sometimes oval ; tapered at both ends, most abruptly at the apex, varying from almost entire to rather prominently toothed ; 1 to $2\frac{1}{2}$ ins. long, $\frac{1}{3}$ to $\frac{3}{4}$ in. wide ; dark glossy green above, conspicuously blue-white, and at first downy beneath. The influence of S. purpurea is seen in the glaucous under-surface of the leaf, and especially in the two stamens being more or less united by their stalks. Like nearly all hybrid willows, S. sordida varies in its approaches now to one parent now to another. It is at its best as a garden shrub when it most resembles S. purpurea.

S. subalpina, *Forbes*

This, a probable hybrid between S. incana and S. repens, is said by Forbes (*Salictum Woburnense*, t. 93) to have been introduced from Switzerland. It is a low shrub of rather neat habit, branches ascending, downy, and retaining their down till the second year. Leaves oblong-lanceolate, usually tapered about equally at each end ; 1 to $2\frac{1}{2}$ ins. long, $\frac{1}{4}$ to $\frac{5}{8}$ in. wide ; margins recurved ; not or very slightly toothed towards the apex, bright green and downy (especially at first) above, permanently grey and woolly beneath ; stalk $\frac{1}{8}$ in. or less long. In his original description Forbes mentions having only seen the male, and the only plants I have seen (at Kew, Cambridge, etc.) are all male. Catkins 1 to $1\frac{1}{4}$ ins. long, slender, yellow ; stamens two.

S. triandra, *Linnæus*.   Almond-leaved Willow

A shrub or small tree up to 30 ft. high, of erect habit ; young shoots glabrous or slightly downy at first, angled or furrowed. Leaves quite glabrous on both surfaces, lance-shaped, rounded or wedge-shaped at the base, sharply pointed, finely toothed ; 2 to 4 ins. long, $\frac{5}{8}$ to 1 in. wide ; green on both sides, but darker above ; stalk $\frac{1}{4}$ to $\frac{1}{2}$ in. long. Catkins produced on very short, leafy shoots in April and May ; males erect, slender, 1 to $2\frac{1}{2}$ ins. long ; stamens three, with stalks about twice as long as the scale.

Native of Europe and N. Asia, wild in Britain, also much cultivated for basket-making, etc. The osiers known under the trade names of " Black Hollander," " Black Italian," " Black Mauls," " French," " Glibskins,"

" Jelstiver," " Mottled Spaniards," " Pomeranian," all belong to this specie
or the following variety.

Var. AMYGDALINA, *Syme* (S. amygdalina, *Linnæus*), is distinguished b
having the leaves pale and glaucous instead of green beneath, but there ar
intermediate forms.

S. VIMINALIS, *Linnæus*. COMMON OSIER

An erect shrub or small tree, up to 20 ft. high ; young shoots grey wit.
fine down at first, becoming glabrous and yellowish later. Leaves rathe
erect, linear or linear-lanceolate, tapering gradually to a fine point, not toothed
4 to 10 ins. long, ¼ to ½ in. wide ; dull dark green and glabrous above, covere
beneath with a shining, silvery grey, close down ; stalk ⅛ to ½ in. long ; midri
prominent. Catkins produced on the naked wood in March and April ; u
to 1 in. long, ¾ in. wide. Stamens two, twice as long as the scale ; ovary downy
Native of Europe (including Britain), spreading eastwards to Siberia an
the Himalaya. Very common on the banks of rivers and lakes, and extensivel
cultivated in Europe for basket-making. The sorts known in the trade a
" Long Skein," " Brown Merrin," " Yellow Osier," belong to this species. I
is very distinct among the willows with long, narrow leaves in the glistening
silvery under-surface.

S. viminalis has hybridised with several other willows. The two mos
important of the hybrids—S. rubra and S. Smithiana—are noticed separately
There are also the following among many others :—

S. FERRUGINEA, *Forbes* (viminalis × cinerea).
S. FRUTICOSA, *Doell* (viminalis × aurita).
S. HIPPOPHÆFOLIA, *Thuillier* (viminalis × triandra).
S. STIPULARIS, *Smith* (viminalis × ? species).—This is one of the most distinc
and striking of this group, a very vigorous shrub, having leaves up to 7 ins. long b
1 in. wide, the down beneath very dense but less shining than in viminalis, and th
stipules much larger. The other parent is cinerea or one of its allies, but the influenc
of viminalis is most apparent.

S. VIRIDIS, *Fries*

This willow occupies a place intermediate between S. alba and S. fragilis
and may be a hybrid between them, although some authorities have regarde
alba and fragilis as extreme forms of one species. In any case, S. viridis fill
the gap between these two willows by an almost complete series of intermediat
forms, sometimes midway between them in most respects, sometimes approach
ing one of them in vegetative characters, whilst resembling the other in repro
ductive ones. What may be termed the central or typical form is a tre
branching at angles of about 60°, with leaves broader and larger than those
of S. alba, and averaging 2 to 5 ins. in length, ⅝ to 1 in. in width ; silky a
first, but soon becoming glabrous ; dark glossy green above, glaucous beneath
The male catkins are longer and more densely flowered than those of alba
and the ovaries are more distinctly stalked and have more distinctly formec
styles. The timber of S. viridis is valued by cricket-bat makers, but ordinarily
is inferior to that of S. cœrulea, being heavier and coarser, and of abou
three-fifths its money value. This refers to the typical or central form o
S. viridis ; as it approaches S. alba in relationship its value improves. By
leaves alone it is sometimes difficult to distinguish between some of the forms anc
S. cœrulea, and the influence of S. fragilis is only to be seen in the stalked, mor
tapered seed-vessels. It is never pyramidal in growth like S. cœrulea.

Native of the lowlands of Britain, where it is widely spread from the
outh and south-west counties of England to Perthshire ; also of continental
Europe. It grows 80 ft. high, and at its middle size has often a broadly
columnar habit.

S. VITELLINA, *Linnæus*. GOLDEN WILLOW
(S. alba vitellina, *Stokes*)

A tree up to 60 or 65 ft. high, with young shoots downy near the buds,
but becoming by winter glabrous and of a brilliant yellow. Leaves narrowly
lanceolate, 2 to 4 ins. long, ⅜ to ½ in. wide, tapering to a slender tail-like point,
glossy green above, glaucous beneath ; not so silky-hairy as in S. alba. The
catkins are longer and more slender than in S. alba, and the scales are longer.
According to Henry, the stamens are occasionally three to each flower.

Of doubtful, perhaps hybrid, origin, this tree is now chiefly planted in
gardens for the fine effect produced in winter by its yellow shoots ; for this
purpose it is pruned hard every spring so as to develop a low thicket of wands.
Several plants should be grouped together. It is also grown in osier beds, but
its twigs are chiefly used for tying purposes ; it is of only second or third-rate
quality for baskets. Var. BRITZENSIS, *Späth*, is a form of S. vitellina with
bright red bark. There is also a weeping form, PENDULA, *Späth*, that is very
elegant and beautiful in winter.

SALVIA. LABIATÆ

Of this very large genus of some hundreds of species, the common
sage (S. officinalis) is probably the only shrubby species that is genuinely
hardy over the British Isles. The other three species here described
are included as being successfully grown in the southern and western
maritime counties.

S. GRAHAMII, *Bentham*. GRAHAM'S SAGE
(Botanical Register, t. 1370)

An evergreen shrub up to 3 or 4 ft. high ; young shoots soft, slender,
square, downy, reddish purple. Leaves opposite, ovate, round-toothed ; ¾ to
3 ins. long, ½ to 1¼ ins. wide ; dull green and slightly downy on both surfaces ;
stalk ¼ to 1 in. long. Flowers produced mostly in pairs on terminal racemes
up to 6 ins. long, opening successively from June onwards. They are about
1 in. long, the lip of the corolla ½ to ¾ in. wide, rich red on first opening, changing
with age to magenta-purple ; the upper, hooded part of the corolla is rosy
red. Calyx tubular, ⅓ in. long, ribbed, downy, reddish above, downy below.

Native of Mexico, where it was originally found about 1830 by Mr J. G.
Graham, after whom it is named, and sent by him to the Horticultural Society's
Garden at Chiswick. It is quite hardy in the south and south-western counties,
and even at Kew will live for several years in a sheltered nook or against a
wall unless a severe winter supervenes. There is no difficulty in keeping up
a stock, as cuttings take root most freely. The most characteristic peculiarity
of the plant is the strong odour given off by the leaves when they are crushed
or rubbed. This almost exactly resembles the odour of black currant leaves.

S. GREGGII, *A. Gray*. GREGG'S SAGE
(Bot. Mag., t. 6812)

This is another Mexican sage of about the same hardiness as the preceding
species. It grows about 3 or 4 ft. high and has square, slender, drooping,

finely downy, very leafy branches bearing at the top glandular-downy, purplish stalked racemes 2 to 6 ins. long, on which the flowers are produced from Jun onwards in pairs or in threes. Lower lip of corolla carmine-red, ¾ in. wide the upper, hooded part more rosy and hairy. Calyx ⅜ in. long, two-lipped purplish, ribbed. It is well distinguished from S. Grahamii by its leaves which are narrowly oblong-lanceolate to oval and ¾ to 1½ ins. long; their odour, too is quite distinct, although slightly suggestive of black currant.

Discovered by Dr J. Gregg in 1848; first flowered in England by M Thompson of Ipswich in 1882. Perhaps scarcely as hardy as S. Grahamii.

S. INTERRUPTA, *Schousboe*. ASH-LEAVED SAGE

(Bot. Mag., t. 5860; Gardeners' Chronicle, 14th July 1923, fig. 6)

A plant with herbaceous shoots and a shrubby base, growing 2 to 3 ft. high of spreading habit; young shoots clothed with soft hairs. Leaves of variabl shape and size, usually oblong-ovate in the main with a pair of lobes at th base, or pinnate with two pairs of leaflets; on weak or flowering shoots the are simply oblong-ovate; the larger leaves are up to 7 or 8 ins. long, th smallest 1½ ins. long, the stalks varying from 4 ins. to 1 in. in length; both surfaces are wrinkled and hairy, the lower one especially; margins round toothed. The inflorescence is a tall, open panicle 2 to 4 ft. long, the flower being borne on a few branches towards the top. The whorls of flowers are 1 to 2 ins. apart with six or nine flowers in each whorl, each on a downy stall ⅛ to ¼ in. long. Corolla blue with a violet tinge, white on the throat and lowe lip; opening dark, it pales with age, 1¼ ins. long, 1 in. wide, downy; lower li three-lobed, the middle lobe notched, ¾ in. wide; upper lip hooded, compressed Calyx viscid, tubular, ½ in. long, ribbed, glandular-downy, two-lipped. Anther attached to the stalk of the stamens by a secondary curved stalk. Style slender exserted.

Native of Morocco; introduced to the Cambridge Botanic Garden in 1798 This handsome sage, which flowers from May to July, although it survive moderate winters unharmed, is not perfectly hardy. Probably for this reaso it has at times disappeared from cultivation. It is sometimes grown in pot for conservatory decoration. It likes all the sunshine it can get.

S. OFFICINALIS, *Linnæus*. SAGE

A sub-evergreen, aromatic shrub, usually 1 to 2 ft. high, but said in favour able places to become three times as high; young stems square, and onl half woody; the whole plant is covered with a short down which gives it a grey appearance. Leaves opposite, oblong, 2 to 3½ ins. long, ½ to 1 in. wide much wrinkled, round-toothed. Flowers arranged in whorls on terminal erect racemes about 6 ins. long. Corolla tubular, ¾ in. long, two-lipped purple; calyx ribbed, funnel-shaped, two-lipped, about half as long as the corolla. Perfect stamens two. Blossoms from June onwards.

Native of S. Europe; cultivated for centuries as a medicinal and culinary herb, and highly valued in former times for making "sage-beer"—supposed to possess many healing virtues. Sage is still much used for flavouring certain meats. The plant likes a sunny position, and is easily increased by cutting placed in a handlight. Although rarely seen except in the kitchen garden this plant is worth growing in a collection of old-fashioned fragrant plants like lavender, rosemary, and such like, for its crowd of erect racemes. There is a variety with white flowers (ALBA), one with stems and leaves of a reddish colour (PURPUREA), and a valueless one with variegated leaves (VARIEGATA).

SAMBUCUS. Elder. CAPRIFOLIACEÆ

About a score species of elder are known, which are widely spread
ver the temperate parts of the globe. Of these about half a dozen
hrubby ones are hardy in Britain. From the remainder of the hardy
hrubs belonging to the same family, the elders are at once distinguished
y their pinnate leaves, which have always an odd number (three to
leven) of toothed leaflets. The flowers are borne in flat, convex, or
yramidal clusters, and are very uniform in size and hue, being from
to $\frac{3}{16}$ in. across, and of some shade of white. The various parts are
ormally in fives. Fruit $\frac{1}{4}$ in. or less in diameter, globose, or nearly so,
ontaining three to five one-seeded nutlets. All the cultivated species
re deciduous, and have opposite leaves, the young shoots are soft and
ull of pith, but the wood of the trunk is hard and bony.

The elders like moisture and a loamy soil ; given these they are not
difficult to accommodate. They can be propagated by cuttings either of
eafless wood put in the open ground in early winter, or by half-ripened
oung wood with a " heel " in frames. The pruning of the sorts grown
or their foliage should be done before growth recommences. The
ollowing is a selection of the best :—

FOR FLOWERS.—S. nigra roseo fl. pl. ; S. canadensis maxima.

FOR FRUIT.—S. nigra and its var. fructu albo ; S. racemosa (where
t succeeds).

FOR COLOURED LEAVES.—S. racemosa plumosa aurea ; S. nigra
urea ; S. nigra albo-variegata.

FOR HANDSOMELY CUT LEAVES.—S. racemosa tenuifolia ; S. racemosa
erratifolia.

S. Ebulus, *Linnæus*, the British plant known as " Dane's blood " is
erbaceous.

The following hardy species are easily divided into two groups according to the
hape of the inflorescence, as follows :—

1. canadensis, cœrulea, nigra, velutina, *flowers in flat or umbrella-shaped umbels.*
2. melanocarpa, pubens, racemosa, *flowers in panicles.*

S. CANADENSIS, *Linnæus*. AMERICAN ELDER

A deciduous shrub, up to 12 ft. high, with white pith ; young branches
glabrous. Leaves pinnate, the leaflets mostly seven (but also five, nine, and
eleven), oval, oblong, or roundish ovate ; the largest $5\frac{1}{2}$ ins. long, $2\frac{1}{2}$ ins. wide ;
aper-pointed, sharply toothed, the lowest pair frequently two- or three-lobed ;
ower surface glabrous or slightly downy. Flowers in convex umbels, 4 to
8 ins. across, white, produced in July. Fruit purple-black.

Native of eastern N. America from Canada to Florida ; introduced in
1761. Nearly allied to S. nigra, it differs in the following respects : it never
assumes a tree-like form or becomes half as high as nigra ; the leaves have
normally one more pair of leaflets ; the flower clusters are more rounded and
appear four weeks later ; the fruit is not absolutely black. I have seen it
making a very pleasing picture growing by the side of a stream in the Arnold
Arboretum, Mass., flowering in July, but it is not so good in this country
as nigra.

Var. ACUTILOBA, *Rehder.*—A cut-leaved form analogous to the var.

laciniata of the common elder, but more graceful owing to the longer and more divided leaf, var. SAUREA, leaf golden yellow.

Var. MAXIMA, *Koehne*.—This, the best and most remarkable form of American elder in cultivation, was originally sent out under the erroneous name of " S. pubens maxima," and, unfortunately, is still grown in many places under that misleading name. It is an extraordinarily robust variety with leaves 12 to 18 ins. long : the leaflets are often eleven to each leaf, and the enormous flower clusters 10 to 18 ins. across.

S. CŒRULEA, *Rafinesque*. BLUE ELDERBERRY

(S. glauca, *Nuttall*)

A tree 13 to 30 ft. (occasionally 50 ft.) high in a wild state, but a robust shrub in this country 5 to 10 ft. high ; young shoots glabrous. Leaves 6 to 10 ins. long, glabrous; the leaflets usually five or seven, occasionally nine ovate or oval ; 2 to 6 ins. long, ½ to 2 ins. wide. Flowers yellowish white produced during June in flat umbels up to 6 or 7 ins. wide. Berries black but covered densely with a pale blue bloom.

Native of western N. America; cultivated in Paris eighty years ago, but now uncommon. It was reintroduced to Kew in 1893, and is still cultivated there. Its two most striking characteristics are its vigorous growth, which makes it even more tree-like in California than S. nigra is in Europe, its trunk being sometimes 18 ins. in diameter ; and the intensely glaucous hue of its berries. These are used as food when cooked, in California. Nearly allied to S. cœrulea and sometimes regarded as a variety of it is

S. VELUTINA, *Durand*, which differs in having the leaves, young shoots, and flower stems thickly clothed with grey velvety down. It has been cultivated in France and England as " S. californica."

S. MELANOCARPA, *A. Gray*

A deciduous shrub, 6 to 12 ft. high, allied to S. pubens and S. racemosa having its flowers and fruits in panicles as in those species, but the panicle are usually broader in proportion to their height. The berries, moreover, are not red but black, and without bloom. Leaflets five or seven (sometimes nine), their chief veins and midrib more or less downy beneath when young but not so downy as S. pubens. Native of western N. America ; introduced to Kew in 1894.

S. NIGRA, *Linnæus*. COMMON ELDER

A deciduous shrub, 15 to 20 ft. high, or a small tree 30 ft. or more high young branches glabrous. Leaves pinnate, 4 to 12 ins. long, composed of three, five, or seven (usually five) leaflets, which are ovate, 1½ to 5 ins. long ¾ to 2 ins. wide ; sharply toothed, glabrous except for a few hairs beneath Flowers yellowish or dull white, with a heavy odour, produced during June in flat umbels 5 to 8 ins. across, each umbel composed of four or five main divisions which are again several times divided. Berries globose, shining black, ¼ in. wide, ripe in September.

Native of Europe (including Britain). One of the best known of native shrubs, and to be regarded more often as a weed in gardens than anything else. Still, the elder, when made to assume the tree form by restricting it to one stem for 6 or 8 ft. up, is not without a certain quaintness and charm Its trunk is rough and crooked, and carries a large rounded head of richly

afy branches, laden with flower in June and with fruit in September. The
:eds are spread by birds, and young elder plants spring up everywhere in
oods, tall shrubberies, etc. In the neighbourhood of more important plants
ˌey must be rigorously pulled up. The species is chiefly represented in
ardens by the numerous varieties that have sprung from it, some of which
:e mentioned below as worth cultivating. The type itself may be left to
ırnish out-of-the-way damp, dark corners, where little else will live.

No plant holds (or perhaps it is safer to say, used to hold) a more
onoured place in domestic pharmacy than the elder. From its berries is
repared, by boiling with sugar, a wine or syrup which, diluted with hot water,
, a favourite beverage in rural districts. It is usually taken just before bedtime
nd is considered a useful remedy for colds, chills, etc.

A large number of varieties have been obtained under cultivation, of which
ˌe following only need be mentioned as the most distinct :—

Var. ALBO-VARIEGATA.—A handsomely variegated shrub whose leaves are
ˌordered with creamy white. Var. AUREO-VARIEGATA is similarly marked
·ith yellow.

Var. AUREA. Golden Elder.—A good yellow-leaved shrub. Useful for
roducing a broad patch of colour ; may be pruned back every spring.

Var. FRUCTU-ALBO (viridis).—The wine made from the greenish white
ˌuits is clear. Also known as " leucocarpa " and " chlorocarpa."

Var. HETEROPHYLLA (linearis).—In this form the blade of many leaflets
ˌ reduced to thread-like proportions, consisting of little more than the stalk
ˌnd midrib. Others are ⅛ to ¾ in. wide, but distorted and shapeless. A curiosity
ˌnly.

Var. LACINIATA. Parsley-leaved Elder.—The handsomest cut-leaved
ˌariety of common elder, the leaflets being pinnately divided into linear
ˌointed lobes. There is also a variegated form of this.

Var. PENDULA.—A weeping form with stiff, pendulous branches.

Var. PLENA.—Flowers with a double row of petals ; ROSEO-PLENA is the
ˌame with rosy coloured flowers.

Var. PYRAMIDALIS.—A stiffly erect, inelegant form.

Var. ROTUNDIFOLIA.—Leaves often with only three leaflets, proportionately
roader, smaller and rounder than the type.

S. PUBENS, *Michaux*. RED-BERRIED AMERICAN ELDER

(S. racemosa pubescens, *Dippel*)

This species, which is found wild over a considerable area in N. America,
ˌn both the eastern and western sides, is so closely allied to the Old World
ˌ. racemosa, that many authors do not separate them. The American shrub
ˌ distinguished by its young shoots, leaves, and flower-stalks being downy, the
ˌith being brown, and the fruit-panicles not so densely packed with berries.

On Vancouver Island, British Columbia, where the typical S. pubens
ˌakes a grand display in partially cleared woods, with its red fruits, a variety
ˌith golden yellow berries is found, var. XANTHOCARPA. A variety with white
ˌruits (LEUCOCARPA) is also known.

S. RACEMOSA, *Linnæus*. RED-BERRIED ELDER

A deciduous shrub, 8 to 12 ft. high, and as much through ; young bark
ˌlabrous, pith white. Leaves pinnate, 6 to 9 ins. long, composed of five
ˌeaflets, which are oval or ovate, 2 to 4 ins. long, ¾ to 1¾ ins. wide ; taper-
ˌointed, sharply and regularly toothed, glabrous on both surfaces. Flowers

produced during April in terminal pyramidal panicles 1½ to 3 ins. hig
scarcely so much wide ; yellowish white. Berries scarlet ; ripe in June an
July ; packed tightly in panicles.

Native of Europe, Asia Minor, Siberia, and W. Asia ; cultivated in Englan
since the sixteenth century. This very beautiful-fruited shrub is on
occasionally seen in perfection in this country, although it grows well an
flowers abundantly. It fruits admirably near Paris, and those who have visite
the upland valleys of Switzerland in July will have marked its great beau
there. Whilst not a native of Britain it has established itself in a remarkabl
way in Scotland. On the slopes of the hills bordering the Tweed in one are
at least, above Peebles, it occurs in broad masses. It evidently likes cool moi
conditions and on the hot dry soil of Kew it bears fruit very sparsely. Bu
if we are denied too frequently its attractive fruits, it has on the other han
sported into a number of coloured and cut-leaved forms, which are among
the best of their particular class, and thrive well. The names and averag
characters of the cut-leaved forms are given below, but they run so much int
each other that no strict distinctions can be drawn between them. Var. plumos
is the least divided, var. tenuifolia the most divided ; the rest are intermediat

Var. LACINIATA.—Leaflets deeply and pinnately lobed ; the lobes linea
pointed, not more than $\frac{1}{12}$ in. wide.

Var. PLUMOSA.—Leaflets up to 5 ins. long and 1¼ ins. wide, the teet
reaching half-way to the midrib. Var. PLUMOSA AUREA, sent out by Messi
Wezelenburg in 1895, is a wholly golden yellow form of this variety, and on
of the most attractive of golden-leaved shrubs.

Var. PURPUREA, *Sweet*.—Petals rose-coloured on the back.

Var. SERRATIFOLIA, var. ORNATA, and var. PTERIDIFOLIA are all inte
mediate in manner of leaf-cutting between laciniata and plumosa.

Var. SPECTABILIS.—Flowers nearly pure white.

Var. TENUIFOLIA.—Leaflets divided quite to the midrib into long narro
segments, often doubly pinnate. A very handsome and graceful shrub wit
fern-like foliage.

SANTOLINA. COMPOSITÆ

Two or three species of Santolina are not uncommon in cultivation
They are plants with semi-woody stems, strong-scented when crushed
and with yellow flower-heads composed of very numerous small florets
and without the ray florets common to so many plants of this Order
They are of very easy cultivation, growing best in full sun in any soi
that is well drained and not too rich. Cuttings taken about July, pu
in pots of sandy soil and placed in heat, root in a few days. Both of then
are seen at their best in a comparatively young state, and are apt t
become shabby with age. S. Chamæcyparissus is valuable for plantin
in masses on the front of a shrubbery, both for its whiteness and for it
abundant blossom.

S. CHAMÆCYPARISSUS, *Linnæus*. LAVENDER COTTON
(S. incana, *Lamarck*)

A white bush, 1 to 2 ft. high in this country, forming a close, leafy mass
foliage persistent ; stems semi-woody, covered the first season with a thicl
white felt. Leaves alternate, very crowded on the shoots, the largest 1 t
1½ ins. long, with clusters of shorter ones in their axils ; all very narrov
(⅛ in. or less wide), and furnished with thick teeth or projections set in row
of about four. The whole leaf is clothed with a white felt. Flower-head

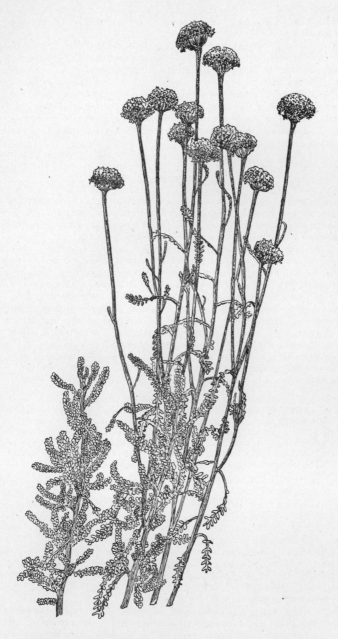

SANTOLINA CHAMÆCYPARISSUS

bright yellow, $\frac{1}{2}$ to $\frac{3}{4}$ in. across, hemispherical, solitary at the end of an erect, slender stalk 4 to 6 ins. long, terminating short lateral twigs of the year. There are no ray-florets.

Native of the Mediterranean region; cultivated in Britain since the middle of the sixteenth century. It is a beautiful and interesting plant, probably the whitest of all hardy shrubs, and bears its showy flower-heads in July so thickly that they almost touch. The plant has a rather agreeable odour when lightly rubbed, but this becomes too strong and acrid to be wholly pleasant when the leaves are crushed. Formerly used in medicine as a vermifuge. The leaf has a curious structure suggestive of the stems of some lycopods; it consists of a central axis on which are set, often in whorls, short, thick, blunt projections.

S. NEAPOLITANA, *Jordan*

An evergreen, rather pleasantly scented shrub 2 to $2\frac{1}{2}$ ft. high, producing a closely packed crowd of erect, slender branches covered with white felt. Leaves 1 to 2 ins. long, $\frac{1}{8}$ to $\frac{1}{4}$ in. wide, either pinnate or with leaflets superposed in four rows; the leaflets (or perhaps better termed "leaf-segments") are $\frac{1}{12}$ to $\frac{1}{4}$ in. long, cylindrical, round-ended, $\frac{1}{36}$ in. in diameter; covered with white down on the young non-flowering shoots, green and less downy on the flowering ones. Flowers bright yellow, borne in a compact, circular, cushion-shaped head, $\frac{3}{4}$ in. wide, in July, each head on a slender erect stalk 3 to 6 ins. long, from six to twelve heads being produced at or near the end of each shoot.

Native of S. Italy. This attractive shrub, often grown wrongly as "S. rosmarinifolia," differs from S. Chamæcyparissus by the longer leaves and by the longer, more slender segments of the leaf. It makes a bright display when in flower. It should be grown in full sunshine and is better in rather poor soil than in rich, the foliage being whiter and the growths sturdier and less liable to fall apart, thus leaving the centre of the plant open and unsightly. Pruned plants produce shoots which are at first quite green.

S. PINNATA, *Viviani* (S. leucantha, *Bertoloni*).—This is one of the less ornamental species in cultivation, from all of which it is distinguished by its white flowers. It is a bushy, leafy shrub $1\frac{1}{2}$ to $2\frac{1}{2}$ ft. high, glabrous or very nearly so. Leaves green, 1 to $1\frac{1}{2}$ ins. long, the segments of the leaf $\frac{1}{8}$ to $\frac{3}{16}$ in. long and arranged in two or four rows. Flowers dull white, produced in July in hemispherical heads $\frac{5}{8}$ in. wide; a single head terminates a slender, erect stalk, 4 to 6 ins. long, one to three of these being borne on a shoot. The foliage has only a slight odour. Native of Italy.

S. VIRIDIS, *Willdenow*. HOLY FLAX

(S. virens, *Miller*)

An evergreen bush about 2 ft. high; stems glabrous, green. Leaves deep green, glabrous; the largest 1 to 2 ins. long, about $\frac{1}{8}$ in. wide; very similar in structure to those of the preceding species, but with the teeth or projections more slender and pointed, and irregularly disposed round the central axis. Flower-heads yellow, $\frac{3}{4}$ in. across; produced in July singly at the end of slender, erect, glabrous stalks, 6 to 10 ins. long.

Native of S. Europe; introduced in 1727. This is not so effective and ornamental a plant as S. Chamæcyparissus, being of an ordinary green colour. Its leaves are longer and thinner, and the plant is not quite so dense in growth nor quite so hardy. The leaves emit an odour when rubbed, but it is neither so strong nor so pleasant as that of S. Chamæcyparissus.

SAPINDUS DRUMMONDII, *Hooker and Arnott.* SOAPBERRY
SAPINDACEÆ

(Sargent's Silva of N. America, tt. 76-77—as S. marginatus)

A deciduous tree up to 40 or 50 ft. high, with scaling bark ; young
shoots warted, slightly downy. Leaves alternate, pinnate, 10 to 15 ins.
long, made up of eight to eighteen leaflets which are lanceolate, slenderly
pointed, tapered and often oblique at the base, not toothed, 1½ to 3½ ins.
long, ½ to 1 in. wide, rather pale green and glabrous above, downy
beneath when young especially at the base of the midrib. Flowers
yellowish white, ⅙ in. wide, produced during June on pyramidal terminal
panicles 6 or 8 ins. long ; sepals narrowly triangular ; petals obovate,
downy inside ; stamens hairy, eight or ten. Fruit a berry about ½ in.
wide, nearly globose, described by Sargent as having a " thin, dark,
orange-coloured, semi-translucent flesh and dark brown seeds " ; the
berry ultimately turns black.

Native of the S. United States, especially towards the west. This tree
is related to Koelreuteria and Xanthoceras, from both of which it differs
in its toothless leaflets. It was introduced in 1915 and has proved quite
hardy. It is not so ornamental in flower as its two allies. The generic
and popular names refer to a detersive principle in the fruits of many
species, which enables them to be used as a substitute for soap in various
parts of tropical and warm temperate regions.

SARCOBATUS VERMICULATUS, *Torrey.* GREASE WOOD.
CHENOPODIACEÆ

(S. Maximilianii, *Nees*)

A deciduous shrub of lax habit, 6 to 9 ft. high, more in diameter,
making a dense thicket of stems, arching and spreading at the top ; twigs
angular, whitish, spine-tipped, usually glabrous. Leaves alternate,
linear ; ½ to 1½ ins. long, 1/16 to ⅛ in. wide ; grey, rather fleshy, stalkless.
Flowers small, greenish, unisexual ; males crowded in a spike ½ to 1 in.
long at the end of short lateral twigs, females appearing singly in the
axils of the lower leaves of the same twig. Neither has any beauty, but
they are interesting botanically. The male flower has neither calyx nor
corolla, the stamens, about three in number, being arranged at the
base of curious cup-like scales. The female flower is also without a
corolla, but has a calyx which persists and enlarges and ultimately
develops into a thin, papery disk, prominently veined, ¼ to ⅓ in. across,
with the seeds in the middle.

Native of the dry, alkaline, and saline regions of western N. America ;
introduced to Kew in 1896 but is no longer there. Like other shrubs
from the same regions, it thrives quite well in ordinary garden soil. It
flowers in July, but, as may be judged from the description, is of more
botanical than horticultural interest.

SARCOCOCCA. BUXACEÆ

A group of evergreen, low shrubs from E. Asia, the cultivated species coming from China and the Himalaya. They are allied to Buxus but have alternate leaves and renew their growth by stems springing directly from the ground, as in butcher's broom. Leaves shining green glabrous, and entire. Flowers unisexual, the two sexes produced on the same axillary raceme, the females at the base. They have no petals the males have four sepals and four stamens, the females four to six sepals. Fruit a fleshy berry, either egg-shaped or globose. The hardy species, all Chinese, are neat and pleasing shrubs with only a modest beauty of flower, but healthy in appearance, the flowers white, fragrant Increased easily by summer cuttings. They will thrive in any moist soil, and have a value in gardens on account of their suitability for shaded spots.

S. HOOKERIANA, *Baillon*

An evergreen shrub up to 6 ft. high, increasing by sucker growths from the base; young shoots minutely downy. Leaves narrowly lanceolate to oblong-lanceolate, slenderly pointed, wedge-shaped at the base; 2 to 3½ ins long, ½ to ¾ in. wide; bright green and quite glabrous; stalk about ¼ in. long Flowers small, fragrant, unisexual, white, crowded in the leaf-axils; styles three; fruit nearly globose, ¼ in. wide, black. Flowers in late autumn.

Native of the W. Himalaya and Afghanistan. It has been cultivated at Kew for more than eighty years past but is not very hardy out-of-doors there unless planted at the foot of a wall or some such place.

Var. DIGYNA, *Franchet.*—This is a variety from W. China, introduced in 1908 by Wilson. It is of dwarfer habit than the Himalayan type and is quite hardy. Its chief botanical distinction is in having only two styles to each flower. From S. ruscifolia it is distinct in its black fruits, that species having dark red ones.

S. HUMILIS, *Stapf*

(Bot. Mag., t. 9449)

An evergreen shrub of neat, tufted habit, 1 to 2 ft. high, stems minutely downy when young. Leaves narrowly oval, pointed, and somewhat more tapered at the apex than at the base; 1 to 3 ins. long, ⅓ to ¾ in. wide; glabrous and glossy green above, paler beneath, with a prominent nerve parallel to each margin; stalk ⅛ to ¼ in. long. Flowers in short, axillary racemes, white very fragrant, produced normally in early spring, sometimes in autumn stamens with flattened stalks, petal-like. Fruit round, ¼ in. diameter, blue black.

Native of W. China; introduced by Wilson for Messrs Veitch in 1907 It differs from ruscifolia in the narrower leaves, with a distinct marginal nerve A neat little shrub sending up new stems from the ground like a butcher's broom. Uppermost leaves often opposite. Rehder and Wilson make it a variety of Hookeriana.

S. RUSCIFOLIA, *Stapf*

(Bot. Mag., t. 9045)

An evergreen shrub, 2 to 4 ft. high; stems erect, branching towards the top, minutely downy when young. Leaves 1 to 2½ ins. long, half as wide ovate, rounded and triple-veined at the base, long and finely pointed; quite glabrous, and of a very dark lustrous green above, paler beneath ; stalk ⅛ to ¼ in. long. Flowers milk-white, fragrant, produced during the winter months in the axils of the terminal leaves. Several flowers appear in each cluster, which has a short stalk ⅓ in. or less long. Sepals four to six, about ¼ in. long ; stamens (of the male flowers) ¼ in. long. Fruit roundish, ¼ in. wide, crimson ; seeds black.

Native of Central China ; discovered by Henry near Ichang in 1887, and introduced from the same neighbourhood by Wilson for Messrs Veitch in 1901. Although its flowers possess only a very modest beauty, this little shrub, with its neat habit and dark polished leaves, is decidedly pleasing ; and as it will thrive in shady situations or under trees, it will obtain a welcome in many gardens.

S. SALIGNA, *Mueller*

(Bot. Reg., t. 1012 ; Buxus saligna, *Don* ; S. pruniformis, *Lindley*)

An evergreen shrub, 2 to 3 ft. high ; stems erect, glabrous. Leaves 3 to 5 ins. long, ½ to 1⅛ ins. wide ; narrow-lanceolate, with a long drawn-out point ; base narrowly wedge-shaped ; glabrous, glossy, with a marginal vein on each side extending all round the leaf ; stalk ¼ to ⅜ in. long. Flowers greenish white, in short axillary racemes opening in winter and spring. Berries egg-shaped, ⅓ to ½ in. long, purple.

Native of the Himalaya ; long cultivated indoors at Kew. From S. humilis and S. ruscifolia it is distinguished by the absence of down from the stems, as well as in stature and length of leaf.

SARGENTODOXA CUNEATA, *Rehder and Wilson*
SARGENTODOXACEÆ

(Bot. Mag., tt. 9111, 9112 ; Holboellia cuneata, *Oliver*)

A unisexual, twining, deciduous climber 25 ft. or more high ; young shoots glabrous. Leaves dark glossy green, alternate, glabrous, composed of three leaflets borne on a common stalk 2 to 4 ins. long. Side leaflets stalkless, obliquely ovate (or like a heart-shaped leaf halved lengthwise), pointed, up to 4½ ins. long, half as much wide ; middle leaflet obovate, oval, or lozenge-shaped, smaller than the side ones and on a stalk ½ in. long. Male flowers greenish yellow, fragrant, borne numerously in pendulous racemes 4 to 6 ins. long ; each flower has six petal-like, narrowly oblong sepals ½ in. long, ⅛ in. wide, and is borne on a stalk ½ to ¾ in. long ; stamens six. Female flowers (borne on separate plants) also in pendulous racemes up to 4 ins. long, with six similar greenish yellow, petal-like sepals, and the carpels crowded on a central cone ¼ in. high. When these carpels mature each develops into a roundish dark purplish blue " berry " ¼ in. wide, carrying a single black seed and borne on a stalk from ¼ to ½ in. long. This stalk is the elongated base of the carpel.

Native of Central China ; discovered by Henry about 1887 ; introduced by Wilson in 1907. It first flowered in this country with the late Mr C. J. Lucas at Warnham Court, Horsham, in May 1922. It may need the protection of a wall in many places. In the shape of its leaflets it is distinct from any other hardy climbing shrub except Sinofranchetia, to which it has much resemblance. It is a plant of great botanical interest, constituting in itself not only a genus but a Natural Order. Its closest affinities are with Stauntonia, Holboellia, and other genera belonging to the same section of Berberidaceæ, as that Order was defined by Bentham and Hooker. Named in honour of the late C. S. Sargent, founder of the Arnold Arboretum, Mass.

SASSAFRAS OFFICINALE, *Nees*.   SASSAFRAS.   LAURACEÆ
(Plate 22)

(S. variifolium, *Kuntze* ; Laurus Sassafras, *Linnæus*)

A deciduous tree, occasionally 70 to 90 ft. high in a wild state ; young shoots sparsely downy at first. Leaves alternate, of variable shape, mostly oval, ovate, or obovate, often with a conspicuous lobe on one or both sides, the sinus always rounded ; 3 to 7 ins. long, 2 to 4 ins. wide. tapering at the base, prominently three-veined ; glossy dark green above, pale and somewhat glaucous beneath, both sides at first downy ; stalk ½ to 1½ ins. long. Flowers greenish yellow, produced in May in downy racemes 1 to 2 ins. long, the sexes usually on separate trees. Corolla absent ; calyx ⅓ in. long and wide, with six narrowly oblong lobes. Stamens nine in the male, and perfect ; six in the female, and aborted. Fruit dark blue, roundish oval, ⅓ in. long.

Native of the eastern United States ; introduced in 1633. The whole tree is pleasingly aromatic, and has many reputed medicinal virtues. Although the Sassafras has no great beauty of flower, it is a striking and handsome tree in foliage. There are very few good specimens in this country ; the best is (or was) at Claremont, near Esher. I measured this tree in May 1910, and made it 50 ft. high, the trunk 7 ft. 2 ins. in girth at 1 ft. from the ground—a fine pyramidal specimen. It should be raised from seed, which can be obtained from American nurserymen cheaply. Although perfectly capable of withstanding severe frost, its young foliage is sometimes crippled in spring by late frost. It likes a warm, loamy soil.

S. TZUMU, *Hemsley*.—This is the only other species of Sassafras in cultivation. It is a Chinese tree, introduced from Hupeh to the Coombe Wood nursery by Wilson in 1900 ; a tree which grew at Kew was the only one known to me. As compared with the American species, it has certain small differences in the structure of the flower, the shoots and leaves are glabrous, and it is remarkably distinct in growth. The original tree at Coombe Wood made enormous, succulent, erect growths every year, perhaps 6 or 7 ft. long, with proportionately large leaves. These shoots were very much cut back in winter, but a woody trunk was gradually being formed, and a tree with age might become quite acclimatised. Leaves with the principal veins reddish ; young wood purple-spotted. The specific name is founded on the native one (" tzu-mu "). According to Henry, who discovered it, the tree grows 50 ft. high, and its timber is valued by the mountaineers where it is wild.

SATUREIA MONTANA, *Linnæus*.   WINTER SAVORY.
LABIATÆ

An evergreen shrub of bushy shape, 1 to 1½ ft. high, aromatically scented ; young shoots slender, downy. Leaves opposite, stalkless, narrowly oblanceolate or linear-oblong, pointed, tapered gradually to the

ase, not toothed; ½ to 1¼ ins. long, $\frac{1}{12}$ to ⅙ in. wide; greyish green
eneath and freely dotted with oil-glands; bristly hairy on the margins.
lowers produced during July and August in axillary racemes ½ to 1 in.
ong and in whorls towards the end of the shoot, the whole forming a
eafy panicle 3 to 6 ins. long. Corolla white to purplish, ⅜ in. long, two-
ipped; upper lip slightly notched, lower lip three-lobed. Calyx tubular,
en- to thirteen-ribbed, downy, with five awl-shaped teeth; stamens four.
  Native of S. Europe eastwards to the Caucasus; long cultivated for
ts pleasing odour and as a flavouring agent in cookery. It was also used
oy the old herbalists in affections of a flatulent nature and Gerard remarks
hat it " doth prevail marvellously against winde." It is the only hardy
hrubby species of a very large genus closely related to the thymes and
iyssop. It can be distinguished from Hyssopus when in flower by the
stamens being almost or quite enclosed in the corolla (conspicuously
exposed in the other). The most ornamental form of the species seems
to be

  Var. VARIEGATA, *Visiani* (S. variegata, *Host*), which has larger flowers
ind an especially broader lower lip to the corolla. Common in Dalmatia.

SAXEGOTHÆA CONSPICUA, *Lindley*. PRINCE ALBERT'S YEW.
TAXACEÆ
(Bot. Mag., t. 8664)

  A low, evergreen tree, sometimes 40 ft. high, with the aspect of a
small-leaved yew; habit bushy, dense, and rounded; branches drooping;
branchlets usually in whorls; bark of trunk peeling. Leaves linear or
linear-lanceolate, ½ to 1⅓ ins. long, $\frac{1}{10}$ in. wide; abruptly narrowed at the
base to a short stalk; tapered more gradually at the apex to a very fine
point; dull dark green above, with two comparatively broad, glaucous
bands of stomata beneath. Male and female flowers on the same plant;
the former in shortly stalked, cylindrical spikes ¼ in. long, produced in a
cluster near the end of the shoot. The fruit is a small cone, solitary at
the end of the twigs, globose in the main, ½ in. diameter; the scales
terminating in a broad, flattened, spine-like point.
  Native of Chile; introduced in 1849 by W. Lobb for Messrs Veitch.
Although similar to the yew, and indeed related to it, this has a very
different fruit. In fruit it differs also from Prumnopitys, which it more
closely resembles in leaf even than the yew; it can, however, be distinguished by the always pointed leaves and the much more conspicuous
lines on their under-surface. The Saxegothæa (this is the only species
known) is not of great value in gardens. Lindley observed of it that it
had " the male flowers of a podocarp, the female flowers of a Dammara,
the fruit of a juniper, the seed of a Dacrydium, and the general aspect of
a yew." Even allowing for Lindley's desire to say something striking,
this statement shows that it is a tree of remarkable interest. It was
named in honour of Prince Albert, consort of Queen Victoria. There
are trees in the south-western counties 39 to 40 ft. high, which are the
finest in the British Isles. At Kew it grows extremely slowly, and of

three plants, two were killed in February 1895, when 30° to 32° of fros
were registered. The third recovered but unfortunately has since bee
lost. Cuttings strike fairly readily in mild heat.

SCHIMA ARGENTEA, *Pritzel*. THEACEÆ
(Bot. Mag., t. 9558)

An evergreen shrub or tree found in a wild state up to 60 ft. or mor
high, but, as seen in cultivation hitherto, a spreading bush 6 ft. or mor
high and as much in width; young shoots dark purplish, minutel
downy. Leaves alternate, 3 to 5 ins. long, ¾ to 2 ins. wide, narrowl
oval-lanceolate or oblanceolate, slender-pointed, tapering to a shor
stalk, entire, rather leathery, glabrous and deep shining green above
glaucous and minutely downy beneath. Flowers solitary or rarely ii
pairs, each on a stalk ½ to 1 in. long and produced as many as nin
together from the terminal leaf-axils; they are 1 to 1½ ins. across, th
five-petalled corolla is ivory-white, camellia-like; stamens fifty to sixty
calyx five-lobed, downy and ciliate.

Native of W. China, Assam and Formosa. Collected by Henry ii
Yunnan in 1898 and freely by Forrest between 1913 and 1925. I
probably reached cultivation through him between 1917 and 1919. I
is most closely akin to Gordonia. The plant best known in cultivatior
was grown at Wisley. It grew to be 8 ft. or more high, which seeme
to justify its being regarded as hardy, but unhappily it has since died,
it is believed through cold. It will be wise to give it a sheltered place
except in the warmer counties.

SCHINUS. ANACARDIACEÆ

Under cultivation in the open air, only one, or at most two, species of
this genus are sufficiently hardy to thrive. These are evergreen shrubs,
with the shoots often becoming spine-tipped, and the leaves alternate.
Flowers very small and numerous on short racemes, yellowish or white.
Fruit a round, one-seeded drupe. The genus is most nearly allied to
Pistacia and Rhus. The species described below were long called
" Duvaua," being distinguished from Schinus proper by the simple
leaves. S. MOLLE, *Linnæus*, the so-called " pepper tree," is very
extensively cultivated in S. France, Italy, etc., where its much divided,
pinnate leaves and drooping branches make it a singularly graceful
tree, laden in autumn with beautiful clusters of red berries about the
size of small peas. It is not hardy with us. Native of S. America.

The two following species do not require a rich soil, making shorter,
hardier growth, and flowering better where it is rather poor. They do
not transplant well. Propagated by cuttings made in August, and placed
in gentle heat.

S. BONPLANDIANUS, *Marchand*
(S. dependens subintegrus, *Engler*)

This evergreen shrub has long been grown on a wall at Kew, where,
however, it was cut to the ground in the winter of 1908-9, when S. dependens
ovatus in the open was not injured. Compared with the ordinary S. dependens,

ts leaves are considerably longer and larger, being linear-oblong, from ¾ to
: ins. long, one-fourth as wide, entire or sparsely toothed. Flowers small,
: in. across, greenish white, produced in small cylindrical racemes less than
in. long during May. First introduced from Buenos Ayres by Mr Low of
Clapton, about 1830. It is probably a more northern and tender form of
5. dependens, which is very widely spread over temperate and subtropical
5. America.

S. DEPENDENS, *Ortega*

(Duvaua dependens, *De Candolle* ; Bot. Reg., t. 1573)

An evergreen shrub, up to 15 ft. high in this country, with stiff, spine-
ipped twigs. Leaves alternate, obovate, ½ to 1 in. long, rounded at the
apex, tapering to a very short stalk at the base, usually entire. Flowers very
numerous, in short axillary racemes about ½ in. long, produced in May from
he spine-tipped twigs of the previous year ; the individual flower greenish
yellow, ⅛ in. wide. Fruit in dense clusters, completely hiding the branches,
each one a dry, deep purple berry about the size of a peppercorn.

Var. OVATUS, Bot. Mag., t. 7406, as S. dependens (Duvaua ovata, *Lindley*).
—This differs from the type in its leaves being smaller, more ovate than
obovate, usually more or less toothed or even with a distinct lobe at each
side near the base.

Both these shrubs are natives of Chile, and have long been in cultivation.
Var. ovatus would appear to be the hardier of the two, and although it was
cut to the ground at Kew in February 1895, it sprang up again freely from
he base. Its flowers have no very bright colour to recommend them, but
hey are borne in such profusion that the shrub gives quite a pleasing effect.
it ascends to nearly 14,000 ft. on the mountains of Chile and Bolivia.

SCHIZANDRA. MAGNOLIACEÆ

A small genus of more or less aromatic twining shrubs, native of
N. America and E. Asia. Two hardy species have for some time been
n cultivation, and they have latterly been augmented by new ones
introduced by Wilson from China. Flowers unisexual, sepals and petals
indistinguishable, nine to twelve ; in the female flowers the carpels are
at first arranged in a head above the petals, but afterwards that part to
which they are attached elongates and bears the globose fruits in a spike.
The species here mentioned are perfectly hardy ; they like a rich
loamy soil, and can be increased by cuttings of half-ripened wood in a
mild bottom heat. The generic name, derived from the Greek, refers
to the cleft anthers of S. coccinea, an American species on which the
French traveller and botanist, Michaux, founded the genus in 1803.

S. CHINENSIS, *Baillon*

(S. japonica, *Hance* ; Maximowiczia chinensis, *Ruprecht*)

A deciduous, climbing shrub, growing 20 to 30 ft. high ; branchlets red,
round, not downy, set with wart-like lenticels. Leaves 2 to 4 ins. long, obovate
or elliptical, tapering at the base to a slender stalk, remotely toothed ; glabrous
except on the principal veins beneath when young. Flowers produced during
April and May, each on a slender stalk 1 in. long, two or three of them being

borne in a cluster at the base of the young growths ; they are pale rose-coloured
fragrant, ½ to ¾ in. across. After the female flowers are past, that portion
bearing the carpels continues to lengthen until it is 2 to 6 ins. long, and on it
the berry-like, scarlet fruits are borne on a sort of pendulous spike. These
remain on the plant during the winter.

Native of China and Japan ; introduced in 1860. Although not showy in
flower (the petals soon drop), its scarlet fruits are very handsome. The dried
wood is charmingly fragrant.

S. HENRYI, *Clarke*

(Gardeners' Chronicle, 1095, ii., fig. 55)

A deciduous, glabrous climbing shrub with twining stems, triangular when
young, each angle winged. Leaves leathery, shining, of variable shape
elliptical, ovate or cordate, pointed or rounded at the apex and sparsely toothed
3 to 4 ins. long ; stalk 1 to 2 ins. long. Flower ½ in. across, unisexual, white
borne on a stout stalk 2 ins. long. The column on which the carpels are
borne elongates after the flowers are faded and becomes fleshy, and 2 to 3 ins
long ; on this the mucilaginous berries are borne. They are eaten by the
Chinese.

Introduced by Wilson for Messrs Veitch about 1900, from W. Hupeh and
Szechuen, but discovered by Henry long previously. It is easily distinguished
from S. chinensis by the lustrous, thicker leaves and triangular branchlets
Quite hardy at Kew. It is wrongly classed as evergreen in *Hortus Veitchii*.

S. RUBRIFLORA, *Rehder and Wilson* (Plate 23)

(Bot. Mag., t. 9146 ; S. chinensis rubriflora, *Franchet* ; S. grandiflora rubriflora
Schneider)

A climbing deciduous shrub 10 to 20 ft. high ; young shoots slender
glabrous, at first reddish. Leaves mostly obovate, sometimes approaching oval
pointed, tapered at the base, toothed ; 2½ to 5 ins. long, 1½ to 2½ ins. wide
quite glabrous ; stalk ½ to 1½ ins. long. Flowers unisexual, solitary in the
leaf-axils at the base of the new shoots, 1 in. wide, deep crimson, each on a
slender, pendulous, red stalk 1 to 1½ ins. long. Sepals and petals five to seven
in all, roundish. Fruit composed of roundish red berries thickly disposed on
the terminal half of a pendulous, red, slender stalk 3 to 6 ins. long, each berry
about the size of a pea and containing two seeds.

Native of W. Szechuen, China ; discovered on Mt. Omei by E. Faber about
1887 ; introduced by Wilson in 1908. This is a handsome climber as regards
both flowers and fruit, the former hanging downwards and in the bud state
resembling ripe cherries. It is quite hardy and is now well established in
cultivation ; it can be trained on a wall or up a stout stake or pole. The fruit
which seems first to have been fully developed at Aldenham, Herts, in 1925
is ripe in September. The species was given an Award of Merit by the Royal
Horticultural Society on 22nd September 1925. Blooms in April and May.

S. SPHENANTHERA, *Rehder and Wilson*

(Bot. Mag., t. 8921)

A deciduous climber growing up to 16 ft. high, devoid of down in all its
parts ; young shoots reddish brown. Leaves 2 to 4 ins. long, obovate to ova
or roundish, tapered at the base, more or less slenderly pointed, minutely and
distantly toothed, pale green beneath ; stalk slender, ¾ to 1½ ins. long. Flower

nisexual, solitary in the lower leaf-axils of the new shoots, about ⅝ in. wide, reenish outside, orange-coloured within, pendulous on slender stalks 1 to 2 ins. ong ; sepals and petals together about nine ; male flowers with ten to fifteen amens. Fruit clusters made up of numerous scarlet berries closely packed n the terminal two or three inches of a pendent stalk, which becomes thickened : the part bearing the berries. The entire length of the fruiting stalk may be p to 6 or 8 ins. It flowers in April and May.

Native of Hupeh and Szechuen, China ; introduced by Wilson in 1907. It as flowered at Kew and Glasnevin and is quite hardy. It is easily distinguished om S. rubriflora, introduced by Wilson at the same time, by the colour of its owers and by the minute, often scarcely noticeable, toothing of the leaves. . chinensis is distinguished by having only five stamens.

Var. LANCIFOLIA, *Rehder and Wilson.*—Well distinguished by its angled oung shoots and its narrow, lanceolate, slenderly pointed leaves which are emotely toothed, 2 or 3 ins. long, 1 in. or less wide. It appears distinct enough) rank as a species.

Closely related to Schizandra Henryi is S. GLAUCESCENS, *Diels.* It has not the ngled young shoots of that species and the leaves are shorter stalked, more glaucous eneath, more tapered at the base and of thinner texture. Flowers orange-red ; uit scarlet. A deciduous climber growing 20 ft. high which flowers in May and June. ntroduced from Central China by Wilson in 1907. Another species of the same roup is

S. PUBESCENS, *Hemsley and Wilson,* easily recognised by the dense covering of hort curled hairs beneath the leaf. Wilson says its " attractive yellow flowers are icceeded by still more conspicuous orange-red fruits." He is credited with intro- ucing it in 1907, but it seems to be very uncommon.

S. NIGRA, *Maximowicz,* a native of Japan and Korea, is a glabrous climber with roadly ovate or obovate leaves 2 to 3 ins. long with stalks often nearly as long as the lade. The flowers are white and ½ in. wide, but the most distinctive feature is the lack berries ½ in. or more long attached to the terminal part of a fruit-stalk 2 to 4 ins. ong. I do not know that it is in cultivation in this country but it would no doubt be erfectly hardy. It is evidently a vigorous grower.

SCHIZOPHRAGMA.   SAXIFRAGACEÆ

Two climbing deciduous shrubs, found in China and Japan, and very early allied to Hydrangea—especially the climbing section of that genus. Leaves opposite, long-stalked. Flowers in a large terminal cyme, the entral flowers small and perfect, the outer ones sterile and reduced to one arge snowy bract borne at the end of a slender stalk. From Hydrangea, he only other genus with which it can be confused, Schizophragma liffers in the sterile flowers consisting of but one bract instead of four, nd in having the four or five styles united into one. The specialised unction of the large bracts is, no doubt, to attract insects to the nflorescence, and thereby bring about the fertilisation of the flowers. n the great majority of flowers each one does its own share in advertise- nent. Fruits top-shaped.

These two shrubs are easily cultivated. They like a good loamy soil nd plenty of moisture, and can be increased by cuttings and layers. The only other necessity is something for them to climb over, and this nay be wall, tree-trunk, or anything to which the aerial roots may ttach themselves.

S. HYDRANGEOIDES, *Siebold and Zuccarini*

(Bot. Mag., t. 8520)

A deciduous, climbing shrub, reaching 40 or more ft. high in a wild state
young stems glabrous, reddish, and furnished with aerial roots. Leave
broadly ovate, with a rounded, heart-shaped or tapering base ; 4 to 6 ins
long, 2½ to 4 ins. wide ; strongly veined, coarsely and angularly toothed, dee
green and glabrous above, but paler, rather glaucous, and with silky hair
beneath ; stalk 1 to 2 ins. long. The leaves near the inflorescence are tapere
at the base, those on sterile shoots heart-shaped. Flowers small, yellowis
white, slightly scented, produced during July in a broad, flattish, cymos
inflorescence 8 or 10 ins. across. The chief feature of the inflorescence ar
the bracts, one of which terminates each main branch of the cyme, and is heart
shaped or ovate, pale yellow, 1 to 1½ ins. long ; flower-stalks furnished with a
thin, loose down.

Native of Japan, where, along with Hydrangea petiolaris it forms a
conspicuous feature in the forests, often covering the trunks of large trees
In gardens it is rare, the plant grown under the name being almost invariabl
Hydrangea petiolaris, which it resembles in habit, but in respect to leaf an
inflorescence is quite distinct. It flowered with the late Mr Chambers a
Haslemere in 1905 for the first time, so far as I am aware, in this country. I
has since flowered in many gardens. The floral bracts are variable in siz
and shape. Distinguished from the following species by its coarsely toothe
leaves.

S. INTEGRIFOLIA, *Oliver*

(Bot. Mag., t. 8991)

A deciduous, climbing shrub of robust growth, reaching probably 40 o
more ft. in height. It produces aerial roots from the branches by which i
attaches itself like ivy to the object upon which it grows ; young stems hair
or glabrous. Leaves ovate, with a heart-shaped or rounded base, tapering t
a long fine point at the apex ; 3 to 7 ins. long, 1½ to 4½ ins. wide ; the margir
entire or sparsely set with small thin teeth ; hairy beneath on the midrib and
veins ; stalk 1 to 2½ ins. long, more or less hairy when young. Flowers
produced in a flat cyme up to 1 ft. in diameter ; the fertile flowers in the
centre each ¼ in. across, and comparatively inconspicuous. But terminating
each division of the inflorescence is the remarkable single sterile blossom
consisting only of one large white bract, narrowly ovate, up to 3½ ins. long
1¾ ins. wide, and veined like a leaf with darker lines.

Native of Central China, where it inhabits rocky cliffs ; introduced by
Wilson for Messrs Veitch in 1901. It grows well and is now well established
in cultivation and is proving to be a free-flowering climber remarkable for the
enormous white bracts accompanying the inflorescence. The stems of ou
young plants are very downy, and the down persists till the following year
but on Wilson's wild flowering specimens they are quite glabrous. Var. MOLLE
Rehder, has the undersurface of the leaves and their stalks very downy.

SCIADOPITYS VERTICILLATA, *Siebold and Zuccarini*.
UMBRELLA PINE. CONIFERÆ (Plate 24)

(Bot. Mag., t. 8050)

An evergreen tree, over 100 ft. high, with a trunk 3 to 4 ft. thick
young shoots brown, not downy. The true leaves of this tree are small
membranous, scale-like bodies, about ⅛ in. long, scattered over the lowe

art of each year's shoot, and crowded into two or three imbricating rows t the apex of the shoot. In the axils of this terminal group of true aves are borne, what, for convenience sake, we usually term leaves, ut which, nevertheless, are really " cladodes " or modified, leaf-like ranchlets. They are produced at the end of the year's shoot in whorls,

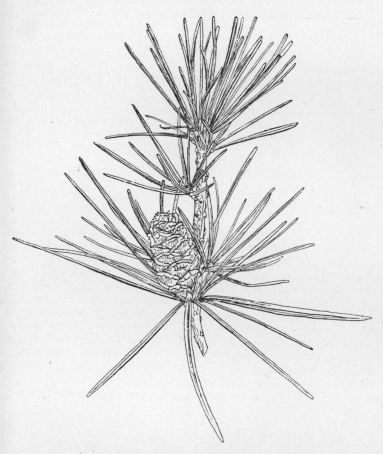

SCIADOPITYS VERTICILLATA

d are 2 to 4½ ins. long, ⅛ in. wide; slightly narrowed at top and ttom, minutely notched at the tip; dark glossy green on both sides, cept that beneath there is a whitish groove traversing the whole length. ese leaf-like organs sometimes show their true nature by branching e *Revue Horticole*, 1884, p. 16). Male flowers in a terminal raceme in. long, carrying about ten flowers, each ⅜ in. long, egg-shaped. nes 2 to 3 ins. long, 1 to 2 ins. wide, borne on a short stout stalk; les with broad reflexed margins.

Native of Japan ; introduced by John Gould Veitch in 1861. In 185
however, a single plant had been sent from Java by Lobb, that had bee
cultivated in the Buitenzorg Garden. The popular name refers to th
arrangement of the so-called leaves, which resemble the ribs of a
umbrella. This remarkable and beautiful tree " stands alone among
Coniferæ with no obvious affinities or immediate allies, and must b
conjectured to have come down to us from a remote geological past whic
has obliterated all trace of its immediate ancestors " (Thiselton-Dyer
In gardens it makes a distinct and striking shrub or small tree
pyramidal form. It should have an isolated position, and thrives in
warm, loamy soil which contains no calcareous substances and is we
enriched with decayed leaves. It is very hardy, but slow growing.

Var. PENDULA.—Sargent observes (*Forest Flora of Japan*, p. 78) th
there is a remarkable specimen with pendulous branches in the Shiba Par
Tokyo. The only plant I have seen with a similar habit in cultivation is,
was, in Gunnersbury Park.

SECURINEGA RAMIFLORA, *Mueller*. EUPHORBIACEÆ

(Geblera suffruticosa, *Fischer*)

A deciduous shrub, 3 to 5 ft. high, with erect stems and long, gracefu
slender, horizontal branches, all the parts devoid of down. Leav
alternate, oval, or slightly obovate ; $\frac{3}{4}$ to 2 ins. long, $\frac{1}{3}$ to 1 in. wide
mostly blunt or rounded at the apex, margin minutely undulated ; du
green above, pale, rather glaucous beneath ; stalk $\frac{1}{8}$ in. long. Plan
unisexual ; flowers greenish yellow, very small ($\frac{1}{10}$ in. across), produce
during August and September in the leaf-axils of the current year
growth. The male flowers are densely packed a dozen or more togethe
opening successively ; each flower on a stalk $\frac{1}{10}$ in. long ; sepals ar
stamens five. The longer-stalked female flowers are borne singly
the leaf-axils. The seed-vessel, borne on a stalk $\frac{1}{4}$ to $\frac{1}{2}$ in. long, is abo
the size of a peppercorn, three-celled, the calyx adherent at the base.
Native of N.E. Asia, including China, Manchuria, and Siberi
introduced from the last named in 1783. It is allied to Buxus ar
Andrachne ; it flowers very freely, but has little to recommend it exce
its graceful habit.

SENECIO. COMPOSITÆ

This is one of the largest genera of flowering plants and compris
over 1000 species, including the common pest of our gardens, t
groundsel. All those included in the following notes are natives
New Zealand and all (except the doubtful S. Haastii) are either shrub
or arborescent. They have alternate leaves and the flowers (or " floret
as they are usually called) are, as in all the Compositæ, crowded
" heads." The florets are usually of two kinds : those in the centre
the head, of tubular shape and known as " disk " florets ; and those
the circumference, tongue-shaped, radiating and known as " ra
florets. (The daisy is the most familiar type.) But sometimes they a

wholly discoid, as in S. elæagnifolius and S. rotundifolius. The generic name, which was used by Pliny, is derived from the Latin *senex*, an old man, and refers to usually grey, hair-like pappus of the seeds.

Provided the climate is sufficiently mild enough for them, they are of easy cultivation and succeed well in a light or sandy loam. S. compactus, Greyi, Haastii, laxifolius and rotundifolius succeed on lime or chalk, as probably do most of the others. The species are not sufficiently planted in sea-side gardens, for which places the toughness of the leathery leaves admirably fits them. Propagation is effected by late summer cuttings placed in very sandy soil and given if possible a mild bottom heat. (See Olearia for the distinction between that genus and this.)

S. COMPACTUS, *Kirk*

An evergreen shrub of compact, much branched habit, 2 to 4 ft. high, spreading twice as wide ; young shoots, under surface of leaves and flower-stalks all clothed with a pure white, dense felt. Leaves obovate or oval, rounded at the apex, tapered at the base, the lower larger ones mostly wavy at the margin, the small upper ones almost or quite entire ; they are ½ to 2 ins. long, ¼ to 1 in. wide, becoming smaller near the inflorescence ; upper surface dark dull green ; stalks ¼ to ½ in. long, felted. Flower-heads ¾ to 1 in. wide, three to ten of them forming a terminal raceme ; ray-florets about twelve, bright yellow.

Native of the North Island, New Zealand. This handsome shrub is unfortunately not quite hardy near London, but is capable of surviving moderate winters if given a sheltered nook and a slight covering during cold spells. In the south and south-west it grows admirably without protection. Its compact habit, small leaves with crinkled margins, and clusters of racemes each terminating a slender shoot of the year, renders it distinct. It flowers in January in New Zealand and in the corresponding antipodal month (July) here, remaining in bloom through August. It occurs wild on limestone. Its nearest relative is S. Monroi which has conspicuously wavy margined, narrower leaves and glandular flower-stalks.

S. ELÆAGNIFOLIUS, *Hooker fil.*

An evergreen shrub 4 to 10 ft. high in a wild state ; young shoots slightly channelled, clothed like the under surface of the leaves and the flower-stalks with a pale, buff-coloured felt. Leaves leathery, mostly oval or obovate, tapered at the base, blunt or rounded at the end ; 2 to 5 ins. long, 1 to 3½ ins. wide ; glabrous and glossy above ; stalk grooved, ½ to 1¾ ins. long. Inflorescence a terminal, pyramidal panicle 3 to 6 ins. high. Flower-heads ½ to ½ in. wide, with nine to twelve very woolly scales surrounding the base of each of them, Florets numerous, with dull white pappus-hairs ; there are no ray-florets.

Native of the North and South Islands of New Zealand, where it ascends to 4500 ft. altitude ; very abundant in some places. Botanically it is related to S. rotundifolius especially in having no ray-florets, but the leaves of that species are almost orbicular in outline and the inflorescence is shorter, often much broader and more rounded. Neither has really much beauty of flower.

Var. BUCHANANII (syn. S. Buchananii, *Armstrong*) is a form smaller in stature, with a smaller leaf (1 to 2½ ins. long) and an inflorescence often merely

a simple raceme. Leaf-stalks very stout. There were two healthy bushes o
this variety in the rock garden at Edinburgh in June 1931 ; the type is als(
hardy there.

S. GREYI, *Hooker fil.*

An evergreen shrub found up to 8 ft. high in a wild state, usually mucl
less with us ; young shoots stout and, like the under surface of the leaves an(
leaf-stalks, densely clothed with a soft white felt, giving them a texture lik
that of .chamois leather. Leaves oblong, .sometimes inclined to ovate
rounded or tapered at the base, rounded to blunt at the apex, entire ; $1\frac{1}{2}$ t(
4 ins. long, 1 to $2\frac{1}{4}$ ins. wide ; dark green and glabrous above except for th(
felted margins ; stalk $\frac{1}{2}$ to $1\frac{1}{2}$ ins. long. Panicles terminal, 4 to 6 ins. long
2 to 5 ins. wide, bearing numerous flower-heads each about 1 in. wide, th
ray-florets twelve to fifteen and of a rich clear yellow ; main and secondar(
flower-stalks glandular-downy, as are also the bracts they bear.

Native of New Zealand in the North Island. It is most closely akin t(
S. laxifolius, but in that species the narrower leaves are more tapered at th(
base and the flower-stalks and bracts are not glandular. S. Greyi is scarcel
so hardy, being a native of the northern, warmer part of New Zealand at altitude
not exceeding 1500 ft., or only half those attained by S. laxifolius in the Soutl
Island. But S. Greyi is perhaps the most beautiful of all the New Zealan(
senecios in cultivation. It gives a blaze of yellow about midsummer an(
there is often a second crop in autumn. It is admirable along the south coas(
even in places exposed to the sea. There is a fine plant 15 ft. in diameter in .
garden at Monreith in Wigtownshire.

S. HAASTII, *Hooker fil.*

The only claim this has to rank as a shrub is in its usually stout wood
root-stock. It is a low, spreading plant, keeping near the ground and sendin(
up its leaves on stalks up to 6 ins. long. The whole plant is white, due to th(
soft felt which covers its various parts. Leaves broadly ovate to orbicula(
rounded or heart-shaped at the base, obscurely round-toothed ; 2 to 5 ins
long, half to nearly as much wide ; the wool on the upper surface of the leave
sometimes wears off towards the end of the season. The flower-heads, eac.
about 1 in. wide, are borne at the top of an erect, terminal, narrow inflorescenc
12 to 15 ins. high, one to three flower-heads being carried by each of the slende
stalks which are clothed with wool and some gland-tipped hairs. The ray
florets are narrow, $\frac{1}{2}$ in. long, yellow. The basal scales of the flower-head ar
very glandular-hairy.

Native of the South Island, New Zealand. This senecio is hardy in place
approaching the south coast and is worth growing for the whiteness of it
foliage, etc.

S. HECTORI, *Buchanan*
(Bot. Mag., t. 8705)

An evergreen or semi-deciduous shrub of erect, sparingly branched, rathe
gaunt habit, growing 6 to 14 ft. high in a wild state ; young branches stou(
covered with loose wool and bases of fallen leaves. Leaves oblanceolate o
narrowly oval, tapered to a narrow, pinnately-lobed base, more abruptl
pointed at the apex, conspicuously toothed (the teeth stand out at right angle
from the leaf margin) ; 6 to 10 ins. long, half as wide ; thinly covered with gre
cottony down beneath, smooth except for minute warts above ; . stalk stou(
quite short. Inflorescence a terminal flattish or rounded corymb up to 10 ins
wide and as much high, opening with us in July. Flower-heads $1\frac{1}{2}$ to 2 ins

in diameter ; the ray-florets twelve to fourteen, pure white, linear, recurved ; the florets of the centre (disk) yellow. Flower-stalks densely glandular-downy. Native of the South Island, New Zealand ; introduced by Major A. Dorrien-Smith in 1910 and flowered by him three years later. It is a handsome species as regards blossom, although of rather ungainly habit. It is easily recognised by the size and shape of the leaves and especially by their curious lobing at the very base. It is not hardy at Kew, but Sir Herbert Maxwell had a plant 6 ft. high by 5 ft. wide in his garden at Monreith in Wigtownshire.

S. HUNTII, *Mueller*

An evergreen shrub or small tree of rounded form 6 to 20 ft. high ; young shoots clothed with glandular down, viscid, stout. Leaves stalkless, narrowly oblong or narrowly obovate, pointed or blunt at the apex, tapered towards the base, entire ; 2 to 4½ ins. long, ¾ to 1 in. wide ; downy above, felted beneath when young, becoming almost glabrous above with age and thinly rusty-downy beneath. Flower-heads very numerous and densely produced in terminal, rounded, or pyramidal panicles 3 to 5 ins. wide. Each flower-head is ½ to ¾ in. wide, with fifteen to twenty yellow ray-florets ; flower-stalks slender, glandular-hairy.

Native of the Chatham Islands, where it is described as forming a small tree handsome in its pale shining green leaves and bright yellow, copious blossoms. It is also of distinct appearance, with leaves rather resembling those of a shrubby spurge in their shape and close arrangement at the end of the branches. It is unfortunately not hardy in most parts of the country, but succeeds on the southern and western seaboards. It is at Monreith in Wigtown-shire, where it commences to flower in June. Major A. A. Dorrien-Smith collected plants in the Chatham Islands in December 1909, when it was just coming into blossom.

S. KIRKII, *Hooker fil.*

(Bot. Mag., t. 8524 ; S. glastifolius, *Hooker fil.*)

An evergreen shrub described as of erect growth in a wild state and from 5 to 12 ft. high, quite devoid of down in all its parts. Leaves very variable in shape ; linear, oblanceolate, obovate, or ovate ; 2 to 5 ins. long, ⅓ to 1½ ins. wide ; always tapered at the base, but either pointed, blunt or rounded at the end and either entire or shallowly and widely toothed ; stalk ¼ to ¾ in. long. Flower-heads produced numerously in a flattish, terminal, much branched corymb 4 to 12 ins. wide. Each flower-head is 1¼ to 2 ins. wide, with ten or less snow-white ray-florets ; disk-florets forming a circular, central, yellow mass ⅓ in. wide.

Native of the North Island, New Zealand ; common in wooded and hilly country up to 2500 ft. altitude. Cheeseman describes it as " a very remarkable and beautiful species, the flowers being so abundantly borne as to conceal the leaves, the multitude of snow-white ray-florets rendering the shrub conspicuous from afar." It was introduced to cultivation here by Major A. A. Dorrien-Smith and was flowered by him at Tresco Abbey in the Scilly Isles in April 1913. It is only in the warmest parts of our islands that it is likely to succeed.

S. LAXIFOLIUS, *J. Buchanan*

(Bot. Mag., t. 7378)

A low, evergreen shrub, 2 to 4 ft. high, of bushy habit ; young stems covered with grey down when young. Leaves alternate, 1½ to 2½ ins. long, ⅓ to 1 in. wide ; oval, lanceolate, or sometimes inclined to ovate or obovate, mostly blunt at the apex, tapering at the base, not toothed, covered above when young with a grey, cobweb-like down, afterwards nearly glabrous ; under-surface clothed with close white felt ; stalk slender, $\frac{1}{2}$ to $\frac{3}{4}$ in. long. Flower-heads 1 in. across, produced in summer in loose, terminal, broadly pyramidal panicles, 5 to 8 ins. long, 3 to 5 ins. wide. Ray-florets twelve to fifteen, golden yellow, fully spread ; disk-florets very small and numerous, forming collectively a reddish brown centre $\frac{1}{4}$ in. across.

Native of the mountains of the Nelson and Canterbury provinces of New Zealand, at 2500 to 5000 ft. It needs somewhat milder climatic conditions than those of east and middle England, and although several times tried in the open at Kew, it has never survived more than two or three winters except in specially sheltered nooks. In the slightly milder parts of the country it succeeds admirably. It is much confused with, and scarcer than, S. Greyi, but is distinguished by its larger, broader leaves, denser corymbs of flowers, and the flower-stalks and bracts are distinct in being glandular.

S. MONROI, *Hooker fil.*

(Bot. Mag., t. 8698)

An evergreen, much branched shrub up to 6 ft. high, usually less with us ; young shoots, leaf-stalks, under surface of leaves and flower-stalks all covered with a whitish felt. Leaves oblong, oval, or rather obovate, conspicuously wrinkled or wavy at the margin, rounded at the apex, tapered at the base ; $\frac{1}{2}$ to $1\frac{1}{2}$ ins. long, $\frac{1}{4}$ to $\frac{5}{8}$ in. wide ; dull green and glabrous above ; stalk $\frac{1}{4}$ to $\frac{3}{8}$ in. long. Flower-heads in terminal compound corymbs, each section carrying three to five ; the flower-head is $\frac{1}{2}$ to $\frac{3}{4}$ in. wide, carrying ten to fifteen bright yellow ray-florets ; flower-stalks long and slender, glandular-downy like the scales that surround the base of the flower-head. Flowers in July.

Native of the South Island of New Zealand, up to elevations of from 1000 to 4500 ft. The species is distinct in its wrinkled leaf-margins and glandular-downy flower-stalks, its nearest ally being S. compactus which has whitish, felted, but not glandular flower-stalks and usually only faintly wrinkled leaves. It is a handsome shrub whose inflorescences may be 4 to 6 ins. wide. No one has succeeded better with it than the late Canon Boscawen at Ludgvan Rectory, near Penzance, or Lord Wakehurst in Sussex, where there was a plant $4\frac{1}{2}$ ft. high and 9 ft. in diameter. At Kew it just misses being hardy in a sheltered nook, but survives our milder winters.

S. PERDICIOIDES, *Hooker fil.*

An evergreen shrub of bushy habit up to 6 ft. or more high ; young shoots slender, slightly ribbed. Leaves oblong or slightly obovate, rounded at the apex, tapered at the base ; numerously toothed ; 1 to 2 ins. long, less than half as wide ; dull green and glabrous ; stalk slender, up to $\frac{1}{2}$ in. long. Inflorescence a flattish or slightly rounded, terminal, erect, many branched corymb, 3 to 6 ins. wide. Flower-heads small, $\frac{3}{8}$ in. long and as much wide, funnel-shaped ray-florets two or three, bright yellow ; disk-florets four to eight.

Native of North Island, New Zealand ; discovered by Sir Joseph Banks and Solander when with Cook on his first voyage to New Zealand (1769-70) and not recorded again until found by Archdeacon Williams in 1870. It is grown by Major A. A. Dorrien-Smith at Tresco Abbey, Scilly ; at Ludgvan Rectory in Cornwall ; and Mrs Vereker, Sharpiton, S. Devon, sent it in flower to Kew in 1922. It is not likely to succeed out-of-doors except in these and similarly mild localities. It flowers during December in New Zealand

during June and July in England. Cheeseman describes it as a handsome
little shrub not closely akin to any other New Zealand species.

S. ROTUNDIFOLIUS, *Hooker fil.*

An evergreen shrub or small tree varying from 6 to 30 ft. high in a wild
state ; young shoots grooved and, like the stalks and under surface of the
leaves and the flower-stalks, clothed with a close, dense, white felt. Leaves
entire, orbicular, heart-shaped, or roundish ovate, blunt or rounded at the
apex ; the largest 5 ins. long by nearly as much wide, the smaller ones 2 to
3 ins. long ; glabrous and dark shining green above ; stalks 1 to 3½ ins. long,
stout, grooved. Flower-heads in large terminal clusters of corymbs from 5 to
10 ins. wide, each flower-head ½ in. long, ⅛ in. wide, white at the sides, yellowish
at the top without any ray-florets. The florets are erect and closely packed in
a faggot-like cluster. Flowers in June and July ; rather unpleasantly scented.

Native of the South Island, New Zealand, where it extends from sea level,
often close to the sea, up to 3500 ft. altitude. Although it has little beauty of
blossom, it is a striking plant because of the size and roundness of its shining
leathery leaves. In September 1928 there was a plant 3 ft. high and 4 ft. in
diameter, growing in an exposed position on the rock garden at Edinburgh.
In Mr Cox's garden at Glendoick, in the valley of the Tay Perthshire, a plant
was 5 ft. high in June 1931. On all but our coldest shores it ought to be a
good seaside shrub. Kirk, in his *Forest Flora of New Zealand*, observes that
its power of withstanding the fiercest gales and dashing sea spray is marvellous,
and that he had never seen a leaf torn by the action of either. (See also
S. elæagnifolius.)

SEQUOIA. CONIFERÆ

Two species of remarkable, coniferous, evergreen trees, confined in
a wild state to California and Oregon, one of them the largest of the
world's trees. They have as their nearest allies the East American
deciduous cypress (Taxodium distichum) and the Japanese Cryptomeria,
but they are not only very distinct from all other conifers, but from
each other. They are not among our hardiest trees, but still thrive well
in suitable parts of the British Isles, being seen at their best, perhaps,
in the southern half of England, planted in good soil and in well-sheltered
spots. S. sempervirens, the redwood, although in many places subject
to injury by late frosts, is, on the whole, a greater success than S. gigantea.
They should be raised from seeds only. The horrible name, " Sequoia-
dendron," has been suggested for S. gigantea.

S. GIGANTEA, *Decaisne*. BIG TREE, WELLINGTONIA

(Wellingtonia gigantea, *Lindley*, Bot. Mag., tt. 4777, 4778)

An evergreen tree, reaching ultimately from 250 to 325 ft. in height, and
forming a trunk 20 to 30 ft. through at the enlarged, buttressed base. Bark
1 to 2 ft. thick, rich brown-red, and of a fibrous texture. The head of branches
in old trees commences at 100 to 150 ft. from the ground, and consists of
comparatively short, horizontal or drooping branches. The final ramifications
of the branches are much divided, the ends forming a dense, bushy cluster
of branchlets. Leaves varying in length from ⅛ to ½ in. long, but always

more or less awl-shaped, triangular in section, tapering from the broad base (by which it is attached to, and extends down the branchlet) to a fine point. They are blue-green and always point forward, adhering for four or five years to the branchlet, which in the early stages they completely cover. Cones 1½ to 3 ins. long, 1¼ to 2 ins. wide ; seeds pale shining brown, ⅛ to ¼ in. long, flattened.

Native of the western slope of the Sierra Nevada, California, at 5000 to 8000 ft. elevation. The "big trees" appear to have first been discovered about the middle of the nineteenth century by hunters and wandering pioneers. A man named John Bidwell is credited with being the first European to see

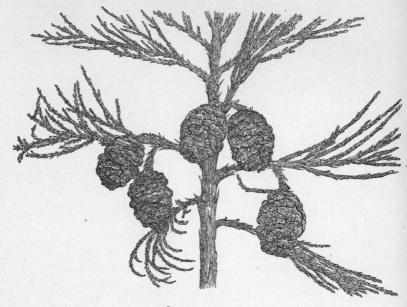

SEQUOIA GIGANTEA

them—in 1841. Seeds were first sent to England in 1853 by Mr J. D. Matthews, and by Veitch's collector, William Lobb. The news of its discovery had created an extraordinary interest over the whole civilised world, and the Wellingtonia (as it had been named by Lindley) was eagerly sought after for nearly all gardens of this country. In many places, as might be expected, it proved a failure, but in many others a great success. As a young tree and up to fifty or sixty years of age, it forms a regular pyramid, furnished to the ground with foliage. In this state it makes an imposing avenue, of which there is a fine example at Linton Park, in Kent. The average increase in height in favourable places (it likes a mild climate, good soil, and shelter) has been 1½ to 2 ft. per annum, and the annual layers of wood ½ to ¾ in. wide.

This tree is one of the marvels of the Vegetable Kingdom, and in bulk, if not in height, surpasses all other of the world's trees. Some of the giants of the Californian forests no doubt antedate the Christian era. It is gratifying to know that their relentless destruction, carried on in the early days for the sake of gain, has been stopped by the action of the State. There does not appear to be any fear of the species becoming extinct, as it is numbered by

tens of thousands even in a wild state. Still, trees between 250 and 300 ft.
high are comparatively few in number. Several varieties have appeared in
cultivation, of which the two following only need be mentioned :—
   Var. AUREA.—A golden-leaved form which originated in the Lough
nurseries, Cork, in 1856, from a seedling.
   Var. PENDULA.—An extraordinary tree with weeping branches, but an
erect leader, forming a tall slender spire. It originated at Nantes in 1863.
Perhaps the finest example known is one in the arboretum of the late Mr Allard,
at Angers in France, which is a tapering spire 65 ft. high.

S. SEMPERVIRENS, *Endlicher*. REDWOOD (Plate 25)

(Taxodium sempervirens, *Lambert*)

An evergreen tree from 200 to over 300 ft. high in nature, and already
over 100 ft. high in this country, where healthy isolated trees form slender
pyramids, furnished from base to summit with leafy branches. Bark of a
rich brown-red, and of a fibrous nature, 6 to 12 ins. thick in the giants of
western N. America ; young shoots and leaves not downy, arranged in two
opposite rows. Leaves linear $\frac{1}{4}$ to $\frac{7}{8}$ in. long, $\frac{1}{20}$ to $\frac{1}{8}$ in. wide ; terminated by
a short abrupt point, very dark lustrous green above, with two broad stripes of
white stomata beneath. On leading shoots the leaves are shorter and arranged
all round the branchlet. Cones roundish oblong, $\frac{3}{4}$ to 1 in. long, about $\frac{1}{2}$ in. wide.
   Native of California and S. Oregon in a narrow felt near the coast ; intro-
duced about 1843. Like its fellow species, S. gigantea, this is one of the
vegetable wonders of the world, having been measured 340 ft. high, and between
80 and 90 ft. in girth of trunk near the buttressed base. The average girth,
however, of big trees is 30 to 50 ft. The age of the largest trees is probably
1300 years. On the tops of adult trees, according to Jepson, the leaves become
small ($\frac{1}{4}$ to $\frac{1}{8}$ in. long), and the branchlets then much resemble those of S.
gigantea. But ordinarily the two are very distinct from each other and have
been separated generically, the branchlets of the redwood much resembling
those of the yew, but with the leaves whiter beneath. On some specimens of
redwood the branches are much less leafy than in others, and stand out as
slender, drooping, rigid arms, from the lower side of which the branchlets hang.
In its finest development in the Californian forests the redwood stands so
thickly and attains to so great a size that it yields enormous amounts of saleable
wood per acre. Jepson gives 500,000 ft., board measure, as the yield of some
limited areas, but three times as much has been recorded. The tree has the
faculty of reproducing itself by suckers from the root—they are occasionally
seen in this country—and, as frequently happens with trees of that propensity,
the germinating power of the seed is low.
   Redwood timber is highly valued for building ; it is reddish, free from
resin, and of a light soft nature ; used also for railway sleepers, shingles,
wine vats, etc. The wood employed in the building of some Californian cities
is almost entirely of this tree.
   Var. ALBO-SPICATA.—Tips of the young shoots creamy white ; leaves only
$\frac{1}{4}$ to $\frac{1}{8}$ in. long.

SHEPHERDIA. ELÆAGNACEÆ

Of the three genera constituting this natural order, Shepherdia differs
from Hippophaë and Elæagnus in its opposite leaves, and in having eight
stamens instead of four. It consists of three scaly N. American shrubs.

with male and female flowers separated on different plants, and both
inconspicuous.   There is no corolla, and the calyx is of four divisions
Fruit a berry.   Named in honour of John Shepherd, curator of the
Liverpool Botanic Garden in the early part of the nineteenth century
The third species, not mentioned below, is S. ROTUNDIFOLIA, *Parry*, an
evergreen shrub not in cultivation.

S. ARGENTEA, *Nuttall*.   BUFFALO BERRY

A deciduous shrub, 3 to 12 ft. high, with opposite, often spine-tipped
branchlets, covered when young with silvery scales.   Leaves opposite, oblong
with a rounded apex and wedge-shaped base ; ¾ to 2 ins. long, ⅛ to ⅝ in. wide
covered with silvery scales beneath, less so above.   Flowers ¼ in. across
produced in small clusters during March from the joints of the previous year's
growth ;   calyx of four oblong green segments, of little or no beauty.   Fruit
roundish egg-shaped, ⅛ to ¼ in. long, scarlet, acid but edible.

Native of the central United States and Manitoba ; introduced in 1818
As with its ally, Hippophaë rhamnoides, it is necessary to have plants of both
sexes in order to obtain fruits, but these are rarely developed in this country
There is great confusion in gardens between this shrub and Elæagnus
argentea.   The latter is often supplied for it, but is easily distinguished by
its invariably alternate, much broader leaves ;   it is also more ornamental
than the Shepherdia, which has not much to recommend it in this country.
S. argentea differs from the following species in having narrower leaves with
a silvery upper surface, and in the often thorn-tipped twigs.

S. CANADENSIS, *Nuttall*

A deciduous, unarmed shrub, up to 6 or 8 ft. high, of bushy habit ; shoots
covered with brownish scales.   Leaves ovate or oval, ½ to 2 ins. long, ¼ to
1 in. wide ;   dull dark green above, and at first furnished with silvery starry
tufts of hairs especially along the midrib and veins ;   the under-surface woolly
and specked with numerous brownish scales ;   stalk ⅛ to ¼ in. long.   Fruit
yellowish red, egg-shaped, ¼ in. long.

Native of N. America, where it is widely spread both in the United
States and Canada ; introduced in 1759, and originally named " Hippophaë "
by Linnæus.   I have seen this shrub growing wild on the cliffs of the
Genesee River gorge in New York State, between Rochester and Lake
Ontario, loaded with its beautiful reddish fruits in July; but in England
they are rarely developed.   The shrub is interesting, and the singular aspect
of the under-surface of the leaf under the lens is worth notice, the thick basis
of silvery hair-tufts being interspersed with brown scales, each scale with a
dark, glistening, eye-like centre.

SHIBATAEA.   GRAMINEÆ

Two species of bamboos, natives of Eastern Asia, with zigzagged
stems flattened between the joints and nearly solid, stem sheaths without
bristles.   The genus is named after K. Shibata, a Japanese botanist.
The following is the only species in cultivation.

S. KUMASASA, *Makino*

(Phyllostachys ruscifolia, *Nicholson* ; Bambusa ruscifolia, *Siebold*)

Stems erect, but very zigzagged, 1½ to 2½ ft. high, very much flattened between the joints, ⅛ in. diameter, the central hollow only large enough to admit a horse hair ; joints 1 to 3½ ins. apart. Branches three or four at each joint, 1 to 2½ ins. long, bearing one to three leaves. Leaves narrowly ovate, broadly tapered at the base, slenderly at the apex ; 3 to 4 ins. long, ¾ to 1 in. wide ; glossy dark green and glabrous above, slightly glaucous and downy beneath, both margins toothed ; secondary veins, five to seven each side the midrib.

Native of Japan ; cultivated by Messrs Veitch at Coombe Wood in the " seventies " of last century as " Bambusa viminalis," and probably introduced for them during the previous decade by John Gould Veitch. A pretty bamboo, being of a neat, tufted habit. It is one of the most distinct of all hardy bamboos, especially in its sturdy, zigzag stems, the great proportionate width of the leaves, their length of stalk, and the uniformly short branches. It is difficult to understand its being associated with Phyllostachys to which it has little resemblance.

SINOFRANCHETIA CHINENSIS, *Hemsley*.
LARDIZABALACEÆ

A large deciduous glabrous climber, covering trees 40 ft. or more high, and with a main stem frequently 3 or 4 ins. thick ; young branches twining, covered with purplish bloom. Leaves composed of three leaflets. borne at the end of a slender purplish stalk 6 to 9 ins. long. Side leaflets obliquely ovate-elliptic ; terminal one broadly obovate, longer-stalked ; all glabrous, glaucous beneath, 3 to 6 ins. long, short-pointed, entire. Flowers unisexual, dull white, small, inconspicuous, and of no beauty, produced in pendent racemes about 4 ins. long, on short leafy shoots. Fruits about the size of a grape, blue-purple, and borne alternately at intervals on an elongated stalk 8 ins. or more long. Seeds black, ⅕ in. long.

Native of Central and W. China, up to 7000 ft. ; introduced by Wilson for Harvard University, U.S.A., and raised at Kew in 1908. This climber is allied to Holbœllia and Stauntonia, but unlike them is quite hardy. Plants less than one year old survived the trying winter of 1908-9 without injury. Its value in gardens will consist in its vigorous habit and fine glaucous foliage ; also in its fine fruits, should they be developed with us. It is the only species of its genus known.

The genus was named in memory of Adrien René Franchet, once attached to the Paris Museum of Natural History, and one of the most capable botanists who ever worked at the Chinese flora. He died 14th February 1900.

SINOMENIUM ACUTUM, *Rehder and Wilson*.
MENISPERMACEÆ

(S. diversifolium, *Diels* ; Cocculus heterophyllus, *Hemsley*)

A deciduous climber, up to 20 ft. high, with twining stems. Leaves very variable in shape, perhaps normally ovate-cordate and entire, but sometimes almost kidney-shaped, sometimes lobed like Catalpa ovata, sometimes deeply three- or five-lobed (with lanceolate lobes), sometimes shallowly so ; often with a lobe on one side only ; the base often truncate ; 2 to 6 ins. long, 1¼ to 4½ ins. wide ; deep bright green, glabrous, with three or five conspicuous veins radiating from the base ; stalk slender, 2 to 6 ins. long. Flowers small, yellow, unisexual, about ⅙ in. wide ; sepals six, in two series of three each, downy beneath ; petals very small ; the flowers are borne in slenderly pyramidal panicles 6 to 12 ins. long, the main and secondary flower-stalks downy. Fruit about the size of a small pea, globose, black, covered with blue bloom.

Native of Central and W. China, also of Japan, where it has been known for at least fifty years, but does not appear to have been introduced to cultivation until Wilson sent it from China to the Coombe Wood nursery in 1901. It first flowered with the late Mr P. D. Williams in Cornwall, in 1912. It is perfectly hardy and a vigorous grower, and is an interesting addition to the few members of the moon-seed family in cultivation (see Cocculus and Menispermum).

SINOWILSONIA HENRYI, *Hemsley*.   HAMAMELIDACEÆ

A deciduous shrub or small tree, occasionally 25 ft. high and upwards in China. Leaves broadly elliptic to obovate, 3 to 6 ins. long, 2½ to 4½ ins. wide ; rather like those of a Tilia, but short-stalked, strongly veined beneath, and covered there with starry hairs (like the young shoots), the margins set with bristle-like teeth. Flowers greenish, in slender, terminal, pendulous racemes 9 ins. long. Fruits very downy, egg-shaped capsules, ⅓ to ½ in. long, stalkless, and arranged on long slender spikes.

Native of the province of Hupeh, China, where it inhabits the banks of mountain streams at 3000 to 4000 ft. ; introduced in 1908, for Harvard University, U.S.A., by Wilson. It is in honour of that famous collector that the genus is named. As a type new to cultivation, belonging to a group of great distinction—the witch-hazel family—it has considerable scientific interest. Its flowers have no great beauty.

Messrs Rehder and Wilson have recently (*Plantæ Wilsonianæ*, i., 427) made a new genus of a shrub nearly allied to Sinowilsonia and Corylopsis. Since 1908 it has been cultivated under Wilson's number, 565. It is now called FORTUNEARIA SINENSIS.

SKIMMIA.   RUTACEÆ

A group of three low, evergreen shrubs, native of China, Japan, and the Himalaya, with alternate, entire, aromatic leaves, terminal flower panicles, and handsome red fruits. Owing to the male and female flowers being frequently confined to separate plants in S. japonica and S. Laureola, it is necessary with them to grow the two sexes together in order that fruit may be obtained, and the fruit constitutes the most attractive feature of the genus. They are of easy cultivation and like a moist loamy soil, and will thrive in a moderately shady spot. Those who make a speciality of growing skimmias for their fruits assist fertilisation by artificial means (see under S. japonica.)

The generic name is derived from "skimmi," a Japanese name for S. japonica. It was given by Thunberg in 1784.

S. FORTUNEI, *Masters*

(S. japonica, Bot. Mag., t. 4719 (not of *Thunberg*) ; S. Reevesiana, *Fortune*)

A low evergreen shrub, usually not more than 2 ft. high, with dark green, narrow elliptical leaves, averaging 2½ to 4 ins. long, and from ¾ to 1 in. wide ; tapering gradually and equally towards both ends. Flowers white, always bisexual, ½ in. across, produced in terminal panicles 2 to 3 ins. long. Fruits rich crimson, distinctly oval or pear-shaped, ⅓ in. long, persisting. Seeds pointed at both ends.

Native of China, whence it was first imported to England by Fortune in 1849. He had found the plant during the previous year in a nursery garden near Shanghai. It was first exhibited in England at the Horticultural Society's Rooms, 21 Regent Street, 23rd October 1852, and was awarded a Knightian medal. Then, and until 1889, when the late Dr Masters cleared up the confusion, it was wrongly known as S. japonica. Being hermaphrodite every plant bears fruit and there is no bother about the sexes, but artificial fertilisation is useful in securing good crops of fruit. Its flowers are abundant and charmingly fragrant. Easily distinguished from the true japonica by the darker, egg-shaped fruits. It dislikes chalky soil.

Var. ARGENTEA, *Masters.*—Leaves with white margins.

S. JAPONICA, *Thunberg*

(Bot. Mag., t. 8038 ; S. oblata, *Moore*)

A low evergreen bush of dense habit, up to 3 or 4 ft. high, considerably more in width. Leaves mostly in a cluster towards the end of the shoot, aromatic when crushed, usually 3 to 4 ins. long, ¾ to 1¼ ins. wide ; pale or yellowish green, narrowly obovate or oval, thickly specked beneath with transparent glands ; leaf-stalk short, stout. Flowers in terminal panicles 2 to 3 ins. long, male and female flowers on different plants ; fragrant, ⅓ in. across ; petals usually four, sometimes five, dull white. Stamens four or five in the male plant, absent or very much aborted in the female. Fruit globular, or depressed at the top like an orange, bright red, ½ in. wide.

Native of Japan. Cultivated at Kew as long ago as 1838, this species did not obtain any general attention from horticulturists until it was introduced from Japan by Fortune in 1861. It was then called S. oblata by T. Moore, under the impression that the species now known as S. Fortunei was the true japonica. Subsequently it became generally cultivated in gardens for its very handsome fruits, which remain long on the branches, and many seedlings were raised. These varied considerably, and a number of named forms were sent out by nurserymen, some male, some female. Brief mention need only be made of the garden names still in common use :—

S. *fragrans* and S. *fragrantissima* are male forms.

S. *macrophylla.*—Another male form with large leaves and flower panicles.

S. FOREMANII.—A fine form with large leaves, and scarlet berries roundish and pear-shaped on the same cluster, suggesting that S. Fortunei has had some part in its origin. Raised by Mr Foreman, Eskbank Nurseries, Midlothian, and given a First Class Certificate when first exhibited before the Royal Horticultural Society in 1888.

S. ROGERSII.—A hybrid, in all probability, between S. japonica and S. Fortunei, having the bisexual flowers and crimson fruits of the latter, but the flattened fruits of S. japonica.

All these forms are easily increased by cuttings, and for the purpose of obtaining fruits one male need only be grown to, say, six females. In order to secure a crop of berries it is advisable to fertilise the flowers artificially. It is necessary, of course, to transfer the pollen from the male to the female, and this is usually done by taking some fluffy material (a rabbit's tail is often used) rubbing it over the male flowers as soon as the pollen is loose, and then dusting over the female flowers with it (the latter are easily recognised by the prominent ovary and stigma, and the absence of stamens). In some districts bees or other insects will do the business themselves, but it is safer to do it by hand. S. japonica grows well in the neighbourhood of towns, but does not, in my experience, fruit freely there, even with artificial fertilisation.

S. LAUREOLA, *Siebold and Zuccarini*

A low evergreen shrub, rarely seen more than 2 or 3 ft. high in this country. Leaves larger than in either of the previous species, and from 3 to 6 ins. long, the largest nearly 2 ins. wide ; they are produced in a cluster at the end of the twig, and vary in outline from lanceolate to obovate and oblong. When crushed they emit (like the young wood and flowers) a very heavy, and to most people unpleasant odour. Flowers crowded in short, terminal panicles about 1½ ins. long, mostly unisexual, yellow or greenish yellow. Fruit red, roundish. or rather longer than wide.

Native of the Himalaya, where it is said to form large thickets up to 11,000 ft. altitude. It is fairly hardy at Kew, but never bears flowers or fruits freely enough to justify its inclusion among first-rate evergreens.

SMILAX. LILIACEÆ

A curious and interesting genus of usually climbing plants, some herbaceous, some shrubby, belonging to the lily family. Of the shrubby species there are both evergreen and deciduous as well as intermediate types. Leaves alternate, prominently three- to nine-ribbed, and net-veined between the ribs ; from the stalks a pair of tendrils are developed by means of which the slender stems are supported. Stems round or angular, usually prickly, often springing from a fleshy or tuberous root-stock, the sexes usually but not always on separate plants : isolated plants having been known to produce fertile seed. The flowers have little beauty, and are always green or greenish. Fruit a black or red berry.

In a monograph published in 1878, over two hundred species were described, but of these a very small proportion are in cultivation.

The chief value of the smilaxes in gardens is in producing rich, graceful masses of handsome foliage. They develop thickets of stems which are constantly being renewed from the base, and are happily placed when they can ramble over a tree-stump or some such support. Seed is rarely seen with us on many of the species, and propagation is best effected by dividing up the plants in spring.

The popular medicine, sarsaparilla, is a product from the root of various tropical American species.

Of the following sorts, S. rotundifolia and S. hispida are the most robust in my experience, but S. excelsa has also been known to make a vigorous tree climber in Surrey ; and for the warmer counties, S. aspera, which has a very graceful inflorescence, is to be recommended.

S. ASPERA, *Linnæus*. ROUGH BINDWEED

An evergreen, semi-scandent plant with four- to six-angled stems and zigzag branches, armed with short, stout spines. Leaves very diverse in shape and size, but nearly always more or less heart-shaped at the base, and prickly on the margins, sometimes on the midrib also. As seen in cultivation the usual type of leaf is of a narrow, elongated, ovate shape, broadest almost or quite at the base, abruptly narrowed above the base, then tapering gradually to the point ; five- to nine-nerved. Sometimes the base is quite straight, and the leaf an elongated triangle ; sometimes the leaf is heart-shaped and nearly as broad as long. They measure from $1\frac{1}{2}$ to 4 ins. long, $\frac{3}{4}$ to 3 ins. wide ; stalk spiny or unarmed, $\frac{1}{4}$ to 1 in. long. Flowers pale green, fragrant, produced in terminal and axillary racemes, along which they are arranged in clusters of four to seven ; the racemes vary from $1\frac{1}{2}$ to 4 ins. long, and the flower-stalk of the individual flower is $\frac{1}{12}$ to $\frac{1}{3}$ in. long. Fruit about the size of a pea, red.

Native of S. Europe, N. Africa, and the Canaries ; cultivated in England since the mid-seventeenth century. It is only hardy in the milder counties or against a warm wall, and is usually seen in cold greenhouses, where if planted out it makes a tangle of numerous stems eventually 8 or 10 ft. high—a handsome cheerful evergreen, with graceful and fragrant, if not showy flowers.

Var. MACULATA, *De Candolle.*—Leaves usually blotched with white. Native of N. India, etc.

Var. MAURITANICA, *Grenier.*—Leaves larger, spines fewer.

S. BONA-NOX, *Linnæus*. STRETCHBERRY

A deciduous or partially evergreen climber, with angular or square branchlets, slightly armed with short, stout prickles. Leaves very variable ; roundish, heart-shaped, fiddle-shaped, spear-shaped or three-lobed ; $1\frac{1}{2}$ to $4\frac{1}{2}$ ins. long ; always pointed, green and glossy on both sides, often bristly or prickly at the margins and on the nerves beneath, five- to nine-nerved ; stalk $\frac{1}{4}$ to $\frac{1}{2}$ in. long. Flowers deep green, produced in umbels, the main-stalk of which is $\frac{1}{2}$ to 1 in. long. Berries black with a bluish bloom, round, $\frac{1}{4}$ in. across ; six to twelve, sometimes more, in an umbel.

Native of the eastern United States from Massachusetts southwards ; introduced in 1739. A hardy species, distinguished from the also black-fruited S. rotundifolia by the longer-stalked umbels and bristly margined leaves.

S. CANTAB, *Lynch*. CAMBRIDGE SMILAX

An evergreen climber reaching 12 ft. or more high ; stems round, armed with sturdy unequal prickles, and furnished with curious minute tufts of bristles ; branches square, often unarmed. Leaves of thin texture, triangular, with the base deeply heart-shaped, the apex pointed ; the largest 5 ins. long, rather more in width ; five-nerved, green on both surfaces, with a few grey spots on the upper one, the margins slightly bristly. Flowers in umbels of eight to twelve, the main-stalk as long or rather longer than the leaf-stalk.

Probably a native of N. America, but of unknown origin, having been first described (*The Garden*, vol. 56, p. 505) by Mr Lynch from a plant growing against a wall in the Cambridge Botanic Garden, where it has stood for many years. It is a male plant, and may prove to be a hybrid or belong to a species previously named.

S. CHINA, *Linnæus*. CHINA ROOT

A deciduous rambling shrub, with round stems sparingly armed with slightly recurved prickles. Leaves 2 to 3 ins. long, very variable, roundish ovate, or broadly oval, or sometimes broader than long, ending in a short abrupt point, the base tapered or truncate or slightly heart-shaped; five- or seven-veined; stalk $\frac{1}{3}$ to 1 in. long. Flowers yellowish green, often numerous in umbels, the main-stalk of which is about 1 in. long. There are often over twenty flowers in an umbel. Fruit $\frac{3}{8}$ in. in diameter, globose, bright red.

Native of China and Japan, where it is frequent and widely spread; introduced in 1759, also by Wilson from China in 1907. It has a large fleshy root-stock, said to be eaten by the Chinese; it also yields the drug known as "China root"—once highly esteemed as a remedy for gout.

S. DISCOTIS, *Warburg*

A deciduous climber growing 10 to 16 ft. high; young shoots grooved or angled; stems armed with decurved spines $\frac{1}{6}$ in. long. Leaves ovate or narrowly oval, mostly heart-shaped at the base and pointed at the apex; $1\frac{1}{2}$ to $3\frac{1}{2}$ ins. long, $\frac{3}{4}$ to $1\frac{3}{4}$ ins. wide; glaucous beneath, three- or five-nerved; stalk $\frac{1}{12}$ to $\frac{1}{5}$ in. long. Flowers greenish yellow, in an umbel terminating a very slender main flower-stalk up to $1\frac{1}{2}$ ins. long; each flower on a stalk $\frac{1}{4}$ to $\frac{1}{3}$ in. long. Fruits blue-black, $\frac{1}{4}$ in. or rather more wide.

Native of Central and Western China; introduced by Wilson about 1908. It is distinct on account of the comparatively large, semi-circular stipules up to $\frac{1}{5}$ in. long, combined with the black fruit, the heart-shaped base of the leaves and their glaucous under surface. It is in cultivation in the Royal Horticultural Society's Garden at Wisley in Surrey, and is hardy there.

Var. CONCOLOR, *Norton*, also introduced about the same time as the type by Wilson, is distinguished by its leaves being green on both sides. The leaves are also larger and the leaf-stalks longer.

S. EXCELSA, *Linnæus*

(Bot. Mag., t. 9067)

A tall evergreen or late deciduous climber, with squarish stems and branches armed with flat, stiff spines, $\frac{1}{4}$ to $\frac{1}{3}$ in. long. Leaves unarmed, broadly ovate, heart-shaped or truncate at the base, pointed; $1\frac{1}{2}$ to $3\frac{1}{2}$ ins. long, often as broad or broader than long; five- or seven-nerved, green on both sides; stalk $\frac{1}{4}$ to $\frac{1}{2}$ in. long. Flowers six to twelve in an umbel, the main-stalk of which is $\frac{1}{2}$ to 1 in. long. Berries red, $\frac{1}{3}$ in. wide.

Native of S.E. Europe and Asia Minor; introduced in 1739. From S. aspera, the other but more western species of Europe, S. excelsa is distinguished by its umbellate inflorescence.

S. GLAUCA, *Walter*. SAW BRIER

(Bot. Mag., t. 1846)

A tall deciduous or partially evergreen climber, with round stems but angled branches, sparsely or not at all prickly. Leaves ovate with broadly tapering or rounded bases and fine points; $1\frac{1}{2}$ to $3\frac{1}{2}$ ins. long, 1 to $2\frac{1}{2}$ ins. wide; green above, glaucous beneath, with usually three prominent nerves and two smaller ones at the margins; stalk $\frac{1}{6}$ to $\frac{1}{3}$ in. long. Flowers green, produced three to eight together in small axillary umbels, the main-stalks of which is $\frac{1}{3}$ to 1 in. long. Berries black with a glaucous bloom, $\frac{1}{4}$ in. wide.

Native of the eastern United States from Massachusetts southwards ;
hardy, and cultivated for seventy years at Kew.   The glaucous colour of the
leaves beneath is its best distinguishing character.

S. HISPIDA, *Muhlenberg*.   HAG BRIER

A climbing deciduous shrub, with round stems furnished with slender
bristles and straight prickles, densely so towards the base ; branches almost
without them.   Leaves heart-shaped or broadly ovate, 2 to 6 ins. long, 1½ to
4½ ins. wide ; five- or sometimes nine-nerved, finely pointed, green on both
sides, margins often minutely jagged ; stalk ¼ to ¾ in. long.   Flowers greenish
yellow, borne on an umbel with a main-stalk 1 to 2 ins. long.   Berries blue-
black, globose, about ¼ in. wide.

Native of the eastern and central United States and Ontario ; introduced
early in the eighteenth century.   This species thrives well in this country,
and is well marked by its large leaves and very bristly stems.

S. LAURIFOLIA, *Linnæus*

A tall evergreen climber with thick, leathery leaves, 2 to 5 ins. long, ⅝ to
2 ins. wide ; three-nerved, dark green and rather glossy above, oblong, tapered
or rounded at the base, and with usually a short, abrupt, fine point ; stalk
¼ to ½ in. long.   Flowers greenish, in umbels, the main-stalk of which is about
as long as the leaf-stalk.   Fruit ¼ to ⅓ in. wide, one-seeded, black when ripe,
but taking two seasons to become so.

Native of the south-eastern United States ; introduced in 1739.   Very
distinct in its three-nerved, leathery, evergreen, and comparatively narrow
leaves, this is, unfortunately, rather tender, and has died out in the open
ground at Kew.   It has succeeded well on a wall in the vicarage garden of
Bitton, near Bath, and is suitable for the south and west generally, where it
will make an interesting evergreen wall-covering.

S. MEGALANTHA, *C. H. Wright*

(Gardeners' Chronicle, 20th Nov. 1920, fig. 116

An evergreen climber growing 15 to 20 ft. high ; young shoots grey, angled,
armed with irregularly scattered, stout spines up to ½ in. long and furnished
with tendrils proceeding from the much thickened leaf-stalk.   Leaves very
variable in size and shape, the largest broadly ovate, rounded at the base,
9 ins. long by 6 ins. wide ; the smaller ones are lanceolate to narrowly oval,
tapered at the base, some of them only 3½ ins. long by 1 in. wide ; all are
of leathery texture, pointed, dark glossy green above, glaucous beneath,
conspicuously three-nerved ; leaf-stalk ½ to 1 in. long.   Flowers (described by
Wilson as greenish) produced from the leaf-axils of small young leaves on
short branches in corymbose umbels ; the perianth of the male flower has six
slenderly pointed lobes ; stamens six.   Fruit globose, nearly ½ in. wide, coral-
red, often one-seeded, borne in umbels over 2 ins. across ; main-stalk 1 in.
long ; individual stalks ½ to ¾ in. long.

Native of Hupeh, W. Szechuen, and Yunnan, China ; originally collected
by A. E. Pratt and E. Faber ; the latter found it on Mt. Omei.   It was
introduced to cultivation by Wilson in 1907.   This fine smilax—in foliage the
most remarkable of all the species that succeed in our average climate—has
grown vigorously without any protection at Kew since its introduction, in good
loamy soil.   It is evidently perfectly hardy.   Its unusually large fruits are very

handsome, but even if it failed to produce them it is well worth cultivating as an evergreen foliage plant. Propagated, like the rest, by division.

S. PSEUDO-CHINA, *Linnæus*. "CHINA" BRIER

Not much is known of this smilax in cultivation, and it is probably rather tender. It appears to be naturally a vigorous climber, deciduous, with the stems almost unarmed. Leaves large, ovate, five- or seven-nerved, green on both sides, up to 4½ ins. long, by 3 ins. wide at the rounded or slightly heart-shaped base; margins minutely jagged. Flowers dark green, and produced numerously in umbels. From all the rest of the umbellate-flowered smilaxes mentioned in these notes this species is easily distinguished by the length of the main flower-stalk, which is 2 to 3 ins. long, flattened. Berries black, ⅓ in. diameter.

Native of the eastern United States; said by Aiton to have been introduced in 1739. The plant has a tuberous root-stock.

S. ROTUNDIFOLIA, *Linnæus*. HORSE BRIER

A vigorous, deciduous or partially evergreen climber, with slender, round or more or less angled stems, armed with one or two short spines between each leaf (not at the nodes); the stems are sometimes 6 or 8 yards long; branches four-angled. Leaves ovate to broadly heart-shaped; 2 to 6 ins. long, often broader than long, with a short abrupt point; prominently five-nerved, glabrous and glossy green on both sides; stalk ¼ to ½ in. long. Flowers greenish yellow, about ⅕ in. across, borne in umbels; main flower-stalk ¼ to ½ in. long, flattened. Berries roundish, black, ¼ in. diameter, covered with glaucous bloom, usually three to six of them in one cluster.

Native of eastern N. America; introduced in 1760. This is the commonest, most vigorous and hardy of all the smilaxes in cultivation, making a dense thicket of stems. It is the common horse brier or green brier of the United States, where its stems are sometimes 30 to 40 ft. long, stretching from tree to tree. In gardens it may be trained up stout oak posts on which the stumps of the side branches have been left 2 or 3 ft. long. Grown in this way it is very elegant.

S. SCOBINICAULIS, *C. H. Wright*

A deciduous climber growing 15 ft. or more high; branches slender, grooved, often very densely furnished with numerous black prickles, often unarmed. Leaves ovate to ovate-oblong, rounded or slightly heart-shaped at the base, finely pointed, five- or seven-veined; 3 to 5 ins. long, 1 to 3 ins. wide; glabrous and green on both surfaces; stalk ¼ to ⅜ in. long, with tendrils attached to it near the blade. Flowers yellowish white, borne in axillary umbels ¾ in. wide, the main-stalk of which is ⅓ in. long, the individual stalks ⅛ to ¼ in. long. Fruit globose, black, ¼ in. wide, in clusters of nine to twelve, each containing one to three seeds.

Native of Central China; discovered by Henry; introduced by Wilson in 1907.

The original type specimen collected in Hupeh by Henry about 1888, on which Mr Wright founded the species, has the stem practically covered with the slender, bristle-like spines he describes. Plants at Kew, however, raised from Wilson's seeds in 1908, have fairly stiff spines sprinkled freely over the stems but no bristle-like ones. The fruits, too, are much smaller. Wilson's No. 627 is certainly true but Nos. 455, 671, and 680, which have also been called scobinicaulis, seem to me to be distinct.

S. Sieboldii, *Miquel*

A deciduous or semi-evergreen species, the stems round or somewhat ribbed, and more or less armed with slender prickles ; branches distinctly angular. Leaves ovate with a heart-shaped base and a long fine point, five- or seven-nerved, margins minutely jagged ; green both sides, 1½ to 3 ins. long, two-thirds as wide. Flowers in small umbels of four to seven blossoms, green ; main flower-stalk ½ to ⅝ in. long. Berries black, ¼ in. diameter, often in threes. Native of Japan ; introduced in 1908, perhaps before. It is a little known species, very distinct from S. China, also Japan, in the smaller black fruits, few-flowered umbels, and triangular-ovate leaves.

S. Walteri, *Pursh*

A deciduous climber, with angled stems, armed only near the base ; branches squarish, unarmed. Leaves ovate to ovate-lanceolate, 2 to 4½ ins. long, ¾ to 2½ ins. wide ; broadly wedge-shaped to slightly heart-shaped at the base, ending in a short fine point ; five- or seven-nerved ; glabrous and green on both sides ; stalk ¼ to ½ in. long. Flowers greenish, in short and flat-stalked umbels. Berries bright coral-red, globose, ⅓ in. wide.

Native of the eastern United States from New Jersey southwards ; introduced early in the nineteenth century ; rarely seen now. It is akin to S. rotundifolia, but has narrower, proportionately longer leaves, and is not so vigorous a grower. S. rotundifolia also has black fruits.

SOLANUM. Solanaceæ

A very large genus said to comprise well over one thousand species. They are mostly herbs, but some are shrubs, climbers, or small trees. The leaves are alternate, the fruit is a berry. The species here mentioned are easily grown in a free loamy soil, provided the conditions are warm enough ; they can be easily propagated by cuttings.

S. crispum, *Ruiz and Pavon.* Solanaceæ
(Bot. Mag., t. 3795)

A scandent, quick-growing, more or less evergreen shrub, with downy, scarcely woody young shoots. Leaves ovate, variable in size, usually 2½ to 5 ins. long, mostly less than half as wide, taper-pointed ; rounded or wedge-shaped, rarely heart-shaped at the base ; minutely downy on both surfaces ; stalk ½ to ¾ in. long. Flowers delicate bluish purple, fragrant, produced from June to September in long-stalked corymbs, 3 to 6 ins. across. Each flower is 1 to 1¼ ins. wide, the corolla with five ovate lobes, the yellow anthers closely packed in the centre. Fruit globose, ¼ to ⅓ in. wide.

Native of Chile ; introduced about 1830. This beautiful plant is only seen at its best in the milder counties of Great Britain, and few plants, even there, are more graceful and lovely. On a south wall at Kew it has grown and flowered for many years, but never with the vigour and profusion one sees in Devonshire and similar localities. It will grow 20 ft. or more high if given support. The most beautiful effect I have seen produced by it was where it had been planted against the wall of a low shed, over the roof of which it had clambered. It may be pruned back in spring before growth commences.

Where the climate is suitable it may be treated as a loose-habited, wide-spreading shrub, by pruning hard back annually. It will thrive in poor soil.

In the gardens of the south-west a beautiful display is made in autumn by SOLANUM JASMINOIDES, *Paxton*, a native of Brazil. It produces its pale blue flowers in great profusion. It is a climber of more slender growth than S. crispum and will grow in similar situations, but it is more tender. Var. ALBUM, with pure white flowers, is the form most often seen.

Of the British bittersweet (S. DULCAMARA, *Linnæus*) there is a variegated form rather handsomely marked with clear creamy white. The soft, semi-woody shoots grow 6 to 8 ft. high, but die back very much in winter, and the base only remains woody. The red berries are poisonous, and the plant may not be desirable where there are children. The flowers are violet-blue, and the leaves frequently unequally lobed at the base.

S. VALDIVIENSE, *Dunal*

(Bot. Mag., t. 9552 ; S. evonymoides, *Remy*)

A deciduous, sucker-producing shrub of loose, lax habit, growing up to 8 or 10 ft. high and developing graceful arching shoots which when young are distinctly angled and downy at the angles. Leaves simple and entire, ovate-lanceolate, pointed, mostly tapered (but sometimes rounded) at the base ; very variable in size, the largest 2 to 2½ ins. long by ¾ to 1 in. wide, the smallest scarcely ½ in. long, downy on the margins ; stalk $\frac{1}{12}$ to ¼ in. long. Flowers produced in short racemes ordinarily of two to seven blossoms, the main-stalk ⅛ to ½ in. long and downy, the individual flower-stalks up to 1 in. long, very slender and glabrous. Each flower is about ½ in. wide, pale mauve, white or lavender, with which the cluster of erect yellow stamens is in good contrast. Fruit globose, ¼ in. wide and of a " dullish slightly translucent olive green." (Comber.)

Native of Valdivia, Chile ; known to botanists since about 1850, but not introduced, so far as I know, until H. F. Comber sent home seeds in 1927. The leaves are not much developed at flowering time (May) and the long sprays, thickly wreathed with blossom, are then very handsome. According to Comber the aim in pruning should be to encourage the growth of long summer shoots which will flower the following spring. Worn out and weedy growths should be removed as soon as the flowering is over. Comber found it growing in " moist sunny meadows." He considers that unless the climate is sufficiently sunny and mild to ripen and preserve the long summer shoots through the winter it will scarcely be worth growing. Still, I have seen it flowering in several places in the south and thought it quite attractive. The sunniest possible spot should be chosen for it.

SOPHORA.   LEGUMINOSÆ

Trees or shrubs with unequally pinnate leaves ; flowers produced in racemes or panicles ; fruit a pod of the necklace pattern, that is, much constricted between each seed. The cultivated species fall into two well-marked groups : 1st, SOPHORA (proper), whose flowers are pea-shaped (or papilionaceous) ; 2nd, EDWARDSIA, whose leaves have smaller and usually more numerous leaflets, and whose flowers are much larger, not papilionaceous, but rather tubular, owing to all the petals pointing forward. The genus is represented on both hemispheres, above and below the equator. The hardy or nearly hardy species come from

N. Asia, New Zealand, and Chile. One species, S. tetraptera, with curiously winged fruits, is found in both the two latter countries—a remarkable phenomenon in plant distribution. The sophoras all like a good loamy soil and a sunny position. The shrubby species can be increased by cuttings ; those which make trees are better from seed.

S. AFFINIS, *Torrey and Gray*

(Sargent's Silva of North America, vol. iii., t. 122)

A deciduous, round-headed tree up to 20 ft. high, with a trunk 8 to 10 ins. in diameter ; young shoots slightly downy. Leaves pinnate, 6 to 9 ins. long, with thirteen to nineteen leaflets which are oval, tapering about equally towards both ends, shortly stalked ; 1 to 1½ ins. long, about ½ in. wide ; slightly downy when young beneath. Flowers in slender downy racemes 3 to 6 ins. long, produced in June in the leaf-axils of the new growths, white tinged with rose, ½ in. or rather more long. Calyx downy, bell-shaped, with broad, shallow triangular teeth. Pods 1½ to 3 ins. long, black, downy, persisting long on the tree. By the constrictions of the pod, each seed has its own oval or globose compartment, the inner wall of which is fleshy ; the pod rather suggests a string of three or four beads.

Native of Texas and Arkansas, often on limestone hills ; discovered in Texas in 1821 ; introduced to cultivation in 1890. Sargent observes that a domestic ink is sometimes made from the resinous exudations of the black fruits. In leaf this sophora resembles S. japonica, but that species is very distinct in having terminal, autumnal flower panicles. S. affinis has not long been in this country and will probably succeed best on the south coast, where it should make a pleasing small tree.

S. FLAVESCENS, *Aiton*

Originally described by Aiton in the *Hortus Kewensis*, vol. ii., p. 43, in 1789, this species has since appeared at intervals, but has never obtained a secure footing in gardens. It is merely sub-shrubby with us, and thrusts up during the growing season shoots 3 ft. or more long, which are, as a rule, cut back to ground-level in winter. The pinnate leaves are 6 to 9 ins. long, with up to nineteen narrowly ovate leaflets 1½ to 2½ ins. long. Flowers yellowish white, ½ in. long, borne during July and August on a terminal cylindrical raceme or panicle up to 1 ft. in length. The pods are 2 to 2½ ins. long and carry one to five seeds.

Native of China, where it has been collected by Delavay, Henry, Wilson, Forrest and others ; also of Formosa. The shoots are really semi-herbaceous and too soft to survive the winters of our average climate, so that it forms in time a woody stool which produces gradually weaker shoots and finally succumbs. In W. Hupeh and E. Szechuen, where Wilson found it a shrub 6 ft. high, he describes it as very common in sandy places.

S. JAPONICA, *Linnæus* (Plate 26)

A deciduous tree, 50 to 80 ft. high, of rounded habit and branching low down when growing in the open, but capable of forming a tall clean trunk when close planted. Bark downy when young, glabrous later and dark greenish brown ; on old trunks it is grey, and corrugated rather like an ash. Leaves rich green, pinnate, 6 to 10 ins. long, composed of nine to fifteen leaflets, which are ovate or oval, 1 to 2 ins. long, half as wide, covered with small appressed hairs beneath. Flowers in terminal panicles 6 to 10 ins. long and wide, creamy white, each about ½ in. long; calyx ⅛ in. long, bell-shaped, green, shallowly toothed. Pod 2 to 3½ ins. long, glabrous, one- to six-seeded ; rarely seen in Britain, but developed in 1911.

Native of China (not of Japan); introduced in 1753. It is one of the most beautiful of all leguminous trees, although it does not flower in a young state—not commencing until thirty to forty years of age. Old trees flower freely, especially after hot summers. The blossoms are not developed until September, and in wet cold summers do not develop at all. They do not fade on the tree, but drop off quite fresh, making the ground white beneath. Perhaps the oldest tree in this country is at Kew—a veteran planted in 1760, whose branches are now held together by steel rods ; its short trunk is 13 ft. in girth. There is a fine tree in the gardens of Petit Trianon, but the finest I have seen is in the old Botanic Garden at Schoenbrunn, near Vienna, which is over 70 ft. high, 18 ft. in girth of trunk, and its head of branches 105 ft. through. The species has purgative properties.

Var. PENDULA.—A very picturesque weeping tree with stiff, drooping branches. It should be grafted on stocks of the ordinary form 10 or 15 ft. high. An admirable lawn tree, or for forming a natural arbour.

Var. VARIEGATA.—Leaves margined with creamy white, but of little value.

Var. VIOLACEA, *Carrière* (S. violacea, *Dippel*).—This variety was introduced from China to the Jardin des Plantes at Paris about 1858. Its flowers, which appear later than those of S. japonica, have the wing-petals and keel stained with rose-violet. A plant has been cultivated at Kew for many years, and has set flower-buds several times, but usually too late in the season to open well. In regard to leaf and young shoot it does not differ materially from the type. (According to Henry the flowers of S. japonica, as he saw them in China vary a good deal in colour, some forms being white, others yellow.)

Var. PUBESCENS, *Bosse*.—Known in gardens as S. Korolkowi, this is no doubt a distinct variety of S. japonica. The most notable tree of the name is growing in the famous Arboretum at Segrez, in France. I saw this tree in July 1904, and it was then covered with panicles of unexpanded flowers. When open they are described as dull white. The leaflets are longer than in japonica (fully 3 ins.), but narrower in proportion ; they are covered beneath with very minute, close down. The young wood too is more downy, and of a lighter colour. The tree at Segrez is over 30 ft. high, with its trunk about 1 ft. in diameter.

S. MACROCARPA, *Smith*

(Bot. Mag., t. 8647 ; Edwardsia chilensis, *Miers*)

An evergreen tree, 20 to 40 ft. high ; young wood covered with reddish brown down. Leaves pinnate, 3 to 5 ins. long, composed of six and a half to twelve and a half pairs of leaflets, which are ¾ to 1½ ins. long, ¼ to ⅜ in. wide, covered beneath and more or less above with reddish brown down. Flowers in short axillary racemes, yellow, 1 to 1¼ ins. long. Calyx ¼ in. long, bell-shaped, shallow-toothed, covered with down like that of the leaves. Pod downy, 4 ins. or more long, ½ in. thick where the seeds are enclosed, but much constricted between them ; not winged, but thickened at the seams.

Native of Chile ; introduced in 1822. This species is nearly akin to, and very much resembles the larger-leaved forms of S. tetraptera. It always differs from them, however, in having no wings to the pods, the flowers are not so large, and the leaves are pretty uniformly of the dimensions given above.

t is not quite hardy at Kew, but thrives very well in S. Devon, Cornwall, nd similar places. There is a fine plant in the garden of Duncan House, orquay, planted there by the late Dr Hamilton-Ramsay.

S. SECUNDIFLORA, *Lagasca*

(Sargent's Silva of North America, vol. iii., t. 121)

An evergreen tree 25 to 35 ft. high with pinnate leaves 4 to 6 ins. long, ade up usually of seven or nine oblong or obovate leaflets which are 1 to ins. long, notched at the end. Flowers produced in racemes 2 or 3 ins. ng at the end of the leafy young shoots of the current year in spring. Each ower (of the normal pea-flower shape) is about 1 in. long, violet-blue and ery fragrant (like violets).

Native of Texas, New Mexico, and North Mexico. It was figured by rtega, the Spanish botanist, 1797, from a plant that flowered in Madrid. ecaisne, who figured it in the *Revue Horticole*, 1854, p. 201, observes that it ithstands easily the climate of the *midi* of France. I do not know that it as been tried out-of-doors yet in this country but it is only likely to succeed the sunniest, warmest localities and is better fitted no doubt for the south of urope. It would be worth while trying it on a south wall, for Sargent escribes it as one of the handsomest of small trees in the Texan forest, and ardy trees with fragrant violet-blue flowers are very rare. Dr Wilfrid Fox ised it from continental seeds a few years ago and has it in his garden at inkworth, near Godalming.

S. TETRAPTERA, *J. S. Miller*. KOWHAI

A shrub or small tree, varying from 15 to 40 ft. high in a wild state, the unk 6 ins. to 2 ft. in diameter. It is deciduous or nearly so in the open, it evergreen in a greenhouse. Branches of young specimens very zigzag, ender, and often interlacing—on older ones the branches become short-inted, or even stunted. Branchlets, leaf-stalks, flower-stalks, and especially e calyx, all covered with a short tawny down. Leaves pinnate, 1½ to 4½ ins. ng ; leaflets ⅛ to ¾ in. long, narrow oblong to roundish ; their number is ery variable, on young plants there are only seven or nine, but on plants at have reached the flowering stage they are much more numerous, and to as many as eighty. Flowers somewhat tubular, golden yellow, 1 to ins. long, pendulous, clustered from four to eight in each raceme, opening in ay. Calyx obliquely bell-shaped, ½ in. or more across, shallow-toothed. Pod to 8 ins. long, four-winged, with constrictions between the seeds.

Var. GRANDIFLORA (Edwardsia grandiflora, *Salisbury*) has larger flowers an the type (full 2 ins. long), and longer, less numerous leaflets.

Var. MICROPHYLLA, *Hooker fil.* (Edwardsia microphylla, *Salisbury* ; Macnabiana, *R. Graham*, Bot. Mag., t. 3735).—Leaflets smaller, more imerous ; flowers 1 to 1½ ins. long.

Native of New Zealand, whence the two forms were both introduced in 72 ; also of Chile. They are not hardy at Kew ; even var. microphylla, nich is considered the less tender, was killed in the open ground during e winter of 1908-9, and plants on walls were badly cut. But in the milder unties or on specially sheltered walls it is most attractive, not only for its owy large flowers, but for its foliage and quaint interesting habit. It will rive in sandy loam. The remarkable necklace-like pod, with four thin ridges aversing it lengthwise, is occasionally seen in this country.

S. VICIIFOLIA, *Hance*

(Bot. Mag., t. 7883)

A deciduous shrub of rounded habit, from 6 to 10 ft. high, and as muc
through, the young branchlets covered with greyish down, the year-ol
branches more or less spiny. Leaves pinnate, 1½ to 2½ ins. long, with seve
to ten pairs of leaflets, which are ¼ to ⅜ in. long, about ⅛ in. wide ; oval c
obovate, with silky appressed hairs beneath. Racemes terminal on shoi
twigs, produced from the buds of the previous year's shoots, 2 to 2½ ins. lon;
Flowers pea-flower-shaped ; petals bluish white ; calyx ⅛ in. long, downy
short-toothed, violet-blue. Pod 2 to 2½ ins. long, about ⅙ in. wide, downy
one- to four-seeded, constricted between the seeds.

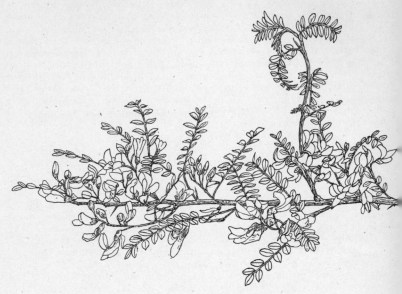

SOPHORA VICIIFOLIA

Native of China in the provinces of Yunnan, Szechuen, and Hupeh, up ♦
13,500 ft. It was introduced in 1897 to Kew, where it has grown well, an
proved to be one of the most charming of recently introduced shrubs, tl
branches being loaded with the blue and white racemes in June, their beau
greatly enhanced by the elegant fern-like foliage. It requires a good loan
soil, and a site exposed to full sunshine. No frost has yet affected it. Accordir
to Henry, in the elevated regions where it grows, it often covers large trac
of barren country, just as gorse does in Britain. It is propagated by cuttin;
made of young shoots with a heel of old wood, in July and August, and plac€
in a gently heated frame.

Nearly related to S. viciifolia is S. MOORCROFTIANA, *Bentham*, wi
similar foliage and habit, but which is more spiny, more downy, has small
leaflets, yellow flowers, and a longer more slender calyx. Native of Kashn
and Tibet.

SORBARONIA. Rosaceæ

A group of some half a dozen hybrids between Sorbus and Aronia.
They are deciduous shrubs or small trees.

S. ALPINA, *C. K. Schneider*

(Pyrus alpina, *Willdenow* ; Aronia densiflora, *Spach*)

A hybrid between Sorbus Aria and Aronia arbutifolia and a deciduous
shrub whose young shoots are at first covered with loose white down, becoming
dark with age. Leaves oval to obovate, tapering equally to both ends or more
abruptly to the apex, finely toothed, 1½ to 3 ins. long, about half as wide, at
first soft and covered beneath with pale down ; stalk ¼ to ½ in. long. Flowers
in terminal corymbs 1 to 2 ins. across, white, opening in May ; styles three
or four. Fruits ovoid to obovoid, dark brownish-red, ⅓ in. wide.
S. alpina is very nearly allied to S. Dippelii but differ in having red fruits
and in the leaves (upper surface especially) being less downy. Var. SUPERARIA
is apparently a reversion towards Sorbus Aria or perhaps a cross between that
species and S. alpina; the leaves are much larger and broader than in the
latter, the flower clusters are also larger, the fruits deep red.
This shrub has been known in gardens since early in the nineteenth century.
A plant obtained from France in 1875 flowered and bore fruit in 1881.

S. DIPPELII, *Zabel*

A bushy-headed shrub ; young wood thickly covered with grey felt.
Leaves 1½ to 3½ ins. long, ⅝ to 1¼ ins. wide ; narrowly oval or oblanceolate,
shallowly toothed, bright green and glabrous above, covered beneath with a
close grey felt, tapering at the base to a stalk ¼ to ⅓ in. long. Flowers ⅓ in.
across, white, with rose-coloured anthers, produced in small downy corymbs.
Fruit top-shaped or roundish, ⅓ in. long, blue-black.
A hybrid between S. Aria and Aronia melanocarpa, of unknown garden
origin. Its affinity with A. melanocarpa is shown in the presence of glands
along the upper surface of the midrib, and in the blackish fruits. It is an
interesting and pretty round shrub, often made into a small tree by grafting on
standards of mountain ash or hawthorn. It is often called " Pyrus alpina " in
gardens.

S. HYBRIDA, *C. K. Schneider*

(S. heterophylla ; Sorbus spuria, *Persoon*)

A deciduous shrub or small tree, 6 to 12 ft. (probably more) high ; young
wood downy. Leaves very variable, but usually more or less pinnate or
pinnatifid ; the smaller leaves, however, are sometimes quite entire, and there
is every intermediate shape ; they are 2 to 3½ ins. long, the three to seven
leaflets or divisions overlapping each other, toothed, slightly downy beneath
in the earlier part of the season. Flowers white, ⅜ in. across, produced at
the end of short leafy twigs in small corymbs. Fruit black-purple, globose,
⅓ in. wide. Although this pretty and interesting little tree has been in gardens
at least 170 years, its origin is not definitely known, but it seems to be a hybrid
between the mountain ash and Aronia melanocarpa. The mountain ash is
no doubt one parent and Aronia arbutifolia is often given as the other. But
it seems doubtful if two trees, both with bright red fruits, would give birth to
one with black-purple ones as S. hybrida does.

III   L

SORBOPYRUS. (Sorbus × Pyrus.) Rosaceæ

So far as is generally known at present this hybrid genus consist of the two trees described below and it may very well be that of then the second one (S. malifolia) is not the result of a separate cross an no more than the offspring of S. auricularis.

S. AURICULARIS, *C. K. Schneider*

(Pyrus bollwylleriana, *De Candolle*)

A deciduous tree, 20 to 40 ft. high (sometimes 50 to 60 ft.), forming rounded bushy head ; young branches more or less covered with loose down

Sorbopyrus auricularis

Leaves ovate or oval, 3 to 4 ins. long, 2 to 2½ ins. wide ; pointed, irregularly and coarsely, sometimes doubly toothed ; rounded or rather heart-shaped a the base ; upper surface covered at first with loose down which falls away as the season advances, lower surface permanently grey-felted ; stalk 1 to 1½ ins long, woolly. Flowers white, ¾ to 1 in. across, produced about mid-May in many-flowered corymbs 2 to 3 ins. across ; anthers rosy red ; calyx with its triangular lobes covered with a conspicuous pure white wool. Fruit pear-shaped, 1 to 1¼ ins. long and wide, red, each on a stalk 1 to 1½ ins. long, with sweet, yellowish flesh.

This interesting and remarkable tree is a hybrid between the common whitebeam (Sorbus Aria) and the pear (Pyrus communis). It is said to have originated at Bollwyller, in Alsace, and is first mentioned by Johannes Bauhin in 1619 and figured by him in 1650. For three hundred years it has been propagated by grafts, for it produces very few fertile seeds, and these do not ome true. The finest tree known to me is at Bramford Hall, Ipswich, which, ccording to information received from Lady Loraine in 1904, was then over o ft. high.

S. MALIFOLIA, *C. K. Schneider*

(Pyrus malifolia, *Spach*)

The only tree with which this is likely to be confused is Sorbopyrus uricularis, the hybrid between Sorbus Aria and Pyrus communis. S. malifolia s also palpably a hybrid, and of an origin very similar to the other. Spach, who named and described this tree in 1834, says the original specimen at that ime grew in the Ménagerie du Jardin du Roi at Paris, and was 30 ft. or more igh. He suggests that it may be a hybrid between S. auricularis and a pear, ut I think it more likely to have been a seedling from S. auricularis, which ccasionally bears fertile seed. As in the manner of hybrids, this rarely repro-luces the mother plant true. It is only necessary to recount the differences etween this tree and S. auricularis : Leaves shorter and comparatively broader, ften roundish oval, not so coarsely toothed, nearly always heart-shaped at he base, not so much felted beneath ; flowers larger, 1 to 1½ ins. across, fewer n the corymb and with stouter stalks, produced in late April and May. Fruit roadly top-shaped, about 2 ins. long and wide, deep yellow when ripe. This nteresting and handsome tree, although not so common as the Bollwyller pear, s on the whole more attractive.

SORBUS

A group of deciduous trees and shrubs for long regarded as a section f the genus Pyrus. The leaves are alternate, simple, or pinnate and hereby form two distinct groups, the former mostly with pinnate veins. Flowers white or pink, produced in terminal clusters ; sepals and petals ive, stamens fifteen or twenty, styles free or united at the base. Fruit a pome, small, usually globose or ovoid with two to five cells each con-aining one or two seeds.

These attractive trees and shrubs are easily cultivated, needing about he same conditions as the apple, *i.e.* a sound open loamy soil and a unny position. Most of them produce viable seeds.

S. ALNIFOLIA, *K. Koch*

(Pyrus alnifolia, *Franchet* ; Bot. Mag., t. 7773 ; Micromeles alnifolia, *Koehne*)

A deciduous tree of rather slender, erect habit, ultimately 40 to 50 ft. high ; ranchlets furnished with short silky hairs when quite young. Leaves of thin exture ; 1½ to 4 ins. long, ¾ to 1½ ins. wide ; the apex pointed, the base ounded, margins double-toothed ; nerves parallel in seven to twelve pairs, ilky-hairy beneath when young, becoming glabrous later ; stalk ¼ to ¾ in. long. Flowers white, ½ in. diameter, produced during May in corymbs, 2 to 3 ins. cross ; calyx and flower-stalks silky ; styles usually too. Fruit ¼ to ½ in. long, val, bright red, no calyx adhering at the top.

Native of Japan, Central China and Korea ; put in cultivation by Mr Späth of Berlin about 1892, but may have been known before. It is one of the reatest and most pleasing of the Micromeles group, and is very appropriately amed. The leaves are bright green beneath, and bear a close resemblance o those of an alder. Fine crops of fruits ripen, and they become very brightly

coloured, and remain long on the tree, but only a small proportion contain
good seeds. Very deserving of cultivation. Leaves orange and scarlet in
autumn.

S. AMERICANA, *Marshall*. AMERICAN MOUNTAIN ASH

(Pyrus americana, *De Candolle*)

A tree 15 to 30 ft. high, ultimately forming a narrow, rounded head of
slender branches ; young shoots glabrous or slightly downy only at first
winter buds ¾ in. long, sharply pointed, gummy, with a tuft of hairs at the
apex. Leaves pinnate, 6 to 12 ins. long, composed of eleven to seventeen
leaflets, which are 1½ to 4 ins. long, ½ to ¾ in. wide, narrowly oblong-lanceolate,
pointed, evenly saw-toothed except at the base, glabrous except when quite
young ; stalkless or nearly so. Flowers creamy white, about ⅛ in. across,
produced about the beginning of June in flattish corymbs 3 to 5 ins. across ;
calyx and flower-stalk glabrous, or slightly downy ; calyx-lobes short
triangular. Fruit bright red, ¼ in. across, slightly longer than broad.

Native of eastern N. America, from Newfoundland to Virginia. It is a
close ally of the European mountain ash, but has larger leaves and smaller
flowers, and is much less downy in its various parts ; in winter it is easily
distinguished by its sticky, only slightly downy buds. It fruits freely in this
country, and its bunches of berries are as handsome as those of the rowan tree,
but it does not thrive so well. Loudon in 1837 observed that although it was
introduced in 1782, he knew of no large old specimen. It is quite hardy, and
grows rapidly in a small state.

Var. DECORA, *Sargent*.—Said by Sargent to be the finest form of
S. americana. " Fruits bright scarlet, often ½ in. in diameter." Leaflets
fewer, larger, and broader than in the type. It appears to cover some of the
same country, and may have been introduced as ordinary S. americana, but
I do not remember to have seen fruits ½ in. across on trees in cultivation. It is
one of the various American mountain ashes known as " Pyrus sambucifolia."
(Syn. S. decora, *C. K. Schneider*.)

S. ARIA, *Crantz*. WHITEBEAM

(Pyrus Aria, *Ehrhart* ; Aria nivea, *Host*.)

A tree usually 30 to 45 ft. high in gardens, but occasionally met with 60 to
80 ft. high ; main branches more or less erect ; young branchlets clothed
with loose white down, becoming nearly glabrous and lustrous dark brown by
winter, and furnished with pale, wart-like excrescences. Leaves with eight to
thirteen pairs of parallel ribs, oval or obovate ; 2 to 4 ins. long, half to two-
thirds as wide ; usually tapering, but sometimes rounded at the base, pointed
or rounded at the apex ; margins doubly toothed ; upper surface bright green,
glabrous except when quite young ; always covered with a close white felt
beneath ; stalk ½ to 1 in. long. Flowers dull white, heavy scented, about ½ in.
across, and produced towards the end of May in corymbs 2 to 3 ins. across ;
stalks and calyx covered with white down. Fruit oval or roundish, ⅓ to ½ in.
long, scarlet-red specked with brownish dots.

Native of the British Isles and pretty general over Europe, also found in
some of its forms in Asia Minor and N. Africa. There is no tree more
characteristic of the chalk hills of Britain or more beautiful in regard to foliage
and fruit, but it is often reduced to a mere shrub. It is very effective in the
breeze when the wind, by lifting the leaves, reveals the pure white under-
surface to the observer in kaleidoscopic glimpses. Although apparently

preferring the limestone in a state of nature, it thrives quite well under cultivation in almost any well-drained soil. A tree well laden with the bright red fruits is also one of the most beautiful of autumn pictures ; only, owing to the depredations of birds, often of short duration. It is best propagated by seeds, but the young plants grow very slowly at first. The timber is hard and heavy, but is too scarce to count for much in the timber trade. The largest tree recorded by Elwes is at Camp Wood, near Henley-on-Thames,

SORBUS ARIA

which in 1905 was 75 ft. high by 4 ft. 9 ins. in girth of trunk. The white-beam has many varieties, some wild, others of garden origin. The most distinct are as follows :—

Var. ANGUSTIFOLIA, *Lindley.*—Leaves narrow, ovate-lanceolate, base very tapering, always more than twice as long as wide.

Var. CHRYSOPHYLLA.—Leaves yellow all the season, rather narrower than in the type. Of garden origin, and sent out by Mr Hesse of Weener, Hanover.

Var. FLABELLIFOLIA.—A very distinct form, sometimes made into a separate species. Leaves smaller and rounder than in S. Aria, snow-white beneath, nearly always wedge-shaped at the base, broad and jagged at the apex, ribs rarely more than six on each side, margins coarsely cut and toothed except at the lower part. A small tree or shrub wild in S.E. Europe and Asia Minor. Fruit not ripe till October.

Var. GRÆCA, *Boissier* (S. græca, *Loddiges*).—A small tree or shrub sometimes confused with the preceding, but with larger, broadly ovate leaves, having as many as ten ribs on each side, and less deeply jagged at the margins. Native of S.E. Europe.

Var. MAJESTICA, *Prain*; Bot. Mag., t. 8184 (Aria Decaisneana, *Lavallée*). —This is the finest of all the varieties of whitebeam, having larger leaves and fruits than any. It is of unknown origin, but is recorded as having existed in the Segrez Arboretum in 1858. It was at one time known in the nurseries near Paris as the "Sorbier du Nepaul," but there is no evidence to show that it ever came from Nepal or any part of N. India. We are thus led to believe that, like many other fine varieties of trees, it originated as a chance and unrecorded seedling under cultivation. Its leaves are sometimes 7 ins. long and 3 to 4 ins. wide, the fruits ⅝ in. long. In other respects it does not differ from S. Aria.

Var. QUERCOIDES.—A form of dwarf habit with leaves evenly lobed like those of common oak, and upturned at the edges.

Var. RUPICOLA (P. rupicola, *Syme*; English Botany, ed. 3, t. 483).—A. dwarfed variety found in several elevated limestone districts of Great Britain. It differs from ordinary S. Aria in the obovate leaves, wedge-shaped towards the base, with fewer veins, and becoming smooth on the upper surface more quickly. According to Mr Syme, the flowers are rather larger than in S. Aria, but the fruit is smaller. Under cultivation it may revert to the type.

Var. SALICIFOLIA.—Leaves narrower than in the type, but not so narrow as in var. angustifolia ; stalks longer as a rule.

Var. SINENSIS, *Henry*.—"Leaves narrow, lanceolate or ovate, with acuminate apex and cuneate base, crenately serrate. A series of forms occur in the mountains of Hupeh, China, where the trees are common at high elevations, and vary from 10 to 40 ft. in height ; very beautiful in foliage, and vigorous in growth." (Henry in *Trees of Great Britain and Ireland*, p. 167.) Introduced by Wilson for Messrs Veitch in 1901.

Var. SULPHUREA.—Leaves as in the type, but pale yellow.

All the varieties are best grafted on stocks of S. Aria, but owing to its slow growth from seed, stocks of mountain ash or even hawthorn are preferred.

S. AUCUPARIA, *Linnaeus*. ROWAN. MOUNTAIN ASH

(Pyrus Aucuparia, *Gaertner*)

A deciduous tree, 30 to 60 ft. high, of erect growth when young, becoming more spreading and graceful with age ; trunk smooth and grey ; branchlets downy when young, becoming glabrous later ; terminal bud very downy throughout the winter, not gummy. Leaves pinnate, 5 to 9 ins. long, composed usually of six and a half or seven and a half pairs of leaflets (sometimes more or less) ; leaflets narrowly ovate-oblong, 1 to 2½ ins. long, smallest towards the apex, pointed, sharply toothed, downy beneath when young, becoming almost or quite glabrous by the autumn. Flowers white, ⅓ in. across, produced very numerously in terminal, flattish corymbs 3 to 5 ins. across ; calyx and flower-stalks clothed with grey wool. Fruits in large showy clusters, ¼ in. to ⅜ in. across, round or slightly oval, bright red.

The mountain ash is widely spread over the cool, temperate parts of Europe and Asia, and is abundant in most parts of the British Isles. It is one of the most beautiful of our native trees alike in leaf, flower, and fruit. Its beauty no doubt is greatest when the branches are laden with the large nodding clusters of ripe fruits in September, but where bird life is abundant that beauty soon passes. Of neat habit and never of large size, it is a useful tree in small gardens, for which, however, some of the varieties mentioned below might be selected, leaving the typical mountain ash for the larger spaces and woodland. It is easily raised from seed, and grows quickly when young. On this account young trees are much used as stocks for grafting varieties of this and allied species on. It likes a moist, cool situation, and is apt to scorch in hot summers in the Thames Valley unless associated with other trees. Of many varieties now in cultivation the following are selected as being most distinct :—

Var. ASPLENIFOLIA.—Leaflets more than usually downy, the marginal teeth twice as deep as in the type, frequently doubly toothed. A very pretty form.

Var. DIRKENI.—Leaves clear yellow when young.

Var. FASTIGIATA.—As already intimated, the mountain ash is usually erect-branched when young. In this variety this characteristic is more strongly marked and is permanent. Raised at Dunganstown, Co. Wicklow.

Var. FRUCTU-LUTEO (Fifeana).—Fruits orange-yellow.

Var. INTEGERRIMA, *Koehne*.—A very distinct variety with leaflets quite entire or with a few obscure teeth near the apex only ; young wood, leaf-stalks, and leaves woolly.

Var. LANUGINOSA (Sorbus lanuginosa, *Kitaibel*).—In Hungary and other parts of Eastern Europe is found this variety, whose leaves are covered with bristly hairs on the upper side and are very downy beneath, also on the inflorescence and young shoots. In other respects it resembles S. Aucuparia, and is not now considered anything more than a variety of that species.

Var. MORAVICA (dulcis). Moravian Mountain Ash.—A native of North Austria ; its fruit is larger than in the type, and is eaten in Germany and Austria. A form of it known as " laciniata," with deeply lobed, even pinnatifid leaflets, is perhaps the handsomest of mountain ashes as regards foliage.

Var. PENDULA.—Branches quite pendulous. There is a form of this whose leaves are spotted with yellow, called PENDULA VARIEGATA.

Var. SATUREIFOLIA.—Three upper leaflets united ; all glabrous beneath. Perhaps a hybrid between S. Aucuparia and hybrida.

S. MEINICHII is intermediate between S. Aucuparia and S. pinnatifida, and was introduced from Norway by the Earl of Ducie about 1904. S. NEUILLYENSIS is of similar origin. Both are very probably seedlings of hybrida (*q.v.*) reverted back in part to S. Aucuparia.

S. POHUASHANENSIS, *Hedlund*, is an ally of S. Aucuparia, discovered in 1874 on the Po-hua mountain, N. China. It has the same woolly winter buds, but rather larger leaflets, and is chiefly distinguished by its larger stipules, which persist until the fruiting season. (In S. Aucuparia the stipules fall earlier.) Fruits $\frac{3}{8}$ in. diameter, bright red.

S. CALONEURA, *Rehder*

(Micromeles caloneura, *Stapf* ; Bot. Mag., t. 8335)

A tree probably 20 to 30 ft. high, with glabrous young shoots and large, ovoid, glabrous winter buds. Leaves oval to oblong, tapered at both ends ; 2 to $3\frac{1}{2}$ ins. long, half as wide ; doubly-toothed, clothed when very young with a loose floss which soon falls away leaving them glabrous above, but with a few hairs on the veins beneath ; veins in nine to sixteen pairs ; stalk $\frac{1}{8}$ to $\frac{1}{2}$ in. long, at first hairy. Flowers white, about $\frac{1}{2}$ in. wide, produced in rounded, dense corymbs, 2 to 3 ins. across; flower-stalks and calyx downy. Fruit somewhat pear-shaped, ⅓ in. long, brown, spotted; the calyx falls away from the apex completely, leaving a small pit there.

Discovered by Henry in Szechuen, China, in 1889; introduced by Wilson in 1904. It belongs to the group or sub-genus Micromeles, distinguished by the naked apex of the fruit, along with alnifolia, Folgneri, etc.

S. CHAMÆMESPILUS, *Crantz*

(Aria Chamæmespilus, *Host*; Pyrus Chamæmespilus, *Ehrhart*)

A shrub of dwarf, compact habit, becoming eventually 5 or 6 ft. high; branches short, stiff; young twigs covered at first with a whitish, cobweb-like substance. Leaves 1¼ to 3 ins. long, ⅔ to 1½ ins. wide; ovate, oval or slightly obovate, green and glabrous on both surfaces, apex rounded or pointed, margins finely toothed.; stalk ⅛ to ¼ in. long. Flowers rosy, crowded in umbels which together form a small terminal corymb; calyx woolly at the base like the flower-stalk, the teeth pointed, erect, almost glabrous outside, but covered with a thick white wool inside; petals erect, never spreading. Fruit ⅓ to ½ in. long, scarcely so wide, scarlet-red.

Native of the Alps of Europe; introduced in 1683, according to Aiton, but not frequent in gardens at the present time. It is very ornamental when in fruit, and is one of the most distinct of the Aria group in its dwarf habit, glabrous leaves, upright petals, and densely packed flowers. It is worth growing as one of the few truly shrubby species, and especially for planting in some sunny spot where a slow-growing shrub is desirable.

SORBUS HOSTII, *Hedlund*, is said to be a hybrid between the above and S. Mougeoti. The foliage is much larger than that of S. Chamæmespilus, and more resembles that of S. Mougeoti in size and in the presence of down on the lower surface; the toothing is sharp and jagged. In the dense, compact inflorescence, and in the upright pinkish petals, the influence of S. Chamæmespilus is apparent. S. Hostii is found wild on the Alps of Austria (see also p. 332).

S. COMMIXTA, *Hedlund*

(S. Aucuparia japonica, *Maximowicz*; Pyrus commixta, *Cardot*)

A deciduous tree belonging to the mountain ash group, often of more or less columnar shape, 25 to 30 ft. high; winter buds glutinous; young shoots glabrous. Leaves pinnate, 5 to 7 ins. long, made up usually of eleven or thirteen leaflets; leaflets ovate-lanceolate, slenderly pointed, sharply toothed; up to 3 ins. long, ⅝ to ¾ in. wide; dark green above, slightly glaucous beneath, glabrous on both sides. Flowers white, ¼ in. wide, produced in May on a flattish branched inflorescence 3 to 5 ins. across. Fruit bright red, globose, ¼ in. wide. Flower-stalks glabrous.

Native of Japan, Korea, and Saghalin; introduced by way of Germany in 1906. Trees at Kew and in Mr Mark Fenwick's garden at Abbotswood, Stow-on-the-Wold, are of comparatively slender columnar habit. S. Aucuparia is at once distinguishable by its shaggy winter buds and the downy young shoots, leaves, and flower-stalks. A nearer relative is S. americana, with the same viscous winter buds, but with leaflets downy when young and of larger average size. The leaflets of S. commixta are more sharply and often doubly toothed. It is a handsome tree, not taking up much space, and the foliage often turns a good red in autumn. Related to it is

S. RUFO-FERRUGINEA, *Schneider*, but very distinct on account of the dark red-brown down which covers the midrib and veins of the undersurface of the leaves. the main leaf-stalks and the flower-stalks. Native of Japan, introduced about 1913 It is grown at Kew and Aldenham.

S. CUSPIDATA, *Hedlund*. HIMALAYAN WHITEBEAM

(Bot. Mag., t. 8259 ; Pyrus vestita, *Wallich*)

A deciduous tree or large size in a wild state, but rarely seen more than 35 ft. high under cultivation. The habit is rather gaunt ; branches few, thick, covered when young with a white wool, which afterwards falls away, leaving the shoots a smooth, purplish brown. Leaves oval or ovate, 5 to 7 (sometimes 9) ins. long by 2½ to 5 ins. wide, the margins toothed, sometimes doubly so or slightly lobed ; upper surface covered at first with a white cobweb-like down, but soon becoming smooth, lower surface covered with a persistent thick felt, at first white or yellowish white, becoming grey later ; nerves parallel, in ten to seventeen pairs ; stalk ⅓ to 1 in. long. Flowers white, ⅝ in. across, produced in late May or early June in substantial corymbs 2 to 3 ins. wide ; petals woolly within ; stalks and calyx very woolly. Fruits globose, ⅝ in. wide, reddish specked with brown dots.

Native of the Himalaya ; introduced in 1820, and the most striking in its foliage of all the whitebeam group. Although nearly a century has elapsed since it was first brought into cultivation, very few specimens of large size exist in this country. The largest I know of is at Buckland St Mary, Chard, which a few years ago was nearly 40 ft. high. It grows well for some years, and then suddenly and without any apparent reason, sometimes in the middle of summer, will droop and die.

S. DISCOLOR, *Hedlund*

(S. pekinensis, *Koehne* ; Pyrus discolor, *Maximowicz*)

A deciduous tree of the mountain ash group up to 35 ft. high ; young shoots purplish, glabrous ; winter-buds hairy. Leaves pinnate, up to 10 ins. long, made up of eleven to seventeen leaflets which are narrowly oblong, pointed, the terminal two-thirds sharply toothed ; 1½ to 3 ins. long, ⅓ to ½ in. wide ; dark green above, greyish beneath ; glabrous except where they join the purplish main-stalk. Flowers ¼ in. wide, white, produced during May in a flattish loose inflorescence 4 to 6 ins. across. Fruit ¼ in. wide, roundish egg-shaped, milk-white.

Native of N. China ; introduced in 1903 to Kew from the Arnold Arboretum. It is probably as well known in gardens by Koehne's specific name " pekinensis." In foliage it resembles the common mountain ash in a general way, but the white fruits distinguish it. It is worth growing for the variety it gives in that respect, but still more for its fine red autumnal colouring. It is perhaps the best of the Aucuparia group in that particular feature.

S. DOMESTICA, *Linnæus*. SERVICE TREE

(Pyrus Sorbus, *Gaertner*)

A deciduous tree, usually 30 to 50 ft. (occasionally 60 to 70 ft. high) ; trunk covered with a scaly, rough bark ; shoots furnished with loose, silky hairs when quite young, which soon fall away ; winter buds glutinous and shining.

Leaves pinnate, 5 to 9 ins. long, composed of thirteen to twenty-one leaflets, which are narrowly oblong, usually pointed, but sometimes rounded at the tip ; 1¼ to 2½ ins. long, ⅜ to ½ in. wide ; margin set with slender teeth except towards the base, which is entire ; glabrous above, more or less downy beneath, but becoming glabrous or nearly so by autumn. Flowers white, about ½ in. across, produced in May in panicles at the end of short branches and from the leaf-axils, the whole forming a rounded or rather pyramidal cluster 2½ to 4 ins. wide. Calyx and flower-stalks downy. Fruit pear-shaped or apple-shaped, 1 to 1¼ ins. long, green or brown tinged with red on the sunny side.

Native of S. and E. Europe. As an ornamental tree this is perhaps scarcely equal to its ally, the mountain ash, but is well worth growing for the beauty of its foliage, and for its flowers, which are larger than usual in Sorbus. It also attains to greater dimensions than any of its immediate allies. The largest tree whose dimensions are recorded by Elwes is growing at Woodstock, Kilkenny, Ireland, which in 1904 was 77 ft. high and 10 ft. 8 ins.in girth.

The most famous of all British service trees was one which grew for some hundreds of years in Wyre Forest, in Worcestershire. The story of this tree was told by Mr Robert Woodward in the *Gardeners' Chronicle*, 13th April 1907. It was first noted by one Edmund Pitt, in 1678, and was mentioned and discussed by various writers up to 1862, when it was set on fire and killed by a vagrant. This tree was considered to be an old one by Pitt in 1678, and there appears to be little doubt that the species lives for five or six hundred years. The Wyre Forest tree is the only one which gives the species any claim to rank as a British tree, for it has never been found truly wild elsewhere. A few of its descendants live, the finest being at Arley Castle, now nearly 60 ft. high.

The fruit of the service tree is sometimes eaten in a state of incipient decay, especially in France, although Loudon observes that it is not highly prized, and is more frequently eaten by the poor than the rich. On the other hand Mr E. Burrell, then gardener to H.R.H. the Duchess of Albany at Claremont, in a letter dated 11th Nov. 1883, observes that " we are sending good fruits of the pear-shaped service for dessert at the present time." This Claremont tree was blown down in 1902, and was then close upon 70 ft. high. The timber is of fine quality, being very hard and heavy, but too scarce to count for much.

The form with pear-shaped fruit, which appears to make the finest tree, is distinguished as var. PYRIFORMIS ; the other, with apple-shaped fruit, as var. MALIFORMIS. Both are easily distinguished at any time from the mountain ash by the rough scaling bark ; in autumn by the big fruits ; and in winter by the glutinous, not very downy buds. The service tree should be raised from seed.

S. ESSERTEAUIANA, *Koehne*

(Bot. Mag., t. 9403 ; S. Conradinæ, *Koehne*)

A deciduous tree up to 35 ft. high ; young shoots grey with down ; buds silky. Leaves pinnate, 6 to 10 ins. long, made up of seven to thirteen leaflets ; main-stalk grey-downy, afterwards purplish. Leaflets stalkless, oblong-lanceolate to ovate-lanceolate, pointed, obliquely rounded at the base, sharply toothed, except towards the base ; 1½ to 3¼ ins. long, ⅝ to 1 in. wide, the central ones the largest ; bright dark green and glabrous above, covered with loose grey down beneath ; veins in twelve to sixteen pairs. Flowers opening in June, white, ½ in. wide, borne on a rounded inflorescence 4 ins. or more across, all the stalks as well as the calyx being covered with loose grey down. Fruit globose, scarlet, ⅕ in. wide.

Native of W. Szechuen, China ; discovered and introduced by Wilson in 1908. Belonging to the Aucuparia or mountain ash group of the genus, its nearest ally is S. Conradinæ, which, according to Koehne, is distinguished by the whiteness of the down beneath the leaflets and in their veins being deeply impressed above ; but Mr Sealy in the *Botanical Magazine* (t. 9403) has united them, finding that the characters relied upon by Koehne do not hold good. It is a very handsome tree, especially when bearing fruit.

S. FOLGNERI, *Rehder*

Micromeles Folgneri, *C. K. Schneider* ; Pyrus Folgneri, *Léveillé*)

A tree up to 30 ft. high, with slender, often semi-pendulous branches ; young shoots at first covered with whitish felt, becoming glabrous by autumn ; winter buds pointed, slender, glabrous. Leaves lanceolate or narrowly ovate, tapering to both ends ; 2 to 3½ ins. long, ¾ to 1¼ ins. wide ; long-pointed, dark green and glabrous above, covered beneath with a close, beautifully silvery white felt ; nerves parallel in eight to ten pairs ; stalk about ½ in. long. Corymbs 3 to 4 ins. across, sometimes rather elongated, carrying numerous rather densely arranged flowers ¼ to ½ in. in diameter and white ; calyx and flower-stalk woolly. Fruit oval or obovate, ½ in. across, red, not crowned by calyx teeth, but with a small pit at the apex.

Native of Hupeh, China ; introduced by Wilson for Messrs Veitch about 1901, and reared in the Coombe Wood nursery. As represented in gardens, it varies considerably in the whiteness of the under-surface, and in the more or less pendent character of its branches. In one form it is beautifully elegant, the branches arching outwards and drooping at the ends, and the leaves are vividly white beneath. Its nearest allies among cultivated sorbuses are S. alnifolia and S. caloneura ; neither white beneath the leaf.

S. GLOMERULATA, *Koehne*

A deciduous shrub or small tree, with glabrous young shoots and winter-buds. Leaves pinnate, 2½ to 6 ins. long, composed of from twenty-one to twenty-nine leaflets which are attached to the grooved, slightly winged, glabrous common stalk at intervals of ¼ to ½ in. Leaflets mostly oblong, sometimes ovate or narrowly oval, toothed towards the apex, pointed ; ¼ to 1⅛ ins. long, ⅛ to ⅓ in. wide ; glabrous or with a little down on the midrib beneath. Corymbs 2 to 3 ins. long and wide, with glabrous stalks, the white flowers, each about ⅓ in. wide, crowded at the top in a rounded cluster ; calyx and styles glabrous. Fruit pearly white, ¼ to ⅜ in. wide, globose.

Native of Hupeh, China ; discovered and introduced by Wilson in 1907. This species is well worth growing for the pretty foliage and pearl-like fruits, whose beauty, however, is apt to be short-lived, through the depredations of birds. It is most likely to be confused with S. Koehneana, which differs in its slightly downy inflorescence, more strongly toothed leaflets, often hairy buds, and in the style being downy at the base. S. glomerulata was grown in the Coombe Wood Nursery under Wilson's number 1494. It flowers in May.

S. GRACILIS, *K. Koch*

A small, deciduous tree or shrub of compact, bushy habit, up to 12 ft., young shoots slender, downy. Leaves pinnate, with a main-stalk 3 to 6 ins. long, carrying seven to eleven leaflets which are roundish oblong to oblong, 1 to 2½ ins. long, toothed towards the rounded or pointed apex, slightly downy and pale beneath ; stipules orbicular, sharply toothed, 1 in. or more across, highly coloured when young. Flowers white, in clusters 1 to 2 ins. across, with large bracts. Fruit oblong, ⅛ in. long, red.

Native of Japan, inhabiting, according to Sargent, mountain forests in Kyushu and Central Hondo. It is a distinct and attractive species, the foliage being bronzy green at first, changing to rich red in autumn. It is considered, in fact, to be one of the best Japanese trees for autumnal colouring. This character, combined with its small size and slow growth, render it well adapted for small gardens.

S. HARROWIANA, *Rehder*

(Pyrus Harrowiana, *Balfour and W. W. Smith*)

A deciduous tree from 25 to 40 ft. high ; young shoots stout, at first clothed with reddish down, soon glabrous, marked with pale lenticels. Leaves pinnate, up to 10 ins. long, consisting of three to nine leaflets ; main-stalk glabrous, the groove on the upper side closed except at the base of the leaflets. Leaflets stout and leathery in texture, oblong or narrowly obovate, rounded or tapered at the base, broad and rounded at the end, minutely toothed except towards the base, the margins slightly rolled back ; 2½ to 8 ins. long, 1 to 2 ins. wide ; glabrous and of a rather glossy green above ; glabrous and glaucous-white beneath with the veins distinctly showing ; scarcely stalked. Corymbs about 6 ins. wide ; flowers dull white, ¼ in. wide, of no beauty, their stalks bearing scattered pale hairs ; fruit pink, roundish ovoid, ¼ in. long, scarcely as wide.

Native of Yunnan, China ; discovered by Forrest in 1912 and introduced by him. In regard to foliage it is the most remarkable of all the mountain ash or pinnate-leaved group. The individual leaflets on adult trees are often more than 8 ins. long and vividly glaucous beneath ; they are much the largest in the group, whereas the flowers and fruits are among the smallest. It flowered at Caerhays, Cornwall, in May 1924. With regard to its hardiness I fear it will be found to succeed really well in the milder counties only. It was 8 ft. high at Exbury, Hants, in 1931. According to Forrest and Farrer the foliage colours well in autumn. It was named in honour of Mr R. L. Harrow, late Curator of the Edinburgh Botanic Garden, afterwards Director of the Wisley Gardens.

S. HOSTII, *Hedlund*

A natural hybrid between S. Chamæmespilus and S. Mougeoti, found wild in Austria, Hungary, and other parts of Central Europe. It is a small deciduous tree up to 12 or 16 ft. high, with oval to obovate leaves 2 to 4 ins. long and 1 to 2¼ ins. wide, sharply toothed, grey-downy beneath and rather like S. Aria but not so white. Flowers pale pink, in clusters about 2 ins. across. Fruits abundant, bright red, roundish oval, ⅓ to ½ in. long.

This is a very convenient representative of the Aria group of Sorbus for a small garden or where space is limited, as it has inherited to a considerable degree the dwarf habit of S. Chamæmespilus. It is very handsome at the fruiting season.

S. HUPEHENSIS, *C. K. Schneider*

A deciduous tree up to 40 ft. high ; young shoots loosely hairy at first, becoming glabrous and dark purplish brown. Leaves pinnate, up to 8 or 10 ins. long, made up of eleven to seventeen leaflets. Leaflets oblong to narrowly oval, pointed, tapered at the base, finely and regularly toothed except at the lower third ; 1½ to 2½ ins. long, ⅜ to ⅞ in. wide ; blue-green above, very pale beneath and downy on the midrib. Flowers small, white, produced in June in several long-stalked corymbs. Fruit globose, ¼ in. wide, white tinged with pink. Native of W. Hupeh, China; discovered by Wilson in 1910. This is a handsome species of the mountain ash (or Aucuparia) group and is nearly related to S. discolor, whose white fruits are more tinged with yellow. Like it, too, its foliage takes on beautiful autumn tints. It differs in having its winter-buds glabrous, and its stipules (persistent in discolor) deciduous. It has borne its white fruits freely in the Duke of Bedford's collection at Woburn.

Var. ROSEA, *Hort. Wisley.*—Calyx bright red; petals blush pink. Given an Award of Merit at Vincent Square, April 1938. Var. APERTA has nine or eleven leaflets, pointed; var. OBTUSA has the same number but blunt and only toothed towards the apex.

S. HYBRIDA, *Linnæus.* BASTARD SERVICE TREE
(Pyrus pinnatifida, *Ehrhart*)

A deciduous tree, 20 to 40, occasionally over 50 ft. high, with ascending branches; twigs covered with loose greyish floss when young, becoming glabrous and of a dark lustrous brown by winter. Leaves 3 to 6 ins. long, 1 to 4 ins. wide; narrowly oblong-ovate in main outline, but usually pinnate or cut nearly to the midrib at the base, the upper portion lobed and toothed, but less deeply so towards the apex, which is merely coarsely toothed; the lower surface is covered with a dull grey, persistent down; leaf-stalk ½ to 1¼ ins. long, downy. Flowers white, about ½ in. wide, produced in May in corymbs 3 to 5 ins. across. Fruit bright red, round oval, ⅝ in. long.

This tree, especially handsome in foliage and fruit, is found wild in N. and Central Europe, and is generally believed to be a natural hybrid between S. intermedia and S. Aucuparia. The influence of the latter is seen in the larger leaves, especially of the sterile shoots, having usually from one to three pairs of leaflets at the base. On the flowering twigs many of the leaves are simple. It is found wild in the Isle of Arran, rarely in England. It is connected with both intermedia and Aucuparia by intermediate forms, but as a rule reproduces itself true from seed. The habit generally is erect, but a form sent out by Messrs Backhouse of York with more than usually erect branches is called var. FASTIGIATA.

S. INTERMEDIA, *Persoon.* SWEDISH WHITEBEAM (Plate 27)
(S. scandica, *Fries*; Pyrus intermedia, *Ehrhart*)

A tree 20 to 40 ft., occasionally more, high, sometimes a shrub in a wild state; shoots very woolly when young, becoming glabrous by winter. Leaves 2 to 4½ ins. long, 1 to 3 ins. wide; broadly oval or ovate, tapering or rounded at the base, rounded or pointed at the apex; margins lobed towards the base, the lobes becoming reduced to double or jagged teeth near the apex; ribs in six to nine pairs; upper surface glabrous, polished green when mature; lower surface covered with a close grey felt. Flowers dull white, ¾ in. across, produced during May in large corymbs up to 5 ins. across; calyx and flower-stalk very woolly. Fruit oval, ½ in. long, red, surmounted by reflexed calyx teeth.

Native of N. and Central Europe, and found in a few places in Wales and the West of England on limestone. It is easily distinguished from S. Aria by the dull grey (not white), felt beneath the leaf. It is nearer, and liable to be confused with S. latifolia, but the leaves are always permanently felted beneath, narrower at the base, not so deeply lobed, and do not suggest those of S. Torminalis as the leaves of S. latifolia do. The groove between the lobes is narrower, often almost closed at the base, in S. intermedia, and the winter buds are darker. This tree is a variable one, and several forms of it have been regarded as species by some authorities. The following is perhaps the most distinct, but there are others of an intermediate character, and some with leaves whose lower lobes are almost cut to the midrib, and thus show affinity with S. hybrida.

Var. MINIMA.—This is described as a small shrub clothing limestone cliffs in two or three places in Breconshire, but the shrubby habit with this (as with other wild forms of S. intermedia) is due apparently to the impoverished conditions under which they grow. Young plants obtained from the natural habitat are, at Kew, making well-formed trees already 19 ft. high, the growths 1 to 2 ft. long in a year. The fruits are described as coral red, bitter, and resembling those of S. Aucuparia ; the leaves, except in being smaller, are like those of S. intermedia ; and the flowers also smaller, have the same whitish woolly covering to the calyx and stalks. The winter buds, too, are the same.

SORBUS MOUGEOTI, *Soyer*, is nearly allied to S. intermedia, differing chiefly in having nine to twelve pairs of ribs in each leaf, and paler felt beneath ; fruits about ⅓ in. wide, red, roundish. Native of S. and E. Europe.

S. KEISSLERI, *Rehder*

(Micromeles Decaisneana ; Pyrus Keissleri, *Léveillé*)

A deciduous tree up to 40 ft. high ; young shoots felted at first, the lenticels numerous and distinct. Leaves obovate to oval, pointed, tapered at the base, finely toothed ; 2½ to 5 ins. long, 1¼ to 2½ ins. wide ; of firm rather leathery texture ; dark glossy green above, paler beneath, at first shaggy, afterwards quite glabrous on both surfaces ; veins in seven to ten pairs ; leaf-stalk ½ in. or less long. Flowers white, ⅓ in. wide, produced in rounded or pyramidal clusters 2 ins. across at the end of short leafy twigs ; stalks woolly ; petals broadly oval ; stamens twenty ; styles two or three, united near the base. Fruit flattish orange-shaped, ½ to ¾ in. wide, dull green, spotted with pale dots ; the calyx falls away from the top and leaves a broad circular pit or scar there. Blooms in April.

Native of Hupeh and Szechuen, China ; discovered by Henry, introduced by Wilson in 1907. It is one of the Micromeles group which is distinguished in the whitebeam tribe by the calyx falling away from the top of the fruit. It is related to S. caloneura, but that species has smaller leaves with more numerous ribs and longer stalks. S. Keissleri is distinct in its large fruits, which are not brightly coloured, and is perfectly hardy at Kew.

S. KOEHNEANA, *C. K. Schneider*

A deciduous shrub or small tree up to 12 or 14 ft. high ; young shoots glabrous, turning very dark ; scales of buds often hairy. Leaves pinnate 2 to 4 ins. long on the flowering twigs, up to 6 ins. long on the barren ones main-stalk slightly downy, grooved on the upper side and slightly winged Leaflets as many as thirty-five to a leaf but usually fewer, oblong to ovate pointed, rounded (often obliquely) at the base, the terminal two-thirds rather strongly toothed ; ¼ to 1¼ ins. long, ⅛ to ⅜ in. wide ; dark green and glabrous above, grey-green and usually slightly downy on the midrib beneath ; scarcely stalked. Flowers ⅓ in. wide, borne on short leafy lateral shoots in corymbose panicles 2 to 3 ins. long and wide ; individual stalks and base of calyx sometimes downy ; petals white ; calyx-lobes triangular, glabrous outside, downy within. Fruit globose, porcelain white, about ¼ in. wide, the stalks becoming reddish.

Native of Hupeh and Shensi, China ; discovered in the former province about 1888 by Henry ; introduced by Wilson in 1907. This pretty shrub is thriving well in this country. It belongs to the Aucuparia group and is closely related to Vilmorini, but that species has rosy-red fruits and the inflorescence and calyx are covered with reddish down. It flowers in May.

S. LATIFOLIA, *Persoon*. SERVICE TREE OF FONTAINEBLEAU

(Pyrus latifolia, *Syme*)

A tree 30 to 45 ft., sometimes over 60 ft. high ; branchlets downy when young, becoming by winter shining and quite glabrous. Leaves roundish ovate, 2 to 4 ins. long, often nearly as wide at the base as they are long ; the apex pointed, the base either truncate or broadly wedge-shaped ; margin either cut into triangular, pointed lobes which are sharply toothed, or simply jaggedly toothed ; glabrous, dark lustrous green above, covered beneath with a greyish felt ; ribs six to ten on each side ; stalk downy, ½ to 1 in. long. Flowers white, ⅝ in. across, borne in corymbs 3 ins. wide during May ; stalks and calyx very woolly. Fruits globular, ½ in. diameter, dull brownish red, dotted.

This interesting tree was first discovered in the forest of Fontainebleau early in the eighteenth century. Its origin has given rise to considerable difference of opinion, but it is generally believed to be a hybrid between S. Aria and S. Torminalis. In many respects, notably in shape and woolliness of leaf, and in colour of fruit, it is certainly intermediate between them. Whether the Fontainebleau tree be a hybrid or not (and it is said to come true from seed), very similar ones found in middle Europe are almost certainly hybrids. The tree in various forms is found in the west of England. It has been much confused with S. intermedia, and in some of its forms approaches that tree in form of leaf. But it is usually much less downy on the lower surface by the end of the summer, the winter buds are paler, and the angle between the marginal lobes of the leaf is wider, often ninety degrees in S. latifolia, whereas in S. intermedia it is frequently a mere slit at the base. There is a very fine old specimen in the Earl of Bathurst's woods at Cirencester, between 70 and 80 ft. high and 11 ft. in girth of trunk.

Var. ARRANENSIS.—This has more deeply lobed leaves, the lower ones reaching more than halfway to the midrib. Isle of Arran.

S. MATSUMURANA, *Koehne*. JAPANESE MOUNTAIN ASH

(Pyrus Matsumurana, *Makino*)

A small tree with glabrous, red-brown young shoots ; winter buds glabrous. Leaves pinnate, 4 to 9 ins. long, made up of nine to thirteen leaflets which are oblong, conspicuously toothed only at the terminal half or less, pointed ; 1½ to 3 ins. long, ½ to 1 in. wide ; the lower pairs only stalked, of thin texture, green above, paler beneath, glabrous except for a few reddish hairs where the leaflets join the main-stalk. Flowers white, ⅜ in. wide, produced in corymbs 2 to 3 ins. across. Styles five ; ovary five-celled. Fruits egg-shaped, ⅜ to ½ in. long, red.

Native of Japan, where it is not uncommon in the mountainous parts of the main island ; introduced in 1912. It is one of the mountain ash group which has been called " Pyrus sambucifolia " wrongly. The true tree of that name differs (according to Mr Makino) from the present species by having

" apparently " a three-celled ovary. The inflorescence of S. Matsumurana, which expands in May and June, seems unusually small as compared with most of the Aucuparia group.

S. MEGALOCARPA, *Rehder*

(Pyrus megalocarpa, *Bean*)

A small tree up to 25 ft. high or a large shrub ; young shoots stout, glabrous, reddish, becoming later dull purple, freely marked with lenticels ; winter-buds very large, ovoid, ½ to ¾ in. long, viscous and shining. Leaves narrowly oval, sometimes obovate or ovate, broadly wedge-shaped or sometimes rounded at the base, finely and closely toothed ; 5 to 9 ins. long, 2 to 4½ ins. wide ; veins parallel, in fourteen to twenty pairs ; glabrous on both surfaces except that when young there are tufts of down in the vein-axils ; stalk ½ to 1 in. long. Corymbs 4 to 6 ins. wide, 3 to 4 ins. high, carrying numerous flowers each ¾ in. wide. Petals dull white, round, ¼ in. wide ; stamens about twenty, ⅛ in. long ; sepals broadly triangular, pointed, ₁₂ in. long, glabrous inside, woolly outside, persisting at the top of the fruit ; styles three or four, united below the middle ; flower-stalks woolly when young. Fruit egg-shaped, ¾ to 1¼ ins. long, up to ⅞ in. wide, russet-brown, minutely wrinkled. Flowers in May.

Native of W. Szechuen, China ; introduced by Wilson for Messrs Veitch in 1903. It is akin to our native whitebeam, although not very closely. It has larger fruit than any of that group and in foliage is one of the finest. The bark of the branchlets is very dark and its winter buds are remarkably large. It is quite hardy, but at Kew, on account of its early growth, is liable to injury by spring frosts. The fruits have no beauty but the foliage occasionally turns a good red.

S. MELIOSMIFOLIA, *Rehder*

(Pyrus meliosmifolia, *Bean*)

A deciduous tree 25 to 35 ft. high ; young shoots glabrous, purplish brown ; winter buds glabrous. Leaves ovate-elliptical, slenderly pointed, tapered at the base, more or less doubly toothed ; 4 to 7 ins. long, half as much wide ; green on both surfaces, woolly on the midrib and veins beneath ; veins parallel, in eighteen to twenty-four pairs ; stalk ¼ in. or less long. Flowers white, in corymbs 2 to 4 ins. wide. Fruit nearly globose, ½ in. long, dull red, the calyx falling away from the summit. It flowers in April.

Native of W. China ; discovered and introduced from Szechuen by Wilson about 1910. It is uncommon in cultivation but is occasionally offered by nurserymen. Belonging to the Micromeles section of the Aria group, it has S. alnifolia and S. caloneura as its closest allies. From both of these it is distinguished by the much more numerous veins of the leaf and the short leaf-stalk.

S. PLURIPINNATA, *Koehne*

(S. foliolosa pluripinnata *C. K. Schneider* ; Pyrus pluripinnata, *Bean*)

A shrub or small deciduous tree whose young shoots, leaf-stalks, and flower-stalks are thickly clothed with grey down. Leaves pinnate, 3 to 5 ins. long, composed of some twenty-one to twenty-five leaflets set about ¼ in. apart on the grooved main-stalk. Leaflets linear-oblong, rounded or abruptly pointed at the apex, obliquely rounded at the base, with a few teeth near the apex only ; ½ to 1⅛ ins. long, ⅛ to ¼ in. wide ; dark green and glabrous above, glaucous grey and woolly beneath. Flowers crowded at the top of branched corymbs 2 to 3½ ins. wide which are borne at the end of short leafy side twigs in May. The flower is quite small (⅛ in. wide), petals roundish ; calyx glabrous. Fruit bright red, ovoid-globose, ⅛ in. wide.

Native of Szechuen, China ; discovered by Henry about 1888, introduced by Wilson to the Coombe Wood Nursery, where it was grown under his number 1620. It belongs to the Aucuparia or mountain ash group and is distinct in its numerous small leaflets combined with the large, coarsely toothed, heart-shaped stipules and the grey downiness of all its young parts. (See note on *S. scalaris*, its nearest ally.)

S. PRATTII, *Koehne* (Plate 28)

(Bot. Mag., t. 9460)

A deciduous shrub or small tree up to 20 ft. high ; winter buds clothed with red-brown down ; young shoots dark grey-purplish, soon glabrous. Leaves pinnate, 3 to 5½ ins. long, consisting of twenty-one to twenty-nine leaflets set ⅙ to ¼ in. apart on the grooved, slightly winged main-stalk. Leaflets stalkless, oblong to oblong-ovate, rounded at the base, pointed, rather coarsely toothed, ½ to ⅞ in. long about ¼ in. wide, more or less cobwebby and rather glaucous beneath. Flowers ⅓ in. wide, white, in clusters 1½ to 2 ins. across, each cluster on a slender stalk 1 to 1½ ins. long, opening in May. Fruit globose, ¼ to ⅓ in. wide, ultimately pearly white.

There are two forms of this mountain ash ; var. SUBARACHNOIDEA, *Koehne*, in which the undersurface of the leaflets is covered with a thin, reddish brown, cobwebby down. Wilson introduced this in 1910 from W. Szechuen under his number 4323. It has borne fine crops of its fruits at Aldenham, Herts, with the late Mr Vicary Gibbs, who described them as of " dazzling pearly whiteness " (see *Gardeners' Chronicle*, 25th September 1920, fig. 66). He remarked that birds are as fond of the fruits as they are of those of ordinary mountain ash. The other variety—TATSIENENSIS, *Koehne*, (Wilson No. 991), differs in having the leaflets glabrous beneath or downy only on the midrib, and smaller.

S. Prattii is related to S. Koehneana and S. glomerulata, both also with white fruits. The latter can be distinguished by its glabrous buds and the former never has the cobwebby down seen in S. Prattii.

S. SAMBUCIFOLIA, *Roemer*

There is no more confusing term in connection with the mountain ash group than " S. sambucifolia." It appears to have been applied to what are by some authors regarded as four distinct species. The true thing is regarded as confined to N.E. Asia, and is probably not in cultivation. In western N. America the tree commonly called " S. sambucifolia " has been made a distinct species by Prof. Greene ; it is SORBUS SCOPULINA, *Greene*. A small erect tree 4 to 12 ft. high, with thick, erect branches. The leaflets, seven to fifteen in number, are broader and more abruptly narrowed at the apex than in S. americana. The flowers and fruits are larger, the latter of a bright red and in trusses 4 to 6 ins. across. S. scopulina is, I think, represented in gardens by the mountain ash known generally as " Pyrus americana nana," the stiffest, stoutest, and most erect branched of any.

The " S. sambucifolia " of the eastern side of N. America is Sargent's S. americana decora, which, he says, is connected with typical S. americana (*q.v.*) by intermediate forms. Finally, in Japan, is S. MATṢUMURANA, *Makino*, a small tree with glabrous shoots and winter buds, the leaflets only toothed at the terminal half.

S. SARGENTIANA, *Koehne*

A deciduous tree 20 to 30 ft. high ; young shoots at first woolly, finally glabrous and conspicuously marked with pale warts (lenticels) ; apex of buds woolly and viscid. Leaves pinnate, 8 to 12 ins. long ; leaflets usually nine or eleven, oblong-lanceolate, slender-pointed, toothed except near the base ; 3 to 5½ ins. long, 1 to 1½ ins. wide ; soon glabrous above, at first downy beneath. Flowers white, ¼ in. wide, densely borne on a hemispherical inflorescence 5 or 6 ins. wide, the stalks of which are thickly clothed with white wool. Fruit scarlet, globose, ⅛ in. wide.

Native of W. China ; discovered by Wilson in 1903, introduced in 1908. It is made one of the most distinct of the mountain ash group by the large size of the leaflets and the large, rounded, woolly stalked inflorescences. The leaflets must, among the cultivated members of this group, be next in size to those of the remarkable S. Harrowiana. It must not, of course, be confused with P. Sargentii of the Malus section of Pyrus.

Var. WARLEYENSIS, *Marquand.*—Leaflets smaller and narrower ; main-stalk dark reddish purple ; inflorescence larger ; fruits smaller. Introduced from W. China by a French missionary, also collected by Wilson in 1903 (*Gardeners' Chronicle,* vol. xciv., fig. 79.)

S. SCALARIS, *Koehne*

A shrub or small tree up to 20 ft. high ; young shoots greyish downy. Leaves pinnate, 4 to 8 ins. long, consisting of twenty-one to thirty-seven leaflets set ¼ to ½ in. apart. Leaflets narrowly oblong, rounded or pointed at the end, toothed at or towards the apex only ; ½ to 1½ ins. long, $\frac{3}{16}$ to $\frac{5}{16}$ in. wide ; covered beneath with a whitish cobwebby down like the main-stalk, which is purplish and grooved above ; stipules large, toothed. Inflorescence 4 to 5 ins. wide, flattish or rounded, much branched ; flowers dull white, ¼ in. wide ; flower-stalks and base of calyx grey-downy. Fruits globose, ⅛ in. wide, bright red.

Native of W. Szechuen, China ; discovered and introduced by Wilson in 1904. It belongs to that section of the mountain ash group from W. China and N. India with leaves made up of numerous small, closely set leaflets, of which S. Vilmorinii is the best known species in gardens. It is very closely related to S. pluripinnata, having the same large, toothed stipules, but that species has on the average a lower number of leaflets to each leaf and they are closer together and smaller ; the inflorescence also is smaller.

S. THIANSHANICA, *Ruprecht*

(Pyrus thianshanica, *Franchet* ; Bot. Mag., t. 7755)

A shrub or small tree, 6 to 14 ft. high, of rounded bushy habit ; young shoots usually glabrous. Leaves pinnate, 5 or 6 ins. long, composed of four and a half to seven and a half pairs of leaflets, which are lanceolate, 1¼ to 2 ins. long, ⅜ to ⅝ in. wide, pointed, finely and evenly toothed, and quite glabrous on both surfaces ; stalkless, except the terminal one. Flowers white, ¾ in. across, produced in late May in terminal, rather loose corymbs, 3 to 5 ins. across ; calyx and flower-stalks quite glabrous except at the margins of the triangular calyx teeth. Fruit roundish, ¼ in. diameter, bright red.

Native of Central Asia (Turkestan, Afghanistan, etc.) ; discovered in 1867, and introduced about 1895. One of the dwarfest of this section, this is also one of the most pleasing. For small gardens or small lawns it is especially adapted, being of slow growth and neat, bushy form. Its flowers are probably the largest in the mountain ash group.

S. THURINGIACA, *Fritsch*

A hybrid between S. Aria and S. Aucuparia, with the leaves partly pinnate, partly simple. The lower part of the leaf is composed of two to four pairs of leaflets, the remaining and smaller upper part consisting of one lobed or pinnatifid segment. It has an origin similar to that of S. pinnatifida, but shows much more the influence of S. Aucuparia in the number of separate leaflets. The Aria influence is shown in the persistent greyish down beneath the leaf, and in the amalgamation of the upper leaflets. There is a tree at Kew 30 ft. high, with a trunk girthing 3 ft. It is usually found in gardens as " Pyrus lanuginosa," but the true S. lanuginosa of De Candolle is merely a variety of S. Aucuparia with densely woolly leaves (wholly pinnate) and hairy young shoots.

S. TORMINALIS, *Crantz*. WILD SERVICE TREE

(Pyrus torminalis, *Ehrhart*)

A tree from 30 to 40 ft. high as a rule, but occasionally 60 to 70 ft., with a trunk girthing over 5 ft., branchlets covered at first with a loose floss, but soon quite glabrous and shining. Leaves 2½ to 5 ins. long, nearly or quite as wide, of a broadly ovate or triangular outline, divided half-way to the midrib into three to five pointed lobes on each side ; margins doubly-toothed ; upper surface glabrous and lustrous dark green ; lower surface paler and at first downy, afterwards glabrous ; stalk 1 to 2 ins. long. Flowers white, ½ in. across ; produced during June in rather lax corymbs 3 or 4 ins. across ; calyx and flower-stalks very woolly. Fruit oval or roundish, ½ in. long, brownish.

Native of Europe (except the extreme north) including Central and S. England. This handsome tree is nowhere apparently very abundant in a wild state, and is rare also in cultivation. Yet few trees of its size are more striking, its leaves being large, boldly cut, and of a healthy polished green, turning crimson or yellowish in autumn. The flowers are not very pure white, but attractive when seen in the mass. The fruits when " bletted " after the fashion of medlars have a similar flavour, but are not to be recommended. It should be raised from seeds, and thrives best in a heavy clayey soil. Elwes records several trees between 60 and 70 ft. high in England, and a tree is known in Germany 82 ft. and 6½ ft. in girth of trunk. In Kent and Sussex the fruits are popularly known as " chequers."

S. VILMORINI, *C. K. Schneider*

(Pyrus Vilmorini, *Ascherson and Graebner* ; Bot. Mag., t. 8241)

A shrub or small tree, 10 to 20 ft. high, of elegant, wide-spreading habit, the young shoots stiff, covered when young with a brownish down. Leaves pinnate, 3 to 5½ ins. long, composed of six and a half to fourteen and a half pairs of leaflets, which increase in size towards the end of the leaf. Leaflets narrow-oblong, or oval, ⅓ to ¾ in. long, ⅛ to ¼ in. wide ; stalkless, toothed towards the apex, glabrous on both sides ; common stalk slightly winged and more or less downy, especially early in the season. Flowers white, ¼ in. diameter, produced in June on slender stalked corymbs at the ends of short twigs, and in the leaf-axils, the whole forming a pretty inflorescence 2½ to 4 ins. across. Fruit globose, ⅓ in. wide, rosy red becoming almost white.

Native of W. China ; originally raised in France by Mr Maurice de Vilmorin from seed he had received from the missionary Delavay in 1889. Introduced to Kew in 1905. This beautiful shrub is apparently quite hardy, and is one of the most elegant species introduced in recent years. The neat, handsomely divided leaves (among the smallest in the mountain ash group), the abundant clusters of pure white blossoms, and finally the fruits of a rosy, not a scarlet, red, all give to this species an air of distinction. It is allied to, and was at first associated with the Himalayan P. foliolosa—a probably tender species with much more woolly leaflets.

SPARTIUM JUNCEUM

SPARTIUM JUNCEUM, *Linnæus*. SPANISH BROOM. LEGUMINOSÆ

(Bot. Mag., t. 85)

A tall shrub of rather gaunt habit, with erect, cylindrical, rush-like stems, glabrous and dark green, which, in the almost entire absence of foliage, fulfil the functions of leaves. It grows 8 to 12 ft. high. Leaves very few and deciduous, simple, linear, ½ to ¾ in. long, with silky hairs beneath. Flowers fragrant, disposed in terminal racemes 12 or even 18 ins. long, on the current season's growth. Each flower is about 1 in. long, pea-shaped (papilionaceous), shortly stalked, rich glowing yellow, with a showy, roundish standard petal nearly 1 in. across. Pod 1½ to 3 ins. long, ¼ in. wide, hairy, five- to twelve-seeded.

Native of S. Europe ; introduced, it is said, in 1518, The name " Spartium " has been given to many leguminous plants, but is now confined to this species. S. junceum is a useful shrub whose value is enhanced by its coming into bloom in June and lasting until September. In July, when it is at its best, it is very showy. It is admirable for planting on hot dry banks, especially if it be associated with a dwarfer shrub (like double-flowered gorse), which will hide its gaunt and naked base. But in the ordinary reaches of the garden also it makes very effective groups, and gives masses of welcome colour when shrubs generally have gone out of flower. It must be raised from seeds (which ripen in abundance), and kept in pots until planted out in permanence, for it dislikes disturbance at the root. Sometimes it is grown as a formal bush, being clipped over with shears in early spring before growth starts ; shoots then spring out all over the bush, which blossom in their due season a few months later.

The shrub has some economic value in the south of Europe, yielding a fibre which is obtained from the branchlets by maceration, and is worked up into thread, cordage, and a coarse fabric.

Var. PLENUM.—A double-flowered form propagated by grafting on young seedlings of the type. It was introduced by Peter Collinson from Nuremberg in 1746. He says : " It cost me a golden ducat ; came from thence down the Rhine, and was brought by the first ship to London in good order. I narched it on the single-flowered broom and gave it to Gray and Gordon two famous nurserymen)." It was, till recently, cultivated at Kew, but unless it had deteriorated, it was scarcely worth Collinson's trouble. In the type, the upper edge of the keel towards the base is sensitive. If it be touched by a pencil point (or the proboscis of an insect) the stamens spring out from the keel, ejecting the pollen in a little cloud.

SPIRÆA. ROSACEÆ

This genus includes herbs as well as shrubs, and the latter show every variation in stature from tufted plants a few inches high to those of almost tree-like dimensions such as the new West Chinese S. arborea, which is 30 ft. high. Spiræa is the chief genus in a tribe of Rosaceæ, and has as it closest allies, Neillia, Exochorda, and Stephanandra—all hardy shrubs represented in gardens. I have followed the Bentham and Hooker conception of the genus, which has for so long been adopted in this country, but there is now a disposition to split it up into several genera, as follows :—

SPIRÆA (proper).—Capsules free ; leaves simple, usually toothed ; e.g. S. japonica, S. Thunbergii, and numerous others.

SIBIRÆA.—Capsules united at the base ; leaves entire ; e.g. S. lævigata (the only species).

SORBARIA.—Leaves pinnate ; e.g. S. Aitchisoni, arborea, Lindleyana, sorbifolia.

CHAMÆBATIARIA.—Leaves doubly pinnate ; e.g. S. Millefolium (the only species).

HOLODISCUS.—Fruit an achene containing one seed not splitting to release it as the capsules of the four previous groups do ; e.g. S. discolor.

Thus, in its more comprehensive sense, Spiræa has simple, pinnate, o
bipinnate leaves, all deciduous. The flowers are very uniform in size
varying in most of the species from about $\frac{1}{4}$ to $\frac{1}{3}$ in. in diameter, but in
a few of the finer garden forms like the double-flowered prunifolia and
cantoniensis, also in S. Millefolium, they are $\frac{1}{2}$ in. across. The blossom
are either white or of some shade of red or pink (all the spring-flowering
sorts have white flowers), and the inflorescence is either a fascicle or short
leafy raceme produced from the buds of the previous year's growths ; o
a panicle or corymb terminating the growths of the current season. The
petals are normally five, the stamens numerous and often so long as to
make a conspicuous feature in the inflorescence, the seed-vessels five
dry, erect, with the style adhering at or near the top, and the calyx
persisting at the base.

The shrubby spiræas, of which about sixty species are known, are
widely spread over Europe, N. Asia, and N. America, but no shrubby
species is a genuine native of Britain, although S. salicifolia has escaped
from gardens and become naturalised in various parts of the kingdom.

As ornaments in the garden, the best of the spiræas fill an important
place. They flower with great freedom, are often very graceful, and
except that some of the earlier flowering kinds are liable to injury by late
frost, they are perfectly at home under cultivation. All like a good loamy
soil, abundant moisture, and full sunlight.

PROPAGATION.—Many of the spiræas spread by means of sucker
growths from the base, and such are easily increased by dividing the
plants into small pieces. The rest can nearly all be propagated easily
by means of cuttings made of moderately firm wood placed in light sandy
soil in gentle bottom heat in July and August. If this be not available
cuttings made of harder wood in September may be placed under bell
glasses out-of-doors in a sheltered spot. For the pinnate-leaved one
root-cuttings may be used.

The spiræas produce fertile seed in abundance, but they cross-breed
with such facility that seed can only be depended on to come true when
the plants are fairly isolated from other species. Some of the very best
spiræas are hybrids, as may be gathered from the following descriptive
notes, but they have become so numerous that they make the genus, as
represented in gardens, excessively difficult to study and classify. Mr
Zabel of Münden has devoted a volume of one hundred and twenty-eight
pages exclusively to their elucidation, but many are so similar to each
other that their differentiation on paper is no longer possible within
convenient limits.

PRUNING.—Few shrubs repay careful pruning better than the spiræas,
and in this matter they may be divided into two groups, viz. (1) those that
flower early and from the buds of shoots made the previous year, such as
arguta, hypericifolia, Thunbergii, Van Houttei, Veitchii, etc. ; and (2)
those that flower later in the year at the ends of the shoots of the current
season, such as japonica, Douglasii, salicifolia, Lindleyana, etc. This
matter is fully discussed in the introductory chapter on pruning, and
from what is there stated it will be evident that the first group must only
be pruned by thinning out the older and weaker wood ; any shortening

SPIRÆA AITCHISONI

back of the shoots must mean a reduction in the next crop of blossom
The second group, on the other hand, is benefited by the shoots bein;
shortened back. This should, of course, be done in late winter or earl
spring, and at the same time superfluous old shoots should be cut clea
out. Unless pruning of either kind is done, many of the spiræas get int
a weedy, thin condition, and their blossoms will not bear compariso
either in quantity or quality with that of properly pruned plants.

The group including Douglasii, tomentosa, salicifolia, Menziesii, an
their hybrids form dense thickets, and spread rapidly by means of under
ground suckers. These should be pruned as in group 2 (being lat
flowering), and it is also advisable at intervals of a few years to dig then
up, divide them into smaller pieces, and after enriching the ground
replant them more thinly. This, of course, applies to ordinary cultivate
shrubberies and borders, but they also make admirable masses for th
wilder portions of the demesne, where they can safely be left to tak
care of themselves. In such places the reddish or rich brown stem
of many spiræas make a cheerful feature in winter.

So many of the spiræas are of similar aspect and value, that fo
gardens a selection suffices. The following kinds may be recommended
or, for smaller gardens, the ten marked * :—

*Arguta.	Douglasii.	Salicifolia paniculata.
Arborea.	Henryi.	Sargentiana.
*Aitchisoni.	*Japonica and its varieties.	Thunbergii.
Brachybotrys.	Media.	Trichocarpa.
Nipponica.	*Margaritæ.	Trilobata.
Canescens.	*Menziesii triumphans.	*Van Houttei.
*Discolor.	*Prunifolia fl. pl.	*Veitchii.

(For the rock garden *bullata and decumbens are very suitable.

S. AITCHISONI, *Hemsley*

(Sorbaria angustifolia, *Zabel*)

A shrub of open, spreading habit, ultimately 10 ft. high ; branches red
when young, perfectly glabrous, and very pithy. Leaves pinnate, 9 to 15 ins
long, composed of eleven to twenty-three leaflets. Leaflets narrowly lance-
shaped with long tapering points ; 2 to 4 ins. long, $\frac{1}{4}$ to $\frac{3}{8}$ in. wide ; evenly
sharply, and rather deeply toothed ; green and quite glabrous on both surfaces,
stalkless. Flowers white, $\frac{1}{8}$ in. across, produced during July and August in
pyramidal branching panicles from 1 to $1\frac{1}{2}$ ft. long, and 9 to 15 ins. through ;
flower-stalks glabrous ; seed-vessels red.

Native of Afghanistan, Kashmir, etc. ; first discovered in the Kurrum
Valley by Dr Aitchison in 1879, and introduced to Kew in 1895 by Mr J. F.
Duthie. It is closely allied to S. Lindleyana, differing chiefly in the red young
bark, the narrower leaves without down and mostly simply (not doubly) toothed
margins, and its larger flowers. On the whole it is superior to S. Lindleyana,
its foliage being more elegant and its flowers more effective. It is said to be
hardy where S. Lindleyana will not succeed.

S. ALPINA, *Pallas*

A shrub 3 to 5 ft. high, with erect stems ; young shoots angled, finely
downy, bright brown. Leaves $\frac{1}{4}$ to 1 in. long, $\frac{1}{8}$ in. or less wide ; narrowly
oblong, or obovate, entire, glabrous, with feathered veins beneath. Flowers

ellowish white, small, produced during May and June in small umbels ;
ower-stalks glabrous.

SPIRÆA ARGUTA (see p. 346)

Native of N.E. Asia ; introduced in 1806. It is allied to S. crenata, but
differs in the feathery veining of the leaf ; also to S. cana, but is distinguished
by the glabrous leaves. Of little garden value.

(This name must not be confused with S. sorbifolia alpina, *Pallas*, the
Sorbaria alpina of later authors, which belongs to one of the pinnate-leaved
spiræas. See S. sorbifolia.)

S. AMŒNA, *Spae*

(S. expansa, *Koch* ; S. fastigiata, *Wallich*)

A shrub up to 6 ft. high, with slender, round, downy stems, erect and nc much branched ; buds hairy. Leaves lanceolate to ovate up to 4 ins. lon by 1¼ ins. wide ; coarsely and sharply toothed (both simply and doubly except at the base, dark green above, hairy on the veins and rather glaucou beneath ; stalks ¼ to ⅓ in. long. Flowers white with a flush of red, borne i flat compound corymbs from 2 to 8 ins. across ; calyx and flower-stalks downy It blossoms on the shoots of the year in July and August.

Native of the Himalaya ; much confused with S. bella, but differing i having round stems, more hairy leaf-buds, and larger, flatter corymbs.

S. ARGUTA, *Zabel* (Plate 29)

A shrub of rounded, bushy habit, 6 to 8 ft. high, and as much wide branches graceful, slender, twiggy, and covered with down. Leave oblanceolate, ¾ to 1½ ins. long, ¼ to ½ in. wide ; entire, or with a few teeth towards the apex ; of a lively green and glabrous above, slightly downy an rather prominently nerved beneath. Flowers ⅓ in. across, pure white, produce during April and May in fascicles of four to eight, each flower on a slende glabrous stalk ½ in. or so long.

Three species are believed to have a share in the parentage of this hybrid viz., Thunbergii, crenata, and hypericifolia. It is the most beautiful of the spring-flowering spiræas, being quite hardy and never failing to produce a wealth of blossom. The flower-clusters are crowded on the upper side o shoots made the previous year, forming snowy white wreaths from 6 ins. t 12 ins. long. It is most conveniently increased by means of layers, its slende lissom branches adapting themselves admirably to this method.

S. ARBOREA, *Bean*

(Sorbaria arborea, *C. K. Schneider*)

A spreading deciduous shrub, usually 10 to 20 ft. high, but said sometimes to be up to 30 ft. ; young shoots and leaf-stalks slightly downy. Leaves pinnate, with thirteen to seventeen leaflets which are oblong-ovate to lanceolate, long and slenderly pointed, 2 to 4 ins. long, doubly toothed, stellately downy beneath but often only slightly so. Flowers white, ¼ in. wide, produced densely in fine, often pyramidal panicles up to and over 12 ins. long, during July.

Native of Central and Western China, introduced by E. H. Wilson in 1908. It is closely akin to S. Lindleyana but superior to that species which differs in the hairs beneath the leaves being simple (not clustered). S. arborea has also a shorter calyx-tube and longer stamens. It is the finest of the Sorbaria or pinnate-leaved group and may be pruned every winter. It likes a good loamy soil and gives finer panicles if top-dressed with manure occasionally.

Var. GLABRATA, *Rehder*, has glabrous shoots and leaves, often purplish, and narrower leaflets.

S. ASSURGENS, *Bean*

(Sorbaria assurgens, *Vilmorin*)

A deciduous shrub up to 8 or 10 ft. high, with more or less erect stems, but making a shapely bush ; young shoots round, not downy. Leaves pinnate, up to more than 12 ins. long, consisting of eleven to seventeen leaflets which

e 2 to 3½ ins. long, ½ to 1 in. wide ; lanceolate, with a long, slender, often
curved point, doubly toothed, sometimes slightly downy on the veins beneath ;
veins in twenty-five or more pairs. Flower-panicles narrowly pyramidal, borne
July and August at the end of leafy shoots ; 6 to 12 ins. long, with their
branches erect. Flowers white, ⅜ in. wide, with about twenty conspicuous
stamens ; calyx glabrous.

Native probably of China. It appears to have been introduced to cultivation by the firm of Vilmorin, who first flowered it at Verrieres, near Paris, in
1900. It was sent by them to Kew in 1903. One of the pinnate-leaved group
of spiræas (now often called Sorbaria), it is nearly related to S. Lindleyana,
but that species has wide panicles with spreading branches. S. sorbifolia,
another close ally, differs in having twice as many stamens to each flower
but fewer (about twenty) veins to each leaflet. It is a worthy member of a
hardy group.

S. BELLA, *Sims*

(Bot. Mag., t. 2426)

A shrub 4 to 6 ft. high, with angular, slightly hairy young branches.
Leaves thin, broadly ovate, pointed, doubly toothed towards the apex ; 1 to
4 ins. long on the barren shoots ; smaller, simply toothed, and about half as
wide on the flowering ones ; upper surface glabrous ; glaucous or whitish, and
more or less downy beneath ; stalks ⅛ to ¼ in. long. Flowers bright rose,
in. across, produced during June in corymbs ¾ to 1½ ins. across.

Native of the Himalaya ; introduced early in the nineteenth century. In
spite of its name this shrub is not one of the best of the spiræas. It has been
much confused with S. amœna, a species nearly allied but having quite round
(not angled) branches. There is also an intermediate form known in gardens
as S. PULCHELLA, *Kunze* (bella × amœna).

S. BRACHYBOTRYS, *Lange*

(S. luxuriosa, *Lavallée* ; S. pruinosa, *Zabel*)

A vigorous shrub, up to 8 ft. high, branches gracefully arching ; young
wood downy, ribbed. Leaves oblong or ovate, ¾ to 1¾ ins. long, ⅓ to ¾ in. wide,
with a few teeth at the apex only ; upper surface dull dark green, and slightly
downy, lower one pale and felted with fine grey down. Flowers bright pink,
small, and crowded densely in stout panicles 1½ to 3 ins. long and about the
same wide ; they are borne at the end of leafy twigs, 3 to 12 ins. long, that
spring from the branches of the preceding year, expanding in June and July ;
flower-stalks and calyx hairy.

A hybrid between canescens and probably Douglasii, inheriting much of
the grace and vigour of the former. This is, indeed, one of the best of the
taller summer-flowering kinds, the long shoots made one year branching
copiously towards the top the following one, when each twig carries its terminal
panicle, the whole forming a fine sheaf of brightly coloured blossom.

S. BULLATA, *Maximowicz*

(S. crispifolia, *Hort.*)

A dwarf shrub of very compact, rounded habit, rarely more than 12 or
15 ins. high ; young shoots erect, covered with rusty coloured down. Leaves
⅜ to 1 in. long, almost or quite as much wide ; broadly ovate, often recurved,
coarsely and irregularly toothed, and nearly or quite glabrous on both surfaces

except for a few hairs at the base and on the stalk ; nerves prominent beneat'
Flowers scarlet-rose, small, produced towards the end of July in great numbe.
in flat branching corymbs 3 ins. wide at the end of the current season's growths
flower-stalks downy.

Native of Japan, and in cultivation by 1881. It is one of the dwarfest c
spiræas and one of the prettiest ; very suitable for the rock garden, or whereve
small dainty shrubs can be accommodated, and protected from strong
growing neighbours. It is a near ally of S. japonica, and may be a garde
form of that species raised in Japan. The old flowering growths may be cu
back in spring. The specific name refers to the puckering of the blade of th
leaf, often noticeable between the veins. The plant is almost hidden by in
flowers in July.

S. CÆSPITOSA, *Nuttall*

(Petrophytum caespitosum, *Rydberg* ; Eriogynia caespitosa, *S. Watson*)

It is, perhaps, stretching the term " shrub " somewhat to include mentio
here of this spiræa, but its base is purely woody and as it occurs in nature th
main stem may be half an inch or more in diameter. The plant is a low
prostrate evergreen forming a close, compact tuft or mat an inch or two high
One writer describes it in the State of Idaho as making dense and perfectl
flat mats of tough woody branches growing over rocks, in the cracks of whic
the seed had originally germinated. Leaves oblanceolate, not toothed, $\frac{1}{4}$ t
1 in. long, $\frac{1}{8}$ in. or less wide, tapering gradually to the base, bluntish at th
apex except for a minute tip ; grey-green covered with silky hairs. Flower
white, very small, produced during July and August densely packed i
cylindrical racemes 1 to $2\frac{1}{2}$ ins. long, the racemes being borne at the top of a
erect stalk 1 to 4 ins. long. The stamens (about twenty to each flower) ar
conspicuously exposed.

Native of the S.W. States of N. America, where it often occurs on limeston
formations. It is hardy even in the E. United States and is grown successfull
in Scotland. It is adapted only for the rock garden, or moraine, where ther
is perfect drainage and unobstructed sunshine. Very distinct from the ordinar
type of spiræa in its dwarfness, its narrow entire leaves, and the close packing
of the small flowers near the top of a quite erect spike. It is often set apar
with four other species in a separate genus—PETROPHYTUM.

S. CANA, *Waldstein and Kitaibel*

A shrub 3 ft. or more high and as much through ; of dense, twiggy habit
the young shoots round and covered with a thick grey down. Leave
narrowly oval or ovate, tapering at both ends ; $\frac{1}{4}$ to 1 in. long, about half a
wide ; nearly always entire ; covered on both sides, but especially beneath
with a grey silky down. Flowers dull white, $\frac{1}{4}$ in. across, produced durin
May at the end of short leafy twigs in dense umbel-like racemes $\frac{3}{4}$ to 1 in. wide
Native of S.E. Europe ; introduced in 1825. The leaf is very like that o
Salix repens in its dense grey down, not, however, so silvery. One of th
least attractive of the spiræas, but of neat habit and quite hardy ; also distinc
in the character of its leaves.

S. CANESCENS, *Don*

(S. flagelliformis, *Hort.*)

A shrub varying considerably in height ; at its tallest 12 to 15 ft. high
more often 6 to 8 ft. high the main stems erect, but producing towards the
top slender, arching or pendulous branches growing 3 ft. or more long in

one season ; the young branches ribbed and downy. Leaves ⅓ to 1 in. long, ⅓ to ⅝ in. wide ; oval or obovate, usually blunt and toothed at the apex, and always more or less tapering to the very short stalk at the base ; dull green and with some down above, grey and more or less thickly downy beneath. Flowers white, or dull creamy white, small, produced during June and July in corymbs 1 to 2 ins. across, at the end of short leafy twigs ; flower-stalks and calyx grey-downy or even felted.

Native of the Himalaya ; introduced in 1837. The chief distinguishing characteristic of this spiræa, and one which gives it a leading place in the genus, is its habit of producing in one season the long, thong-like shoots to which the popular name " flagelliformis " refers. When, the following year, there springs from every bud a short erect twig, each crowned with its dense cluster of flowers, there are few more strikingly beautiful shrubs, especially at the date when it blossoms. The species is somewhat variable in the shape and size of the leaf, in the amount of down it bears, also to some extent in habit. It has, in consequence, received many names. The small greyish leaves tapering at the base, and the abundant clusters of white flowers set on the upper side of long arching branches, generally distinguish it.

S. CANTONIENSIS, *Loureiro*

(S. Reevesiana, *Lindley*, Bot. Reg., vol. 30, t. 10)

A deciduous or partly evergreen shrub, 4 to 6 ft. high, of wide-spreading, graceful habit, producing a thicket of erect and outwardly arching stems ; young stems glabrous. Leaves lozenge-shaped, 1 to 2½ ins. long, ½ to ¾ in. wide ; deeply and irregularly toothed (sometimes almost lobed), on the upper part, green and quite glabrous on both sides, with a glaucous tinge especially beneath ; stalk slender, ¼ to ⅓ in. long. Flowers white, ⅓ in. across, produced during June in hemispherical corymbs 1 to 2 ins. across, each corymb on a leafy stalk 1 to 2 ins. long.

Native of China and Japan. This shrub is scarcely known in gardens except in its double-flowered state, var PLENA, in which the many-petalled blossoms are nearly ½ in. across ; when freely borne they make a charming display. In the gardens of the south of France, Italy, and Dalmatia this double-flowered form is perhaps the most beautiful white-flowered shrub in April, its long sprays arching in every direction and laden with blossom. But in the Thames Valley it is rarely seen to perfection owing to injury by spring frosts. It can be got in better condition on a wall. Nearly allied to this species is S. chinensis (*q.v.*), also with fragrant white flowers in corymbs, but readily recognised by the yellowish felted under-surface of its leaves. A hybrid between them is S. BLANDA, *Zabel*, which has leaves furnished beneath with a greyish down, and white flowers in downy corymbs. All of this group are spring tender.

Var. LANCEATA, *Zabel.*—Leaves lanceolate ; flowers double.

S. CHAMÆDRYFOLIA, *Linnæus*

(Bot. Reg., t. 1222)

An erect shrub, up to 6 ft. high, the young shoots yellowish, glabrous, angular, zigzag. Leaves ovate or ovate-lanceolate, 1½ to 3 ins. long, ¾ to 1½ ins. wide ; coarsely, irregularly, often doubly toothed ; dark green and glabrous above, somewhat glaucous and slightly downy beneath. Flowers ⅓ in. across, white, produced in a corymb or corymbose raceme 1½ ins. across ;

flower-stalks glabrous, slender, the lower ones $\frac{3}{4}$ in. long, becoming shorter towards the summit. Stamens conspicuously long.

Var. ULMIFOLIA.—Leaves ovate, the upper two-thirds coarsely often doubly toothed. The inflorescence is more of a raceme than a corymb, and from $1\frac{1}{2}$ to 2 ins. long; flowers white, $\frac{1}{2}$ in. across. This is the handsomest form of S. chamædryfolia, distinct in its broader leaves and more elongated inflorescence.

S. chamædryfolia is a rather variable species with a very wide natural distribution; its most westerly habitat is E. Europe, and it reaches thence to Siberia, Dahuria, Manchuria, and Japan. In all its forms it is an attractive and reliable shrub, usually escaping late frosts and flowering during May; var. ulmifolia opening towards the end of the month. It renews itself by sending up every year strong erect sucker-growths from the ground, which produce flowers on short twigs the following year; and, to give these their best chance, sufficient of the older shoots should be pruned out after flowering to enable them to develop freely and strongly.

S. SCHINABECKII, *Zabel*, is a handsome hybrid between var. ulmifolia and S. trilobata. It is 6 ft. high, a twiggy bush with white flowers in stalked umbels— at their best in June.

S. FLEXUOSA, *Fischer* (S. chamædryfolia flexuosa, *Maximowicz*), is closely allied to the above, but is distinguished by the more conspicuously angled (or winged) stems, the dwarfer habit, the smaller narrower leaves simply-toothed on the upper third or half only, sometimes almost entire, and by the flowers being fewer in the cluster. Native of S. Siberia; probably nothing more than a variety of chamædryfolia.

S. CHINENSIS, *Maximowicz*

(S. pubescens, *Lindley*; Bot. Reg., vol. 33, t. 38)

A shrub 3 to 5 ft. high, of dense very leafy habit; young shoots downy. Leaves 1 to $1\frac{3}{4}$ ins. long, $\frac{1}{2}$ to $1\frac{1}{4}$ ins. wide; varying from rhomboidal and tapering at both ends, to broadly ovate with a nearly truncate base, sometimes obscurely three-lobed; the upper part sharply and coarsely toothed, the teeth gland-tipped; upper surface furnished with scattered hairs, under-surface clothed with yellowish felt; stalk $\frac{1}{4}$ to $\frac{1}{3}$ in. long. Flowers white, nearly $\frac{1}{2}$ in. across, produced during June in stalked umbels or corymbs 1 to 2 ins. wide; flower-stalks and calyx downy. The leaves remain very late on the branches.

Native of N. China and allied to S. cantoniensis, but readily distinguished by its downy shoots, flower-stalks, and yellowish felted leaves, the last named being considerably broader in proportion to their length than those of cantoniensis. It is not very hardy, and is killed to ground level in hard winters.

S. CORYMBOSA, *Rafinesque*

A dwarf shrub, 1 to 3 ft. high, with glabrous, erect, mostly unbranched stems. Leaves of firm texture, oval, ovate or roundish; $1\frac{1}{2}$ to 3 ins. long, two-thirds as wide; coarsely and often doubly toothed in the upper half; glabrous on both surfaces and rather glaucous beneath; stalk $\frac{1}{8}$ to $\frac{1}{4}$ in. long. Flowers white, $\frac{1}{8}$ in. wide, borne on the shoots of the year in dense, rounded, branching corymbs 2 to 4 ins. across; seed-vessels glabrous, sepals erect at the fruiting stage; flower-stalks very downy.

Native of the United States, from the mountains of Georgia north to New Jersey. A handsome shrub allied to S. BETULIFOLIA, *Pallas* (under which name it is often grown), flowering from June to August. Like that species it renews itself by stems pushed from the base annually, and these should be encouraged by pruning out the older wood. In the true S. betulifolia the sepals are much reflexed at the fruiting stage.

S. CRENATA, *Linnæus*

(S. crenifolia, *C. A. Meyer*)

A shrub 3 to 5 ft. high, bushy, with slightly angular stems ; young twigs at first more or less downy, becoming glabrous later. Leaves narrowly to broadly obovate, ½ to 1⅛ ins. long, ¼ to 1 in. wide ; toothed only at the apex, slightly downy or glabrous beneath, with three distinct veins running length-wise. Flowers white, small, produced during May in small hemispherical umbels at the end of short, leafy twigs.

Native of S.E. Europe, the Caucasus, Siberia, etc. ; long known in cultiva-tion. From its immediate allies (S. alpina and S. cana) its three veins running the whole length of the leaf distinguish it. It is also often confused with S. hypericifolia, but that species has its flowers wholly or almost wholly in stalkless umbels. There is a hybrid between S. crenata and cana called S. CONFERTA, *Zabel*, which has three-veined leaves like S. crenata, but more and persistently downy.

S. DECUMBENS, *W. Koch*

(S. procumbens in gardens)

A dwarf shrub, 3 to 8 ins. high, with slender, glabrous, often prostrate stems, from which the thin, wiry flowering branches ascend. Leaves obovate or oval, tapered at both ends, sharply, angularly and rather coarsely toothed towards the apex ; ½ to 1½ ins. long, ¼ to ½ in. wide ; quite glabrous on both surfaces ; stalk about ⅛ in. long. Flowers white, ¼ in. across ; in corymbs 2 ins. wide ; seed-vessels glabrous, with the sepals deflexed.

Native of the Tyrol, especially in the Carnic Alps. It is a pleasing little shrub, one of the dwarfest of spiræas, and very suitable for the rock garden.

S. HACQUETII, *Fenzl* (S. decumbens tomentosa, *Poech*).—A dwarf shrub similar in habit to S. decumbens, but differing in the young bark, leaves, flower-stalk, and calyx being downy ; in the more prominent nerves beneath the leaf, which on the whole is proportionately narrower, and not so coarsely toothed ; also by the sepals being more erect in fruit. Native of N. Italy and the Tyrol.

S. DENSIFLORA, *Nuttall*

A deciduous shrub up to 2 ft. high, with glabrous, round, rich brown young shoots. Leaves oval or ovate, rounded at both ends, rather coarsely toothed towards the apex ; ⅔ to 1¾ ins. long ; glabrous on both surfaces, deep green above, paler beneath ; stalk $\frac{1}{12}$ in. or less long. Flowers rose-coloured, densely packed in dome-shaped corymbs 1 to 1½ ins. wide, opening in June.

Native of western N. America, from British Columbia to Oregon. It was no doubt gathered by early collectors like Douglas and Lobb, and, as it was growing in Veitch's nursery at Exeter in 1861, was probably introduced by the latter. It is useful as a very hardy, low-growing shrub that will keep dwarf without pruning, and its rose-coloured flowers are pretty and attractive.

S. DISCOLOR, *Pursh*

(S. ariæfolia, *Smith* ; Holodiscus discolor, *Ascherson*)

A large deciduous shrub, usually 8 to 12 ft. high, considerably more in width. Stems erect at the base, but branching and gracefully arching or pendulous at the top ; young branches downy and slightly ridged. Leaves

ovate, with a straight or broadly wedge-shaped base ; 2 to 3½ ins. long, 1½ to
3 ins. wide on the barren stems, smaller on the flowering branches ; each
margin cut up into four to eight lobes which are themselves sharply toothed
upper surface slightly hairy, lower one covered with a grey felt ; stalk ¼ to
⅝ in. long. Flowers creamy white, small, produced during July in pendulous
plume-like panicles 4 to 12 ins. long ; flower-stalks and calyx downy. Frui
an achene, non-splitting, woolly.

Native of western N. America ; introduced by Douglas in 1827. It is
better known in gardens as S. ariæfolia—an appropriate name recalling the
resemblance of its leaves to those of some of the Aria group of Pyrus, but
given to the plant five years later than Pursh's name of 1814. In any selection

SPIRÆA DISCOLOR

of spiræas this must be placed in the best half-dozen. It produces an
extraordinary profusion of blossom, and is exceedingly graceful in habit
Many fine plants are scattered over the south of England ; there is one at
Saltwood, in Kent, 12 ft. high and 40 ft. across. In 1906, in Sir A. Buchan
Hepburn's grounds in E. Lothian, I saw one 20 ft. high. This shrub is seen
to best advantage as an isolated specimen with a dark green background
say of holly. In thin woodland it also thrives admirably, as one may see i
in the beautiful demesne of Dropmore.

Var. DUMOSA, *S. Watson* (S. dumosa, *Nuttall*; Holodiscus dumosus
Heller).—A smaller growing and distinct variety 2 to 6 ft. high ; leaves
¾ to 2 ins. long, nearly as wide, silky white beneath ; flowers in erect
panicles. California, Oregon, etc. Probably a distinct species, now rare in
gardens.

These two spiræas differ from all the rest here included in having an
indehiscent seed-vessel.

S. DOUGLASII, *Hooker*

(Bot. Mag., t. 5151)

A shrub 4 to 6 ft. high, forming a thicket of erect stems, reddish, covered when young with a very fine felt. Leaves narrow oblong, 1½ to 4 ins. long, ½ to 1 in. broad ; coarsely and unequally toothed on the terminal part only, dark green above, covered with a fine grey felt beneath. Flowers purplish rose, produced in an erect terminal panicle 4 to 8 ins. high, very closely packed ; flower-stalks and calyx grey-downy ; stamens pink, standing out well beyond the petals ; ovaries glabrous.

Native of western N. America ; discovered by David Douglas in British Columbia about 1827, and first raised in the Glasgow Botanic Garden from his seed. It flowers from the end of June to the end of July, and a patch several feet across makes a rather striking display. The shoots that flowered the previous summer should be pruned back in February or early March, and the plants are all the better if broken up every few years as advised in the introductory notes to this genus, and the soil enriched. It thrives especially well near water. It is allied to tomentosa, but differs in its glabrous ovaries, its longer more oblong leaves, and in flowering earlier.

S. GEMMATA, *Zabel*

A shrub 4 to 8 ft. high, with slender, arching, more or less angular stems, quite glabrous ; buds slender, pointed, longer than the leaf-stalk. Leaves narrowly oblong, from ½ to 1 in. long, ⅛ to ⅓ in. wide ; often entire with a short abrupt tip, but sometimes blunt and with about three teeth at the end ; green and quite glabrous on both surfaces. Flowers white, small, produced during May in corymbs about 1 in. across ; flower-stalk glabrous, slender.

Native of Mongolia, and usually found in gardens as " S. mongolica." A pretty, white-flowered shrub distinct amongst others of its group by reason of its long, slender leaf-buds.

S. HENRYI, *Hemsley*

(Bot. Mag., t. 8270)

A shrub of lax, spreading habit, 6 to 9 ft. high, more in diameter ; branches reddish brown, slightly hairy when young. Leaves of the barren shoots 2½ to 3½ ins. long, ¾ to 1¼ ins. wide ; narrowly oblong or oblanceolate, coarsely toothed near the apex ; those of the flowering twigs much smaller, ¾ to 1½ ins. long, oblong or obovate, more shallowly toothed at the apex than the others, sometimes entire ; all covered more or less with loose, greyish down beneath. Flowers white, ¼ in. across, produced in June on rounded corymbs, 2 ins. across, which terminate short, leafy twigs ; flower-stalk and ovary downy.

Native of Central China ; named in honour of Dr A. Henry, who first discovered it near Ichang in 1885 ; introduced for Messrs Veitch by Wilson in 1900. It is a fine shrub, and stands in the front rank of spiræas, but on account of its wide-spreading habit needs plenty of space for lateral development ; it is better as an isolated plant than grouped in a shrubbery. Shoots 5 ft. or more long are made in a season.

S. WILSONI, *Duthie* (Bot. Mag., t. 8399), is closely allied to, perhaps only a variety of S. Henryi. It is distinguished among other points by its glabrous ovary, and glabrous or slightly silky flower-stalks. Leaves of flowering shoots entire, downy above, duller green. Introduced in 1900 from N.W. China.

III   M

S. HYPERICIFOLIA, *Linnæus*

A bushy shrub, 5 or 6 ft. high, with graceful, arching, twiggy branches, which, when young, are brown and usually covered with fine down, becoming grey with age. Leaves obovate, with a tapering base, and about three teeth at the apex, or none at all ; ¾ to 1¼ ins. long, ¼ to ½ in. wide ; of a greyish green, slightly downy beneath, three or five nerves running lengthwise ; stalk very short. Flowers pure white, ¼ in. across, produced during early May in clusters from the buds of the previous summer's shoots ; each flower on a usually downy stalk about ⅔ in. long.

A widely spread and variable species extending in a wild state from S.E. Europe and Asia Minor across N. Temperate Asia. It is naturalised but not truly wild in N. America. At its best this is a pretty shrub, although not in the very first rank of spiræas ; starting later into growth than several other of its white-flowered allies, it escapes the damaging influence of late spring frosts.

S. ACUTIFOLIA, *Willdenow*, is closely allied to hypericifolia, and by some authors is made a variety of it. It differs mainly in the flowers being yellowish white, and about half the size only, and in the narrower leaves. Of little value for gardens.

S. JAPONICA, *Linnæus fil.*

(S. callosa, *Thunberg* ; S. Fortunei, *Planchon*, Bot. Mag., t. 5164)

A shrub of rather open habit, from 3 to 5 ft. high, stems erect, round or slightly angled, ultimately glabrous and shining brown. Leaves lanceolate or narrowly oval ; 3 to 4 ins. long, 1 to 1½ ins. wide ; coarsely, sharply and irregularly toothed, each tooth gland-tipped ; tapering at the base, dark green above, rather glaucous beneath, glabrous on both sides, or soon becoming so. Flowers ¼ in. across, rich rosy red, produced during July and August in large, flat, compound corymbs terminating the current season's shoots. The inflorescence, which may be anything up to 12 ins. across, consists really of a series of corymbs springing from the uppermost leaf-axils, the lower ones with stalks long enough to bring the flowers to about the same level as the upper ones ; calyx and flower-stalk downy.

Native of Japan and China. S. japonica may be taken as the type of a large and valuable group of spiræas which flower in summer on the shoots of the year, and produce the blossoms in a large flattish inflorescence. They are all handsome, and should be pruned in spring by cutting clean out sufficient of the older wood to prevent crowding, and then shortening back those selected to remain.

Var. ALBA (S. albiflora, *Zabel* ; S. callosa alba, *Hort.*).—A shrub of dwarfer, weaker growth than the type ; young shoots downy and distinctly ribbed ; leaves shorter-stalked and smaller ; flowers white. Some authors regard this as a distinct species.

Var. BUMALDA (S. Bumalda, *Hort.*).—A dwarf, neat, yet elegant variety usually under 18 ins. high. Flowers in flat corymbs, and of a beautiful carmine shade. Var. ANTHONY WATERER.—This fine form is a sub-variety of Bumalda, and originated in the Knap Hill nursery about 1890. It has the same habit as the ordinary Bumalda, but its flowers are of a much more brilliant shade of carmine. It is, perhaps, the most highly coloured of spiræas. In both, the leaves frequently come partially variegated. By removing the flowers as they fade, both may be kept flowering until late September.

Var. GLABRA (S. glabrata, *Lange*).—A strong-growing form with corymbs

often over 1 ft. in diamter, flowers rosy pink.   Leaves much broader than in
the type, the largest 4 to 5 ins. long and 2½ to 3 ins. wide, of broadly ovate form,
rounded at the base, and, like the young wood and flower-stalks, glabrous.

Var. MACROPHYLLA, *Zabel*.—Leaves as large or larger than the preceding
variety, but curiously inflated, " bullate " ;   inflorescence poor and small.
Only worth growing as a curiosity.

Var. RUBERRIMA.—Flowers deeper rose than the type.

S. LÆVIGATA, *Linnæus*

(Sibiræa lævigata, *Maximowicz*)

A deciduous shrub of sturdy, bushy habit, 2 to 5 ft. high, with thickish,
rather sparse, perfectly glabrous, brown branchlets.   Leaves entire, narrowly

SPIRÆA LÆVIGATA

obovate ;   2 to 4½ ins. long, ⅓ to ⅞ in. wide ;   stalkless, tapering at the base,
the apex with a short abrupt point ;   glaucous green and quite glabrous.
Flowers white, produced from late April to early June in terminal spreading
compound panicles 3 to 5 ins. high.

Native of Siberia ;   introduced to Britain in 1774.   This species, whilst
not particularly showy, is quite distinct from all other spiræas in its foliage,
which in shape and colour is more suggestive of a spurge (Euphorbia) than
the genus to which it belongs.   Shrubs 4 ft. high are often as much as 7 ft.
through.

S. LINDLEYANA, *Wallich*

(Sorbaria Lindleyana, *Maximowicz* ; S. tomentosa, *Rehder*)

A shrub of graceful spreading habit, up to 20 ft. high ; branches very pithy, green, glabrous. Leaves 10 to 18 ins. long, pinnate, consisting of eleven to twenty-three leaflets, which are lanceolate or ovate-lanceolate ; 2 to 4½ ins. long, ½ to 1½ ins. wide (the terminal one often larger and pinnately lobed) ; usually deeply and doubly toothed, glabrous above, furnished with loose, simple hairs beneath, especially about the midrib and veins. Flowers ivory white, scarcely ¼ in. wide, produced in terminal pyramidal, branching panicles 1 to 1½ ft. long and 8 to 12 ins. through ; flower-stalks downy. Seed-vessels in panicles, often more or less pendulous.

Native of the Himalaya ; flowering from July to September, the individual blossom being, however, rather short-lived. A very handsome robust shrub which, flowering on the branches of the year, may be pruned back every winter or early spring. It is allied to S. Aitchisoni, but differs in its downy flower-stalks, and in the leaflets being broader, doubly toothed and hairy beneath. From S. sorbifolia it differs very much in its strong spreading habit.

S. LONGIGEMMIS, *Maximowicz*

A shrub 4 or 5 ft. high, with glabrous, erect, angular stems, and curiously flat, leaf-like winter buds often ⅓ in. long. Leaves ovate-lanceolate, wedge-shaped at the base, sharply and deeply, often doubly, toothed ; 1½ to 3 ins. long, ¾ to 1¼ ins. wide ; bright green and glabrous above, rather glaucous and hairy on the veins beneath when young ; stalk ⅛ to ¼ in. long. Flowers white, ¼ in. across, produced towards the end of May in broad, rounded, corymbose panicles 2 to 3½ ins. across and 1 to 2 ins. long ; stamens prominent ; flower-stalk and calyx downy.

Native of N. China in the province of Kansu ; also found by Wilson in W. China. It is a very pretty white-flowered spiræa blossoming late enough to escape injury by frost. I have seen it in excellent condition in the garden at Grayswood Hill, near Haslemere—the upper side of the branches wreathed with corymbs terminating leafy twigs.

S. MARGARITÆ, *Zabel*

A shrub 4 or 5 ft. high ; its stems erect, reddish brown, and downy. Leaves 2 to 3½ ins. long, ¾ to 1½ ins. wide ; narrowly oval or oblong, coarsely, sharply, and irregularly toothed at the terminal part, entire and narrowly wedge-shaped at the base. Flowers bright pink, ⅓ in. diameter, produced from July onwards in large, flat corymbs 3 to 6 ins. across, terminating the growths of the year.

If the origin of this spiræa is correctly deduced by the author of the name, it is a hybrid in which three kinds are united, viz., japonica, corymbosa, and japonica alba. However that may be, it is certainly one of the very best of the late summer-flowering group. A large mass of it makes a very striking effect from July to September. It should be pruned every winter or early spring in the same way as recommended for the japonica group, *i.e.*, to cut out entirely the older shoots and prune the younger ones back to within 1 ft. of the ground, leaving only sufficient—say one every 6 ins. or so—to furnish the plant during the ensuing summer. Treated in this way the shrub does not get to be more than 3 ft. high, and becomes a sheet of blossom. If the corymbs are cut off as they fade, a succession of flowers may be obtained until September.

S. MEDIA, *F. Schmidt*

(S. confusa, *Regel*)

An erect shrub, up to 4 or 6 ft. high, with glabrous, round stems sometimes downy when young. Leaves ovate or oblong with a wedge-shaped base, 1 to 2 ins. long, ⅓ to ¾ in. wide; the terminal part sharply toothed or with a few large teeth only near the apex, sometimes entire; upper surface glabrous, lower one more or less hairy or sometimes glabrous; stalk ⅛ in. or less long. Flowers white, ¼ in. across, produced during late April and early May in long-stalked racemes 1 to 1½ ins. across each terminating a short leafy twig.

Native of E. Europe to Japan and Sachalin. It is a pretty species, but liable to be injured by late spring frosts. Several varieties of it have been distinguished chiefly by the shape, hairness, and toothing of the leaf.

Var. GLAB-RESCENS, *Zabel.*— Leaves quite glabrous or soon becoming so.

Var. MOLLIS, *C. K. Schneider.* — Leaves silky on one or both sides.

SPIRÆA MEDIA

S. oblongifolia, *Waldstein*, appears to be a form of S. media whose leaves are entire except for one to three teeth at the apex.

In gardens S. media is sometimes used for forcing early into blossom under the name of " S. confusa."

S. MENZIESII, *Hooker*

A shrub 3 to 5 ft. high, stems brown, erect, slightly downy or glabrous. producing suckers freely; leaf-buds hairy. Leaves lanceolate, oblong or broadly oval, 1½ to 3½ ins. long, toothed towards the apex, more or less grey-green and downy beneath, or sometimes green. Flowers bright purplish rose, crowded in an erect, pyramidal panicle terminating the shoots of the year and 3 to 8 ins. high. It blossoms in July and August.

This fine spiræa is found wild in western North America, whence it was introduced in 1838. Some authors regard it as a distinct species, some as a variety of S. Douglasii. Mr Zabel considers it to be a natural hybrid between S. Douglasii and S. salicifolia, and places under it, as varieties, a series of forms whose leaves are more or less intermediate between those of S. Douglasii (with a grey-downy under-surface), and those of S. salicifolia (with both surfaces green and glab-rous). All the forms of S. Menziesii should be pruned back nearly to the previous year's wood every spring, and old worn-out stems removed.

Var. ANGUSTI-FOLIA, *Zabel.* — Leaves narrowly oblong, more taper-ing at the base than at the apex, toothed only towards the apex, lower surface grey downy.

Var. EXIMIA.— Leaves oval or obovate, 3 ins. long, ½ to 1 in. wide, toothed from the middle, or below it to the apex, under-side more or less grey-felted. Panicles broadly pyramidal

SPIRÆA MENZIESII TRIUMPHANS

and much branched, the lower branches 3 or 4 ins. long and leafy. Some of the finer panicles measure 8 ins. long by 6 ins. wide.

Var. MACROTHYRSA, *Zabel* (S. californica, *Hort*.).—Leaves broadly obovate, about 2 ins. long, often more than half as wide, felted beneath. Panicles dense, usually about 5 to 7 ins. high, nearly half as wide at the base.

Var. TRIUMPHANS.—Leaves oval-lanceolate, 1½ to 2½ ins. long, ½ to ¾ in. wide, toothed nearly to the base, green beneath and slightly downy, especially on the veins. Panicles broadly pyramidal, branching at the base, up to 8 ins. high and 4 ins. wide. Flowers bright purplish rose. This, perhaps the finest of all the Menziesii group, makes a splendid display from mid-July onwards.

S. MILLEFOLIUM, *Torrey*

(Bot. Mag., t. 7810 ; Chamæbatiaria Millefolium, *Maximowicz*)

A shrub 3 to 5 ft. high, the erect branches covered with glandular down, sticky when young, and having a balsamic odour. Leaves 2 to 3½ ins. long, ½ to 1 in. wide ; doubly pinnate and very like those of the common milfoil, the ultimate subdivisions ₁⁄₁₂ in. long, narrowly oblong, downy ; common stalk slightly winged. Flowers white, ⅓ to ½ in. diameter, produced in erect, terminal branching panicles, 3 to 5 ins. high ; flower-stalks and calyx densely covered with tufted hairs ; petals roundish, surrounding a cluster of yellow stamens. Flowers in July.

Native of western N. America ; first discovered in 1853 by Dr Bigelow ; introduced to Kew in 1891. It occurs up to 10,000 ft. altitude in California, and is quite hardy in the south of England, but likes a well-drained soil and as sunny a position as possible. The plant has a pungent aromatic odour. Its much divided foliage makes it quite distinct from any other spiræa ; it has indeed been placed in a genus by itself under the name given as a synonym above.

S. MOLLIFOLIA, *Rehder*

A deciduous shrub up to 6 ft. high, with arching branches ; young shoots very hairy at first, becoming purple, nearly glabrous and very distinctly angled the second year ; buds up to ¼ in. long, brownish purple. Leaves oval, oblong or obovate, tapered at both ends, usually more abruptly so at the apex, mostly entire, sometimes three-toothed at the apex ; ½ to ¾ in. long, half as wide ; silky all over. Flowers white, ¼ in. diameter, borne during June and July in corymbs about 1 in. across, terminating short leafy twigs that spring from the growths of the previous year ; stamens twenty.

Native of W. Szechuen, China ; discovered by Wilson in 1904 ; introduced in 1909. As it occurs up to 14,000 ft. in a wild state it is likely to be very hardy. It is quite distinct from all other cultivated spiræas in the combination of its silky leaves, and long, slender winter buds.

S. NIPPONICA, *Maximowicz*

(S. bracteata, *Zabel* ; Bot. Mag., t. 7429)

A deciduous shrub of rounded, bushy habit, growing 4 to 8 ft. high ; the branches, leaves, and flower-stalks quite glabrous ; young wood reddish. Leaves very broadly obovate or oval, sometimes nearly round, ½ to 1 in. long, sometimes entire, but usually with a few broad teeth at the rounded apex ; stalk ¼ to ½ in. long. Flowers pure white, ⅓ in. across, crowded densely in rounded or conical clusters, 1 to 1½ ins. wide. Each cluster is borne at the end of a leafy twig, 1½ to 3 ins. long, springing from the wood of the previous year ; petals overlapping. It is at its best in June. The synonym refers to the leaflike bracts on the stalks of the lower flowers.

A native of Japan ; first introduced by Siebold to his nursery at Leyden, and originally sold as " S. rotundifolia alba." It is sometimes injured by late frosts, but when these are escaped, few June-flowering shrubs are more lovely. The flower-clusters are all borne on the upper side of the horizontal

SPIRÆA NIPPONICA

or arching branches. It is perfectly hardy, but needs liberal conditions at the root, even more than the majority of spiræas do. The great thing is to get a comparatively few long shoots rather than a crowd of small twiggy ones. Old shoots should be removed as soon as they produce nothing but twiggy shoots.

S. PECTINATA, *Torrey and Gray*

(Eriogynia pectinata, *Hooker* ; Luetkea pectinata *Bongard*)

An evergreen sub-shrub a few inches high, of tufted habit, spreading by underground suckers ; young growths and leaves glabrous. Leaves glossy green, three-lobed, the lobes usually again divided into two or three secondary lobes, so that one leaf may have from three to nine (occasionally more) segments. The entire leaf is $\frac{1}{3}$ to 1 in. long and all its divisions are linear, pointed, $\frac{1}{24}$ to $\frac{1}{16}$ in. wide ; the winged leaf-stalk is somewhat wider. Flowers white, $\frac{1}{4}$ to $\frac{1}{3}$ in. wide ; produced in May and June in racemes 1 to 2 ins. long borne at the end of erect leafy branchlets which give the plant when in flower a height of 3 to 6 ins. ; flower-stalks downy. Calyx of five glabrous, pointed sepals ; stamens twenty, united at the base to form a ring round the five carpels. There are from ten to twenty flowers on each raceme.

Native of western N. America, from Alaska to California. The oldest specimen in the Kew Herbarium, received from St Petersburg in 1835, was collected during the Russian voyage round the world (1826-1829) under Admiral Luetke, after whom the plant was named in one of the generic synonyms given above. It was, apparently, long after that before it got into cultivation. In its lower latitudes it occurs at high elevations ; on Vancouver Island, for instance, it ascends to altitudes of 5000 to 6000 ft. It requires, therefore, cool moist conditions such as suit the mossy saxifrages. Given these it makes a charming plant for the rock garden.

S. PRUNIFOLIA, *Siebold and Zuccarini*

This species is scarcely known in cultivation except by the double-flowered form, to which the following description refers : A shrub 4 to 6 ft. high, the branches gracefully arching and forming a dense bush as much in diameter as it is high ; young shoots downy. Leaves ovate, 1 to 1¾ ins. long, ½ to ¾ in. wide ; downy beneath (especially when young), finely and evenly toothed ; stalk ⅛ in. or less long. Flowers produced during late April and May in fascicles three to six together, each flower on a glabrous, slender stalk, ½ to ¾ in. long ; petals pure white and so numerous as to form a flower like a small " batchelor's button," ½ in. across.

Native of China, and much cultivated there ; it was found by Wilson in its double-flowered state in W. Hupeh. This form was originally introduced from Japan by Dr Siebold about 1845. In the *Gardeners' Chronicle* for 20th February 1847, an advertisement sets forth that "the stock of this magnificent novelty bought at Dr Siebold's sale, is now in the possession of Louis van Houtte, florist at Ghent," and plants to be delivered the following April are offered at one guinea each. It is still one of the most beautiful of hardy shrubs, producing during the summer slender shoots, 1 to 2 ft. long which, the following May, are wreathed from end to end with blossom. For the needs of most gardens it can be increased sufficiently quickly by taking off the side suckers from old plants and potting them, then placing them in a mild bottom heat ; but if such conveniences are not available they can be planted in the open ground—a slower, less certain process.

The single-flowered plant is in cultivation, and is distinguished as S. prunifolia "flore simplex." In my experience it is an absolutely worthless shrub because of its extraordinary sterility. A plant was obtained from the Continent for Kew in 1887, but although I have known this and others raised from it for twenty years, I have never yet seen it in flower. But this, of course, is more likely to be an individual than a racial characteristic, seeing the floriferousness of the double-flowered form.

S. ROSTHORNII, *Pritzel*

A deciduous shrub up to 6 ft. high, of spreading habit ; young shoots slightly downy. Leaves ovate to lanceolate, slenderly pointed, broadly wedge-shaped or almost rounded at the base ; sharply, jaggedly, unevenly toothed ; ½ to 3 ins. long, ¾ to 1¼ ins. wide ; bright green above, more or less downy on both surfaces but especially beneath ; stalk ⅛ to ¼ in. long. Flowers white, about ¼ in. wide, produced in early June in flattish corymbs 2 to 3½ ins. across that terminate leafy shoots ; flower-stalks all downy.

Native of W. Szechuen, China ; introduced under Wilson's No. 965 in 1909. Nearly related to S. longigemmis and having the same curious elongated winter buds, but that is a glabrous shrub as regards the young shoots and early so as regards the leaves.

S. PRATTII, *C. K. Schneider*, made synonymous with this species in *Plantæ Wilsonianæ*, vol. i., p. 451, seems to differ in its sturdier growth ; more compact, densely flowered, rounded corymbs ; smaller, more abundant and more densely pubescent leaves. It was found by A. E. Pratt in W. Szechuen (No. 190).

S. SALICIFOLIA, *Linnæus.* BRIDEWORT

A shrub 3 to 6 ft. high, with running roots and forming ultimately a dense thicket of erect stems, which are soon quite glabrous. Leaves lanceolate or narrowly oval, but sometimes broadest above the middle ; $1\frac{1}{2}$ to 3 ins. long, $\frac{1}{2}$ to 1 in. wide ; pointed, sharply and often doubly toothed, glabrous and green on both surfaces. Flowers rose-tinted white, crowded on erect, terminal, slightly downy panicles about 4 ins. high, and 2 ins. wide at the base.

This, which may be considered the typical form, is a native of E. Europe, Asiatic Russia to Japan. It is not a native of Britain, but is naturalised in several places, notably in some parts of N. Wales. When once it obtains a footing, it appears to be able to hold its own against any other vegetation, spreading by its creeping suckers and forming an almost impassable thicket. Left to itself in this way, its inflorescences become poor ; but cultivated in good garden soil and occasionally divided, it makes a handsome show in June and July.

Var. LATIFOLIA, *Aiton* (S. latifolia, *Borkhausen*).—Stems reddish or purplish brown ; leaves oval or ovate, unequally and rather coarsely toothed, $\frac{3}{4}$ to $1\frac{3}{4}$ ins. wide ; panicles large, conical, not downy, flowers white or blush-coloured. Eastern N. America from Newfoundland to Virginia, commonly known there as " Meadow-sweet."

Var. PANICULATA, *Aiton* (S. alba, *Duroi*).—This is the finest form of S. salicifolia. Leaves narrowly oval or ovate ; inflorescence 8 to 12 ins. long, as much wide, much branched, slightly downy. Flowers white or rosy tinted. This spiræa is sometimes regarded as a distinct species (S. alba) and the preceding one (latifolia) as its variety. They differ from typical salicifolia in the much larger, compound panicles of pyramidal rather than cylindrical shape. Native of N. America, with a more western distribution than var. latifolia.

S. SANSSOUCIANA, *K. Koch*

(S. Nobleana, *Hocker*, Bot. Mag., t. 5169)

A shrub 4 or 5 ft high, with erect, brown stems covered with a close grey felt. Leaves oblong to narrowly oval, 2 to 4 ins. long, $\frac{3}{4}$ to $1\frac{1}{4}$ ins. wide, mostly tapering, sometimes rounded at the base ; irregularly and rather jaggedly toothed except near the base ; green, downy on the veins above, covered with a dull greyish, close down beneath. Flowers bright rose, produced during July, and densely crowded in broad, corymbose panicles which form an inflorescence 3 to 10 ins. across, terminating the shoot of the year ; flower-stalk and calyx grey-felted.

A hybrid between japonica and Douglasii, first described by K. Koch under the above name in 1857. Two years later it was sent to Kew by Mr Chas. Noble of Bagshot, and named Nobleana by Sir Wm. Hooker. In an accompanying letter, still preserved at Kew, Mr Noble states that it had been raised from a plant of Douglasii growing by the side of one of japonica. Hooker nevertheless identified it with a spiræa that had been collected by W. Lobb in California ; and for many years S. Nobleana was regarded as native of that State. There is no doubt, however, that Lobb's plant is different, and that Noble's plant had the origin he indicated. It appears to have also been raised about the same time independently at Paris and Woking.

The Californian plant wrongly identified with S. sanssouciana by Hooker is apparently a natural hybrid between S. Douglasii and perhaps S. densiflora, *Nuttall* (S. SPLENDENS, *Baumann*).

S. SARGENTIANA, *Rehder*

A deciduous shrub 4 to 6 ft. high, with long, slender, arching, round young shoots, at first downy, soon glabrous. Leaves narrowly oval to narrowly obovate, wedge-shaped and entire at the base, more or less toothed towards the tip ; ½ to 1 in. long, ⅛ to ½ in. wide ; dull green above, paler and downy beneath, the few veins running lengthwise; stalk 1/16 to ⅛ in. long. Flowers creamy white, ¼ in. wide, produced during June in rounded clusters 1 to 1¾ ins. wide that terminate short leafy twigs springing from the virgin shoots of the previous year ; main and secondary flower-stalks downy.

Native of W. Szechuen, China ; discovered and introduced by Wilson in 1908-9. In its graceful habit, small leaves and mode of flowering this resembles the well-known S. canescens (flagelliformis) which can be distinguished by its ribbed stems. It is also closely related to S. Henryi, which has much larger but similarly toothed leaves. S. Sargentiana is a distinctly pretty shrub, perfectly hardy and well worth cultivation.

S. SINOBRAHUICA, *W. W. Smith*

A deciduous shrub 4 to 7 ft. high ; young shoots covered with a thick tawny down ; buds white-woolly. Leaves broadly ovate or obovate, lobed and toothed at the upper part, entire and tapered towards the stalk ; ½ to 1⅛ ins. long, from two-thirds to nearly as much wide ; dull green and downy above, grey-tawny and velvety beneath ; stalk 1/16 to ⅛ in. long. Flowers creamy white, ⅛ in. wide, produced during June in rounded clusters 1 in. across at the end of short leafy twigs. There are ten to twenty flowers in a cluster, each borne on a slender downy stalk ; petals roundish ; calyx downy like the flower-stalk ; stamens twenty.

Native of Yunnan, China ; discovered by Forrest in 1910 and introduced by him. He found it at upwards of 10,000 ft. altitude, varying apparently in height from 3 to 8 ft. It is very distinct in the tawny down that covers the young shoots, under surface of the leaves, flower-stalks and calyx ; also in the goodly size (for a spiræa) of the blossoms. It is evidently nearly akin to S. chinensis and may be the same as S. yunnanensis, *Franchet*.

S. SORBIFOLIA, *Linnæus*

(Sorbaria sorbifolia, *A. Braun*)

A shrub 3 to 6 ft. high, which suckers freely ; stems erect, very pithy, varying from nearly glabrous to downy. Leaves 8 to 12 ins. long, composed of thirteen to twenty-five leaflets, which are lanceolate, 2 to 3½ ins. long, ½ to 1 in. wide ; sharply and conspicuously double-toothed, green on both sides ; usually quite glabrous above and the same beneath. Flowers ⅛ in. across, white, produced during July and August in a stiff erect raceme 6 to 10 ins. high ; flower-stalks downy and glandular ; ovaries glabrous or nearly so.

Native of N. Asia from the Ural Mountains to Japan ; introduced in 1759. It is distinguished from its near allies S. Lindleyana and S. Aitchisoni by its comparatively dwarf, stiff habit, and narrower, stiffer flower-panicles. Grown in rich soil it makes a handsome shrub.

Var. ALPINA, *Pallas* (Sorbaria alpina, *Dippel* ; S. grandiflora, *Maximowicz*).—This is distinguished from the typical S. sorbifolia by its dwarf habit (1 to 3 ft. high), fewer and shorter leaflets with somewhat blunter teeth, and by the larger flowers (½ to ⅝ in. across).

Nearly allied to S. sorbifolia is S. STELLIPILA, which differs chiefly in the leaves being clothed with stellate hairs beneath, and in the downy ovaries. In habit and leaf form it resembles S. sorbifolia. Native of Japan.

S. THUNBERGII, *Siebold*

A shrub 3 to 5 ft. high, often more in diameter, of very twiggy, bushy habit ; branchlets slender, angled, downy. Leaves linear-lanceolate, 1 to 1½ ins. long, ⅛ to ¼ in. wide ; taper-pointed, the margins set with a few incurved teeth, smooth and pale green on both sides. Flowers pure white, ¼ in. across, produced on the leafless, wiry twigs during March and April in clusters of two to five, each flower on a glabrous, slender stalk, ¼ to ⅓ in. long ; calyx shallow, smooth.

Native of China ; but first introduced from Japan, of which country, however, it is doubtfully native. This is the earliest of all the spiræas to flower in the open, and in ordinary seasons is at its best by the middle of April. The fascicles of blossom spring directly from the shoots made the previous summer, and if the season has been sufficiently sunny and hot to have thoroughly ripened the wood, the plants will be almost hidden by the profusion of flowers. The habit of the plant is graceful owing to the arching form of the slender branches, and altogether there are few more attractive shrubs in bloom in early April.

S. TOMENTOSA, *Linnæus*. STEEPLEBUSH

A shrub 3 to 5 ft. high, with spreading underground roots, ultimately forming a thicket of erect angled stems which when young are covered with brownish felt. Leaves ovate, 1½ to 3 ins. long, ¾ to 1½ ins. wide ; coarsely and irregularly toothed almost to the base, dark green and nearly glabrous above, covered with a close, yellowish grey felt beneath. Flowers purplish rose, densely produced in erect, terminal, branching panicles 4 to 7 ins. long, 1½ to 2½ ins. wide during late summer.

Native of the eastern United States ; introduced, according to Aiton, in 1736. It is allied to the western S. Douglasii, and is often confused with it ; it is, however, distinguished by the thicker, browner (or yellowish) felt beneath the leaves, which are toothed much nearer the base ; by flowering some weeks later, and by the ovaries being woolly (glabrous in Douglasii).

Var. ALBA is a pretty white-flowered form.

The cultivation of these handsome spiræas is the same as for S. Douglasii (*q.v.*).

S. TOSAENSIS, *Yatabe*

(S. nipponica tosaensis, *Makino*)

A deciduous shrub up to 6 ft. or perhaps more high, of erect habit, free from down in all its parts ; young shoots slightly angled and dotted with dark lenticels, wholly very dark brown the second year. Leaves linear oblong, tapered at the base, entire or with two or three teeth quite at the apex ; ⅓ to 1 in. long, ⅛ to ¼ in. wide ; dark dull green above, slightly glaucous and net-veined beneath ; stalk ⅛ in. or less long. Flowers white, ¼ in. or less wide, opening ten to twenty together in flattish corymbs less than 1 in. wide that terminate short leafy twigs. Calyx green, funnel-shaped, grooved lengthwise with five short triangular lobes.

Native of Japan, where it was discovered on the banks of the river Watari-gawa in the province of Tosa in 1891 ; introduced to Kew in 1923. It is a neat shrub, distinct in its erect habit, very dark year-old twigs, and abundant narrow leaves which occur on the slender twigs seven to ten to the inch. It is perfectly hardy and grows well at Kew, where it flowers in June, but it is too modest in regard to its blossom to secure much notice.

S. TRICHOCARPA, *Nakai* (Plate 30)

(Gardeners' Chronicle, 11th Aug. 1923, fig. 32)

A deciduous shrub 4 to 6 ft. high, with rigid, spreading branches; young shoots glabrous, distinctly angled. Leaves oblanceolate to oblong, abruptly pointed, tapered at the base, with a few teeth near the apex or none at all; 1 to 2½ ins. long, ½ to 1 in. wide; vivid green above, rather glaucous beneath, quite glabrous; stalk ¼ in. or less long. Flowers white, ⅛ in. wide, produced during June on rounded corymbs 1 to 2 ins. wide, growing upwards, and terminating short leafy twigs that are clustered on the preceding year's shoots, the whole forming a handsome arching spray sometimes over 1 ft. long. Petals roundish, notched; flower-stalks and seed-vessels downy.

Native of Korea; discovered in 1902; introduced to cultivation in 1917 from the Diamond Mountains by Wilson, who considered it one of the best of all spiræas. It is distinct in its glabrous, nearly entire leaves, very pale beneath. It is considered to be nearest to S. nipponica and has similar leafy bracts on the inflorescence, but S. nipponica has much shorter, more oval leaves and a more compact, less spreading habit. There is a good example in Mr Cox's garden at Glendoick in the Tay Valley near Perth.

S. TRILOBATA, *Linnæus*

A twiggy shrub, 3 to 4 ft. high, of broad but compact habit, young shoots and leaves glabrous; stems round, often zigzagged in growth. Leaves roundish, ½ to 1 in. (rarely 1½ ins.) long, and about as much wide, coarsely toothed, sometimes obscurely three- or five-lobed, the base rounded or sometimes slightly heart-shaped, rather glaucous green. Flowers white, small, produced during June, packed very numerously in umbels ¾ to 1½ ins. across; each umbel terminating a short leafy twig, springing from the previous year's growth, every flower having a slender, glabrous stalk ⅓ to ¾ in. long.

Native of N. Asia, from N. China and S. Siberia to Turkestan; introduced in 1801. Although its flower-buds are sometimes injured by frosts, this is a very pretty shrub of neat habit.

S. BLUMEI, *Don*, found in China and Japan, is nearly allied to S. trilobata, but differs in the shape of the leaf, which is ovate or lozenge-shaped, longer than it is wide, the base wedge-shaped. Flowers white, crowded in umbels 1 in. wide. A shrub 3 to 6 ft. high.

S. VAN HOUTTEI, *Zabel*

A shrub 6 ft. high, with gracefully arching, glabrous brown stems. Leaves rhomboidal or obovate, sometimes distinctly three-lobed, more or less broadly tapering and entire at the base, coarsely toothed on the upper half; ¾ to 1¾ ins. long, ½ to 1¼ ins. wide; dark green above, rather glaucous beneath, glabrous on both sides. Flowers white, ⅛ in. across, produced during June in umbel-like clusters 1 to 2 ins. across; calyx-lobes erect.

A hybrid between S. trilobata and probably S. cantoniensis; raised by Mr Billiard, a nurseryman at Fontenay-aux-Roses, near Paris, about 1862.

At its best it is probably the finest of all the white-flowered spiræas, except perhaps S. arguta ; in low-lying situations it is subject to injury by late spring frosts. In more elevated gardens, or where the plant is not forced into premature activity by unseasonable warmth, there is no more desirable shrub, for it is very hardy. Its stems, at first erect, afterwards arching outwards at the top, bear the extraordinarily profuse blossoms on the upper side of the branches. It is one of the spiræas which should have the older wood thinned out after flowering to allow light and air to enter and help in the development of the younger growths. It is very valuable for forcing early into bloom for indoor decoration, and is often exhibited in this state at the spring shows under the erroneous name of S. confusa, a synonym of S. media—a less vigorous shrub with longer stamens and the calyx-lobes ultimately reflexed.

S. VEITCHII, *Hemsley*

(Bot. Mag., t. 8383)

A strong-growing shrub, probably 10 or 12 ft. high eventually, producing gracefully arching shoots, 2 to 3 ft. long in a season ; young branches reddish, slightly downy. Leaves ¾ to 2 ins. long, ⅓ to ¾ in. wide ; oblong or obovate, not toothed, glabrous on both surfaces or very slightly downy beneath. Flowers white, small, crowded in dense corymbs, 1½ to 2½ ins. across ; calyx and flower-stalks covered with a fine down ; fruits glabrous when ripe.

Native of Central China ; discovered by Wilson in W. Hupeh in 1900, and introduced by him for Messrs Veitch. It is a fine species (Mr Wilson told me he considered it the best of Chinese spiræas), somewhat similar in general aspect and in producing its flowers on short leafy twigs from the growths of the previous summer, to the well-known S. canescens (flagelliformis). It is readily distinguished from that species, however, by its glabrous, entire leaves and glabrous fruit. Its entire leaves also distinguish it from two other allies—S. Henryi and S. Wilsoni. I saw the plants first introduced in their young state in the Coombe Wood nursery, when they were making shoots as much as 8 ft. long in a season ; when these, the following June, were wreathed from end to end with clusters of pure white blossom, they made a picture of remarkable beauty.

S. VIRGATA, *Franchet*

(S. myrtilloides, *Rehder*)

A deciduous shrub 4 to 8 ft. high, with angular downy shoots, becoming glabrous and dark coloured the second year. Leaves oval, mostly rounded at the apex, broadly tapered at the base, entire, or obscurely toothed towards the apex ; ¼ to ⅝ in. long, about half as much wide ; glabrous on both surfaces, glaucous beneath ; stalk $\frac{1}{20}$ in. long. Flowers white, scarcely ¼ in. wide, produced in early June in rounded clusters ½ to 1 in. wide at the end of short leafy shoots springing from the growths of the previous year ; flower-stalks downy ; calyx glabrous except near the flower-stalk, its lobes triangular ; petals roundish obovate ; ovary glabrous.

Native of Yunnan, China ; discovered by the Abbé Delavay ; introduced to cultivation by Forrest, who found it on the eastern flank of the Lichiang Range in 1910. I do not think it is common in cultivation, but Mr L. de Rothschild showed some pleasing flowering sprays at Westminster, in June 1929. It appears to be most nearly related to S. media, which has round (not angled) young shoots and much more distinctly toothed leaves.

STACHYURUS PRÆCOX, *Siebold*. TERNSTRŒMIACEÆ

(Bot. Mag., t. 6631)

A deciduous shrub, said to become as much as 10 ft. high in Japan, but rarely more than half as high in England. Leaves ovate-lanceolate,

STACHYURUS PRÆCOX

glabrous, 3 to 7 ins. long, with a long slender apex; toothed at the margin. Flowers twelve to twenty together, in stiff drooping racemes 2 to 3 ins. long, each flower ⅓ in. across, pale yellow.

Native of Japan, and quite hardy. Its greatest merit in the garden is its early-flowering nature. In favourable years it will be in full flower by the middle of February, and ordinarily, not more than a month later. The flower-spikes are formed in the axils of the leaves and attain their full length in autumn, and, although exposed to whatever inclemencies the winter may bring, remain unscathed. Unseasonable warmth in the early part of the year, followed by a rough cold spell, will sometimes injure the flowers. But on the whole they are very hardy, and when the reddish leafless branches are hung with yellow racemes 1 in. or less apart there are few things in the garden more pleasing at that early season.

In China this species is represented by S. CHINENSIS, *Franchet*, which has recently been introduced in considerable quantity by Wilson. Although, as seen growing side by side, they appear distinct, there is really very little on which one can seize to differentiate them. In habit S. chinensis is the stronger and more vigorous, sending up strong arching shoots, varying from green to dark brown, sometimes red as in S. præcox. The racemes and flowers are to all intents the same, but the fruits, which I have not seen, are said to be smaller than in S. præcox. It flowers at Kew about a fortnight later than S. præcox, and is as hardy and, if anything, more attractive.

When planting out either of these species it is advisable to mix peat and leaf-soil with the loam, especially if the last be of a heavy nature. S. præcox can be propagated easily by cuttings made of fairly firm wood in July with a " heel " attached, and placed in gentle heat, also by division.

STAPHYLEA. BLADDER-NUT. STAPHYLEACEÆ

A genus of deciduous bushes occasionally large enough to be considered small trees, with opposite, trifoliolate or pinnate leaves, usually made up of three or five leaflets. The flowers are produced in terminal racemes or panicles, and are of some shade of white ; the sepals, petals, and stamens five. The most distinctive feature of the genus is the fruit— a membranous, inflated, two- or three-celled capsule.

The bladder-nuts are planted in gardens for the beauty of the foliage and flowers, and for their interesting fruits. All those given separate mention below are hardy. Their needs are simple—a good, loamy, moist soil and a fairly sunny spot. They can be increased by cuttings. All flower in May.

Besides the species of which a more detailed account is given below, the two following may be briefly mentioned :—

S. BOLANDERI, *A. Gray*.—A native of N. California ; discovered in 1874, on a branch of the Sacramento River, near Mount Shasta. It has three oval or roundish, glabrous, short-pointed leaflets, up to 2½ ins. long ; greenish white flowers, capsules three-celled, 2½ ins. long. I have not met with it in gardens.

S. EMODI, *Wallich*.—Native of the north-western Himalaya. A shrub or small tree with trifoliolate leaves, each leaflet 3 to 6 ins. long ; flowers white, in rather dense cymes, 1½ to 4 ins. wide.   Capsules 2 to 3 ins. long. This bladder-nut is allied to S. trifolia, but has less downy leaves, whose margins are simply and less conspicuously toothed.   Plants under the name have recently been distributed from nurseries.

The bladder-nuts have a rather remarkable distribution over the North Temperate Zone. They spread all round the world, but most of the species have each their own separate area. Thus, starting at home, we have S. pinnata, which extends through Europe to Asia Minor, then come S. colchica in the Caucasus, and S. emodi in the Himalaya and Afghanistan. Crossing into China, there is S. holocarpa (and perhaps one or two more species) ; then S. Bumalda carries the genus to the western shores of the Pacific. Across that ocean the roll is taken up on the western side of N. America by S. Bolanderi, and on the Atlantic side by S. trifolia.

The following species may be grouped as follows :—

1. Leaves trifoliolate

S. trifolia, 10 to 15 ft. high. Leaflets very downy all over beneath.
S. Bumalda, 2 to 6 ft. high. Leaflets downy only on midrib and veins.
S. holocarpa, 20 to 30 ft. high. Leaflets downy at the base only.

2. Leaves tri- or quinquefoliolate

S. pinnata. Leaflets dull and pale beneath.
S. colchica. Leaflets lustrous green beneath ; capsules 3 to 4 ins. long.
S. Coulombieri. Leaflets lustrous green beneath ; capsules 1½ to 2 ins. long.

S. Bumalda, *De Candolle*

A deciduous shrub 3 to 6 ft. high, of neat habit. Leaves of three leaflets which are 1½ to 3 ins. long, ovate-lanceolate, sharply toothed, downy on the midrib and veins. Flowers greenish white, ¼ in. long, borne in a terminal cymose cluster 1½ to 3 ins. long. Fruit a membranous inflated capsule about 1 in. long and wide, in two flattened obovate parts, each terminated by the bristle-like, persistent style ; seeds yellowish.

Native of Japan, where it inhabits mountainous regions ; also of Central and W. China. The Japanese form has not proved of much value in gardens, being rather tender and having few attractions. It flowers in May and June. The Chinese form recently introduced by Wilson may be hardier.

S. colchica, *Steven*

(Bot. Mag., t. 7383)

A deciduous shrub, 6 to 10 ft. high, with stiff, erect branches. Leaves composed of three or five leaflets, which are ovate-oblong, 2½ to 3½ ins. long, nearly or quite glabrous, shining beneath, the margins set with fine, rather bristle-like teeth ; the terminal leaflet is stalked, the lateral ones stalkless. Flowers in erect panicles terminating the young shoots and lateral twigs, the largest up to 5 ins. long, and as much wide ; each flower ¾ in. long and wide, the sepals spreading, narrow oblong, very pale green ; petals white, erect, narrow, recurved at the tips. Fruit a two- or three-celled inflated capsule, 3 to 4 ins. long, 2 ins. wide, the apex of each division ending in a long, fine point. Seeds ⅓ in. long, pale brown. Flowers in May.

Native of the S. Caucasus, and the handsomest of cultivated staphyleas
It is now largely employed for forcing early into bloom for conservatory
decoration. It is distinguishable from S. pinnata in leaf, by the shining lower
surface, and in fruit by the much larger capsules.

S. Coulombieri, *André*

A deciduous shrub of vigorous habit, considered by some to be a hybrid
between S. colchica and pinnata. The leaves are composed of three or five
leaflets, which are larger than in either of the reputed parents, the terminal

Staphylea Coulombieri

one often 5 to 6 ins. long ; they are ovate-oblong, toothed, dark green on both
sides, and very lustrous beneath. Flowers white, and intermediate in size
between those of the parents ; the panicles are not so large as in S. colchica, the
blossoms more compact, and the sepals and petals wider and shorter. The
fruit is intermediate in size, being a two- or three-celled capsule, $1\frac{1}{2}$ to 2 ins.
long, the seeds rather larger.

This handsome shrub was first noticed as showing hybrid characters in
the nursery of Mr Coulombier, at Vitry, in France, in 1887. It had been
obtained by him from the famous arboretum of Segrez in 1872, beyond which
date its history is unknown. But it may well have originated there as a chance
hybrid. It is most closely related to S. colchica, especially in the shining
green under-surface of the leaves, but the much smaller fruits and the differences
in the sepals and petals distinguish it.

Var. GRANDIFLORA, *Zabel.*—A very distinct form with much longer, laxer panicles, and larger individual flowers ; the leaflets are rather longer than in ordinary S. Coulombieri, but proportionately narrower.

S. HOLOCARPA, *Hemsley*

(Bot. Mag., t. 9074)

A deciduous shrub, 20 to 30 ft. high in a wild state, and often tree-like ; young shoots glabrous. Leaves of three leaflets, which are oblong-lanceolate, abruptly acuminate, the terminal one stalked and 2 to 4 ins. long, the side ones almost stalkless ; all finely toothed, and downy at the base beneath. Flowers white or pink, borne in short, broad corymbs, 2 ins. or more long ; each flower ½ in. long. Fruit a three-celled, pear-shaped inflated capsule, 2 ins. long, 1 in. wide, tapering gradually at the base, but terminating in a short, sharp point. Seeds shining grey, about the size of large shot.

Native of Central China ; first discovered in the province of Hupeh by Henry. It was introduced to cultivation by Wilson in 1908 when collecting for Harvard University, and by him was considered likely to prove attractive in gardens. It has indeed proved very beautiful where it has flowered well.

S. PINNATA, *Linnæus.* BLADDER-NUT

A deciduous shrub up to 12 or 15 ft. high. Leaves pinnate, composed of usually five leaflets, occasionally three, rarely seven ; they are 2 to 4 ins. long, ovate or ovate-oblong, toothed, dull green above, pale and dull beneath, with down near the base of the midrib. Flowers in terminal drooping panicles 2 to 4 ins. long, white, each flower about ½ in. long, the sepals as well as petals erect. Fruit a two-celled, bladder-like capsule 1 to 1½ ins. long, about the same wide, each cell containing one or more seeds about the size of a large pea, brownish yellow.

Native of Europe from the West to Asia Minor. It is the best known of the bladder-nuts, and although not a native of Britain is now naturalised in the hedgerows and copses of some parts. In 1596, according to Gerard, it grew in the Strand " by the Lord Treasurer's House." It is not so handsome and notable a shrub as S. colchica, from which, as well as from Coulombieri, it is distinguished by the dull under-surface of the leaves and erect sepals, and from S. colchica in particular by the much smaller fruits, containing seeds twice as large. It merits a place in the garden for its curious and interesting fruits as well as its flowers and foliage.

S. TRIFOLIA, *Linnæus*

A deciduous shrub up to 10 or 15 ft. high. Leaves of always three leaflets, which are broadly ovate, 2 to 4 ins. long, occasionally doubly toothed ; pale and downy all over the lower surface, dark green and less downy above ; the middle leaflet is long-stalked, the side ones very shortly so. Panicles short, drooping, 1½ to 2 ins. long, either terminating the leading shoot or small side twigs ; flowers bell-shaped, dingy white. Fruit a usually three-celled capsule, 1¼ to 1½ ins. long, less in width ; seeds yellowish, $\frac{3}{16}$ in. long.

Native of the eastern United States ; cultivated in England in 1640, but not ornamental enough ever to have been extensively grown. It is easily distinguished from the other species in cultivation by the very downy leaves. There appears to be rarely more than one seed to each cell, often none.

STAUNTONIA HEXAPHYLLA, *Decaisne.*

LARDIZABALACEÆ

An evergreen climbing shrub, whose main stem is sometimes 4 or 5 ins. thick near the base. Leaves long-stalked, compound, consisting of three to seven leaflets radiating from a common centre. Leaflets ovate to elliptical, acutely pointed, the side ones usually oblique, of leathery texture, glabrous, 2 to 5 ins. long; stalks 1 to 2 ins. long. Flowers, unisexual, produced three to seven together in a raceme, white tinged with violet, ¾ in. across; they have six fleshy sepals, but no petals; the males with six stamens, the females with three ovaries. Fruit of the size of a walnut, purple, sweet and watery; eaten by the Japanese.

Native of Korea and Japan. The genus commemorates Sir George Staunton, who accompanied Lord Macartney on his famous embassy to China in 1792. From the closely allied Holbœllia it is distinguished by the stamens being united instead of free. It has been grown since 1876 on a wall at Kew, but needs warmer conditions than are there afforded to be seen at its best. It is admirably adapted for the south-western counties, but in more northern localities is best suited in a winter garden or cool conservatory.

STEPHANANDRA.   ROSACEÆ

An Asiatic genus of deciduous shrubs, comprising four species. They are closely allied to Spiræa, but have small, dull white, or greenish flowers; sepals and petals five. Leaves alternate. Fruit a dry capsule enclosed by the persistent sepals. They like a moist, loamy soil, and are easily propagated by cuttings or by division of the plants; S. incisa also by root-cuttings put in heat in March.

S. INCISA, *Zabel*

(S. flexuosa, *Siebold and Zuccarini*)

A deciduous shrub of graceful habit, with glabrous, wiry, zigzag branches, forming a dense, rounded bush ultimately 4 to 8 ft. high, sending up sucker growths freely from the base. Leaves triangular in the main, truncate or heart-shaped at the base, tapering to a slender apex; 1½ to 3 ins. long, somewhat less in width at the base; the margins cut into deep lobes, the lobes toothed; stipules linear, toothed, ¼ in. long. Flowers greenish white, ⅛ in. wide, crowded on panicles 1 to 3 ins. long and terminating short side-twigs from the previous year's shoots; stamens ten.

Native of Japan and Korea; introduced to Kew, in 1872, by way of St Petersburg. It has proved quite hardy, and is now generally cultivated for the beauty of its handsomely cut, fern-like foliage, and for the brown of its naked stems and branches in winter. The finest specimen I have seen is in Lord Annesley's garden at Castlewellan, which some years ago was 8 ft. high and more in diameter—an exceedingly elegant bush. The flowers appear in June, but have little beauty.

S. TANAKÆ, *Franchet*
(Bot. Mag., t. 7593)

A deciduous shrub of twiggy habit, up to 6 ft. or perhaps more high, with labrous, slender branches. Leaves broadly ovate or triangular, 2 to 5 ins. ong and from two-thirds to quite as much wide ; the point long and slender, he base rounded or heart-shaped ; the margins double-toothed, and frequently vith one or two pairs of angular lobes more or less developed near the base ; eins hairy when quite young, becoming glabrous ; stipules heart-shaped, oothed, ¼ in. long. Flowers yellowish white, produced in June and July in a lax, branching panicle 2 to 4 ins. long ; each flower ⅕ in. across on a stalk about as long ; stamens fifteen to twenty.

Native of Japan ; introduced to Kew in 1893. It differs from S. incisa n the larger, less deeply cut leaves (which turn an orange colour in autumn), n the broader stipules, the more numerous stamens, and in the longer, more lender, and less densely flowered panicles. The flowers become a purer white ander sunnier skies than ours. The species is hardier than S. incisa and its stems are brighter brown.

STERCULIA PLATANIFOLIA, *Linnæus*. STERCULIACEÆ
(Firmiana simplex, *W. F. Wight* ; Firmiana platanifolia, *R. Brown*)

A tree up to 60 ft. high, with noble foliage and a trunk smooth even n age. Leaves variable in size, but averaging from 6 to 8 ins. in length and as much or more wide ; on vigorous young plants they are over 1 ft. long. Ordinarily, the leaves have three rather shallow, pointed lobes towards the end, but often they are five-lobed, with the general outline of a maple-leaf, the base heart-shaped ; they are either furnished with stellate down beneath, especially in the vein-axils, or are glabrous. The leaf-stalk is two-thirds to quite the length of the blade. Flowers small, yellow, produced on a branching panicle as much as 18 ins. long and 9 ins. wide. Fruit a kind of pod (follicle), 3 to 4 ins. long, tapering to a beak at the end, and containing several seeds about the size of peas.

Native of China, but introduced in 1757 from Japan, where it is much cultivated. It was long treated as a greenhouse plant, and is, indeed, better suited in Cornwall and such-like localities than in the London districts, where, to be safe, it needs wall protection. Its beauty, however, is only fully shown in a spot where it can develop freely on all sides. It is very fine on the Riviera, especially in the Casino Gardens at Monte Carlo.

STEWARTIA. TERNSTRŒMIACEÆ

This genus, sometimes spelt " Stuartia," was so named in honour of John Stuart, the Earl of Bute who acted as chief adviser to Augusta, Princess Dowager of Wales, when she founded the Botanic Garden at Kew, in 1759-60. About eight species are known, two from the East United States the others from Japan and China. They are shrubs or trees with alternate leaves, white petals, and numerous stamens ; the other parts of the flower in fives. Allied to Camellia, but deciduous.

Stewartias have been too much neglected in gardens ; they have great beauty, and flower in July and August, when few shrubs remain in blossom. They are evidently not among the most robust, for the American species, although first introduced more than a hundred years ago, must still be classed with the rarest inhabitants of our gardens. A sheltered sunny position should be selected for them, and care should be taken that they do not suffer from excessive drought. Whilst a peaty soil is not essential for them, they are undoubtedly benefited by having some of it, as well as leaf-soil, mixed with the ordinary loam of the garden, especially when young. Still a warm, sandy loam free from lime suits them well. I find that the root shelter they obtain by being planted in a bed of Erica mediterranea is very grateful to them, and the soil which suits heaths suits them also. Stewartias are not easy to propagate except by seeds which are occasionally borne by good-sized plants. They should, like most of those of the Camellia family, be sown as soon as obtained. Failing them, cuttings may be used. These should be taken from ripened wood in late summer and inserted in very sandy soil under a cloche in a cool frame, or even in pure sand. It is wise to put plants in their permanent sites as early as possible.

STYLES SEPARATE . . . . *S. ovata*
STYLES UNITED
  Ovary glabrous . . . . *S. serrata*
  Ovary hairy; bracteoles leafy, as long as, or longer than
    the calyx
    Flower 1 to 1¼ in. across . . . . . . *S. monadelpha*
    Flower 2½ to 3 in. across . . . . . . *S. sinensis*
  Ovary hairy; bracteoles leathery, much smaller than the calyx
    Filaments purple . . . . *S. malacodendron*
    Filaments yellow, flower cup-shaped . . . . *S. pseudo-camellia*
    Filaments yellow, flower opening wide . . . . *S. koreana*

S. KOREANA, *Rehder* (Plate 31)

(Flora Sylvatica Koreana, part xvii., t. 16; S. pseudocamellia var. Koreana,
Sealy; Bot. Mag. N. Ser. t. 20)

A deciduous tree up to 45 or 50 ft. high; young shoots glabrous. Leaves oval to ovate, with a short slender point and a broadly tapered or occasionally rounded base, shallowly toothed; 1¼ to 4 ins. long, ¾ to 3 ins. wide; silky-hairy when very young, the hairs soon falling away except for a few on the midrib and stalk; stalk ⅛ to ½ in. long. Flowers solitary in the leaf-axils or sometimes terminal, each on a glabrous or slightly downy stalk ½ in. long, white, 2¼ ins. wide. Petals spreading, oval, 1 in. wide, silky at the back except at the wavy margin; stamens with white stalks; sepals roundish, ⅜ in. wide, silky outside; styles reddish, united. Seed-vessel woody, ovoid, beaked, ¾ in. long, silky.

Native of Korea; introduced to America by Wilson in 1917. It is closely related to S. pseudo-camellia, which it much resembles. The flowers, however, are larger and flatter and do not take on the cup shape of that species. In S. koreana, too, the leaves are wider, not slenderly tapered, and less silky-hairy. Mr A. Osborn, late of Kew, who saw small trees in the Arnold Arboretum in late June 1930, informed me that they were beautifully in flower then and showed the species to be definitely one of the best of the stewartias. This opinion was amply confirmed at Vincent Square on 3rd July 1945, when Major E. de Rothschild showed flowering specimens. Dr Rehder observes that the leaves change to bright brownish-orange or orange-red in autumn.

S. MALACODENDRON, *Linnæus*

(Bot. Mag., t. 8145; S. virginica, *Cavanilles*)

A deciduous small tree or shrub, 15 ft. or more high. Leaves 2 to 4 ins. long, ovate, oval, or obovate, more tapered at the base, and less distinctly

STEWARTIA MALACODENDRON

stalked than in S. pentagyna ; the apex is pointed or blunt, the margins toothed, the lower surface more or less hairy. Flowers solitary in the leaf-axils, 2½ to 3½ ins. across ; calyx ¾ in. across, with five broad, pointed, hairy divisions ; petals white, silky behind ; stamens purple, with bluish anthers, forming a conspicuous and beautiful centre to the flower. Fruit woody, egg-shaped, ½ in. diameter.

Native of the south-eastern United States, and from S. pentagyna easily distinguished by the united styles and by the smaller and differently shaped leaves. Mark Catesby, the famous author of the *Natural History of Carolina*, flowered this tree in his garden at Fulham in 1742, and Peter Collinson grew it at Mill Hill, near Hendon, in 1761, but it is now one of the rarest of American shrubs. Commencing to flower in July, it continues into August, being at that season one of the handsomest and most distinguished shrubs in flower. The largest plant of whose existence I am aware is in a garden at Stoke Poges—over 20 ft. high. There is also a good example at Syon.

S. MONADELPHA, *Siebold and Zuccarini*

A deciduous tree 50 to 80 ft. high ; young shoots hairy at first, slender. Leaves ovate to ovate-lanceolate, 1½ to 3 ins. long, ⅝ to 1¼ ins. wide, rounded to widely cuneate at the base, the apex narrowed to a slender point, serrate, appressed downy beneath at first ; stalk ½ in. or less long. Flowers white, 1 to 1⅓ ins. wide, petals spreading, silky downy at the back ; stamens united at the base ; anthers violet ; fruit ovoid, beaked, ⅖ in. long, covered with yellowish closely appressed hairs.

Native of S. Japan ; introduced about 1903 ; Wilson found it abundant on the island of Yakushima with a smooth, pale trunk sometimes 3 ft. in diameter. The fruit is the smallest in the genus and the flowers, which I have not seen, must be the same.

S. OVATA, *Weatherby*

(Bot. Mag., t. 3918 ; S. pentagyna, *L'Heritier* ; Malacodendron ovatum, *Cavanilles*)

A deciduous shrub, up to 15 ft. in height, with erect branches but a bushy habit ; young shoots, leaf-stalks, and often the leaves tinged with red. Leaves ovate, 2½ to 5 ins. long, about half as much wide ; rounded at the base, pointed, toothed more or less distinctly on the margin, or entire ; hairy beneath, more especially when young. Flowers produced singly in the leaf-axils, on hairy stalks, about ¼ in. long. Sepals five, about ½ in. long, broadly strap-shaped or ovate, densely hairy ; petals five or six, creamy white, prettily crenulated, one of them often deformed. A conspicuous feature of the flower is the cluster of normally whitish, but sometimes purple stamens ; styles three to five, not united ; the finest flowers are over 4 ins. across, others under 3 ins.

Native of several of the southern United States, most abundant perhaps in Tennessee. This species has for more than one hundred years been an inhabitant of our gardens, but never a common one. Yet it is one of the most interesting and beautiful of American shrubs, especially in July and August, when in bloom. It is said to have been 10 to 12 ft. high in the gardens of Dropmore and White Knights seventy years ago, but large plants appear now to be very scarce. Botanically, its most distinctive character is the disunited styles.

Var. GRANDIFLORA.—I distinguish by this name the beautiful form with purple stamens, which give a much more striking character to the flower than the ordinary whitish ones, especially as it measures 4 to 4½ ins. across

he petals. This form is found along with the white-stamened one in the woods
f Georgia ; there appears to be no other character to differentiate them, but
he stamens are always purple.

S. PSEUDO-CAMELLIA, *Maximowicz*

(Bot. Mag., t. 7045)

In Great Britain this species has only as yet attained the dimensions of
a shrub or small tree of dense habit, but in Japan it was seen by Sargent up
o 50 ft. in height, with a trunk 6 ft. in girth. It is deciduous, the branchlets
nd often the leaves quite glabrous, the latter sometimes silky beneath. Leaves
to 3½ ins. long, ovate or obovate, tapering at the base to a short stalk, finely
oothed. Flowers produced singly in the leaf-axils on a short stalk, ½ in. or
ess in length ; each flower 2 to 2½ ins. across, white and cupped. Petals five,
oundish, concave, covered with silky hairs behind, the margins irregularly
agged ; sepals densely hairy ; stamens numerous, incurved, orange-yellow.
)vary conical, surmounted by five united styles, the stigmas only spreading.
Fruit a broadly ovoid, hairy capsule, 1 in. long.

Native of Japan ; introduced to England by Messrs Veitch, but cultivated
previously in the United States and in France, where it first bore fruit in
he nursery of Messrs Thibaut and Keteleer at Sceaux, near Paris, in 1878.
t is not, perhaps, quite so striking as either of the American species, but
s still a beautiful tree, and is evidently more at home in English gardens.
When the seasons are suitable the leaves turn brilliant yellow and red before
alling. The ugly specific name refers to the resemblance of the flowers to
hose of a single camellia.

S. SERRATA, *Maximowicz*

(Bot. Mag., t. 8771)

A deciduous tree probably 30 ft. and upwards high ; young shoots often
eddish and slightly hairy at first, becoming glabrous. Leaves oval or obovate,
apered towards the base, more abruptly so towards the pointed apex, margins
et with incurved teeth ; 1½ to 3 ins. long, half as much wide ; dull green and
glabrous above ; paler, downy in the vein-axils and usually hairy on the midrib
)eneath ; stalk ⅛ to ½ in. long. Flowers solitary in the leaf-axils of the young
hoots, cup-shaped, 2 to 2½ ins. wide, opening in June ; flower-stalk ⅛ to ¼ in.
ong, hairy. Petals five, creamy white, stained with red outside, scoop-shaped,
i in. wide, the margins jagged. Stamens numerous, free, their stalks silky
at the base ; anthers yellow. Sepals five (occasionally six), ovate-oblong,
ʒ to ¾ in. long, pointed, glabrous except for minute hairs on the margin ;
)ersisting to the fruiting stage and then much reflexed. Seed-vessel woody,
ovoid, ¾ in. long, quite glabrous, each of the five divisions tapered to a beak at
he top. Seeds winged like those of an elm.

Native of Japan, where it appears to be uncommon. I first became
acquainted with it in 1915, when it was sent in flower to Kew by the late Sir
Edmund Loder ; it had also then been in cultivation for some time at Nymans,
n Sussex. Like all its kind it is an attractive tree. Its nearest ally, perhaps,
s S. sinensis, but that species is amply distinguished by its hairy ovary and
seed-vessel, by its stamens being united at the base, and by having no tufts of
down in the vein-axils of the leaf beneath. Branches beautifully in flower were
hown by Lt.-Col. Stephenson Clarke at Westminster on 21st June 1932.

S. SINENSIS, *Rehder and Wilson*

(Bot. Mag., t. 8778)

A deciduous shrub or small tree, 30 ft. high ; bark peeling, young shoot‑clothed at first with fine hairs. Leaves oval or ovate-oblong, 1½ to 4 ins. long, ⅝ to 1¾ ins. wide ; wedge-shaped at the base, tapered at the apex toothed ; at first hairy on both surfaces (but more densely so above) and a the margin, becoming almost glabrous ; bright green on both sides ; stall hairy, ⅛ to ¼ in. long. Flowers solitary in the leaf-axils, 1½ to 2 ins. across white, fragrant ; stamens numerous, downy ; styles united into one column five-rayed at the top ; ovary hairy ; sepals and petals silky at the back.

Native of China ; introduced by Wilson about 1901. It is nearly allied to S. monadelpha, which is, however, a native of Japan only. Messrs Rehder and Wilson observe, moreover, that the " capsule of S. sinensis is the larges in the genus (⅖ in. in diameter), that of S. monadelpha is the smallest " (⅓ in in diameter). *Plantæ Wilsonionæ*, ii., p. 396.

STRANVÆSIA.   ROSACEÆ

A small genus of evergreens inhabiting Tibet, China, and the Himalaya, very similar to Photinia. Propagated by cuttings made o half-ripened wood, placed in gentle heat. They thrive in sandy loam The generic name was given by Lindley in honour of Mr Fox Strangways.

S. DAVIDIANA, *Decaisne*

(Bot. Mag., t. 9008 ; Photinia Davidiana, *Cardot*)

The typical S. Davidiana is figured in the *Botanical Magazine* from a plan of Forrest's introduction grown by the late Marquis of Headfort in his garder near Kells, Co. Meath. As depicted there, the leaves have pretty much the same outline as those of S. undulata, but Forrest's specimens show them to be considerably larger and as much as 4½ ins. long by 1¾ ins. wide. It wil become difficult apparently to distinguish S. salicifolia from S. Davidiana by the foliage, as it is possible to find leaves from both identical in shape, never theless in typical Davidiana they are on a whole considerably wider in proportior to their length and the plant itself more vigorous and tree-like. The fruit: of the latter are globose, brilliant red, ¼ in. or rather more wide and generally larger. There does not appear to be anything distinctive in the angles at which the leaf-veins join the midrib, or in their number, or in the degree of downines of the inflorescence.

S. Davidiana is a native of the mountains which separate the valleys of the Yangtse, Mekong, and Salwin rivers. Forrest found it over 30 ft. high Originally discovered by Père David, near Moupin, in 1869. Plants at Exbury are over 20 ft. high.

S. NUSSIA, *Decaisne*

(S. glaucescens, *Lindley* ; Bot. Reg., t. 1956)

A small evergreen tree, the branchlets covered when young with a loose whitish down, ultimately glabrous. Leaves leathery, lanceolate to obovate 2½ to 4 ins. long, ¾ to 2 ins. wide ; dark shining green and glabrous above paler, glossy and slightly downy on the midrib beneath, finely toothed. Flower white, about ½ in. across, produced in July in flattish, terminal hairy-stalkec orymbs, 2 to 4 ins. across ; flower-stalk and calyx woolly. Fruit hoary with own when young, becoming pale red and glabrous, ¼ in. long, pear-shaped. Native of the outer ranges of the Himalaya ; introduced to England in 1828. t is not hardy in the open at Kew, but grows vigorously on a wall, where, owever, it rarely flowers. There is a good specimen in the gardens of Osborne House, Isle of Wight, which flowers and produces fruit in abundance and here is one in Lt.-Col. Stephenson Clarke's garden at Binstead, Isle of Wight, which was 20 ft. high in 1939.

S. SALICIFOLIA, *Hutchinson*

(Bot. Mag., t. 8862 ; S. Davidiana salicifolia, *Rehder*)

An evergreen shrub with erect branches, perhaps ultimately a small tree ; oung shoots densely clothed with brown down which persists more or less on he year-old branchlets. Leaves narrowly oblong or lance-shaped, pointed, apered towards both ends, not toothed ; 1½ to 4 ins. long, ⅜ to 1 in. wide ; bright green above, paler beneath and glabrous on both sides except for a ine of down on the midrib above ; stalk ½ to ¾ in. long, downy like the young hoots. Flowers in terminal corymbs 3 ins. wide ; stalks downy. Each flower s ¼ in. wide, with five round white petals ; stamens about twenty, with red anthers which give a pretty tinge to the flower clusters. Fruits red, globose, in. wide.

Native of W. China. I saw this shrub in the nursery of the Arnold Arboretum in 1910 and obtained a plant for Kew which I believe represents its irst introduction to England. It had been introduced to America by Wilson in 1907. As noted above under S. Davidiana, it is difficult to find any really distinctive character from that species and it is probably merely a form of it. A handsome-fruited, quite hardy shrub. Both flower in June.

S. UNDULATA, *Decaisne*

(Bot. Mag., t. 8418 ; S. Davidiana undulata, *Rehder and Wilson*)

A low, spreading evergreen shrub, or a tree over 20 ft. high, with very downy young branchlets. Leaves leathery, oval-lanceolate, pointed, glossy green, 1½ to 3½ ins. long, ½ to 1¼ ins. wide, entire, downy only on the midrib and margins ; stalk ⅛ to ½ in. long, downy. Flowers white, produced in June in terminal, hairy-stalked corymbs, 1½ to 2½ ins. wide ; each flower about ⅜ in. across ; petals soon falling ; calyx with five triangular lobes, silky hairy when young ; stamens about twenty. Fruit brilliant red, of the size of common haws but rounder.

Native of China ; introduced by Wilson for Messrs Veitch about 1901. It appears to be quite hardy. It flowers with great freedom, but the blossoms last in beauty a very short time. Its great charm as a garden shrub is in its abundant crop of bright red fruits. The leaves (as in Photinia) turn red some-imes before falling. The specific name refers to the frequently wavy margin-of the leaves. There is a plant at Exbury only 6 or 7 ft. high, but twice as wide.

Var. FRUCTU-LUTEO.—The typical form of S. undulata is now becoming fairly well known and is valued for its orange or orange-red fruits. In January 1920 Mr Coey of the Donard Nursery Co., Newcastle, Co. Down, sent to Kew a specimen bearing bright yellow fruits but it has since been lost. Mr Coey wrote that " three plants of a batch I raised have these yellow fruits. The young wood seems to be as red as in the red-fruited plants." This form may be distinguished as var. FRUCTU-LUTEO.

STYRAX. STORAX. STYRACACEÆ

A large genus of trees and shrubs found in Europe, N. America India, China, and Japan. Only a small proportion of these are hard in Britain, but no group possesses greater beauty and distinction. Leave alternate, and often clothed, like the young wood and other parts of th plant, with stellate (or rosette-like) down. Flowers white, usually i racemes. From Halesia and Pterostyrax, its nearest allies, Styrax i distinguished by the relative position of the fruit and calyx. In th present genus the fruit sits in the persistent cup-shaped calyx ; in th other two the fruit is below the calyx, which is persistent in Pterostyra only.

All the species of Styrax need careful attention when young. The like a sheltered spot, and when first planted out should have a sand loam, to which decayed leaves and, if available, some finely broken-u peat has been added. Once established, they will root into the surround ing ground. Cuttings of S. japonicum and americanum may be rooted but they and the rest succeed better raised from seed.

S. AMERICANUM, *Lamarck*. AMERICAN STORAX

A deciduous shrub, 3 to 8 ft. high ; young shoots nearly glabrous. Leave narrowly oval, or obovate, 1½ to 3½ ins. long, ½ to 1¼ ins. wide ; the bas wedge-shaped, the apex mostly pointed ; minutely toothed, dark green above paler beneath, almost or quite glabrous on both sides ; stalk ⅛ in. or less long Flowers white, pendulous, ¾ to 1¼ ins. across, produced in June and July on to four near and at the end of short leafy twigs ; each flower on a slende stalk ¼ to ½ in. long. Petals ⅛ to ³⁄₁₆ in. wide, pointed ; calyx triangular-lobed stamens erect, ½ in. long. Fruit roundish oval, ¼ in. wide, covered with fin grey down, and supported at the base by the persistent five-lobed calyx.

Native of the south-eastern United States ; introduced in 1765. Thi shrub has long been cultivated at Kew, but grows slowly, really needing warmer climate. It was killed to the ground by the frosts of February 1895 but sprang up again later. It is better adapted for our south-west counties where it is a pretty shrub ; yet neither as hardy nor as beautiful as S. japonicum to which in its pendulous blossoms it bears some resemblance but is easil distinguished by its narrower petals.

S. DASYANTHUM, *Perkins*

A deciduous shrub or small tree, the young branchlets furnished at firs with reddish brown down, becoming glabrous. Leaves obovate to broadl oval, 2 to 4 ins. long, 1½ to 3 ins. wide ; tapered more or less at the base pointed, the upper part minutely toothed ; the lower surface when youn is covered with tufted hairs, which mostly fall away before the end of th season. Flowers white, ½ to ¾ in. long, produced in July in slender termina racemes 2 to 4 ins. long, augmented by clusters of two to four flowers in th uppermost leaf-axils. Corolla segments lanceolate, covered outside with tufted, yellowish white down. Calyx cup-shaped, felted outside, ¼ in. long with several short but unequal, pointed teeth.

Native of Hupeh, China ; discovered by Henry, and again by Wilson i 1900. The best plant I know of was at Aldenham, where it has succeede against a wall, and flowered several times in recent years. It is also very goo at Tower Court, near Ascot.

S. HEMSLEYANUM, *Diels*

(Bot. Mag., t. 8339)

A deciduous tree, 20 ft. or more high, young shoots covered at first with ﹍ufted down. Leaves obovate or unequally ovate, 3 to 5½ ins. long, 2 to 3½ ins. ﹍ide ; usually more gradually tapered at the base than at the apex ; finely ﹍nd rather distantly toothed, prominently veined ; glabrous and pale green ﹍bove, sparsely furnished beneath with tufted (stellate) down ; stalk ¼ to ﹍in. long. Flowers pure white, produced in June on terminal downy

STYRAX HEMSLEYANUM

﹍acemes or few-branched panicles, 4 to 6 ins. long, each flower on a stalk ﹍in. long. Corolla ¾ in. long, about 1 in. wide, the five lobes narrowly oval, ﹍owny outside, joined at the base into a tube ¼ in. long. Calyx bell-shaped, ﹍in. long, slender-toothed, covered with reddish brown tufted down.

Native of Central and W. China ; introduced by Wilson in 1900. It is ﹍ultivated at Caerhays, Cornwall, and is a vigorous small tree, 10 or 12 ft. ﹍igh, of remarkable beauty when in blossom ; striking also in size of leaf. ﹍t bears a certain resemblance to S. Obassia, but the leaves of that species are ﹍ounder, more coarsely toothed, and much more downy beneath, and the bud ﹍s enclosed by the base of the leaf-stalk.

S. JAPONICUM, *Siebold and Zuccarini*

(Bot. Mag., t. 5950 (wrongly as S. serrulatum))

A small deciduous tree, 10 to 25 ft. high, of very graceful habit ; th
branches slender, sometimes drooping ; young shoots at first furnished wi
scattered tufts of down, which soon fall away. Leaves usually oval, taperir
about equally at both ends, 1 to 3½ ins. long, ½ to 1½ ins. wide ; but occasional
obovate or even roundish ; margins set with minute, shallow, distant glandula
teeth ; dark glossy green above, glabrous on both surfaces except for tuf
of down in the vein-axils ; stalk ⅓ in. or less long. Flowers pure white, perfect
pendulous, ¾ in. diameter, borne on short lateral shoots carrying about thre
leaves and three to six blossoms ; each flower on a glabrous slender stall
1 to 1½ ins. long. Corolla of five pointed divisions, which are united ne
the base, ⅝ in. long, downy outside. Calyx glabrous, funnel-shaped, ¼ i

STYRAX JAPONICUM

long, persisting at the base of the roundish, egg-shaped fruit, which is ½ i
long. Flowers in June.

Native of Japan and Korea ; introduced to Kew by Richard Oldham
1862. It is a small tree of singular grace and beauty, very hardy, bu
preferring a sheltered spot and one, if possible, shaded from morning su
for the flower-buds and the young shoots are liable to injury by late sprir
frosts. It should be given a light loamy soil to which either peat or lea
soil, or both, have been added. Apart from its susceptibility to late fros
especially in low-lying situations, it is one of the most desirable of all harc
trees of its type, and amply repays the trouble of preparing a suitable mediur
for the roots, if that does not already exist.

S. LANGKONGENSE, *W. W. Smith*

A deciduous shrub of bushy habit up to 6 ft. high as found in a wild stat
young shoots covered with minute, brownish, starry down. Leaves alternat
indistinctly toothed, ovate or obovate, rounded to tapered at the base, ofte
narrowed abruptly at the end to a short point ; 1 to 2½ ins. long, ¾ to 2 in
wide ; dark dull green and strewn with pale minute down above, white ar
soft with starry down beneath ; veins in four to six pairs, yellowish ; stalk ¼ i
or less long. Flowers white (pure or with a creamy tint), about 1 in. wid
borne singly or in pairs in the leaf-axils and at the end of shoots 1 to 2 in
long, thus forming a kind of short raceme. Corolla five-lobed, shortly tubul
at the base, downy (especially outside) ; stamens ten, anthers yellowish ; caly
cup-shaped, ¼ in. long, five-toothed, velvety with brown down. Fruit nut-lik
egg-shaped, ⅝ in. long, ½ in. wide, at first covered with down.

Native of Yunnan, W. China; found in 1910 by Forrest on hills at the
outh end of the Langkong Valley, " in dry, open, stony, pasture." This
pecies appears to be very rare in cultivation and I have only seen it at Caerhays,
here it flowers in June and July and is very pleasing then. It occurs wild
t altitudes of 7000 to 9000 ft., but quite what degree of hardiness that suggests
am not certain about. I should judge it to be tender in a place like Kew.

There are at Caerhays in Cornwall and at Headfort in Co. Meath examples of
yrax which appear to be hybrids between langkongense and Wilsonii, the relationship
the latter being suggested by their taller, freer habit (some are already 10 ft. high),
inner twigs, and especially by a more markedly angular toothing of the leaves
nd the closer, tighter covering of down beneath them. They resemble langkongense
the larger leaves and flowers and in the whiteness of the leaves beneath, but appear
me to be handsomer than either of their presumed parents.

S. OBASSIA, *Siebold and Zuccarini*
(Bot. Mag., t. 7039)

A small deciduous tree, 20 to 30 ft. high, of rather narrow proportions ;
oung wood covered at first with tufted hairs, soon glabrous. Leaves broadly
val or almost round, 3 to 8 ins. long, and from two-thirds to as much wide ;
istantly toothed, except near the base ; upper surface deep green and
labrous except on the veins, the lower surface densely clothed with velvety
fted down ; stalk ¼ to 1 in. long, the base enclosing the bud. Flowers
agrant, about 1 in. long, pure white, drooping, produced in June on terminal
acemes 6 to 8 ins. long, each flower on a downy stalk ½ in. long ; the common
alk is almost glabrous. Corolla deeply five-lobed, the lobes about ¾ in. long,
in. wide, minutely downy. Calyx between funnel- and bell-shaped, from
ve- to ten-lobed, downy, ¼ in. long, persistent and enlarging with the fruit,
hich is egg-shaped, about ¾ in. long, velvety.

Native of Japan ; introduced for Messrs Veitch in 1879 by Maries. This
one of the most beautiful and striking even of Japanese flowering trees.
: grew to over 20 ft. high in the Coombe Wood nursery, but needs a sheltered
ot. For newly planted specimens it is an advantage if peat and leaf-soil
mixed with the ordinary soil. It grows slowly in our climate, and abhors
ryness at the root.

S. OFFICINALIS, *Linnæus*. STORAX
(Bot. Mag., t. 9653)

Repeated experiment has shown that it is useless to attempt to grow this
eautiful shrub without protection near London. Against a south wall it
ay grow and thrive for some years, but even there is not permanently safe.
onsequently, although introduced in the sixteenth century, it is still very
re. There is, however, a plant growing in one of the outside recesses of the
emperate House at Kew facing south which flowers beautifully in June.
is 10 ft. high. I have also seen it very beautiful at Binstead in the Isle of
ight. It is a shrub or small tree, 12 to 20 ft. high in nature, the young shoots,
aves, and flower-stalks covered with whitish down. Leaves up to 3½ ins. long,
vate, often broadly so, and sometimes heart-shaped at the base. Flowers
orne in June in short terminal clusters of three to eight orange-like, fragrant
ossoms ; each flower is 1¼ ins. wide, the six to eight divisions of the corolla
hite, very downy, narrow-oblong. Fruit globose, ¾ in. wide, with the remains
the style at the top, and the woolly calyx beneath.

Native of Greece and Asia Minor up to elevations of 3600 ft. The fragrant
sin known as " storax " is obtained from this shrub by wounding the stem.

A correspondent in Greece informs me that a worm attacks the wood, and that the dust resulting from its borings is used by the natives as incense. The shrub is very suitable for Cornwall and similar localities.

S. SHIRAIANUM, *Makino*

A small deciduous tree; young shoots covered with minute stellate down. Leaves mostly obovate and tapered at the base, sometimes roundish; coarsely and unevenly toothed (or almost lobed) above the middle, entire towards the base; 1½ to 4 ins. long, 1 to 3 ins. wide; stellately downy beneath, more especially on the midrib, thinly so elsewhere; veins in six to eight pairs; stalk ⅛ to ½ in. long. Flowers white, very shortly stalked, produced during June in racemes of eight or ten that terminate young, leafy, lateral shoots and are about 2½ ins. long. Corolla ⅝ to ¾ in. long, funnel-shaped, five-lobed; the lobes ovate, pointed and about half as long as the tubular part, downy. Calyx bell-shaped, with five triangular, sometimes bifid, lobes, thickly covered with tawny down. Fruit globose to egg-shaped, ½ in. long.

Native of Japan, where it is said to be sparingly distributed; introduced to the United States in 1915. This is a very distinct species, firstly in the tube of the corolla being twice as long as the lobes (usually it is shorter) and secondly, in the shape of the leaves with their broad ends and deep toothing. They bear a considerable resemblance to those of Hamamelis japonica. I do not know if this styrax exists in this country, but if not it should be introduced as it is undoubtedly a handsome tree, and it should be hardy in most parts of the British Isles. In the United States it flowers in June.

S. SHWELIENSE, *W. W. Smith*

A deciduous shrub up to 25 ft. high in a wild state, with reddish brown stellately downy young shoots. Leaves elliptical, pointed, usually tapered but sometimes rounded at the base, shallowly toothed; 2 to 4 ins. long, ¾ to 2 ins. wide; dark dull green above, greyish beneath, both sides soft and velvety to the touch; chief veins in five to seven pairs; stalk ⅛ in. or less long. Flowers white, about 1 in. wide, produced on short leafy shoots as in langkongense. Corolla lobes downy outside and at the margins. Calyx bell-shaped, ¼ in. long, very downy, minutely toothed or almost entire; flower-stalk about ¼ in. long, often thickening towards the calyx and giving it a funnel-like shape.

Native of the Tengyueh-Shweli divide, Yunnan, W. China, at altitudes of about 7000 ft.; discovered by Forrest in 1913. I only know it as growing at Caerhays, where it was, in 1932, some 6 or 8 ft. high; it blossoms there in late June and July. S. langkongense, to which it is akin, has smaller leaves, whiter beneath and less velvety, and its calyx is more distinctly toothed.

S. VEITCHIORUM, *Hemsley and Wilson*

A small tree, 12 to 15 ft. high; young shoots, leaf-stalks, and calyx covered with a close, grey, starry down. Leaves lanceolate, with a long tapered point, and a wedge-shaped or slightly rounded base, remotely and shallowly toothed; 3 to 5 ins. long, 1 to 1¾ ins. wide; of thin texture, downy on both surfaces, but especially on the midrib and veins beneath; stalk ¼ to ⅓ in. long. Flowers white, nearly 1 in. across, produced at the end of the shoot and in the uppermost leaf-axils on the current season's growth, forming a group of slender panicles each 4 to 8 ins. long. Calyx minutely five-toothed.

Native of Hupeh, China, where it was discovered and introduced for Messrs Veitch in 1900 by Wilson. Mr Wilson only saw it once, and I only know it from his specimen (2015) preserved at Kew, and the living plants raised at Coombe Wood, where it was hardy and vigorous. The leaves of cultivated young trees are more uniformly downy than the flowering specimens collected in China, which have only tufts in the vein-axils beneath, but Mr Wilson claimed them to be true ; probably this is a juvenile character.

S. WILSONI, *Rehder*

(Bot. Mag., t. 8444)

A deciduous shrub, sometimes of tree-like form, 6 to 10 ft. high, of much-branched, twiggy habit ; young shoots furnished with starry down. Leaves ovate, $\frac{1}{2}$ to 1 in. long, half to two-thirds as wide ; rounded or broadly tapered at the base, often bluntish at the apex, the lower half not toothed, the terminal part either three-lobed or sparsely toothed ; green and minutely downy on both sides when young. Flowers nodding, pure glistening white, $\frac{5}{8}$ to $\frac{3}{4}$ in. across, produced one to four in the leaf-axils, and at the end of short lateral twigs in June. Corolla lobes ovate-oblong, $\frac{1}{3}$ in. long, pointed, covered with minute starry down outside ; calyx green, scurfy, with lance-shaped lobes $\frac{1}{12}$ in. long. Stamens clustered in an erect columnar group, $\frac{3}{8}$ in. high, their stalks white, the anthers yellow.

Native of W. China ; introduced by Wilson when collecting for Harvard University in 1908. It is a very pretty shrub, remarkable in flowering when a few inches high and when only two or three years old. I am afraid it will prove rather tender in some parts of the country, at least when young, but it is likely to be a delightful shrub for the warmer parts. In June, 1913, I saw in Mr Chenault's nursery at Orleans, a plant 6 ft. high in full blossom. It was one of the most beautiful objects I have ever seen.

SUÆDA FRUTICOSA, *Forskal*. SHRUBBY GOOSEFOOT.
CHENOPODIACEÆ

(Chenopodium fruticosum, *Linnæus*)

A sub-evergreen shrub, 3 or 4 ft. high, with glabrous, erect branches. Leaves alternate, linear, nearly cylindrical, fleshy, $\frac{1}{4}$ to $\frac{3}{8}$ in. long, blue-green, borne at very close intervals on the stem. Flowers small, green, stalkless, one-third as long as the leaves, produced during July in the leaf-axils of the current year's shoots, either singly or two or three together, insignificant.

Native of the maritime districts of Europe, including some parts of the east and south coasts of Britain. It has rather a heath-like aspect, with its slender, erect stems and closely set, short leaves—but the latter are, of course, much more thick and fleshy. The shrub has no beauty of flower, but the habit and foliage are sufficiently interesting and graceful for it to be planted in brackish places, or in positions exposed to salt spray where comparatively few shrubs will thrive. It succeeds well in sandy soil, and can be increased by cuttings placed under a handlight. If it gets too ungainly in form it should be pruned back in spring, but the semi-woody shoots are frequently cut back by winter frost.

SYCOPSIS SINENSIS, *Oliver*.   HAMAMELIDACEÆ

An evergreen bushy shrub or a small tree, up to 20 ft. high in China ;
young shoots at first scaly.   Leaves rather leathery, strongly nerved, entire

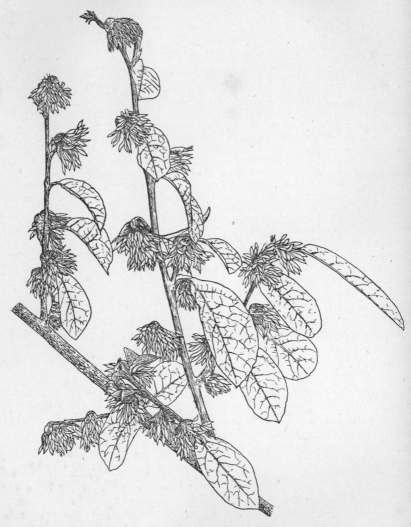

SYCOPSIS SINENSIS

or slightly toothed towards the apex, ovate or ovate-lanceolate ; 2 to 4½
ins. long, one-third to half as wide ; glabrous and dark green above, paler
and quite glabrous beneath ; leaf-stalk and young wood slightly warted.
Flowers in short dense clusters less than 1 in. long, the chief features

of which are the ten yellow stamens and the reddish brown bracts that enclose the inflorescence. The flowers are unisexual and without a corolla, both sexes appearing on the same plant. Fruit a dry, woolly, egg-shaped capsule, ⅓ in. long.

Native of Central China at 4000 ft. altitude ; introduced by Wilson for Messrs Veitch in 1901. It is perfectly hardy at Kew, and can be increased by means of cuttings made of fairly ripened wood and placed in heat. Its neat habit and distinct appearance, combined with its ever-green nature, make it welcome in gardens, and when as well flowered as I have seen it at Wakehurst, in Sussex, is quite handsome. It blossoms usually in March. Our figure was drawn from a plant which flowered at Coombe Wood in 1910.

SYMPHORICARPOS. CAPRIFOLIACEÆ

An unimportant genus of shrubs, of which about half a dozen species are in cultivation. Until recently the genus, as known to botanists, was confined to N. America, but Wilson has recently found a species in W. China. They have no beauty of flower, and with the exception of S. orbiculatus, which has red fruits, and S. sinensis, which has dark blue ones, they are chiefly remarkable for their snow-white berries, well exemplified in most gardens by the common snowberry—S. albus. Leaves opposite, not toothed, but sometimes with a wavy lobing, deciduous. The genus is allied to Lonicera, but differs in the regular corolla and two-seeded berry.

The differences between the West American species are not very readily defined, but they consist chiefly in the relative lengths of stamens, style, and corolla. All the species grow well in any moist soil, and are easily propagated by cuttings, several by division. The West Chinese species alluded to above—S. sinensis, *Rehder*—differs from all the rest in having dark blue fruits, which are ovoid, ⅓ in. long, and covered with a plum-like bloom, and in the flowers being borne on a " terminal peduncled inflorescence." It is cultivated in the Arnold Arboretum, whence it was introduced to this country in 1912.

S. ALBUS, *Blake*. SNOWBERRY

(S. racemosus, *Michaux*)

A deciduous shrub 3 to 4 ft. high ; young shoots slender, usually somewhat downy. Leaves oval to oval-oblong, roundish at the base, sometimes lobed, downy beneath, ¾ to 2 ins. long, apex blunt. Flowers of little beauty, ¼ in. long, produced at the end of the twigs during June and July in spikes or clusters up to 1½ ins. long ; corolla pink, downy inside ; stamens and style rather longer. Fruit globose or ovoid, ½ in. wide, snow-white, pulpy when ripe.

Native of eastern N. America from Nova Scotia to Virginia.

Var. LÆVIGATUS, *Blake* (S. rivularis *Suksdorf*).—A taller shrub and up to 3 to 6 ft. high, forming dense thickets of erect, many-branched, glabrous stems. Leaves up to 3 ins. long, glabrous ; fruit rather larger than in the type. This variety is a native of the western side of N. America and is the one most commonly grown in Britain and known generally as " snowberry." Introduced in

1817. This well-known shrub ripens its fruit in October, and having apparently no attraction for birds, they remain on the twigs up to New Year or later, interesting for their pure whiteness. Whilst the plant repays good cultivation by the greater size and abundance of the fruit (which often weigh down the branches in graceful arches), there are few shrubs more useful for filling up dark out-of-the-way corners. Although deciduous, its stems and twigs are dense enough to make an effective screen.

S. MOLLIS, *Nuttall*

(S. ciliatus, *Nuttall*)

A low or prostrate shrub ; young shoots covered with soft down. Leaves roundish to oval, sometimes shallowly lobed, ½ to 1 in. long, velvety and grey with down, especially beneath. Flowers few and small, produced singly or in short clusters at and near the end of the twigs ; corolla widely bell-shaped, about ⅛ in. long and broad, pinkish white, enclosing the glabrous style. Fruit white, globose, about ¼ in. wide.

Native of California northward on the Pacific coast region to British Columbia ; distinct and interesting for its decumbent habit and densely downy leaves.

S. OCCIDENTALIS, *Hooker*. WOLFBERRY

A deciduous shrub up to 6 ft. high. Leaves oval or oblong, stout, up to 2 ins. or more long, glabrous or more or less downy beneath. Flowers in dense spikes or racemes, both in the leaf-axils near the end of the shoot and at the end itself. Corolla open funnel-shaped, deeply five-lobed, densely hairy inside, ¼ in. long, pinkish ; style and stamens slightly protruded, the former glabrous. Fruit dullish white, globose, about ⅜ in. wide.

Native of N. America from Oregon eastwards to Michigan. It has been confused with S. albus, but is an inferior shrub with smaller, duller fruits ; it differs also in the deeper-lobed corolla and in the protruded style and stamens. Of little garden value.

S. ORBICULATUS, *Moench*. CORAL BERRY

(S. vulgaris, *Michaux*)

A deciduous shrub, 3 to 7 ft. high, of dense, bushy habit ; branches thin, densely leafy, spreading, very downy. Leaves oval or ovate, with a rounded base, ½ to 1¼ ins. long, ¼ to ¾ in. wide ; dark dull green above, hairy and somewhat glaucous beneath ; stalk $\frac{1}{12}$ in. long. Flowers produced in August and September in short, dense clusters in all the leaf-axils from the lower side of the twigs. Corolla bell-shaped, ⅛ in. long, dull white, the style hairy. Berries purplish red, between egg-shaped and globose, ¼ in. long.

Native of the eastern United States ; introduced in 1730. A neat bush with the leaves arranged in opposite rows on the branches, but with little beauty of flower. The fruits are pretty, and when freely borne make the shrub extremely ornamental in autumn and winter, but it does not bear fruit so freely in this country as in its native one, except after a hot summer like that of 1911.

Var. VARIEGATUS.—Leaves smaller than in the type, bordered unevenly with yellow. A good variegated shrub.

S. orbiculatus differs from all the rest of the species here mentioned in having a downy style and red berries. These characters and the long array of short flower-spikes beneath the branches make it the most distinct of the cultivated members of this genus.

S. OREOPHILUS, *A. Gray*

A deciduous shrub, 2 to 3 ft. high, of spreading habit, with either glabrous or downy young shoots and leaves, the latter narrowly to broadly oval, 1½ to 2 ins. long, ¾ to 1 in. wide on strong barren shoots, half or less than half as large on the flowering twigs. Flowers mostly in pairs in the leaf-axils of short twigs. Corolla pinkish white, tubular or slightly tapering towards the base, ⅓ to ½ in. long, the tube four or five times as long as the lobes ; style glabrous, half or less than half the length of the corolla. Fruit white, oval, ⅓ in. long.

Native of western N. America ; introduced in 1898. It is a distinct species because of its comparatively long, tubular corolla and short style. It is distinguished from rotundifolius by the flattened seeds being pointed at one end. Chiefly of botanical interest.

S. ROTUNDIFOLIUS, *A. Gray*

A deciduous shrub, 2 to 3 ft. high ; branches very leafy, covered at first with minute down. Leaves roundish to oval or ovate, ⅓ to 1 in. long, pointed or blunt at the apex, more or less downy beneath, sometimes with sinuous margins, but otherwise entire. Flowers stalkless, produced in June and July in two- to five-flowered spikes in the upper leaf-axils, and the end of the shoot. Corolla pinkish white, ¼ to ⅓ in. long, between funnel and bell-shaped, shallowly five-lobed ; hairy towards the base inside ; style glabrous and, like the stamens, enclosed within the corolla. Fruit white, oval or nearly globose, ¼ in. wide.

Native of western N. America ; of but little garden value. It is allied to S. oreophilus but has a shorter corolla, and the two nutlets (popularly " seeds ") in the fruit are shorter and equally broad and blunt at both ends.

SYMPLOCOS PANICULATA, *Miquel.* SYMPLOCACEÆ

(S. cratægoides, *Buchanan-Hamilton*)

A deciduous shrub or small tree, of light and elegant aspect ; young shoots hairy. Leaves oval, ovate, or somewhat obovate ; 1½ to 3½ ins. long, ¾ to 1¾ ins. wide ; tapering at both ends, finely toothed, slightly hairy above, more so on the veins beneath ; stalk ⅛ to ⅓ in. long, hairy. Flowers fragrant, white, ⅓ in. across, produced during late May and early June in terminal hairy panicles, and in the leaf-axils on small lateral twigs ; the whole inflorescence is 1½ to 2½ ins. long. The stalk of the axillary inflorescence appears to spring from the stem some distance above the leaf-axil itself, which seems to be due to its union to the branchlet. Petals five, united only at the base ; stamens about thirty in five clusters, one cluster attached to the base of each petal. Fruit roundish oval, mostly one-seeded, becoming bright blue in autumn.

Native of China, Himalaya, and Japan ; introduced from the last-named country to the United States about 1871 ; afterwards to England. Although it flowers freely it seems to develop fruit shyly, perhaps only in hot seasons. In the Arnold Arboretum, Mass., it bears fruit profusely ; they are described as of " a brilliant ultramarine blue," and hanging in pendulous clusters. It is best propagated by imported seeds, which usually lie dormant a year.

S. TINCTORIA, *L'Heritier*. Horse Sugar.—Native of the south-eastern United States ; introduced to this country in 1780 and several times since, but not hardy. It got its name from the sweet taste of its leaves, which are greedily eaten by horses and cattle. The fruit is yellowish brown, ⅓ in. long, oval, and produced in a cluster of three or four close to the stem.

Symplocos is allied to Halesia and Styrax, but differs in the arrangement of the stamens noted above. The hairs, too, on the leaves, etc., are simple (not stellate).

SYRINGA. LILAC. OLEACEÆ

A group of small trees and shrubs, consisting of about two dozen species, confined to the Old World. One or two are found in E. Europe, the rest in N.E. Asia. The cultivated species are deciduous, and have opposite leaves, usually neither toothed nor lobed ; but in one species they are pinnate (S. pinnatifolia), and in another pinnately lobed (S. persica laciniata). The flowers appear in panicles, often pyramidal, but sometimes of indeterminate shape. Corolla tubular, with four lobes ; calyx bell-shaped, unevenly toothed ; stamens two. Seed-vessel a capsule of flattened or spindle shape, composed of two valves, which split from the top downwards when ripe.

There are two distinct sections of the genus :—

1. *The true lilacs.*—Corolla-tube long, enclosing the stamens. Flowers usually purple, sometimes white.
2. *The Ligustrina or privet-like group.*—Corolla-tube short, the stamens protruded well beyond the mouth. Flowers white. This group is composed of three species.— S. amurensis, japonica, and pekinensis.

Among the true lilacs there is a well-marked section which form a terminal bud and flower on the leafy shoots of the year ; it is distinguished as the Section VILLOSÆ. The remainder, forming the Section VULGARES, of which S. vulgaris is the type, flower on naked or leafless panicles, often in terminal pairs.

In 1929 Mrs Susan McKelvey of Boston, Mass., published a fine quarto volume, *The Lilac* (pp. 581 and profusely illustrated), in which by a generous and wholesome reduction of false species, she has very much simplified the study of this genus. The following names, several of them now well known in gardens, are suppressed :—

Sargentiana	as synonymous with		Komarowii.
Dielsiana			
Schneideri	,,	,,	microphylla.
tetanoloba	,,	,,	Sweginzowii.
Adamiana			
Wilsonii	,,	,,	tomentella.
albo-rosea			
Rehderiana	,,	,,	tomentella Rehderiana.
Koehneana			
Palibiniana	,,	,,	velutina.
formosissima	,,	,,	Wolfii.

In the making of them too much stress was placed on the presence or absence on the various parts of the plant of mere downiness, which Mrs McKelvey has shown to be a most unreliable character in this genus. The very handsome lilac known as " Lutèce " is a hybrid raised by L. Henry in the Jardin des Plantes, Paris, by crossing S. Josikæa and S. villosa. The name " S. Henryi " has been given by C. K. Schneider as a collective term to this and other hybrids of the same origin.

Mr Emile Lemoine of Nancy, France, in 1911 introduced to notice in his catalogue a race of early flowering lilacs which he had raised by crossing S. oblata Giraldii with forms of common lilac. The variety named " Lamartine " is especially good at Kew. The varieties " Descartes," " Necker," and " Villar " (single-flowered), also " Vuaban " and " Claude Bernard " (double) are well worth cultivating for their late April or early May flowers. The name " Syringa hyacinthiflora," first used in 1878 by Lemoine for a hybrid with double flowers between oblata and vulgaris azurea plena, has been adopted as a collective term for this group.

The cultivation of the common lilac is dealt with under the heading of S. vulgaris, and the soil and general treatment are the same for the rest of the genus. All of them can be propagated by layers, most of them by cuttings. Cuttings should be made of mature shoots in August, and placed in a sheltered position under handlights. Softer cuttings taken earlier will often take root in gentle heat.

S. AMURENSIS, *Ruprecht*

(Ligustrina amurensis, *Regel*)

Of the three species now in cultivation which represent the section Ligustrina (or privet-like lilacs), this is the least satisfactory in my experience. It was discovered in Manchuria by Radde, a Russian botanist, in 1857, and like many other shrubs from the same region, its flower-buds are easily excited into premature growth by warm January and February days, and are almost invariably cut off by late frosts. I have never seen a perfect panicle at Kew, although the flowers " set " freely enough. The species is a sturdy bushy shrub, 6 to 8 ft. high, or a small tree. Leaves 2 to 4 ins. long, 1 to 2 ins. wide, ovate or oval, usually with a drawn-out apex, the base more or less tapered ; stalk about ½ in. long. Flowers dull white, not very pleasantly scented, produced during June in panicles which, when perfectly developed, are 4 to 6 ins. long, 3 to 4 ins. wide ; tube of corolla very short.

S. CHINENSIS, *Willdenow*. ROUEN LILAC

(S. dubia, *Persoon* ; S. rothomagensis, *Richard*)

A deciduous bush of dense rounded habit, 10 to 15 ft. high. Leaves ovate, 1½ to 2½ ins. long, ⅝ to 1¼ ins. wide ; rounded or broadly wedge-shaped at the base, taper-pointed, glabrous ; stalk ⅓ to ½ in. long. Flowers of the common lilac shade, intermediate in size between those of the common and Persian lilacs, somewhat loose ; corolla tube ½ in. long, lobes ¼ in. long.

A hybrid between the Persian and common lilacs, said to have been raised in the Botanic Garden of Rouen by Mr Varin in the last quarter of the eighteenth century ; introduced to Britain in 1795. There is nothing improbable in this story, but the plant has been known in China for more than one hundred years, and is still common in cultivation about Pekin. It is quite possible the plant had two separate origins. It is a bush of great beauty when in flower, the growths made during the summer producing the following May a pair of flower-trusses 3 to 6 ins. long at each joint towards the end, so that the whole makes a heavy, arching, compound panicle. It sometimes produces fertile seed.

Several forms of the Rouen lilac are in cultivation: *alba*, flowers pale pink; *duplex* and *La Lorraine*, double; *metensis*, rosy lilac; *rubra* (*Saugeana*) lilac-red.

S. EMODI, *Wallich*. HIMALAYAN LILAC

A large robust shrub, 10 to 15 ft. high, the branchlets dark olive green or brownish, but freely spotted with long, narrow, pale excrescences. Leaves 3 to 8 ins. long, and about half as wide; oval or sometimes ovate or obovate, tapering at the base; dark dull green above, pale, or almost white beneath. Panicles mostly columnar, 3 to 6 ins. long, one or three of which terminate the young shoots. Flowers not pleasantly scented, expanding in June. Corolla ⅜ in. long, scarcely as much wide across the lobes, white or slightly purple tinted. Calyx bell-shaped, very shallowly lobed. Seed-vessels ¾ in. long, each half ending in a slender, almost tail-like point. Native of the Himalaya; long known in gardens, but not common. It is useful in flowering rather late. Closely allied to villosa, it is scarcely as good a shrub, and differs in its leaves being

SYRINGA EMODI

whiter beneath and downy only on the midrib, or glabrous. The seed-vessel also differs in being rather longer and in having the more attenuated apices mentioned above. S. emodi never seems to have the magnificent inflorescences characteristic of vigorous specimens of S. villosa—nor are the flowers ever so richly coloured. (*Villosæ section.*)

Var. VARIEGATA has leaves broadly, irregularly, and rather effectively margined with yellow.

S. JAPONICA, *Decaisne*

(Ligustrina amurensis japonica, *Maximowicz*)

A deciduous tree up to 30 ft. high, of erect habit, often a shrub ; young shoots not downy, but marked with small, round, pale dots. Leaves ovate with a long tapering point, rounded or broadly wedge-shaped at the base ; 3 to 8 ins. long, about half as wide ; and either glabrous or slightly downy beneath, glabrous above ; stalk ½ to 1 in. long. Flowers white, not fragrant, produced at the end of the branch, usually in a pair of broad pyramidal panicles, 8 to 12 ins. long, 6 to 8 ins. through. Corolla ¼ in. across, the short tube almost hidden in the calyx, which is bell-shaped and scarcely lobed. Seed-vessel ¾ in. long, scimitar-shaped, glabrous, blunt at the end.

Native of Japan ; introduced to the Arnold Arboretum in 1876 and thence to Kew in 1886. Professor Sargent, who saw it wild on the hills of central Yezo, says that there it is an ungainly, straggling tree, 25 to 30 ft. high, with a trunk rarely 12 to 18 ins. thick. I saw it flowering in June, 1910, in the Arnold Arboretum and other places near Boston, Mass., and it was the most striking tree then in flower, some being specimens over 30 ft. high, of shapely, rather columnar habit, and laden with blossom. In Britain it does not succeed so well and remains more a shrub than a tree, but even here it is very attractive at the end of June. (Bot. Mag., t. 7534, erroneously as S. amurensis.)

S. JOSIKÆA, *Jacquin*. JOSIKA LILAC

(Bot. Mag., t. 3278)

Belonging to the same group of lilacs as S. villosa and S. emodi, this is inferior in many respects to both. Its flowers, however, are of a deeper lilac than either. The leaves are whitish beneath, as in S. emodi, and of the same shape, 2 to 5 ins. long. Panicle slender, 4 to 8 ins. long, 2 to 4 ins. wide. Corolla ½ in. long, ¼ in. or less across the lobes. Seed-vessel ⅝ in. long, bluntish at the end. Blossoms in early June. (*Villosæ section.*)

This lilac was first noticed in Hungary about 1830, having been sent by the Baroness von Josika to Jacquin the botanist of Vienna, who named it in compliment to her. Her specimens came from Siebenburgen in E. Hungary, which has since been usually regarded as the native home of this lilac. This, of course, is quite probable, and the plant has since been found apparently wild there. But some authorities consider it more likely to be of N. Chinese origin—possibly a deeper coloured variety of villosa with glabrous leaves. It is distinguished from S. villosa in flower by the much denser arrangement of the flowers in whorls.

S. JULIANÆ, *C. K. Schneider*

(Bot. Mag., t. 8423)

A deciduous spreading shrub of stiff, bushy habit, about 6 ft. high ; young shoots slender, very downy, the down persisting for two years. Leaves 1 to 2 ins. long, ½ to 1 in. wide ; oval (sometimes inclined to ovate or obovate), tapered at the base, finely pointed ; dull dark green, with appressed hairs above ; grey and very hairy beneath ; stalk ⅛ to ⅓ in. long, hairy. Panicles 2 to 4 ins.

long, usually in pairs from the terminal buds of the previous year's shoots, sometimes from the two or three uppermost pairs ; hairy like the shoots. Flowers fragrant, $\frac{1}{4}$ to $\frac{1}{3}$ in. long, $\frac{1}{8}$ to $\frac{1}{4}$ in. across the lobes. Calyx violet-coloured, glabrous, with short pointed lobes. The hairy flower-stalks (about $\frac{1}{8}$ in. long) carry one to three blossoms. Corolla deep lilac outside, pale inside the lobes. (*Vulgares section*.)

Native of W. China ; introduced for Messrs Veitch about 1900. It is allied to S. pubescens and S. VELUTINA, *Komarov*, but is much more downy than the first (*q.v.*) and its flowers are more deeply coloured. The second species may not be in cultivation, but has a downy calyx. S. Julianæ flowers in May and June and is both distinct and pretty, but not equal to the best lilacs.

S. KOMAROWII, *C. K.* *Schneider*

(McKelvey's The Lilac, tt. 29-33)

A deciduous shrub up to 15 ft. high ; young shoots pale brown, distinctly warted. Leaves mostly oval, but sometimes obovate or ovate-lanceolate, tapered sometimes slenderly and equally towards both ends, sometimes more

SYRINGA JULIANÆ

abruptly towards the apex ; 3 to 7 ins. long, 1 to $2\frac{3}{4}$ ins. wide ; dark green above and downy on the sunken midrib when young ; yellowish green beneath and downy more or less all over ; stalk $\frac{1}{3}$ to $\frac{3}{4}$ in. long. Inflorescence borne on a leafy shoot, nodding, 4 to 6 ins. long, 2 ins. wide, of cylindric shape, made up of whorls of densely packed flowers, the main-stalk strongly warted and sparingly downy. Flowers deep rose, pink, or lilac-coloured, about $\frac{1}{2}$ in. long, the four lobes of the corolla $\frac{1}{12}$ in. long, erect or rather spreading ; calyx cup-shaped, $\frac{1}{12}$ in. long, with shallow triangular lobes or truncate, rather downy like the short flower-stalk. Seed-vessel $\frac{1}{2}$ in. long, nearly glabrous. Flowers in June. (*Villosæ section*.)

Native of W. Szechuen, China ; introduced by Wilson in 1908, but apparently represented in the St Petersburg Herbarium in 1893. It is a handsome lilac closely related to S. reflexa, which differs in its more slender, longer and more recurved panicles and usually more warted fruits.

Var. SARGENTIANA, *C. K. Schneider* (S. Sargentiana, *C. K. Schneider*).— At first given specific rank by Schneider, this was afterwards reduced by him to a variety. It is considered to differ from typical Komarowii in the more downy under surface of the leaves, more downy longer panicles, and very downy calyx. Mrs McKelvey has made the name synonymous with S. Komarowii, not allowing it even varietal rank.

S. MEYERI, *C. K. Schneider.* MEYER'S LILAC

This lilac was introduced by the late F. N. Meyer from Chihli, N. China, in 1908 to the United States Dept. of Agriculture by means of cuttings. It is a deciduous shrub of dense, compact habit growing up to 5 or 6 ft. high, with slightly downy, squarish young shoots. Leaves oval, sometimes inclined to obovate ; ¾ to 1¾ ins. long, not quite so wide ; glabrous except occasionally for down on the veins beneath. Two pairs of veins run from the base of the leaf to the apex parallel with the margins. The violet-purple flowers are produced in May and June, densely packed in panicles up to 4 ins. long and 2½ ins. wide. Corolla ½ in. long, with spreading lobes giving it a diameter of over ¼ in. Calyx and flower-stalks either glabrous or slightly downy. Seed-vessel ½ to ¾ in. long, warted. (*Vulgares section.*)

Meyer's lilac is only known as a cultivated plant in N. China. It is most closely related to S. pubescens, whose leaves are not generally so tapered at the base, more downy beneath, and have three or more pairs of veins. Mrs McKelvey thinks it may eventually prove to be a selected form of that species. As a dwarf, compact, ornamental lilac it is well worth cultivation. It will flower when scarcely 1 ft. high and a plant at twenty years old in the Arnold Arboretum, Mass., was only 5 ft. high. There used to be a plant at Kew, received from France in 1923 under this name and said to have been collected by Mr J. Hers in N. China, which was quite hardy.

S. MICROPHYLLA, *Diels.* SMALL-LEAVED LILAC

(McKelvey's The Lilac, tt. 74-79 ; S. Dielsiana, *C. K. Schneider* ; S. Schneideri, *Lingelsheim*)

A deciduous shrub 5 ft. or more high, of spreading habit, with slender, downy young shoots. Leaves roundish ovate, pointed or rounded at the apex ; ½ to 2 ins. long, ⅓ to 1¼ ins. wide ; dark green above, greyish green beneath, slightly downy on both surfaces, ciliate ; stalk ⅛ to ¼ in. long. Panicles 2 to 4 ins. long and 1½ to 2 ins. wide ; produced in pairs at the end of the shoot and often supplemented by lateral ones. Flowers very fragrant, lilac-coloured, the corolla slender-tubed, ⅜ in. long, with the spreading lobes oblong, round-ended, ⅛ in. long ; calyx downy, helmet-shaped, 1/16 in. long, with very short triangular lobes. Seed-vessel spindle-shaped, ½ in. long, warted.

Native of N. and W. China ; discovered by Père Giraldi in 1893 ; introduced to Coombe Wood Nursery by Purdom in 1910. It is a June flowering lilac belonging to the *Vulgares section.* As with some other species, its nomenclature has been confused owing to the varying degree of downiness of the leaves, etc. The lilacs named S. Dielsiana and S. microphylla glabriuscula are now considered to be merely forms of this species with glabrous or nearly glabrous shoots, leaves, and calyx, and are connected with the type by many intermediate forms. A second crop of flowers is sometimes produced in autumn on the current year's leafy shoots. It is a very distinct lilac on account of the small size and often nearly orbicular shape of the leaves.

S. OBLATA, *Lindley*

(Bot. Mag., t. 7806)

A deciduous shrub, 10 to 12 ft. high, or a small tree, similar in habit to the common lilac ; young shoots glabrous, round ; buds purplish. Leaves very broadly heart-shaped to reniform, often considerably wider than long, being

1½ to 4 ins. wide, 1½ to 3 ins. long ; short-pointed, glabrous on both surfaces ; stalk ¾ to 1 in. long. Flowers pale lilac, produced at the beginning of May in short broad panicles, usually in pairs from the uppermost joints of the previous year's wood. Corolla-tube ½ in. long, about ⅔ in. across the lobes ; calyx slightly glandular, with pointed lance-shaped lobes. Seed-vessel ⅝ in. long, slender-pointed. (*Vulgares section.*)

Native of N. China ; introduced by Robert Fortune from a garden in Shanghai in 1856. It is closely allied to S. vulgaris, but is easily distinguished by the wider leaves and by flowering about a fortnight earlier. My experience of it is that it is the most unsatisfactory of all the lilacs except S. amurensis. It is excited into growth by mild weather in early spring, only to have its young leaves and flowers destroyed by later frost. Probably in higher localities it may succeed better, for the shrub itself is perfectly hardy, and in climates with a much harder but more settled winter than ours flowers abundantly. The leaves turn red in autumn.

S. AFFINIS, *L. Henry*, is a white-flowered lilac very near S. oblata ; it has been called " S. oblata alba." The young shoots are finely downy the leaves on the average smaller. Native of N. China. (Syn. S. oblata alba.)

S. PEKINENSIS, *Ruprecht*

(Ligustrina pekinensis, *Regel*)

A deciduous small tree of spreading, graceful habit, up to 20 ft. high eventually ; young shoots glabrous. Leaves ovate, oval, or ovate-lanceolate, 2 to 4 ins. long, 1 to 2 ins. wide ; mostly tapering, sometimes rounded at the base, long and tapering at the apex, quite glabrous on both surfaces ; stalk slender, ½ to ¾ in. long. Flowers white, very densely clustered in numerous loose panicles 3 to 6 ins. long, produced in pairs. Seed-vessel ⅝ to ¾ in. long, glabrous, pointed at the end.

Native of the mountains of N. China, where it was discovered by the Abbé David. It was raised at Kew in 1881 from seed sent from Pekin by the late Dr Bretschneider. Botanically allied to S. japonica, it is very distinct as seen growing. It has much more slender branches, the leaves are smaller, the inflorescence instead of being sturdy, pyramidal, and erect, is smaller and is a loose, rather shapeless panicle ; the seed vessel, too, differs in the more pointed apex. It is perfectly hardy, and has grown more quickly at Kew than S. japonica, having now a trunk more than 20 ins. in girth, and flowering freely towards the end of June.

Var. PENDULA.—Raised from Chinese seed in the Arnold Arboretum, Mass., and a very graceful, pendulous tree.

S. PERSICA, *Linnæus*. PERSIAN LILAC

(Bot. Mag., t. 486 ; S. afghanica, *C. K. Schneider* (wild type))

A deciduous shrub, 4 to 6 ft. high, of dense, bushy, rounded habit ; young shoots slender, glabrous. Leaves lance-shaped or ovate lance-shaped (rarely three-lobed), with a long tapering apex and a more abruptly tapered base ; green and glabrous on both sides ; 1 to 2½ ins. long, ¼ to ½ in. wide ; stalk ⅛ in. long. Flowers of the common lilac shade and fragrance, produced in May from the uppermost buds of the preceding summer's growth in small, sometimes branching panicles, 2 to 3 ins. long and as much wide. Corolla-tube about ¼ in. long, the four spreading lobes rather shorter.   Calyx funnel-shaped with four short, pointed lobes.   Seed-vessels ½ in. long, cylindrical.

Native of Persia to N. China ; said to have been introduced to England in 1640.   Cultivated from time immemorial in Persia and India.   (*Vulgares section.*)

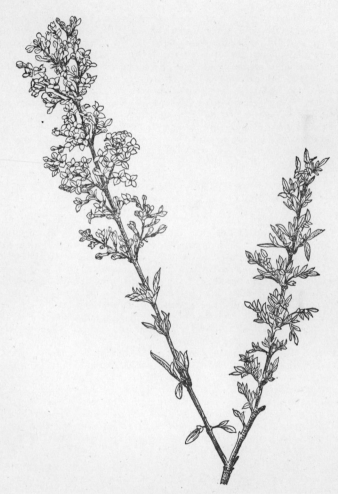

SYRINGA PERSICA LACINIATA

Var. ALBA, *Aiton.*—Flowers white.

Var. LACINIATA, *Aiton.*—Leaves cut back to the midrib into five, seven, or nine parallel oblong lobes.   This variety appears to produce seed under cultivation more freely than either the typical or white forms.

The Persian lilac, in all its forms, is a delightful shrub, both in its neat habit and fragrant blossom.   Increased by cuttings of nearly ripe wood.

S. PINNATIFOLIA, *Hemsley*

A deciduous shrub, 8 to 12 ft. high, of elegant bushy habit; the young shoots and every other part of the plant free from down. Leaves pinnate, 1½ to 3½ ins. long, composed of seven, nine, or eleven leaflets, which are dull green, stalkless, ovate-lanceolate; ¾ to 1¼ ins. long, ¼ to ⅜ in. wide; pointed, the base rounded, or in the case of the terminal leaflets frequently attached to the common stalk by a portion of the blade. Flowers white, with a slight lilac tint, produced in May in panicles 1½ to 3 ins. long, which spring usually in opposite pairs from the joints of the previous year's wood. Corolla-tube ½ in. long, the lobes at the mouth spreading and giving the flower a diameter of ¼ in.; calyx-lobes rounded.

Native of W. China; discovered by Wilson in 1904 at an elevation of 9000 ft. The pinnate leaves of this species at once suggest an affinity with the cut-leaved variety of the Persian lilac, but they are divided (except sometimes near the apex) into quite distinct leaflets, and not merely lobed as in the other. It has flowered several times, and is quite hardy. It has great interest as a new and distinct lilac, but its garden value will never, I think, equal that of the Persian lilac.

S. POTANINII, *C. K. Schneider*. POTANIN'S LILAC

(Bot. Mag., t. 9060)

A deciduous shrub of graceful habit ultimately 9 to 12 ft. high; young shoots minutely downy. Leaves mostly oval, slenderly pointed, tapered at the base; 1½ to 3 ins. long, ¾ to 1½ ins. wide; dark green and minutely but densely downy above, thickly covered with soft down beneath; stalk ⅛ to ¼ in. long. Inflorescence loosely pyramidal, erect, 3 to 6 ins. long, 2 to 3 ins. wide; main and secondary flower-stalks downy. Flowers fragrant, ⅓ to ½ in. long, white to pale rosy purple, the tube very slender, the four lobes ⅛ in. long, narrowly oblong; anthers yellow. Calyx downy, cup-shaped, shallowly toothed or nearly truncate. Seed-vessel ⅝ in. long, pointed, glossy, smooth or minutely and sparsely warted. Flowers in June.

Native of W. China in the provinces of Yunnan, Szechuen, and Kansu; discovered in the latter, in 1885, by the Russian traveller, Potanin, after whom it is named. Wilson found it near Tachien-lu in 1904 and again in 1908. A fine plant, about 10 ft. high when I saw it in 1930, was growing in Col. Stern's chalk garden at Highdown, near Worthing. This was raised in 1914 from Farrer's seeds collected in Kansu and has almost white, delightfully fragrant flowers with yellow anthers. It is related to S. Julianæ, but that species has smaller leaves, dark violet anthers, and a glabrous calyx. Both belong to the *Vulgares section.* Nearly related to them is

S. PINETORUM, *W. W. Smith.*—According to Forrest, who collected it in June 1914, in Yunnan, this is a shrub 4 to 8 ft. high with pale lavender-rose flowers. They have yellow anthers and the leaves, 1 to 1½ ins. long, are hairy on the midrib and veins beneath. It is doubtful whether the true plant is in cultivation.

S. PUBESCENS, *Turczaninow*

(S. villosa of Bot. Mag., t. 7064—not of *Vahl*)

A deciduous shrub or small tree, 12 to 15 ft. high, forming a rounded head of branches; young shoots glabrous. Leaves 1 to 2½ ins. long, ¾ to 1½ ins. wide; broadly ovate, sometimes roundish, tapered abruptly at the apex to a short point, rounded or broadly wedge-shaped at the base; dull green and glabrous above, pale and with a little scattered down beneath, most abundant on the midrib; stalk ¼ to ½ in. long. Flowers fragrant, pale lilac or nearly white, produced along with the young leaves during early May in leafless panicles from one or both of the terminal buds of last year's shoots. The panicles are 3 to 5 ins. long, 2 to 3 ins. wide, the corolla-tube slender, ½ in. long; lobes ⅛ in. long, the incurving of the margins making them cupped. Calyx very short, with triangular lobes.

Native of N. China; introduced by the late Dr Bretschneider in 1881. It is only a second-rate lilac in this country, owing to the frequent injury of the young growths and panicles by late frost. In the United States, where the summer heat is greater, and the seasons better defined, it is very beautiful. The confusion in the naming of this shrub and S. villosa, *Vahl*, is alluded to under that species. (*Vulgares section.*)

S. REFLEXA, *C. K. Schneider*

(Bot. Mag., t. 8869; McKelvey's The Lilac, tt. 21-28)

A deciduous shrub up to 12 ft. or perhaps more high; young shoots somewhat angular, stout, warty, becoming grey the second season. Leaves oval-oblong, sometimes obovate or ovate-lanceolate, pointed, mostly tapered at the base; 3 to 8 ins. long, nearly half as much wide; dark green above, paler beneath; there are many short hairs on the midrib and chief veins beneath, otherwise they become nearly glabrous before falling. Flowers densely packed in a series of whorls on a terminal, leafy, arching or pendulous, cylindrical or narrowly pyramidal panicle, 4 to 10 ins. long and 1½ to 4 ins. wide; opening in June, not fragrant. Each flower has a narrow funnel-shaped tube about ⅓ in. long, rich pink or purplish pink outside, whitish within; and four ovate, pointed lobes inflexed at the tip which give the flower a diameter of ⅜ in. Calyx cup-shaped, with small erect teeth; glabrous or slightly downy. Seed-vessel cylindrical, ¾ in. long, warted.

Native of Hupeh, Central China; discovered by Henry in 1889; introduced in 1910 by Wilson, who found it at elevations of 8000 to 9000 ft. It is undoubtedly one of the handsomest of the Chinese lilacs and perfectly hardy. The most distinctive character is afforded by the shape and pose of the inflorescence which, in being densely packed with blossom, in being of cylindrical shape and more or less pendulous, differs from all other cultivated lilacs except S. Komarowii (*q.v.*). It belongs to the *Villosæ section*.

S. SWEGINZOWII, *Koehne and Lingelsheim*

(McKelvey's The Lilac, tt. 55-60; S. tetanoloba, *C. K. Schneider*)

A deciduous shrub up to 12 ft. high, with slender, glabrous, purplish-grey young shoots. Leaves of thin texture, ovate-lanceolate or oval-lanceolate, often long and slenderly pointed, sometimes more abruptly pointed, the base tapered or almost rounded; 2 to 4 ins. long, 1 to 2 ins. wide; dark green and glabrous above, paler and hairy on the chief veins beneath, ciliate; stalk ¼ to ½ in. long. Panicles terminal, erect, usually 6 to 8 ins. long, opening in June, sometimes supported by lateral ones; flower-stalks mostly glabrous, purplish. Flowers fragrant, pale rosy lilac, white inside the corolla lobes. Corolla ⅓ in. long, slender-tubed; lobes spreading; anthers yellow, inserted near the top. Calyx truncate or with shallowly triangular teeth, glabrous, purplish. Seed-vessel ½ in. long, pointed, smooth, shining. (*Villosæ section.*)

Native of China; first named in 1910 from a cultivated plant in a private garden near Riga; it must, therefore, have been introduced to Europe early in the century, if not before. It was collected in Szechuen by Wilson for Messrs Veitch in 1904, and he found it again in August 1910 at Sungpan, in the northern part of the same province. It is a very hardy, charming lilac of graceful habit which first came into notice in this country through being exhibited by the Hon. Vicary Gibbs at Westminster on 8th June 1915, when it received an Award of Merit. Mr Lemoine has sent out a lilac which he calls "S. Sweginzowii superba." Except that it has panicles somewhat larger than ordinary, such as might be developed under very good cultivation, it does not seem to differ from the type. The species is akin to S. villosa, but has thinner, smaller leaves and a more slender corolla tube, from which the anthers do not protrude.

S. TOMENTELLA, *Bureau and Franchet*

(S Wilsonii, *C. K. Schneider*, Bot. Mag., t. 8739 ; S. alborosea, *N. E. Brown* ; S. Adamiana, *Balfour fil.*)

A deciduous shrub up to 10 or 15 ft. high ; young shoots usually without down but sprinkled with pale warts. Leaves oval to ovate, pointed, more or less wedge-shaped at the base ; 2 to 6 ins. long, half as much wide ; dark green, glabrous or slightly downy above, pale and downy (sometimes very much so) beneath, ciliate ; stalk ¼ to ½ in. long. Panicles erect, terminal, up to 8 ins. long and 5 ins. wide, rather loose ; flower-stalks reddish, more or less downy, sometimes glabrous. Flowers pale lilac-pink, white inside, with a fragrance resembling, but not so strong as, that of common lilac. Corolla-tube about ½ in. long with four lobes spreading sufficiently to give the flower a diameter of ⅓ in. Calyx cup-shaped, reddish, $\frac{1}{16}$ in. long, truncate or slightly toothed, glabrous or downy. Seed-vessel shining, spindle-shaped, ⅔ in. long, not downy. (*Villosæ section.*)

Native of W. China ; first described in 1891 from material collected by Prince Henri d'Orleans the previous year. It had been collected a year previously by A. E. Pratt, but did not reach cultivation until 1904, when Wilson introduced it from W. Szechuen to Veitch's nursery at Coombe Wood. This sending was named " S. alborosea " by N. E. Brown. In 1908 Wilson again collected it in W. Szechuen and of part of his material Schneider made a new species, viz., S. Wilsonii, and identified the remainder as S. tomentella. Mrs McKelvey now regards them as one species, the differences consisting chiefly in the degree of pubescence.

Var. REHDERIANA, *Rehder* (S. Rehderiana, *C. K. Schneider*), has densely downy shoots, panicles and under surface of leaves, and more hidden anthers. I have not seen living plants, but Mrs McKelvey sinks this also under S. tomentella.

In all its forms S. tomentella is very handsome and, like others of the *Villosæ* group, valuable in coming into flower in June after the common lilac and its varieties are past. The often very densely downy undersurface of the leaves is distinctive.

S. VELUTINA, *Komarow*. KOREAN LILAC

(McKelvey's The Lilac, tt. 67-73 ; S. Palabiniana, *Nakai* ; S. Koehneana, *C. K. Schneider*)

A deciduous shrub up to 10 ft. high, with slightly downy or glabrous, sometimes glandular, purplish young shoots. Leaves oval, ovate or rhomboidal to lanceolate, long- to short-pointed, tapered at the base ; 2 to 2½ ins. long, ½ to 2 ins. wide ; dark dull green and glabrous or slightly downy above, paler and more or less downy beneath ; leaf-stalk ¼ to ½ in. long. Panicles often in pairs from the terminal pair of buds of the previous season's shoots, each 4 to 6 ins. long, rather thinly set with blossom. Flowers opening in late May and June, fragrant. Corolla very slender, ⅜ in. long, less in diameter, of various shades of lilac outside, white within ; anthers purple, near to but not reaching the mouth. Flower-stalks and calyx often purplish, varying from downy to glabrous. Seed-vessel ⅔ in. long, pointed, warty. (*Vulgares section.*)

Native of Korea and N. China ; discovered in the former country in 1897 ; introduced to St Petersburg soon after. Mrs McKelvey, in her recent monograph, has sunk several names under S. velutina which were previously regarded as specific. Amongst them is S. Palibiniana, which had been cultivated under that name since 1917, but only differs in the amount of down carried by the various parts. There appears, indeed, to be in this species every gradation between glabrousness and the velvetiness the specific name implies. Wilson found a white-flowered form in Korea in 1917—var. LACTEA.

S. VILLOSA, *Vahl*

(S. Bretschneideri, *Lemoine*, Bot. Mag., t. 8292 ; S. emodi rosea, *Cornu*.

A deciduous shrub, 10 ft. or more high, of robust habit ; branches erect, stout, stiff, nearly or quite glabrous when young, marked with a few pale dots. Leaves oval or oval lance-shaped, pointed, rounded or wedge-shaped at the base ; 2 to 6 ins. long, 1 to 2½ ins. wide ; glabrous and dark green above, glaucous and thinly furnished with bristle-like hairs or nearly glabrous beneath ; stalk ¼ to 1¼ ins. long. Panicles terminal and axillary, often three at the end of a leafy shoot ; they are usually 6 to 10 ins. long (but I have measured exceptionally fine ones 18 ins. long) ; half to two-thirds as wide. Corolla lilac-rose, ½ in. long, the lobes ⅛ in. long, rounded, spreading. Calyx bell-shaped with four short, pointed lobes ; slightly hairy or glabrous. Seed-vessel about ½ in. long. (*Villosæ section.*)

Native of N. China; discovered early in the eighteenth century by Père d'Incarville, the Jesuit missionary ; introduced to cultivation about 1885. Much confusion has existed as to the correct name of this shrub. The name villosa has been given to the species above described as S. pubescens (see Hooker in *Bot. Mag.*, t. 7064), but an examination of Vahl's original specimen shows that the plant latterly cultivated as S. Bretschneideri is the true villosa.

This beautiful lilac, perhaps the most robust of its section of the genus, flowers at the end of May and early in June, after the flowers of the common lilac and its varieties have faded. It is one of the most desirable of hardy shrubs, vigorous in constitution, and free flowering. It differs from the vulgaris group in forming a true terminal bud, and in flowering on the current year's shoots. As will be noticed by the synonyms recorded above, it has by different authors been referred to as S. emodi and S. Josikæa, to both of which it is allied, but from both of which it differs in its larger, more open inflorescence.

S. VULGARIS, *Linnæus.* COMMON LILAC

(Bot. Mag., t. 183)

A deciduous shrub or small tree, up to 20 ft. high, usually producing a crowd of erect stems, but occasionally a single trunk over 2 ft. in girth, clothed with spirally arranged flakes of bark ; shoots and leaves quite glabrous. Leaves heart-shaped or ovate, 2 to 6 ins. long, from three-fourths to almost as much wide near the base ; stalk ¾ to 1¼ ins. long. Panicles pyramidal, 6 to 8 ins. long, usually in pairs from the terminal buds. On cultivated improved varieties, panicles 12 to 18 ins. long are produced. Flowers " lilac," delightfully fragrant ; corolla-tube ⅓ to ½ in. long, the lobes concave ; calyx and flower-stalks more or less furnished with minute gland-tipped down. Seed-vessels smooth, ⅝ in. long, beaked. (*Vulgares section*.)

Native of the mountainous regions of E. Europe. Introduced to W. Europe in the sixteenth century. It has been cultivated in England for over three hundred years, and is now as characteristic a feature of village scenery as almost any native shrub.

The garden varieties of lilac, to be obtained at their best, must be given generous treatment. They like a deep, rather stiff, but well-drained loam, and should be mulched every second winter with rotted manure or bone meal. An important item in the cultivation of the finer lilacs is the removal of the flower-trusses as soon as they fade, so as to prevent the formation of seed, thereby concentrating the energies of the plant in the new growth and the succeeding crop of blossom. They need no systematic pruning, but in order to obtain fine trusses the weaker and superfluous shoots may be cut out at the same time as the old inflorescences are removed. Named lilacs should always be obtained on their own roots. The practice of grafting them on either privet or common lilac should never be encouraged ; with the former as a stock they do not live so long or grow so well, and with the latter, unless a watch is maintained, the variety in time becomes overwhelmed by suckers. They are best propagated by layers, but cuttings also may be used. Isolated bushes—and a fine shapely lilac is an admirable ornament for a lawn—should be trained to a single stem by removing all the lower buds and subsequently the lower branches. As the lilac does not form a terminal bud, and naturally forks its branches every year, some training and pruning is at first needed to get a tree-like example. A selection of garden varieties of lilac planted in a broad mass, with the dwarfer Persian and Rouen lilacs on the margins, makes a splendid feature in May.

So many varieties are being raised, chiefly in France, that only a selection can be given here ; many of them indeed are scarcely to be distinguished from each other :—

1. SINGLE-FLOWERED

Alba grandiflora. White, large.
Dr Mirabel. Claret coloured ; trusses fine.
Jacques Callot. Reddish lilac.
Madame Francisque Morel. Very large trusses—rosy lilac.
Marie Legraye. White ; buds cream-coloured.
Negro. Deep blue-purple.
Pasteur. Flowers large, claret-coloured, in fine trusses.
Philemon. Flower red, in broad trusses.
Princess Marie. Pale lilac.
Prof. Sargent. Bright rosy lilac.
Souvenir de Louis Späth. Deep purple ; perhaps the finest of this shade.
Ville de Troyes. Reddish lilac.

2. DOUBLE-FLOWERED

Abel Carrière. Blue-lilac.
Comtesse Horace de Choiseul. Greyish white.
Condorcet. Lilac-blue.
La Tour d'Auvergne. Purple-lilac.
Madame Casimir Périer. Large, creamy white.
Madame de Miller. White.
Madame Lemoine. White.
Marc Micheli. Pale lavender blue, white behind.
Michael Buchner. Pale rosy lilac.
Miss Ellen Willmott. Snow-white, with fine trusses and flowers.
President Loubet. One of the darkest purple double-flowered kinds.
William Robinson. Violet-mauve.

S. WOLFII, *C. K. Schneider*

(McKelvey's The Lilac, tt. 16-20 ; S. formossisima, *Nakai*)

A deciduous shrub up to 20 ft. high ; young shoots glabrous or nearly so, turning grey. Leaves oval-lanceolate, slenderly pointed, more or less abruptly tapered at the base, glabrous except for down beneath (especially on the veins) ; 3 to 7 ins. long, about half as wide ; dark green above, pale beneath ; stalk ½ to 1 in. long. Panicle terminal, up to 12 ins. long, opening in June ; flower-stalks downy. Flowers lilac, fragrant ; corolla ½ in. long, the lobes erect ; anthers inserted half-way down the tube, primrose yellow. Calyx usually more or less downy, sometimes glabrous ; cup-shaped, scarcely or not at all lobed. Seed-vessel ¼ in. long, glabrous, blunt ended. (*Villosæ section.*)

Native of Korea and Manchuria ; introduced about 1909. This handsome and very hardy lilac is related to S. villosa, which differs, however, in the corolla lobes being spreading and in the anthers being near the mouth. It is still more closely allied to S. Josikæa, the Hungarian lilac, which has the same erect corolla lobes but has smaller anthers inserted even lower than those of S. Wolfii. S. Josikæa is not so vigorous, has smaller leaves paler beneath, and is not so handsome a shrub.

S. YUNNANENSIS, *Franchet*. YUNNAN LILAC

(McKelvey's The Lilac, tt. 6-10)

A deciduous shrub up to 12 ft. high, of rather erect, slender habit ; young shoots minutely downy or glabrous, reddish, thinly but conspicuously warty. Leaves oval, oblong-lanceolate or narrowly obovate, tapered at the base, pointed ; 1½ to 3½ ins. long, ¾ to 1½ ins. wide ; dull green above, glaucous beneath, glabrous on both surfaces but margined with minute hairs ; stalk reddish, ½ to ¾ in. long. Panicle terminal, up to 8 ins. long and 6 ins. wide, flower-stalks minutely downy. Flowers fragrant, opening in June. Corolla pale pink, becoming almost white, ¼ to ⅜ in. long, ¼ in. across the spreading lobes ; anthers yellow, reaching the mouth of the tube. Calyx glabrous, cup-shaped, with very small teeth, reddish. Seed-vessel glabrous, ⅔ in. long. (*Villosæ section.*)

Native of Yunnan, China ; first named in 1891 from specimens collected by Delavay ; first introduced to this country by Forrest when collecting for Mr A. K. Bulley, 1904-7. It is a pleasing lilac and is most closely related to the Himalayan S. emodi. It has, especially, the same smooth, pale, almost glaucous under-surface of the leaves. The Himalayan lilac is distinct in its much larger leaves and in the anthers being more protruded. Plants grown at Kew and Aldenham as S. yunnanensis appear to fit the type in every way except that the panicles are quite glabrous. The typical plant is growing at Moreton Paddox in Warwickshire.

TAIWANIA CRYPTOMERIOIDES, *Hayata*. CONIFERÆ

(Plate 32)

(Gardeners' Chronicle, 30th Oct. 1920, fig. 99—young tree)

An evergreen tree averaging in its adult state 150 to 180 ft., but occasionally over 200 ft. in height, the trunk (sometimes 30 ft. in girth) clothed with reddish brown bark separating from it in loose strips. As in so many conifers, the leaves of juvenile trees are quite distinct from

those of adult ones.   The former are arranged equally all round the
stem, about twenty to the inch, awl-shaped, $\frac{1}{4}$ to $\frac{5}{8}$ in. long, $\frac{1}{12}$ in. wide
at the base, spine-tipped and of hard texture.   Leaves and twigs of
adult trees very like those of Athrotaxis laxifolia, the former being
$\frac{1}{8}$ to $\frac{1}{6}$ in. long, triangular in cross section, incurved at the shortly pointed
apex, with stomata on all three surfaces ; they are close enough together
completely to hide the stems.   Cones terminal, ovoid-cylindrical, $\frac{1}{2}$ in.
long, $\frac{1}{4}$ to $\frac{3}{8}$ in. wide ; scales numerous, rounded, overlapping.
     Native of Formosa, especially on Mt. Morrison, also of Yunnan,
China ; first introduced to England in 1920 by E. H. Wilson, who
had raised plants in the Arnold Arborteum from seed he had himself
collected in Formosa.   This tree is one of the tallest conifers in the Old
World and is only surpassed in height by some native of the Himalaya.
The shoots of young trees are very like those of Cryptomeria japonica
and the adult tree is in general aspect also similar.   In youth it is
extremely elegant, the branches curved gracefully upwards, the
branchlets slender and more or less drooping.   The taiwania has lived
in the open in the National Pinetum at Bedgebury since 1926, although
it suffered in the winter of 1928-9.   The late Marquis of Headfort showed
a fine young tree at the Conifer Congress at Westminster in November
1931, which he had grown outside in Co. Meath.   It will no doubt be
quite hardy in the maritime counties of the south and west.   The
generic name is adapted from " Taiwan," the Chinese name for the
island of Formosa.

TAMARIX.   TAMARISK.   TAMARICACEÆ

     A group of shrubs or small trees, natives of the Old World, and often
inhabiting maritime situations or places where the soil is permeated with
saline substances.   Some half a dozen species are grown in British
gardens, all distinguished by the feathery character of their branches,
the minute scale-like leaves resembling those of some junipers, and the
small flowers crowded on short racemes.   There are few genera of
shrubs whose nomenclature is more obscure and involved, many of the
species needing microscopical examination for their identification.
     The tamarisks are easily cultivated, and none of them appears to find
the peculiar conditions under which they occur wild essential, although
perhaps they do not thrive so well in their absence.   Although some of
them come from hot, dry regions, the saline substances which are
absorbed by the plant in such places prevent excessive transpiration.
But when these are absent from the soil, and nature's safeguard against
too great a loss of moisture no longer exists, a more regular supply of
moisture at the root becomes necessary.   This simply means that in
inland districts they need a fairly good, deep loam.   No shrubs are more
easily propagated than these.   It is only necessary to make cuttings of
the previous summer's wood about the thickness of a lead pencil and,
say, 8 ins. long, and place them in the open ground in early winter,
burying about two-thirds of the cutting.   On the south coast of England,
where hedges are often made of T. anglica, the process consists of simply

utting out pieces the length and thickness of a stout walking-stick,
harpening them at one end, and driving them in the ground where
he hedge is to be.

For exposed seaside places there are few shrubs so beautiful and so
onveniently managed as the tamarisks. In gardens the late summer or
autumn flowering species may be cut back every February if it be
lesirable to keep them low.

T. ANGLICA, *Webb*. ENGLISH TAMARISK

An evergreen shrub, 3 to 10 ft. high, inhabiting maritime districts on the
coasts of England and France. In habit it is erect, the young wood reddish
brown. Leaves minute, bright green; ovate-lanceolate, narrowed towards
he base, glabrous. Flowers in slender racemes 1 to 2 ins. long, white tinged
with pink outside, each flower $\frac{1}{8}$ in. across, ovate in bud, and produced in the
axil of a narrow bract. Stamens five, the disk on which they are inserted not
showing rounded teeth (as in gallica) between the points of attachment.

Closely allied to T. gallica and by some botanists treated as a form of it,
he English tamarisk differs chiefly in the shape of the flower-bud, and in the
absence of lobing on the disk on which the stamens are inserted. It may
be seen at some of our seaside resorts, especially at Felixstowe and Bognor,
where great masses of it, planted and wild, make a charming display in late
summer and early autumn. It evidently prefers maritime rather than inland
positions. On the coasts of Dorset and Devon it flowers up to Christmas.

T. GALLICA, *Linnæus*. FRENCH TAMARISK

An evergreen or deciduous shrub or small tree, in this country 10 to 12 ft.
high, but as much as 30 ft. in more southern localities. Branches erect, the
young ones with smooth, purplish bark. Leaves lanceolate or ovate-lanceolate,
broad at the base, glaucous. Racemes slender, cylindrical, 1 to 2 ins. long,
densely set with flowers, which are pink when open, globose in bud. Stamens
five, the disk on which they are attached having ten shallow, rounded lobes.

The Gallic tamarisk is a species of very uncertain limits, both botanical and
geographical. By some writers it is made to include plants growing as far
apart as N. Africa and China, and some make it include the English tamarisk
described above. The species as we know it under cultivation is a native of the
west coast of France. It flowers very prettily in late summer and autumn.

T. HISPIDA, *Willdenow*
(T. kashgarica, *Hort.*)

A deciduous shrub, up to 3 or 4 ft. high, distinct from all other cultivated
tamarisks in the downiness of its young branches and leaves. It has a rather
erect, compact habit, and the leaves are very glaucous; the largest less than
$\frac{1}{8}$ in. long, sharply pointed, but comparatively broad at the base; the smallest
are only one-third or one-fourth the size. Flowers bright pink, opening in
late August and September, and borne in erect racemes 2 or 3 ins. long
terminating the branchlets.

This handsome tamarisk, easily distinguished from the others here
mentioned by its hairy twigs and leaves, was introduced to cultivation by
the Russian traveller Roborowsky, who collected seeds near Kashgar in
W. Asia and sent them to Messrs Lemoine of Nancy. It was put on the
market in 1893. It has also been found in the deserts east of the Caspian

Sea. Whether it is not quite hardy, or whether (as is more likely) it doe
not get enough sun in England to ripen its wood properly, this species ha
not proved long-lived at Kew. Its glaucous white colour, its handsom
flowers, and the fact that it blooms during the whole of September, make i
a charming acquisition wherever it thrives, but it is evidently better suite
for a continental climate than for ours.

T. JUNIPERINA, *Bunge*

(T. chinensis, *Siebold* ; T. japonica, *Hort.* ; T. plumosa, *Hort.*)

A deciduous shrub or small tree, becoming in time gaunt in habit, th
very distinct plumose branches covered with pale green foliage. In thei
final subdivisions the branchlets are the thinnest of cultivated tamarisks
scarcely thicker than threads, but through its close branching, this specie
is the densest in habit. The larger leaves scattered on the thicker branchlet
are $\frac{3}{16}$ in. long, pointed, and ultimately decurved ; they become smaller o
each subdivision until, on the final ramifications they are about $\frac{1}{32}$ in. long
Flowers bright pink in the bud state, paler after opening ; produced in Ma
on the twigs of the preceding season ; racemes $1\frac{1}{2}$ to 2 ins. long.

Native of N. China, Manchuria, and perhaps Japan. It is the mos
graceful of hardy tamarisks, and is worth growing for the fine plumose effec
of its branches, which stand out very prominently when associated with othe
shrubs, not only for their elegance but also for the peculiar freshness of thei
pale green. It has lived outside for many years at Kew, and forms a rugge
trunk, but rarely flowers. It is cut back in hard winters.

T. PENTANDRA, *Pallas*

(Bot. Mag., t. 8138 ; T. hispida æstivalis, *Hort.* ; T. Pallasii, *Desvois*)

A deciduous shrub or small tree, ultimately from 12 to 15 ft. high, o
upwards, with long, slender, plumose branches. Leaves very small, pointed
the largest $\frac{1}{8}$ in. long, arranged at intervals along the flowering shoots ; th
smallest one-fifth as large, and crowded fifty or more to the inch. Flower
arranged densely in slender, sometimes branching racemes, 1 to 5 ins. long
each tiny blossom $\frac{1}{8}$ in. across, rosy pink ; they cover the whole terminal par
of the current year's shoot, which is thus transformed during August int
a huge plume-like panicle of blossom as much as 3 ft. long. Sepals, petals
and stamens, all five in number.

Native of S.E. Europe and Asia Minor, especially on the banks of tida
rivers. This beautiful tamarisk is quite hardy, and one of the most pleasing
of late-flowering shrubs. It should be planted in groups large enough fo
its soft rosy plumes to produce an effect in the distance. To obtain it at it
best, it is necessary to cut it back every winter almost to the old wood. It
then sends up the long slender branches which flower for six weeks or so
in August and September. It is propagated with the greatest ease by making
cuttings, 6 to 9 ins. long, in early winter of the stoutest part of the season's
growth, and putting them in the ground out-of-doors like willows. It has
been called a variety of T. hispida, but that species, as stated above, is very
distinct in its downy twigs and leaves.

T. TETRANDRA, *Pallas*

A deciduous shrub, 10 to 15 ft. high, with glabrous dark branches which
are usually arching in plants a few years old. The minor branchlets or twigs
are very thin, clothed densely with minute, scale-like leaves, which under

he lens are seen to be closely imbricated, pointed, and incurved at the apex.
'lowers very small and closely set on slender, cylindrical, straight racemes,
to 2 ins. long, which develop in May from the branches of the previous year.
'hey are bright pink, very freely borne, and have each four stamens.
    Native of the eastern Mediterranean region, the Crimea, Caucasus, etc.

TAMARIX TETRANDRA

It is the commonest species in gardens, being supplied by continental nurserymen under at least five names, such as " africana," " algeriensis," " caspica,"
" indica," and " parviflora," some of which belong rightly to distinct species.
Among cultivated tamarisks it is distinct in flowering early from the old wood
and in having four stamens. A shrub of great beauty and grace, admirable
in masses. Introduced in 1821.
    The true T. PARVIFLORA, *De Candolle*, is sometimes grown as " T. tetrandra
purpurea." It has dark reddish purple shoots and darker flowers than the
above ; stamens four.

TAPISCIA SINENSIS, *Oliver*. STAPHYLEACEÆ

A deciduous tree, usually about 30 ft. high (very rarely as much a 80 ft., with a trunk 12 ft. in girth). Leaves pinnate, 12 to 18 ins. long composed of five to nine leaflets, which are ovate, heart-shaped at th base, pointed, toothed, 3 to 5 ins. long, greyish beneath. Flowers small yellow, in axillary panicles 4 to 6 ins. long, the divisions of the panicl very slender ; they have a charming honey-like fragrance. Fruit egg shaped, black, ⅓ in. long.

Native of the mountains of W. Hupeh, China, at elevations of 250c to 3000 ft., where it is rare ; also of Szechuen at similar elevations where it is more common. It is the only species of the genus known Introduced by Wilson for the Harvard University in 1908. I am doubtful of its proving hardy except in the south-west ; where it i hardy its chief garden value will be in its bold pinnate leaves and scented blossoms. The generic name is an anagram of Pistacia, a genus to which this tree bears a strong resemblance.

TAXODIUM DISTICHUM, *Richard*. DECIDUOUS CYPRESS. CONIFERÆ

A deciduous, usually pyramidal tree, 100 to 150 ft. high, the tapered trunk erect, buttressed at the base, and measuring above it 4 to 6 ft. ir diameter. In damp situations the roots produce curious woody protuber ances, which occasionally stand up several feet out of the ground, being several inches thick, and hollow. The young shoots are of two kinds . (1) the leading ones, which are persistent and have the leaves spirally arranged ; (2) the others, very slender, annual, and falling away in autumn along with the leaves ; this latter kind of shoot has no buds. Leaves spirally attached, but spreading (except in the leading shoots) in two opposite horizontal rows ; linear, pointed, ⅜ to ⅝ in. long, $\frac{1}{16}$ to $\frac{1}{12}$ in. wide, of a soft yellowish green. Male and female flowers separate, but on the same tree ; the former in slender panicles 4 or 5 ins. long. Cones globular, ¾ to 1½ ins. wide.

Native of the southern United States, mostly in swamps, where its base is submerged during a portion of the year; introduced in 1640 by John Tradescant.

This tree is one of the most beautiful and interesting that can be grown in wet places, although it thrives well, too, in ordinary soil. Its fine feathery foliage, of the tenderest green in spring, and dying off a rich brown in autumn, has nothing similar to it in the whole range of hardy trees. It is perfectly hardy near London, and very accommodating. A dry hollow at Kew, in which a deciduous cypress was growing, was turned into a lily pond in 1896 by puddling it over with clay. The taxodium was left standing, and its trunk became permanently immersed in 2 or 3 ft. of water. The tree showed no ill effects from the sudden and drastic change in its root conditions, but on the contrary has grown much better ever since ; only the immersed part of the trunk has become swollen and spongy. The finest trees I have seen are (or were) in

Whitton Park, Hounslow, one of which some years ago was 110 ft. high. This grew by the side of the pond, and there is no doubt such a spot is best for the tree. There are some fine examples at Syon, from one of which the sprays of male racemes here figured were taken. In these flowering sprays, it will be noticed, the leaves are always spirally arranged.

Var. PENDULUM (T. distichum imbricarium, *Sargent*; Glyptostrobus pendulus, *Endlicher*, Bot. Mag., t. 5603).—A smaller tree than the type ; the

TAXODIUM DISTICHUM (male flowering shoots)

leaves smaller, never in two opposite rows, but always spirally arranged or more or less flattened to the twig, sometimes scale-like. According to Sargent, it is not rare in a wild state. This variety is sometimes grown as Glyptostrobus heterophyllus," but the true plant of that name, closely allied and very similar to the Taxodium, is a native of China.

T. MUCRONATUM, *Tenore*. MEXICAN SWAMP CYPRESS

Taken altogether this tree seems distinct enough from the familiar swamp cypress of the S.E. United States (Taxodium distichum) to rank as a species, although the botanical differences appear to consist in the leaves being shorter, in its flowering in autumn instead of spring, in the panicles of the male flowers being longer, and in the tree being generally of a more evergreen type. It is a more southern tree, being found at its best in Mexico, and is not so well adapted for our climate. It has, nevertheless, grown to a height of about 40 ft. at Kew at the margin of water without any artificial protection and is there

well distinguished by a proportion of its leaves hanging on throughout th
winter. According to Henry the leaves generally remain on the trees for tw
years in Mexico.

There are some trees in that country very remarkable for their size an
age, the most wonderful of them all being one growing in the churchyard c
Santa Maria del Tule, about eighteen miles south-east of the city of Oaxaca
The height of this tree is about 140 ft. and the diameter of its trunk upward
of 40 ft. Its age has been calculated as 5000 years (from the number of annua
rings in a scooped-out portion of the trunk) and it is generally regarded as th
oldest tree in the world. It has been suggested, however, that it may be real!
a cluster of several trees originally growing so close together that the trunk
have amalgamated.

TAXUS. YEW. TAXACEÆ

The six or seven reputed species that make up this genus have, b
more than one authority, been regarded as but geographical variation
of a single one. The type of the genus is T. baccata, and the other
do not differ from it in fruit, only in characters of bud, leaf, and habi
It is for garden purposes more convenient to avoid the cumbersom
varietal designations, and adopt simple specific names. The generi
characters of flower and fruit will be found under the notice of th
common yew. Yew timber possesses remarkable strength and durability
and was once highly valued in this country, especially for indoor us
(furniture, etc.) ; it is also very resistant to decay from wet out-of-doors

T. BACCATA, *Linnæus*. COMMON YEW

A tree 30 to 40, rarely 50 or 60 ft. high, forming in age a short, enormousl
thick trunk, clothed with red-brown peeling bark, and crowned with a rounde
or wide-spreading head of branches. Leaves spirally attached to the twig
but by the twisting of the stalks brought more or less into two opposed ranks
they are of a dark, glossy, almost black-green above, grey, pale green c
sometimes yellowish beneath, the stomatic lines indistinct ; linear, $\frac{1}{2}$ to $1\frac{1}{4}$ in
long, $\frac{1}{16}$ to $\frac{1}{12}$ in. wide ; more gradually tapered to a fine point than any othe
of the species here mentioned. Flowers unisexual, with the sexes almo
invariably on separate trees, produced in spring from the leaf-axils of th
preceding summer's twigs. Male a globose cluster of stamens ; female born
close to the end of the shoot, and consisting of an ovule surrounded by sma
bracts. What is usually termed the " fruit " is a fleshy cup developed from
disk in which the ovule is set. This cup is bright red (sometimes yellow
juicy, and encloses the nut-like seed except at the top.

Native of Europe (including Britain), N. Africa, and W. Asia. No tre
has become more woven into the history and folk-lore of Great Britain tha
the yew. All through the Middle Ages and until gunpowder came into genera
use, yew wood was more valued than any other for the manufacture of bow
long the national weapon of offence ; but Spanish-grown wood was considere
the best. In earlier ages still, before the conversion of this country t
Christianity, yews were, no doubt, sacred trees, and the Druids erected the
temples near them. The early Christians made a practice of building the
churches on sites previously held sacred by the Britons, and thus perpetuate
that association of the yew with religious edifices which has lasted until nov

Many famous yews are scattered over the country to which space does not admit of reference. The tree is probably capable of attaining to a greater age than the oak. The noted yews of Fountains Abbey in Yorkshire were large enough for the monks to shelter and worship under whilst the abbey was being built, nearly 800 years ago. The oldest yew in Britain is the Fortingal yew in Perthshire, its perfectly hollow trunk, now split in two, was originally 7 ft. in diameter near the ground.

A peculiar mystery is attached to the poisonous quality the yew is known to possess, owing to its uncertain and apparently capricious effects. One may go into parks where yews are standing, and see them eaten off by cattle up to the grazing line as other trees are, and yet no case of poisoning heard of; on the other hand, deaths of horses, cattle, and calves turned into fresh fields where they were able to get at yew bushes have occurred so often as to leave no doubt that the yew is poisonous. It appears as if the poison acts only on certain states of the stomach. In my opinion it is more virulent when the stomach is empty, perhaps only then. It also appears that semi-dried twigs and foliage are more dangerous than green ones, and it has been surmised that the male tree is more poisonous than the female. The poison does not appear to be of an acrid or irritant nature, but brings about death rather by arrest of the heart's action. Neither the Canadian nor the Himalayan yew is known to be poisonous. The red fleshy cup that surrounds the seeds is frequently eaten by children without ill effects, but the seeds themselves contain the alkaloid known as taxine that is found in the leaves, and may be the principle that has caused so many fatalities.

The yew bears clipping exceptionally well, and on that account makes excellent evergreen hedges. It is also the best, frequently the only tree used for topiary work, *i.e.* training and clipping into formal and fantastic shapes. The most remarkable examples in this country are at Levens Castle, in Westmoreland, and at Elvaston Castle, in Derbyshire. The Levens trees were planted about two hundred years ago, and have been annually clipped ever since—a remarkable testimony to the adaptability and vitality of the yew.

The tree is an extremely hardy one, and is adapted to almost any soil, but like most trees is best suited on a good loam. It is one of the best evergreens for calcareous soils. Common yew is mostly raised from seed which, collected when ripe in autumn, should be kept a year before sowing, mixed with sand or soil and turned occasionally. Named varieties are easily raised from cuttings of small shoots placed under a cloche in late July or August. There is now a great number of varieties of yew cultivated, mostly of seedling origin ; here follows a selection of the most notable :—

Var. ADPRESSA.—A very striking and handsome form that would be considered a distinct species if its origin were not known. It is a wide-spreading shrub of dense habit (female), with leaves only $\frac{1}{4}$ to $\frac{1}{2}$ in. long, $\frac{1}{2}$ in. wide, abruptly pointed at the apex. According to the late Mr F. T. Dickson, it was found by his father in a bed of seedling yews about 1838, and called by him " brevifolia "—a name now in disuse, as it belongs rightly to the Californian yew.

Var. ADPRESSA AUREA.—A very effective form, with golden young foliage, which originated in the Handsworth Nurseries, Sheffield. ADPRESSA STRICTA is of erect habit.

Var. AUREA. Golden Yew.—Habit compact ; leaves golden yellow when young, changing to green after autumn.

Var. BARRONI.—Leaves golden, becoming a rich coppery shade.

Var. CAVENDISHII.—Procumbent, 1 to 2 ft. high.

Var. CHESHUNTENSIS.—A form intermediate and probably a hybrid between the common and Irish yews ; it has a wider habit than the latter but the leaves are similarly arranged all round the twig.

Var. DOVASTONI. Westfelton Yew.—One of the most distinct and hand some forms. The tree makes an erect stem, its branches are horizontal, an its branchlets, or spray, pendulous. It was raised about 1777 by Mr John Dovaston of Westfelton, near Shrewsbury, and the original tree, in additio to its striking habit is of interest in having, although mostly male, produce a branch which bears fruits. A sub-variety has golden young leaves.

Var. ERICOIDES.—A dwarf form with narrow crowded leaves $\frac{1}{4}$ to $\frac{1}{2}$ in. lon —a curiosity merely.

Var. FASTIGIATA. Irish Yew.—Of columnar habit, with its branches an branchlets quite erect and its leaves standing out all round the twigs. Tw trees, both female, were originally found in the Fermanagh Mountains abou 1780 by a Mr Willis ; one he planted in his own garden where it lived until 1865 the other, which is still alive, he sent to Florence Court. From the latter hav come most, if not all, of the Irish yews in existence, but recently several mal trees have been found at North Mundham in Sussex. Their origin is no known. There is a sub-variety with golden young leaves—FASTIGIATA AUREA

Var. FRUCTU-LUTEO.—Differs from the type in the yellow fruits ; firs noticed about 1817 at Glasnevin, Dublin.

Var. GLAUCA.—Leaves at first very glaucous beneath.

Var. GRACILIS PENDULA.—Of the Dovastoni type. Stem erect, branche horizontal, branchlets slender, elongated, pendulous.

Var. HORIZONTALIS.—Branches horizontal, like Dovastoni, but with th branchlets not pendulous ; a form with golden young leaves is calle HORIZONTALIS ELEGANTISSIMA.

Var. NANA.—Dwarf and spreading in habit.

Var. PENDULA.—A low spreading form with branches more or les pendulous.

Var. PROSTRATA.—A prostrate-branched variety.

Var. RECURVATA.—Branches horizontal, leaves recurved.

Var. SEMPERAUREA.—Young shoots and leaves yellow, retaining thei colour through the first winter.

Var. WASHINGTONI.—A low spreading shrub, with leaves of a golden hu and up to $1\frac{1}{4}$ ins. long.

T. BREVIFOLIA, *Nuttall*. CALIFORNIAN YEW

A small tree 20 to 30, rarely 50 to 70 ft. high, the trunk clothed with thi reddish brown bark ; branchlets slender, winter buds clothed with loos yellowish, pointed scales. Leaves $\frac{1}{4}$ to $\frac{2}{3}$ in. long, $\frac{1}{16}$ in. wide, linear, rathe abruptly narrowed at the apex to a fine point ; dark green above, paler gree beneath, arranged in two opposite horizontally spreading rows and persistinj four or five years. Fruit as in T. baccata.

Native of western N. America, from British Columbia to California introduced in 1854. This yew is rare in cultivation, the form so-called being usually a form of T. baccata. On the other hand, the yews differ so little fron each other in essential points that it may easily be lost among the numerous forms of common yew.

T. CANADENSIS, *Marshall*. CANADIAN YEW

A shrub of spreading habit, often low and straggling, sometimes 4 to 6 ft high ; winter buds small, roundish, the scales loose, roundish at the apex ridged at the back. Leaves $\frac{1}{2}$ to $\frac{3}{4}$ in. long, $\frac{1}{16}$ to $\frac{1}{12}$ in. wide ; linear, terminatec

ɔy a fine rather abrupt point, shortly stalked ; dark glossy green above, paler
ʒreen beneath. Fruit red, as in T. baccata.

Native of eastern N. America, from Newfoundland to Virginia ; introduced
ɩn 1800. The Canadian yew is distinguishable from the English yew by the
ɩnvariably shrubby habit, by the more abruptly pointed leaves, and by the
ɩeaf-buds, but can scarcely be said to differ from it more than the varieties of
ɔommon yew do among themselves. It has little to recommend it beyond its
ɔotanical interest, except that it is the hardiest of the yews and can be grown
ɯhere it is too cold for T. baccata.

T. CHINENSIS, *Rehder*. CHINESE YEW

(T. cuspidata chinensis, *Rehder and Wilson* ; T. baccata chinensis, *Pilger*)

This tree was introduced in 1908 from Central and Western China by
Wilson, who observes that it is scattered throughout Western Hupeh and
Szechuen, especially in regions where hard, carboniferous limestone prevails.
He found it occasionally 50 ft. high with a rich red-brown trunk 3 to 4 ft. in
ɩiameter. The plants at Kew raised from his seeds are distinguished from
T. baccata by the leaves being longer ($\frac{3}{4}$ to $1\frac{1}{2}$ ins.), by their being set usually
ɯider apart on the branchlet, by being more curved, and by spreading
ɩorizontally. They seem to represent a type found in Szechuen. Other
ɩpecimens collected in Hupeh by Henry and Wilson have leaves only $\frac{1}{3}$ to $\frac{1}{2}$ in.
ɩong and closely set on the twig. These appear to be of a quite distinct yew
ɔompared with the Szechuen plants, but they are the form to which Pilger first
ɯsed the name " chinensis." The yews of China seem to need further
ɩlucidation.

T. CUSPIDATA, *Siebold and Zuccarini*. JAPANESE YEW

A tree 40 to 50 ft. high in Japan, with a trunk girthing about 6 ft. ; in
ɔultivation a low tree or spreading shrub ; older bark reddish brown. Leaves
ɩ to 1 in. long, $\frac{1}{12}$ to $\frac{1}{8}$ in. wide ; linear, tapered rather abruptly at the apex to
ɩ fine point ; rounded, and with a distinct stalk at the base $\frac{1}{12}$ in. long ; dark
ʒreen above ; with a broad, tawny yellow strip composed of ten to twelve
ɩtomatic lines on each side of the green midrib beneath. The leaves are
ɩrranged approximately in two ranks, and stand more or less erect from
ɩhe twig, often forming a narrow V-shaped trough. Fruit red, as in T.
ɔaccata.

Native of Japan ; introduced by Fortune about 1855, and very hardy
ɩlthough slow-growing. It thrives extremely well in the trying New England
ɔlimate, and is apparently one of the best evergreens introduced there. There
ɩre two distinct forms of it in cultivation, the one a tree, the other, var.
COMPACTA, a compact, low bush, wider than it is high. Whilst the general
ɩspect is the same as that of the English yew, it can be distinguished by the
ɩarked yellow tinge of the under-surface of the leaves, and by the longer, more
ɔblong winter buds with looser, more pointed scales.

T. MEDIA, *Rehder*, is a hybrid between T. cuspidata and T. baccata raised in the
Jnited States about 1900. According to Rehder the foliage is similar to that of
ɩuspidata but more distinctly two-ranked. Its var. HATFIELDII is of the same type as
ɩhe Irish yew, the shoots being erect, the leaves spreading all round the shoot, not in
ɩwo ranks. Introduced to Kew in 1931 but has since been lost. Var. HICKSII is
ɔf the same type but of columnar shape, Hatfieldii being of compact, conical shape.

TELOPEA TRUNCATA, *R. Brown.* TASMANIAN WARATAH.
PROTEACEÆ

An evergreen, varying from a shrub of low, spreading habit to a small
tree up to 25 ft. high ; young shoots stout, round, covered with brownish
down. Leaves alternate, of stiff leathery texture, usually closely set on
the branchlets where some persist for two years. They are of oblanceolate
shape, tapered gradually to the base, more abruptly to the apex which
may be rounded or pointed, sometimes having two or three large teeth,
or sometimes (especially on young cultivated plants) being deeply
bilobed ; 2 to 5 ins. long, $\frac{1}{6}$ to $\frac{3}{4}$ in. wide ; dullish green above, rather
glaucous beneath. Flowers rich crimson, crowded in a terminal head
2 to 3 ins. wide, each blossom of much the same shape as those of
Embothrium coccineum ; the slender curved perianth is about 1 in.
long, splitting and showing the conspicuously exposed, curving style
1 to $1\frac{1}{4}$ ins. long, with the large knob-like stigma at the end. The flower
is filled with honey. Seed-pod woody, cylindrical, curved, 2 to 3 ins.
long, terminated by a " tail " $\frac{1}{2}$ to $\frac{3}{4}$ in. long.

Native of Tasmania and especially abundant on Mt. Wellington,
where it flowers in December and January, but where it is said to be
becoming scarce in the frequented parts because of the spoliation of the
blossom for Christmas decoration. One writer remarks that " the vivid
scarlet colouring of the flowers shining out amongst the sombre blue-
greens of the gum forests is certainly one of the most beautiful sights the
Tasmanian bush affords." A hundred years ago a Tasmanian correspondent of Kew wrote : " I really think this plant will do well in the
open air in Britain ; it is only found in the cool mountainous parts of
the island and I have tried in vain to coax it to grow in my garden, but
the summer heats have always destroyed it." A plant which grew in the
rock garden at Kew for several winters, reaching a height of about 18 ins.,
was quite healthy ; there is a large example in the garden at Wakehurst
in Sussex. I suppose these plants were raised from seeds collected by
Comber and I cannot find that it has ever been cultivated here before.
It should flower with us in early summer. Comber suggests a peaty
soil for it, in a young state at any rate.

TERNSTRŒMIA JAPONICA, *Thunberg.* TERNSTRŒMIACEÆ

An evergreen shrub or small tree with a much-branched head, and
warted, not downy branchlets. Leaves alternate, crowded at the apex
of the shoot, obovate or oblanceolate ; $1\frac{1}{2}$ to 3 ins. long, $\frac{1}{2}$ to $1\frac{1}{2}$ ins.
wide ; tapered gradually at the base to a short, stout, purplish stalk ;
more abruptly tapered to a rounded or bluntish apex ; they are dark
varnished green, thick and leathery, and quite glabrous. Flowers
fragrant, solitary on stalks about $\frac{3}{4}$ in. long, nodding, of short duration,
produced in July and August from the leaf-axils, and from the axils of
fallen scales on the lower naked part of the shoot. Corolla yellowish
white, about $\frac{1}{3}$ in. across ; petals five. Fruit globose, and about the size

of a cherry, yellow, tinged with rose on the sunny side, the rounded sepals persisting at the base.

Native of Japan ; introduced in the early part of last century, but probably incapable of withstanding our hardest winters, for it had nearly or quite disappeared from gardens until reintroduced a few years ago. It has withstood 20° of frost at Kew, but is no doubt better adapted for the south-west counties than for our average climate. This species has been confused with Eurya japonica, but the latter has broader ended, more distinctly obovate leaves.

TETRACENTRON SINENSE, *Oliver*. TROCHODENDRACEÆ

A deciduous tree, 50 to 90 ft. high allied to and resembling Cercidiphyllum japonicum, especially in having, on the year-old branches, short or obsolete twigs, each producing a single leaf and an inflorescence. It differs, however, in its invariably alternate leaves. Young branches dark, glabrous, freely marked with pale lenticels. Leaves ovate or heart-shaped, long-pointed, with usually five or seven prominent nerves radiating from the base ; 3 to 4½ ins. long, 2 ins. wide, the margins evenly set with blunt teeth. Flowers numerous, stalkless, on a pendulous spike 4 to 6 ins. long, very small, yellowish ; sepals, stamens, and carpels four ; petals absent.

Native of the province of Hupeh, China, where it was originally discovered by Henry ; introduced by Wilson for Messrs Veitch in 1901. It is apparently quite hardy, although I have seen it much injured by late spring frosts. It flowers freely at Caerhays, Cornwall, in midwinter, its wealth of catkins making a picture of great elegance and beauty.

TEUCRIUM. GERMANDER. LABIATÆ

A large genus mostly of herbaceous plants, a few of which are shrubby. They are related to the rosemary and lavender, having opposite leaves and a corolla tubular at the base, expanding at the mouth into two " lips," as is typical of this Natural Order ; the upper lip, however, is split down as far as the calyx so that the bottom half of it appears to belong to the lower " lip." Stamens four, protruding through the slit of the upper lip. The genus is said to be named after Teucer, a prince of Troy. These two species are very hardy, very easily cultivated, and very readily propagated by cuttings, but of no particular garden value.

T. CHAMÆDRYS, *Linnæus*. WALL GERMANDER
(Syme's English Botany—Ed. iii., t. 1094)

An evergreen, semi-shrubby plant, herbaceous at the top, woody at the base, with a creeping root-stock and ascending, very downy branches ; 8 to 12 ins. high. Leaves opposite, mainly ovate, but conspicuously toothed or almost lobed, tapering at the base to a winged stalk ; ½ to 1¼ ins. long, almost half as much wide, bright green above, hairy on both sides. Flowers arranged on a terminal raceme 2 to 5 ins. long, two or three together in the axils of the leaves or bracts. Corolla rose-coloured, ½ to ⅝ in. long, two-lipped, the lower lip veined with darker rose. Calyx ¼ in. long, tubular, with five sharp lobes, hairy and, like the floral bracts, purplish.

Native of Central and Southern Europe ; cultivated in England in the middle of the eighteenth century and now naturalised in many parts of Britain. Very hardy and easily grown. It flowers from July to September, earlier in warm countries. At one time it was considered to be a valuable specific for gout and was an important ingredient in the popular medicine known as " Portland powder," a name it acquired through its having (reputedly) cured an eighteenth-century Duke of Portland of that complaint. The plant has a pleasant, slightly aromatic odour when crushed.

T. FRUTICANS, *Linnæus*. SHRUBBY GERMANDER

An evergreen shrub of diffuse habit, naturally 7 or 8 ft. high, stems square, and covered with a close white felt. Leaves opposite, ovate, ½ to 1½ ins. long, about half as wide, broadly wedge-shaped or rounded at the base, bluntish at the apex ; dark, rather bright green and glabrous above, white, with a close felt beneath, fragrant when crushed ; stalk ¼ in. or less long. Flowers produced during the summer and autumn singly in the axils of the small uppermost leaves or bracts—the whole forming a raceme 3 or 4 ins. long. Calyx ¼ in. long, with five ovate, pointed, leaf-like lobes, white beneath. Corolla pale purple or lavender-coloured, forming a short tube at the base, to which the four long stamens are attached, then developing into a large five-lobed lip 1 in. long (like the lip of an orchid flower in shape), the basal pair of lobes the smallest and palest ; flower-stalk white, ¼ in. or less long.

Native of S. Europe and N. Africa ; introduced by the then Duchess of Beaufort in 1714. It is very pretty, and distinct among shrubs because of the pure white under-surface of the leaf and the curiously shaped labiate flower. At Kew it can be grown on a wall, but is not hardy in the open. Easily increased by cuttings during the summer, and preferring a rather light soil.

T. MONTANUM, *Linnæus*. MOUNTAIN GERMANDER

(Sibthorp and Smith's Flora Græca, t. 534)

An evergreen, semi-shrubby plant prostrate and woody at the base, 6 to 12 ins. high, often reduced to tufts one-third those heights in dry, barren, rocky places ; young shoots slender, wiry, erect, downy. Leaves opposite, crowded, linear to narrowly oblong, tapered towards both ends ; ¼ to 1 in. long, 1⁄12 to ⅛ in. wide ; bright green and thinly downy above, grey-white with thick down beneath ; margins decurved. Flowers densely packed in terminal, roundish clusters 1 in. across. Corolla ½ in. long, yellow, upper lip veined with purple ; calyx tubular, downy, ¼ in. long, with five teeth.

Native of Central and S. Europe to Asia Minor, introduced in 1710 ; easily distinguished from T. Chamædrys by its yellow flowers and narrow usually toothless leaves. It flowers from July to September. Often found growing on calcareous formations in the Swiss Alps.

THUYA. CONIFERÆ

In the now generally accepted ·interpretation of the word, Thuya comprises six or seven species of evergreen trees with thin, scaling bark, belonging to the same group of conifers as the Chamæcyparis or flat-leaved group of cypresses. They are very distinct in the cones, which are egg-shaped or rounded, and have flat, oblong, and (except in T. orientalis and T. dolabrata) thin scales ; very different from the peltate or top-shaped scales of the cypresses. The flat, pinnately divided branchlets and the leaf arrangement, however, are very similar, and the leaves are similarly scale-like. Juvenile types of foliage are sometimes permanently retained in T. occidentalis and T. orientalis, and are popularly known as " Retinisporas " (see also under Cupressus). Small as the number of species is—and one of them, T. SUTCHUENENSIS, *Franchet*, is not in cultivation unless recently introduced from China— they have been placed in three separate genera, viz., Biota (see T. orientalis), Thujopsis (see T. dolabrata), and Thuya proper. Biota and Thujopsis have both roundish or globose cones and thick scales, the former distinct also in its wingless seeds.

They all like a moist, loamy soil, and though best raised from seeds can be increased by cuttings.

T. DOLABRATA, *Linnæus fil.*

(Thujopsis dolabrata, *Siebold*)

A tree up to 40 or 50 ft. high, or a shrub of pyramidal form ; branchlets arranged in opposite rows (distichous), the ultimate subdivisions much flattened, about ¼ in. wide, dark glossy green above, with conspicuous glaucous patches beneath. Leaves hard and rigid, borne in four ranks ; those of the lateral ranks strongly keeled, ⅛ to ¼ in. long, incurved at the point, their edges overlapping the leaves of the middle ranks, which are appressed and rounded at the apex. Cones ½ to ¾ in. long, subglobose ; the six or eight scales thick, woody, ending in a horn-shaped boss ; seeds winged.

Native of Japan ; first introduced to Messrs Veitch's at Exeter by way of the botanic garden at Buitenzorg, in Java, 1853. Its effective introduction, however, took place in 1861, when seeds were sent to England by both J. G. Veitch and Fortune. Seen at its best, this is a striking and beautiful shrub, very distinct from the other thuyas in its broad branchlets and its rounded cones with thick woody scales. When young it is very dense in habit at the base, but as it increases in height the upper growth is apt to become thin and attentuated. There are trees 35 ft. high in Devon and Cornwall, and I have seen good specimens in Scotland over 20 ft. high. It enjoys a sheltered spot.

Var. NANA, *Siebold* (Thujopsis lætevirens, *Lindley*).—A curious dwarf, form, growing very slowly. Branchlets more slender, leaves smaller.

Var. VARIEGATA.—Young spray variegated with patches of creamy white.

Var. HONDAI, *Makino*, attains heights of up to 100 ft. Its branches are more closely set and partly overlapping ; leaves smaller, the lateral ones incurved at the tips ; cones globose.

T. JAPONICA, *Maximowicz.* JAPANESE ARBOR-VITÆ

(T. Standishii, *Carrière* ; Thujopsis Standishii, *Gordon*)

An evergreen tree rarely more than 20 to 30 ft. high in the British Isles, but said to grow twice that height in Japan, of rather open habit, pyramidal, slow-growing ; bark reddish, peeling. Branches curved upwards at the ends ; branchlets drooping ; ultimate subdivisions about 1/10 in. wide, flattened, aromatic when crushed. Leaves scale-like, about ⅛ in. long, the lateral pairs with their edges turned inwards and clasping the flatter ones above and below the twig, blunt, thickened and incurved towards the apex ; rather pale yellowish green on the upper side the twig, glaucous on the lower side, except at the points. Cones oblong, $\frac{1}{3}$ in. long, composed of about ten broadly oval, overlapping scales, two pairs only of which bear seeds.

Native of Japan ; introduced by Fortune for Standish of Ascot in 1860. Fortune only saw it as a cultivated tree about Tokyo, and it was not until about 1878 that it was discovered wild by Maries on the mountains of the Central Island. This thuya has the most open branching of the cultivated species and (with the exception of T. dolabrata) the coarsest branchlets. It is a distinct and handsome evergreen.

T. KORAIENSIS, *Nakai*. KOREAN ARBOR-VITÆ

(T. kongoensis, *Nakai*)

According to Wilson, who describes this thuya in the first volume of the *Journal of the Arnold Arboretum*, p. 186, as he saw it in Korea, it is " remarkable in its variation in habit from a sprawling shrub of nondescript shape to a slender, graceful, narrowly pyramidal tree." He gives its maximum height as 25 to 30 ft., but this it rarely attains and usually it forms an impenetrable tangle 1 to 2 yards high. The bark is thin, scaly, and of a chocolate-brown colour. The branching and leafage are quite of the ordinary thuya type, the sprays being flat, the leaves scale-like and much compressed, the lateral ones with incurved tips. The sprays are unusually glaucous beneath for this genus. I do not know that cones have as yet been produced in this country, but on Wilson's native specimens they are ovoid, erect, $\frac{1}{3}$ in. long, with eight oblong brown scales.

Introduced to the Arnold Arboretum, Mass., from the Diamond Mountains of Korea by Wilson in 1917 ; soon afterwards to Kew, where it is quite hardy and very healthy. A group of half a dozen plants are mostly low and spreading, but one is of slender pyramidal shape, thus tallying with Wilson's description of the varying habit of growth and confirming his recommendation of the shrubby type for ground cover. In Korea it is abundant as undergrowth in forests of pine, spruce and fir. The odour of the crushed branches, whilst suggesting that of T. occidentalis, is not the same but rather more agreeable. The species is most closely akin to T. japonica, which has less flattened branchlets much less glaucous beneath, and more agreeably scented when crushed.

T. OCCIDENTALIS, *Linnæus*. ARBOR-VITÆ

An evergreen tree, 50 to 60 ft. high, with a trunk 2 to 3 ft. in diameter ; in cultivation a pyramidal shrub or tree rarely more than half as high ; branches usually upturned towards the end ; branchlets three or four times pinnate, the ultimate subdivisions much flattened, $\frac{1}{16}$ to $\frac{1}{12}$ in. wide. Leaves scale-like, about $\frac{1}{12}$ in. long, the lateral ones pointed, prominently keeled and overlapping the middle ones ; they are a dull yellowish green above, paler and grey green beneath (not with whitish patches, as in T. plicata), the middle ones beneath are furnished with a raised roundish gland in the centre. Cones about $\frac{1}{3}$ in. long, oblong, with eight or ten scales.

Native of eastern N. America, from Nova Scotia to Virginia, usually on swampy or moist ground. It has been cultivated in English gardens since the sixteenth century, but is not in the first rank of conifers, being often thin in habit (especially on dry soils) and dull in colour, frequently putting on a yellowish brown appearance in winter. It often grows slowly. For forming evergreen shelter hedges, especially in nursery grounds, it has proved very useful. As an ornamental evergreen for gardens, it is much inferior to T. plicata or Cupressus Lawsoniana. Very numerous forms of garden origin have been named, only a few of which need mention here. In all its forms this thuya has a distinctive, heavy, rather acrid odour when rubbed or crushed.

Var. BUCHANANI.—Branchlets very slender, with the subdivisions thin and far apart.

Var. CRISTATA.—Dwarf, very distinct in the penultimate subdivisions being curiously curved like a cock's comb, the ultimate divisions often developed on one side only.

Var. DUMOSA.—Dwarf and rounded, rarely more than 2 ft. high. (Vars. globosa, minima, and pygmæa are similar.)

Var. ELLWANGERIANA.—An inelegant lanky shrub with slender, curving branches, some of which bear typical leaves, others the needle-like leaves of the seedlings, ¼ in. long, still others with both. Shrubs over forty years old retain this dimorphic character.

Var. ERICOIDES.—In this the whole of the foliage is needle-like and of the juvenile or seedling type ; the plant always remains a dwarf rounded shrub, glaucous in summer, brown in winter. Known in gardens as Retinispora dubia. It has an odour similar to that of the type.

Var. LUTEA.—Young branchlets yellow the first summer and winter, becoming green the second year.

Var. PLICATA (not to be confused with T. plicata or gigantea).—Branches rigid, and arranged in the vertical plane as in T. orientalis. Leaves brownish green, very glandular.

Var. SPÄTHII.—A curious dwarfed form, with erect branches distinctly four-sided, the upper ones with juvenile, awl-shaped leaves.

Var. VERVÆNEANA.—Branchlets and spray golden yellow at first, brownish in winter, green the second year. Dwarfer in habit and deeper in colour than lutea.

Var. WAREANA.—Raised by Mr Ware at Coventry about one hundred years ago ; dwarf, dense in habit, the branchlets often vertical as in var. plicata but of a brighter green.

T. ORIENTALIS, *Linnæus*.   CHINESE ARBOR-VITÆ

(Biota orientalis, *Endlicher*)

A shrub or small tree, 30 to 40 ft. high, very distinct among the thuyas and cypresses by reason of the more or less erect or upward-curving branches bearing the spray or branchlets in the vertical plane, and in being of the same colour on both sides. There are two distinct types in cultivation ; the one tall, somewhat columnar, and comparatively thin-branched, sometimes called var. pyramidalis ; the other a dense, rounded or broadly pyramidal shrub with numerous branches springing from near the ground. The latter is the more effective for gardens. Ultimate subdivisions of the branchlets $\frac{1}{16}$ in. wide, flattened ; green on both sides. Lateral leaves with their edges overlapping the middle ones, about $\frac{1}{12}$ in. long, scale-like ; middle ones grooved ; all marked with numerous white stomata. Cones roundish egg-shaped, ¾ in. long, erect, purplish ; scales six, rarely eight, thick and woody, with a hooked, horn-like boss near the apex. Seeds wingless.

Native of N. and W. China ; cultivated in Europe since the first half of the eighteenth century. The dense-growing, broader, and more shrubby form is a very effective garden plant, easily known by the yellow-green, flattened spray set up edgewise and, in healthy plants, densely packed. It likes a good loamy soil, and is more likely to suffer from drought than from cold. At the same time it should not be exposed on bleak situations. Numerous varieties are offered for sale, many of but little value. The following are the most notable :—

Var. AUREA.—Branchlets yellow-tipped in summer.

Var. DECUSSATA (Biota Sieboldii, *Gardeners' Chronicle*, 18th Feb. 1888, fig. 36).—A dense pyramidal shrub with erect branches and terete branchlets bearing awl-shaped leaves in opposite, decussate pairs. A juvenile form of the same type as var. pendula, but with erect, more slender shoots and smaller, juniper-like leaves, turning brownish in winter.

Var. ERICOIDES (Retinispora ericoides).—Leaves soft, glaucous, linear, $\frac{1}{4}$ to $\frac{1}{3}$ in. long. A juvenile state of the same type as Cupressus pisifera squarrosa. It differs from T. occidentalis ericoides in odour.

Var. MELDENSIS.—Foliage mostly juvenile and blue green, but partly adult.

Var. PENDULA.—The most remarkable but least ornamental of all the forms. Its branches are often pendulous and cord-like, but stiff, producing the branchlets in crowded clusters. Leaves slender, awl-shaped, $\frac{1}{3}$ in. long, produced in pairs or in threes. Although the foliage is of a juvenile type, this form occasionally produces fertile cones ; the seed giving ordinary Thuya orientalis.

T. PLICATA, *D. Don*. GIANT THUYA

(T. Craigiana, *Hort.* ; T. gigantea, *Nuttall* ; T. Lobbii, *Hort.* ; T. Menziesii, *Douglas*)

A tree up to 200 ft. high in a wild state, with a trunk sometimes 15 ft. in diameter at the buttressed base ; in cultivation a slender, pyramidal tree in some places already approaching 100 ft. in height. Unless close-planted it retains its branches to the ground, but is inclined to become thin at the top. Branches curving upwards at the ends, branchlets drooping, strong-smelling and slightly aromatic when crushed ; ultimate subdivisions $\frac{1}{16}$ to $\frac{1}{12}$ in. wide, flattened. Leaves dark glossy green, scale-like, $\frac{1}{12}$ to $\frac{1}{8}$ in. long ; the lateral ones the longer, with their edges infolded and overlapping the flatter ones above and below the twig ; they are all sharply pointed and have glaucous patches beneath. Cones egg-shaped, $\frac{1}{2}$ in. long ; scales about ten, with a small triangular boss just beneath the apex.

Native chiefly of British Columbia, Oregon, and Washington ; to a small extent also of California. Introduced by W. Lobb for Messrs Veitch in 1853, it has proved by far the handsomest and best growing of the thuyas. In gardens it is often grown as T. Lobbii and T. gigantea, but it was first given the name " plicata " by Don in 1824, ten years previous to Nuttall's name " gigantea " and thirty years before " Lobbii " came into use. To add to the confusion, Libocedrus decurrens was for long called " Thuya gigantea." T. plicata is distinguished from the E. American T. occidentalis by the glaucousness and comparative scarcity of glands beneath the branchlet, and by its much more rapid, cleaner growth. From T. japonica it differs in its denser habit, finer spray, and different odour. It is considered very promising as a forest tree in many parts of England.

Var. AUREA.—Much of the young growth yellow.

Var. GRACILIS.—Spray finer, and with smaller leaves.

Var. PYRAMIDALIS.—Of slender columnar form ; distinct, and worthy of cultivation.

Var. ZEBRINA.—Spray with curious patches of yellow interspersed with the ordinary green of the current year's shoots.

Young trees of Thuya plicata grown in large batches have been attacked by a parasitic fungus, *Botrytis cinerea*.

THYMELÆA NIVALIS, *Meissner*. THYMELÆACEÆ

(Passerina nivalis, *Ramond*)

A semi-prostrate evergreen shrub, 4 to 8 ins. high, with half woody, slightly hairy, unbranched shoots. Leaves densely arranged in whorls of threes (about seven whorls to the inch), stalkless, linear, $\frac{1}{3}$ to $\frac{1}{2}$ in. long, about $\frac{1}{10}$ in. wide, bluntish pointed, slightly hairy about the margins, dull greyish green, rather fleshy. Flowers solitary in each leaf-axil, stalkless, $\frac{1}{4}$ in. across, scarcely so long, yellow. Calyx tubular at the base, dividing at the top into four ovate lobes, two of which are conspicuously broader than the other two. Stamens yellow, eight, in two series of four, inserted near the apex of the calyx-tube; very shortly stalked.

Native of the Pyrenees. A pleasing little evergreen for the rock garden, flowering abundantly in March. It is closely allied to the daphnes, and has the same supple, tough shoots and corolla-like calyx. It has no true corolla. It is quite hardy in the rock garden at Kew. Closely allied to and sometimes regarded as a variety of T. tinctoria, *Endlicher*.

THYMUS. THYME. LABIATÆ

Small evergreen plants of an aromatic character, with a woody base. Leaves small, opposite, usually dotted with oil-glands. Flowers in axillary whorls or terminal. Corolla indistinctly two-lipped; calyx cylindric, with ten or more conspicuous ribs, five-toothed; stamens four. The following species are very hardy and thrive in light, sandy, or calcareous soils. Bees are very fond of the flowers.

T. SERPYLLUM, *Linnæus*. WILD THYME

(Syme's English Botany, t. 1043)

An evergreen sub-shrub forming dense tufts a few inches high, often with trailing rooting stems, woody only at the base; young shoots wiry, with two strips of white down running lengthwise on opposite sides, or downy pretty nearly all round. Leaves ovate or oval, blunt, $\frac{1}{8}$ to $\frac{1}{3}$ in. (sometimes $\frac{1}{2}$ in.) long, furnished beneath and at the margins with comparatively long white hairs, or sometimes glabrous; dotted with oil-glands. Flowering stems erect, bearing the rosy purple flowers in dense, rounded terminal heads $\frac{1}{2}$ in. wide. Corolla scarcely $\frac{1}{4}$ in. long; calyx similar to the leaves in hairiness. Blossoms in summer and early autumn.

Native of Europe, N. Africa, and W. Asia; it occurs abundantly all over Britain, even on the outlying islands of St Kilda, Orkney and Shetland of the north, and the Channel Islands of the south. It is the "wild thyme" of Shakespeare, always loved for its sweet scent. On the dry chalk downs it is usually very dwarf. Many varieties of it have been named, such as CITRIODORUS (lemon thyme); LANUGINOSUS with stems hairy all round, also on both sides of the leaves and the inflorescence; ANGUSTIFOLIUS with very narrow leaves; and ERICOIDES with very tiny ones.

T. CHAMÆDRYS, *Fries*, is nearly related to T. Serpyllum, of which it is sometimes regarded as a variety or sub-species. The leaves are larger as a rule and less hairy and the flowers come in elongated spikes up to 2 or 3 ins. long, instead of being almost confined to one terminal head. The flowering shoots are also taller. The flowers are larger and have the upper lip of the corolla shorter and more rounded. It is widely spread in Britain, but not so abundantly and ubiquitously as T. Serpyllum.

T. VULGARIS, *Linnæus*. GARDEN THYME

An evergreen shrub, much branched, 6 to 12 ins. high, with a woody base and slender, semi-herbaceous, greyish, downy young shoots. Leaves stalkless, $\frac{1}{4}$ to $\frac{1}{2}$ in. long, $\frac{1}{16}$ to $\frac{1}{8}$ in. wide, linear to ovate, toothless, grey downy, dotted with numerous oil-glands ; margins recurved. Flowers lilac-coloured or pale purple, opening from May to July in axillary whorls, the whole forming a terminal spike 1 to 2 ins. long and $\frac{1}{2}$ in. wide. Corolla about $\frac{1}{4}$ in. long ; calyx hairy, about as long as the corolla-tube, cylindric, with three very short triangular teeth and two longer, awl-shaped ones.

Native of S. Europe from Portugal to Greece, especially in the Mediterranean region ; also of Corsica and the Balearic Isles. It has been grown in Britain from ancient times chiefly as a flavouring herb and for its pleasant aromatic odour. Oil of thyme, produced from the plant by distillation, chiefly in the south of France, is used for scenting soaps and as a local external stimulant. According to Gerard, the herbalist, thyme taken internally has many virtues, some curiously diverse, such as being " good against winde in the belly " and " profitable for such as are fearfull melancholicke and troubled in minde." It is scarcely employed at all in English medicine to-day.

TILIA. LIME or LINDEN. TILIACEÆ

A genus of about thirty species of large or medium-sized, deciduous trees, with more or less zigzagged young shoots ; winter buds prominent. The inner bark is tough and fibrous, and that of some species is used for making rough ropes and mats. Leaves alternate, but set in two opposite rows on the branches, toothed, usually heart-shaped at the base. Flowers produced in summer on the shoots of the current year, in axillary, slender, long-stalked cymes. One of the most characteristic features of the genus is the large membranous bract, several inches long, to whose midrib the lower part (sometimes more than half) of the main flower-stalk is united, thus giving it the appearance of rising directly from the centre of the bract. The flowers are very uniform in the limes, being fragrant, $\frac{5}{8}$ to $\frac{3}{4}$ in. across, dull or yellowish white. Sepals and petals five. In several species (all the American ones) there are also five petal-like scales to which the base of the stamens is united. Fruit dry, nut-like, about the size of a pea, usually one-seeded.

The limes belong to the North Temperate Zone, but do not occur in western N. America or the Himalaya. They are all thriving trees in gardens, preferring a rich moist soil. Such species as euchlora and petiolaris ought to replace to a great extent the common lime. The American species are not of much account with us, but some of the Asiatic ones, like T. Oliveri, are promising.

As with all forest trees, the limes should, if possible, be raised from seed. Failing that, they may be raised from layers, or, in the case of named varieties, by grafts. Grafted plants, however, frequently make very unshapely trees. The graft is taken, as a rule, from side branches, with the distichous (or two-ranked) arrangement alluded to above. The leading shoot often retains this character for many years, and shows a tendency to grow horizontally rather than erect. Often, too, the stock grows in thickness less quickly than the scion, or *vice versa*, with the result that there is formed an unsightly break in the trunk.

There has been considerable confusion in gardens over the nomenclature of the limes, largely due to a great number of hybrid or intermediate types. They interbreed with great facility under brighter skies than ours.

A selection of the best limes would include the following : *euchlora*, *petiolaris*, *platyphyllos*, *tomentosa*, and *Moltkei*. Of a smaller type are *cordata*, *platyphyllos* var. *asplenifolia*, and *mongolica*.

T. AMERICANA, *Linnæus*. AMERICAN LIME

A tree usually 60 to 70 ft. high in a wild state (occasionally nearly twice as much), the trunk 9 to 12 ft. in girth ; young shoots quite glabrous. Leaves roundish ovate, usually heart-shaped at the base, occasionally cut off straight ; pointed at the apex ; 5 to 8 ins. long and 3 to 6 ins. wide on young trees, smaller on adult wild trees, coarsely toothed ; dark dull green above ; paler, shining, and quite glabrous beneath, except for minute tufts of down in the axils of the veins ; stalk 1½ to 2 ins. long. Flowers rarely seen in this country ; the floral bract is 4 to 5 ins. long, 1 to 1½ ins. wide ; the inflorescence pendulous on a stalk 3 to 4 ins. long ; flowers ¾ in. across, yellowish white.

Native of eastern and central N. America ; introduced, according to Aiton, in 1752. It is not one of the first-rate limes in this country, being apt to die back, and is chiefly noteworthy for the occasionally enormous leaves, as much as 15 ins. long by 10 ins. wide, that appear on thick, succulent shoots. From its allies, T. Michauxii and T. heterophylla, it is distinguished by the glabrous leaves, glossy green beneath. It probably needs a sunnier climate than that of Great Britain, and apparently flowers freely enough on the Continent, from the fact that several hybrids have originated there (see T. Moltkei and spectabilis). T. FLAVESCENS, *A. Braun*, cultivated at Carlsruhe as long ago as 1836, is believed to be a hybrid between this species and T. cordata.

T. CORDATA, *Miller*. SMALL-LEAVED LIME

(T. parvifolia, *Ehrhart* ; T. microphylla, *Ventenat* ; T. ulmifolia, *Scopoli*)

A tree sometimes 80 to 90 ft. high on the Continent, usually much smaller in Britain ; young shoots glabrous or nearly so. Leaves rounded, heart-shaped, 1½ to 3 ins. long, nearly or quite as much wide ; with a short tapered apex, sharply and rather finely toothed ; dark green and glabrous above ; pale, sometimes whitish beneath, with tufts of red-brown hairs in the axils of the veins ; stalks slender, glabrous, 1 to 1½ ins. long. Flowers yellowish white, fragrant, produced in the latter part of July in pendent, slender-stalked cymes 2 or 3 ins. long. Floral bract 1½ to 3½ ins. long, ⅜ to ¾ in. wide, glabrous. Fruit globose, covered (especially at first) with a loose greyish felt, not ribbed, thin-shelled.

Native of Europe, especially of the north, and found wild in Britain. It is not frequently planted in gardens, although it makes a neat slow-growing small tree, flowering after both T. platyphyllos and T. vulgaris. The finest trees I have seen are on the Continent ; one in the Grosser Garten at Dresden has a trunk 8 ft. in diameter near the ground, and is 80 to 90 ft. high. T. vulgaris differs from this species in its larger leaves, green, and with paler tufts beneath ; its earlier flowers ; and its thicker-shelled fruits.

There is in Japan a lime very closely allied to T. cordata ; it is T. JAPONICA, *Simonkai*, probably only a geographical form with more numerous (up to forty) flowers in a cluster.

T. EUCHLORA, *C. Koch*

(T. dasystyla, *Hort.*, not *Steven*)

A tree as yet about 50 ft. high in this country, but probably considerably higher naturally, of graceful, often rather pendulous growth ; young shoots glabrous. Leaves roundish ovate, oblique and heart-shaped at the base, with short, tapered points ; 2 to 4 ins. long, often more in young trees, and as much or more wide ; rich glossy green and glabrous above, pale green beneath and glabrous, except for tufts of hairs in the axils of the veins ; marginal teeth small, regular and slender ; stalk glabrous, 1 to 2 ins. long. Flowers produced in the latter half of July, three to seven together in cymes 2 to 4 ins. long, yellowish white. Floral bract linear-oblong, or narrowly lance-shaped, 2 to 3 ins. long, ¼ to ⅝ in. wide, glabrous, shortly stalked. Fruit distinctly ovoid, tapered to a point, shaggy, with pale brown wool, ¼ to ⅓ in. long.

Of doubtful origin ; introduced about 1860. In some respects this is the most beautiful of the limes on account of its bright green large leaves and pleasing form. It is remarkably free from insect pests. In the summer of 1909, when not only limes but nearly every other tree and shrub was infested with aphides and other pests, I examined specimens of this lime at intervals during the summer, and never found a single parasite on the leaves. Yet it is quite uncommon in this country. On the Continent, however, its qualities are better appreciated, and it is being much planted in streets. Its brilliantly glossy, rounded, nearly glabrous leaves and pendulous branches very well distinguish it. It has been suggested that it is a hybrid between T. cordata and the scarcely known T. caucasica found in the Caucasus.

T. HENRYANA, *Szyszylowicz*

A tree 30 to 50 ft. high, the branchlets at first stellately downy, ultimately glabrous.[1] Leaves obliquely and broadly ovate, heart-shaped or cut off straight at the base, shortly taper-pointed, 2 to 5 ins. long, 1½ to 3 ins. wide ; the margin set with bristle-like teeth ¹⁄₁₀ in. long, the midrib and veins downy above, the whole under-surface covered with dull brownish stellate down ; there are tufts of down in the vein-axils ; stalks 1 to 1½ ins. long. Flowers whitish, numerous (twenty or more), on cymes 4 to 6 ins. long ; floral bracts of similar length, ½ to ¾ in. wide, stellately downy, especially behind.

Native of Central China ; discovered by Henry in 1888 ; introduced for Messrs Veitch by Wilson in 1901, and quite hardy. It is distinct from all the species here mentioned in the almost hair-like teeth of the leaves.

T. HETEROPHYLLA, *Ventenat*

It is doubtful if there be any living trees of this lime in the British Isles ; what are cultivated under the name being usually T. Michauxi, which is believed to be a natural hybrid between T. americana and T. heterophylla, and in some of its forms closely approaches the latter. But, according to Sargent, T. heterophylla can always be distinguished by having no tufts of hairs in the vein-axils beneath the leaf. The leaves are always covered beneath with a close layer of silvery down. It is a tree 50 to 80 ft. high in a wild state, with a trunk 9 to 12 ft. in girth, and is a native of the eastern United States from New York to Alabama, reaching its largest size in the forests of the mountains of N. Carolina and Tennessee. Its leaves are 4 to 8 ins. long, with slender stalks up to 3½ ins. long. It is hardy in the Arnold Arboretum, Mass., but appears to have always been a neglected tree.

T. INSULARIS, *Nakai*

A deciduous tree 40 to 80 ft. high, with a grey-barked trunk 1 to 3 ft. in diameter ; young shoots glabrous or sparsely hairy. Leaves of firm texture, roundish ovate, sometimes almost kidney-shaped, coarsely toothed, rounded or shortly pointed, heart-shaped at the base ; 2 to 3½ ins. long, usually as wide or even wider than long ; glabrous except for tufts of pale down in the vein-axils; stalk 1 to 1½ ins. long. Flowers ½ in. wide, numerous on the cyme, borne on slender stalks, the bract 1½ to 2½ ins. long, ½ in. or more wide, not downy. The whole inflorescence is 3 to 4 ins. long ; fruit obovoid, $\frac{3}{10}$ in. long.

Native of Korea ; introduced to Kew from the Arnold Arboretum in 1924. It was collected by Wilson during his expedition to Korea in 1917. Except that it is quite hardy and grows well, little is as yet known of its qualities under cultivation.

T. INTONSA, *Rehder and Wilson*
(T. tonsura, *Hort. Veitch*)

A deciduous tree up to 65 ft. high, with a trunk up to 9 ft. in girth ; young shoots densely clothed with short, yellowish brown hairs, glabrous the second year. Leaves roundish heart-shaped, often obliquely so, terminated by a short abrupt point ; margins evenly and distinctly toothed ; 1½ to 4 ins. long, rather less wide ; glabrous above except for some minute hairs on the chief veins ; grey-green and densely clothed with starry down beneath, especially on the midrib and the seven to nine pairs of lateral veins ; there are also tufts of down in the vein-axils ; leaf-stalk 1 to 2 ins. long, downy. Flowers solitary or three on the cyme, yellowish white, the bract narrowly oblong, clothed with starry down, especially at the back, the flower-stalk united with it as far as the middle. Petals ⅛ in. long, $\frac{1}{10}$ in. wide. Fruit egg-shaped, ⅜ in. long, distinctly five-ribbed, covered with a pale close felt.

Native of W. Szechuen, China, where Wilson discovered it in 1903 and introduced it at the same time. It is quite hardy and grows well at Kew, where it has flowered and borne fruit. Its most distinctive character perhaps is the woolliness of its shoots and general downiness, to which the specific name (" unshorn ") refers. It promises to be of neat habit and is apparently one of the smaller lindens.

T. MANDSHURICA, *Ruprecht and Maximowicz*.
MANCHURIAN LIME

The only specimen I know of this lime in cultivation in Britain is a small tree at Kew, now about 45 ft. high. Like so many Manchurian trees and shrubs, it starts early into growth (before any other species), and is almost invariably cut back by spring frosts. It might prove a handsome tree in the south-western counties, but near London is of no value. It is described as growing 60 ft. high in Manchuria. Leaves (on the tree at Kew), 2½ to 6 ins. wide, the same or rather more long, heart-shaped, widely and coarsely toothed, with occasionally a lobe at the side ; green with a thin stellate down above, grey and with abundant stellate down beneath, but with no tufts in the vein-axils. Young shoots downy. It has never flowered at Kew, but on preserved wild specimens the floral bracts are 4½ ins. long, 1 in. wide, downy ; the fruit globose, warted, downy and not or indistinctly ribbed. Introduced to Kew in 1871.

T. MAXIMOWICZIANA, *Shirasawa*

A tree 70 to 100 ft. high ; young shoots downy. Leaves roundish ovate, 3 to 6 ins. long, scarcely as wide ; contracted at the apex to a short point, heart-shaped at the base, coarsely toothed ; dark green and slightly downy above, covered beneath with grey stellate down, and furnished with conspicuous tufts in the axils of the veins ; stalk 1½ to 3 ins. long. Flowers not seen in this country but described as being produced in clusters of ten to eighteen, the floral bracts 3 to 4 ins. long, downy. Fruit ⅔ in. long, ribbed.

Native of Japan ; sent to Kew by Prof. Sargent in 1890. It is a noble forest tree in Japan, but the few trees in Britain do not promise well, although they seem to be hardy. This lime differs from the others with starry pubescent leaves and branches in having tufts of brownish hairs in the vein-axils.

T. MICHAUXII, *Nuttall*

(T. heterophylla Michauxi, *Sargent*)

A deciduous tree, 70 to 80 ft. high in a wild state, with a trunk 6 to 9 ft. in girth ; young shoots and buds glabrous. Leaves broadly ovate, very variable in size, in adult specimens 4 to 8 ins. long, 3 to 6 ins. wide ; obliquely heart-shaped or rarely truncate at the base, taper-pointed, coarsely and sharply toothed, dark green and glabrous above, more or less covered with starry down beneath ; stalk 1½ to 2 ins. long. Floral bract narrowly obovate, 5 to 6 ins. long, downy above, glabrous below ; flowers yellowish, produced in a cyme at the end of a slender stalk, 1¾ ins. long. Fruit ⅛ in. long, felted, roundish oval.

Native of eastern N. America ; long in cultivation, but confused with T. americana, between which and T. heterophylla it is in most respects intermediate. From T. americana it is easily distinguished by the dull downy under-surface of the leaves, but the down is variable in amount. I have not seen it in flower in this country. It occasionally produces enormous leaves on young succulent shoots ; I have gathered them 17 ins. by 12 ins. Like T. americana, the branches are liable to die back. It is sometimes found in gardens under the name " T. pubescens," but the true T. PUBESCENS, *Aiton*, is not in cultivation, and probably not hardy.

T. MIQUELIANA, *Maximowicz*

A tree 40 ft. high, the young shoots, leaf-stalks, and especially the under-surface of the leaves covered with a dull grey felt. Leaves ovate, 2 to 5 ins. long, 1½ to 3½ ins. wide ; heart-shaped at the base, taper-pointed, coarsely toothed (sometimes lobed) ; dark glossy green above, without tufts in the vein-axils beneath. Flowers numerous, sometimes over twenty on the cyme ; floral bracts 3 to 4½ ins. long, ⅝ to ¾ in. wide, with scattered starry down. Fruit globose, felted, ⅜ in. long.

Not known in a wild state, but much planted in Japan near temples ; introduced to Kew in 1900. It is distinct among limes with a similarly felted under-surface in the long-pointed, ovate leaves. Among cultivated limes it keeps its leaves longer than any other, I have seen them quite green in mid-November. It is, however, possible that this character may disappear as the trees grow older. (E. China has lately been given as its native country.)

T. MOLTKEI, *Späth*. MOLTKE'S LIME

This tree was first noticed in Mr Späth's nursery, near Berlin, over sixty years ago, and was offered in his catalogue of 1883. He considered it to be a hybrid between T. americana and T. tomentosa, the former of which it resembles in the leaves, except that they are somewhat grey and downy beneath—a character presumably inherited from the silver lime. Later observers have, however, substituted as a parent in place of T. tomentosa, the pendulous, long-stalked T. petiolaris, from whose silvery leaves, of course, nearly similar characters would be inherited. Some years ago I saw a tree of T. Moltkei, which had been planted in 1888 by the famous field-marshal whose name it bears, in Mr Späth's grounds near a specimen of T. tomentosa planted by Bismarck. It has thriven remarkably well, and is a handsome pyramidal tree about 40 ft. high, of great vigour. Professor Sargent states that in the Arnold Arboretum a tree identical with the above has been raised from a seed of T. petiolaris, fertilised, it is assumed, by a tree of T. americana standing near.

Very similar to T. Moltkei is T. SPECTABILIS, *Dippel*, probably a hybrid between T. Michauxii and T. tomentosa. The leaves have the same grey-white, downy under-surface ; winter buds downy at the points.

T. MONGOLICA, *Maximowicz*. MONGOLIAN LIME

A tree about 30 ft. high, with smooth, reddish shoots. Leaves 1½ to 3 ins. long, about as much wide, maple-like in form, in young trees often three-lobed or obscurely five-lobed, the lobes and apex taper-pointed ; coarsely toothed, the teeth triangular with slender points ; glabrous and glossy above ; pale beneath, and glabrous except for conspicuous tufts of down in the vein-axils ; stalk about 1 in. long, glabrous, reddish. Flowers produced in late July, often numerous (sometimes thirty or more) on the cyme ; floral bract 2 to 3 ins. long, ½ in. wide. Fruit obovoid, downy.

Native of N. China and Mongolia ; introduced to the Jardin des Plantes at Paris in 1880. From this source all the trees in cultivation have been raised. I saw it in several continental establishments in 1904, and the plants then obtained for Kew represent, I believe, its first introduction to Britain. This lime is apparently very hardy, and has already flowered at Kew ; it promises to make a small elegant tree. The lobing of the leaf renders it very distinct in a young state, but this is evidently less marked in adult trees.

T. OLIVERI, *Szyszylowicz*

A tree 40 ft. high, with glabrous young shoots. Leaves roundish ovate, 3 to 4 ins. long, scarcely as wide ; abruptly taper-pointed, heart-shaped at the base, with short teeth at the margin ; dark green and glabrous above, pure white beneath with dense close felt ; axil-tufts of down absent ; stalk 1 to 2 ins. long.

Native of Central China ; discovered by Henry in 1888 in the province of Hupeh ; introduced by Wilson in 1900 for Messrs Veitch. The species is very promising. It is allied to T. tomentosa, but differs in its glabrous young shoots. Henry says that its flowers are similar to those of that species, but smaller. His specimens in the Kew Herbarium show the fruit to be oval or globose, $\frac{1}{3}$ to $\frac{1}{2}$ in. long, warted, white with down. The white under-surface of the leaves of this lime makes it distinct, and it is altogether a very attractive tree for smallish gardens.

T. ORBICULARIS, *Jouin*

This tree originated in the nursery of Messrs Simon-Louis, near Metz, about 1870. Mr E. Jouin, who described it and gave its history in *La Semaine Horticole*, 26th Aug. 1899, says that it was raised from a seed of T. petiolaris, and he offers the suggestion that it may be a hybrid between that species and T. euchlora. It much resembles T. petiolaris, but the leaves (of a very glossy green above) have shorter stalks, and the felt on the under-surface is grey rather than silvery. They remain on the trees until late October. The branches are pendulous, and, according to M. Jouin, the tree is of very vigorous growth and forms a conical head. Trees at Kew thrive admirably and give every indication of making fine specimens.

T. PAUCICOSTATA, *Maximowicz*

A small deciduous tree, the young shoots glabrous. Leaves very obliquely ovate, the base cut straight across in a slanting direction or slightly heart-shaped, the apex acuminate, margins conspicuously and fairly regularly toothed except at the apex and the base ; 2 to 3½ ins. long and 1½ to 2½ ins. wide in adult trees, much larger (up to 5 or 6 ins. long) in young, cultivated ones ; dull dark green and glabrous above, green beneath, and with tufts of rusty brown down in the axils of the veins, but not at the base, where the main veins join the leaf-stalk ; stalk glabrous, ¾ to 1½ ins. long. The cymes carry seven to fifteen flowers and the bract is glabrous, 2 to 3 ins. long. Fruit roundish or slightly obovoid and ribbed.

Native of N.W. China ; discovered in the province of Kansu by Potanin in 1875. The plant is believed to have been grown at Coombe Wood under the name " T. Miqueliana chinensis," having been introduced in 1901 by Wilson. The leaves of this plant, however, are more downy beneath, especially at the base of the blade, than in wild adult specimens. It appears to resemble most closely T. cordata in general aspect and differs much from ordinary T. Miqueliana.

T. PETIOLARIS, *De Candolle.* PENDENT SILVER LIME

(Bot. Mag., t. 6737 ; T. americana pendula, *Hort.*)

A round-topped tree, 60 to 80 ft. high at present in Britain, probably 100 ft. high ultimately, with pendulous branches and a singularly graceful habit ; young shoots downy. Leaves roundish ovate, heart-shaped or nearly straight across at the base, mostly oblique, pointed, regularly and sharply toothed ; 2 to 4½ ins. long, about three-fourths as wide ; dark green and slightly downy above, white with a close felt beneath ; stalk downy, up to 2½ ins. long. Flowers dull white, three to ten together in drooping cymes 2 to 3 ins. long. Floral bract as long as the cymes, narrowly obovate, sprinkled with minute tufted down. Fruit globose to orange-shaped, grooved, warty, ⅜ in. wide.

Of doubtful origin, but, if truly wild, a native no doubt of S.E. Europe. Some authorities consider it a garden form of T. tomentosa, which it resembles in some particulars, but is very distinct in its weeping habit, the long leaf-stalks, and the short, broad, grooved fruit. It appears to have been introduced to Britain about 1840, and was for long known in nurseries as " T. americana pendula "—a name which should be dropped, as the tree has not the least connection with T. americana, either botanically or geographically. One of the most beautiful of limes, it should be planted in place of the common lime, which is too abundant. There is a good specimen at Kew which flowers every year in late July and August, and whose fragrance

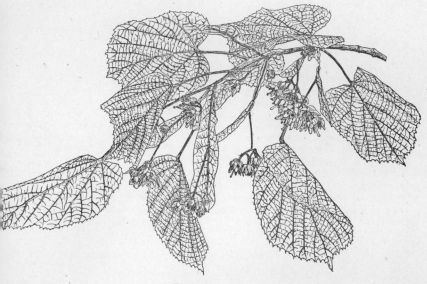

TILIA PETIOLARIS

is then perceptible yards away. Bees find something narcotic in the flowers, as they may be seen in the evenings lying in scores beneath the tree, and many do not recover.

T. PLATYPHYLLOS, *Scopoli*

A tree of the largest size, 100 ft. or more high, with a straight, clean trunk, and a shapely, rounded head of branches; young shoots downy. Leaves roundish heart-shaped, occasionally oblique, 2 to 5 ins. long, nearly or quite as much wide; shortly taper-pointed, sharply toothed, dark green and slightly downy above, densely so beneath, especially on the veins and midrib; stalk downy, ½ to 2 ins. long. Flowers yellowish white, produced in late June, usually in three- but sometimes six-flowered, lax, pendent cymes, 3 or 4 ins. long. Floral bracts 2 to 5 ins. long, ½ to 1¼ ins. wide; downy, especially on the midrib and behind. Fruit somewhat pear-shaped, ⅓ to ½ in. long, prominently five-ribbed, downy.

Native of Europe, especially the central and southern part. Although not so commonly grown in England as T. vulgaris, it is a more shapely and cleaner grown tree. The trunk does not produce the numerous swollen burrs covered with adventitious buds that are so characteristic of T. vulgaris. From T. vulgaris and T. cordata this lime is easily distinguished by its larger downy leaves, the downy shoots, and the larger five-ribbed fruit. These three limes, it may be mentioned, together constitute the T. europæa of Linnæus, T. cordata being the representative in N. Europe, T. platyphyllos in the south.

Numerous varieties of garden origin are offered in nurseries, of which the most notable are :—

Var. ASPLENIFOLIA (syns. laciniata and filicifolia).—A much smaller, denser-habited tree than the type, with the leaves raggedly, deeply, and irregularly lobed, often cut to the midrib into three or more long, narrow, deeply toothed divisions.

Var. AUREA.—Young branchlets golden yellow.

Var. FILICIFOLIA NOVA.—Leaves narrow-triangular, often irregularly lobed in the way of asplenifolia, but not so deeply.

Var. OBLIQUA.—In the south of Europe is found a form of T. platyphyllos, with glabrous shoots and much less downy leaves. It has been suggested that the lime known in gardens as T. obliqua may be that form. The leaves are very oblique at the base.

Var. PYRAMIDALIS.—Of pyramidal habit ;· possibly a wild form.

Var. TORTUOSA.—Young branches curiously curled and twisted, often forming loops. First shown at a meeting of the R.H.S. in December 1888.

Var. VITIFOLIA.—Leaves with several pointed, slender lobes standing out ½ to 1 in. beyond the average margin.

There is a worthless lime known in gardens as " T. sublunata variegata·" or " europæa variegata," which may belong to T. platyphyllos, or be a hybrid between it and T. cordata.

In S.E. Europe, T. platyphyllos is replaced by T. CORINTHIACA, *Bosc*, and, still farther east, in Persia, Armenia, and the Caucasus, by T. CAUCASICA, *Ruprecht*. Both are closely allied to it, but neither is in cultivation.

T. TOMENTOSA, *Moench*. SILVER LIME

(T. argentea, *De Candolle* ; T. alba, *Aiton*)

A tree 60 to 100 ft. high, usually of broadly pyramidal habit, and with rather stiff, erect branches ; young shoots woolly. Leaves 2 to 5 ins. long, about as wide, roundish, heart-shaped, or nearly straight at the base, shortly and slenderly pointed, frequently with small lobes at the margins as well as the sharp, sometimes double teeth ; dark green above and slightly downy at first ; silvery white with a close felt beneath ; stalks ¾ to 1½ ins. long, felted. Flowers dull white, produced in late July and early August in five-to ten-flowered cymes, 1½ to 2½ ins. long. Floral bract downy, rather longer than the cymes. Fruit ⅓ to ⅔ in. long, egg-shaped, with a short point, white with down and minutely warted, and faintly five-angled.

Native of S.E. Europe ; introduced in 1767. This tree, especially when fully grown, is handsome ; in the young and intermediate states it is stiff and rather formal in habit. It thrives admirably in the south of England, and some fine examples exist there, notably one at Albury about 100 ft. high. In a breeze this tree presents a lively aspect, through the flashing of the under-surface of the leaves as they are turned by the wind. It is not likely to be confused with any but the other limes whose leaves are silvery white beneath, viz., T. petiolaris and Oliveri. From the former it differs much in habit and in the short leaf-stalks ; and T. Oliveri has no down on the shoots.

T. TUAN, *Szyszylowicz*

A tree 40 to 50 ft. high, young branches glabrous, or soon becoming so. Leaves thin, 2½ to 5½ ins. long, 1½ to 3½ ins. wide ; broadly ovate with a very oblique, sometimes slightly heart-shaped base, apex slender-pointed ; margins distantly and minutely toothed towards the point, but quite entire at the lower half ; upper surface nearly glabrous, lower one covered with a close grey felt, and with small tufts in the vein-axils ; stalks slender, downy, 1 to 2½ ins. long ; floral bract 3 to 5 ins. long, ½ to ¾ in. wide, stellately downy. Native of W. China ; discovered by Henry in 1888. The specific term " Tuan " is the native Chinese name for all limes. Henry observes that the bark of this species is much used for making shoes.

T. VULGARIS, *Hayne.* COMMON LIME

(T. intermedia, *De Candolle* ; T. europæa, *Linnæus* (in part))

A tree reaching well over 100 ft., sometimes 130 ft. high ; young branches glabrous. Leaves 2½ to 4 ins. long, nearly as wide ; obliquely heart-shaped at the base, with a short, tapered apex, sharply toothed, dark green and smooth above, pale green beneath, with tufts of hairs in the main axils ; stalk slender, 1 to 2 ins. long, glabrous. Flowers yellowish white, fragrant, produced in pendent, slender-stalked cymes, 3 or 4 ins. long, during early July. Floral bracts 3 to 4½ ins. long, ½ to ⅞ in. wide ; slightly downy on the midrib at the back. Fruit roundish oval, the shell thick and tough with ribs only faintly showing.

This tree is of uncertain origin, but is now generally believed to be a hybrid between T. cordata and T. platyphyllos. It is the common lime of the British Isles, and one of the most popular of all trees for avenues, streets, gardens, and parks. It has the defect of dropping its leaves early, especially in dry summers, and is very subject to the attacks of aphides, whose excrement turns black on the leaves and renders them very unsightly in late summer. With better limes available, it is, I think, planted much more abundantly in towns and gardens in these days than its merits justify. Rarely producing fertile seed, it is propagated by layering from stools, and owing possibly to this process, now centuries old, it often has an objectionable propensity to form huge burrs on the trunk, that sprout into dense thickets of succulent shoots, which if not removed ultimately completely hide the trunk.

The common lime reaches to great age, and has the faculty of keeping alive for many years after the centre of the trunk has decayed. In consequence, many famous and historical trees and avenues exist, especially in cathedral towns and university cities. So far as I have seen, most of the large limes of Central Europe are T. cordata.

Several gall-producing insects infest the leaves, the commonest being one which produces the curious " nail-gall," a conical, pointed growth on the surface of the leaf, ¼ to ⅓ in. long. None of these pests appear to do much permanent damage.

The timber of the lime is useful for indoor purposes, being white and soft ; it is used in pianoforte manufacture. The inner bark is very tough, and furnishes the material out of which the well-known " bast " mats are made.

TORREYA. TAXACEÆ

A group of four species of evergreen trees, named in honour of Dr John Torrey, a famous American botanist. They are closely allied to Cephalotaxus *(q.v.)* and Taxus, and have opposite branchlets and linear, firm, sharp-pointed leaves terminated by a fine hard point, and arranged in opposite spreading ranks. Flowers unisexual, the sexes either on the same or separate trees (solitary examples have borne fertile seed in this country) ; the male flowers are solitary in the leaf-axils, and composed of six to eight whorls of stamens. Fruit egg-shaped, a thin, tough, fleshy layer enclosing a large, bony seed.

Like allied groups, the torreyas are of interest in representing on a few isolated spots—Florida, California, China, and Japan—a type of vegetation that in earlier geological periods occupied much of the earth's surface. They are, perhaps, of more scientific than horticultural interest, but T. nucifera and T. californica are well worth a place in warm, sheltered gardens. They like a good loamy soil, and the Floridan species is found on limestone. They should, if possible, be increased by seeds, failing which cuttings may be employed. T. TAXIFOLIA, *Arnott*, the " Stinking Cedar " of Florida, does not appear to be in cultivation.

T. CALIFORNICA, *Torrey*. CALIFORNIAN NUTMEG

(T. Myristica, *Hooker*, Bot. Mag., 4780)

A tree 50 to 70 ft. high in California (rarely 100 ft.), with a straight, erect trunk and whorled branches ; branches horizontal ; branchlets pendulous, bearing the leaves in two flattish ranks. Leaves spreading at angles of 45° to 70° to the twig ; 1½ to 3 ins. long, about ⅛ in. wide ; slightly convex, linear, with a slender spine-tipped point ; dark glossy green above ; yellowish green with a glaucous band of stomata each side the midrib beneath. The foliage as a whole is hard, stiff, and well armed by the needle-like points. Male flowers egg-shaped, ⅓ in. long, pale yellow. Fruit olive-like green, ultimately streaked with purple, about 1½ ins. long by 1 in. wide, a thin, resinous flesh covering the grooved shell of the seed.

Native of California, where it is widely spread, but not abundant ; introduced in 1851. This interesting and handsome tree appears to be best suited for the milder parts of the country, and one of the best specimens in the country is at Tregothnan, in Cornwall, 50 ft. high. It has, nevertheless, withstood 32° of frost at Kew, and, among other places, has borne fertile seed as far north as Orton Hall, Peterborough. Its foliage much resembles that of Abies bracteata, and is distinct in its length from the other species. In the south of England this tree deserves a wider trial than it has yet received. The popular name refers to the outward likeness of the seed to a nutmeg, but it has, of course, no similar qualities.

T. NUCIFERA, *Siebold and Zuccarini*

A tree in Japan occasionally 80 ft. high, oftener a shrub or small tree 20 to 30 ft. high ; in cultivation, so far as I have seen, always of a shrubby character, and not more than 10 or 12 ft. high. Young shoots green, becoming in succeeding years purplish and shining. Leaves linear, ¾ to 1¼ ins. long, ⅛ to 3/16 in. wide ; tapered at the upper part to a slender, stiff point ; very dark glossy green above, and with two glaucous stomatic strips beneath. The leaves (somewhat convex on the upper surface, stiff and hard in texture) are borne in two spreading ranks, which form a broad V-shaped channel. Fruits green, elliptical, 1 to 1⅛ ins. long, ¾ in. wide. They are occasionally borne in abundance at Kew.

Native of Japan ; first introduced in the eighteenth century. Prof. Sargent, who saw this tree 80 ft. high in Japan, says that " with their bright red bark and compact heads of dark green, almost black, lustrous foliage, they possess extraordinary beauty." The kernels of the nuts have an agreeable, slightly resinous flavour.

Nearly allied to the above is T. GRANDIS, *Fortune*, of which a few plants are in cultivation. There is a specimen about 18 ft. high at Kew which is quite hardy. Its leaves are shorter and thinner in texture than those of T. nucifera, and when crushed do not emit a pungent aromatic odour as in that species. This comparatively odourless character distinguishes it from all other torreyas. The tree was discovered in China by Fortune in 1855 ; it attains there the same height as T. nucifera does in Japan.

TRACHELOSPERMUM. APOCYNACEÆ

The two species grown out-of-doors are evergreen twining shrubs, with opposite, leathery leaves, and more or less hairy stems, exuding a milky juice when cut. Flowers in slender, stalked cymes, very sweetly scented. They both need wall protection, and may be grown in a light loamy soil. When young or newly planted, a little peat added is an advantage. Increased by July or August cuttings.

T. ASIATICUM, *Nakai*

(T. crocostemon, *Stapf* ; T. divaricatum, *Kanitz*)

An evergreen climber at least 15 ft. high, of dense, much branched habit ; the young shoots very hairy, and the hairs persisting more or less for several years. Leaves leathery, opposite, oval or slightly ovate ; ¾ to 2 ins. long, ⅜ to ¾ in. wide ; mostly blunt at the apex, dark glossy green, glabrous ; stalk ⅛ in. or less long. Flowers yellowish white, fragrant, produced in July and August in slender terminal cymes, 2 to 2½ ins. long. Corolla with a tube ⅓ in. long, and with five spreading obovate lobes, giving it a diameter of ¾ in. Calyx-lobes erect, narrow, pointed.

A native of Korea and Japan. All the plants in cultivation have originated from one which for many years has grown on the west wall of the herb garden at Kew, which often flowers with great profusion. It has smaller leaves and yellower flowers than T. jasminoides, and is readily distinguished when in flower by the erect calyx-lobes, which in T. jasminoides are larger and distinctly turned back. It has never been injured by any frosts of the last thirty years at Kew. (Syn. T. crocostemum *Stapf.* and our 1st Ed.)

T. JASMINOIDES, *Lemaire*

(Rhyncospermum jasminoides, *Lindley*, Bot. Mag., t. 4737)

An evergreen twiner, growing 10 or 12 ft. high, young shoots hairy. Leaves oval-lanceolate, 1½ to 3½ ins. long, ½ to 1 in. wide ; tapering at both ends, the tip blunt, downy beneath when young, becoming glabrous ; dark glossy green above ; stalk about ⅛ in. long. Flowers very fragrant, produced in July and August on glabrous, slender-stalked cymes, 1½ to 2 ins. long, usually on short lateral twigs. Corolla scarcely 1 in. across, pure white, five-lobed, the lobes spreading, wavy ; the tube ¼ in. long, narrowed towards the base. Calyx with five lanceolate reflexed lobes.

Native of China ; introduced by Fortune from Shanghai in 1844. Usually seen in greenhouses, where its flowers are prized for their fragrance, this species can also be grown on walls along the south coast and in the west.

Var. VARIEGATUM has shorter, broader leaves, bordered and blotched with creamy white.

TRACHYCARPUS FORTUNEI, *Wendland.* CHUSAN PALM.
PALMACEÆ (Plate 33)

(T. excelsa, *Wendland* ; Chamærops excelsus, *Martius,* not *Thunberg* ; C. Fortunei, *Hooker,* Bot. Mag., t. 5221)

This palm, which is the only species that can be termed really hardy in this country, varies in height according to the circumstances under which it is grown. In the Temperate House at Kew there is an example about 50 ft. high, but in the open air plants at least seventy years old are only about 12 or 15 ft. high. In the warmest counties, however, it is 25 to 30 ft. high. The stem is erect, cylindrical, clothed with coarse, dark, stiff fibres, which are really the disintegrated sheathing bases of the leaves. These fibres are employed by the Japanese and Chinese to make ropes and coarse garments. The leaves, which persist many years, are fan-shaped, $1\frac{1}{2}$ to $2\frac{1}{2}$ ft. long, $2\frac{1}{2}$ to 4 ft. wide, divided at the outside into numerous deep, narrow, folded segments, 2 ins. wide, tapering to a ragged point. The stalk is two-edged, and varies in length according to the age of the specimen and the conditions under which it is grown ; it is usually between 2 and 3 ft. long, and $\frac{1}{2}$ to 1 in. wide, with small jagged teeth on the margins. The flowers are borne in a large, decurved, handsome panicle from near the top of the stem among the younger leaves ; they are yellow, small, but very numerous. The panicles bear flowers usually of one sex only, the female ones being the smaller and less ornamental. Fruit a blue-black drupe about the size of a boy's marble.

Although the Chusan palm is perfectly hardy in the south and west of Britain, in so far as it will, when properly established, withstand a temperature of 32° or more of frost, it likes a spot screened from the north and east winds. Exposed to blasts from those quarters it will live, but has usually a miserable, battered appearance. When it was first experimented with in the open air it was usual to cover it with mats or branches, but this has been found to be unnecessary. On account of its slow growth in the open air when young, it is usually the practice to put out-of-doors plants which have already attained some size in the cool greenhouse, in order that an immediate effect may be produced. Such plants it is advisable to protect during severe (but only severe) weather for a few years. For the rest this palm likes a rich loamy soil. It is a gross feeder, and is much helped by an occasional thick top-dressing of cow-dung.

Native of Central China. Its first introduction to Europe has to be credited to Siebold, who sent seeds from Japan (where it is cultivated, but doubtfully indigenous) to Leyden in 1830. Not many germinated, but of the few that did, one was sent to Kew in 1836. In 1860 this plant was 28 ft. high, but no one suspecting its hardiness, it was grown in the tropical palmhouse. Fortune introduced plants and seeds in 1849, and it was with some of the plants so obtained that experiments were made in the open air—with such successful results.

In the garden at Leonardslee there is a very interesting palm obtained some years ago from Japan. Its leaves are smaller, stiffer, and not so prickly on the stalks as in ordinary T. Fortunei, and it produces suckers

freely. The flowers of this palm are like those of T Fortunei, and
Henry has named it var. SURCULOSA, but it is possibly the T. NANA,
Beccari (see *Webbia*, vol. iii., p. 187).

TRICUSPIDARIA. TILIACEÆ

A Chilean genus of two species, both evergreen shrubs or small trees,
with alternate leaves, and solitary, bell- or urn-shaped flowers produced
on pendulous, thickened stalks from the leaf-axils. They both delight
in a cool, moist, peaty soil, or loam, and can be increased by cuttings
of half-ripened wood placed in a close frame with gentle bottom heat.
Excellent and attractive shrubs in the milder counties, they need protection near London.

T. DEPENDENS, *Ruiz and Pavon*

(Bot. Mag., t. 8115 ; Crinodendron dependens, *C. K. Schneider*)

An evergreen shrub or small tree, up to 30 ft. high, the young shoots
reddish and faintly downy. Leaves oval or ovate, 1 to 3 ins. long, ½ to 1½ ins.
wide ; shallowly and rather coarsely toothed, dark green and glabrous above,
much paler beneath ; stalk reddish, ⅛ to ¼ in. long, slightly hairy. Flowers
white, bell-shaped, ¾ in. long, produced singly on a pendulous stalk 1 to
2 ins. long, from the leaf-axils. Corolla of five rather fleshy petals, which
are three-toothed at the ends, downy at the margins, oblong.
Native of Chile ; introduced by Mr H. J. Elwes in 1901. Its name was
for a long time wrongly attached to its fellow species in gardens. It appears
to thrive better than T. lanceolata as a wall shrub at Kew, but is considered
to be more tender in the open in Ireland. It is certainly a much more rapid
grower. On a wall at Kew it has stood quite uninjured for several winters,
and blossoms freely in late summer. It is very distinct from T. lanceolata in
its white, more bell-shaped flowers. Easily increased by cuttings.

T. LANCEOLATA, *Miquel*

(T. dependens, *Hort.*, Bot. Mag., t. 7160 ; T. hexapetala, *Turczaninow* ;
Crinodendron Hookerianum, *Gay*)

An evergreen shrub or small tree, up to 10 or 30 ft. high, sometimes more,
of a stiff, bushy growth ; young wood felted with grey down. Leaves oblong-
lanceolate, pointed ; 1½ to 5 ins. long, ½ to 1¼ ins. wide ; coarsely toothed
except towards the tapering base, dark green above and downy on the midrib,
paler beneath and downy on the midrib and chief veins, stiff and hard in
texture ; stalk ¼ in. or less long, downy. Flowers produced singly from the
terminal leaf-axils each on a stout, stiff, downward-pointing, stalk 2 to 3 ins.
long. Corolla urn-shaped, 1 to 1¼ ins. long, rich crimson, very fleshy, grooved,
toothed at the narrow mouth ; calyx downy.
Native of Valdivia, Llanquihue, and the Island of Chiloe in Chile ;
introduced by William Lobb for Messrs Veitch in 1848, and for the same
firm by Pearce about ten years later. It thrives best in such places as the Isle
of Wight, Cornwall, Ireland, and the west of Scotland, and where it succeeds
it is one of the most attractive of all shrubs. At Kilmacurragh, Co. Wicklow,
it was 26 ft. high. It has the curious habit of pushing out its flower-stalks in
autumn, but the flowers do not open until the following May. It likes a partially

shaded spot ; the leaves are often " scorched " and brown at the margins when the plant stands fully exposed to sunshine or wind. This species was long grown in gardens as " T. dependens." The two species are very distinct in shape of leaf and colour of flower.

TRICUSPIDARIA LANCEOLATA

TRIPATELEIA. ERICACEÆ

A genus of two Japanese deciduous shrubs closely related to the N. American Elliottia, with which Bentham and Hooker united it, also to Cladothamnus. From both these genera Tripetaleia is distinguished by the flower having usually three petals only. Elliottia, moreover, has eight stamens to a flower whilst this genus has only six. Both species will succeed under conditions suitable for rhododendrons.

T. BRACTEATA, *Maximowicz*

(Elliottia bracteata, *Bentham and Hooker*)

A deciduous shrub 3 to 6 ft. high, with glabrous, pale brown young shoots. Leaves alternate, obovate, tapered towards the base, mostly rounded at the apex or tapered to a short mucro, entire ; 1 to 2 ins. long, $\frac{3}{8}$ to 1 in. wide, quite glabrous on both surfaces; stalk $\frac{1}{8}$ in. or less long. Racemes erect, terminal on the current year's leafy twigs, slender, 3 to 6 ins. long, bearing the flowers at intervals of ¼ to ½ in., each on a slender stalk ¼ to ⅜ in. long. Each flower springs from the axil of an oval or obovate, leafy, ciliate bract ¼ in. long and there are also smaller bracts on the individual flower-stalk. Petals white, tinged with pink, usually three but sometimes four or even five, narrow-oblong, ⅜ in. long, recurved at the end ; sepals usually five, narrowly oval, $\frac{3}{16}$ in. long ; stamens six. Style stout, standing out ⅜ in. above the petals and strongly curved. Seed-vessel a dry, usually three-valved capsule, ¼ in. wide.

Native of Japan. This shrub has been in intermittent cultivation at Kew and probably elsewhere during the last forty years, but it is quite uncommon. It was growing in the Arnold Arboretum in 1910. It flowered during July and August when grown at Kew and the copious racemes made it worth growing. It is easily distinguished from the following species by its glabrous foliage, its racemose (not paniculate) inflorescence furnished with larger, more conspicuous bracts, and by the larger segments of the calyx. (Syn. Botryostege bracteata, *Stapf*.)

T. PANICULATA, *Siebold and Zuccarini*

(Elliottia paniculata, *Bentham and Hooker*)

A deciduous shrub 3 to 6 ft. high, with angled young shoots. Leaves lanceolate to narrowly ovate or obovate, entire, pointed, tapered at the base to a short stalk ; upper surface dark dull green and glabrous except along the midrib ; lower surface pale green and glabrous except for copious white hairs on the midrib and base of the veins ; chief veins in two or three pairs. Flowers borne on erect panicles 2 to 6 ins. high, commencing to open in July and continuing until September. They are terminal on the young leafy shoots. The flowers are white, tinged with pink, and have three (occasionally four or five) linear-oblong petals ⅜ in. long ; calyx cup-shaped ; style slender, ⅜ in. long, glabrous, standing out horizontally well beyond the petals. The bracts on the flower-stalks are small and linear.

Native of Central Japan and of Yesso, where it was collected by Maries about 1877. It had, however, been known as long before as 1840, when Siebold described it. It has several times been introduced but has not been successfully established at Kew. It is probably more amenable to cultivation than T. bracteata but neither has sufficient beauty to have induced cultivators in general to study their needs very closely. The numbers of the various parts of the flower are curious and unusual ; thus we may see a flower with three spreading petals, a five-lobed calyx and six stamens.

TRIPTERYGIUM. CELASTRACEÆ

A genus of two or three species of shrubs deciduous and more or less scandent. Leaves large, alternate ; flowers small in terminal panicles ; petals and stamens five ; calyx five-lobed. The name refers to the three-winged fruit. Both species are easily cultivated in good loamy soil.

T. REGELII, *Sprague and Takeda*

A deciduous shrub of rambling or climbing habit, with angular, warted stems. Leaves alternate, oval or ovate, broadly wedge-shaped to rounded at the base, tapered at the apex to a long and slender point ; 2½ to 6 ins. long, 1½ to 4 ins. wide ; the margin set with rounded, blunt, incurved teeth ; dark green above, and except for minute down on the midrib when quite young ; stalk $\frac{1}{4}$ to $\frac{3}{4}$ in. long. Flowers yellowish white, about $\frac{1}{3}$ in. wide, produced in a panicle at the end of the shoot, supplemented by clusters in the axils of the terminal leaves, the whole forming an inflorescence up to 8 or 9 ins. long and 2 or 3 ins. wide ; petals five, roundish obovate ; calyx small, with five rounded lobes ; stamens five. Fruit three-angled, each angle conspicuously winged ; the wings erect, about $\frac{5}{8}$ in. long, $\frac{1}{4}$ in. wide, membranous. The whole inflorescence is covered with short brown felt.

Native of Japan, Korea, and Formosa ; discovered in 1858 by Wilford, the Kew collector ; introduced by Mr J. G. Jack to the Arnold Arboretum in 1905, thence to Kew, where it is apparently fairly hardy but slow-growing. In foliage it resembles Celastrus, but is very distinct in the fruit, which is more like that of wych elm with an extra wing. The flowers are said to be sweetly scented.

T. WILFORDII, *Hooker fil.*
(Bot. Mag., t. 9488 ; T. Forrestii, *Loesener*)

A deciduous scandent shrub from 10 to 40 ft. high in a wild state ; young shoots often long and unbranched, angular, downy. Leaves alternate, oval or ovate, mostly rounded at the base, contracted at the apex to a short, slender point, finely toothed ; 2 to 5 ins. long, about half as much wide ; glabrous above, sometimes downy beneath on part of the midrib and stalk ; the stalk $\frac{1}{2}$ in. or less in length. Flowers very small, whitish, produced in a terminal panicle 6 ins. long, flower-stalks thickly covered with pale brown down. Fruit three-winged, $\frac{5}{8}$ in. long and wide, the wings thin and membranous like the wings of an elm fruit, chocolate brown and yellowish.

Native of Yunnan ; discovered by Forrest in 1906. I have not seen its living flowers and there is some variation in the description of their colour as given by collectors. Forrest describes them in the type specimen (No. 4290) as " greenish brown," but in Nos. 24753 and 24319 as " creamy white " and " grey yellow " respectively. Judging by the fine panicles of fruit, which may be 6 or 7 ins. long and 3 ins. or more in diameter and which Forrest describes as " dull purplish crimson," this shrub should give a striking effect in autumn. There is a fine plant 20 ft. high in the cool rhododendron house at Exbury, Hants, but it should be hardy in the milder parts of the country at any rate.

The plant figured in the Botanical Magazine, quoted above, flowered and bore fruit at Caerhays. Its nomenclature is very involved as is shown by the list of synonyms accompanying the plate which consists of eight species in four genera.

TROCHODENDRON ARALIOIDES, *Siebold and Zuccarini.*
TROCHODENDRACEÆ
(Bot. Mag., t.7375)

An evergreen glabrous shrub of rather spreading habit in this country, becoming a small tree 15 to 30 ft. high in the mountain forests of Yezo and the main island of Japan, where it is indigenous. Leaves rhododendron-like, 3 to 5 ins. long, narrowly oval or lanceolate, leathery, shallowly toothed at the upper end, lustrous green ; leaf-stalks half the length of the blade. Flowers produced from April to June in erect, terminal racemes, each flower on a slender stalk 1 or $1\frac{1}{2}$ ins. long. There are no sepals or petals, and the numerous stamens are set round the edge of a green hemispherical disc, which is really the calyx-tube. Across the stamens the flower is ¾ in. in diameter. Carpels about ten, arranged in a ring within the stamens.

The only known representative of its genus, this shrub gives the name to a small and peculiar natural order once united with Magnoliaceæ. T. aralioides is a handsome-foliaged shrub, interesting as well as striking when in blossom, its flowers being a vivid green. First introduced from Japan by Messrs Veitch, in whose nursery at Coombe Wood it bore its green flowers for the first time in 1894. It likes a moist loamy or peaty soil.

TROCHODENDRON ARALIOIDES

TSUGA. HEMLOCK FIRS. CONIFERÆ

A group of eight or ten evergreen trees of great beauty and elegance, represented on both sides of N. America, in China, Japan, and the Himalaya. They have very slender twigs, and short linear leaves, arranged, except in one species (T. Pattoniana), mainly in two opposite ranks, each leaf seated on a cushion-like projection (as in Picea), and closely set on the twigs—twelve to twenty-four to the inch. Cones solitary, rarely more than 1 in. long, and usually pendulous at the end of the twigs. Seeds winged. In places where they thrive, which is where the rainfall is abundant and the soil is deep and well-drained, they are not exceeded in beauty of form by any other evergreen trees. They are best propagated by means of seed ; but the Japanese and Chinese species, perhaps the others also, can be propagated by cuttings.

T. ALBERTIANA, *Sénéclauze.* WESTERN HEMLOCK (Plate 34)
(T. heterophylla, *Sargent*)

A tree up to 200 ft. high, of pyramidal habit, with a reddish brown trunk 4 to 6 ft. in diameter ; young shoots very slender and leafy, downy with intermingled hairs, which are still perceptible on shoots five or six years old. Leaves ¼ to ⅞ in. long, 1/16 to 1/12 in. wide ; linear, of uniform width, rounded at the ends, shortly stalked, toothed at the margins ; glossy dark green above, the midrib sunken ; nearly covered beneath with dull grey-white stomata.

Cones not stalked, oblong-conical, ¾ to 1 in. long, ½ in. wide before expanding
scales broadly obovate, rounded, often with a minute, velvety down on the
outer surface.

Native of western N. America from California to Alaska ; introduced
in 1851. It thrives remarkably well in good soil and a moist climate, such
as W. Wales, Devonshire, and in Perthshire, where there are many fine
specimens exceeding 100 ft. in height. It always forms a graceful, tapering
conical tree with the extremities of the branches drooping, and is one of the
most pleasing of evergreens ; but it is worthless on dry hungry soil. The
distinctions between this species and T. canadensis are noted under the latter

T. BRUNONIANA, *Carrière*. HIMALAYAN HEMLOCK

(T. dumosa, *Eichler*)

A tree 120 ft. high in a wild state, of cedar-like habit, with spreading
branches pendulous at their extremities ; young shoots downy on the upper

TSUGA BRUNONIANA

side. Leaves linear, ½ to 1⅓ ins. long, 1/16 to 1/12 in. wide ; tapered at the apex,
shortly stalked, minutely toothed ; dark green above, with the midrib deeply
sunk, the lower surface silvery white, being almost entirely covered with
stomata. Cones not stalked, egg-shaped, ¾ to 1 in. long ; scales roundish,
downy at the base outside.

Introduced in 1838 from the Himalaya, where, twelve years later, Sir Joseph Hooker found it with a trunk sometimes 28 ft. in girth. In this country, according to Elwes, the best specimen is at Boconnoc, in Cornwall—about 55 ft. high. The finest I have seen is at Fota, a beautiful rounded bushy tree about 45 ft. high and through, feathered to the ground with its graceful branches. At Dropmore there is also a good example. But the species is only adapted for the milder parts of the British Isles. At Kew it has time after time been destroyed by frost. Of all the hemlock firs it is the one whitest beneath the leaf; this character, with its downy shoots and toothed leaves, will enable it to be recognised.

T. CANADENSIS, *Carrière*. CANADIAN HEMLOCK

(Abies canadensis, *Michaux*)

A tree 70 to 100 ft. high, with a trunk 6 to 10 ft. in girth, and a head of often rounded form; bark reddish brown; young shoots bright grey, minutely hairy. Leaves very shortly stalked, $\frac{1}{4}$ to $\frac{2}{3}$ in. long, linear, but often broadest ($\frac{1}{16}$ to $\frac{1}{12}$ in.) near the rounded base, tapering thence to a bluntish point; margins toothed; dark green above, with a clear, well-defined band of stomata each side the midrib beneath. The leaves are mainly in two opposite, spreading ranks, but there are also smaller leaves on the upper side of the branchlet pointing forward, flattened to the branchlet, often inverted and showing the white-lined lower surface. Cones $\frac{1}{2}$ to $\frac{7}{8}$ in. long, oval, borne on a short downy stalk; the scales broadly obovate, about as wide as long, minutely downy except on the exposed part.

Native of eastern N. America; introduced early in the eighteenth century. This beautiful tree thrives very well in the moister parts of our islands, especially where the soil is good and retentive of moisture. There are good specimens in the west of England, and I have also seen excellent ones at Murthly, and elsewhere in Perthshire. The tree as grown in this country has a strong propensity to branch into several stems near the ground, and to form a large rounded head of branches very distinct from the slenderly tapered form of T. Albertiana. From that species it is also distinct in the usually (not invariably) tapered leaf, in the much more clearly defined, whiter lines beneath, and in the cones being shortly stalked (stalkless in Albertiana). Visitors to Boston, Mass., have an opportunity of conveniently inspecting a primæval wood of hemlock, which covers one of the hills in the beautiful Arnold Arboretum near that city. Here they have formed clean straight trunks, one of which (it may not have been the largest) I found in 1910 to be over 9 ft. in girth.

Several varieties of the hemlock fir are cultivated, but none except var. pendula possesses any particular merit.

Var. ARGENTEA (albo-spica).—Tips of the young shoots white.

Var. FRIENDII.—Habit stiff and pyramidal.

Var. PARVIFOLIA.—A thin-habited tree of little beauty, with tiny leaves $\frac{1}{4}$ in. long, not or very slightly toothed.

Var. PENDULA.—A very attractive shrub or small tree forming a hemi-spherical mass of pendulous branches, completely hiding the interior.

Var. PROSTRATA.—I saw this perfectly prostrate variety of the Canadian hemlock in the garden of Mr Renton, Branklyn, Perth, in June 1931. It is quite distinct in habit from Sargent's hemlock, which forms a compact pendulous-branched shrub 6 ft. or more high.

Var. SARGENTII.—Another pendulous form of more compact shape than the preceding. Found about 1870 in the Fishkill Mountains, New York.

T. CAROLINIANA, *Engelmann.* CAROLINA HEMLOCK

(Gardeners' Chronicle, 1886, ii., fig. 153)

A tree usually 50 to 80 ft. high ; young shoots glossy, pale brown, downy on the upper surface. Leaves linear, ¼ to ¾ in. long, mostly of uniform width, rounded, and sometimes slightly notched at the apex ; margins not toothed ; dark green above, with two bands of stomata beneath. The lower leaves spread in two opposite ranks, but the shorter ones on the upper side the branchlets are more or less erect. Cones shortly stalked, 1 to 1½ ins. long ; scales oblong, considerably longer than wide.

Native of the south-eastern United States, where it has a restricted habitat ; introduced to Kew in 1886 from the Arnold Arboretum ; first discovered in a wild state in 1850. It has never succeeded really well, although capable of withstanding severe cold. It is easily distinguished from both canadensis and Albertiana by the much less downy twigs and by the entire leaves of adult plants. Seedling plants have them toothed.

T. CHINENSIS, *Pritzel.* CHINESE HEMLOCK

(Bot. Mag., t. 9193)

A tree 6 to 8 ft. high whose young shoots are furnished, especially on the upper side, with dense, short down. Leaves ⅓ to ⅞ in. long, $\frac{1}{12}$ in. wide, linear or slightly tapered towards the apex, minutely toothed on the margin (at least on young cultivated plants), dark glossy green above ; paler beneath, with two narrow, rather slim bands of white stomata ; stalk $\frac{1}{20}$ in. long. Cones stalkless, erect, ovoid to globose, the scales bright as if varnished.

Native of Szechuen in W. China ; discovered by Père Farges ; introduced about 1903 by Wilson, who found it at 9-11,000 ft. altitude. Adult trees have entire leaves. The plants in cultivation are thriving well ; one at Borde Hill, Sussex, had a head of branches 25 ft. across in July 1939.

T. DIVERSIFOLIA, *Masters.* JAPANESE HEMLOCK

(Abies Tsuga nana, *Hort.*)

A tree 70 or 80 ft. high in Japan, with red trunks 6 or 7 ft. in girth ; young shoots downy. Leaves ¼ to ⅝ in. long, $\frac{1}{16}$ to $\frac{1}{12}$ in. wide ; linear, and of uniform width, margins not toothed, distinctly notched at the apex, abruptly tapered to a short stalk at the base ; dark glossy green above, with two clearly defined white lines of stomata beneath. Cones egg-shaped, ½ to ¾ in. long.

Confined in a wild state to Japan, whence it was introduced in 1861 by John Gould Veitch, and subsequently distributed by his firm as Abies Tsuga (or Sieboldii) nana. It is still found under that name in many gardens. It is at once distinguished from T. Sieboldii by its closer habit and downy shoots, its shorter leaves, and by always commencing to grow earlier in spring. It is a neater, smaller tree in gardens than T. Sieboldii, although Sargent observes (*Forest Flora of Japan,* p. 81) that in the great forest of it covering the Nikko mountains at 5000 ft. altitude, it grows to great size. T. Sieboldii has a more southern habitat. On account of its dainty habit (it is more a shrub than a tree with us) it makes a very pleasing lawn plant, especially in spring, whilst the young twigs are still bright yellow-green.

T. Pattoniana, *Sénéclauze*. Patton's Hemlock

(T. Hookeriana, *Carrière* ; T. Mertensiana, *Sargent*)

A tree 70 to over 100 ft. high, the trunk 12 ft. or more in girth ; bark red-brown ; young shoots downy. Leaves shortly stalked, set all round the branchlet, although more crowded on the upper side, linear, curved ; $\frac{1}{2}$ to 1 in. long, $\frac{1}{20}$ to $\frac{1}{16}$ in. wide ; rounded at the apex, margins not toothed ; sometimes grey-green, sometimes conspicuously blue-green. There are inconspicuous lines of stomata on both surfaces. Cones without stalks, rich purple when young, becoming red-brown ; oval-cylindric, 1$\frac{1}{2}$ to 3 ins. long, $\frac{1}{2}$ to $\frac{3}{4}$ ins. thick. Native of western N. America from Alaska to California ; introduced by Jeffrey in 1854. It is distinguished from all other tsugas by having stomata on both surfaces of the leaf. There has arisen much confusion in regard to the naming of this tree. It is represented in cultivation by two forms—one of a beautiful blue glaucous tint, which in gardens is usually called " Hookeriana " ; the other of a darker greener shade, and called " Pattoniana." The tree, however, originally called " Abies " Pattoniana, appears to have been the blue form, which is commonest in a wild state. There is no doubt they belong to the same species, as there are intermediate degrees of blueness. The confusion in the naming of this tree has been increased by the adoption of the name " Mertensiana " (given to it by Bongard in 1832 in conjunction with Pinus) by American authors. " Tsuga Mertensiana," *Carrière*, has been much used in late years for T. Albertiana.

In all its forms, but more especially the blue one, this tree is remarkably beautiful. It likes a moist climate and a pure atmosphere. At Murthly Castle, near Perth, there is a group of several trees (one with pendulous branchlets) which makes one of the most beautiful garden pictures one can imagine, produced by foliage alone. I saw them in 1906, when they ranged from 40 to 50 ft. in height.

Besides the greenish grey and glaucous forms of T. Pattoniana there is a third form, which has green leaves, less than $\frac{1}{2}$ in. long, minutely toothed, and with the stomatic lines on the upper side imperfectly developed (see article by A. Murray in *The Garden*, 19th Sept. 1874). Henry has called this var. Jeffreyi, and says it is only known in cultivation. According to Rehder it is a hybrid between Pattoniana and Albertiana.

T. Sieboldii, *Carrière*. Siebold's Hemlock

(Abies Tsuga, *Siebold*)

A tree up to 100 ft. high in Japan, with a trunk 9 ft. or more in girth ; but only a small bushy tree with us, although a very elegant one ; young shoots perfectly glabrous. Leaves linear, of uniform width, $\frac{1}{3}$ to 1 in. long, $\frac{1}{16}$ to $\frac{1}{10}$ in. wide, rounded and distinctly notched at the apex, not toothed, abruptly narrowed at the base to a short stalk ; rich glossy green above, with two clearly defined white lines of stomata beneath. Cones $\frac{3}{4}$ to 1 in. long, egg-shaped ; scales rounded.

Confined in a wild state to Japan, whence it was introduced about 1853. Although slow-growing and not in the least likely to make a large tree in this country, the grace and beauty of Siebold's hemlock fir makes it well worth cultivation. It is admirable for some sheltered nook on a lawn, where the soil is good and well-drained. Distinguished among tsugas by the entire margins of the leaf, and glabrous shoots.

The shrub known in gardens as T. Sieboldii nana appears to be T. diversifolia. I know of no dwarf form of the true Sieboldii.

T. YUNNANENSIS, *Masters*. YUNNAN HEMLOCK

An evergreen tree 60 to 150 ft. high, with a trunk up to 20 ft. in girth young shoots reddish grey furnished with stiff down. Leaves up to ¾ in. long ¹⁄₁₆ in. wide, rounded or shortly pointed and not notched at the apex ; margin not or very obscurely toothed ; dark glossy green above, with two broad, very white stripes beneath ; grooved above, midrib prominent beneath ; stalk very short. Cones dull coloured, egg-shaped, ¾ in. long, not stalked ; scales of fibrous texture, finely ribbed lengthwise.

Native of Yunnan and W. Szechuen, China ; originally discovered by the Abbé Delavay ; introduced in 1908. It is nearly akin to T. chinensis and has been confused with it, but that species has yellowish or yellowish-grey young shoots, leaves notched at the apex and with dull inconspicuous lines of stomata beneath ; its lustrous cones are also distinct. The Himalayan T. Brunoniana is another near relative with leaves of similarly conspicuous whiteness beneath, but up to 1⅜ ins. long. The true T. yunnanensis appears to be quite rare, but a fine young plant was shown by the Marquis of Headfort from his collection in Co. Meath at the Conifer Congress of 1931. It was also growing in the late Lt.-Col. Stephenson-Clarke's fine collection at Borde Hill in Sussex.

ULEX. LEGUMINOSÆ

A genus of very spiny shrubs allied to the brooms, but differing in having the calyx as well as the petals yellow. Only three species, all natives of England, are worth cultivating ; several others, mostly found in Spain and Portugal, are too tender to be of any value. The leaves are small and spine-tipped, often reduced to mere prickles ; and all the species have the quality of evergreens, from the dark green of their spines and branches.

In gardens they are often useful for covering dry sunny banks or breadths of poor gravelly soil, where most shrubs would not thrive. In such places the double-flowered variety of U. europæus is particularly effective in spring. The two other species have a value in flowering in late summer and autumn. None of them will thrive in shade, and they are never satisfactory in rich soil ; in either case flowers will be sparsely borne, and the plants apt to get lank and ungainly. Where the soil is of good quality it is advisable not to dig it over when planting, with the view of keeping it as hard as possible. Propagation by cuttings is referred to under the notice of U. europæus plena. Seeds should be sown singly in small pots and the plants put in their permanent places at their first planting, for they transplant badly. The common gorse should be sown *in situ*. The three hardy species are easily differentiated as follows :—

1. SPRING-FLOWERING

U. *europæus*.

2. AUTUMN-FLOWERING

U. *Gallii*. Spines stiff and long ; wing-petals long.
U. *nanus*. Spines slender ; wing-petals short.

U. EUROPÆUS, *Linnæus.* GORSE, FURZE, WHIN

A shrub usually 2 to 4 ft. high as seen wild, but occasionally 6 ft. or even more high ; excessively spiny. The main branches are hairy, and from them spring numerous short side branches which grow horizontally and always end in a stout, sharp spine, the whole forming an intricate formidable mass. Leaves simple, ¼ to ½ in. long, linear, sharply pointed or reduced to mere spines. Flowers produced singly from the leaf-axils of the previous year's shoots, on hairy stalks ¼ in. long, transforming the end of the branch into a brilliant raceme of gold. Calyx large, hairy, yellow like the petals, persistent. Pod ⅝ in. long, covered with brown hairs, two- or three-seeded.

Native of W. and Central Europe, and abundant in the British Isles, where it covers thousands of acres of moor, common, and heath. Whilst April and early May is the time when the gorse is in its full beauty, it commences to flower in February, and odd flowers may be found at almost all times—a characteristic on which is based the country saying, " When furze is out of bloom, then is kissing out of fashion." There is but little use for the gorse in gardens. It may be employed for covering dry banks, but even there the double-flowered variety described below is much to be preferred.

Var. PLENUS. Double-flowered Gorse.—In this variety the stamens disappear from the flower, either partially or entirely, and are replaced by petals of varying size. The variety does not produce seed, and must be propagated by cuttings, which should be made of the current season's wood in August, 3 or 4 ins. long, and placed in a cold frame in very sandy soil, and kept close. They will commence to root and grow the following spring. When the roots are 1 in. long, the young plants should be potted in 3-in. pots, ready for planting out whenever required the following winter. It is lower-growing and more compact in habit than the type, and is in every way superior to it as an ornamental shrub for gardens, lasting longer in flower. Like common gorse, it needs a dry, hungry soil and a sunny position to develop its full beauty. In rich soil it grows rank and does not flower so freely. This variety first appeared in the nursery of Mr John Miller of Bristol, about 1828.

Var. STRICTUS, *Webb* (U. strictus, *Mackay*). Irish Gorse.—A variety of erect, rather columnar growth, of little value in the garden, as it flowers sparsely. Found in Co. Down in the early part of the nineteenth century, native also of Spain. Known also as U. hibernicus and U. fastigiatus.

Dried furze was at one time much used in country places for heating bakers' ovens, and is still often woven into hurdles for sheltering cattle, forming a good wind screen, not rubbed against or soon knocked down. Owing to the amount of dead twigs and spines inside the outer living layer, gorse plants are very inflammable during hot summer spells. Gorse, therefore, even the double-flowered variety, should not be planted where its firing would be a source of danger to buildings or even to valuable trees.

U. GALLII, *Planchon*

A dwarf, sturdy bush allied to U. nanus, and by some writers made a variety of it. In general appearance, however, it more resembles U. europæus, having the same hairy branches and stout spiny branchlets, but it is much dwarfer, usually under 2 ft. The flowers, each ⅝ in. long and bright yellow, are borne from August to October ; the wing-petals are curved and longer than the keel, the calyx finely downy. Pod ¼ to ½ in. long, one- or two-seeded.

Native of W. Europe, and abundant in the south-west of England, where it makes (often in company with Erica cinerea and E. Tetralix) most charming displays in autumn. The moors behind Bournemouth, covered with these

plants, will be familiar to many. It is in some respects intermediate between
U. europæus and U. nanus, resembling the former in its branches, but the
latter in time of flowering
and in the absence of
hairs from the calyx. It
is not so hardy as either
of them, but apparently
withstands all except the
very hardest winters at
Kew, especially when the
plants are a few years
old. In gardens it is
scarcely known—being
confused with U. nanus
—but is very pretty
planted in poor soil,
especially if associated
with the two heaths just
named.

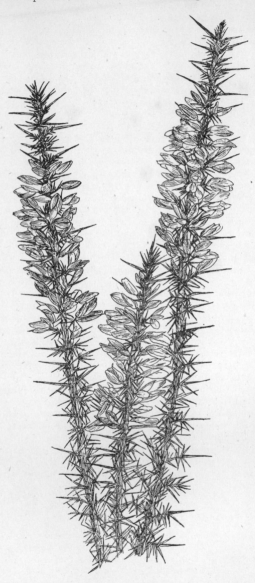

ULEX NANUS

U. NANUS, Forster.
DWARF GORSE

A dwarf shrub of
dense, close habit, some-
times procumbent in a
wild state, but changing
its character when intro-
duced to the garden, and
sending up slender, erect
branches, 1 to 2 ft. long
in a single season;
branchlets hairy. Leaves
and branchlets as in U.
europæus, only smaller
and less rigid. Flowers
golden yellow, about half
the size of common gorse;
the calyx not hairy but
slightly downy; wing
petals straight, shorter
than the keel. Pod ½ in.
long, hairy.

Native of W. Europe,
and abundant in many
parts of Great Britain.
Atlhough some botanists
profess to find it a variety
of U. europæus, it is
really very distinct. It is
autumn-flowering, being
at its best in September,

when the ordinary gorse is in seed. This is its most valuable characteristic in
gardens, for its long, slender stems set with flowers are often very pretty when

ew other shrubs are in blossom. But it needs a poor dry soil to develop
ts greatest beauty. In rich garden soil it gets to be 6 ft. high, and very
anky.

ULMUS. ELM. ULMACEÆ

A group of about twenty species of deciduous trees, some of them of
the largest size, with alternate, toothed leaves, usually unequal-sided at
he base. Flowers produced in clusters or short racemes from axillary
buds, either on the naked shoots in early spring, or on the leafy ones in
autumn. They have no beauty, being very small, green, or tinged with
ed ; the perianth or calyx is somewhat bell-shaped, with four to nine
usually about five) lobes, and the same number of stamens. The fruit
s most characteristic, being a flat, membranous, semi-transparent disc
(" samara "), enclosing the seed in a cavity at the centre or towards the
apex, where it is slightly or deeply notched. The leaves of elms usually
die off yellow in autumn. There are three elms in cultivation which
flower on the leafy shoots of the year in autumn ; they are crassifolia,
parvifolia, and serotina. The remainder are spring-flowering, and ripen
their seeds by midsummer. If new stocks are required, the seeds should
be sown as soon as ripe. The varieties are chiefly grafted on seedlings
of U. montana, this being preferred because its roots do not produce
suckers like campestris or nitens.

All the elms are gross feeders, and the roots travel enormous distances
in search of food. Whilst not very particular, they thrive best on deep
alluvial soil. A bad enemy of the elms, the English elm in particular,
is a boring beetle (*Scolytus scolytus*). The female of this insect burrows
a channel beneath the bark, along which she distributes her eggs ; when
these hatch out they burrow at right angles to the parent channel, the
whole brood producing a curious and very characteristic fishbone-like
marking. The attacks of this beetle .itself about ¼ in. long, usually cause
he death of the tree. It is, I think, most destructive in dry, hot summers,
and trees that have been injured at the roots appear more liable to its
attacks than healthy ones. There is probably no cure, but the trees may
be assisted by feeding and watering. In the case of important trees,
outward applications in spring of coal tar or train oil, after the rough
outer bark has been shaved off, have been recommended. Trees badly
affected should be cut down and not left lying about for the young larvæ
to hatch out, which they do about the end of May.

Much concern amongst foresters and tree-planters in general has
been aroused by the depredations of a parasitic fungus which attacks
elms and is usually fatal to them. Mycologists know it as CERATOS-
TOMELLA ULMI, *Buisman* and from the fact that it first appeared about
1919 in Holland it has become generally known as the " Dutch Elm
Disease." But it is widely spread also in Belgium, N. France, and
Germany. First noted near London in 1927, it has since proved fatal
to many English elms, especially in the southern, eastern, and midland
counties.

The presence of the disease is first indicated during the season of
growth by the leaves withering, becoming discoloured and soon falling.

Internal evidence of its existence can be found by making a cross section of a branchlet, when dark brown spots will be found on the latest formed annual rings. According to the researches of the Forestry Commission, the most susceptible age of elms is between fifteen and forty years. In 1931, two very healthy trees of Van Houtte's variety of common elm, about thirty-six years old and growing in the Pagoda Vista at Kew, succumbed in a few months after the first visible evidences of the disease.

No satisfactory method of dealing with the disease has been, nor is likely to be found, but it may be worth while to cut off isolated affected branches such as occasionally appear on old trees as soon as the existence of the fungus becomes apparent. Partially affected trees in some cases appear to be recovering. The Forestry Commission's report on the elm disease, published in 1932, records a somewhat decreased virulence, but this may be only temporary. It is a curious fact that, in Belgium and Holland, whilst almost entire avenues have been destroyed, a few scattered trees along them have escaped. This has engendered a hope that these exceptions may represent immune types. If that proved to be true, the propagation of them would afford a means of replacing the lost trees. But the whole problem is as yet too obscure for anything definite to be stated on this point.

U. ALATA, *Michaux*. WAHOO or WINGED ELM

It is doubtful if this elm be at present in cultivation, although according to Loudon it was introduced in 1820. For a long time the corky-barked form of U. nitens (suberosa) did duty for it, the two resembling each other in the corky wings of the branches. They are amply distinct in other respects, for U. alata has leaves downy all over the midrib and veins beneath, and the fruits are downy and distinctly hairy. It is a tree found wild in the south United States, where it is 40 to 50 ft. high; its young shoots glabrous or nearly so, its leaves narrowly obovate or ovate-oblong, not downy above; 1¼ to 3 ins. long, ½ to 1¼ ins. wide; doubly toothed, sharply pointed. Fruits hairy oval, ⅓ in. long, in short-stalked clusters. The corky wings on the branches are two in number and set on opposite sides.

U. AMERICANA, *Linnæus*. AMERICAN or WHITE ELM

A tree up to 100 or 120 ft. high, with a trunk 6 ft. or more in diameter forming in isolated positions a wide-spreading head of branches gracefully pendulous at the ends, the whole as much in diameter as the tree is high bark ashy grey; young shoots slender, at first downy. Leaves ovate to obovate or oval, contracted at the apex to a long, slender point; unequal at the base, one side of the midrib being rounded, the other tapered; doubly toothed; 4 to 6 ins. long, 1 to 3 ins. wide; downy beneath and at first somewhat hairy above; lateral veins up to about eighteen pairs; stalk about ¼ in. long. Fruit oval or obovate, nearly ½ in. long, produced in short-stalked clusters, beautifully fringed with pale hairs, the two incurved horns at the apex meeting and forming a small aperture.

Native of eastern and central N. America; introduced in 1752. The American elm is one of the finest and most picturesque trees of its native country, always marked by its beauty and grace of branching; but in Britain it is a very rare tree.

U. BELGICA, *Burgsdorf.* BELGIAN ELM
(U. hollandica, *Späth*)

In the streets of Holland and Belgium is a very common tree, usually called U. hollandica. It is, no doubt, a hybrid, of which U. glabra is one parent (and the one it more closely follows), U. nitens the other. As one usually sees it, it is a clean-growing, erect-stemmed tree of pyramidal form, but that is probably due to pruning. Naturally, it is said to assume a broad head of branches. It has leaves up to 5½ ins. long, much the same in character as those of U. glabra, but with stalks often more than twice as long. In some of the large continental nurseries this is grown for sale more extensively than any other elm. Said to have first appeared in a plantation at Bruges. It differs from U. glabra in the young shoots becoming glabrous towards the end of the season, and being more slender, also in the narrower leaf with a coarsely toothed, more elongated apex.

U. CORITANA, *Melville.* CORITANIAN ELM (see p. 554)

U. CRASSIFOLIA, *Nuttall.* CEDAR ELM

A tree up to 80 ft. high in nature, but in cultivation in England very slow-growing and forming a round-headed small tree ; young shoots clothed with fine, soft, very short down ; winter buds often in pairs. Leaves ovate to oblong, obliquely rounded or slightly heart-shaped at the base, bluntish or rounded at the apex ; ¾ to 2 ins. long, ½ to 1¼ ins. wide ; toothed (sometimes doubly), of firm rather hard texture ; very harsh to the touch above, more or less downy beneath ; stalk $\frac{1}{12}$ to ⅛ in. long. Flowers produced in clusters in the leaf-axils in August and later. Fruit ⅛ in. long, oval, tapered at both ends, deeply notched at the top, downy all over, especially on the margin.

Native of the southern United States and hardy at Kew, where it was introduced by Prof. Sargent in 1876. Although quite healthy it increases very slowly in height, and no doubt needs a hotter summer than ours to be seen at its best. Sargent describes it as the " common elm tree of Texas." Allied to U. crassifolia is

U. SEROTINA, *Sargent,* first recognised as a distinct species in 1899. It has the same habit of flowering in the axils of the leaves in autumn, but is distinguished by the longer, larger, sharply pointed leaves of thinner texture, but less harsh to the touch above ; the oval fruits are ⅛ to ½ in. long, borne in racemes 1 to 1½ ins. long and much more conspicuously fringed. It is a native of the south-eastern United States, and was first sent to Kew by Prof. Sargent in 1898. These two species in their habit of autumnal flowering are allied to U. parvifolia (*q.v.*).

U. DIVERSIFOLIA, *Melville.* EAST ANGLIAN ELM
(see p. 555)

U. ELLIPTICA, *Koch.* CAUCASIAN ELM

Like U. pedunculata in its relationship to U. americana, this species affords an example of close affinity between an Old World and a New World elm. In many respects it does not differ from the following species (U. fulva), although it is native of the Caucasus, Persia, Turkestan, and W. Siberia. It differs in its less fissured bark and in the thinner, more sharply toothed leaves. The fruit is obovate, ⅝ to 1 in. long, and, like that of U. fulva, is downy only on the part covering the seed ; it is, however, longer and not so round, and in shape is more like that of U. glabra. Trees under this name were introduced in 1891 and are quite hardy. The tree grown as " U. Heyderi " belongs either to this species or to U. fulva, but the late Prof. Henry believed the true U. elliptica is not in cultivation.

III   P

U. FULVA, *Michaux.* SLIPPERY ELM

(U. rubra, *Michaux fil.*)

A tree 60 to 70 ft. high, with a trunk up to 2 ft. thick, supporting a spreading head of branches ; young shoots very downy ; winter buds $\frac{1}{4}$ in. long, covered with brown hairs. Leaves oblong-ovate, 3 to 8 ins. (sometimes in young trees 10 ins.) long, about half as wide, abruptly tapered to a long, slender point, obliquely rounded at the base ; jaggedly or doubly toothed ; upper surface very harsh to the touch through minute excrescences ; lower surface downy ; stalk $\frac{1}{4}$ to $\frac{1}{3}$ in. long. Flowers very short-stalked and crowded in clusters. Fruit orbicular or obovate, $\frac{1}{3}$ to $\frac{3}{4}$ in. long, slightly notched at the top, the part covering the seed (which is in the centre) coated with red-brown hairs, naked elsewhere.

Native of central and eastern N. America. This elm gets its popular name from its mucilaginous inner bark. It thrives very well as a young tree at Kew, making strong growths several feet long each summer. In the size and roughness of the upper surface of the leaves, it resembles U. glabra, but the stalk is longer and the fruit distinct. Its specific name refers to the brown hairy buds which, together with the hairy patch in the centre of the fruit, well distinguish it.

U. GLABRA, *Hudson.* WYCH OR SCOTCH ELM

(U. montana, *Withering* ; U. scabra, *Miller*)

A tree from 100 to 125 ft. high, with a trunk sometimes 6 ft. in diameter ; head of branches wide-spreading, rather open ; young shoots stout, downy ; bud scales hairy. Leaves usually 3 to 7 ins. long (sometimes more on young trees) $1\frac{1}{2}$ to 4 ins. wide ; oval to obovate, slender-pointed, sometimes three-lobed towards the top, very unequal-sided at the base ; coarsely and doubly toothed, upper surface dull green, very rough ; lower one downy ; stalk very short, never more than $\frac{1}{4}$ in. long, often quite hidden by the rounded basal half of the blade, downy ; veins in fourteen to twenty pairs. Flowers in dense, stalkless clusters. Fruit oval, $\frac{3}{4}$ to 1 in. long, downy only at the slightly notched apex, the seed situated in the middle.

Native of N. Europe, including Britain. It is rare in the south and east of England, but common in Scotland and Ireland, where it is one of the noblest of native trees. In the open it forms a stout, shortish trunk of great thickness, and a head of branches often pendulous at the ends. It is apt to be confused in gardens with some of the hybrids (major, vegeta, etc.) that have originated between it and U. nitens, but may always be distinguished among those and other British elms by the seed being in the middle of the fruit, the very short leaf-stalks, very rough leaves, and the absence of any corkiness on the two-year-old shoots. Moreover, the tree does not produce suckers as nitens and procera do, and on that account is valued as a stock for other elms. Several very distinct varieties of wych elm are in cultivation, but no doubt some commonly referred to this species are hybrids. The specific name " glabra " refers to the bark (at first downy) remaining smooth for many years.

Var. CAMPERDOWNI.—A pendulous branched tree, the branches forming a globose head. Originally found at Camperdown House, near Dundee.

Var. CRISPA, *Loudon* (U. asplenifolia and U. urticæfolia of gardens).— Leaves narrowly oblong-oval, $1\frac{1}{2}$ to $3\frac{1}{2}$ ins. long, $\frac{3}{4}$ to $1\frac{1}{2}$ ins. wide ; rather infolded, the margins very jaggedly and deeply cut into slender, often double, teeth. A curious, slow-growing form.

Var. DAUVESSEI (U. Dauvessei, *Henry*) has shorter more rounded leaves of thinner texture ; perhaps a hybrid.

ULMUS GLABRA (in fruit)

Var. FASTIGIATA, *Loudon*.   Exeter Elm.—Branches and branchlets erect, the latter as well as the leaves frequently twisted.   There is a tree 12 ft. in girth in the vicarage garden at Bitton. The elm known as U. WREDEI is perhaps a form of this ; it has yellow leaves. Both these elms have leaves rounder than in the type, and with more laciniate margins.

Var. LIBERO-RUBRO.—Inner bark purplish red.

Var. LUTESCENS.—Leaves yellow.

Var. NANA.—A dwarf rounded bush rarely more than 5 or 6 ft. high.

Var. PENDULA, *Loudon.*—Branches stiffly pendulous, forming a low, spreading, arbour-like tree, admirable as a lawn specimen. It should be grafted high on the typical form. Originated early in the nineteenth century, in a nursery at Perth.

Var. PURPUREA.—Leaves purple. The colour is more lasting in the form called ATROPURPUREA. There are big-leaved forms known by such names as gigantea, macrophylla, superba, etc., some of which are no doubt hybrids.

U. JAPONICA, *Sargent.* JAPANESE ELM
(U. campestris japonica, *Rehder*)

A tree up to 110 ft. high in Japan, forming, according to Sargent, broad heads of graceful, pendent branches ; young shoots very downy, sometimes winged. Leaves oval, inclined to obovate ; 3 to 4½ ins. long, 1½ to 2½ ins. wide ; unequal at the broadly tapered base, abruptly narrowed at the apex to a slender point, rather coarsely toothed ; furnished with stiff hairs above at first, afterwards very harsh to the touch ; lower surface clothed with pale down, especially on the veins and midrib ; veins in fourteen to sixteen pairs, stalk about ⅛ in. long. This elm was introduced in 1895 to the Arnold Arboretum where, fifteen years later, I saw trees already 28 ft. high. In 1897 it was sent to Kew. It has not yet flowered, and I only know the fruits from samples collected near Sapporo, where the tree is much grown ; they are obovate, ⅝ in. long, nearly ½ in. wide, tapered at the base, the seed being situated close to the notch, the inner edges of which are edged with down. Elsewhere the fruit is glabrous. The young shoots are fawn-coloured.

U. LACINIATA, *Mayr*
(U. montana laciniata, *Trautvetter*)

A tree mostly about 30 ft. high in Japan according to Sargent, but sometimes thrice as high in Central Yezo according to Mayr ; young shoots nearly or quite glabrous. Leaves 3 to 7 ins. long, about half as wide, obovate, with three, sometimes five, very conspicuous acuminate lobes at the broad end ; upper surface rough with minute tubercles. lower surface densely downy ; doubly toothed. Fruits about ⅞ in. long, ½ in. wide, glabrous, the seed in the centre.

Native of Japan, N. China and Manchuria, and remarkably distinct for the large terminal lobes of the leaves. It has been in cultivation since 1900. Henry records that the Ainos of N. Japan take off the inner bark of this tree in narrow strips and, after soaking it in water, weave it into a coarse cloth from which they make garments.

U. LÆVIS, *Pallas.* EUROPEAN WHITE ELM
(U. pedunculata, *Fougeroux* ; U. effusa, *Willdenow*)

A tree over 100 ft. high, with a trunk up to 6 ft. in diameter, supporting a wide-spreading, rather open head of branches ; bark brownish grey ; young shoots clothed with grey down, at least at first. Leaves obliquely obovate, 2½ to 5 ins. long, rather more than half as wide; with double incurved teeth at the margins ; the base very unequal, being rounded at one side of the midrib, abbreviated and tapered at the other ; the apex narrowed abruptly to a slender point ; bright green, glabrous, or slightly harsh above, usually clothed beneath with a dense grey down ; side veins up to eighteen pairs ; stalk ⅛ to ¼ in. long. Fruit oval, about ½ in. long, fringed with pale hairs, and having two incurved horns at the apex ; the fruits are borne on slender pendulous stalks in crowded clusters.

Native of Central and E. Europe, but very closely allied in botanical characters to U. americana, from which it is indeed difficult to distinguish it. It thrives better in this country, and the leaves seem more uniformly downy, more unequal at the base, and more frequently broadest above the middle ; the winter buds are more elongated and sharply pointed. Of European elms it most resembles U. glabra, but is easily distinguished by the smoother, smaller leaves, and especially by the fringed samara (fruit). There is a fine tree at Syon, 90 ft. high, and 12 ft. 8 ins. in girth, long regarded as U. americana, and certainly possessing the characteristic form of the New World tree.

U. MACROCARPA, *Hance.* LARGE-FRUITED ELM

A deciduous tree sometimes bushy but occasionally 50 ft. high ; young shoots hairy, often becoming furnished with two corky wings after the second year. Leaves broadly obovate to oval, obliquely rounded at the base, narrowed abruptly to a short slender apex, doubly toothed ; 2 to 4 ins. long, 1¼ to 2½ ins. wide ; very rough with short bristles on both surfaces and with axil-tufts of down beneath ; veins in ten to fourteen pairs ; stalk ¼ in. or less long. Fruits flat, winged, orbicular or broadly oval inclined to obovate, slightly notched at the top ; ¾ to 1¼ ins. long, harshly bristly like the leaves, ciliate, with the seed in the centre.

Native of N. China and originally described in 1868 from specimens collected by the Abbé David. It was afterwards found by Komarow in Manchuria and by Purdom in Shen-si ; Mr Mori, the Japanese botanist, includes it in his *Flora of Korea.* Introduced to America in 1908, and cultivated by the late Mr Vicary Gibbs at Aldenham. From all other elms in cultivation it is easily distinguished by the large size of its winged fruits ; in other respects it is very like an ordinary elm, but is evidently a much smaller tree.

U. MAJOR, *Smith.* DUTCH ELM

(U. hollandica, *Miller*)

A large tree up to 120 ft. in height, of somewhat open, thin branching, the branchlets often pendulous ; trunk 4 to 5 ft. in diameter ; young shoots slightly hairy. Leaves oval or ovate, 2½ to 5 ins. long, 1½ to 3 ins. wide ; taper-pointed, one side cordate at the base, and developed farther down the stalk than the other side, which is tapered ; upper surface dark shining green, glabrous or nearly so, the lower one also bright green, downy in the vein-axils and along the midrib, nearly glabrous elsewhere ; veins in ten to fourteen pairs ; stalk downy, ¼ to ⅜ in. long. Fruit between ovate and obovate, ¾ to 1 in. long, with the seed close to the terminal notch.

A British tree and probably a hybrid between U. glabra and U. nitens. It is quick-growing, and several fine specimens exist in the older part of Kew Gardens. One of them when felled, I found to be 150 years old, 92 ft. high, and 13 ft. 6 in. in girth. The sucker-like shoots produced directly from the trunk are often corky. It produces enormous crops of seed, infertile so far as I have seen. The botanical characters of this elm most resemble those of U. nitens, but the leaves and fruit are much larger, and the habit more open.

Var. SERPENTINA, *Henry.*—Usually placed as a pendulous form of U. glabra, this curious elm is apparently of hybrid origin. The branchlets are curiously twisted and contorted as well as pendulous. In the ten to fourteen pairs of veins, and in the down being chiefly confined to tufts in the vein-axils and along the midrib and veins, it closely resembles U. major.

U. NITENS, *Moench.* SMOOTH-LEAVED ELM

(U. carpinifolia, *Gleditsch* ; U. glabra, *Miller,* not of *Hudson*)

A tree 100 ft. high, represented in Great Britain by several forms varying in habit from slender, cone-shaped trees to beautifully pendulous-branched ones. The typical form is a pyramidal tree, at least up to middle age, the branches often corky, sometimes extremely so ; young shoots almost or quite without down in the adult tree, slender. Leaves obliquely oval or ovate, doubly toothed, narrowing at the apex to a shortish point, very unequal at the base (one side of the blade being tapered, the other rounded or semi-cordate) ; 1½ to 4 ins. long, 1 to 2 ins. wide ; (on vigorous shoots considerably larger) ; upper surface glossy green and glabrous ; lower surface downy only in the vein-axils or along the midrib ; stalk ¼ to ½ in. long ; veins in ten to thirteen pairs. Flowers crowded in dense clusters close to the leafless shoot. Fruit oval or obovate, glabrous, ½ to ⅝ in. long, notched at the top, with the seed close to the notch.

Native of Europe and W. Asia, and one of the two undisputed species of British elms. The other, U. glabra, is amply distinguished by the seed being in the middle of the fruit, by the very downy shoots and much larger, downy leaves. The common elm, U. procera, differs in its rounder leaf ; downy all over beneath and rough above. A tree at Madingley turns red every autumn, but the usual decaying colour of the leaf is yellow.

Var. BERARDII.—A very interesting little elm raised in the nursery of Messrs Simon-Louis, near Metz, in 1863. Its leaves are oval, ½ to 1½ ins. long, ¼ to ⅝ in. wide, with four to seven coarse triangular teeth down each side ; glabrous on both surfaces. The slender twigs and leaf-stalks are downy. The parent tree was said to be a large elm on the ramparts of Metz, and judging by the glabrous leaves of this variety it would appear to have been U. nitens. It may, however, have been a hybrid.

Var. PENDULA, *Rehder.*—A tree with pendulous branches, very vigorous, and large-leaved ; makes a handsome specimen isolated on a lawn.

Var. SUBEROSA. Cork-barked Elm.—Like the type in leaf, but of stiff, spreading, low habit, the branches two or more years old becoming furnished with usually four conspicuous, corky ridges. It has to be noticed, however, that the corkiness of the branches is often noticeable in a greater or less degree in what we regard as the typical U. nitens, and if seeds of the most suberous tree were sown, it is probable that there would appear many ordinary U. nitens among them. Common in forests of Central Europe.

Var. VARIEGATA.—Leaves marked more or less copiously with white, especially on the margin.

Var. WEBBIANA.—Leaves small, rounded ; habit columnar.

U. PARVIFOLIA, *Jacquin.* CHINESE ELM

(U. chinensis, *Persoon*)

A small tree up to 60 ft. high, with a slender trunk supporting a rounded head of branches ; branchlets very slender, clothed with a close, minute, grey down ; winter buds small, conical. Leaves leathery, ¾ to 2½ ins. long, ⅓ to

1⅓ ins. wide ; oval, ovate or obovate ; unequally rounded at the base (or one side of the midrib tapered) ; pointed, the margins rather evenly toothed, the teeth triangular, often blunt ; upper surface lustrous green, and smooth on the smaller twigs, rather rough on vigorous shoots ; lower surface pale, bright green, with tufts of down in the vein-axils, or smooth ; stalk ⅟₁₆ to ¼ in. long, downy, veins in ten to twelve pairs. Flowers produced in September and October in the leaf-axils. Fruit ovate-oval, ⅓ in. long, not downy ; seed in the centre.

Native of N. and Central China and Japan. This tree retains its leaves until the New Year quite fresh and green, and is well worth growing for its elegance. It is sometimes confused with U. pumila in gardens, but that species flowers in spring. From the other autumn-flowering elms—U. crassifolia and U. serotina—it is distinct in retaining its leaves so late, in the almost complete absence of down from beneath the leaves, and in their brighter smoother surfaces. Introduced in 1794.

U. Plotii, *Druce*.   Plot Elm

(U. minor, *Henry*, not *Miller*)

A tree up to 80 or 90 ft. high, with a few short spreading main branches and pendulous branchlets, the latter slender, minutely and sparsely downy when young. Leaves obovate to oval, up to 2½ ins. long, and 1½ ins. wide ; unequal sided and often heart-shaped at the base ; upper surface smooth, dull green, lower one at first densely clothed with glands which later fall away, downy in the vein-axils ; margin doubly toothed, veins in eight to ten pairs ; leaf-stalk downy, ⅕ in. long. Fruit elliptic, ½ in. long, notched at the tip, bearing the seed in the upper part.

Native of Middle England. It is a tree of very elegant and characteristic appearance, allied closely, no doubt, to U. nitens, and producing suckers like that elm, but differing in its smaller, duller leaves, with fewer veins and shorter stalk.

U. procera, *Salisbury*.   English Elm

(U. campestris, *Miller*)

A tree up to 120, or even 150 ft. high, with a trunk 6 ft. or more in diameter ; young shoots hairy. Leaves roundish ovate, to broadly oval, very unequal at the base, terminated by a short, abrupt point, coarsely and doubly toothed ; 2 to 3½ ins. long, about two-thirds as wide ; dark green and very harsh to the touch above ; paler beneath and downy all over, with conspicuous tufts of white down in the vein-axils, along the midrib, and at the base of the chief veins—of which there are ten to twelve pairs. Flowers clustered closely to the branchlet, opening early in the year, reddish. Fruit a round disk, ½ in. across, not downy, bearing the seed close to the notch at the top.

In old books on trees the English elm is usually said to be a native of Europe introduced to Britain at the time of the Romans. It is now fairly certain that it is genuinely wild nowhere but in southern England, the elm called campestris on the Continent being a distinct tree. (See var. australis.) The English elm produces fertile seed extremely rarely. I have not myself seen a genuine seedling, but Henry states that he raised four plants out of twenty batches of seed sown in 1909. In many parts of southern England the elm is the dominant tree, especially in hedgerows ; all these trees, however, have sprung from root suckers, which the elm produces freely, and which afford the best means of propagation.

The origin of the English elm still remains a mystery. It occurs in some parks and gardens of Spain, but apparently always planted, and there is no evidence that it was ever introduced to England from Spain. On the other hand, there is a tradition that the Spanish trees originally were sent from England. Against its being a genuine native of Britain, there is the curious fact that it is almost invariably infertile. I am inclined nevertheless to think that this last may be accounted for by its extreme facility in producing suckers from the roots. There are plenty of instances of trees that propagate themselves easily by parts of the old plant, losing much of their ferility of seed— our native willows and poplars are instances, as is also the North American Robinia hispida. In the tropics, too, there is the banana, which has wholly, and the sugar cane, which has largely, lost its power of reproduction by seed after long-continued increase by offsets or cuttings. There is always the possibility that it originated as a hybrid from the other British elms.

As a tree in the English landscape the elm impresses one by its noble stature and bulk, its rich leafiness, and its singular beauty in winter when the finely fretted outline of its naked branches shows in delicate tracery against the sky. In the autumn the foliage dies off rich yellow, and lingers on the branches longer perhaps than that of any of our native trees. This elm has an unfortunate propensity in age of dropping its limbs, which snap off without any warning. This usually happens on still evenings in late summer and early autumn when the trees are still in full leaf. It is also liable to occur during a heavy rain following a period of heat and drought. This habit makes the elm a very unsuitable tree to plant in crowded thoroughfares.

The timber of elm is valuable for its toughness and the absence of any tendency to split. It has also considerable beauty of graining and colour. Kept permanently dry or permanently wet, it is very durable. At one time, before the introduction of iron pipes, hollowed-out trunks of elm were used as water-pipes. Although many varieties of elm have been placed under campestris by nurserymen and others, it seems to me there are but two genuine garden varieties of English elm, both no doubt branch sports :—

Var. LOUIS VAN HOUTTE.—Leaves entirely yellow, retaining their colour throughout the summer. The best yellow-leaved elm.

Var. VARIEGATA.—For those who admire variegated trees this may be recommended as one of the best. The leaves are conspicuously blotched, striped, and margined with creamy white. Some years ago I saw a fine specimen of this form on the main road between Warwick and Coventry, whose suckers were as variegated as the parent.

Var. AUSTRALIS, *Henry.*—This is the tree referred to above as the continental form of U. campestris. Henry (*Trees of Great Britain and Ireland*, p. 1904) distinguishes it as a tree often pyramidal in habit, with short branches. Leaves thick and firm in texture, oval, 2 to 3 ins. long, $1\frac{1}{4}$ to $1\frac{3}{4}$ ins. wide, with a longer, more cuspidate and tapered apex than in the type, and with the tufts of down in the vein-axils beneath not so well developed. Fruit not so round, but more obovate. The tree is best distinguished from the English elm by its thicker textured leaves with more prominent veins beneath. It is quite fertile. Native of Europe from Belgium to the Riviera and Switzerland. Probably a distinct species.

U. PUMILA, *Linnæus.* DWARF ELM

A small tree, 10 to 30 ft. high, sometimes a shrub. Leaves oval or ovate-lanceolate, acute to acuminate at the apex, tapered or rounded at the base,

and not unequal-sided there as elms usually are ; rather coarsely toothed
except at the base ; $\frac{3}{4}$ to $2\frac{1}{4}$ ins. long, $\frac{1}{3}$ to 1 in. wide ; dark green and quite
glabrous (or with minute tufts of down in the vein-axils) beneath ; stalk downy,
$\frac{1}{12}$ to $\frac{1}{6}$ in. long. Flowers borne on the naked shoots in spring, on very short
stalks, and in clusters. Fruit circular or rather obovate, deeply notched at the
top, $\frac{1}{2}$ in. across, the seed about the middle.

Native of N. Asia, from E. Siberia to N. China. It has been confused in
gardens with U. parviflora (*q.v.*). Under the name of

U. PINNATO-RAMOSA, *Dieck*, a very elegant, vigorous-growing, small-leaved elm
was sent out from the Zoeschen Arboretum about fifty years ago. The more downy
branchlets are arranged in two opposite rows (distichously), and the leaves are longer
pointed, but otherwise very similar to U. pumila. It flowers in spring. Introduced
from W. Siberia and Turkestan. (Syn. U. pumila pinnato-ramosa, *Henry.*)

U. SEROTINA, *Sargent*. RED ELM

A tree 60 to 70 ft. high of spreading habit, with slender, glabrous or nearly
glabrous young shoots, often becoming more or less corky-winged. Leaves
oblong, often inclined to obovate, 2 to $3\frac{1}{2}$ ins. long, slender-pointed, very unequal
at the base, doubly toothed, with about twenty pairs of veins, glabrous and
glossy above, downy on the veins beneath ; stalks about $\frac{1}{4}$ in. long. Flowers
in pendulous racemes $1\frac{1}{4}$ ins. long, opening in September. Fruits $\frac{1}{2}$ in. long,
oblong-elliptical, deeply divided at the apex, fringed along the margins with
silvery white hairs ; they are ripe in November.

According to Sargent (*Silva of N. America*, vol. xiv. plate 718) it inhabits
limestone hills from Tenessee to Georgia. It is occasionally planted as a shade
tree in Alabama and Georgia where it is distinguished by its broad, handsome
head of pendulous branches.

U. STRICTA, *Lindley*. CORNISH ELM (Plate 35)

(U. nitens stricta, *Henry* ; U. cornubiensis, *Hort.*)

A tree 80 to 100 ft. high, of slender, tapering, or columnar form, young
shoots more or less downy. Leaves very like those of U. nitens but smaller,
being 2 to $2\frac{1}{2}$ ins. long, 1 to $1\frac{1}{2}$ ins. wide, broadly obovate or oval ; dark green,
smooth and glossy above, paler beneath, with conspicuous tufts of down in
the axils of the veins ; doubly toothed ; veins in ten to twelve pairs ; stalk
$\frac{1}{3}$ in. long, downy. Fruit like that of U. procera but $\frac{5}{8}$ in. long, and $\frac{1}{2}$ in. wide,
carrying the seed near the notch at the apex.

Native of Cornwall, Devon, and Somerset in England, and of Brittany in
France. This elm produces suckers freely, but does not often bear perfect fruit.

Var. WHEATLEYI (U. sarniensis, *Loddiges*). Guernsey or Jersey Elm.—
This is very closely allied to the Cornish elm, of which Henry regarded it as
probably a seedling. Its branches are more stiffly erect, and the tree more
tapered, the leaves are proportionately broader and less conspicuously downy
in the vein-axils beneath. Fruit as in U. procera.

Both these elms, but especially the latter, are admirable for street planting,
retaining without artificial aid the slender, tapering form essential for trees
planted in all but the widest streets of towns. They are immediate allies of
U. nitens. A yellow-leaved form of the Jersey elm originated in the nurseries
of Messrs Dickson at Chester in 1900.

U. Thomasii, *Sargent*. Rock Elm

(U. racemosa, *Thomas*)

A tree 80 to 100 ft. high, with a trunk up to 3 ft. in diameter, supporting a narrow roundish head of branches. In a young state the trees are pyramidal ; winter buds and young shoots downy. Leaves oval to obovate, with an abrupt, slender point and an unequal, oblique base ; 2 to 4½ ins. long, 1¼ to 2¾ ins. wide ; doubly toothed, glabrous, dark glossy green above, downy beneath ; side veins in often over twenty pairs ; stalk up to ¼ in. long, sometimes partially covered by the overlapping bases of the blade. Flowers in racemes 1 to 2 ins. long. Fruit oval, ½ to ¾ in. long, downy all over as well as on the thickened margins, with a slight open notch at the apex ; the two points erect.

Native of eastern N. America, where it produces a valuable timber. I know of no fine tree in this country, although there are small ones at Kew. It is slow-growing, even in the Arnold Arboretum, Mass., where there is an interesting group of very characteristic young trees. Its distinctive points are its large downy winter-buds, ¼ or ⅓ in. long, its racemose inflorescence and shallowly notched, hairy fruits.

U. vegeta, *Lindley*. Huntingdon or Chichester Elm

This fine elm, according to information given to Loudon by Mr John Wood of Huntingdon, in 1836, was raised in the nursery of his firm about the middle of the eighteenth century from seed gathered in Hinchingbrook Park. It is, no doubt, a hybrid between U. glabra and U. nitens, and like many hybrid trees, is of remarkably vigorous growth. One of the largest of all elms, it reaches 140 ft. in height, forming a thick short trunk 5 or 6 ft. in diameter with ascending branches. Leaves up to 5 or 6 ins. long, more than half as wide, glabrous above and downy beneath only in the leaf-axils. Fruit oval, up to ⅞ in. long, the seed not reaching to the notch at the top. This last character and its less downy leaves distinguish it from U. major, of presumably the same percentage. The veins, too, are more numerous (fourteen to eighteen pairs) than in U. major. According to Elwes it has the defect of splitting in the trunk due to its habit of forking low down. This, however, can be prevented by timely pruning. The tree produces suckers. Lord Sandwich kindly informs me that his famous tree at Hinchingbrook is 140 ft. high, its trunk girthing 24 ft. at 5 ft. from the ground.

U. viminalis, *Loddiges*

A narrow-headed, rather slender tree with drooping branches ; young shoots slightly downy, slender. Leaves oblanceolate or narrowly oval, nearly always tapered at the base, terminated by a long slender point ; 1 to 2 ins. long, ⅓ to ¾ in. wide ; very deeply toothed, the teeth narrow, often blunt ; upper surface very rough, lower one downy especially in the vein-axils and on the veins. I have never seen it bearing fruit although it flowers. Several varieties of U. viminalis are in gardens :—

Var. aurea (syns. Rosseelsii ; antarctica aurea).—Leaves yellow.
Var. variegata.—Leaf margins variegated with creamy white.
U. viminalis is a charming small tree for gardens, very elegant and not growing fast. It is of uncertain origin, but is probably a seedling of some hybrid elm.

U. BETULÆFOLIA, *Loddiges*, appears to be allied to U. viminalis, and is also of uncertain origin, possibly a hybrid in whose origin U. nitens has shared. The leaves are narrowly obovate, up to 2½ ins. long by 1½ ins. wide, the margins deeply toothed, the teeth narrow, incurved, often again toothed, very harsh to the touch above, downy in the vein-axils beneath. The habit is elegant on account of the pendulous young branchlets.

U. WILSONIANA, *C. K. Schneider.* WILSON'S ELM

A deciduous tree up to 80 ft. high, with a trunk occasionally a yard in diameter ; young shoots downy. Leaves ovate to oval, often with a short, slender, drawn-out apex, obliquely unsymmetrical at the base, rather evenly doubly-toothed ; 2 to 4½ ins. long, 1¼ to 2½ ins. wide ; veins in sixteen to twenty-two pairs, parallel, those in the centre of the leaf forking towards the margin ; dark green and very harsh to the touch above, paler and downy beneath, especially on the midrib and veins beneath ; stalk stout, downy, ⅛ to ¼ in. long. Fruit (samara) smooth, obovate, notched at the rounded apex of the wing, the seed situated just below the notch.

Native of W. China ; discovered by Wilson in 1900 ; introduced by him to the Arnold Arboretum in 1910 by means of graftwood. It is related to U. japonica, but that species has leaves with usually not more than sixteen pairs of veins, also the inner margins of the notch of its fruit-wing are edged with down. Wilson's elm often develops corky bark after the fashion of our native U. nitens.

UMBELLULARIA CALIFORNICA, *Nuttall.* CALIFORNIAN LAUREL. LAURACEÆ

(Oreodaphne californica, *Nees* ; Bot. Mag., t. 5320)

An evergreen tree, 80 to 100 ft. high in favourable situations in California, with a dense head of very leafy branches ; young shoots at first minutely downy. Leaves alternate, leathery, with a pungent aromatic odour when crushed, narrowly oval or oblong, but tapered at both ends ; 2 to 5 ins. long, ¾ to 1½ ins. wide ; not toothed, dark green and glossy above, paler beneath, almost glabrous on both surfaces except when just unfolding. Flowers ¼ in. across, yellowish green, produced during April in terminal and axillary umbels ¾ in. wide, on a common stalk 1 in. long. Fruit roundish pear-shaped, 1 in. long, ¾ in. wide ; green changing to purplish.

Native of California and Oregon ; introduced by Douglas in 1829, and the only known species. This fine tree is hardy in the open at Kew, and is 32 ft. high, being only occasionally injured by severe frost. On a wall it flowers, and has borne fruit. A tree near the porch of Bitton Vicarage, Bristol, frequently bears good crops of fruit. Jepson says that the finest grove in California is near Eel River, where for several miles there is a wood composed entirely of this tree. It likes a sheltered spot in gardens, where it is about equal to the bay laurel as an ornamental evergreen. It is very fine in the gardens of Osborne House, Isle of Wight, and there is a tree at Binstead, Isle of Wight, 50 ft. high, its trunk girthing 7 ft. I have only raised it from seed, but it could no doubt be layered if not propagated by cuttings.

VACCINIUM. VACCINIACEÆ

A large genus of shrubs, or occasionally trees, widely spread over the northern hemisphere, and existing in considerable numbers on the mountains of S. America. They have alternate leaves, and are both deciduous and evergreen. The corolla is more or less bell-shaped, globose, or cylindrical, except in V. erythrocarpum and V. japonicum; calyx persistent; stamens eight or ten. Fruit a juicy berry. Some authors unite this and allied genera with the Ericaceæ, from which they only differ in the corolla being superior (*i.e.*, situated above the ovary), whilst the relative position of these two parts of the flower is reversed in the Erica family.

As garden shrubs, the vacciniums are chiefly valued for their fruits and the autumnal colour of their foliage. Many are pretty in flower, but none makes the fine display provided by so many of the heath family. In nature they are nearly always found on mountain and moorland, and the genus is one of the most characteristic of the lonely parts of the northern hemisphere. Many produce very palatable fruits.

Under cultivation they prefer a peaty soil, or a light loamy one devoid of lime, and improved by adding decayed leaves. They are all moisture-loving plants. All the hardier ones produce seed which should be treated as advised for rhododendrons, and the others can be propagated by cuttings made of half-ripened wood in July, and placed in sandy peaty soil in gentle bottom heat.

There is considerable confusion in the identification of the N. American species of the V. corymbosum group, and American authors are by no means unanimous in their estimates of the number it contains; but they are all hardy, free-growing, and handsome shrubs, the leaves turning red before they fall, but frequently persisting well into the winter.

V. ARBOREUM, *Marshall*. FARKLEBERRY

(V. diffusum, *Aiton*, Bot. Mag., t. 1607)

A shrub, or small tree, up to 30 ft. high in some of its native localities, and varying also from deciduous to evergreen, according to locality; young twigs downy. Leaves ovate, obovate or oval; ½ in. to 2 ins. long, half as wide; very shortly stalked, mostly pointed, minutely and sparsely glandular-toothed, the margins slightly recurved; of leathery texture, glabrous and of a very glossy dark green above, slightly downy beneath. Flowers produced during July and August singly in the axils of the leaves or in the axils of bracts on terminal racemes 1 to 2 ins. long, each on a slender stalk ¼ to ⅝ in. long, with two minute bracts about the middle. Corolla white, bell-shaped, ¼ in. long, five-lobed, the lobes reflexed. Calyx small, the five lobes triangular. Fruit ¼ in. wide, black, roundish. The flower is jointed to the stalk.

Native of the south and east United States, as far north as N. Carolina; introduced to Kew by Mr John Cree in 1765. In the British Isles it is a deciduous shrub, said by Loudon in 1837 to have been 10 ft. high in the walled garden at White Knights. It was quite hardy when grown at Kew, pretty and free-flowering, but slow in growth. The form in cultivation is, no doubt, from the northern limits of its distribution, but the evergreen tree form ought to be tried in the mildest counties.

V. ARCTOSTAPHYLOS, *Linnæus*. CAUCASIAN WHORTLEBERRY

(Bot. Mag., t. 974)

A deciduous shrub, probably 10 ft. high ultimately ; young wood glabrous or slightly downy. Leaves ovate-oblong, pointed, finely toothed ; 1½ to 4 ins. long, ¾ to 1½ ins. wide ; dark dull green and downy on the veins above, paler and more downy beneath ; stalk $\frac{1}{12}$ in. long. Flowers produced during June, each in the axil of a bract on slightly downy racemes 1 to 2 ins. long

VACCINIUM ARCTOSTAPHYLOS

from the previous year's wood ; corolla greenish white tinged with purple, bell-shaped, ⅓ in. long and wide ; stamens ten, hairy ; calyx with five shallow triangular lobes. The flower is distinctly jointed to the stalk just below the ovary. Berry globose, purple, ¼ to ⅓ in. across.

Native of the Caucasus ; introduced in 1800. It is allied to V. padifolium from Madeira, but is a hardier shrub and (in cultivation at least) has larger leaves and differs in the hairy stamens. Its leaves, which are the largest among hardy vacciniums, die off a pretty purplish red. It occasionally bears a second crop of flowers in September in the leaf-axils of the current year's shoots. A decoction of the leaves is used in the Caucasus as a tea, especially by the Circassians. When dried they have the appearance and aroma of black tea, but are very dissimilar and inferor in flavour. It is known as " Broussa tea."

V. ATROCOCCUM, *Heller*. BLACK HUCKLEBERRY

A deciduous shrub, 4 to 10 ft. high, with the leaves not toothed, and very downy, even woolly beneath, the down persis' .ng to the end of the season. Berries black and shining, without any bloom, ¼ in. ide.

Native of the eastern United States and Canada. Except in its much more downy leaves, its broader, shorter corolla, and especially its bright black berries, this species resembles V. corymbosum, of which A. Gray made it a variety.

V. BRACTEATUM, *Thunberg*

(Andromeda chinensis, *Loddiges*)

An evergreen shrub 3 to 6 ft. high ; young shoots glabrous or nearly so. Leaves narrowly oval, tapered at both ends, of thin firm texture, distantly or scarcely toothed at all ; 1 to 3 ins. long, ½ to 1 in. wide ; dark green, glabrous ; stalk ⅛ in. or less long. Racemes 1 to 2 ins. long, minutely downy, carrying a dozen or more flowers, sometimes forming a kind of panicle of short flowering twigs ; each flower is in the axil of a small, persistent, leafy bract of linear-lanceolate shape and ⅛ to ⅜ in. long. Corolla white, slender, cylindrical, ¼ in. long, tapering slightly to the mouth which has tiny triangular lobes, minutely downy outside ; calyx lobes triangular, downy ; stamens downy. Fruit globose, ¼ in. wide, red, downy.

Native of Japan, Korea, and China ; apparently first introduced by Mr Reeves of Canton to Loddiges' nursery at Hackney in 1829 ; it was figured in their *Botanical Cabinet* (t. 1648) the following year. Reintroduced from China by the late Maurice de Vilmorin in 1914. Its distinctive characters are its downy, slender corolla and conspicuous bracts like tiny leaves which are borne on the main flower-stalk. Although perhaps best suited for the south-western counties and similarly mild localities, where it should make a cheerful evergreen, it is hardy enough and flowered freely when grown at Kew in August or September, reaching 5 ft. in height there.

V. CÆSPITOSUM, *Michaux*. DWARF BILBERRY

(Bot. Mag., t. 3429)

A dwarf deciduous shrub of tufted habit, 4 to 10 ins., sometimes only 2 or 3 ins. high ; branches round, minutely downy or glabrous. Leaves obovate to narrowly wedge-shaped, tapered towards the base, toothed, usually ¼ to 1½ ins. long, about half as wide ; glabrous and shining. Flowers appearing in May with the young shoots, and produced singly on decurved stalks ⅛ in. long. Corolla pitcher-shaped, ⅕ in. long, pale pink, five-toothed at the much contracted mouth. Berry globose, about ¼ in. wide, black with a blue bloom, sweet.

Native of N. America, spreading across the continent from Labrador to Alaska and southwards to New York on the east, to California on the west, inhabiting mountain summits at its more southerly limits. Introduced in 1823. A neat little shrub now rare in cultivation, but recently reintroduced from California ; very suitable for the rock garden. A form known as MAJOR grows 1 ft. high, and has leaves up to 1½ ins. long.

V. CANADENSE, *Rich*. SOUR-TOP, VELVET LEAF

(Bot. Mag., t. 3446)

A low, much-branched deciduous shrub usually under 1 ft. high ; shoots very downy, even bristly. Leaves ¾ to 1½ ins. long, ⅛ to ½ in. wide ; narrowly oval, pointed, not toothed ; downy on both sides. Flowers produced during May along with the young leaves in short dense clusters. Corolla bell-shaped, ¼ in. or less long, white tinged with red. Berries blue-black, ¼ in. or more wide, very agreeably flavoured.

Native of eastern N. America ; introduced in 1834, but first distinguished in 1748 by Kalm, the Swedish traveller. It has been much confused in gardens with the various forms of V. pennsylvanicum, but is readily distinguished by its very downy entire leaves. Like that species, it gives a valuable wild fruit, its berries ripening later, and forming a useful succession to the other in N. America.

V. CORYMBOSUM, *Linnæus*.   SWAMP BLUEBERRY

(Bot. Mag., t. 3433)

A deciduous shrub, 4 to 12 ft. high, forming a dense thicket of erect, much-branched stems ; young shoots downy to nearly glabrous. Leaves ovate to oval-lanceshaped, 1 to 3½ ins. long, half as wide ; tapering at both ends, very shortly stalked, downy beneath on the midrib and veins, not toothed. Flowers produced during May in a series of short, few-flowered clusters near and at the leafless ends of the previous season's twigs. Corolla cylindrical,

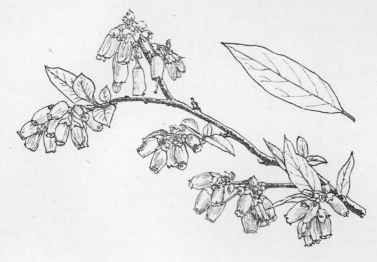

VACCINIUM CORYMBOSUM

but narrowed near the mouth, ¼ to ½ in. long, white or pale pink. Berries black, covered with a blue bloom, and from ¼ to ½ in. wide, variable in size, colour, and flavour.

Native of eastern N. America ; introduced in 1765. In British gardens this is the commonest, often the only N. American vaccinium. It not only grows well and blossoms freely, but its leaves turn to beautiful shades of red before falling in the autumn. It is a very variable species, and there are at least half a dozen forms that may be distinguished. The most distinct are :

Var. AMŒNUM, *A. Gray* (V. amœnum, *Aiton*).—Like the type in habit, but with the leaves minutely toothed, and hairy on the margins when young.

Var. FUSCATUM, *A. Gray* (V. fuscatum, *Aiton*).—Leaves covered beneath with brownish hairs. Introduced in 1770.

Var. PALLIDUM, *A. Gray* (V. pallidum, *Aiton*). Mountain Blueberry.— Leaves bluish beneath, and glabrous except for the minutely toothed margins being hairy. Berries deep blue.

All the varieties are by some writers considered to be distinct species like atrococcum (*q.v.*), which Gray made a variety of V. corymbosum also.

V. CRASSIFOLIUM, *Andrews*

(Bot. Mag., t. 1152)

An evergreen shrub of more or less procumbent habit; young wood covered with fine down. Leaves set about ¼ in. apart on the twigs, oval; ⅓ to ¾ in. long, ⅛ to ⅜ in. wide; slightly toothed, quite glabrous, shining green, and of leathery texture; stalk ¹⁄₁₆ in. long, reddish like the young twigs. Flowers produced in May and June in short lateral and terminal racemes; corolla bell-shaped, rosy red, ¼ in. long. Berries black.

Native of the south-eastern United States; introduced in 1787. It is not very hardy in the London district, and is better adapted for the south-western counties. It was in cultivation early in the nineteenth century, but was lost sight of until recently offered by American nurserymen. The only other evergreen vaccinium in cultivation with which it could be confused is V. Vitis-idæa, which is a much sturdier shrub with larger leaves, speckled beneath with black dots.

V. DELAVAYI, *Franchet*

A compact evergreen shrub, 1 to 3 ft. high; young shoots angled, bristly. Leaves much crowded on the shoots (ten or twelve to the inch) obovate, rounded or notched at the end, tapered to the base, not toothed, margins decurved; ⅜ to ½ in. long, half as much wide; glabrous, rather leathery; stalk very short. Racemes ½ to 1 in. long, usually terminating the shoot, main flower-stalk bristly. Corolla roundish urn-shaped, ⅛ in. long, described by Forrest as creamy yellow, tinged with rose outside, also as white flushed with rose, and bright rose; calyx lobes triangular, ciliate. Fruit globose, ⅛ in. wide, described by Forrest as " dark crimson " and " purplish red."

Native of Yunnan, China; discovered by Delavay; described and named by Franchet in 1895; introduced to cultivation by Forrest. In general appearance it much resembles V. moupinense and, like that species, grows in its wild state on cliffs, rocks, and as an epiphyte on trees. It differs from it in the leaves having a notch at the end, in the inflorescence being terminal, and in the flower-stalks being bristly. It makes a neat little evergreen with small, box-like foliage.

V. DELICIOSUM, *Piper*

It was in 1915 that this species was first distinguished and named. Previous to that date it was probably confused with V. cæspitosum, to which it is closely related. It grows 4 to 12 ins. high, has the same tufted habit and the same round, glabrous young shoots, but the leaves are of thicker texture and instead of being bright green on both sides are pale and rather glaucous beneath. In shape they are obovate to oval, pointed, tapered at the base, roundish-toothed, ½ to 1¼ ins. long. Flowers solitary, drooping from the leaf-axils; corolla rather globose, pinkish, ⅛ in. long. Fruit globose, black with a blue bloom, sweet.

Whilst V. cæspitosum is distributed right across N. America, V. deliciosum appears to be confined to the north-west, more especially to Washington. Piper, the author of the name, describes it as abundant in the Alpine meadows at about the limit of trees in the Cascade and Olympic Mountains. It is a neat, deciduous shrub suitable for a moist spot in the rock garden and was introduced some years ago to this country by Mr F. R. S. Balfour of Dawyck. I have not seen the fruit but it is to that that the specific name presumably refers. Its near relative, V. cæspitosum, has a comparatively narrower corolla.

V. Dunalianum, *Wight*

An evergreen shrub up to 20 ft. high in its wild state, or almost a tree ; quite devoid of down in all its parts ; young shoots lightly ribbed. Leaves oval or oval-lanceolate, with a long, slender, often tail-like end, and a broadly tapered base, not toothed ; 3 to 5 ins. long, 1 to 1¾ ins. wide ; dark green, of leathery texture ; stalk ⅛ to ¼ in. long. Racemes axillary, 1½ to 3 ins. long ; corolla waxy white, bell-shaped, ⅕ in. long, with five triangular teeth ; fruit black, globose, ¼ in. wide.

Native of Sikkim, Bhotan, Khasia Mountains, and W. China ; introduced many years ago from India. Wilson found it on Mt. Omei in 1904 and it had previously been collected there by Henry. It is one of the strongest growing of vacciniums and is worth growing as a handsome evergreen in the south-western counties. Near London it needs cool greenhouse treatment. The slender tail-like apex of the leaf, often 1 to 1½ ins. long, is distinctive.

V. erythrocarpum, *Michaux*. Mountain Cranberry

(Bot. Mag., t. 7413 ; Oxycoccus erythrocarpus, *Persoon*)

A deciduous shrub, from 3 to 6 ft. high, with downy young branches. Leaves short-stalked, ovate or ovate lance-shaped, taper-pointed ; 1 to 3 ins. long, scarcely half as wide ; bristle-toothed, tinged with red and slightly hairy when young. Flowers produced in June singly on slender pendulous stalks, about ½ in. long, from the axils of the young leaves. Corolla pale red, deeply four-lobed ; the lobes narrow, ⅓ in. long, and curled back, leaving the long anthers exposed and standing close together in a sort of column. Berries acid, roundish, ¼ in. wide, turning red, then purplish black.

Native of the mountains of the south-eastern United States ; introduced in 1806 by Loddiges of Hackney, but never common. It is a pretty shrub and of peculiar interest in forming a connecting link between Vaccinium and Oxycoccus (the true cranberries). It has the shrubby habit of the former, but the flower structure and arrangement of the latter. When first introduced it was hoped that it might prove of value as a fruiting bush, but like the rest of the imported species, it has never borne fruit freely enough to count for much.

V. fragile, *Franchet*

(V. setosum, *Wright*)

An evergreen shrub 1 to 3 ft. high ; young shoots round, densely bristly. Leaves ovate to oval, tapered to both ends ; finely and regularly toothed ; ½ to 1 in. long, ¼ to ⅜ in. wide ; nearly or quite glabrous above, downy beneath especially on the midrib. Flowers produced in a cluster of racemes during May and June from the terminal leaf-axils ; racemes 1 to 2 ins. long, downy ; corolla urn-shaped, white to rosy red, ⅛ to ¼ in. long, with five small reflexed teeth at the mouth ; calyx-lobes ciliate. Fruit black, globose, ³⁄₁₆ in. wide.

Native of W. China ; discovered by Delavay and Henry, also collected by Wilson as early as 1904, but whether he introduced it I do not know. It is, however, at present in cultivation at Exbury and elsewhere, raised from Forrest's seeds. Mr Lionel de Rothschild thought highly of it as a dwarf evergreen. According to the field notes of its various collectors, it varies considerably in its wild state in the colour of its flowers. Some are given as white, others as white tipped with rose, white stripped and tipped with vermilion, salmon red, pale rose. The beauty of the inflorescence is heightened by the red bracts on the raceme in whose axils the flowers are borne.

V. GLAUCO-ALBUM, *Hooker fil.*

(Bot. Mag., tt. 8924, 9536)

An evergreen shrub, 2 to 4 ft. high ; young stems soon glabrous. Leaves stiff and hard in texture, oval or ovate, 1½ to 2½ ins. long, ⅝ to 1¼ ins. wide ; pointed, with bristle-like teeth on the margins, green and glabrous above, of a vivid blue-white and slightly bristly on the midrib beneath. Racemes slightly downy, 2 to 3 ins. long, produced from the leaf-axils, and conspicuous for their large, persistent, blue-white bracts, edged with bristles. Corolla pinkish white, ¼ in. long, cylindrical, contracted at the mouth ; calyx glabrous shallowly lobed. Berries ⅓ in. diameter, globose, black, covered with blue-white bloom.

Native of the Himalaya at 9000 to 10,000 ft. altitude ; only hardy in the milder parts of the kingdom. It is remarkable for the vivid blue-white bloom on the fruit, bracts, and under-surface of the leaves. It used to grow well with the late Mr T. Acton of Kilmacurragh, Co. Wicklow, Ireland.

V. HIRSUTUM, *Buckley.* HAIRY HUCKLEBERRY

A low, deciduous shrub, 2 to 3 ft. high, spreading by underground rhizomes ; young shoots very downy, and remaining so the second year. Leaves ovate to oval, 1 to 2½ ins. long, ½ to 1¼ ins. wide, shortly stalked, pointed, deep green and slightly downy above, paler and more downy beneath ; not toothed. Flowers in broad, short racemes, produced towards the end of May. Corolla cylindrical, narrowed towards the mouth, ⅜ in. long, white tinged with pink, hairy ; calyx-lobes pointed, and like the flower-stalks, very hairy. Berries ¼ in. in diameter, nearly globular, blue-black covered with gland-tipped hairs.

Native of the mountains of N. Carolina and southwards, discovered by Mr Buckley about 1836, but lost sight of until rediscovered and brought into cultivation by Prof. Sargent in 1887. Given a position that is moist and not too sunny, it spreads rapidly by underground suckers. It is rendered very distinct by the hairiness of all its parts, more especially of its fruits, which have a sweet, pleasant, but not very pronounced flavour.

V. INTERMEDIUM, *Ruthe*

A natural hybrid between V. Myrtillus and V. Vitis-Idæa which has been found wild on the continent of Europe, and in Staffordshire in England. It is fairly intermediate between its parents, but resembles V. Myrtillus more closely in habit. The stems are not so markedly angular as in that species, and it inherits from V. Vitis-Idæa an evergreen or almost evergreen character. The leaf-margins are toothed, but the under-surface is not dotted. Berry dark violet. It was originally discovered in this country in Maer Woods, Staffordshire, by Mr Robert Garner, in 1870 ; and in 1886 by Prof. Bonney on Cannock Chase.

V. JAPONICUM, *Miquel*

A deciduous shrub 2 to 3 ft. high, with angular, glabrous young shoots. Leaves ovate to ovate-oblong, pointed, heart-shaped, rounded or tapered at the base, very finely toothed ; 1 to 2½ ins. long, ½ to 1¼ ins. wide ; glabrous, very shortly stalked. Flowers solitary in the leaf-axils, each borne in June and July on a very slender stalk ½ to ¾ in. long. Corolla pink, deeply divided into four narrow lobes which are curled back so as to leave ⅜ in. of the long anthers exposed and clustered together in a sort of column ; calyx with triangular lobes. Fruit globose, ¼ in. wide, bright red, pendulous.

Native of Japan and Korea ; introduced about 1893. It belongs to the
same section of Vaccinium as the American V. erythrocarpum, and with it
forms a connecting link with the cranberries (Oxycoccus). Both have the
shrubby habit of Vaccinium but the corolla is deeply split as in Oxycoccus, the
lobes similarly recurved.

Var. SINICUM, *Rehder*, is the Chinese form which has proportionately
narrower leaves with down on the midrib beneath. Introduced by Wilson in
1907. V. erythrocarpum differs from both in its downy shoots and more
downy leaves ; the flower-stalks are all very slender.

V. MEMBRANACEUM, *Douglas*

(V. myrtilloides, *Hooker*, not of *Michaux* ; Bot. Mag., t. 3447)

A deciduous shrub from 1 to 5 ft. high, erect-growing ; branchlets angular,
glabrous. Leaves ovate to oblong, pointed, rounded or tapered at the base,
minutely toothed ; $\frac{3}{4}$ to $2\frac{1}{2}$ ins. long, $\frac{1}{4}$ to 1 in. wide ; bright green and glabrous
on both surfaces ; stalk $\frac{1}{16}$ in. or less long. Flowers solitary in the leaf-axils
on stalks $\frac{1}{4}$ to $\frac{1}{3}$ in. long. Corolla between globose and urn-shaped, $\frac{1}{4}$ in.
across, greenish or pinkish white ; calyx entire. Berries $\frac{1}{4}$ to $\frac{1}{3}$ in. diameter,
purplish black, sweet, but rather acid.

Native of N. America from Lake Superior west to California, and north
to Alaska, discovered by Douglas about 1828. It is allied to V. Myrtillus in
its angled branchlets and solitary nodding flowers. Of little garden value.

V. MORTINIA, *Bentham*. MORTINA

An evergreen shrub, 2 to 4 ft. high, the young shoots covered with a dark
minute down. Leaves densely set on the twigs (about $\frac{1}{8}$ in. apart), ovate,
minutely toothed, $\frac{1}{3}$ to $\frac{1}{2}$ in. long, very uniform ; dark green above and
glabrous except for a little dark down on the midrib ; paler and minutely
pitted beneath with a tiny bristle in each cavity ; stalk downy, $\frac{1}{12}$ in. long.
Flowers produced during June in short, dense racemes from the leaf-axils,
and on the lower side of the twigs. Corolla rosy pink, cylindrical, about
in. long ; stamens hairy ; calyx with five triangular lobes ; flower-stalks
downy. Berry red, $\frac{1}{5}$ in. diameter.

Native of Ecuador, on the slopes of Mount Pinchincha ; introduced by
Hartweg about 1840. It is not hardy at Kew, surviving the mildest winters
only, but farther south, as at Leonardslee, near Horsham, it succeeds
admirably. It is a particularly neat and pleasing shrub, although its flowers,
as they grow, are hidden by the foliage. It is of peculiar interest also as
affording one of very few instances of a shrub found wild within a few miles
of the equator, yet hardy enough to grow and flower in some of the home
counties. The fruits are sold in the market of Quito, and from the name,
" Mortina," by which they are known there, the specific name has been adapted.

V. MOUPINENSE, *Franchet*

A low evergreen shrub of close, dense habit, 1 to 2 ft. high ; young shoots
grooved, downy. Leaves leathery, entire, crowded (ten or twelve to the inch),
narrowly obovate or oval, usually tapered more abruptly to the bluntish or
rounded apex ; $\frac{1}{3}$ to $\frac{1}{2}$ in. long, $\frac{1}{8}$ to $\frac{1}{16}$ in. wide ; dark glossy green, quite
glabrous except for the short stalk which is downy. Racemes $\frac{3}{4}$ to 1 in. long,
carrying nine to fifteen nodding flowers, the main and individual flower-stalks
quite glabrous, chocolate-red. The racemes spring mainly from the axils of
the terminal leaves. Corolla $\frac{3}{16}$ in. long, urn-shaped, five-angled, contracted

at the top to a small orifice where are five tiny triangular lobes ; deep shining chocolate-red. Calyx glabrous, coloured like the corolla, its lobes triangular. Stamens included in the corolla, their stalks hairy. Fruit a globose berry ¼ in. wide, purple-black.

Native of W. Szechuen, China ; discovered by David in 1869 ; introduced by Wilson in 1909. In the original description by Franchet the flowers are described as white and Wilson describes them as rose-pink, but on the plants which have flowered at Kew they are dark red or chocolate crimson. Wilson observes that, in its wild state, it often occurs as an epiphyte on old trees. It is a pleasing little evergreen, suitable for the rock garden and growing well in peaty or light loamy soil. No doubt it dislikes chalk. It blooms in May and June. Very similar to V. Delavayi, it can be distinguished by its leaves not being notched at the apex and by its glabrous inflorescence.

V. MYRSINITES, *Lamarck*. EVERGREEN BLUEBERRY

(V. nitidum, *Andrews*, Bot. Mag., t. 1550)

An evergreen shrub, often low and spreading, sometimes up to 2 ft. high ; young shoots slender, mostly downy, minutely warty. Leaves narrowly oval or obovate, pointed, tapered at the base, indistinctly toothed, scarcely stalked ; ¼ to 1 in. long, ⅛ to ¼ in. wide (sometimes larger) ; glossy green above ; paler, conspicuously veined and sometimes bristly beneath. Flowers produced in April and May in terminal and axillary clusters towards the end of the shoots. Corolla tubular, ¼ in. long, white or tinged with pink, with five small teeth ; calyx triangularly toothed, glabrous like the flower-stalk. Fruit ¼ in. wide, blue-black.

Native of S.E. United States from Virginia to Florida ; cultivated by Loddiges of Hackney in 1813. It is not very hardy near London, but should succeed farther south and west, where the decumbent form would make a neat ground cover. The upright form suggests Pernettya mucronata by its small leaves closely set on the branchlets.

Var. GLAUCUM, *Gray*, has the leaves glaucous beneath.

V. MYRTILLUS, *Linnæus*. WHORTLEBERRY, BILBERRY

A deciduous shrub, usually 6 to 12 ins. high, sometimes more ; the young branches distinctly angled, glabrous. Leaves ovate, ½ to 1 in. long, often somewhat heart-shaped, regularly and bluntly toothed, bright green and quite glabrous, scarcely stalked. Flowers produced in May usually singly on drooping stalks from the leaf-axils. Corolla nearly globular, pale pink, ¼ in. long. Berries black, with a blue bloom, ⅓ in. diameter, globular.

Native of Britain, where it is one of the commonest of mountain and moorland shrubs, also of N. and Central Europe. The bilberry is one of the most valuable wild fruits of Britain, and is frequently offered in considerable quantities in the markets of north country towns. They are used for making tarts, jelly, and are especially delicious eaten with cream and sugar. A very hardy plant, it manages to survive on the summits of our loftiest mountains. It is scarcely of sufficient interest for the garden, and does not always thrive well translated to low-level gardens, in the south at any rate. Its angled stems distinguish it from the other British species.

Var. LEUCOCARPUM.—Fruits white.

Var. MICROPHYLLUM, *Hooker* (V. microphyllum, *Howell*).—Native of western N. America from the Sierra Nevada, where it occurs at 7000 ft. into British Columbia. It is about half the size of the European plant in all its parts.

V. NEGLECTUM, *Fernald*

A deciduous shrub 2 to 4 ft. high, of bushy, much branched shape; young shoots, leaves and flower-stalks all without down, at least at maturity. Leaves 1½ to 3½ ins. long, ½ to 1½ ins. wide; narrowly oval or obovate, pointed, rounded or widely tapered at the base, not toothed; often glaucous beneath when young; stalk $\frac{1}{12}$ in. long. Flowers produced during May in racemes 1 to 2 ins. long that spring from the joints of the previous year's growth, each flower coming from the axil of a small leaf-like bract. Corolla white or pink, ¼ in. long, bell-shaped with five comparatively large lobes; stamens with their anthers distinctly protruded; calyx with five triangular lobes; flower stalk very slender, up to ½ in. long. Fruit globose to obovoid, ¼ in. wide, green or yellow.

Native of the S.E. United States and very closely related to (possibly only a variety of) V. stamineum. They belong to a group of American species distinguished by their conspicuously exposed anthers, and by the leaf-like bracts on the racemes. These bracts are mostly oblong and ¼ to 1 in. long. V. stamineum differs from this species by its downy young shoots, leaves, etc., V. neglectum being quite glabrous. But there are intermediate forms. Both are pleasing when in flower, their beauty being enhanced then by the pale colour of the thin young leaves. Belonging to the same group is

V. MELANOCARPUM, *C. Mohr*, which is a deciduous bush of a similar type with downy young shoots and leaves downy beneath, thereby differing from V. neglectum. It is more conspicuously downy than V. stamineum and the fruits, instead of being yellowish or green, as in that species and V. neglectum, are of a dark plum-purple, shining, ⅓ in. diameter, edible but rather acid. Flower-stalks decurved, hairy, slender. Native of the S.E. United States, often in mountain woods. Still another of this groups is

V. CANDICANS, *C. Mohr*, which has also downy leaves, but they are glaucous beneath, and the globose fruit is also glaucous. It has been introduced to this country, and when in bloom in May and June is very charming with its thin glaucous young leaves and bracts, and nodding white flowers with exposed yellow anthers.

V. NUMMULARIA, *Hooker fil.*

A low evergreen shrub often found growing wild in the forks of trees and having pendulous branches there. Young shoots rather slender, but made to look thicker by their dense covering of pale brown bristles, which give them an almost mossy appearance. Leaves scarcely stalked, of firm, even hard texture, bright green, wrinkled but not downy above, conspicuously veined and glabrous beneath; broadly oval to ovate, rounded or bluntish at the apex, rounded at the base; ½ to 1 in. long, ⅜ to ⅝ in. wide; margins recurved, sparingly set with bristles. The leaves are set on the twigs six or eight to the inch. Flowers opening in May and June, crowded on several racemes, each ½ to ¾ in. long, clustered at the end of the shoots. Corolla rose-red to pink or pinkish white, ⅕ in. long, $\frac{1}{10}$ in. wide, tapering from the base to the narrow mouth; stamens hairy; calyx shallowly lobed, ciliate. Fruit globose, ⅕ in. wide, each on a stalk ¼ to ½ in. long, black, said to be edible.

Native of N. India, especially in Sikkim and Bhotan at altitudes of 8000 to 10,000 ft. Introduced about 1850, it is still rare but occasionally offered by nurserymen. It is a very distinct species on account of the mossy twigs, small thick wrinkled leaves, and rose-coloured or pinkish blossom. Although it has been found by Mr I. Burkill at 11,600 ft. altitude near Phallut in Sikkim, it is only just hardy enough for our average climate. But it succeeds well in the maritime counties of the south and west and is better worth cultivation there than many of this genus. Suitable for a moist spot in the rock garden.

Forrest found a similar vaccinium in Yunnan at an altitude of 12,000 ft. which ought to be hardier.

V. OLDHAMII, *Miquel*

(V. ciliatum, *Thunberg*)

A deciduous shrub up to 12 ft. high in Japan, of bushy habit; young shoots glandular-downy. Leaves ovate, oval or obovate, pointed, tapered or sometimes rounded at the base; edged with fine, bristle-like teeth; 1 to 3 ins. long, $\frac{1}{2}$ to $1\frac{1}{2}$ ins. wide; green on both surfaces, sprinkled with bristles above, bristly on the midrib and veins beneath; stalk $\frac{1}{8}$ in. or less long. Racemes $1\frac{1}{2}$ to $2\frac{1}{2}$ ins. long, carrying eight to twenty nodding flowers; flower-stalks glandular-downy with leaf-like bracts at the base. Corolla bell-shaped, $\frac{1}{6}$ in. long, reddish; stamens downy, somewhat shorter than the corolla; calyx-lobes triangular. Fruit globose, $\frac{1}{3}$ in. wide, black, edible. Blooms in June.

Native of Japan and Korea; it was collected in the latter country by Wilford in 1859 and by Richard Oldham in 1863, but does not seem to have reached cultivation until 1892. Although quite hardy, it is not a particularly attractive species, but the leaves sometimes turn a good red before falling.

V. OVALIFOLIUM, *Smith*

A deciduous shrub of slender shape from 4 to 12 ft. high; young shoots angular, not downy. Leaves oval, ovate, not toothed, blunt at the apex, rounded at the base, 1 to $2\frac{1}{2}$ ins. long, $\frac{5}{8}$ to $1\frac{1}{4}$ ins. wide; pale green above, rather glaucous beneath, quite glabrous; stalk $\frac{1}{16}$ in. long. Flowers solitary on a glabrous drooping stalk about $\frac{1}{4}$ in. long. Corolla egg-shaped, much narrowed at the mouth, $\frac{3}{8}$ in. long, pinkish; calyx shallowly ten-toothed. Fruit bluish purple, $\frac{2}{5}$ in. wide, acid.

Native of the high latitudes of N. America from Quebec and Michigan to Alaska and Oregon. It has long been known but has not sufficient flower beauty to have secured for itself a permanent place in gardens. It was first collected by Archibald Menzies on the N.W. coast of N. America during Vancouver's great voyage of survey, 1790-5. He found it in "shady Alpine woods" and alludes to its "very useful fruit." Its chief garden value is in the occasional rich colouring of its foliage in autumn. Flowers in June.

The name "V. ovatifolium" occurs in catalogues, probably in mistake for the above. It has at any rate no standing.

V. OVATUM, *Pursh*

(Bot. Mag., t. 4732)

An evergreen shrub of bushy habit, 10 to 12 ft. high in this country; young wood purple, covered with short, dense down. Leaves $\frac{1}{4}$ to $\frac{1}{2}$ in. apart, sometimes slightly heart-shaped at the base, but usually rounded or tapering; $\frac{1}{2}$ to $1\frac{1}{2}$ ins. long, $\frac{1}{3}$ to $\frac{3}{4}$ in. wide; of firm leathery texture, finely and regularly toothed, dark glossy green above, paler beneath and glabrous except for some short, scattered bristles beneath and some down on the midrib above. Flowers produced in May and June four to six together in short, nodding racemes from the leaf-axils, white, roundish, bell-shaped, with five small, recurved, triangular lobes. Berry black, round, $\frac{1}{3}$ in. diameter.

Native of western N. America; discovered by Menzies towards the end of the eighteenth century; introduced by Douglas in 1826. Whilst hardy enough to survive the hardest winters experienced at Kew, it often suffers in severe frost through the cutting back of the younger growth. At Bearwood, in Berkshire, there was and still may be a specimen 10 to 12 ft. high, which is one of the finest in the country. It is a handsome bush when seen at its best. The fruit rarely ripens with us ; they were said by Douglas to be agreeably flavoured, although acid.

V. PADIFOLIUM, *Smith*. MADEIRAN WHORTLEBERRY

(Bot. Mag., t. 7305 ; V. maderense, *Link*)

A deciduous shrub, 6 to 8 ft. high in this country, but becoming a small tree in Madeira ; young wood downy except for glabrous strips extending from the base of one leaf to the axil of the next below. Leaves ovate to oval, 1 to 2¼ ins. long, ½ to 1 in. wide ; rounded or tapering at the base, pointed, finely toothed, dark green and downy on the midrib above, paler and downy at the base of the midrib below ; stalk $\frac{1}{12}$ in. long. Flowers produced in June in racemes 1 to 2 ins. long, from the wood of the previous year, each flower drooping and jointed at the base of the ovary to a short stalk springing from the axil of a bract about ¼ in. long. Corolla bell-shaped, ¼ in. long, dull yellow tinged with purple, the five lobes triangular ; stamens ten, glabrous. Berries blue, globose, ¼ to ½ in. across.

Native of the mountains of Madeira at altitudes of 3000 to 5000 ft. ; introduced to Kew by Masson on his return in 1777 from his famous collecting expedition to the Cape of Good Hope. What was believed to be one of his plants was still growing in the Botanic Garden at Kew until a few years ago. But whilst it may thus be considered hardy, it thrives better where the climate is warmer—in such a garden, for instance, as that of Abbotsbury, near Weymouth. There has been much confusion between this species and the Caucasian V. Arctostaphylos, but seen together they are quite distinct. The latter has larger leaves, is of more open growth, the stamens are hairy, and it is quite deciduous.

V. PARVIFOLIUM, *Smith*

A deciduous shrub, varying in height from 1 to 6 ft. ; the stems and twigs slender, sharply angled (like V. Myrtillus) when young, glabrous. Leaves oval, obovate, or nearly round, thin, ¼ to ½ in. long, not toothed. Flowers solitary in the leaf-axils, nodding ; corolla globular, pinkish white. Berry bright red, acid but very palatable, ¼ in. across.

Native of western N. America from California to Alaska and the Aleutian Islands. It is but little known in gardens, and so far as I have seen its chief value as an ornament is in the beautiful red its leaves turn in autumn before they fall.

V. PENNSYLVANICUM, *Lamarck*. LOW BLUEBERRY

A low, deciduous shrub, usually under 2 ft. high ; young shoots warted and more or less downy. Leaves nearly stalkless, lance-shaped to narrowly oval or oblong ; ¾ to 1½ ins. long, ⅛ to ¼ in. wide ; minutely toothed, pointed, glabrous and bright green, the midrib downy on one or both sides. Flowers produced in April and May in short dense clusters. Corolla white tinged with red, cylindric to bell-shaped, ¼ in. or rather more long. Berries round, ¼ to ⅝ in. wide, normally black, covered with a blue bloom, but variable in colour, being in some forms red, and in one (var. LEUCOCARPUM, *Gray*) white ; very sweet.

Native of the eastern United States and Canada ; introduced in 1772. The berry has a pleasant flavour, and is one of the most valuable wild fruits of N. America, ripening earlier than those of any other species. It covers large areas of poor sandy soil. In this country it has little or no value as a fruit-bearer, but makes a pleasing low cover on peaty or light sandy soils.

Var. ANGUSTIFOLIUM, *A. Gray*, is a dwarf mountain form, with lanceolate leaves not exceeding ⅓ in. in width.

V. PRÆSTANS, *Lambert*

A low deciduous shrub with a creeping root-stock ; its glabrous or downy mostly unbranched shoots growing 3 to 6 ins. high. Leaves obovate, sometimes broadly oval, usually rounded at the apex except for a small mucro, or broadly tapered to a point ; always slenderly tapered at the base to a short stalk ; indistinctly toothed ; 1 to 2¼ ins. long, ½ to 1½ ins. wide ; both surfaces green, glabrous above, sparsely hairy on the veins beneath. Flowers white, tinged with pink, produced in June two or three together or solitary at the base of the leafy part of the stem, each on a short downy stalk that is furnished with two narrow, leaf-like bracts. Corolla bell-shaped, ¼ in. or less long, with erect lobes at the mouth ; stamens downy ; calyx-lobes rounded, ciliate. Fruit ⅖ to ½ in. wide, globose, bright glossy red, sweet and fragrant.

Native of Japan, Kamtschatka, and Saghalien. It was first named and shortly described by Aylmer B. Lambert in the *Transactions of the Linnæan Society*, vol. x., t. 9, in 1810, from a specimen that had been collected in Kamtschatka, but does not seem to have reached cultivation until Wilson introduced it from Saghalien in 1914. It is remarkably distinct for a vaccinium in its low creeping habit, in the shape and size of its leaves, and in its large fruits, which are said to have a fragrance like that of a strawberry. Inured as it is to severe cold in winter it will probably succeed best in the north and in Scotland. It is often found growing in sphagnum. It resembles Rhododendron kamtschaticum in mode of growth.

V. Sprengelii, *Sleumer*

(V. Donianum, *Wight* ; V. mandarinorum, *Diels*)

A deciduous shrub up to 10 ft. high ; young shoots round, mostly glabrous. Leaves 1½ to 3½ ins. long, ½ to 1¼ ins. wide ; ovate-lanceolate, slender-pointed, tapered at the base, glabrous ; stalk ⅛ in. long. Flowers produced in May on the lower side of axillary racemes 1 to 3 ins. long ; corolla white (either pure or pink tinted), cylindrical, ¼ in. long, with five teeth at the narrow mouth ; glabrous outside, downy within ; calyx-lobes triangular ; stamen-stalks hairy. Fruit ⅓ in. wide, black-purple.

Native of the Khasia Mountains and Assam in India ; also of China. Collectors describe it as a beautiful shrub in a wild state but it is only hardy in the milder parts of the British Isles. Plants of Chinese origin are in Cornish gardens, probably raised from seeds sent home by Wilson, who observes that it is an exceedingly variable plant common in the woodlands and thickets of Hupeh and Szechuen. It bears fruit very freely at Caerhays. The original Indian type has glabrous young shoots and flower-stalks, but downy forms have been found in China.

V. STAMINEUM, *Linnæus*. DEERBERRY

A deciduous shrub, 2 to 4 ft. high, of bushy, much-branched habit ; twigs downy. Leaves oval or ovate, ¾ to 3 ins. long, about half as wide ; pointed ; dark dull green above, and downy on the midrib, paler or more or less glaucous and downy beneath ; leaf-stalk ⅛ in. or less long. Flowers white, with bright yellow projecting anthers, produced during May and June in downy racemes, 1 to 2 ins. long, furnished with leaf-like bracts ¼ to ¾ in. long. Corolla open, bell-shaped, ¼ to ⅓ in. wide ; calyx glabrous except on the ciliate margins, flower-stalk slender, downy, ⅛ to ½ in. long. Fruit greenish or yellowish, round or pear-shaped, ⅓ in. wide, not edible.

Native of eastern N. America ; introduced in 1772. This is one of the prettiest of vacciniums in its blossoms, which are freely borne on short, broad racemes, springing from the joints of the previous year's wood. It is distinct among cultivated vacciniums for the protruding stamens and large, leafy bracts on the racemes. Nearly allied to this species is V. NEGLECTUM, *Fernald*, which differs in having quite glabrous leaves and branches.

V. ULIGINOSUM, *Linnæus*. BOG BILBERRY

A deciduous shrub, 1 to 2 ft. high, with very minutely downy or glabrous round branchlets. Leaves obovate, or almost round, not toothed, glabrous or finely downy beneath, dull glaucous green, ½ to 1 in. long, with scarcely any stalk. Flowers produced during May singly or in pairs or threes from the uppermost joints of the previous year's wood, each on a drooping stalk about ¼ in. long. Corolla pale red or white, bell-shaped, ⅛ in. long, with usually four teeth. Berries black with a blue bloom, sweet.

Native of the mountain heaths and bogs of the Northern Hemisphere and common in the north of Britain. The fruit is edible, but is said to produce headache and giddiness if eaten in quantity. It furnishes a valuable food for mountain game, but is scarcely worth cultivating in gardens. From its companion deciduous species in Britain (V. Myrtillus), it is easily distinguished by its round stems, entire leaves, and in the parts of the flower being mostly in fours.

V. URCEOLATUM, *Hemsley*

An evergreen bush up to 6 ft. high in its wild state ; young shoots at first covered thickly with fine down. Leaves of firm, leathery texture, ovate-oblong, narrowed at the apex to a long fine point, rounded at the base, not toothed ; 2 to 4 ins. long, 1 to 2½ ins. wide ; dark green, downy only when quite young ; veins very deeply impressed on the upper surface ; stalk very short, about $\frac{1}{12}$ in. long. Flowers in racemes 1 to 1½ ins. long, springing from the leaf-axils in June. Corolla urn-shaped, ¼ in. long, pink ; calyx-lobes triangular ; stamens with slightly exposed anthers, their stalks downy. Fruit black, globose, ¼ in. wide.

Native of W. China ; first discovered about 1887 on Mt. Omei, in Szechuen by the Rev. E. Faber. Wilson found it on the same mountain in 1904 when collecting for Messrs Veitch and in Wa-shan in 1908. Introduced to Kew from Messrs Vilmorin of Paris in 1923. It is scarcely hardy enough to grow really well at Kew and was severely injured by the winter of 1928-9, but it succeeds well at Caerhays in Cornwall. Wilson observes that it is partial to sandstone boulders. It is more notable perhaps for its striking evergreen foliage than for any beauty of blossom.

V. VACILLANS, *Kalm*. BLUE HUCKLEBERRY

A deciduous shrub, 1 to 4 ft. high, with mostly glabrous, yellowish green, warted branchlets. Leaves mostly oval to obovate, 1 to 2 ins. long, about half as wide ; nearly entire, or minutely toothed except towards the base ; very shortly stalked, minutely pointed, glabrous, firm, pale or glaucous beneath.

Flowers produced during May in short clusters on the leafless tips of the previous year's shoots. Corolla pink, cylindrical, about ¼ in. long ; calyx often reddish. Berries roundish, ¼ to ⅓ in. wide, black, usually covered with a blue bloom, very sweet.

Native of the eastern United States from Maine southwards to Georgia. This is a stiffly branched species with firm textured leaves, and is one of the most ornamental in its flowers, which, like the fruits, cover the terminal (and naked) 2 or 3 ins. of the twigs. Said to favour dryish situations in a wild state.

V. VIRGATUM, *Aiton*

(Bot. Mag., t. 3522)

A deciduous shrub of erect habit 4 to 10 ft. high ; young shoots minutely downy. Leaves ovate-lanceolate to oval-oblong, 1 to 3 ins. long, 1 to 1½ ins. wide, tapered to both ends, finely toothed or entire, bright green and glabrous above, pale or glaucous beneath ; shortly stalked. Flowers white or pink, in short axillary clusters of six to ten ; corolla ⅓ in. long, cylindrical but slightly tapered towards the mouth, where are five tiny, reflexed teeth ; calyx five-lobed, lobes triangular. Fruit globose, black, ¼ in. wide, sometimes slightly covered with bloom.

Native of eastern N. America from New York southwards, often in swamps. Much confused in gardens with V. corymbosum which has a more urceolate, less cylindrical corolla. Probably some of the plants called virgatum in gardens and valued for their autumn tints are really V. corymbosum.

Var. TENELLUM, *Gray* (V. tenellum, *Aiton*).—A smaller shrub with smaller (½ to 1¼ ins.) leaves and shorter, denser flower-clusters.

V. VITIS-IDÆA, *Linnæus*. COWBERRY

A low, evergreen, creeping shrub, 6 to 10 ins. high, with round, wiry, few-branched stems, covered when young with short, black down. Leaves dark lustrous green, box-like, obovate, often notched at the apex, shortly stalked ; ¼ to 1 in. long, about half as wide ; the lower surface sprinkled with black dots. Flowers produced during May and June, five to twelve together in terminal racemes less than 1 in. long. Corolla white or pinkish, bell-shaped, rather deeply four-lobed, ¼ in. long. Berries dark red, globular, acid and harsh in flavour, ⅖ in. wide.

Native of Britain on moors, heaths, and in woods ; also of Europe, N. Asia, and N.E. America. Its fruit is only palatable when cooked with sugar. As a shrub, the cowberry is the handsomest of native species, the dark glossy foliage making neat, dense tufts. In suitable positions it spreads quickly by means of its creeping root-stock.

Var. MAJOR, *Loddiges*.—Leaves larger than in the type, up to 1⅛ ins. long.
Var. MINOR.—Leaves smaller than in the type, ⅛ to ½ in. long.

VELLA. CRUCIFERÆ

A genus of shrubs consisting of three species, two of which are occasionally found in cultivation. They are natives of S.W. Europe. Flowers yellow ; petals four ; seed-vessel a compressed, two-celled pod, with one or two seeds in each cell.

V. Pseudocytisus, *Linnæus*.   Cress Rocket

(Bot. Reg., t. 293)

A low, evergreen shrub, usually less than 2 ft. high near London, but larger in milder localities ; branches erect, covered the first two or three years with spiny bristles, ultimately glabrous. Leaves obovate, ½ to ¾ in. long, rounded at the apex, tapering to a short stalk at the base, covered on both surfaces and at the margin with stiff bristly hairs. Flowers on an erect, elongated, terminal raceme, 4 to 8 ins. long, more crowded towards the top, the calyx erect, green, hairy ; petals somewhat spoon-shaped, the terminal part yellow, and roundish ; the lower part contracted into a long, slender, purplish claw ; each petal about ⅓ in. long ; flower-stalk 1/16 in. long.

This curious shrub is a native of the mountains of Central Spain. It is not really hardy, but has stood unprotected on the rock garden at Kew for several years at a time. Our hardest winters kill it. A sunny, rather dry position should be given it. It was cultivated by Miller at Chelsea, in 1759. Propagated easily by cuttings of half-ripened wood in gentle heat. It flowers from the end of May to July. Very suitable for the Isle of Wight and similar climates.

V. spinosa, *Boissier*

A dwarf, deciduous shrub of dense, compact habit about 1 ft. high, with rigid, erect stems, the upper branchlets of which become spine-tipped ; young shoots glabrous except for a few pale bristles at first. Leaves dull greyish green, linear, ½ to ¾ in. long, 1/20 in. wide ; fleshy, often showing a tendency to become pinnate ; glabrous except for an occasional bristle like those on the young shoots. Flowers few in terminal corymbs ; each flower about ⅝ in. across ; petals four, yellow with brown veins, roundish obovate, narrowed at the base to a slender claw about as long as the blade. Calyx tubular, ¼ in. long, green, with four erect pointed teeth. Seed-vessel a dry two-celled pod, erect, ¼ in. long, somewhat heart-shaped, terminated by a flat, pointed beak ⅓ in. long.

Native of Spain, it was quite hardy in the rock garden at Kew, where a plant scarcely 1 ft. high grew for twenty years, flowering in June. It is an interesting, but not very showy shrub. Propagated by cuttings of young wood. The bristles and spines on the stems and leaves are much more numerous and conspicuous in wild plants.

VERBENA tridens, *Lagasca*.   Mata Negra.   Verbenaceæ

(V. Carroo, *Spegazzini* ; Princeton Univ. Exped. to Patagonia, t. 23)

An evergreen shrub of virgate habit, 3 to 6 ft. high ; young shoots slender, stiffly erect, downy. The leaves on the first year shoots are arranged oppositely, seven to fourteen pairs to the inch, and are downy, from 1/12 to ⅙ in. long, stalkless, consisting of three stout, sharply-pointed lobes, each lobe grooved beneath on either side of its prominent midrib. From the axils of these leaves, during the second year and afterwards, proceed short branches on which the short, simple, thick, blunt leaves are packed closely together decussately (*i.e.*, in four superposed rows), the whole making a quadrangular arrangement of leaf and stem ¼ in. wide. The second type of leaf is about 1/12 in. long. On the older wood the leaf-clusters form curiously contorted masses. Flowers white to rosy-lilac,

sweetly and powerfully scented, produced in terminal spikes, often one
spike on each of a cluster of short twigs near the apex of the shoot; a
spike carries six to twelve flowers. Corolla $\frac{1}{4}$ to $\frac{1}{3}$ in. long, $\frac{1}{4}$ in. wide,
tubular, five-lobed, downy; calyx tubular, grooved, downy, with jagged
margins; stamens four, attached to and hidden in the upper half of the
corolla-tube, anthers yellow; bracts three-lobed, resembling the leaves,
one flower in the axil of each.

Native of Patagonia; originally named in 1816. It appears to be
widely spread from Port San Julian in the north to Lake Laguna Blanca
in the south, in places abundant enough to provide fuel. We owe the
introduction of this extraordinary shrub to Mr Clarence Elliott of the
Six Hills Nursery, Stevenage, who found it in flower in February 1928.
It is quite unlike any other plant in our open-air gardens, especially in
the change of the tiny leaves from the three-lobed and sharply-pointed
ones of the shoots in their first year to the undivided, blunt and decussate
ones of subsequent years. I learn from Mr Elliott that it is proving
absolutely hardy in his nursery and flowered there in July 1932. The
vanilla-like fragrance of the blossom is very strong and perceptible several
yards away from the plant, which grows well in ordinary loam and should
be given as sunny a place as possible.

VERONICA. Speedwell. SCROPHULARIACEÆ

The greater part of the genus Veronica consists of herbaceous plants.
Of those that have a claim to mention in this work all are natives of New
Zealand, and with the exception of V. elliptica, which is found also in
S. America, they belong exclusively to New Zealand. In the *Manual of
the New Zealand Flora* (1906), Mr Cheeseman enumerates about seventy
woody species, ranging from small trees to dwarf shrubs, all evergreen.
V. PARVIFLORA, *Vahl* (V. arborea, *Buchanan*), is sometimes a tree 25 ft.
high, with a trunk 2 to 3 ft. in diameter. They have opposite, mostly
stout or leathery leaves, usually superposed in four vertical rows, but in
a few species, like cupressoides and Hectori, the leaves are tiny, scale-
like, and more or less appressed to the stem, as in cypresses. The older
parts of the stems are conspicuously ringed with the scars of fallen leaves.
The growth of these veronicas, except in a few, is continuous, that is
to say, no terminal bud is formed at the end of the growing season.
Flowers crowded in usually axillary, sometimes terminal panicles,
racemes, or spikes, and produced near the ends of the growing shoots.
The individual flowers are very much alike in all the following species
except in colour. The calyx has four sepals, and the corolla (usually
about $\frac{1}{4}$ in. across) consists of a tubular base expanding at the mouth
into four more or less spreading lobes. Stamens two, the stalks attached
to the top of the corolla tube. Seed-vessel a two-celled, often flattened
capsule.

These New Zealand veronicas are of the easiest cultivation, provided
the climate is not too severe for them. They can be very readily
increased by means of young wood cuttings, and thrive in a sandy loam.
Unfortunately, very few of them are sufficiently hardy to withstand

our severest winters. The hardiest are anomala, buxifolia, carnosula, cupressoides, Darwiniana, Hectori, and brachysiphon. Most of them flower from May onwards.

The species hybridise freely, and some of the most ornamental kinds are of hybrid origin. The majority of these hybrids, however, are of the more tender class, and should really be classed as cool greenhouse plants, except in the south-western counties. All the sorts appear to thrive well in maritime districts. The Edinburgh Botanic Garden contains a fine collection, and several survived the winter of 1894-5 there that succumbed at Kew.

The following descriptions are mostly checked by those of Mr Cheeseman in his valuable *Manual* above mentioned. But it is difficult to distinguish with certainty many of the species in cultivation, owing to the different aspects the plants assume at different stages of their career, and to the differences that arise from the changed environment of plants under cultivation. The difficulty is further increased by the shy-flowering character of several.

Besides the species described below, there are many hybrids available for, and well worth cultivation in mild localities. The number increases annually, largely owing to cross-fertilisation by bees, and there are some fine hybrids without published names that have been raised in private gardens. The following are obtainable in nurseries : *Bowles' Hybrid*, up to 18 ins. high, flowers mauve, on short spikes ; *Blue Gem*, fine, blue-flowered ; *edinensis*, dwarf, leaves small, flowers pale blue (a cross between V. Hectori and pimeleoides raised at Edinburgh in 1904) ; *Gauntlettii*, flowers in long spikes, deep salmon rose ; *Girdwoodiana*, a distinct hybrid of erect growth with slender stems and small leaves, flowers pale lavender ; *Headfortii*, a handsome hybrid raised by the late Marquis of Headfort, purplish blue ; *Evelyn*, flowers rich carmine ; *La Seduisante*, an old hybrid from V. speciosa with reddish-lilac flowers ; *Simon Delaux*, very large racemes of bright crimson flowers ; *Purple Queen*, bright purple ; *Veitchii*, a fine robust shrub with very large racemes of deep violet flowers.

The shrubby veronicas are particularly valuable for seaside gardens, not only because they enjoy the greater mildness and dampness of the climatic conditions there, but because many of them are not injured even by salt spray.

It has to be noted that some authorities use HEBE as the generic title of these shrubs as distinct from the herbs and sub-herbs called VERONICA.

V. AMPLEXICAULIS, *Armstrong*

(Bot. Mag., t. 7370)

A shrub, 1 to 3 ft. high, with the branches erect or ultimately prostrate. Leaves glaucous, ½ to 1 in. long, ⅓ to ⅔ in. broad ; broadly oblong or oval, cupped, superposed in four vertical rows and closely set together ; rounded at the apex, the bases overlapping, heart-shaped, not stalked, but partially clasping the stem. Flowers white, ¼ in. across, stalkless, borne from leaf-axils near the end of the shoot in simple or branched spikes 1 to 1½ ins. long, the main-stalk of which is minutely downy.

Native of the South Island of New Zealand in the Canterbury province; discovered by Armstrong about 1880 and soon after introduced. It is allied to, and about as hardy as V. carnosula and V. pinguifolia. From the former it is distinguished by its downy ovary and round-tipped seed-vessel, and from both by its stem-clasping leaves, heart-shaped at the base, and in the longer, often branched inflorescence.

V. LINDSAYI, *Hort.*, was raised by the late Mr R. Lindsay of Edinburgh, a well-known cultivator of New Zealand veronicas, from seeds of V. amplexicaulis ripened in his garden. It is of more compact habit than that species, the leaves are not glaucous, and the flowers are pink. No doubt of hybrid origin.

V. ANGUSTIFOLIA, *A. Richard*
(V. parviflora angustifolia, *Hooker fil.* ; Bot. Mag., t. 5965)

A shrub, 3 to 5 ft. high, occasionally more, of rather thin, loose habit ; branches slender, erect, glabrous and shining, turning dark brown towards the end of the season. Leaves stalkless, linear, $1\frac{1}{2}$ to $3\frac{1}{2}$ ins. long, $\frac{1}{8}$ to $\frac{1}{4}$ in. wide ; tapering to a point, perfectly glabrous, often pointing downwards. Racemes in pairs from the leaf-axils near the summit of the shoot, 2 to 5 ins. long, $\frac{3}{4}$ in. wide ; the basal flowers opening long before the terminal ones. Flowers white, tinged more or less with lilac, $\frac{1}{6}$ to $\frac{1}{4}$ in. diameter ; tube of

corolla twice or thrice as long as the sepals, which are erect, oblong, edged with minute hairs. Individual flower-stalk slender, $\frac{1}{8}$ to $\frac{1}{4}$ in. long, and, like the main-stalk of the raceme, minutely downy.

Native of the North Island of New Zealand ; introduced about 1868, perhaps before. It is very distinct in its narrow leaves and purple-brown stems, and has considerable merit as a flowering shrub, producing its graceful racemes from July until November in successive pairs near the top of the growing shoot. It succumbs in severe winters.

V. ANOMALA, *Armstrong*
(Bot. Mag., t. 7360)

A shrub, 3 to 5 ft. high, of erect, narrow habit, with slender branches, minutely downy in a strip above each leaf-axil when young. Leaves $\frac{1}{3}$ to $\frac{3}{4}$ in. long, oval-lanceolate or narrow-oblong, pointed, entire, tapering at the base to a very short, broad stalk, somewhat keeled, dark shining green and quite glabrous. Flowers white or pale pink, produced in June and July in a cluster of spikes at the end of the shoot, and thus forming a panicle, or several panicles, each 1 to $1\frac{1}{2}$ ins. long, and nearly as wide.

VERONICA ANOMALA

Corolla $\frac{1}{4}$ to $\frac{1}{3}$ in. across, with a slender tube about twice the length of the calyx. Anthers blue. Seed-vessel ovate-oblong, glabrous.

Native of the South Island of New Zealand ; introduced about 1883. It is one of the hardiest of New Zealand veronicas, and flowers regularly every summer. With age (at least under cultivation) it assumes a lanky, broom-like, fastigiate habit, but on the whole is one of the most satisfactory of the group.

V. ARMSTRONGII, *Johnson*

(Gardeners' Chronicle, 12th Aug. 1899, fig. 50)

A small evergreen shrub 1 to 3 ft. high, much branched, the clusters of twigs often spreading like the rays of a fan ; twigs, when covered with appressed overlapping leaves, $\frac{1}{16}$ to $\frac{1}{12}$ in. in diameter. Leaves of two types : (1) $\frac{1}{10}$ to $\frac{1}{8}$ in. long, linear, pointed, more or less spreading ; this type is characteristic of juvenile plants, but shoots of adult ones frequently revert to it ; (2) the normal or adult state, $\frac{1}{10}$ in. long, appressed to the stem, closely overlapping, roundish or blunt at the apex ; margins furnished with minute hairs. In the latter or adult type each pair of leaves are united for the greater part of their margins and thus form a kind of socket into which the base of the next pair is set. Flowers white, $\frac{1}{4}$ in. wide, in terminal heads of three to eight blossoms ; flower-stalks downy ; calyx minutely downy on the margin.

Native of the South Island, New Zealand, inhabiting mountain districts up to 5000 ft. It is hardy and flowered in the Edinburgh Botanic Garden as long ago as 1894. It belongs to the same group as V. propinqua, V. Hectori, and V. lycopodioides, but the curious funnel-like structure of each pair of adult leaves is distinctive. Flowers during July and August.

V. BALFOURIANA, *Hooker fil.* BALFOUR'S SPEEDWELL

(Bot. t. Mag., 7556)

A shrub about 3 ft. high, with erect purplish stems, minutely downy above the leaf-axils. Leaves $\frac{1}{3}$ to $\frac{3}{4}$ in. long, $\frac{1}{6}$ to $\frac{1}{4}$ in. wide ; oval or somewhat obovate, scarcely stalked, pale glossy green and quite glabrous except for minute marginal hairs near the base. Flowers pale purplish blue, $\frac{1}{3}$ to $\frac{1}{2}$ in. in diameter, produced about midsummer in handsome stalked racemes, 2 to 3 ins. long, $\frac{3}{4}$ in. wide. The racemes are axillary and usually opposite in a pair. Sepals about $\frac{1}{8}$ in. long, minutely downy, as long as the corolla-tube.

Originally raised at the Edinburgh Botanic Garden from New Zealand seeds ; the native locality apparently not known, as it has not since been found wild. Its affinities are considered to be with V. brachisiphon, but its racemes are handsomer in their larger blue flowers. The corolla-tube of V. brachisiphon differs in being about twice the length of the calyx. V. Balfouriana is hardy in ordinary winters, but will not stand so much frost as V. brachisiphon.

V. BRACHYSIPHON, *Bean* (Plate 36)

(V. Traversii, Bot. Mag., t. 6390 ; Hebe brachysiphon, *Summerhayes*)

An evergreen shrub up to 6 ft. high, or more, forming a wide-spreading, rounded bush of dense habit ; branches erect, at first minutely downy, soon becoming quite glabrous. Leaves densely arranged on the shoot (ten or twelve to the inch), superposed in four vertical rows ; narrowly oval or oblong, sometimes slightly obovate ; $\frac{1}{2}$ to 1 in. long, $\frac{1}{8}$ to $\frac{1}{4}$ in. wide ; pointed, tapered at the base to a short, broad stalk ; dark, rather dull green. Racemes produced in July from the leaf-axils near the end of the shoot, usually about 2 ins. long,

¾ in. wide, the main-stalk minutely downy. Flowers ¼ to ⅓ in. in diameter, white ; sepals ovate with minute hairs at the edges, corolla-tube about twice as long. Anthers purple-brown. Seed-vessel ⅙ in. long, much compressed, about twice as long as the sepals.

Native of New Zealand ; introduced about 1868. This has proved the most hardy, and on the whole the most ornamental of New Zealand veronicas in gardens. The only time I have seen it killed by cold was in February 1895. It makes a handsome and shapely evergreen, worth growing on that account alone, but it has the additional attraction of flowering freely and regularly after midsummer, when shrubs in flower cease to be abundant. It is pleasing as an isolated specimen on a lawn.

In an article in the *Kew Bulletin*, 1927, p. 395, Mr Summerhayes points out that the well-known veronica grown as V. Traversii in gardens and figured as such in the *Botanical Magazine*, t. 6390, is not the typical species of that name as originally defined by Hooker. It appears to differ chiefly in the corolla-tube being much shorter as compared with the calyx, for which reason he proposes for it the specific name BRACHYSIPHON. He also adopts for it Commerson's generic term HEBE as applicable to the shrubby veronicas in general.

V. BUCHANANII, *Hooker fil.*

A dwarf, much branched evergreen shrub up to 12 ins. high, compact in habit ; young shoots glabrous. Leaves ⅛ to ¼ in. long, closely set together on the twigs and overlapping, oblong to orbicular, rounded at the apex, slightly concave, quite glabrous and rather glaucous. Flowers white, ⅕ in. wide, stalkless, produced in a cluster of two to four spikes near the end of the shoot. Each spike is ½ to ¾ in. long with a very downy main-stalk. Seed-vessel downy.

Native of the South Island, New Zealand, up to 6000 ft., where it flowers in December and January, equivalent to our June and July. A rock garden shrub and quite hardy. The late Mr Cheeseman places it next to V. pimeleoides in relationship, but that is a shrub of much laxer habit. I have seen V. Buchananii very healthy in the rock garden at Edinburgh.

V. BUXIFOLIA, *Bentham*

A neat shrub, 2 to 5 ft. high, with erect branches ; young shoots pale green, glabrous, except for a thin strip of down reaching from the axil of one leaf to the opening between the pair next above it. Leaves in four super-posed rows, ⅓ to ½ in. long, $\frac{3}{16}$ to ¼ in. wide ; oblong inclined to obovate, pointed, rounded at the base, dark glossy green, perfectly glabrous, covered with minute dots beneath ; stalk about $\frac{1}{12}$ in. long, dilated where it joins the stem and slightly hairy there. Flowers white, ¼ to ⅓ in. across, produced in June and July at and near the apex of the shoots in closely packed clusters, ½ to 1 in. long, which are often branched and collectively form a corymb, 1 to 2 ins. across, the stalks minutely downy. Sepals narrow oblong, rounded at the end, edged with minute hairs ; seed-vessel about twice as long.

Native of the North and South Islands of New Zealand. The plant in cultivation under this name and described above is very distinct in general appearance from native grown specimens, which have the leaves much more densely arranged on the stem, and less distinctly stalked. But in all essential particulars they appear to be the same. Probably the differences are due to the different environment of cultivated plants. It reaches up to 4000 ft. altitude in New Zealand, and is one of the hardiest members of this group. It flowers annually, but not freely.

V. CARNOSULA, *Hooker fil.*

A shrub usually more or less prostrate, and rarely more than 1 ft. high with us, occasionally 3 ft. high in New Zealand, young shoots with a vertical strip of down above each leaf-axil. Leaves glaucous green, scoop-shaped, obovate, pointed; $\frac{1}{3}$ to $\frac{3}{4}$ in. long, $\frac{1}{4}$ to $\frac{2}{3}$ in. wide; narrowing to a stalkless base, closely superposed in four rows. Flowers densely crowded in spikes near the end of the shoot, the whole forming a dense terminal cluster; flower-stalks very downy. Flowers $\frac{1}{4}$ in. across, white; sepals erect, as long or rather longer than the corolla-tube, edged with minute hairs. Ovary, style and seed-vessel free from down, the last pointed.

Native of the South Island of New Zealand up to 4500 ft. altitude. It is a very pleasing little evergreen, making low densely leafy tufts of a striking glaucous hue, and of neat appearance. It is also one of the hardiest of this group. Nearly allied to V. pinguifolia (*q.v.*).

V. CATARRACTÆ, *Forster*

A deciduous shrub or sub-shrub up to 12 ins. high; young shoots purplish, slender, often with a line of down extending upwards from the axil of each leaf. Leaves ovate-lanceolate to lanceolate, pointed, tapered at the base, coarsely saw-toothed; $\frac{1}{2}$ to $1\frac{1}{2}$ ins. long, $\frac{1}{4}$ to $\frac{1}{2}$ in. wide; dark green above, paler below, glabrous; stalk $\frac{1}{12}$ to $\frac{1}{4}$ in. long. Racemes slender, erect, 3 to 9 ins. high, produced in late summer from leaf-axils at the upper part of the shoots. Flowers white with rosy purple lines, $\frac{1}{3}$ to $\frac{1}{2}$ in. wide; flower-stalks downy, the individual ones about $\frac{1}{4}$ in. long, very slender.

Native of New Zealand. This is a variable species and specimens with stems 2 ft. long and leaves 4 ins. long are included under it. The form described above and cultivated at Kew is the same as Forster's type on which he based the name in 1786. It is evidently the same as Hooker's var. minor. A neat spreading plant, flowering continuously through late summer into autumn.

V. LYALLII, *Hooker fil.*, is a near relative of the above but smaller in all its parts. It is of prostrate habit, the branches taking root in the ground. Young shoots with usually two lines of down as in V. catarractæ. Leaves thick and leathery, ovate to orbicular, $\frac{1}{4}$ to $\frac{1}{2}$ in. long, with a few coarse teeth on each margin. Flowers white, veined with rose, $\frac{1}{3}$ in. wide, produced in late summer and autumn on erect racemes 2 to 6 ins. high; anthers blue. Native of both islands of New Zealand up to 4500 ft. It is hardy and has been cultivated at Kew for fifty or more years. (See also V. linifolia.)

V. COLENSOI, *Hooker fil.*

(V. Hillii, *Colenso*)

An evergreen shrub of bushy habit 1 to 2 ft. high; young shoots carrying leaves eight to twelve to the inch. Leaves obovate-oblong, abruptly pointed, scarcely stalked, $\frac{3}{4}$ to $1\frac{1}{4}$ ins. long, $\frac{1}{6}$ to $\frac{1}{2}$ in. wide; rather glaucous when young, becoming dark green, quite glabrous. They appear to be mostly entire but are sometimes sparsely toothed. Flowers white, $\frac{1}{4}$ in. wide, produced densely in racemes about 1 in. long from the terminal leaf-axils during July and August. Corolla-tube shorter than the calyx.

Native of the North Island of New Zealand, collected first on the Ruahine Mountains by W. Colenso, whose original specimens have some distinctly toothed leaves. The plant figured as "V. Colensoi" in the *Botanical Magazine*, t. 7296, is not the true plant, nor are some of the plants going by this name in cultivation. V. Hillii is considered to be a synonym of V. Colensoi ; the leaves and racemes in the original type specimens are rather longer than in Colensoi and the leaves are more distinctly toothed.

V. CUPRESSOIDES, *Hooker fil.*

(Bot. Mag., t. 7348)

A shrub usually seen 2 to 4 ft. high in this country, but said to be as much as 6 ft. in a native state. It has a rounded, dense habit, much like that of a dwarf cypress or juniper, the branches being very much forked and subdivided, the final ramifications very slender and short ($\frac{1}{2}$ to 1 in. long). Branchlets about $\frac{1}{30}$ in. thick, often minutely downy. Leaves on adult plants scale-like, about $\frac{1}{16}$ in. long, glabrous except for minute hairs on the margin, rounded at the apex ; they do not, as in Hectori and lycopodioides, completely hide the stem, although usually appressed to it ; the bases of each pair are united and clasp the stem. In young plants (occasionally on odd branches of older ones), the leaves are as much as $\frac{1}{4}$ in. long, narrowly oblong, ovate or somewhat obovate, and vary from entire to irregularly or pinnately lobed, pointed and distinctly stalked. Flowers pale blue, $\frac{1}{4}$ in. diameter, produced three to eight together at the ends of the branches in a small head about midsummer.

Native of the South Island of New Zealand ; long cultivated. It is fairly hardy, and during some seasons blossoms quite freely in June and July. It is worth growing for its neat appearance and remarkable cypress-like growth—one of many instances of curious " mimicry " in plants.

V. DARWINIANA, *Colenso.* DARWIN'S SPEEDWELL

(V. glaucophylla, *Cockayne*)

A shrub up to 3 ft. or probably more high, branches erect, glabrous except for a strip of down above each leaf-axil when young. Leaves in four superposed rows, oval-lanceolate, pointed, scarcely stalked, $\frac{5}{8}$ to $\frac{3}{4}$ in. long, $\frac{1}{8}$ to $\frac{1}{4}$ in. wide ; slightly concave, somewhat glaucous on both surfaces ; quite glabrous except for some minute hairs on the margins when young. Racemes usually in one or two pairs near the tops of the branches, $\frac{3}{4}$ to $1\frac{1}{2}$ ins. long ; flowers densely arranged, white, $\frac{1}{4}$ in. diameter. Sepals broadly ovate, about as long as the corolla-tube, which is downy within the throat. Individual flower-stalks scarcely so long as the calyx, and, like the main-stalk of the raceme, downy.

Native of both the main islands of New Zealand. Mr Cheeseman regarded this as more nearly related to V. brachysiphon than any other. It differs in the hairy throat of the corolla, and in the glaucous foliage. It is a neat bush, but does not flower with the freedom of V. brachysiphon.

V. DECUMBENS, *Armstrong*

An evergreen decumbent plant, 1 to 3 ft. high, with purplish black shoots that have two opposite vertical strips of down proceeding upwards from each pair of leaf-axils. Leaves usually closely set on the branches, mostly oval or inclined to oblong or obovate ; $\frac{1}{3}$ to $\frac{3}{4}$ in. long, about half as much wide ; of thick, rather fleshy texture, quite glabrous, dark green, red on the margins. Flowers densely packed in two or four racemes near the end of the shoot, each $\frac{1}{2}$ to $\frac{3}{4}$ in. long ; main flower-stalk downy. Corolla white, $\frac{1}{4}$ in. wide, four-lobed, lobes oblong and blunt, the tube twice as long as the calyx ; calyx-lobes edged with minute down.

Native of the South Island of New Zealand, up to 4500 ft. Cheeseman, the New Zealand botanist, described it as a very beautiful plant well distinguished from its allies by the polished purplish black young shoots, red margins to the leaves, shortly stalked flowers and long corolla-tube. It is one of the hardiest species and flowers during July and August.

V. DIEFFENBACHII, *Bentham*
(Bot. Mag., t. 7656)

A shrub of wide-spreading habit, 3 to 4 ft. high. Leaves narrow-oblong, 2 to 4 ins. long, ½ to 1 in. wide ; pointed, thick in texture, rather pale green ; the base stalkless and partially clasping the stem. Racemes showy, produced in pairs a little below the apex of the shoot in the leaf-axils ; 3 or 4 ins. long, ¾ to 1 in. wide, densely crowded with blossom. Flowers ¼ in. diameter, purplish lilac.

Native of the Chatham Islands, where it was discovered in 1841 by Dieffenbach. It is closely allied, and bears a considerable resemblance to V. speciosa, from which it differs in its generally narrower, paler green leaves, its round, not angled stems, and in the seed-vessel being about thrice (instead of twice) the length of the calyx. It is, perhaps, only an outlying form of V. speciosa and, like it, needs winter protection.

V. DIOSMÆFOLIA, *R. Cunningham*
(V. diosm. trisepala, *T. Kirk*, Bot. Mag., t. 7539 ; V. jasminoides, *Hort.*)

A much-branched evergreen shrub 2 to 5 ft. high ; young shoots often minutely downy. Leaves closely arranged in the usual four superposed rows, narrowly oblong, tapered about equally to both ends, finely pointed, mostly quite entire ; ½ to 1 in. long, ¹⁄₁₀ to ⅛ in. wide ; dark bright green above, paler beneath, midrib prominent beneath, but with no visible veins ; stalk very short. Flowers produced near the ends of the shoots in June in usually one or three rounded, corymbose clusters ¾ to 1 in. wide. Corolla pale lavender-blue to white, ¼ to ⅓ in. wide, with a short funnel-shaped tube and four lobes, the rearmost (or inner) lobe the largest. Calyx usually three-lobed, one lobe broader than the others or more or less deeply notched. Flower-stalks minutely downy.

Native of the North Island, New Zealand, discovered by Richard Cunningham in 1834 in the Bay of Islands. Its distinguishing characters are the downy shoots and flower-stalks, the corymbose inflorescence, the usually three-lobed (rarely four-lobed) calyx. It is a neat and pleasing shrub and has been successfully cultivated in the Edinburgh Botanic Garden for over half a century. At Kew it is killed or injured in severe winters. The so-called variety " trisepala " has no proper standing, being based merely on the absence of a bilobing of one calyx segment, thereby making the calyx three-lobed, which is its normal condition in this species. Nearly related to this species is

V. MENZIESII, *Bentham*, a native of the South Island up to 3000 ft., where it was discovered in Dusky Bay in 1791. It has flowers similarly coloured, but differs in its broader leaves, deeply four-lobed calyx, and glabrous shoots.

V. ELLIPTICA, *Forster*
(V. decussata, *Aiton* Bot. Mag., t. 242)

A tree up to 20 ft. high, or a shrub a few feet high, in a wild state ; branches round, with a downy strip above each leaf-axil, or wholly downy. Leaves oval or obovate, narrowed abruptly at the apex to a short point ; ½ to 1¼ ins. long, ¼ to ½ in. wide ; standing out at right angles from the stem, the base rounded and distinctly but shortly stalked, the stalk flattened to the stem ; pale green and glabrous except chat the margin is downy. Racemes crowded near the ends of the branches, 1 to 1½ ins. long, erect, not or slightly downy. Flowers the largest among these shrubby veronicas, being sometimes ⅔ in. diameter, white, fragrant, four to twelve of them appearing on a raceme. Seed-vessel twice the length of the sepals.

Native of New Zealand, Chile, Tierra del Fuego, and the Falkland Islands, whence it was, according to Aiton, introduced by Dr Fothergill in 1776. It is one of numerous instances showing the close affinity of the flora of New Zealand with that of southern S. America. Lately reintroduced from the Falkland Islands by Mr Clarence Elliott.

V. EPACRIDEA, *Hooker fil.*

A low or prostrate evergreen shrub, the young stems completely clothed with leaves arranged in opposite, overlapping pairs on the stem. Leaves about $\frac{3}{16}$ in. long, ovate, pointed, united at the base, distinctly recurved, V-shaped in cross section, glabrous except for a streak of down where the leaves join at the base, dark dull green with pale margins ; they persist on the stems for several years. Flowers closely packed in compact, egg-shaped, terminal heads, ½ to 1¼ ins. long by ¾ in. wide. Each flower is about ⅛ to $\frac{3}{16}$ in. wide, white, the tube of the corolla slender. Calyx deeply four-lobed, the lobes narrow oblong, as long as the corolla tube, margined with fine hairs.

Native of the South Island of New Zealand ; discovered by Dr Sinclair, in 1860, at Tarndale, a few miles from the Wairau Gorge, Nelson. It is a species distinct in the very stiff, thick, rigid leaves, dense compact head of flowers and long slender corolla tube. It occurs wild at elevations of 3000 to 5000 ft. and is quite hardy. Suitable for the rock garden. Flowers in July.

V. HAASTII, *Hooker fil.*, is closely related but has not the V-shaped (" keeled ") leaves of V. epacridea. Native of the same regions and elevations.

V. GIBBSII, *T. Kirk*

An evergreen shrub of thin habit, 9 to 18 ins. high ; young shoots completely hidden by the closely packed leaves twelve to sixteen to the inch. Leaves ovate, mostly pointed, stalkless, overlapping at the base ; ¼ to ¾ in. long, ⅛ to ½ in. wide ; glaucous, often tinged with purplish red, of stout texture, glabrous except for the margins which are conspicuously fringed with pale hairs. Flowers white, ⅕ in. wide, produced during July and August in two or four clusters about 1 in. long near the end of the branches. The bracts, flower-stalks, and margins of the calyx-lobes all furnished with white hairs.

Native of the South Island, New Zealand, up to 4000 ft. altitude. It is a native of the Nelson Provincial District and appears to have a restricted distribution, having been found on two peaks only of the Dun Mountain Range —Mt. Rintoul and Ben Nevis. If all the New Zealand veronicas were as distinct as this, their study would be simple. The hairy margins of the leaves distinguish it from any other. Coming from such a lofty altitude it is quite hardy, but it is still uncommon in cultivation although one of the best of the glaucous-leaved species.

V. GIGANTEA, *Cockayne*
(V. salicifolia gigantea, *Cheeseman*)

A tree rivalling V. parviflora in stature and bulk and ranging from 20 to 30 ft. in height and forming a well-defined trunk. It is not a native of New Zealand proper, but Cheeseman records that in the Chatham Islands it attains occasionally a height of 40 ft. It has leaves 2 to 4 ins. long, $\frac{1}{3}$ to $\frac{1}{2}$ in. wide, with minutely hairy margins. Flowers white, $\frac{1}{5}$ in. wide, produced in racemes about as long as the leaves. Besides the greater stature and shorter racemes, this veronica differs from V. salicifolia in having the calyx and the corolla-tube of about the same length. There is a picture of a tree growing on Chatham Island in the Kew Bulletin for 1910, p. 123, taken by Capt. Dorrien Smith in December 1909. The plant was introduced to cultivation by him at the same time.

V. HECTORI, *Hooker fil.* HECTOR'S SPEEDWELL

(Bot. Mag., t. 7415)

A shrub 6 ins. to 2 ft. high, with stiffly erect, much-branched, round stems, covered and hidden by closely flattened, scale-like leaves. The shoots of the year, with their covering of leaves, are from $\frac{1}{12}$ to $\frac{1}{8}$ in. thick. Leaves $\frac{1}{10}$ to $\frac{1}{6}$ in. long, closely overlapping, each pair united by their margins at the lower half; and thus entirely clasping the stem; tapered to a bluntish apex margins, at first minutely hairy. Flowers $\frac{1}{4}$ in. wide, white or pinkish, crowded in a small terminal head. Sepals narrowly oblong, about as long as the corolla-tube; margins minutely hairy.

Native of the South Island of New Zealand, up to 8000 ft. It is one of the very hardiest of New Zealand veronicas and makes an interesting small evergreen, but is rather shy-flowering. Like V. lycopodioides it bears much resemblance to the juvenile condition of some conifers. V. lycopodioides differs from it in having distinctly square stems, and in the leaves not being so much united towards the base. (See also V. cupressoides.)

V. HULKEANA, *F. von Mueller*

(Bot. Mag., t. 5484)

A loose-habited, straggling shrub, occasionally reaching a height of 4 to 6 ft. or even more when grown against a wall—as it usually is in this country. Leaves in pairs somewhat far apart on the branches, broadly ovate; 1 to 2 ins. long, $\frac{1}{2}$ to $1\frac{1}{4}$ ins. wide; broadly wedge-shaped or rounded at the base, coarsely toothed, the teeth and apex either blunt or sharp, dark glossy green; stalk $\frac{1}{4}$ to $\frac{1}{2}$ in. long. Flowers $\frac{1}{4}$ to $\frac{1}{3}$ in. diameter, of a delicate lavender or lilac shade, produced in May and June in huge branching panicles which terminate the shoots. These panicles are sometimes 18 ins. long, with side branches 3 to 7 ins. long. The flowers themselves are without stalks, but the ramifications of the panicle are downy.

Native of the South Island of New Zealand; introduced about 1860. It is, unfortunately, one of the more tender species and is only really happy out-of-doors in the mildest counties. Even there it is usually treated as a wall shrub. It used to thrive well with Miss Willmott on a warm wall at Warley. A species of remarkable beauty and distinction, it is, unhappily, frequently short-lived in cultivation, dying suddenly without any ostensible cause other than its excessive production of blossom. The panicles should be removed as soon as the flowers fade.

V. FAIRFIELDII, *Hooker* (Bot. Mag., t. 7323), is a shrub of dwarfer, sturdier habit, with leaves $\frac{1}{2}$ to 1 in. long, and shorter, broader flower panicles. It first appeared in the Fairfield Gardens, near Dunedin, N.Z. Mr Cheeseman suggests it may be a hybrid between V. Hulkeana and V. LAVAUDIANA, *Raoul*, the latter a dwarf shrub under 1 ft. high, with pink flowers (Bot. Mag., t. 7210).

V. LEIOPHYLLA, *Cheeseman*

(V. parviflora phillyreæfolia, *Hooker fil.*)

An evergreen shrub 4 to 12 ft. high in a wild state ; young shoots slender, glabrous, with the leaf-pairs about ¼ in. apart. Leaves linear-oblong, blunt or pointed, scarcely or not at all stalked ; ¾ to 1¼ ins. long, ⅛ to ⅓ in. wide ; glabrous. Racemes 2 to 4 ins. long, ½ in. wide ; flower-stalks minutely downy. Flowers ⅛ to ⅙ in. wide, white, closely packed. Corolla-tube about twice as long as the calyx, which has oblong, round-ended lobes, fringed with minute hairs.

Native of the South Island, New Zealand, from sea level up to 3000 ft. It was first discovered by Mr J. C. Bidwill in the Nelson District. Hooker originally considered it to be a variety of parviflora, the tree-like, tender species of the North Island. V. leiophylla is, however, reasonably hardy. The main and secondary flower-stalks and margins of the calyx are finely but distinctly downy, although Cheeseman described the plant as " perfectly glabrous." Flowers in July and August.

V. LIGUSTRIFOLIA, *A. Cunningham*

An evergreen shrub up to 3 ft. high, of lax habit ; young shoots glabrous. Leaves ¼ to over 1 in. apart on the branchlets, scarcely or not stalked, narrowly oblong to narrowly lanceolate ; 1 to 2¼ ins. long, ¼ to ½ in. wide. Flowers produced in slender cylindrical racemes 2 to 3 ins. long from the terminal leaf-axils. Corolla white, small, scarcely ¼ in. wide, with a funnel-shaped tube shorter than the calyx and four spreading pointed lobes. Calyx deeply divided into four lobes of ovate-lanceolate shape, pointed and often minutely downy on the margins. Blossoms in July and August.

Native of the North Island of New Zealand. Related to V. salicifolia which has much larger, more slenderly pointed leaves, racemes much longer, the corolla tube longer than the calyx, and altogether a stronger, bigger shrub.

V. LINIFOLIA, *Hooker fil.*

An evergreen, sub-shrubby plant, 2 to 4 ins. high, of tufted habit ; branchlets slender, woody at the base only, glabrous, with leaves set twelve to sixteen to the inch. Leaves linear, ⅓ to 1 in. long, 1/16 to ⅛ in. wide, not toothed, bluntish at the tip, tapered at the base to a broad, membranous, flattened stalk, which clasps the stem and is margined with pale hairs. Flowers white, up to ½ in. wide, produced in May and June several together close to the ends of the shoots, each on a slender stalk ¼ to 1 in. long. Corolla-tube very short, with four broad, spreading, veined lobes. Calyx deeply four-lobed.

Native of the South Island of New Zealand, up to altitudes of 4500 ft. This is a charming dwarf plant for the rock garden, very hardy and covering itself with white flowers in May and June. The lower branches are procumbent and self-rooting. Although both Hooker and Cheeseman describe it as a herb, it is certainly woody at the base. The racemes are very distinct from those of the type common to the New Zealand veronicas, the flowers being rarely more than four to a raceme, which may be 1 to 2 ins. long, each blossom on a slender glabrous stalk which springs from the axil of a leaf-like bract and is one-third to half as long as the entire raceme. Akin to V. catarractæ and V. Lyallii, both of which have toothed leaves.

V. LOGANIOIDES, *Armstrong*

(Bot. Mag., t. 7404)

A dwarf, conifer-like shrub, usually well under 1 ft. in height ; often only 4 to 6 ins. Stems erect, becoming decumbent with age ; when young, furnished with soft, pale hairs. Leaves ⅛ to ¼ in. long, ovate or lanceolate, tapering from a broad stalkless base to a bluntish point, sometimes entire, sometimes with one or two comparatively large teeth at each side, erect or spreading, keeled at the back, dull green, glabrous. Flowers pure white (sometimes pink-veined), ¼ to ⅓ in. across, produced in June and July in a terminal, single or three-branched inflorescence, on which the flowers open successively for some weeks. Sepals ovate-oblong, pointed, with hairy margins ; corolla-tube short, scarcely so long as the sepals. Main and secondary flower-stalks hairy.

Native of the South Island of New Zealand, and a pleasing dwarf evergreen distinct among this group in its hairy stems and racemes ; its small, closely set, spreading, frequently toothed leaves ; and in the flattish seed-vessel splitting across the narrowest diameter.

V. LYCOPODIOIDES, *Hooker fil.*

(Bot. Mag., t. 7338)

A shrub 1 to 2 ft. high, with stiff, erect branches densely clothed with overlapping scale-like leaves and much resembling a lycopod. The branchlets, as clothed with leaves, are four-sided, each face about ⅛ in. wide. Leaves on adult plants about $\frac{1}{10}$ in. long, rather more wide, triangular, flattened to the branches and strongly keeled at the back (it is the prominent keel that gives the quadrangular form to the branchlets), each pair united at the base. On young plants, and on occasional " reverted " branches of older ones, the leaves are twice as long, not pressed to the branches, awl-shaped with a broad base, and often more or less linear-lobed. Flowers produced about midsummer in a small head ½ in. across at the end of the branches ; the corolla ¼ in. diameter, white, against which the large blue anthers are in effective contrast.

Native of the South Island of New Zealand up to 5500 ft. It is about as hardy as V. cupressoides and is equally shy-flowering in this country. From that species it is easily distinguished by the much less dense habit, the final subdivisions of the branches being longer, thicker, and more open. (See also V. Hectori.)

V. MACRANTHA, *Hooker fil.* LARGE-FLOWERED VERONICA

An evergreen shrub of sparse, rather ungainly habit, 1 to 2 ft. high, with the leaves about eight to the inch on the young shoots. Leaves obovate, often narrowly so, pointed or rounded at the apex, tapered at the base, conspicuously toothed at the upper half ; ⅓ to 1 in. long, ¼ to ½ in. wide ; of thick fleshy texture, thickened at the margins, glabrous bright green ; stalk short and thick. Flowers pure white, ¾ in. wide, produced from the terminal leaf-axils in clusters of three to eight.

I do not know that this species is, or ever has been, in cultivation, but if it does not exist in gardens it would seem to be worth introducing. It is remarkably distinct in the leathery toothed leaves, but more especially in the flowers being ¾ in. wide and the largest borne by any shrubby New Zealand species. As it occurs up to 5000 ft. altitude on the South Island it should be one of the hardiest. Cheeseman observes that in growth it is by no means so attractive as many other species, but that when in flower few have a more charming appearance. "The sight of a rocky slope covered with multitudes of the pure white flowers is a spectacle not easily paralleled."

V. MATTHEWSII, *Cheeseman*

An evergreen shrub up to 4 ft. high, with quite glabrous, often purplish-red young shoots. Leaves closely set on the branches, of thick, leathery texture, stalkless, oblong or oval, rounded at the apex and base; $\frac{3}{4}$ to $1\frac{1}{2}$ ins. long. Racemes slenderly cylindrical, produced in June and July from the leaf-axils towards the tips of the branches; 2 to 4 ins. long, $\frac{1}{3}$ to $\frac{5}{8}$ in. wide; the main-stalk downy, naked at the base for about an inch. Flowers white or purplish, $\frac{1}{4}$ to $\frac{1}{3}$ in. wide; corolla spreading, four-lobed, the lobes rounded at the end; calyx deeply four-lobed, the lobes blunt, with the margins edged with down and often purplish; flower-stalks downy.

Native of the South Island, New Zealand; found originally near Lake Wakatipu in the Humboldt Mountains. It is a popular shrub in the gardens of the South Island, especially near Dunedin, where it has been known as "V. Traversii crassifolia." It is, of course, quite distinct from V. Traversii (*i.e.* V. brachysiphon) and is considered to be more nearly related to the handsome V. Balfouriana, whose calyx-lobes, however, are pointed, and its leaves smaller.

V. OBOVATA, *T. Kirk*

An evergreen shrub up to 4 or 5 ft. high, of erect habit; young shoots purplish at the joints, glabrous. Leaves arranged in about four pairs to the inch, obovate, mostly rounded at the apex, gradually narrowing at the base to a short, broad stalk; about $\frac{3}{4}$ in. long and $\frac{3}{8}$ in. wide; of stout leathery texture. Flowers in slender racemes 1 to 2 ins. long, $\frac{1}{2}$ in. wide, produced near the end of the shoots; main-stalk finely downy. Corolla white, $\frac{1}{5}$ in. wide, the tube short and broad, the lobes oblong, blunt. Calyx about as long as the corolla tube, with blunt, ovate-oblong lobes.

Native of the South Island, New Zealand, where it ascends up to 4500 ft. altitude, and should therefore be amongst the hardier species. It flowers at Kew in July and August.

V. PARVIFLORA, *Vahl*

(V. arborea, *Buchanan*)

A diffusely branched, evergreen shrub 6 ft. and upwards high, but described as being in a wild state sometimes a tree 20 to 25 ft. high with a trunk 6 ft. in girth near the base; young shoots slender, bearing the leaf-pairs from $\frac{1}{8}$ to $\frac{1}{2}$ in. apart. Leaves linear or linear-lanceolate, pointed, stalkless; 1 to $2\frac{1}{2}$ ins. long, $\frac{1}{6}$ to $\frac{1}{4}$ in. wide; quite free from down. Flowers white with a tinge of lilac, $\frac{1}{6}$ in. wide, densely produced during July and August on slender racemes up to 3 ins. long from near the end of the branchlets; main flower-stalks downy. Calyx-lobes oblong, round-ended, margined with minute hairs; corolla-tube one and a half times the length of the calyx.

Native chiefly of the North Island, New Zealand, up to 2000 ft. altitude, but occurring also near Queen Charlotte Sound at the north of the South Island. It appears to be the largest of all New Zealand veronicas and a tree 28 ft. high with a trunk 2 ft. in diameter is recorded. I am not sure that the true plant is at present in cultivation and it is probably somewhat tender. Trained into tree form, it should make an interesting feature in the south-western counties.

V. PIMELEOIDES, *Hooker fil.*

(Bot. Mag., t. 8967)

A prostrate or partially erect shrub, with downy (sometimes very downy) young branches. Leaves closely set in four vertical rows, ovate, oval, or obovate; $\frac{1}{4}$ to $\frac{1}{2}$ in. long, $\frac{1}{8}$ in. wide; tapered towards both ends, concave, glaucous, glabrous. Flowers purplish blue, $\frac{1}{4}$ to $\frac{1}{3}$ in. diameter, stalkless, produced during June, July, and August in solitary or branched, cylindrical spikes $\frac{3}{4}$ to 2 ins. long, the main-stalk of the spike downy like the young branchlets. Corolla-tube very short.

Var. GLAUCO-CŒRULEA, *Cheeseman* (V. glauco-cœrulea, *Armstrong*).—A more robust plant with leaves up to $\frac{1}{2}$ in. long, and shortly stalked, more conspicuously glaucous than the type. Flowers darker blue-purple.

Both these are very pleasing dwarf shrubs, forming a dense covering to the ground, the blue flowers contrasting admirably with the glaucous leaves, which, with the conspicuously downy stems and flower-spikes, distinguish the species. Native of the South Island of New Zealand, up to 3500 ft.

V. PINGUIFOLIA, *Hooker fil.*

(Bot. Mag., t. 6147 (and t. 6587 as carnosula))

A shrub 1 to 3 ft. high, branches at first erect, often ultimately prostrate; minutely downy when young, stained with purple beneath each pair of leaves. Leaves closely superposed in four rows, obovate, blunt at the apex, tapered to a broad stalkless base, $\frac{1}{2}$ to $\frac{3}{4}$ in. long, $\frac{1}{4}$ to $\frac{3}{8}$ in. wide; quite entire, concave or scoop-shaped, dull glaucous green. Flowers white, $\frac{1}{4}$ to $\frac{1}{3}$ in. diameter, stalkless, crowded on spikes $\frac{3}{4}$ to 1 in. long which are borne in the terminal leaf-axils; stalk of spike downy. Calyx with four minutely downy, oblong, blunt divisions. Corolla-tube scarcely as long as the calyx; ovary and style downy. Seed-vessel oblong or obovate, rounded at the apex, downy, nearly twice as long as the calyx.

Native of the South Island of New Zealand; introduced about 1868. It is killed by very severe frosts, but survives most of the winters in the South of England, flowering about midsummer, although not abundantly nor regularly. It is very similar to, and much confused with V. carnosula, under which name it was figured in the *Bot. Mag.*, t. 6587. The differences between the two are in the often comparatively broader leaves of V. carnosula, its glabrous ovary and style, and its ovate, pointed, glabrous seed-vessel. They occur wild in the same region.

V. PROPINQUA, *Cheeseman*

(V. cupressoides variabilis, *N. E. Brown*; V. salicornioides, *Hort.*, not *Hooker fil.*)

This is very closely related to the well-known V. cupressoides, having the same small, scale-like leaves and bearing considerable resemblance in leaf and twig to a cypress. The leaves, however, are more closely set on the twigs, blunter and thicker; the plant is dwarfer (1 to 3 ft. high), the seed-vessel is $\frac{1}{8}$ in. long ($\frac{1}{12}$ in. in cupressoides) and of ovoid instead of obovoid shape. The flowers are white (pale blue in cupressoides), about $\frac{1}{4}$ in. wide, produced in small clusters of four to eight near the end of the twigs.

Native of the South Island of New Zealand; cultivated in this country for fifty or more years (Edinburgh, Kew, Leonardslee, etc.) but often under the wrong name of " V. salicornioides." The true veronica of that name is a very distinct species with stouter stems completely hidden by the overlapping, closely and wholly appressed leaves, and white flowers ¼ in. wide, produced in small heads. It is a native of the South Island of New Zealand up to 5000 ft. latitude and was hardy when grown at Kew, where it bloomed in July and August.

V. SALICIFOLIA, *Forster*

A shrub up to 10 ft. high in a wild state, branchlets round, glabrous or very minutely downy when young. Leaves narrowly lanceolate or oblong-lanceolate, 2 to 5 ins. long, ½ to ⅞ in. wide; tapering to a long slender point, more abruptly tapered at the base; stalkless or nearly so; pale green and glabrous; midrib slightly downy above, prominent beneath. Racemes slenderly cylindrical, 4 to 6, sometimes 10 ins. long, ¾ in. wide; very thickly crowded with blossom except at the base, which is naked for 1 or 2 ins. Flowers small, ¼ in. long, variable in colour, being white tinged with lilac, bluish purple or of intermediate shades; corolla-lobes narrow, not spreading; the tube nearly twice as long as the narrow pointed sepals. The main-stalk of the racemes, the flower-stalks (slender and ⅛ in. long), and the margins of the sepals minutely downy.

Native of New Zealand, where according to Cheeseman, it is the most widely spread and the most variable of all the veronicas. It is one of the tender sorts, only adapted for the milder parts of Britain. It has hybridised very freely with other species, and some of the fine garden varieties are descended in part from it. V. ANDERSONI, *Lindley*, a variegated form of which was once very popular for summer bedding, is a hybrid between this species and V. speciosa.

V. SPECIOSA, *R. Cunningham*

(Bot. Mag., t. 4057)

A shrub up to 5 ft. high; branches spreading, very stout even when young, gabrous, two-edged at first. Leaves 2 to 4 ins. long, ¾ to 1¾ ins. wide; obovate, rounded or bluntish at the apex, tapered at the base to a very short stalk; dark shining green, leathery, glabrous except that the midrib above and the margins near the base are minutely downy. Racemes produced in the upper-most leaf-axils, 1½ to 3 ins. long, 1 to 1½ ins. thick. Flowers dark reddish purple, ⅓ in. diameter.

Native of the North Island of New Zealand, where it was discovered in December 1833, by Richard Cunningham, at the south head of Hokianga Harbour. It occurs also in the South Island, but is very rare and confined to small areas, always on cliffs near the sea. I am not sure that the typical plant is now in cultivation, but it is very striking in the great width of its round-ended or broadly tapered leaves. It has, however, by hybridisation with other species given birth to a very valuable series of evergreen flowering shrubs, in which its influence is seen in the purple, violet, or reddish flowers, and in the compressed two-angled shoots. Unfortunately they inherit, too more or less of its tenderness, so that in all but the warmest counties of the British Isles they need winter protection. A variety called " Autumn Glory," possessing, however, little of the " blood " of V. speciosa, is an exception. It is one of the hardiest and best, producing its bright blue flowers from August to November. It is a neat bush with oval or obovate leaves ⅝ to 1½ ins. long, and erect racemes (sometimes branched) 1½ to 3 ins. long.

V. TETRASTICHA, *Hooker fil.*

An evergreen, small, freely branching shrub, 3 to 6 ins. high, forming tufts up to 1 ft. across ; shoots decumbent below, upper ones erect, hollowed on four sides and thus making them sharply tetragonous. Leaves very densely set, $\frac{1}{12}$ to $\frac{1}{10}$ in. wide, narrowly spatheolate, ciliate, imbricated in four vertical rows, each pair joining at the base to clasp the stem. Flowers white, $\frac{1}{8}$ to $\frac{1}{6}$ in. wide, borne in short two- to four-flowered spikes near the tips of the branches, stalks downy.

Native of the South Island of New Zealand at altitudes of 3000 to 6000 ft. and quite hardy. A distinct and interesting rock garden shrub often found in fissures of rocks on its native mountains.

VERONICA VERNICOSA

V. VERNICOSA, *Hooker fil.*

(V. canterburiensis, *Armstrong*)

A low, spreading shrub, 1 to 3 ft. high ; shoots furnished with extremely minute down. Leaves densely packed on the stem, $\frac{1}{4}$ to $\frac{1}{2}$ in. long, $\frac{1}{8}$ to $\frac{3}{16}$ in. wide ; oval to obovate, pointed, tapered at the base to a short stalk, dark glossy green, glabrous ; on the spreading branches the stalks of the lower leaves are often twisted so as to bring the faces of all the leaves to pretty much the same plane. Racemes in pairs towards the ends of the shoots, $\frac{1}{2}$ to 1 in. long, four-to eight-flowered ; stalks downy. Flowers white, $\frac{1}{4}$ to $\frac{1}{3}$ in. diameter ; calyx-lobes narrow oblong, blunt, about half the length of the seed-vessel.

Native of the South Island of New Zealand, in mountainous districts up to 4000 or 5000 ft. As represented at Kew this is one of the daintiest of New Zealand veronicas and flowers freely.

VIBURNUM. CAPRIFOLIACEÆ

Few genera have received a greater accession of new material in recent years than this—chiefly through the exploration of Central and W. China. In a recent enumeration of viburnums from E. Asia, where the genus has its headquarters, Dr Rehder included sixty-five species, which, with others from India, Europe, and N. America, will bring the total to over a hundred. Of these about one-half are grown in the open air in Britain. The leading characteristics of the genus, which is a well-marked one, are as follows : Shrubs, rarely small trees, either deciduous or evergreen ; with opposite, simple leaves ; white or pinkish flowers borne most frequently in flattish or rounded cymose clusters, or sometimes in pyramidal panicles, always terminal. Corolla five-lobed, spreading, bell-shaped or rarely tubular ; calyx small, five-toothed ; stamens five. Fruit a one-seeded drupe, usually blue, black, or red.

A curious feature of several species of Viburnum is the presence of two distinct types of flower in the one inflorescence—the one sterile and showy, consisting of a corolla without stamens or pistil, the other much smaller but perfect and fertile. The function of the large sterile flower is that of advertisement and to attract insects to the inflorescence. This really represents an interesting and unusual division of labour, for most insect-fertilised flowers do their own advertising by means of the petals attached to the individual flower. In three species—Opulus, macro-cephalum, and tomentosum—gardeners, by cultivation, have obtained an inflorescence made up entirely of sterile blossoms, which represents a striking increase in flower beauty. These phenomena are also exhibited by several species of Hydrangea.

Viburnums as a rule are of easy cultivation, but there are some exceptions and some are not very hardy. They love moist conditions and a deep, rich loamy soil. V. alnifolium and V. furcatum are said to love shade. So far as I know there is no viburnum that cannot be increased by means of cuttings, although some, like alnifolium, are better from layers. Most of them take root easily if made of nearly ripe wood in late July or August and placed in gentle bottom heat.

V. ACERIFOLIUM, *Linnæus*. DOCKMACKIE

A deciduous bush 3 to 6 ft. high ; young branches at first softly downy, becoming glabrous. Leaves maple-like, three-lobed ; the side lobes with divergent, slender points, all coarsely toothed ; 1½ to 4 ins. long and about the same wide ; rounded or heart-shaped at the base, with scattered down above, softly downy (especially at first) and covered with black dots beneath ; stalk ½ to 1 in. long, downy. Flowers white, ⅛ in. diameter, uniform and all fertile, produced during June in terminal, long-stalked cymes 2 to 3 ins. across. Fruits first red, then purple-black, oval, ⅓ in. long.

Native of eastern N. America ; introduced in 1736. Although one of the earliest introduced of American viburnums this is now very scarce in gardens ; it has little beauty of flower, but is attractive in autumn for its crimson foliage. I have seen it growing along the roadsides in New Hampshire just as V. Opulus does at home, but never so vigorous a shrub.

V. PAUCIFLORUM, *Rafinesque*, resembles the above in the often three-lobed and palmately veined leaves, and in all the flowers of the cyme being perfect. It differs from it in the nearly glabrous leaves and in the bright red (not finally black) fruits. It is a shrub 3 to 5 ft. high, the cymes small, about 1 in. across, borne on short, two-leaved lateral twigs. Widely spread over the high latitudes of N. America from Labrador to Alaska, found also in mountainous regions farther south. Of little garden value and rarely seen.

V. ORIENTALE, *Pallas*, native of the Western Caucasus and Asia Minor, is also closely allied to V. acerifolium, but can always be distinguished by the absence of the minute black dots beneath the leaf so characteristic of the American species. It is not so downy, the hairs beneath being almost confined to the vein-axils ; otherwise very similar. Rare in gardens.

V. ALNIFOLIUM, *Marshall*. HOBBLE BUSH

(Bot. Mag., t. 9373 ; V. lantanoides, *Michaux*)

A strong-growing, rather coarse-habited, deciduous shrub, 6 to 10 ft. high ; the central shoots erect, the lower ones spreading, often prostrate ; young bark covered with a thick scurfy down. Leaves in distant pairs, broadly ovate to roundish, the points short and abrupt, the base heart-shaped ; margins irregularly toothed ; 4 to 8 ins. long, nearly as broad ; upper surface dark green, at first downy, but becoming glabrous ; lower surface with much stellate down on the midrib and veins, especially when young ; stalk 1 to 2½ ins. long, scurfy downy. Flowers white, produced in stalkless cymes with usually five divisions, and 3 to 5 ins. across ; marginal flowers sterile, and ¾ to 1 in. across ; central ones perfect and much smaller. Fruit red, turning black-purple, ⅓ in. long, broadly oval.

Native of eastern N. America ; introduced in 1820. This, perhaps the most striking of the Lantana group, is rarely seen in our gardens, where it does not seem to thrive. The best plants I have seen in Europe were in Mr Hesse's nursery at Weener, in Hanover. Mr Hesse was of opinion that it needs shade and abundant moisture, and I have also seen it in New England in positions that support that opinion, although not invariably so. It is very distinct in its large leaves, which turn deep claret-red in autumn ; and from our native V. Lantana is well distinguished in having large, sterile marginal flowers. The popular name refers to its prostrate lower branches, which often take root and trip up the unwary traveller through its native haunts. The venation of the leaves is handsome ; the primary veins branch on the lower side only, and are connected by thin parallel nerves almost at right angles. The nearest ally in cultivation to this species is

V. FURCATUM, *Blume*, a native of Japan. This also has the showy sterile marginal flowers, but its stems are more uniformly erect. It differs also in the shorter stamens, which are only half the length of the corolla, and in the shape of the furrow in the seed. It succeeds in gardens no better than V. alnifolium, although there was a healthy plant at Abbotsbury, near Weymouth, a few years ago. It is a native of N. Japan at low levels, and of the mountainous parts of the south. The foliage turns brilliant scarlet to reddish purple in autumn. It is a bush 12 ft. or more high in a wild state. Introduced in 1892.

V. SYMPODIALE, *Graebner*, is closely allied to both the preceding, especially to V. furcatum, but differs in having stipules on the leaf-stalks, and in its smaller, ovate, more finely toothed leaves. It was collected in Central China by Wilson in 1900, and may be in cultivation.

V. BETULIFOLIUM, *Batalin*

(Bot. Mag., t. 8672)

A deciduous shrub up to 10 or 12 ft., branchlets glabrous, becoming brown or purplish brown. Leaves ovate to diamond-shaped, broadly wedge-shaped at the base, and often entire there, the terminal part more gradually tapered and coarsely toothed ; 2 to 4 ins. long, 1¼ to 3 ins. wide ; dark green and glabrous above, paler and also glabrous beneath, except for a few simple hairs on the veins, and sometimes tufts in the vein-axils ; veins in four to six pairs ; leaf-stalk ½ to ¾ in. long, usually slightly hairy. Cymes 2¼ to 4 ins. across, the main, and especially the secondary, flower-stalks usually covered with a close, pale brown, stellate down ; main branches of corymb seven. Flowers white, ⅙ in. across, all perfect ; stamens protruded, anthers yellow. Fruit red, roundish, ¼ in. long.

Native of Hupeh and Szechuen, China ; discovered in 1885 by Potanin, introduced by Wilson in 1901, in 1907, and in 1910. A handsome fruiting shrub of the same character as V. Wrightii, but with more coarsely toothed, cuneate, fewer-veined leaves.

V. BITCHIUENSE, *Makino* (Plate 37)

(V. Carlesii syringiflorum, *Hutchinson*)

A deciduous shrub up to 10 ft. high, of loose, thinly branched habit; young shoots clothed with dense stellate down. Leaves ovate, $1\frac{1}{2}$ to $3\frac{1}{2}$ ins. long, two-thirds as much wide, pointed, rounded or broadly tapered at the base, with small outstanding teeth at the margin; both surfaces furnished with stellate down but more thickly beneath; stalk $\frac{1}{8}$ to $\frac{1}{4}$ in. long; veins in five to seven pairs. Flowers sweetly fragrant, produced in April and May in a flattish or slightly rounded corymb $1\frac{1}{2}$ to $2\frac{1}{2}$ ins. across. Each flower is about $\frac{3}{8}$ in. wide, pink changing to white, the corolla having a slender tube $\frac{1}{4}$ in. long, and five rounded lobes. Stalks of stamens twice as long as the anthers. Fruit black, $\frac{2}{5}$ in. long, $\frac{1}{5}$ in. wide, crowned with the short style and five-lobed calyx.

Native of W. Japan in the mountains of the province of Bitchiu; introduced as "V. Carlesii" about 1911 and for some years regarded in gardens as an inferior form of that species. It differs in its taller, more straggling habit, less downy leaves, smaller flowers, and is well distinguished by the slender stalk of the stamens being twice as long as the anthers, whereas in V. Carlesii the anthers are twice as long as the stalks. It has suffered in reputation somewhat from invidious and persistent comparisons with that species, but is really a handsome shrub. I remember well seeing a fine bush about 9 ft. high in the late Mr J. G. Millais' garden at Horsham on a day in May some years ago, fully in blossom, and it struck me as about as handsome a viburnum as I had seen.

V. BUDDLEIFOLIUM, *C. H. Wright*

A deciduous shrub about 6 ft. high; the young shoots densely covered with pale, star-like down. Leaves oblong-lanceolate, 3 to 5 ins. long, 1 to 2 ins. wide; pointed, rounded or slightly heart-shaped at the base, shallowly toothed; upper surface furnished with simple or forked hairs; the lower one felted with pale, stellate down; stalk $\frac{1}{4}$ to $\frac{1}{2}$ in. long. Flowers white, funnel-shaped, $\frac{1}{3}$ in. across, all perfect, produced on a short-stalked, numerously branched cyme, 3 ins. across. Fruit oval, $\frac{1}{3}$ in. long, black.

Native of Central China; discovered and introduced by Wilson in 1900. It belongs to the Lantana group, differing from V. Lantana in its narrow, oblong leaves.

V. BUREJÆTICUM, *Regel and Herder*

(V. burejanum, *Herder*)

I am doubtful if the true plant to which this name belongs is now in cultivation, although it may be among recent introductions from China. What is usually seen under the name is V. Lantana or one of its near allies. The true burejæticum is quite distinct. A deciduous shrub whose young shoots are covered at first with a dense, stellate down, becoming almost white and glabrous the second year. Leaves ovate, oval or slightly obovate; tapered, rounded, or slightly heart-shaped at the base, tapered and often blunt at the apex; 2 to 4 ins. long, 1 to 2 ins. wide; evenly and angularly toothed, with scattered, mostly simple hairs above, and scattered stellate ones beneath, chiefly on the veins, becoming almost glabrous; stalk $\frac{1}{4}$ to $\frac{1}{2}$ in. long, scurfy. Flowers white, uniform and perfect, $\frac{1}{4}$ in. wide, produced in stalked usually five-branched cymes, 2 ins. across; the stalks covered with stellate scurfy down. Native of Manchuria and China.

V. BURKWOODII, *Hort.*

This charming hybrid was raised by Messrs Burkwood and Skipwith in their nursery at Kingston-on-Thames in 1924. It was raised from V. utile pollenised with V. Carlesii and has inherited the evergreen character of the seed parent. Its ovate, pointed leaves are 1½ to 4 ins. long, ¾ to 1¾ ins. wide, rounded or slightly heart-shaped at the base, indistinctly toothed; dark, slightly burnished green above, thickly covered beneath with pale brown stellate down; leaf-stalks ¼ in. or less long, covered (like the young shoots) with the same kind of down as the leaves. Flowers charmingly fragrant, produced in late April and May in rounded, five-rayed, terminal, well-filled clusters 2½ to 3½ ins. across. Each flower is about ½ in. wide, the corolla having five spreading, rounded lobes, pinkish when quite young, afterwards pure white; anthers pale yellow.

Considering its parentage, there is no reason why this viburnum should not be quite hardy, and it has, indeed, passed through several hardish winters without a trace of injury. This, with the beauty of its flowers, their pleasant fragrance, and its easy propagation by cuttings, should secure it a place in many gardens.

V. CARLESII, *Hemsley*

(Bot. Mag., t. 8114)

A deciduous shrub of rounded habit 4 to 8 ft. high; young shoots densely

VIBURNUM CARLESII

clothed with starry down. Leaves broadly ovate, with often a slightly heart-shaped base, pointed, irregularly toothed; 1 to 3½ ins. long, ¾ to 2½ ins. wide:

dull green above, greyish below, both surfaces soft with starry down ; stalk about ¼ in. long. Inflorescence a terminal, rounded cluster 2 to 3 ins. across, composed of very fragrant flowers, all fertile. Corolla ½ in. across, at first pink then white, with a slender tube ⅓ in. long. Fruit jet-black, ¼ in. long, egg-shaped but flattened.

Native of Korea ; introduced from that country to Japan in 1885, by Mr Unger of the firm of L. Boehmer & Co., Yokohama. A single plant was sent to Kew by the same firm in 1902, which represented its first introduction to Europe. It is undoubtedly one of the most delightful of viburnums, not only for the beauty of the flowers, but for a fragrance unrivalled for sweetness in the genus. Although apparently quite hardy when fully established, a little nursing helps when young, and is better grown in pots and wintered in a cool frame the first winter. It roots readily from cuttings made in late summer, and put in heat. The inflorescence reaches the bud state in autumn, and remains exposed through the winter, the flowers expanding in April and May.

V. CASSINOIDES, *Linnæus.* WITHE-ROD

A deciduous shapely bush of rounded form, rarely more than 6 to 8 ft. high in Britain, but said to be occasionally a small tree in the southern United States ; young wood scurfy. Leaves ovate to oval with a short, slender, often bluntish apex, rounded or wedge-shaped at the base ; 1½ to 4½ ins. long, ¾ to 2¼ ins. wide ; irregularly and shallowly round-toothed, or merely wavy at the margin, thick and firm in texture ; dull dark green and glabrous or nearly so above, somewhat scurfy beneath ; stalk scurfy, ¼ to ¾ in. long. Flowers all uniform and perfect, yellowish white, ⅕ in. wide, produced in early June in cymes 2 to 4 ins. across, the main-stalk of which is shorter than the branching portion. Fruit blue-black when ripe.

Native of eastern N. America ; introduced, according to Aiton, in 1761. There is much confusion between this species and V. nudum (*q.v.*), but cassinoides has dull green leaves and very scurfy young shoots, leaf-stalks, and flower-stalks, and a short-stalked inflorescence. In nudum the leaves are glossy, the shoots, etc., comparatively free from scurf, and the inflorescence usually long-stalked.

V. COTINIFOLIUM, *D. Don*

A deciduous shrub 6 to 12 ft. high, whose young branchlets, under-surface of leaves (upper surface to a less extent) and the flower-stalks are clothed with a dense, grey, stellate down. Leaves ovate, oval or nearly round ; the base rounded, the apex shortly pointed or rounded ; 2 to 5 ins. long, two-thirds to nearly as wide, finely toothed. Flowers white, tinged with pink, widely funnel-shaped, ¼ in. long, produced during May in rounded usually five-branched cymes 2 to 3 ins. across. Fruit ovoid, red, ultimately black, ⅓ to ½ in. long.

Native of the Himalaya from Bhutan to Beluchistan ; introduced about 1830. This species is closely allied to V. Lantana, and is very similar in foliage and general appearance, but differs in the following respects : cymes more often five-rayed than seven-rayed, corolla tinged with pink, and distinctly funnel-shaped, the corolla-tube longer than the lobes. The true plant is rare in gardens, and not so hardy as V. Lantana, but it thrives and flowers at Grayswood Hill, near Haslemere.

V. CYLINDRICUM, *Hamilton*

(V. coriaceum, *Blume*)

An evergreen shrub (in some of its native habitats a tree 40 to 50 ft. high), branchlets warted, otherwise glabrous. Leaves oval, oblong, or somewhat obovate, 3 to 8 ins. long, 1½ to 4 ins. wide ; wedge-shaped or sometimes rounded at the base, slender-pointed at the apex, the terminal half usually remotely toothed ; upper surface dark dull green and covered with a thin, waxy layer, which cracks and turns grey when the leaf is rubbed or bent ; both surfaces quite glabrous ; stalk ½ to 1½ ins. long. Flowers white, quite tubular, about ⅕ in. long, produced from July to September in usually seven-rayed cymes 3 to 5 ins. across. The cymes are rendered pretty by the protruded bunch of lilac-coloured anthers. Fruit egg-shaped, ⅛ in. long, black.

Native of the Himalaya and China ; introduced to Kew from India in 1881, and later from Yunnan through the Jardin des Plantes, Paris, in 1892. Most of the plants now in cultivation are Chinese, and these are probably hardier than the Indian ones. They have at any rate succeeded very well. Two characters make this species very distinct, viz., the tubular corolla with erect, not spreading lobes, and the curious waxy covering of the leaves ; the latter only shows itself when the leaf is touched or bent ; ordinarily they are of a dingy dark green.

V. DASYANTHUM, *Rehder*

(Sargent's Trees and Shrubs, t. 149)

A deciduous shrub up to 8 ft. high, with glabrous, glossy branchlets becoming dark or purplish brown the second year. Leaves ovate, rounded at the base, tapered to a long, slender point, rather distantly and shallowly toothed, the teeth often standing out at right angles to the margin ; 2 to 4½ ins. long, 1 to 2¼ ins. wide ; dark green, glabrous on both surfaces except for simple hairs on the midrib and veins beneath and tufts of down in the vein-axils ; veins in six or seven pairs ; leaf-stalks slender, ⅛ to ¾ in. long, glabrous. Corymbs 3 to 4 ins. across, usually seven-branched ; the main and secondary flower-stalks are glabrous, the final subdivisions, like the ovary and calyx, felted with pale brown wool ; corolla woolly outside, ¼ in. across. Fruit egg-shaped, ⅓ in. long, red.

Native of Hupeh and Szechuen, China ; discovered by Wilson in 1900, and introduced by him in 1907. It is allied to betulifolium and to lobophyllum, from both of which it differs in its woolly corolla ; also to hupehense, which has the leaves downy on both surfaces.

V. DAVIDII, *Franchet*

(Bot. Mag., t. 8980)

An evergreen shrub of apparently low, compact habit, and about 3 to 5 ft. high ; young branches warted. Leaves leathery, narrowly oval or slightly obovate, tapered at the base, more slenderly so at the apex ; 2 to 6 ins. long, 1 to 2½ ins. wide ; strongly and conspicuously three-veined, often obscurely or shallowly toothed near the apex, dark green above, pale below, glabrous on both surfaces except for small tufts of down in the vein-axils beneath ; stalk ¼ to 1 in. long. Flowers dull white, ⅛ in. wide, densely crowded in stalked stiff cymes, 2 to 3 ins. across. Fruits blue, ¼ in. long, narrow oval.

Native of W. China ; introduced by Wilson for Messrs Veitch in 1904. In its large, conspicuously three-nerved leaves and low compact habit, this shrub is quite distinct from most other viburnums in cultivation. It has little beauty of flower, but is interesting and pretty in fruit, and quite hardy. Another

VIBURNUM DAVIDII

W. Chinese species with conspicuously three-nerved leaves very similar to the above is

V. CINNAMOMIFOLIUM, *Rehder* ; but it is a bigger shrub, or sometimes a tree 20 ft. high, and its inflorescence is much larger and more lax, its almost entire leaves not so thick, its fruits smaller. Wilson discovered this species on Mount Omi, and it is in cultivation. I saw it at Borde Hill a few years ago 15 ft. high and 16 ft. in diameter.

V. DENTATUM, *Linnæus*. ARROW WOOD

A deciduous bush up to 15 ft. high, with glabrous, young wood. Leaves broadly ovate (roundish on the flowering shoots), 1½ to 3 ins. long, two-thirds to nearly as wide ; rounded or heart-shaped at the base, pointed at the apex, coarsely and sharply toothed ; glossy green and glabrous above, downy in the vein-axils only, or even quite glabrous beneath ; veins in six to ten pairs ; stalk ½ to 1 in. long. Flowers uniform and perfect, white, ⅕ in. across, produced in long- and slender-stalked cymes, 2 to 3 ins. wide. Fruit roundish, egg-shaped, blue-black, ¼ in. long.

Native of eastern N. America from New Brunswick to Georgia ; introduced, according to Aiton, in 1736. The young shoots that spring from the base are straight and erect, and it was their use by the native Indians as arrows that gave rise to the popular name. The plant usually called dentatum in gardens is really V. pubescens, a species which differs from the true dentatum in having stellate down. The true V. dentatum is not common.

V. DILATATUM, *Thunberg*

(Bot. Mag., t. 6215)

A deciduous shrub, 6 to 10 ft. high, with erect stems ; young branchlets very downy. Leaves broadly ovate, roundish or obovate ; 2 to 5 ins. long, and from half to about as much wide ; widely toothed, pointed, tapering, rounded or heart-shaped at the base ; hairy on both sides ; stalk ¼ to ¾ in. long ; veins in five to eight pairs. Flowers pure white, all fertile, ¼ in. across, produced in June in hairy, stalked, mostly five-rayed cymes, 3 to 5 ins. across. Fruit bright red, roundish ovoid, ⅓ in. long.

.Native of Japan and China ; first flowered by Messrs Veitch in 1875. This fine viburnum is remarkably profuse in its flowering ; the trusses being produced not only at the top of the branch, but from short twigs down the sides as well. It is even more beautiful in its fruits, but unfortunately does not set them so freely here as it does in sunnier countries. It is distinct among the red-fruited species in its very hairy character, the corolla even being hairy outside.

V. EROSUM, *Thunberg*

A deciduous shrub of erect habit up to 6 ft. high ; branches slender, covered with pale brown down when young. Leaves oval-ovate or somewhat obovate, wedge-shaped or rounded at the base, pointed ; 1½ to 3½ ins. long, 1 to 2 ins. wide ; sharply toothed, stellately downy on both surfaces, especially beneath ; stalks ¼ in. or less long. Flowers white, ⅛ in. across, produced in May in rather loose, slender, scurfy-stalked,. usually five-branched cymes, 2 to 3½ ins. across ; stamens rather longer than the corolla. Fruit red, roundish-ovoid, ¼ in. long.

Native of Japan. It has been introduced several times ; first probably by Fortune in 1844, later by Maries and Sargent. It was cultivated for some years in the Royal Hort. Society's garden at Chiswick, but never seems to have secured a permanent place in gardens. It is, perhaps, not perfectly hardy. Among the red-fruited viburnums this species is marked by the stalks of the leaves being so short.

V. ICHANGENSE, *Rehder* (V. erosum ichangense, *Hemsley*), Sargent's Trees and Shrubs, t. 150.—This close ally of V. erosum was discovered in Hupeh by Henry, and introduced by Wilson in 1901, and several times since. It flowered at Coombe Wood in 1906. The leaf-stalks are very short, as in V. erosum, but the blades are smaller, ovate-lanceolate, and slender-pointed. The flowers are in smaller cymes, 1 to 1½ ins. wide, the stamens are shorter than the corolla ; the calyx-tube is conspicuously and densely woolly. Fruit red, as in V. erosum.

V. FOETIDUM, *Wallich*

(Bot. Mag., t. 9509 ; V. ceanothoides, *C. H. Wright*)

A semi-evergreen shrub up to 10 ft. high ; young shoots angular and reddish, downy, the hairs either simple or clustered. Leaves 1 to 3 ins. long, about half as wide, either broadly ovate with a rounded base and more or less trilobed towards the apex, or, on the older shoots, varying to broadly lanceolate and obovate, coarsely toothed, more or less finely downy, especially on the three or four pairs of veins and the reddish stalks. Flowers individually stalkless, in rounded branched clusters 2 ins. wide, opening in July, each about ¼ in. wide ; petals white, anthers violet. Fruits closely packed, scarlet-crimson, broadly oval to orbicular, ¼ in. wide.

Native of India and China. The plants in cultivation were raised from seed collected by Forrest in China. His seed germinated very freely at Kew, but the young plants found the climate too cold and gradually faded out. In warmer climates it is quite handsome in fruit and I saw it very attractive at Exbury as long ago as 1934, in the autumn of which year it was given an Award of Merit at Vincent Square. The unpleasant odour referred to in the specific name is most conspicuous in dried specimens.

V. FRAGRANS, *Bunge* (Plate 38)

(Bot. Mag., t. 8887)

A deciduous shrub 10 ft. or more high, and as much in diameter, with nearly glabrous young shoots. Leaves obovate or oval, pointed, much tapered towards the base, strongly toothed, with about six pairs of parallel veins ; 1½ to 4 ins. long, 1 to 2¾ ins. wide ; glabrous except for tufts of down in the vein-axils beneath, stalk ⅓ to ¾ in. long. Flower-clusters terminal and lateral, 1½ to 2 ins. wide ; flower-stalks slightly hairy or glabrous. Each flower is ⅓ to ⅝ in. wide, white, or tinged with pink on opening, the corolla lobes rounded and spreading, the tube slender and ⅜ in. long. Calyx ⅛ in. long, with five small, rounded, membranous lobes. Stamens short and inserted about midway on the tube. Fruit said to be brilliant red and edible.

Native of Kansu, China ; first introduced by W. Purdom for Messrs Veitch under his numbers 689 (" white flowers ") and 690 (" pink "). The first flowers I saw were sent to me from Wakehurst, Sussex, in March 1920, which had been gathered from one of Purdom's plants obtained from the Coombe Wood Nursery some years previously. As a rule it commences to bloom in November and continues through the winter, the flowers being able to bear ten or twelve degrees of frost without injury. They have a very charming heliotrope-like fragrance. According to Farrer, this is the best beloved and most universal of garden plants all over N. China, and it is curious that so popular a shrub should have been so long in reaching this country. A dried specimen at Kew is dated from St Petersburg as long ago as 1835 ; and the Russian traveller, Potanin, found it wild and cultivated in Kansu in 1885. But nothing was heard of it until Farrer found it, wrote about it, and sent home seeds. In his *On the Eaves of the World*, vol. i., pp. 96, 97, he alludes to it as " this most glorious of shrubs." This is a courageous statement to make, but, seen at its best on a winter's day well in bloom and filling the air with its fragrance, it is a singularly delightful shrub. Farrer found it 10 ft. high and more in diameter, growing wild in cold bleak regions, so it is absolutely hardy. He describes the fruit as well-flavoured and of a " glossy scarlet." There are two forms in cultivation, one with bronzy young leaves and shoots and flowers that are pink in bud ; and another with green shoots and foliage and pure white flowers. They vary also in mode of growth. Some are stiffly erect whilst others are more sprawling, their lower branches layering themselves freely. This is certainly the best midwinter blossoming shrub introduced since the advent of Hamamelis mollis.

V. GRANDIFLORUM, *Wallich*

(Bot. Mag., t. 9063 ; V. fœtens, *Decaisne* ; V. nervosum, *Hooker fil.*, not *Don*)

A deciduous shrub of stiff habit, or, in a wild state, sometimes a small tree ; young shoots softly downy at first, becoming dark brown by winter. Leaves of firm texture, dullish green, narrowly oval, tapered towards both ends, pointed, finely and regularly toothed ; 3 to 4 ins. long, half as much wide ; veins parallel in six to ten pairs, very downy beneath ; stalk ¾ to 1 in. long, purplish. Flowers fragrant, produced in February and March (sometimes earlier) in a cluster of stalked corymbs at the end of the preceding summer's growth, the whole making a many-flowered inflorescence 2 to 3 ins. across. The tube of the corolla is slenderly cylindrical, ½ in. long, spreading at the mouth into five roundish ovate lobes and measuring there ½ to ¾ in. wide. On first opening the corolla is flushed with pale rose, afterwards it is almost pure white ; anthers pale yellow. Calyx reddish, with five minute, pointed lobes.

Bracts linear, ¼ to ½ in. long and, like the main and secondary flower-stalks, downy. Fruits oval, ½ to ¾ in. long, ultimately blackish purple, said to be edible. Native of the Himalaya at 7000 to 12,000 ft. ; introduced from Bhutan by Mr R. E. Cooper for Mr A. K. Bulley in 1914. At present this viburnum is rare and the degree of cold it will bear doubtful, but it should be nearly or quite hardy. At Kew it is grown in the open, where it produces its charmingly scented blossom early in the year. It is related to V. fragrans, which is distinguished from it by the nearly or quite glabrous leaves and flower-stalks, the fewer veins of the leaf, and the smaller flowers. The flowers of both bear several degrees of frost without injury.

V. BODNANTENSE is a hybrid between V. fragrans and V. grandiflorum (Bot. Mag. N.S. t. 113).

V. HARRYANUM, *Rehder*

An evergreen shrub ultimately 6 to 8 ft. high, of bushy habit ; young shoots clothed with a minute, dark down. Leaves orbicular to obovate or broadly ovate, tapered at the base, rounded at the apex except for a small mucro ; margins entire, or with a few obscure teeth ; ¼ to 1 in. long, from two-thirds to nearly as wide ; dark dull green above, paler beneath, quite glabrous on both surfaces ; leaf-stalk about ¹⁄₁₂ in. long, reddish. Inflorescence a terminal, compound umbel, 1½ ins. across. Flowers pure white, ⅛ in. across. Fruit ovoid, pointed, ⅛ in. long, shining, black.

Native of W. China ; discovered and introduced in 1904 by Wilson, who remarks that it is rare on mountains at 9000 ft. It is quite distinct from any other cultivated evergreen viburnum in its small privet-like leaves. It appears to be fairly hardy, and flowered for the first time in cultivation in 1914. It was named in compliment to Sir Harry Veitch.

V. HENRYI, *Hemsley*

(Bot. Mag., t. 8393)

An erect, evergreen shrub becoming 10 ft. high, and having a tree-like habit ; branchlets stiff, glabrous. Leaves narrowly oval, oblong or obovate ; 2 to 5 ins. long, 1 to 1¾ ins. wide ; shortly pointed, wedge-shaped or rounded at the base, shallowly toothed, dark shining green above, paler beneath, glabrous on both sides or slightly furnished with stellate down on the stalk and midrib ; stalk slightly winged, ½ to ¾ in. long. Panicles stiff, pyramidal, 2 to 4 ins. wide at the base, and about as long ; flowers perfect and uniform, white, ¼ in. across, opening about midsummer. Fruits oval, ⅛ in. long, at first red, then black.

Native of the Patung district of Central China, discovered there by Henry in 1887 ; introduced by Wilson for Messrs Veitch in 1901. It is distinct among hardy viburnums through its long, narrowish, nearly or quite glabrous leaves, its stiff, thin, erect habit, and especially its pyramidal panicles. It was given a First Class Certificate at Vincent Square in September 1910 for its beauty in fruit.

V. HESSEI, *Koehne*

A deciduous shrub allied to and sometimes made a variety of V. Wrightii, but of dwarfer habit and more densely branched. Leaves roundish or broadly ovate, 2½ to 3 ins. long, 2 to 2¼ ins. broad ; rounded or slightly heart-shaped at the base, slender-pointed, with short broad teeth ; hairy in the vein-axils beneath. Flowers pure white in short-stalked cymes ¾ to 1¾ ins. across. Fruits coral red, about ¼ in. wide.

First described in a German periodical in 1909, this plant was put into commerce by Mr Hesse, of Weener in Hanover, the following winter. It is apparently a dwarf form of V. Wrightii, or a closely allied species. We know little of it or of its value in gardens. A native, no doubt, of Japan.

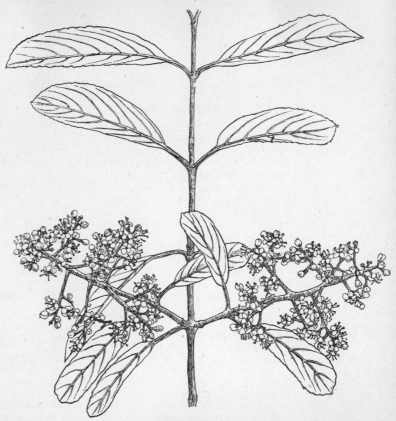

VIBURNUM HENRYI

V. HUPEHENSE, *Rehder*

A deciduous shrub, the young shoots stellately hairy the first year, purplish brown the second. Leaves roundish ovate, long-pointed, truncate or slightly heart-shaped at the base, coarsely toothed, dark green and covered with loose stellate down above, paler and more downy beneath; 2 to 3 ins. long, 1¼ to 2¼ ins. wide; veins in seven or eight pairs; leaf-stalk grooved, ½ to ¾ in. long, densely downy; stipules narrowly lanceolate, downy. Corymbs about 2 ins. wide, the main and secondary flower-stalks covered densely with stellate down; branches of the corymb usually five. Fruit egg-shaped, red, ⅓ to ⅖ in. long.

Native of Hupeh, China; discovered by Henry; introduced by Wilson in 1908. The above description is adapted from the original one of Dr Rehder, who observes that it is most nearly related to V. dilatatum (from which it differs in its orbicular-ovate leaves, and stipuled leaf-stalks), and to V. betuli-folium, from which it is distinct in being downy on both leaf surfaces.

V. JAPONICUM, *Sprengel*

(V. macrophyllum, *Blume*)

A sturdy, evergreen bush up to 6 ft. high in this country, with thick. glabrous young shoots. Leaves leathery, usually ovate (sometimes very broadly so), but also roundish, oval or obovate ; 3 to 6 ins. long, half to nearly as much wide ; abruptly pointed or with a short, slender apex ; the base entire and rounded or tapering, the terminal part remotely and shallowly toothed or merely wavy ; both surfaces quite glabrous, the upper one dark glossy green, the lower one paler but with innumerable tiny dark dots ; stalk ½ to 1¼ ins, long. Flowers uniformly perfect, ¾ in. wide, white, very fragrant, produced in rounded short-stalked, often seven-rayed cymes 3 to 4½ ins. across. Fruit round-oval, ¼ in. long, red.

Native of Japan ; probably first introduced by Maries in 1879. Richard Oldham, who collected it in Nagasaki in 1862, describes it as " a small tree on the hills," but it gives no promise of being more than a sturdy bush with us. It appears to be quite hardy at Kew, but grows slowly in the open, and is no doubt happier in a warmer climate. On a wall it makes a pleasing and striking evergreen. This species has been much confused in gardens with V. odoratissimum (the V. Awafuki of gardens), but it may be distinguished in the following respects : The young wood is not so warted as in V. odoratissimum ; the secondary veins run out to the margin of the leaf ; the inflorescence is rounded and umbel-like rather than paniculate.

V. KANSUENSE, *Batalin*

A deciduous shrub, 4 to 8 ft. high, with glabrous, ultimately greyish branchlets. Leaves ovate to roundish in main outline, but deeply three- or five-lobed, the lobes coarsely toothed and taper-pointed ; the base wedge-shaped, rounded or slightly heart-shaped ; 1 to 2 ins. long, and from two-thirds to fully as much in width ; dark green, and with appressed hairs above, especially on the veins ; much paler beneath, with conspicuous tufts of pale down in the vein-axils, and with hairs along the midrib and veins ; leaf-stalk ½ to 1 in. long, slender, glabrous ; three or five main veins radiate from the top of the leaf-stalk. Corymbs without sterile flowers, 1 to 1½ ins. across, often seven-rayed. Flowers pinkish white, ¼ in. wide ; calyx glabrous. Fruit red, ⅓ to ½ in. long, oval to roundish.

Native of China, where it is apparently widely spread, being found in Kanzu, Szechuen, and Yunnan ; introduced by Wilson in 1908. It belongs to the Opulus group, but is distinct in having no marginal showy sterile flowers, which the other Chinese species (V. Sargentii) has. The leaves also are very distinct in their frequently small size and deep lobing, some suggesting a small maple leaf. An elegant shrub.

V. LANTANA, *Linnæus*. WAYFARING TREE

A vigorous deciduous bush, sometimes almost tree-like, 12 to 15 ft. high ; young shoots, buds, lower surface of leaves and flower-stalks all covered with a dense coat of pale, minute, starry down. Leaves broadly ovate or inclined to oblong, the base heart-shaped, the apex pointed or bluntish ; minutely toothed ; 2 to 5 ins. long, 1½ to 4 ins. wide ; upper surface velvety with stellate down, at least at first ; stalk ½ to 1¼ ins. long. Flowers white,

¼ in. across, uniform and perfect, produced in May and June in stalked, usually seven-rayed cymes, 2 to 4 ins. wide. Fruit oblong, ⅓ in. long, at first red, ultimately black.

Native of Europe, including the south of England. It is the type species of the Lantana group of viburnums, characterised by naked winter buds, deciduous foliage, a scurfy stellate down, and fruits at first red, then black. V. Lantana is itself an ornamental shrub, pretty in flower, in fruit, and sometimes in its red autumn tints ; useful for planting in tall shrubberies or in thin woodland. There is a variety which goes under various names (" aureis variegatis," " punctatum," and " pulverulentum ") whose leaves are blotched and spotted with yellow, but I have never seen it in a condition that would justify one in planting it.

Var. RUGOSUM has leaves even more wrinkled than the type.

V. LENTAGO, *Linnæus.* SHEEPBERRY

A robust deciduous shrub or small tree up to 20 or 30 ft. high ; young wood with a slight reddish scurf ; winter buds grey. Leaves ovate to obovate, wedge-shaped or rounded at the base, the apex as a rule long and taper-pointed ; finely, sharply and regularly toothed ; dark, shining green above, smooth on both sides except for a short, scurfy down on the midrib and veins ; 2 to 4 ins. long, half as wide ; stalks mostly winged, ½ to 1 in. long. Flowers creamy white, ¼ in. across, agreeably fragrant, all perfect, produced in May and June in a terminal stalkless cyme, 3 to 4½ ins. across. Fruit oval, blue-black, ½ to ⅝ in. long, covered with bloom.

Native of eastern N. America from Canada to Georgia ; introduced in 1761. Although this species does not bear fruit freely in this country it is well worth growing for its flowers, and as a small and handsome tree. It is closely allied to, and confused in gardens with, V. prunifolium, but differs in the leaves being long and taper-pointed with winged stalks [see also V. rufidulum]. The wood has a disagreeable odour, according to Sargent.

V. LOBOPHYLLUM, *Graebner*

(Sargent's Trees and Shrubs, t. 148)

A deciduous shrub, with young shoots glabrous or soon becoming so, dark reddish brown when mature. Leaves ovate to roundish or broadly obovate, abruptly narrowed at the apex to a short point ; mostly rounded, sometimes broadly wedge-shaped at the base ; coarsely toothed except towards the base ; 1½ to 4 ins. long, ⅞ to 3¼ ins. wide ; glabrous or downy only on the midrib and veins ; veins in five to seven pairs ; leaf-stalk ¼ to 1 in. long. Corymbs 2 to 4 ins. wide, with seven main branches, which, like the secondary ones, are minutely downy and glandular. Flowers white, ¼ in. across, stamens longer than the corolla, anthers yellow. Fruit bright red, roundish, ⅛ in. long.

Native of W. China ; introduced by Wilson in 1901, and again in 1907 and 1910. It belongs to the confusing group of red-fruited Asiatic viburnums containing Wrightii, betulifolium, dilatatum, etc.

V. MACROCEPHALUM, *Fortune*

(Bot. Reg., 1847, t. 43)

A deciduous or partially evergreen shrub up to 12 or 20 ft. high, forming a large rounded bush, the young shoots covered with a close scurf which, seen under the lens, is found to be minute stellate down. Leaves ovate, occasionally oval or oblong, rounded at the base, rounded or pointed at the apex ; 2 to 4 ins. long, 1¼ to 2½ ins. wide ; dull green, and with scattered hairs above, covered with stellate down beneath ; stalk ¼ to ¾ in. long. Flowers pure white, all sterile, 1 to 1¼ ins. across, forming a huge, globular truss 3 to 6 ins. wide.

This, which is Fortune's type, was introduced by him from China in 1844 for the Royal Hort. Society, and described in the second volume of the Society's Journal. Being perfectly sterile, it has, of course, no place in nature, and is a purely garden plant, and should really be distinguished as var. STERILE. It is the most striking, if not the most beautiful of viburnums, its truss exceeding in bulk that of any other species. Near London, it lives in a sheltered spot in the open, but is better on a wall, where a well-grown plant makes a very fine display in May. Fortune saw it 20 ft. high in Chusan.

The wild form of V. macrocephalum (V. KETELEERI, *Carrière* ; V. arborescens, *Hemsley*) is a native of China, and has only the marginal flowers of the showy sterile kind, the small perfect ones filling the centre of the cyme, which is 3 to 5 ins. across, and comparatively flat. It is somewhat hardier than the wholly sterile plant.

V. MOLLE, *Michaux*

(V. Demetrionis, *Deane*)

A deciduous shrub of bushy habit, 6 to 12 ft. high ; young shoots glabrous and bright green at first, soon turning grey ; older bark peeling. Leaves broadly ovate to roundish ; 2 to 5 ins. long, 1¾ to 3¾ ins. wide ; mostly heart shaped at the base, slender-pointed, coarsely triangular toothed ; upper surface dark green and glabrous ; paler and more or less downy beneath ; stalk ½ to over 1 in. long. Flowers white, all perfect, ¼ in. across, produced in long-stalked cymes 2 to 4 ins. wide. Fruit scarcely ½ in. long, oval, much compressed, blue-black.

Native of eastern N. America. The true V. molle of Michaux is quite uncommon in gardens. The plant which has for long been going under the name is V. scabrellum. V. molle is very distinct in this blue-fruited group of American viburnums in the loose peeling bark of the older branches, also because of a pair of glandular-downy stipules on each leaf-stalk.

V. NUDUM, *Linnæus*

A deciduous shrub up to 10 ft. high ; young shoots slightly scurfy and downy. Leaves oval, ovate or lance-shaped, 2 to 4½ ins. long, 1 to 2¼ ins. wide ; minutely and irregularly toothed to almost entire ; dark glossy green and glabrous above ; paler, somewhat scurfy or glabrous beneath ; stalk ¼ to ⅝ in. long. Flowers yellowish white, uniform and perfect, ⅙ in. across, produced in early June on cymes 2 to 4 ins. wide ; the main-stalk as long or longer than the branched flowering portion. Fruit ⅓ in. long, oval, blue-black.

Native of eastern N. America ; introduced in 1752. This viburnum is closely akin to V. cassinoides, under which species the distinctions between the two are explained. It is a handsome, shiny-leaved shrub which flowers freely. It has a more southern distribution than cassinoides, and does not, apparently, reach into Canada.

V. ODORATISSIMUM, *Ker-Gawler*

(Bot. Reg., t. 456 ; V. Awafuki, *Hort.*)

An evergreen shrub, 10 to 25 ft. high, with warted bark, free from down. Leaves leathery, oval to obovate, 3 to 8 ins. long, 1½ to 4 ins. wide ; wedge-shaped at the base, rounded or with a short, blunt tip at the apex ; entire or with a few obscure teeth towards the end ; glossy green and glabrous above,

paler beneath and glabrous except for tufts of down in the vein-axils ; stalk
½ to 1¼ ins. long. Flowers pure white, fragrant, all perfect, produced in
stalked, broadly pyramidal panicles, 3 to 6 ins. high, 2½ to 5 ins. wide at the
base. Fruit red at first, ultimately black.

Native of Japan, China, and India ; introduced about 1818. This shrub
grows well and makes a handsome bush in the south-western counties, but
is not very hardy near London—not so hardy even as V. japonicum, with
which it is much confused. Its pyramidal inflorescence best distinguishes
it from that species, but the venation of the leaf also is different in the veins
splitting up and not running out to the margin, a character which enables it
to be recognised when out of bloom. There is a specimen about 20 ft. high
in the gardens of Greenway House, Churston Ferrers, S. Devon.

V. OPULUS, *Linnæus*. GUELDER ROSE

A deciduous shrub forming a thicket of erect, grey stems, 10 to 15 ft.
high ; young wood glabrous, ribbed. Leaves three- (sometimes four- or five-)
lobed, maple-like, 2 to 4 ins. long, often as much or more wide, the base
truncate, the lobes pointed ; coarsely and irregularly toothed ; dark green and
glabrous above, more or less downy beneath ; stalk ½ to 1 in. long, with two
thin linear stipules at the base and glands near the leaf-blade. Cymes 2 to
3 ins. across, with a border of sterile, showy white flowers, ¾ in. diameter,
the centre composed of small fertile flowers ; anthers yellow. Fruits bright
red, globose, ⅓ in. wide. It blossoms in early June.

Native of Europe, including the British Isles. Whilst in beauty of flower
the Guelder rose is inferior to many viburnums, it is inferior to none in this
country in its fruits, or in the rich hues of its decaying foliage. Many other
species, no doubt, have fruits as beautiful, but they do not set them in our
gardens with the certainty of this. Of several varieties the most attractive is

Var. STERILE, *De Candolle*. The Snowball Tree.—In this form all the
flowers are of the large sterile kind, and the cyme becomes in consequence
transformed into a globose head of white closely packed blossom, 2 to 2½ ins.
across. This is one of the most beautiful of hardy shrubs, but of course the
fruiting beauty of the common Guelder rose is sacrificed. It is supposed to
have originated in the Netherlands, but has been known in English gardens
since the sixteenth century, and possibly before. Easily increased by cuttings.
There is a rosy-tinted form of it called ROSEUM.

Var. LUTEUM.—Flowers like the type ; fruits translucent yellow.

Var. NANUM.—A curious dwarf form of tufted habit, growing 1 to 3 ft.
high. Its leaves are ¾ to 1½ ins. wide ; so far as I have seen, it never flowers.

The American or naturalised form of V. Opulus (V. AMERICANUM, *Miller*)
scarcely differs from the Old World type. Its growth is said to be more vigorous,
its leaf-stalks to have a shallower, broader channel and smaller glands, the
main-stalk of the inflorescence to be shorter, and the stamens not so long.

V. SARGENTII, *Koehne*, which was introduced in 1892 from N. China to Europe
through Prof. Sargent, is a close ally to V. Opulus. It is a coarser growing shrub
with often larger leaves, a corky bark, purple anthers, and smaller fruit. It is not so
useful and well doing a shrub as V. Opulus in Britain, starting earlier into growth,
and being subject to injury by spring frosts. In the Arnold Arboretum Dr Rehder
says its fruits are not so brilliantly coloured, and are less abundant.

V. PROPINQUUM, *Hemsley*

An evergreen shrub of bushy habit, with glabrous, shining, angular young
shoots. Leaves three-veined, ovate-lanceolate to oval, wedge-shaped or
rounded at the base, pointed, shallowly and sparsely toothed ; 2 to 3½ ins.

ong, $\frac{3}{4}$ to $1\frac{1}{4}$ ins. wide; dark glossy green and glabrous; stalk $\frac{1}{4}$ to $\frac{5}{8}$ in. long. Flowers greenish white, $\frac{1}{6}$ in. across, all perfect, produced in usually seven-branched cymes $1\frac{1}{2}$ to 3 ins. wide. Fruit blue-black, egg-shaped, $\frac{1}{5}$ in. long.

Native of Central and W. China; discovered by Henry and introduced by Wilson for Messrs Veitch in 1901, and again later. It has lived outside for some years in this country, but whether it will eventually prove quite hardy remains to be seen. It is distinct from all other cultivated viburnums except V. Davidii and V. cinnamomifolium in its evergreen three-veined leaves. Those two species have larger more conspicuously veined leaves, which in V. cinnamomifolium are scarcely toothed.

V. PRUNIFOLIUM, *Linnæus*. BLACK HAW

A deciduous, tall shrub or sometimes a small tree, 20 to 30 ft. high; branchlets rigid, glabrous and reddish when young. Leaves glabrous, ovate, oval or obovate, sometimes roundish; $1\frac{1}{2}$ to $3\frac{1}{2}$ ins. long, 1 to 2 ins. wide; rounded or wedge-shaped at the base, blunt or short-pointed at the apex; pale below; stalks not so slightly winged, reddish, $\frac{1}{3}$ to $\frac{3}{4}$ in. long. Flowers white, $\frac{1}{4}$ in. across, uniformly perfect, produced during June in scarcely stalked cymes 2 to 4 ins. across. Fruit dark blue, oval, $\frac{1}{2}$ to $\frac{2}{3}$ in. long, sweet and eatable.

Native of eastern N. America; introduced in 1731. This makes a very handsome small tree, especially if kept to a single stem when young, forming a shapely rounded head of branches. It is allied to V. Lentago and V. rufidulum (*q.v.*).

V. PUBESCENS, *Pursh*

(V. venosum, *Britton*)

A deciduous shrub, 10 to 12 ft. or even more high; young branches covered with starlike down. Leaves broadly oval or ovate, often orbicular, $1\frac{1}{2}$ to 4 ins. long, 1 to 3 ins. wide; coarsely toothed, rounded to heart-shaped, at the base, dark green above, paler and covered with starlike down beneath; stalk slender, $\frac{1}{2}$ to $1\frac{1}{4}$ ins. long; veins in seven to nine pairs. Flowers all perfect and uniform, white, $\frac{1}{6}$ in. wide, on cymes 2 to 4 ins. across, the main-stalk slender, stellately downy. Fruit blue-black, $\frac{1}{4}$ to $\frac{1}{3}$ in. long; roundish oval.

Native of the eastern United States; long cultivated in gardens as V. molle. It is allied to that species in its blue fruits and downy leaves, but differs in its close (not peeling) bark, and its downy shoots (see also V. dentatum.)

Var. CANBYI, *Blake*.—A form with thinner, less downy leaves, often downy only on the midrib beneath. Leaves and inflorescence larger, the latter only slightly downy. Superior to the typical V. venosum.

Var. LONGIFOLIUM, *Blake*.—A cultivated form with longer leaves than the preceding, downy on both sides, especially beneath. This has been cultivated as V. dentatum longifolium. Apparently not known wild.

V. SCABRELLUM, *Chapman*.—This species is one of those involved in the confusion with molle and pubescens. It is very similar to the latter, but differs in the reddish brown branchlets, the often obovate (sometimes oval or oblong, rarely orbicular) leaves with shorter stalks and only five to seven pairs of veins. The cymes are similar to those of V. venosum, but the individual flower is rather larger.

Native of the eastern United States from Pennsylvania southwards. It has long been in cultivation under other names, chiefly "molle" and "pubescens."

V. RHYTIDOPHYLLUM, *Hemsley*

(Mag. Bot., t. 8382)

An evergreen shrub 10 to 20 ft. high, and more through ; the stout branches thickly covered with starry down. Leaves ovate-oblong ; 3 to 7½ ins. long, 1 to 2½ ins. wide ; pointed or blunt at the apex, rounded or slightly heart-shaped at the base ; upper surface glossy, not downy, but deeply and conspicuously wrinkled ; lower one grey with a thick felt of starry down ; stalk ½ to 1¼ ins. long. Flowers produced on large terminal umbel-like trusses 4 to 8 ins. across, which form into bud in the autumn and remain exposed all through the winter,

VIBURNUM RHYTIDOPHYLLUM

and until the blossoms expand the following May or June. They are a dull yellowish white, about ¼ in. diameter. Fruit oval, ⅓ in. long, at first red, then shining black.

Native of Central and W. China ; introduced by Wilson for Messrs Veitch in 1900. This remarkable shrub is one of the most distinct and striking, not only of viburnums but of all the newer Chinese shrubs. It appears to be quite hardy, and flowers well in spite of the curious habit of forming its infloresences and partially developing them in autumn. Its beauty is in its bold, wrinkled, shining leaves and red fruits. The flowers are dull and not particularly attractive. It was given a first-class certificate by the Royal Hort. Society in September 1907. During that month of the year its fruits are red.

In July 1939 I saw a plant at Borde Hill, Sussex, 20 ft. high and 30 ft. across.

V. RIGIDUM, *Ventenat*

(Bot. Reg., t. 376; V. rugosum, *Persoon*, Bot. Mag., t. 2082)

An evergreen shrub of bushy rounded habit and rather open branching, 6 to 10 ft. high and as much wide; young shoots covered with hairs. Leaves ovate or oval, toothless, pointed to rounded at the apex, wedge-shaped at the base; 2 to 6 ins. long, 1 to 3 ins. wide; dark dull green and roughish with appressed hairs above, paler and furnished beneath with soft grey hairs, especially on the prominent midrib and veins; margins ciliate; stalk up to $\frac{3}{4}$ in. long. The inflorescence is a flattish corymb 3 to $4\frac{1}{2}$ ins. wide, carrying numerous white flowers, each about $\frac{1}{5}$ in. wide; stigma rose-coloured; main and secondary flower-stalks hairy. Fruit egg-shaped, $\frac{1}{4}$ to $\frac{1}{3}$ in. long, blue, finally black.

Native of the Canary Islands; introduced by Masson, the Kew collector, on his way home from S. Africa in 1778. This evergreen is not hardy at Kew except against a wall, but succeeds well in the southern and western maritime counties. At Caerhays in Cornwall, where it is 9 or 10 ft. high, it blossoms from February to April. Most nearly akin to V. Tinus, it is well distinguished by its much larger, dull, very hairy leaves; nor is it so densely leafy in habit.

V. RUFIDULUM, *Rafinesque*. SOUTHERN BLACK HAW

(V. rufotomentosum, *Small*)

A deciduous shrub of very rigid, thin habit, described as becoming a tree often 40 ft. high in a wild state; young shoots more or less covered with a rust-coloured down; winter buds reddish brown. Leaves stiff and leathery, oval, ovate, or obovate; rounded, blunt, or shortly pointed at the apex, wedge-shaped or rounded at the base, toothed; 2 to 4 ins. long, 1 to $1\frac{1}{2}$ ins. wide; dark shining green above, covered beneath when young with a reddish short down, much of which falls away before the leaf drops; stalks $\frac{1}{4}$ to $\frac{1}{2}$ in long, stout, more or less winged, and densely covered with rusty coloured down. Flowers white, all perfect, $\frac{1}{3}$ in. across, borne on cymes 3 to 5 ins. across. Fruit blue, $\frac{1}{2}$ to $\frac{2}{3}$ in. long.

Native of the south-eastern United States; introduced to Kew in 1902. It belongs to the same group as V. prunifolium and V. Lentago, from both of which it differs in its dense covering of rusty down especially on the leaf-stalk and midrib. Its habit, too, as a young shrub, is curiously rigid and its foliage narrower. It has hitherto been shy of flowering under cultivation, but may improve with age. According to Sargent the wood has a disagreeable odour.

V. SCHENSIANUM, *Maximowicz*

A deciduous shrub with slender branches; young shoots, under surface of leaves, leaf-stalks and flower-stalks clothed with starry down. Leaves oval or ovate, often blunt or rounded at the end, toothed; 1 to $2\frac{3}{4}$ ins. long, $\frac{3}{4}$ to $1\frac{1}{2}$ ins. wide; veins in five or six pairs; stalks $\frac{1}{6}$ to $\frac{1}{3}$ in. long. Flowers dullish white, $\frac{1}{4}$ in. wide, borne in May and June on a five-branched cyme, $1\frac{1}{2}$ to $3\frac{1}{2}$ ins. across. Fruit egg-shaped, $\frac{1}{3}$ to $\frac{1}{2}$ in. long, turning red, finally black. Ovary glabrous.

Native of N.W. China; introduced about 1910. It belongs to the same group in the genus as the well-known V. Lantana, in which it is distinguished by its comparatively small leaves, whose veins do not run out fully to the margins, but subdivide and die out before reaching them. Its nearest ally is

V. burejæticum, which is distinguished by its downy ovary and more generally pointed leaves. It does not appear to have any great garden value.

V. SETIGERUM, *Hance*

(V. theiferum, *Rehder*; Sargent's Trees and Shrubs, t. 121)

A deciduous shrub of erect habit, up to 12 ft. high, with glabrous grey stems. Leaves ovate-lanceolate, rounded at the base, long, and taper-pointed, widely and sharply toothed; 3 to 6 ins. long, 1¼ to 2½ ins. wide; dark green above, and glabrous on both surfaces, with the exception of long hairs on the midrib and on the parallel veins beneath, which mostly fall away by autumn; veins in six to nine pairs, running out to the teeth; stalk ½ to 1 in. long, hairy like the midrib. Cymes 1½ to 2 ins. across, five-branched, terminal on short, lateral, two-leaved twigs. Flowers white, ¼ in. wide, all perfect. Fruit red, egg-shaped, nearly ½ in. long.

Native of Central and W. China; introduced in 1901 by Wilson. It is allied to V. phlebotrichum, but has larger, longer stalked leaves. Rehder's specific name refers to the use of the leaves by the monks of Mount Omi as a kind of tea.

V. SIEBOLDII, *Miquel*

(V. reticulatum, *Hort.*)

A deciduous, strong-growing shrub 6 to 10 ft. high, or a small tree with stiff, spreading branches, stellately downy and grey when young. Leaves mostly obovate or approaching oblong, pointed or rounded at the apex, and tapered at the base; prominently parallel-nerved, coarsely toothed except towards the stalk; 2 to 5 ins. long, 1½ to 3 ins. wide; dark glossy green and glabrous above, glabrous beneath or downy, chiefly on the veins; stalk ¼ to ¾ in. long. Flowers creamy white, ⅓ in. across, all perfect, produced in long-stalked cymes 3 to 4 ins. across. Fruit oval, about ½ in. long, at first pink then blue-black.

Native of Japan. This is a vigorous and handsome shrub usually more in diameter than it is high, distinguished by its large, strongly veined, often obovate leaves, which have a disagreeable scent when crushed. A viburnum is grown in nurseries under this name which is really V. japonicum, an evergreen of quite distinct species described on a previous page. The V. Sieboldii usually found in cultivation and commonly known as " reticulatum " has leaves almost entirely glabrous.

V. SUSPENSUM, *Lindley*

(V. Sandankwa, *Hasskarl*, Bot. Mag., t. 6172)

An evergreen shrub 6 to 12 ft. high; branchlets warted and furnished with starry down when quite young only. Leaves leathery, ovate or inclined to oval, pointed, rounded or broadly wedge-shaped at the base, toothed at the terminal two-thirds or scarcely toothed at all; 2 to 5 ins. long, 1½ to 3 ins. wide; glossy green and quite glabrous; chief veins in four or five pairs; stalk ¼ to ½ in. long. Inflorescence a corymbose panicle 2½ to 4 ins. long and nearly as wide. Flowers fragrant, white, faintly tinted with rose; corolla-tube cylindrical, spreading at the top into five rounded lobes and measuring ⅓ in. in diameter. Calyx five-toothed, the teeth triangular, pointed, ciliate; bracts awl-shaped, ⅓ in. long; flower-stalks minutely downy. I have not seen the fruit, but it is described as globose, red, crowned with the presisting style.

Native of S. Japan; introduced to Belgium about 1850. This has been tried out-of-doors at Kew with indifferent success even on a wall, but it succeeds very well in the Scilly Isles and Cornwall and it is occasionally sent to Kew to be named from other mild parts of Britain. So far as my experience goes, this shrub does not flower freely in this country, probably for lack of sufficient sunshine, for it flowered well in several gardens in March 1922, owing no doubt to the phenomenal heat and dryness of the previous summer.

V. TINUS, *Linnæus*. LAURUSTINUS

A dense-habited, much-branched evergreen shrub of rounded form, 6 to 12 ft. high, often more in diameter, and furnished to the ground; young shoots smooth, or slightly hairy. Leaves not toothed, narrowly ovate, approaching oblong, tapered at both ends; 1½ to 4 ins. long, ¾ to 1½ ins. wide; dark glossy green above, paler beneath, and with tufts of down in the lower vein-axils; stalk ⅓ to ¾ in. long, often more or less hairy. Flowers white, about ¼ in. across, uniform and perfect, produced in winter and spring in terminal cymes 2 to 4 ins. across. Fruit ovoid, tapering towards the top, ¼ in. long, deep blue, finally black.

Native of the Mediterranean Region and S.E. Europe; cultivated in South Britain for over three centuries. In southern gardens the laurustinus is one of the most useful of all evergreen shrubs, forming rich masses of greenery and opening its flowers any time between November and April, according to the weather. It will thrive in moderate shade, but flowers more freely in full sun. The fruits, indigo-blue, ultimately black, are not frequently seen with us. From all other cultivated hardy viburnums this is distinguished by its luxuriant masses of entire, evergreen leaves.

The laurustinus is represented in gardens by several varieties, and even among plants we regard as typical, variation is noticeable.

Var. HIRTUM, *Aiton.*—In this variety the shoots, the stalks, and bases of the leaves are clothed with bristly hairs. The leaves also are larger and of different shape, being as much as 3 to 4 ins. long, and 2 ins. wide, rounded or even slightly heart-shaped at the base. Scarcely so hardy as the type, and sometimes grown for early flowering in cool greenhouses. There are bushes 16 ft. high in the botanic garden at Bath.

Var. LUCIDUM.—In habit this is more open, and less compact than the type, and altogether a stronger grower. It also bears larger leaves and trusses, and the individual flower is nearly ½ in. across, sometimes pinkish. The largest leaves are 4 ins. long, and 2½ ins. wide. Very useful and effective in the milder counties, it is not so hardy as the type. The varietal name refers to the glabrous, burnished young shoots, and to the glossy surfaces of the leaf, the lower one with only a few tufts of hairs in the vein-axils.

Var. PURPUREUM.—Leaves of a dull purple tinge.

Var. VARIEGATUM.—A portion of the leaf, sometimes all one side, yellow.

A more erect-habited form has been distinguished as STRICTUM or pyramidale. All the forms of laurustinus are easily increased by cuttings put in a cool frame, or, more quickly, in mild heat.

V. TOMENTOSUM, *Thunberg*

A deciduous shrub of bushy habit, 6 to 10 ft. high, the branches mostly horizontal, covered when young with a minute, starry down. Leaves ovate or oval, tapered to a point, rounded or wedge-shaped at the base, 2 to 4 ins. long, 1 to 2½ ins. wide; toothed except at the base, dull dark green above with scattered hairs at first; pale, greyish, and stellately downy beneath; stalk ½ to ¾ in. long. Inflorescence a flat umbel 2½ to 4 ins. across, borne at the end of a short, usually two-leaved twig; the centre is filled with the small perfect flowers, surrounded by a few large, white sterile ones, 1 to 1½ ins. across. Fruit roundish egg-shaped, at first coral red, finally blue-black. Blossoms in early June.

Native of China and Japan; introduced about 1865. Although not so well known or so effective as its variety plicatum, this shrub is very pretty when in flower with the trusses set along the branches in two rows. Messrs Veitch had a variety they called MARIESII, with the trusses and sterile flowers larger. Wilson also found in Hupeh a very fine form with its sterile flowers 1½ to 2 ins. across.

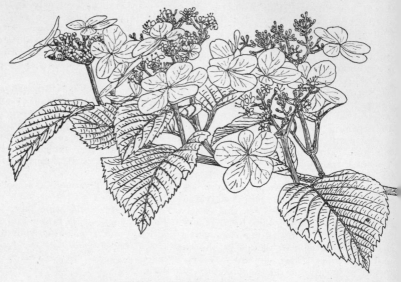

VIBURNUM TOMENTOSUM

Var. PLICATUM, *Maximowicz* (V. plicatum, *Thunberg*). Japanese Snow-ball.—Under its commoner name of V. plicatum, this shrub is now well known in gardens, both in the open and as a plant forced early into blossom for greenhouses. It stands in the same relation to V. tomentosum as our common snowball tree does to V. Opulus, the whole of its flowers being transformed into the sterile showy kind, and the inflorescence from a flat umbel to an almost globose one. V. plicatum is in the very first rank of deciduous shrubs, and probably if one were confined to a dozen sorts it would be among them. Its flower-trusses are 2 to 3 ins. across, pure white, and come from the branches of the previous year in two opposite rows at the end of short two-leaved twigs. Two forms of it are offered by nurserymen, viz., grandiflorum and rotundifolium. Although introduced from China (where, as in Japan, it has long been cultivated) by Fortune, in 1844, it is only within the last forty-five years that much use of it has been made as a hardy shrub. Young plants rooted from cuttings are apt to be injured the first year after being put out, but when once established they withstand at least 30° of frost without injury. Typical V. tomentosum is not, I think, quite so hardy.

Nearly allied to the above species is V. HANCEANUM, *Maximowicz*, from China. It is distinguished by its rounder, shorter-pointed leaves, shallowly toothed above the middle only. Perhaps not at present in cultivation.

V. UTILE, *Hemsley*
(Bot. Mag., t. 8174)

An evergreen shrub of rather thin, open habit, 5 or 6 ft. high, the slender branches clothed at first with a pale, starry down. Leaves usually narrowly ovate or nearly oblong; 1 to 3 ins. long, ¼ to 1¼ ins. wide; of firm texture, glabrous and dark glossy green above, prominently veined and white beneath, with a dense covering of starry down; margins entire; apex tapered but bluntish; base rounded to wedge-shaped; stalk ¼ to ⅓ in. long. Flowers all fertile, produced during May densely packed in terminal, rounded trusses, 3 ins. across, the branches of the inflorescence stellately downy. Each flower is ⅓ in. wide, white. Calyx glabrous, with shallow, rounded lobes. Fruit blue-black, oval, ¼ in. long.

Native of China; introduced in 1901 by Wilson. It has proved quite hardy since its introduction, and is a pretty, graceful shrub. According to Wilson, it grows on limestone.

V. VEITCHII, *C. H. Wright*

A deciduous shrub about 5 ft. high; young branches, leaf-stalks, and under-surface of leaves densely clothed with stellate down. Leaves ovate, pointed, heart-shaped at the base; 3 to 5 ins. long, 2 to 3 ins. wide; sharply and widely toothed; upper surface with scattered stellate down. Flowers white, uniform and perfect, ¼ in. across; produced on a stoutly stalked, very scurfy-downy cyme, that is 4 or 5 ins. across. Fruit red, then black.

Native of Central China, discovered and introduced in 1901 by Wilson, for Messrs Veitch. It is one of the Lantana group, differing from V. Lantana itself in the more remote marginal teeth, and in the calyx being felted with starlike down. Wilson found it as a bush about 5 ft. high, but rare; he considers it to be about the most ornamental of the Lantana group.

V. WILSONII, *Rehder*

A deciduous shrub 6 to 10 ft. high with very downy young shoots. Leaves ovate to roundish oval, or broadly tapered at the base, the apex slender or even tail-like, toothed; 1½ to 3½ ins. long, half as much wide; dark green and with usually some hairs above, at least on the veins; clothed beneath either on the veins and midrib with mostly simple hairs, or all over the lower surface with star-shaped hairs and some long simple ones; veins in six to nine pairs; stalk ¼ to ⅜ in. long, hairy and starry-downy. Flowers white, all fertile, ¼ in. wide, opening in June in a terminal five- or six-branched corymb 2 to 3 ins. wide; main and secondary flower-stalks velvety with down. Corolla ⅕ in. wide, the lobes roundish ovate; calyx downy. Fruit bright red, egg-shaped, ⅓ in. long, slightly hairy.

Native of Szechuen, China; discovered by Wilson in 1904 and introduced by him in 1908 to the Arnold Arboretum, Mass., whence it was obtained for Kew the following year. The plants which were raised from Wilson's No. 1120 flower and bear fruit regularly at Kew. Dr Rehder compares it with V. hupehense, but that species has stipules attached towards the base of the leaf-stalks which are absent in V. Wilsonii. In the downiness of leaf and inflorescence they are very similar.

V. WRIGHTII, *Miquel*

A deciduous shrub, 6 to 10 ft. high, with erect stems ; young branches glabrous. Leaves 2 to 5 ins. long, 1 to 2½ ins. wide ; mostly ovate and rounded at the base, but sometimes obovate and tapered at the base ; slenderly and often abruptly pointed, somewhat distantly toothed ; bright green and almost glabrous above, paler beneath with tufts of hairs in the vein-axils ; veins in six to ten pairs ; stalk ¼ to ¾ in. long. Flowers all perfect, produced in May on glabrous or downy-stalked, five-rayed cymes, 2 to 4 ins. across, the flowers themselves scarcely stalked, white. Fruit round-ovoid, red, ⅓ in. long.

Native of Japan. This handsome-fruited species is closely related to V. dilatatum, but that species is at once distinguished by the extremely downy character of its leaves, young branches, and inflorescence. V. Wrightii is sometimes united to V. PHLEBOTRICHUM, *Siebold*, with which, indeed, it appears to be connected by forms intermediate in several respects. The typical V. phlebotrichum is, nevertheless, very distinct in the smaller, narrower, ovate to oblong, shorter-stalked leaves, the more numerous, silky, whitish hairs on the veins beneath, the quite glabrous and slender-stalked cymes, the purple calyx, and especially the very short stamens. Native of Japan.

VILLARESIA MUCRONATA, *Ruiz and Pavon*. OLACACEÆ
(Bot. Mag., t. 8376)

An evergreen tree up to 60 ft. high ; young shoots downy, ribbed. Leaves alternate, of hard leathery texture like those of a holly, ovate or oblong, pointed ; 1½ to 3½ ins. long, ¾ to 2 ins. wide ; entire on the flowering shoots of adult trees ; spiny, much larger, and more rounded at the base on young ones ; glabrous and dark glossy green ; stalk ⅛ to ¼ in. long, downy. Flowers fragrant, ⅔ in. wide, yellowish white and densely crowded in a cluster of panicles, each 1 to 2 ins. long and produced in the terminal leaf-axils and at the end of the shoot in June. The individual flower, which has its various parts in fives, is almost stalkless, but the main and secondary flower-stalks are clothed with brown down. Fruit an egg-shaped drupe ⅔ in. long, containing one fleshy seed surrounded by a hard shell.

Native of Chile and grown in the Temperate House at Kew. The finest tree I know of in the open air is at Abbotsbury in Dorset. I was informed by Mr Kempshall, the gardener, that it was introduced to the gardens there by the Hon. W. Fox-Strangways about 1840 and that the tree is now between 50 and 60 ft. high, rather pyramidal in shape and resembles a holly. Like a holly, its leaves are spiny on young trees, entire on old ones. Some of the leaves beneath are curiously pitted near the vein-axils. The Abbotsbury tree flowers in June but has not, I believe, borne fruit. The villaresias are sometimes unisexual. The generic name commemorates Matthias Villarez, a Spanish botanist.

VINCA. PERIWINKLE. APOCYNACEÆ

Two species of periwinkle are common in gardens, and a third, V. difformis, is occasionally seen. They are evergreen trailing shrubs, propagated with the greatest ease by means of cuttings a few inches long, or by taking up old patches and dividing them. The parts of the calyx and corolla are in fives, the latter consisting of a basal tubular part and broad, horizontally expanding lobes. Flowers solitary in the leaf-axils. Leaves opposite. V. major is sometimes attacked by a parasitic fungus which turns the leaves yellow and ultimately kills them.

V. DIFFORMIS, *Pourret*

(Bot. Mag., t. 8506 ; V. media, *Hoffmannsegg and Link* ; V. acutiflora, *Bertolini*)

A trailing sub-shrubby plant in Britain usually dying back in winter, probably evergreen in S. Europe, of spreading growth, quite glabrous in leaf and stem. Leaves ovate, broadly wedge-shaped or rounded at the base, more tapered towards the apex ; 1½ to 3 ins. long, ¾ to 2 ins. wide ; entire, rich green on both surfaces, but rather paler beneath ; stalk ⅛ to ¼ in. long. Flowers solitary in the leaf-axils, produced in November and December on stalks 1 to 1½ ins. long. Corolla 1½ ins. across, very pale lilac-blue, the lobes obovate or rather rhomboidal, pointed ; calyx-lobes awl-shaped, ¼ in. long. Fruit awl-shaped, 1½ ins. long.

Native of S.W. Europe and N. Africa. It resembles V. major in general appearance, but is easily distinguished by the absence of hairs on stem and leaf-margin and by the non-ciliate sepals. It is not so hardy as V. major, but thrives well in the vicarage garden at Bitton. At Kew it flowers too late to expand properly out-of-doors, but taken up and put under glass provides a continuous display during the darkest months of the year.

V. MAJOR, *Linnæus*. LARGER PERIWINKLE

An evergreen shrub whose barren stems are long and trailing, its flowering ones erect and 1 to 2 ft. high, glabrous except for a few dark bristles at the joints. Leaves opposite, ovate, 1 to 3 ins. long, half to two-thirds as wide, pointed, dark green, glossy on both surfaces, glabrous, but edged with minute hairs ; stalk ⅛ to ¼ in. long Flowers bright blue, solitary in the leaf-axils on a slender stalk 1 to 2 ins. long ; corolla 1½ ins. across, the base a funnel-shaped tube spreading at the mouth into five deep, broadly obovate lobes ; calyx-lobes five, narrowly linear, nearly ½ in. long, with hairs on the margin. Fruit glabrous, awl-shaped, long-pointed, 1½ to 2 ins. long.

Native of Central and S. Europe eastward to the Caucasus. It is seemingly wild in parts of England, but from the fact that it rarely perfects its seed, a doubtful native. Useful for growing in semi-shaded positions where it makes pleasant ground cover, but not flowering so well there as in the full sun. The first flowers appear in May and continue until September. It should be trimmed over annually in spring, cutting away the old growths. Distinct from V. minor in its large, broad-based, often heart-shaped leaves, and from V. difformis in its ciliate leaves and calyx-lobes.

V. MINOR, *Linnæus*. LESSER PERIWINKLE

An evergreen trailing shrub rarely more than 6 ins. above the ground, forming in time a dense mat ; stems glabrous, wiry. Leaves oval, or slightly obovate, always tapered at the base ; ¾ to 2 ins. long, ½ to ¾ in. wide ; quite glabrous and of a deep glossy green on both sides. Flowers 1 in. across, bright blue, produced from April until autumn. Corolla-lobes obovate ; calyx glabrous, its lobes about ⅛ in. long.

Native of many parts of Europe, and found as far east as the Caucasus and Asia Minor. Like V. major, it is found apparently wild in England, but is doubtless an escape from cultivation. It is, of course, easily distinguished from that species by the smaller flowers, whose calyx-lobes are shorter and broader, and by the smaller narrow-based leaves.

Var. ALBA.—Flowers white.

Var. ARGENTEO-VARIEGATA.—Leaves shorter, proportionately broader, blotched with white.

Var. AUREO-VARIEGATA.—Leaves blotched with yellow.

Var. AZUREA.—Flowers sky-blue.

Var. PLENA.—Flowers double.

Var. PUNICEA (purpurea).—Flowers purplish.

All the forms of Vinca minor make excellent ground cover for shady places, but flower better fully exposed. The stems root freely at the tips.

VISCUM ALBUM, *Linnæus*. MISTLETOE. LORANTHACEÆ

An evergreen shrub of tawny, yellowish aspect, parasitic on various trees, usually in the form of a rounded, pendulous bush ; branches glabrous, bifurcating at each joint. Leaves opposite, narrowly oblong or obovate, tapering at the base, rounded at the apex ; $1\frac{1}{2}$ to 4 ins. long, $\frac{1}{4}$ to 1 in. wide ; not stalked. Flowers inconspicuous, almost stalkless, and produced in the forks of the branches, the sexes often on separate plants. Fruit a white, translucent berry $\frac{1}{3}$ in. wide, whose single seed is embedded in a very viscid pulp ; ripe in midwinter.

Native of Europe, where it is widely spread, and of N. Asia. It is found commonly in the south of England, but not in Scotland or Ireland. The mistletoe is frequently cultivated in gardens for its interest and associations, and nurserymen supply it growing on apple trees. The two sexes should be obtained if possible on the same or separate host plants. It must be propagated by seed, and this is best done by bursting the berry on the youngish bark of the host plant. The glutinous substance in which the seed is embedded soon hardens and attaches the seed securely. It is not necessary to make a slit in the bark for the seed.

In nature the mistletoe is spread by birds. They eat the fruits, but a thick coating of gluten remains on the seeds which is made even more adhesive by partial digestion. It grows most commonly perhaps on apple trees, so much so as to be a pest in some of the west country orchards. Although, because of its association with the rites of the ancient Druids, its most famous host plant is the oak, it is in reality very rarely seen on that tree. Nor, in this country, is it common on coniferous trees, although I have seen it abundant on Scotch pine in Switzerland (Val d'Anniviers). But from a list of host trees of the mistletoe published some time ago in the horticultural press, there appear to be few of our native trees on which it will not grow. (See *Journal of Botany*, 1916, p. 292.)

LORANTHUS EUROPÆUS, *Jacquin*.—The mistletoe is the only parasitic shrub native of Britain, but this loranthus, a parasite also, is found in Central and Eastern Europe. Some years ago a plant was introduced to Kew from Austria growing on an oak (which, contrary to the mistletoe, it favours).

Although the oak grew vigorously, the parasite never flourished or grew much, and after lingering ten or twelve years, died. Probably our climate is not sunny enough for it. It is deciduous, and bears its fruit in a terminal spike of four or five pairs.

VITEX. VERBENACEÆ

Of this large genus of Old World shrubs and small trees, two species can be grown on walls in the southern parts of the country. They require a sunny spot and not too rich a soil. Propagated by cuttings.

V. AGNUS-CASTUS, *Linnæus*. CHASTE-TREE

A deciduous shrub of free, spreading habit ; young shoots covered with a minute grey down. Leaves opposite, composed of five to seven radiating leaflets borne on a main-stalk 1 to 2½ ins. long ; leaflets linear lance-shaped ; 2 to 6 ins. long, ¼ to ¾ in. wide ; tapering gradually towards both ends, not toothed ; dark green above, grey beneath with a very close felt ; stalks of leaflets ¼ in. or less long. Flowers fragrant, produced during September and October in whorls on slender racemes which are 3 to 6 ins. long, sometimes branched, and borne in numbers on the terminal part of the current season's growth, at the end and in the leaf-axils, the whole forming a large panicle. Corolla violet, tubular, ¼ in. long, with five expanding lobes ; stamens four, protruded ; calyx funnel-shaped, downy, shallowly lobed.

Native of the Mediterranean region ; cultivated in Britain in 1570. Near London it needs the protection of a wall ; given this it is quite safe. A plant has lived on a west wall at Kew for at least sixty years. It flowers freely in warm seasons, and its crowd of panicles is sometimes very effective. The entire plant has an aromatic, pungent odour. The popular name is said to come from the Greeks, whose women at the festival in honour of Ceres strewed their beds with it. There is a white-flowered variety, ALBA.

V. INCISA, *Lamarck*. CHINESE CHASTE-TREE

Introduced in 1785 from China, this species is rarely seen at the present time. It requires the protection of a wall, and in competition with the many finer plants adapted for wall cultivation, it scarcely keeps its place in gardens. It has digitate leaves like the preceding species, the leaflets being usually five, but varying from three to seven in each leaf. They differ from those of V. Agnus-castus in having distinct stalks, up to 1 in. long ; in being coarsely toothed, and in being sometimes 1½ ins. wide Flowers violet-blue, arranged in distant whorls on slender racemes 6 to 9 ins. long, the whole forming a large, thinly furnished panicle terminating the shoots of the year ; calyx downy, deeply and sharply lobed. A deciduous shrub up to 10 ft. high. (*Syn.* V. Negundo incisa, *Clarke.*)

VITIS. VINE. VITACEÆ

(Including Ampelopsis, Cissus, Parthenocissus)

Vitis shares with Clematis the distinction of being the most important genus of hardy climbers in gardens. The flower beauty of Clematis is lacking in the vines, but is compensated for by the greater luxuriance of growth, nobler foliage, and above all by the colour beauty in autumn many of them possess. No species is native to the British Isles, or, excepting the doubtful V. vinifera, is wild in Europe. It is mainly to China, Japan, and to E. and Central N. America that we owe that wealth of species from which cultivators may now make their choice. As defined by Bentham and Hooker, Vitis is a very large genus of perhaps four hundred species. Owing to the inconvenience that would be involved by changing the names, I have not departed from their estimate of the genus ; but there is a general disposition among botanists nowadays to split up Vitis into several genera, thus following the admirable monograph of the late Mr Planchon, published in 1887. Below, an arrangement of the species here dealt with is given, in which each one is placed under the genus as defined by Planchon, so that anyone preferring to adopt the more recent nomenclature may do so. After all, it is a matter of opinion.

With the exception of a single species, V. (or Cissus) striata, all the vines here described are deciduous and, with the exception of another, V. rupestris, they are all climbers. Leaves alternate, with frequently a tendril or an inflorescence opposite to each on the stem. Flowers small, greenish, and of no beauty, but occasionally fragrant ; they are sometimes perfect, but others are unisexual, and not infrequently the sexes are segregated on different plants. Fruit a black, blue, red, or yellow berry, with or without bloom ; seeds one to four, embedded in juicy pulp.

The ornamental vines are of very easy cultivation, provided the climate is warm enough for them. They like a good loamy soil and plenty of root room, although V. heterophylla, which is grown for the beauty of its fruit, is more fertile with a restricted root run. The most inconvenient thing in their cultivation is the provision of suitable support. Best of all, perhaps, is a pergola on which the shoots can be trained and pruned back annually as much as is necessary. They can also be trained up posts, when, if the shoots are allowed to hang loosely, they are very elegant. Whole trees or large shrubs may be given up to them, over which they can ramble at will, and this, approaching nature as it does, shows the more vigorous ones at their best. The splendid form of V. Coignetiæ in the nursery of Knap Hill was growing in this way. The clinging sorts like inconstans, quinquefolia, and himalayana are useful for walls, tree trunks, or any surface in need of a summer covering. Many species colour best in autumn when grown on walls.

Some species, like Coignetiæ, are difficult to increase except by seeds and layers, but most of the true vines can be propagated by cuttings, or preferably by " eyes." An " eye " consists of a single bud of the previous summer's shoot, with about half an inch of wood at each side, cut slanting fashion, so that the cut surfaces almost meet beneath the bud. These are made in early spring, each one placed on the surface of a small pot of sandy soil, the bud only uncovered, then put in gentle bottom heat. Cuttings are made one or two joints long, at the time the leaves are falling in autumn, and put under a handlight or in a cool frame. The Ampelopsis, Parthenocissus, and Cissus groups are easily rooted from leafy cuttings made in July and August of firm growth.

V. Bourquiniana, *Munson*, a relative or variety of V. aestivalis, the " summer grape " of N. America, is a very vigorous large-leaved vine which grows rampantly and bears its black fruits freely at Kew. From the S.W. United States comes V. Longii, *Prince*, a hardy strong-growing vine that is possibly a hybrid between V. arizonica and V. rupestris; also V. Treleasei, *Munson*, of more shrub-like habit and scarcely a climber.

The ampelopsis described in the original edition under the then accepted name of "V. leeoides" is now V. Chaffanjoni (syn. Ampelopsis Watsoniana, *Wilson*). For other alterations, see notes below on V. micans and V. pulchra.

I. Vitis (proper). True Grape Vines

Stems with peeling bark (except rotundifolia). Leaves undivided except in Pagnucci and Piasezkii. Flowers in panicles; petals united by their ends into a sort of cap, and falling before they separate :—*æstivalis, amurensis, arizonica, bicolor, californica, candicans, Champini, cinerea, Coignetiæ, cordifolia Davidii, Doaniana, flexuosa, Labrusca, monticola, Munsoniana, Pagnucci, Pentagona, Piasezkii, pulchra, Romanetii, rotundifolia, rupestris, Thunbergii, vinifera, vulpina.*

II. Parthenocissus (or Psedera)

Leaves divided into three to seven leaflets; tendrils mostly with viscous disks at the tips; petals separate and expanded. Flowers in compound cymes :—*Henryana, himalayana, inconstans, quinquefolia, semicordata, Thomsoni, vitacea.*

III. Ampelopsis

Tendrils coiling, never with viscous tips. Leaves simple to much divided. Petals separate and expanding; ovary surrounded by a disk : *aconitifolia, arborea, brevipedunculata, Chaffanjoni, Delavayana, heterophylla, indivisa (cordata), megalophylla, micans, orientalis, serjanæfolia.*

V. striata belongs to the section Cissus, and is the only one of that section we can grow out-of-doors. It has much divided leaves, and the disk below the ovary is four-lobed. In other respects much like Ampelopsis.

A Himalayan vine, V. capreolata, *D. Don*, has been many times introduced, but is not hardy. It is distinguished by having the inflorescence produced from the axil of the leaf instead of opposite to it. It belongs to Planchon's genus Tetrastigma as T. serrulatum. Leaves digitate, composed of five leaflets, one or both lower pairs united on one stalk. V. obtecta, recently introduced from China, is of the same group.

V. ACONITIFOLIA, *Hance*

(Ampelopsis aconitifolia, *Bunge*)

A slender-stemmed, luxuriantly leafy, deciduous climber; young shoots glabrous. Leaves very variable in shape and size, composed either of three or five stalkless leaflets radiating from the end of a common stalk which is ½ to 2 ins. long. The leaflets are lanceolate or diamond-shaped in general outline, but always deeply and coarsely toothed, and often conspicuously three- or five-lobed, the lobes reaching sometimes to the midrib. The entire leaf is 2 to 5 ins. across, the leaflets 1 to 3 ins. long, deep glossy green above, pale beneath, and glabrous on both sides except for small tufts of down in the vein-axils beneath. Flowers produced in August and September in numerous forked cymes. Fruits scarcely ¼ in. long, roundish obovate, dull orange.

Native of China. Of the vines with compound leaves and deeply cut leaflets this is the hardiest and most luxuriant in growth. It can be trained up a tall post, which it will soon cover with a beautiful tangle. There has been some confusion in gardens between this species and another vine, also of the Ampelopsis group, viz. :—

V. serjanæfolia, *Maximowicz* (Ampelopsis serjanæfolia, *Bunge*).—This is a native of Japan, Korea, and China, and quite distinct in foliage from V. aconitifolia.

The leaflets are in threes or fives, and in the latter case are arranged pinnately on the common stalk (not all radiating from its end as in the other). Another distinction is that the leaf-stalk between the pairs of leaflets is winged. Sometimes the lowest pair of leaflets are themselves pinnately divided. In other respects the leaflets are dark green above, pale glossy green beneath, glabrous. Fruit ¼ in. wide, violet-blue. The plant has a tuberous root like a Dahlia.

V. ÆSTIVALIS, *Michaux*. SUMMER GRAPE

A very vigorous deciduous climber, growing to a great height when support is available ; branchlets round, glabrous or loosely downy. Leaves very large, 4 to 12 ins. across, about as much long ; varying from deeply three- or five-lobed to scarcely lobed at all ; teeth shallow and broad, pointed at the apex, deeply heart-shaped at the base ; dull green, ultimately glabrous above, covered beneath with more or less persistent floss which is rusty red at first, changing to brown with age. Flowers in panicles up to 8 or 10 ins. long. Berries globose, ⅓ in. diameter, black with a blue bloom, agreeably flavoured.

Native of the eastern and central United States ; introduced in the seventeenth century. It is the parent of a race of American grape vines, including " Herbemont," " Cynthiana," and " Virginia Seedling." On the young stems there is a tendril missing from every third joint, and in its large-leaved state can thus be distinguished from V. Labrusca, which has a tendril or panicle opposite every leaf.

Var. BOURQUINIANA, *Bailey*.—Leaves only slightly downy beneath, the down grey or dun-coloured. Fruit larger, black to amber-coloured. Dr Rehder suggests that it is possibly a hybrid. V. Bourqúiniána, *Munson*.

V. CINEREA, *Engelmann*. SWEET WINTER GRAPE.—This vine, a native of the central United States, is allied to, and was at one time regarded as a variety of V. æstivalis. It has angular downy branchlets (as contrasted with the round, almost glabrous ones of æstivalis) ; the down beneath the leaf is grey or whitish, and the berries have little or no bloom.

V. AMURENSIS, *Ruprecht*. AMURLAND GRAPE

A strong-growing, deciduous vine of somewhat similar character to, but quite distinct from, V. vinifera, with reddish young shoots, flossy when young, a thick, hard disk of wood dividing the pith at the joints. Leaves 4 to 10 ins. wide, somewhat longer ; five-lobed, often deeply so, the middle lobe then of broadly ovate form, with a slender abrupt point ; the base has a deep, round, broad sinus ; under-surface somewhat downy.

Native of Amurland, Korea, and N. China. Worth growing for its vigorous habit, and for the usually fine crimson and purple autumn hues of its noble foliage.

V. ARBOREA, *Linnæus*. PEPPER VINE

(Ampelopsis arborea, *Koehne* ; A. bipinnata, *Michaux*)

A deciduous climber, with slender, purplish, nearly or quite glabrous, somewhat angular, zigzag shoots, slightly marked with lenticels ; tendrils slender, forked. Leaves 5 to 8 ins. long, about as much wide, doubly (sometimes trebly) pinnate, and composed of numerous stalked leaflets, which are ovate, ½ to 1¾ ins. long, ⅓ to 1¼ ins. wide ; sometimes lobed, always with very large, sharp, triangular teeth, the apex pointed, the base narrowly to broadly wedge-shaped ; dark green and glabrous above ; at first downy on the veins and in the vein-axils beneath, ultimately nearly or quite glabrous. Flowers in open, long-stalked cymes. Berries dark purple, about ⅓ in. diameter.

Native of the southern United States; introduced in 1700, and quite hardy, although better against a wall than in the open. It belongs to what is now considered the "true" Ampelopsis group, in which the petals are distinct and spreading and, like the sepals, in fives. It is a very handsome climber when in vigorous growth, but although it flowers occasionally, rarely develops fruit with us. Perhaps partially or wholly evergreen in warmer climates. (See also V. orientalis.)

V. ARIZONICA, *Engelmann*. CAÑON GRAPE

A shrubby or weakly climbing vine, deciduous; branchlets angular, at first clothed with cobwebby down, tendrils mostly perishing when young. Leaves heart-shaped, sometimes unlobed, sometimes more or less distinctly three-lobed; 1½ to 3 ins. wide, about the same long; the sinus at the base broad and rounded, the apex pointed, the margins coarsely and fairly regularly triangular toothed; cobwebby above, woolly beneath when young; stalk one-third to half as long as the blade. Berries black, with abundant bloom, ¼ to ⅓ in. wide, agreeable in flavour.

Native of the south-western United States; introduced to Kew in 1898 but unfortunately has since been lost. It has little to recommend it for gardens in general.

V. BICOLOR, *Le Conte*. BLUE GRAPE

(V. argentifolia, *Munson*; V. Lecontiana, *House*)

A vigorous deciduous climber, with round shoots free from down, but usually very glaucous, a tendril missing from every third joint. Leaves 4 to 12 ins. wide and long, three- or five-lobed, irregularly and shallowly toothed, usually glabrous on both surfaces, and vividly blue-white beneath. In other respects this vine is similar to V. æstivalis, to which it is most nearly allied. It is a native of the eastern and central United States, and in cultivation in Britain makes a luxuriant climber. Visitors to Goat Island, Niagara Falls, will have noticed its abundance there, associating with Celastrus scandens and other climbers in the production of a beautiful and luxuriant effect; this vine is conspicuous in the blue-white young shoots and under-surface of the leaves, to which the popular name refers.

V. BREVIPEDUNCULATA, *Dippel*

(Ampelopsis brevipedunculata, *Trautvetter*)

A vigorous climber, with roughly hairy young shoots. Leaves distinctly three-, rarely five-lobed, the side lobes spreading and pointed; heart-shaped at the base; 2 to 6 ins. long and wide, coarsely toothed, the teeth rounded, but ending in a minute abrupt point (mucro); dark green above with scattered short hairs at first; bristly hairy beneath; stalk from three-fourths to as long as the blade, very hairy, especially at first. Inflorescence hairy, once or twice forked, each fork terminated by a cymose flower-cluster. Fruit ¼ to ⅓ in. across, amethyst blue.

Native of Japan and of the region of the Amur and Ussuri rivers; cultivated for the last forty years in gardens under various names, such as V. amurensis, Regeliana, heterophylla var. cordata. It is certainly closely allied to V. heterophylla, but is well distinguished by its bristly hairy young shoots, etc., and less angular teeth. One of the true Ampelopsis.

V. CALIFORNICA, *Bentham.* CALIFORNIAN GRAPE

A deciduous climber, reaching 20 to 30 ft. in height, the young shoots covered at first with grey cobwebby down, nearly glabrous later. Leaves roundish cordate or kidney-shaped, occasionally three-lobed ; 2 to 4 ins. wide, and about as long ; rounded at the apex, the sinus at the base often wide and rounded ; the margins set with fairly even, broadly triangular teeth, scarcely ⅛ in. deep ; upper surface glabrous, lower one usually grey with down ; stalk 1 to 2 ins. long, grey downy like the young shoot. Berry ¼ in. in diameter, black, covered with purple bloom.

Native of California. This is a very well-marked vine in the round-ended, shallowly and evenly toothed leaves. It has no value, even in its own home, as a fruit-bearer, but is certainly very handsome in autumn, its leaves turning a deep crimson before they fall.

V. CANDICANS, *Engelmann.* MUSTANG GRAPE

A vigorous deciduous climber, shoots covered with a dense white wool, a thick disk interrupting the pith at the joints. Leaves 2 to 4½ ins. wide, broadly heart-shaped to kidney-shaped, sometimes entire or with only a wavy outline, sometimes obscurely three-lobed ; on young plants or strong sucker shoots the leaves are sometimes deeply three-, five-, or seven-lobed, but even then scarcely or very shallowly toothed. On first expanding the upper surface is woolly, but the wool soon falls away, leaving it a dull, dark green, whilst the under-surface remains covered with a thick white felt. The stalk is one-fourth to half as long as the blade, and white-woolly. Berries globose, about ⅔ in. wide, purplish, and unpleasantly flavoured.

Native of Texas, often found on limestone. It is one of the most distinct of American grape-vines in the broad, almost entire leaves and vivid white wool beneath, suggesting a white poplar leaf. It was quite hardy when grown at Kew. Allied to it, and perhaps a hybrid from it, is

V. DOANIANA, *Munson.* Doan's Grape.—The leaves of this vine, however, are always three-lobed and coarsely toothed, and the upper surface is bluish green strewn with patches of white wool. The young shoots and leaves are quite white all over at first, and much of the wool persists beneath. It was found wild in Texas and New Mexico ; although no longer grown there, it was introduced to Kew in 1892 where it was quite hardy.

V. CHAFFANJONI, *Léveillé and Vaniot*

(Ampelopsis Chaffanjoni, *Léveillé* ; A. Watsoniana, *Wilson* ; V. leeoides, *Hort. Veitch*)

A deciduous climber of the Ampelopsis group, and allied to V. megalophylla ; leaves pinnate, up to 1 ft. in length. Leaflets five or seven, oval or oblong, 1½ to 4½ ins. long, ¾ to 2 ins. wide ; rounded or broadly tapered at the base, terminating in a long, slender point ; sparsely toothed, lustrous green above, claret purple beneath, and, like the young shoots, perfectly smooth.

This vine was discovered in Western Hupeh, China, by Wilson and introduced in 1900. It was distributed by Messrs Veitch from the Coombe Wood nursery erroneously as " V. leeoides," and appeared as such in previous editions of this work where, however, I suggested it might eventually prove to be a new species. It differs from the true V. leeoides by its leaves being simply pinnate, never bipinnate. It does not seem to be very vigorous grown in an exposed position, but was very handsome trained up a pole in the Coombe Wood nursery. It succeeds well grown on a south wall.

V. COIGNETIÆ, *Pulliat*

(V. congesta, *Hort.* ; V. Thunbergii, *Hort.*, not *Siebold*)

A very vigorous deciduous climber, reaching the tops of the highest trees ; young shoots round, ribbed, and at first covered with a loose greyish floss ; there is a tendril missing at every third joint. Leaves perhaps the largest among vines, being sometimes 12 ins. long and 10 ins. broad, ordinarily 4 to 8 ins. wide ; they are roundish in the main, rather obscurely three- or five-lobed, the lobes and apex pointed, the base deeply heart-shaped ; shallowly to coarsely toothed ; dark green and glabrous above, covered beneath with a thick rusty brown felt ; stalk from 2 to 6 ins. long, somewhat woolly. Berries black with a purple bloom, ½ in. wide.

Native of Japan ; first introduced apparently to Mr Anthony Waterer's nursery long ago through Messrs Jardine and Matheson, East India merchants. The original plant grew over some trees at Knap Hill, and made a glorious display of crimson every autumn. Owing to difficulty in propagating, it spread very little in cultivation. But about 1893 a quantity of seeds were imported from Japan, and the species became more common in gardens. The seedlings, however, have not yet proved quite equal in autumn colouring to the Waterer stock, which is generally but wrongly named V. Thunbergii. The true V. Thunbergii (*q.v.*) is very distinct. Seeds of V. Coignetiæ had been introduced from Japan to France by Madame Coignet as long ago as 1875, and the plants raised from them were greatly admired for their magnificent autumn colour. They experienced there the same difficulty in propagation, and owing to this and the phylloxera regulations this vine did not spread out of France. In the absence of seed, layering appears to be the only method of propagation available. In the forests of Yezo, according to Sargent, " it climbs into the tops of the largest trees, filling them with its enormous leaves, which in autumn assume the most brilliant hues of scarlet." It was in this way that it grew at Knap Hill. It is also very fine at Castlewellan and Narrow Water, in Ireland, in both places on a wall, developing a remarkable size of leaf—frequently 1 ft. or more across. In this respect, and in the richness of its colour in autumn, it is undoubtedly the finest of all true vines. Seedling plants have leaves very much more deeply lobed than fully grown ones.

V. CORDIFOLIA, *Michaux.* FROST or CHICKEN GRAPE

A very vigorous vine, whose main stem in a wild state is sometimes from 1½ to 2 ft. thick ; young shoots smooth or only slightly hairy, a tendril missing from every third joint. Leaves thin, roundish ovate, with a heart-shaped base (the sinus pointed and narrow) ; 3 to 5 ins. wide, rather more in length ; slenderly pointed, coarsely and irregularly toothed, unlobed or sometimes obscurely three-lobed, glossy and glabrous above, glabrous or downy on the veins beneath ; stalk often as long as the blade. Flowers in drooping panicles, 4 to 12 ins. long. Berries globose, ¼ to ½ in. in diameter, black.

Native of the eastern United States ; introduced in 1806. The berries are moderately well-flavoured after they have been touched by frost in America, harsh and acid before ; in one form (var. FŒTIDA, *Engelmann*) they have a pungent, fœtid odour. The species has been confused with vulpina (*q.v.*).

V. DAVIDII, *Foëx*

(V. armata, *Diels* ; Spinovitis Davidii, *Carrière*)

A luxuriant, deciduous climber, the young shoots not downy, but covered with spiny, gland-tipped, somewhat hooked bristles, which give them a very rough appearance. Leaves heart-shaped, slender-pointed, toothed ; 4 to 10 ins. long, $2\frac{1}{2}$ to 8 ins. wide ; shining dark green and glabrous above ; bluish or greyish green beneath, and downy only in the vein-axils, but more or less glandular-bristly, as is also the leaf-stalk, which is from half to nearly as long as the blade. Fruit said to be about $\frac{2}{3}$ in. diameter, black, and of a pleasant flavour.

Native of Central China ; introduced by Wilson for Messrs Veitch in 1900, but if, as I believe, the vine called Spinovitis Davidii is the same, it has been cultivated in France and in England since about 1885. The plant cultivated at Kew under the latter name has leaves more deeply lobed and more coarsely toothed than Wilson's V. armata, and the spines are smaller ; but in other respects it does not appear to differ. According to Carrière, the leaves are very variable in shape.

Var. CYANOCARPA, *Sargent*, is described as a more vigorous form than the type, and as having larger leaves of unsurpassed richness in autumn colouring. Ordinary V. armata changes to brilliant red. (V. Veitchii, *Hort.*)

V. DELAVAYANA, *Franchet*

(Ampelopsis Delavayana, *Planchon*)

This species was introduced by Wilson for Messrs Veitch in 1900, and appears to be quite hardy and vigorous. It is a climber with hairy young stems, swollen at the joints. Leaves composed of three or five leaflets, the middle one of which is shortly stalked, narrowly oval, tapered at both ends, especially towards the point ; side lobes stalkless, unequal at each side of the midrib, sometimes with a lobe on the lower side and oblique at the base. All are coarsely toothed, roughish above, downy (at least when young) on the veins beneath. Leaflets from $1\frac{1}{2}$ to 4 ins. long, $\frac{3}{4}$ to $1\frac{1}{2}$ ins. wide (larger on vigorous young plants). Fruits small, dark blue. Young shoots and leaf-stalks pinkish. Native of W. China.

V. FLEXUOSA, *Thunberg*

A slender-stemmed, elegant climber ; shoots glabrous, or downy only when quite young. Leaves roundish ovate and heart-shaped at the base, or triangular and truncate at the base, often contracted at the apex to a slender point : amongst the smallest in the genus, being ordinarily 2 to $3\frac{1}{2}$ ins. across, of thin firm texture ; glabrous and glossy above, downy on the veins and in the vein-axils beneath. Inflorescence slender, 2 to 6 ins. long. Fruits about the size of a pea, black.

Native of Japan, Korea, and China ; long cultivated in gardens, but recently brought more prominently into notice by new forms introduced from China. It is a variable species, but the typical form is known by its quite small, unlobed (or indistinctly three-lobed) leaves, glabrous and very glossy above.

Var. PARVIFOLIA, *Gagnepain*.—Leaves smaller, shining bronzy green above, purple beneath when young. One of the daintiest in leaf of all true vines. Sent out about 1904 as " var. Wilsonii " by Messrs Veitch.

V. HENRYANA, *Hemsley*

(Parthenocissus Henryana, *Graebner* ; Psedera Henryana, *C. K. Schneider*)

A vigorous deciduous climber, with sharply four-angled stems free from down ; tendrils forked, ending in disks by which it adheres to flat surfaces. Leaves composed of three to five leaflets borne on a stalk $1\frac{1}{2}$ to $4\frac{1}{2}$ ins. long. Leaflets obovate, oblanceolate, or narrowly oval, slender-pointed, tapered at the base to a short stalk, coarsely toothed except near the base ; 1½ to 5 ins. long, one-third to one-half as wide ; dark velvety green, variegated with silvery white and pink along the midrib and primary veins, which are slightly downy beneath. The green part turns red in autumn. Inflorescence a terminal leafy panicle of cymes up to 6 or 7 ins. long.

Native of Central China ; discovered by Henry about 1885 ; introduced by Wilson for Messrs Veitch in 1900. It is a remarkably handsome vine closely allied to the true Virginian creeper, and having the same power of attaching itself to walls, etc., by means of its adhesive disk-tipped tendrils. It thrives quite well against a wall or where it gets a little shelter, but fully exposed in the open it is not quite hardy. A large batch of year-old plants were killed in the winter of 1908-9 at Kew. Its variegation is better defined on a north-west or even north wall, than when the plant is fully exposed to the sun.

V. HETEROPHYLLA, *Thunberg*

(Bot. Mag. (as var. humulifolia), t. 5682 ; Ampelopsis heterophylla, *Siebold*)

A luxuriant, deciduous climber, with the shoots and leaf-stalks reddish, glabrous, or only slightly downy when quite young. Leaves extremely variable in shape ; sometimes broadly heart-shaped and not lobed at all, sometimes slightly three-lobed, sometimes deeply three- or five-lobed, several shapes to be seen on the same shoot ; 2 to 4 ins. long and wide ; the lobes and apex slenderly pointed, the base straight or more or less heart-shaped ; margins sharply toothed ; dark green above, pale bright green beneath, with a slight pubescence at first on the veins ; stalk from half to nearly as long as the blade. Flowers in small cymose clusters, each cluster terminating a division of the forked inflorescence. Berries porcelain blue, dotted with black, ¼ in. across.

Native of China, Japan, and Korea ; introduced about 1860. Several attempts have been made to distinguish by name the various forms of this vine, but the leaves are so extremely variable, even on the same plant, that it seems best to keep to the name heterophylla. The great beauty of this vine is in its blue fruits, and these are only produced where the plant is fully exposed to the sun. The best results are obtained by planting it against a south wall, where it has a rather restricted root run. It is most nearly allied to V. indivisa, but that never has distinctly lobed leaves (see also brevipedunculata).

Var. ELEGANS, *Regel* (V. heterophylla variegata).—Leaves handsomely splashed with pink and white, and the young shoots pink. It is too delicate to thrive away from a wall.

The climber known in gardens as V. citrulloides, with very deeply five-lobed leaves, which seem constant, may belong to heterophylla.

V. HIMALAYANA, *Brandis*

(Psedera himalayana, *C. K. Schneider*)

A vigorous deciduous climber, with semi-woody, glabrous young stems ; the tendrils terminated by clinging disks. Leaves composed of three leaflets, each shortly stalked and borne at the end of a slender, common stalk 2 to 5 ins. long. Central leaflet ovate, oval or obovate ; the side ones very obliquely ovate (two or three times as much blade on one side of the midrib as on the other), and often somewhat heart-shaped at the base on one side only. They are all abruptly tapered at the apex, toothed ; dark green and glabrous above, paler, slightly glaucous beneath, with a few short hairs on the midrib only ; 2 to 6 ins. long, 1¼ to 4 ins. wide. Fruit globose, ¼ in. wide, in loose clusters several times forked.

Native of the Himalaya up to 11,000 ft. It is a rather tender species, and only thrives well on a wall. Its leaves change to rich red in autumn.

V. SEMICORDATA, *Wallich*, is perhaps not specifically distinct from himalayana' but it has smaller leaves and its young shoots and under-surface of leaves are bristly. It may be a form from higher altitudes, as plants raised at Kew from seed sent by the Calcutta Botanic Garden are hardier than V. himalayana.

V. INCONSTANS, *Miquel*

(Ampelopsis Veitchii *of gardens* ; Parthenocissus tricuspidata, *Planchon*, Bot. Mag., t. 8287)

A lofty deciduous climber reaching the tops of trees over 60 ft. high ; young shoots glabrous, attaching themselves to their supports by means of viscous disks terminating the tendrils. Leaves extremely variable, but of three main types : 1, broadly ovate with a heart-shaped base, shallowly or coarsely toothed, but not, or very slightly, lobed ; 2, composed of three distinct, stalked leaflets, the middle one obovate, the side ones obliquely ovate ; 3, conspicuously and deeply three-lobed, the side lobes erect or spreading. The two first types are characteristic of young plants and young shoots, and the leaves average from 2 to 5 ins. across ; the last are found on old plants that have reached the flowering and fruiting stage, and the leaves are large and coarse, 8 ins. or even more across. In all forms they are glabrous above, finely downy on the veins beneath. Flowers yellow-green, produced in cymes mostly on short two-leaved shoots. Fruit dull, dark blue with a bloom, flattish, ¼ to ⅓ in. wide.

Native of Japan and China ; introduced by John Gould Veitch about 1862. No climbing plant ever introduced has secured so important a place in British horticulture. Owing to its abundance, it is now becoming the vogue to decry it. It certainly requires watching, and should never be allowed to grow over and shroud beautiful architectural detail, as has happened on some of the colleges at Oxford. On the other hand, the stark ugliness of innumerable brick walls in urban districts has been hidden by it. It is really one of the least troublesome of climbers, being self-supporting and attaching itself readily and securely to walls, etc., by means of the viscid tips of the tendrils, and spreading with remarkable rapidity. The leaves of the young climbing branchlets are at first pressed to the wall. In autumn the foliage turns one of the loveliest of crimsons. The large leaves that appear on old plants near the base are coarse in appearance, and the plant then loses much of its charm. It does not bear fruit except during hot summers ; there was a good crop in 1911. Cuttings made of firm pieces of young branchlets, 3 or 4 ins. long, and put in gentle heat about August strike root readily. The young plants should be grown in pots until planted out permanently, as they dislike transplanting.

Var. LOWI (Ampelopsis Lowi, *Hort.*).—A seedling form raised by Messrs Low of Enfield, and first exhibited by them in 1907. It has small three- to seven-lobed leaves, at least when young, very elegant, and colouring as well as the type.

V. INDIVISA, *Willdenow*

(Ampelopsis cordata, *Michaux*)

A vigorous deciduous climber ; young bark warted, not or very slightly downy ; tendrils forked, sometimes absent. Leaves roundish ovate, more or less heart-shaped at the base, shallowly but sharply toothed ; glabrous or slightly downy along the veins and in the vein-axils beneath ; 2 to 5 ins.

long, scarcely as wide ; stalk often downy, shorter than the blade. Flowers on slender-stalked cymes 1½ to 3 ins. broad. Fruits blue or greenish blue.

Native of the south-east and south central United Sates ; introduced in 1803. It is quite hardy and grows vigorously at Kew, but has no special attraction. The ends of the shoots are herbaceous and die back in winter, disarticulating at the nodes. Although the leaves have the typical Vitis shape, it is a true Ampelopsis, the sepals and petals being in fives, the latter separate and expanded, the bark not peeling.

V. LABRUSCA, *Linnæus.* NORTHERN FOX GRAPE

A vigorous deciduous climber, with very woolly young shoots carrying a tendril or an inflorescence at every joint. Leaves thick-textured, unlobed, or three-lobed (sometimes deeply) towards the top ; shallowly and irregularly toothed, broadly ovate or roundish, 3 to 7 ins. wide and long ; the base heart-shaped ; upper surface dark green, becoming glabrous, lower one covered with rusty-coloured (at first whitish) wool ; stalk more than half as long as the blade. Panicles 2 to 4 ins. long. Berries globose, ⅔ in. diameter, thick-skinned, dark purple with a musky or foxy aroma.

Native of eastern N. America from New England southwards ; introduced in 1656. Of the wild grape vines of N. America this is the most important in an economic sense, and has produced more varieties cultivated for their fruit than any other. It is a vigorous species, and although it has not the least value as a fruiting vine in this country, it is worth growing for its fine foliage and luxuriant growth. It is distinguished among all the true Vitis by having a tendril or an inflorescence opposite each leaf.

V. MEGALOPHYLLA, *Veitch*

(Ampelopsis megalophylla, *Diels*, Bot. Mag., t. 8537)

A vigorous deciduous climber ; young shoots rather glaucous, and, like the rest of the plant, quite glabrous. Leaves doubly pinnate (the upper and smaller ones simply pinnate), from 1½ to 2 ft., sometimes more, long, and nearly as wide. The larger ones are composed of seven or nine segments, the one or two lowest pairs of which are again pinnately divided. Leaflets of variable shape and size, but mostly ovate or ovate-oblong, deep green above, glaucous beneath ; 2 to 6 ins. long, 1 to 3 ins. wide ; coarsely toothed, each tooth terminated by a minute abrupt point. Flowers produced in August in a sparse, slenderly branched inflorescence, each branch terminating in a cyme. Fruit top-shaped, ¼ in. diameter, black.

Native of W. China ; introduced to France in 1894 by Mr Maurice de Vilmorin, and by him distributed as V. cantoniensis—a different and probably not hardy vine. Wilson introduced V. megalophylla for Messrs Veitch in 1900, and from their nursery it was largely distributed. In some respects it is the most remarkable of all hardy vines. Its leaves are larger than those of any other in cultivation, suggesting at their biggest the leaves of Aralia cordata. Planted in good soil and trained up a lofty post (it should be 15 ft. high), this vine provides a very striking effect. It has made growths 8 to 10 ft. long in one season at Coombe Wood.

V. MICANS

(V. repens, *Veitch* ; Ampelopsis micans, *Rehder*

A deciduous climbing vine up to 20 ft. high ; young shoots glabrous and purplish on the sunny side. Leaves roundish to triangular-ovate, three-lobed (often inconspicuously so), shallowly heart-shaped to truncate at the base, slenderly pointed, coarsely and triangularly toothed ; 2½ to 5 ins. long, glabrous on both sides, but of a glittering green above and pale or rather glaucous beneath ; stalk purplish, 1½ to 3 ins. long. Flowers crowded in a branching cluster at the end of a slender stalk 1 to 2 ins. long. Fruits dark blue, flattened —globose, ⅕ in. wide.

Native of Hupeh and Szechuen, China ; introduced by Wilson in 1900 to the Coombe Wood Nursery. It was first put in commerce by them under the name " V. repens " and was figured as such in their *Catalogue of Novelties*, 1905. It is apparently one of the two plants that have been called " V. flexuosa Wilsonii," but the charming little vine more generally known under that name in this country and well marked by its small, glittering leaves being purple beneath should, according to Rehder, be called V. FLEXUOSA PARVIFOLIA, *Gagnepain*.

V. micans belongs to the section *Ampelopsis*, and is represented by a vigorous plant on the vine pergola at Kew.

V. MONTICOLA, *Buckley*. MOUNTAIN GRAPE

A deciduous climber up to 30 ft. high, with slender, angled, slightly downy branchlets. Leaves 2 to 4 ins. across, about the same in length ; heart-shaped at the base, the sinus broad and rounded ; sharply, sometimes slenderly pointed, coarsely triangular-toothed, and slightly three-lobed ; of thinnish texture, dark green above, greyish beneath, both surfaces shining ; woolly on the veins beneath when young ; stalk about half the length of the blade. Berries globose, ¼ in. wide, black and sweet.

Native of Texas ; introduced in 1898. There is a thin diaphragm interrupting the pith at the joints. V. CHAMPINII, *Planchon*, is another Texan species introduced at the same time, and allied to V. monticola, but has larger fruits, also black.

V. ORIENTALIS, *Boissier*

(Ampelopsis orientalis, *Planchon* ; Cissus orientalis, *Lamarck*)

A laxly bushy, or sometimes climbing, deciduous shrub, with glabrous, slightly ribbed shoots. Leaves variable ; often doubly trifoliolate (each of the three chief divisions being subdivided into three leaflets), sometimes simply pinnate, sometimes bipinnate. Leaflets ovate, diamond-shaped or obovate, tapered at the base ; 1 to 3 ins. long, ⅝ to 2 ins. wide ; the upper part coarsely toothed ; dark dull green and glabrous above ; paler, grey-green, also glabrous beneath, or with tiny tufts in the vein-axils. Flowers with the parts in fours, produced on long-stalked cymes. Fruit roundish, top-shaped, ¼ in. diameter, red.

Native of Asia Minor, Syria, etc., up to 5000 ft. on the mountains ; introduced in 1818. It is, no doubt, closely allied, and very similar to the American V. arborea, but its foliage is coarser and not so distinctly bipinnate, and it falls sooner in autumn. The leaves are usually composed of nine leaflets (but sometimes eleven or fifteen), which are considerably larger on the average, and appear to be never downy on the veins beneath, as are frequently those of V. arborea. A handsome foliaged shrub, which used to fruit with Canon Ellacombe at Bitton, near Bath. He compared them to clusters of red currants.

V. PAGNUCCI, *Du Caillaud*

A slender-stemmed climber ; young shoots soon quite glabrous. Leaves 1½ to 4 ins. long and wide, variable ; sometimes composed of three distinct leaflets, sometimes deeply three-lobed with a heart-shaped base , or with a lobe on one side only. On the trifoliolate leaf the middle leaflet is stalked, ovate or oval ; the side leaflets obliquely ovate and stalkless. For the rest, they are all rather coarsely and angularly toothed, the upper surface somewhat rough to the touch, the lower one downy on the midrib and veins ; stalks ¾ to 2 ins. long, slightly hairy.

Native of Central China ; introduced to Kew in 1899, but it had previously been cultivated in France. It is a vine of moderately vigorous gorwth, the leaves turning a glorious blood-red in autumn. Dr Rehder makes it a variety of V. Piasezkii.

V. PENTAGONA, *Diels and Gilg*

(V. ficifolia pentagona, *Pampanini*)

A deciduous climber of the true vine character ; young shoots clothed with a whitish felt, and attaching themselves to their supports by twining tendrils, which are also felted. Leaves ovate with a heart-shaped or truncate base and pointed apex, usually but not always shallowly three- or five-lobed, unevenly and shallowly toothed ; 3 to 6 ins. long, three-fourths as wide ; dark green above and at first downy, becoming glabrous ; clothed beneath with a vividly white, close felt which remains until the leaves fall ; stalk 1 to 3 ins. long ; veins in six to nine pairs. Berries globose, ⅓ in. wide, blue-black, borne in slender bunches 4 to 6 ins. long.

Native of W. Hupeh and Szechuen ; introduced by Wilson in 1907, in the autumn of which year seeds were sent to Kew from the Arnold Arboretum (Wilson No. 134). This is a very distinct and ornamental species on account of the conspicuous white felt which covers the under surface of the leaf. No cultivated species of Vitis has this character more marked. It is a vigorous grower and very hardy.

Var. BELLULA, *Rehder and Wilson.*—Described as differing from the type chiefly in the much smaller leaves, 1½ to 2½ ins. long.

V. PIASEZKII, *Maximowicz*

(Bot. Mag., t. 9565 ; Parthenocissus sinensis, *Diels* ; Psedera sinensis, *C. K. Schneider*)

A vigorous, deciduous handsome climber, with rarely branching tendrils, young shoots at first flossy, then glabrous. Leaves very variable, 3 to 6 ins. long, 2½ to 5 ins. wide ; three-lobed with a heart-shaped base, or composed of three or five taper-based leaflets, the middle one of which is stalked and oval or obovate, the side ones or at least the lower pair obliquely ovate and stalkless. The merely lobed leaves differ much in the depth of the lobes, which are sometimes little more than large triangular teeth, but showing every intermediate condition between that and the tri- or quinque-foliolate ones. The margins are sharply toothed, the upper surface dark green, downy on the veins, the lower surface more or less brown-felted ; stalks purplish, half to two-thirds as long as the blade. Fruit black-purple, globose, ⅓ in. wide, in slender, sometimes forked branches 4 or 5 ins. long.

Native of Central China ; introduced in 1900 by Wilson. It has remarkably variable leaves, resembling in that respect V. Pagnucci.

V. PULCHRA, *Rehder*

(V. flexuosa major, *Hort. Veitch*)

In previous editions, under " V. flexuosa," a brief note is given about this vine. It was originally sent out under the name " V. flexuosa major " from Veitch's Nursery, but in 1913 Dr Rehder described it in a German periodical and gave it the above name. It is a vigorous deciduous climber with reddish, soon quite smooth young shoots. Leaves roundish ovate, 3 to 6 ins. wide, often as broad as, or broader than long, sometimes slightly three-lobed, oftener coarsely toothed, the base widely and shallowly heart-shaped, the apex shortly or slenderly pointed ; glabrous or nearly so above, covered with grey down beneath ; stalk 1½ to 4 ins. long. Flowers produced in June on slender panicles up to 4 ins. long.

The native country of this vine is not definitely known, but it is almost certainly North Asiatic and probably Japanese. Its chief value is in the rich purple and blood-red tints of its dying leaves, which are also coloured when unfolding. Amongst other places, it succeeded very well with Mr Robinson at Gravetye, near East Grinstead. It appears to be related to, possibly a hybrid of, V. Coignetiæ and appeared in cultivation about 1880.

V. QUINQUEFOLIA, *Lamarck*. TRUE VIRGINIA CREEPER

(V. hederacea, *Ehrhart* ; Psedera quinquefolia, *Greene* ;
Parthenocissus quinquefolia, *Planchon*)

A tall, deciduous climber, reaching to the tops of lofty trees, free from down in all its parts ; stems slender, reddish at first, clinging to its support by means of a disk at the end of each branch of the tendril. Leaves composed of five leaflets (sometimes three) radiating from the end of a common stalk 1 to 4 ins. long. Leaflets oval to obovate, 1 to 4 ins. long, ⅓ to 2½ ins. wide, slenderly pointed, tapered at the base to a stalk ⅛ to ½ in. long, coarsely toothed except at the base ; dull green above, pale and rather glaucous beneath. Inflorescence several times forked, the final subdivisions terminated by an umbel of three to eight flowers. Fruit globose, about ¼ in. diameter, blue-black.

Native of eastern N. America from New England southwards to Florida ; introduced in 1629 ; originally named Hedera quinquefolia by Linnæus. It is one of the finest of all climbers, its leaves turning a rich crimson before they fall. As it clings of itself to walls and tree trunks it is very useful. But, very strangely, it had, until a few years ago, become quite scarce in cultivation, having been replaced by V. vitacea, a species without the sucker disks on the tendrils, and therefore not able to attach itself to flat surfaces. The true plant has comparatively recently been reintroduced under the names of " muralis " and " Engelmannii." At Kew, without artificial support, it has climbed the naked trunks of lofty pine trees and reached the top.

Var. HIRSUTA (Ampelopsis hirsuta, *Donn*).—A distinct variety, sometimes regarded as a separate species, with hairy shoots, leaf-stalks, leaflets (both surfaces), and inflorescence. Native of the south-eastern United States.

Var. ST PAULII.—Young shoots, leaf-stalks, and under-surface of leaflets as well as the midrib above clothed with down of a finer nature than in var. hirsuta, from which it also differs in the sharper, deeper teeth, and in being a better wall-climber.

V. ROMANETI, *Du Caillaud*

A vigorous, deciduous climber ; young shoots downy, and mixed with the down are numerous gland-tipped, stiff, erect bristles. Leaves of firm texture, three-lobed with a deep, narrow opening where the stalk is attached, shallowly toothed, each tooth ending in a bristle-like tip ; 6 to 10 ins. long ; 4 to 7 ins. wide ; upper surface slightly downy on the nerves, or almost smooth and dark green ; lower surface covered with a dense grey felt, with the midrib and veins hairy, a few large gland-tipped bristles mixed with the hairs. Stalk one-third to one-half as long as the blade, with a mixture of down and glandular bristles as on the shoot, but with the bristles more numerous. Fruit black, $\frac{1}{3}$ to $\frac{1}{2}$ in. diameter.

Native of China; introduced about 1881, and one of the finest of the true vines except that it is rather tender in a young state, and until the main stem becomes quite woody. From V. armata it is very distinct in the felted under-surface of the leaves, and it is not possible to confuse it with any other species.

V. ROTUNDIFOLIA, *Michaux*. SOUTHERN FOX GRAPE

A vigorous, deciduous climber, with stems up to 90 ft. in length, in a wild state, the bark adhering (not shredding); young shoots warted; tendrils unbranched. Leaves broadly ovate or roundish, always broadly heart-shaped at the base, pointed; 2 to $4\frac{1}{2}$ ins. long and wide; of firm texture, seldom lobed, but with the marginal teeth large, irregular, triangular; upper surface glossy dark green, glabrous; the lower one yellowish green, also glossy, with down in the vein-axils and sometimes on the veins; stalk usually shorter than the blade. Berries roundish, $\frac{2}{3}$ to 1 in. diameter, dull purple without bloom, skin thick and tough; flavour musky.

Native of the southern United States; sometimes wrongly named " V. vulpina." Nearly allied to it is Munson's grape (V. MUNSONIANA, *Simpson*), which has smaller fruits with a tender skin and acid flesh; it has been in cultivation, but is not very hardy, coming from Florida. These two species are distinguished from all the grape vines by the pith running uninterrupted through the joints of the stem, and by the non-shredding bark and unforked tendrils.

V. RUPESTRIS, *Scheele*. BUSH GRAPE

A deciduous bush up to 6 or 7 ft. high, usually without tendrils; young shoots glabrous or nearly so. Leaves kidney-shaped or broadly heart-shaped; 2 to $4\frac{1}{2}$ ins. wide, scarcely so long; abruptly and slenderly pointed; coarsely, irregularly, and sharply toothed, but not or only slightly lobed; glossy, bluish green on both surfaces and glabrous, except that the veins beneath are sometimes downy; stalk rather shorter than the blade. Berries roundish, about $\frac{1}{4}$ in. wide, purple-black with a slight bloom, agreeably flavoured.

Native of the south-eastern United States. Interesting as a bushy, not climbing vine.

V. STRIATA, *Baker*

(Ampelopsis sempervirens, *Hort.*; Cissus striata, *Ruiz and Pavon*)

An evergreen climber; young stems slender, angled, hairy and very leafy; tendrils thread-like. Leaves $1\frac{1}{2}$ to 3 ins. across, composed of five scarcely stalked leaflets, radiating from the end of a common stalk $\frac{3}{4}$ to $1\frac{1}{2}$ ins. long. Leaflets obovate or oblanceolate, $\frac{1}{2}$ to $1\frac{1}{2}$ ins. long, $\frac{1}{4}$ to $\frac{3}{4}$ in. wide; tapered at the base, coarsely toothed towards the apex, each tooth tipped abruptly with a short gland; dark glossy green and glabrous on both surfaces. Flowers green, produced in small cymes. Fruits about the size and shape of small red currants, but of a reddish purple colour.

Native of Chile and S. Brazil; introduced about 1878. Against a wall this survives all but the hardest winters, but is tender in the open. It is a very elegant plant, luxuriantly leafy, and with beautifully cut leaves. Tweedie, the Kew collector in S. America, called it the " ivy of Uruguay," and says it covers the bushes with red berries in winter. It thrives very well in the south and west, and bore large crops of fruit at St Leonard's as long ago as 1885, but the berries were purplish rather than red. When cut down to the ground by frost it will often break up again the following summer, but on the whole it is only well adapted for the mildest counties.

V. THOMSONII, *Lawson*

A slender, deciduous climber of the quinquefolia group ; young stems slightly downy at first, ribbed. Leaves composed normally of five leaflets, borne on a slender downy stalk 1½ to 4½ ins. long. Leaflets oval or obovate, 1 to 4 ins. long, ½ to 1½ ins. wide ; slenderly pointed, the upper half shallowly but sharply toothed, the base entire and tapered to a stalk, ⅛ to ¾ in. long ; under-surface sparsely downy on the midrib, glossy. The entire leaf, leaf-stalk, and young shoots are of bright claret purple when young, becoming greenish purple later, changing finally to deep reddish purple. Flowers in cymes on a slender stalk.

Native of China ; introduced by Wilson for Messrs Veitch in 1900. It was awarded a first-class certificate by the Royal Hort. Society, 1st Sept. 1903, and is, indeed, one of the most charming acquisitions of recent years amongst hardy climbers. It appears to be nearly related to V. Henryana, but is decidedly hardier. I have never seen it suffer from frost.

V. THUNBERGII, *Siebold and Zuccarini*. FIG-LEAVED VINE
(Bot. Mag., t. 8558 ; V. Seiboldii, *Hort.*)

A slender-stemmed, only moderately vigorous, deciduous climber, the young shoots angled, more or less woolly. Leaves variable, but deeply three- or five-lobed, usually 2½ to 4, sometimes 6 ins. across, heart-shaped at the base. Lobes ovate, often penetrating half or more than half the depth of the blade, the space (or sinus) between the lobes often expanding and rounded at the bottom ; sharply, shallowly, and irregularly toothed, dark dull green and glabrous above, covered with a rusty brown felt beneath. Leaf-stalk about half the length of the blade. Berries in bunches 2 or 3 ins. long, black with a purple bloom, ⅜ in. or less in diameter.

Native of Japan ; introduced probably by Siebold. The name has generally in this country been wrongly applied to a fine form of V. Coignetiæ (*q.v.*), from which it is quite distinct in its comparatively small leaves, deeply lobed like those of a fig, and its slender, less woody, five-angled young shoots. It is much nearer V. FICIFOLIA, *Bunge* ; in fact the distinctions between these two are not very clear. It has also been associated with V. Labrusca, but that species must be regarded as purely N. American, and as more nearly allied to V. Coignetiæ than V. Thunbergii, both of which, however, are distinguished from it by having a tendril missing from every third joint of the young shoot. V. Thunbergii is grown at Kew and at Bitton, where it turns rich crimson in autumn, and occasionally bears fruit. In my experience it is a rather weak grower, the ends of the shoots dying back considerably every winter.

V. VINIFERA, *Linnæus*. COMMON GRAPE VINE

A deciduous climber, growing 50 ft. or more in length if given support ; young shoots sometimes glabrous, sometimes cobwebby. Leaves usually 3 to 6 ins. wide and long ; three- or five-lobed, coarsely toothed. When deeply lobed the sinus between the lobes is rounded and almost or quite closed by the overlapping of the upper parts of the lobes. Upper surface glabrous, or downy on the veins ; lower one always more or less downy (sometimes felted), especially on the veins ; stalk more than half as long as the blade. Berries oval, black with a blue bloom.

The grape vine has been cultivated in all the warm temperate parts of Europe, and in parts of Asia back into the unrecorded past, and its real native country is now a matter of conjecture. But the general opinion is that it originated in Asia Minor and the Caucasian region. It is perfectly hardy in most parts of Britain, and has, in past times, been cultivated for the production of wine. Of modern vineyards in Britain that of the Marquis of Bute near Cardiff was the most famous, but it was uprooted in 1920. On sunny walls palatable grapes can be grown in this country, especially in hot summers ; but it has to be said that the results generally offer but little inducement to take up out-door cultivation of grapes, especially now that glasshouses can be erected so cheaply and give such infinitely better results. Still, for several centuries after the Norman Conquest, vineyards were common enough in the south and west of England. Winchester, or Winton, is said to take its name from its excellent vintage. It is not within the province of this work to deal with the numerous varieties of grape vine that are grown for their fruit, but there are three varieties that require mention for their distinct or ornamental qualities as hardy climbers.

Var. APIIFOLIA, *Loudon* (V. laciniosa, *Linnæus*). The Cut-leaved or Parsley Vine.—The striking and handsomely cut leaves of this variety consist of three to five main divisions, sometimes stalked. These are again variously cut into deep narrow lobes, pointed or bluntish. It makes a very effective climber, although the leaves are certainly not subdivided enough to suggest parsley. Cultivated in Britain since the middle of the seventeenth century.

Var. INCANA. The Miller Grape.—Leaves three-lobed or unlobed, smaller than in the type, the upper surface as well as the lower one covered with a grey, cobweb-like down, giving them, when young especially, a whitish appearance as if dusted with flour. Its aspect is curious and interesting rather than attractive.

Var. PURPUREA. Teinturier Grape.—Leaves at first of a beautiful claret red, deepening later in the season to lurid purple. One of the richest hued of purple shrubs.

A variety of no particular merit as an ornament, but of interest, is var. CORINTHIACA, the vine that produces the " currants " of the grocers' shops. It has smaller, more rounded leaves than the type, and tiny, black, very often seedless fruits. The name " currant " is a corruption of " Corinth," whence most of the dried fruits of this vine are exported.

V. VITACEA. COMMON VIRGINIA CREEPER

(Parthenocissus dumetorum *Rehder*; P. vitacea, *Hitchcock*; Psedera vitacea, *Greene*; P. inserta, *Fritsch*; Cissus quinquefolia, *Sims*, Bot. Mag., t. 2443)

This is the common Virginian creeper of gardens, especially town gardens, in this country, where it has long been grown under the name of Vitis (or Ampelopsis) quinquefolia. It is not, however, the true plant of that name, although the two were not separated specifically until 1894. It is very widely spread over N. America in its various forms, but the type appears to be east N. American. The best and most obvious distinction between it and the true V. quinquefolia is in the absence of disks at the end of the tendrils, on account of which it is unable to attach itself to flat surfaces. It supports itself, as most vines do, by twining its tendrils round whatever is available. It is useful for covering arbours and flattish surfaces generally; trained along a rafter or similar horizontal support it will send down a thick curtain of branches. It has the same five, obovate-lanceolate leaflets radiating from the end of a long, slender common stalk as in V. quinquefolia, but it differs in their being larger, greener beneath, brighter green above, and in the deeper, sharper teeth; the inflorescence is cymose and flatter. The leaves turn red in autumn. Where a self-supporting climber is not needed it is the better and more handsome vine. Cultivated in 1824, when it was believed to be of Brazilian origin (see *Bot. Mag.*, t. 2443).

Var. LACINIATA (V. quinquefolia incisa of gardens).—Leaves very deeply, sometimes doubly toothed, some of the teeth being ½ in. deep, with a roughness on the surface due to scattered minute hairs; the main-stalk of the leaf and the stalks of the leaflets are both longer than in the type. The variety is found wild in the western and south-western United States.

Var. MACROPHYLLA (V. quinquefolia major of gardens).—Leaflets very large, 6 or 8 ins. long and 3 to 4½ ins. wide.

V. VULPINA, *Linnæus*. RIVERBANK GRAPE

(V. riparia, *Michaux* ; V. odoratissima, *Donn*)

A vigorous, deciduous, scrambling bush or climber with glabrous young shoots. Leaves thin, 3 to 8 ins. wide, usually somewhat longer, broadly heart-shaped, with a finely tapered point and coarse, triangular, unequal teeth; usually more or less three-lobed; shining green on both surfaces, downy on the veins beneath; stalk from half to quite as long as the blade. Flowers sweetly scented like mignonette, produced in panicles 3 to 8 ins. long. Berries globose, ⅓ in. diameter, black-purple, covered thickly with blue bloom.

Native of eastern N. America from New Brunswick to the southern United States; introduced in 1806. The name vulpina has been wrongly applied to V. rotundifolia, the " Southern fox grape " (*q.v.*), a very well-marked vine with unforked tendrils and close bark. The riverbank grape is really most closely allied to V. cordifolia, and both have a tendril missing from every third joint, but the present species differs in its more commonly three-lobed leaves with larger more persistent stipules, and in its blue-bloomed fruits. It is worth growing for its vigorous, leafy habit and sweet-scented flowers. It strikes very readily from cuttings and has, in consequence, been much used as a phylloxera-proof stock on which the wine-producing vines of France have been grafted.

V. PALMATA, *Vahl*, is nearly related to V. vulpina, and is a native of the south central United States, where it is known as the " Red grape." It has glabrous, bright red young branches and leaf-stalks, three- or five-lobed leaves, the lobes long and slenderly pointed. Berries black, without bloom.

V. WILSONÆ, *Veitch*

(Gardeners' Chronicle, 2nd Oct. 1909 ; fig. 101. V. reticulata *Pampanini*)

A very vigorous deciduous climber with woolly young shoots. Leaves roundish ovate, more or less heart-shaped at the base, short-pointed, wavy-toothed, 3 to 6 ins. wide, woolly all over when young, becoming glabrous above but remaining cobwebby beneath especially on the veins. The fruits are black covered with a purplish bloom and scarcely ½ in. long, borne in slender bunches 3 to 5 ins. long, often unbranched.

Native of Hupeh, China; discovered by Wilson in 1902 and introduced then or in 1904 when collecting for Messrs Veitch, who showed it at Westminster in

October 1909, under the present name, V. Wilsonæ. It was then given an Award of Merit for its fine deep red autumn colour. It grows very vigorously on the vine pergola at Kew. This vine was named " V. reticulata " by both Pampanini and Gagnepain in the years 1910 and 1911 respectively, but that name had already been used for a species of the Cissus section of Vitis by M. A. Lawson, over forty years previously, in the *Flora of British India*, vol. i., p. 655.

WEINMANNIA TRICHOSPERMA, *Cavanilles*. SAXIFRAGACEÆ

An evergreen tree 40 ft. and upwards high in a wild state, with a trunk 1 to 2 ft. in diameter ; young shoots and flower-stalks furnished with brown down. Leaves opposite, pinnate, 1½ to 3 ins. long, composed of nine to nineteen leaflets set ¼ to ½ in. apart, the space between each pair filled on each side of the main-stalk with a triangular wing. Leaflets stalkless, oval or obovate, ⅜ to ¾ in. long, with two to six conspicuous teeth on each side ; dark lustrous green and glabrous except for a few bristles at the base of each pair of leaves. Flowers fragrant, quite small, white, packed closely on a cylindrical mignonette-like raceme 1½ to 2 ins. long, opening in May, the stamens with their pink-tipped anthers being the most conspicuous feature. Fruit a dry, two-celled capsule, ⅛ in. long, red when young.

Native of the Chilean Andes. Apart from its flowers, which are not very conspicuous, this is one of the handsomest evergreens brought from Chile. Its leaves, rather fern-like in character, are distinct among evergreens by the conspicuously winged leaf-stalks. The species is not quite hardy near London but can be grown against a wall there. It succeeds admirably in Sussex and of course in Devon and Cornwall. Although usually seen as a shrub, there is a small columnar tree of it in the garden at Wakehurst, near Hayward's Heath, and it is 10 ft. high in the Ludgvan Rectory garden, near Penzance. Easily propagated by cuttings taken in July and put in gentle bottom heat.

Weinmannia is a genus of over fifty species of shrubs or trees found in S. America, Australasia, Malaya, Madagascar, etc. It was named by Linnæus after Johann Wilhelm Weinmann, an apothecary of Ratisbon, in the early part of the eighteenth century.

WISTARIA. LEGUMINOSÆ

A small genus of exceedingly ornamental climbers, represented in the eastern United States and in N.E. Asia. The leaves are alternate, deciduous, and unequally pinnate. Flowers in handsome axillary or terminal racemes, and mostly of a pale bluish lilac or white. Pods rather resembling those of kidney beans in shape. The genus was named in honour of Caspar Wistar, a professor of anatomy in the University of Pennsylvania in the early part of the nineteenth century. It is sometimes spelt Wisteria.

Wistarias are of easy cultivation, and quite hardy in the southern half of England. In some places to the north-east they should be grown on walls. They like a good loamy soil, but are not fastidious at the root; a sunny position, however, is essential. The only problem in connection with their culture is the provision of suitable support. For W. sinensis, walls and pergolas afford the best means of displaying its attractions, and for the display of the long racemes of W. floribunda macrobotrys an overhead trellis work is desirable. An arbour framed in iron will quickly be covered by either of these species, and as the branches twist round the rods any unsightliness is soon hidden.

Seeds are not frequently produced, and do not afford a reliable means of increase. But layering may be adopted, and shoots grafted in spring on pieces of root from the same species, or sinensis, unite readily under glass. Cuttings of August wood made of the lower part of the season's shoots may also be tried.

Since the publication of the first edition of this work in 1914, the Asiatic species of Wistaria have been reviewed in Sargent's *Plantæ Wilsonianæ*, vol. ii., p. 509, by Rehder and Wilson, and by the latter author in the *Gardeners' Chronicle*, 5th August 1906, p. 61.

The W. brachybotrys of Siebold, whose identity has so long been a puzzle, is shown to be the W. floribunda of De Candolle. Wilson observes that the short racemes implied by the specific name " occur occasionally in the spring, but are much more common in late summer, when some plants bear a second sparse crop of flowers." Wilson found that on wild plants the racemes varied from 4 to 14 ins. in length. This species is easily distinguished from W. sinensis by the more numerous (thirteen to nineteen) leaflets to each leaf, smaller flowers, and by flowering two or three weeks later.

According to Rehder and Wilson, the proper name for the well-known Wistaria " multijuga," *Van Houtte*, is W. FLORIBUNDA MACROBOTRYS. It is really a cultivated form of W. floribunda with phenomenally long racemes. Wilson found them 5 ft. 4 ins. long in a garden at Kasukabe in Japan, but I have not seen them over 4 ft. long in this country. The following corrections in nomenclature have to be made :—

W. multijuga is			W. floribunda macrobotrys.		
,,	,,	alba is	,,	,,	alba.
,,	,,	rosea is	,,	,,	rosea.
,,	,,	Russelliana is	,,	,,	Russelliana.
,,	sinensis plena is		,,	,,	violacea plena.
,,	,,	variegata is	,,	,,	variegata.
,,	,,	alba plena is	,, venusta.		

W. FLORIBUNDA, *De Candolle* (Plate 39)

(W. brachybotrys, *Siebold* and *Zuccarini*, Flora japonica, t. 45)

A deciduous climber with twining branches growing 30 ft. or more high. Leaves 10 to 15 ins. long, consisting usually of eleven to nineteen leaflets which are downy when young, soon almost or quite glabrous and of a glossy dark green; of ovate shape and 1½ to 2½ ins. long. Racemes borne on short leafy shoots, normally 5 to 10 ins. long, slender, the flowers opening successively from the base, each on a slightly downy stalk ½ to 1 in. long; they are (normally) violet- or purplish-blue and fragrant; standard petal ¾ in. wide; calyx ⅓ in. long, bell-shaped, with triangular teeth. Pod 3 to 6 ins. long, velvety.

Native of Japan, whence it was imported to Belgium by Siebold in 1830.
In the text accompanying the figure in his *Flora japonica*, he states that he found it cultivated in several places, but only once wild, which was near Nagasaki. His description of the plants he saw as being only 3 to 5 ft. high, and the main flower-stalk as only 2 to 3 ins. long, is what seems to have misled people, although the plants he saw evidently formed a tangle on a hillside and were not genuinely climbing. It is said to be able to withstand a colder climate than W. sinensis.

Var. MACROBOTRYS, *Rehder and Wilson.* — Leaflets up to 4 ins. long; racemes 1½ to 3½ ins. long, sometimes over 5 ft. This is a cultivated variety never, I believe, found truly wild. It is more generally named " W. multijuga " and was introduced to Belgium by Siebold and thence to Kew in 1874. There is a very famous plant at Kameido, which has often been illustrated and described by travellers. It forms a huge arbour, extending partly over a piece of water spanned by a semicircular Japanese bridge. With its thousands of slender, pendulous racemes 3 to 4 ft. long, crowded with lilac blossoms " odorous of honey and buzzing with bees," it makes, no doubt, one of the most remarkable floral exhibitions on the globe. This variety is not so well adapted for walls as W. sinensis; it should be trained in such a way as to allow the racemes to hang freely, such as on overhead trellises.

WISTARIA FLORIBUNDA MACROBOTRYS

Some authorities have considered it a variety of W. sinensis, but it is quite distinct. The most obvious difference is the length of raceme, but the leaves also have more leaflets, and it flowers two or three weeks later. Where climbing space is not available, it can be treated as a bush. A plant in the Kew collection has been grown for over forty years like this, and is now only about 8 ft. high. Its branches are spurred back every year, and it produces an amazing profusion of racemes. All the forms of this wistaria can be increased by layers and by grafting twigs on the pieces of its own roots in spring.

Var. ALBA.—Flowers white, tinged with lilac, racemes shorter than in the type ; a very beautiful plant.

Var. ROSEA.—Flowers pale rose-coloured.

Var. RUSSELLIANA.—Flowers darker than in the type, marked with creamy blotches.

W. FORMOSA, *Rehder*

A hybrid between W. sinensis and W. floribunda alba, raised in the late Professor C. S. Sargent's garden at Holm Lea, Brookline, Mass., in 1905. Leaflets nine to fifteen to a leaf ; racemes about 10 ins. long ; flowers $\frac{4}{5}$ in. long, each on a stalk $\frac{1}{5}$ to $\frac{1}{3}$ in. long, pale violet, produced in May and June. Young shoots silky downy as are the leaves at first, afterwards becoming bright green on both surfaces and glabrous above. Rehder observes that all the flowers of one raceme open at nearly the same time, unlike those of W. floribunda which open successively from the base onwards ; also that this hybrid is superior in beauty to both parents. It was introduced to Kew in 1922.

W. FRUTESCENS, *De Candolle*

(Glycine frutescens, *Linnæus* ; Bot. Mag., t. 2103)

A deciduous climber, spreading 30 to 40 ft. from its base, and enveloping trees and shrubs in its wild state ; young shoots yellowish. Leaves pinnate, 7 to 12 ins. long, with four and a half to seven and a half pairs of leaflets of nearly uniform size ; ovate, $1\frac{1}{2}$ to $2\frac{1}{2}$ ins. long, up to $1\frac{1}{8}$ ins. wide ; slightly downy only when young. Racemes terminal on the shoots of the year, very downy, 4 to 6 ins. long, the shorter ones erect. Flowers much crowded, fragrant, each about $\frac{3}{4}$ in. long, pale lilac-purple, with a yellow spot ; calyx slenderly bell-shaped, $\frac{1}{4}$ in. long, downy, with five short triangular teeth, and like the flower-stalk, downy. Pod glabrous, much more cylindrical and swollen where the seeds are fixed, than in the Asiatic species. Seeds also rounder. Native of the south-eastern United States ; introduced in 1724. It is not so strong a grower as either W. sinensis or W. floribunda macrobotrys, nor does it ever produce so fine a display. Commencing to blossom in the latter part of June, it continues until the end of August.

Var. ALBA.—Flowers white.

W. JAPONICA, *Siebold and Zuccarini*

(Millettia japonica, *A. Gray*)

A deciduous climber with slender twining stems. In a state of nature it climbs up bushes and small trees, which eventually become almost entirely enveloped by it. Leaves 6 to 9 ins. long, composed of nine to thirteen leaflets, which are ovate, rounded, or slightly heart-shaped at the base ; $1\frac{1}{2}$ to $2\frac{1}{2}$ ins. long, $\frac{1}{2}$ to $\frac{3}{4}$ in. wide ; bright glossy green and glabrous below. Racemes axillary, often branched, very slender, many-flowered, 6 to 12 ins. long. Flowers white or pale yellow, $\frac{1}{2}$ in. or so long (the smallest of wistarias), each produced on a stalk $\frac{1}{6}$ in. long. Calyx bell-shaped, $\frac{3}{16}$ in. long, glabrous except for the ciliate margins, five-toothed. Pod 3 to 4 ins. long, $\frac{1}{3}$ in. wide, quite glabrous, six- to seven-seeded.

Native of Japan ; introduced for Messrs Veitch by Maries, in 1878. It first flowered in August 1884 at the Coombe Wood nursery. One of the most distinct of wistarias, belonging, perhaps, to another genus, this species never appears to have had full justice done to it in this country. It is worth growing if only for the lateness of its flowers (July and August). The often branching racemes, small flowers, and almost entire absence of down, distinguish it clearly. According to Siebold, a tree enveloped by this wistaria in full flower forms a " magnificent *coup d'œil,* giving to vegetation an aspect of wild beauty."

W. MACROSTACHYA, *Nuttall*

Under the name of " W. frutescens magnifica," this wistaria has long been in cultivation. In habit, foliage, and flower characters it is very like W. frutescens, but is a much handsomer plant and differs in the following respects : Leaflets rather larger ; racemes 8 to 12 ins. or even more long, with up to ninety flowers on each ; calyx teeth longer in proportion to the tube ; flower-stalk and calyx very glandular as well as hairy. Well worthy of cultivation. Native of Missouri, Arkansas, Tennessee, etc.

W. SINENSIS, *Sweet*

(Glycine sinensis, *Sims* ; Bot. Mag., t. 2083)

A strong-growing, deciduous climber, capable of covering lofty trees. The trunks of old specimens, although often decayed and hollow, attain great dimensions for a climber, and on some of the older plants in this country are over 5 ft. in circumference. The branches, which are covered with silky down when young, support themselves by twining round whatever support is available. Leaves pinnate, 10 to 12 ins. long, consisting usually of eleven leaflets, which are elliptical or ovate, deep rich green and glabrous above, somewhat hairy beneath, especially on the midrib ; $1\frac{1}{2}$ to 4 ins. long, $\frac{1}{2}$ to $1\frac{1}{2}$ ins. wide ; increasing in size towards the end of the leaf. Racemes 8 to 12 ins. long, produced in May from the buds of the previous season's growth. Flowers mauve or lilac-coloured, borne singly on stalks $\frac{1}{2}$ to $\frac{3}{4}$ in. long ; each flower is about 1 in. long, pea-flower shaped, with a fine, rounded standard petal $\frac{3}{4}$ in. wide. Pod rather like that of a kidney bean, 5 or 6 ins. long, club-shaped, $\frac{3}{4}$ in. wide towards the end, tapering gradually towards the base, covered with a velvety pile, and containing two or three seeds.

Native of N. China ; first introduced in 1816 from a garden in Canton. No climber ever brought to this country has added more to the beauty of gardens. It flowers towards the end of May, and there is frequently a second smaller crop in August. It is as remarkable for its rapid growth as for its wealth of blossom. Where wall space is available, it will extend forty yards or more from each side of the stem. In full blossom, when every twig is garnished with pale lilac flowers, few plants are so lovely. It may be used in several ways ; the commonest is as a wall plant on houses, also as a pergola plant, and for covering arches. At Kew, an old specimen which up to 1860 grew on a house there, was trained over a large iron cage erected for it when the house was demolished ; it was old then, but is still a fine feature. On the Continent, especially in Italy, it is frequently planted so as to overrun large trees ; in such a way it makes gorgeous displays there in April. When the plant has filled its destined space, it becomes necessary to prune the long, slender shoots back to within an inch or two of the older wood ; otherwise it soon becomes an inextricable tangle. This is done in late summer. This wistaria may also be treated as a shrub, 5 to 8 ft. high, by an annual hard pruning. Seed is only ripened in unusually hot years.

Var. ALBA has white flowers. The wistaria known in gardens as " W. alba plena " is now identified as a variety of venusta.

Var. PLENA.—In this the flowers are lilac, but owing to the stamens becoming transformed into petals, they lose their pea-flower shape and become rosettes. To my mind, this spoils rather than improves the flower, and the plant does not blossom so freely. Introduced from Japan to America, about 1863, and thence to England.

Var. VARIEGATA.—Leaflets blotched with white. Not a desirable plant.

W. VENUSTA, *Rehder and Wilson*

(Bot. Mag., t. 8811)

A deciduous climber growing 30 ft. and upwards high ; young shoots softly downy. Leaves pinnate, 8 to 14 ins. long, composed usually of eleven leaflets, sometimes nine or thirteen ; main-stalk downy. Leaflets oval to ovate, with a tapered apex and usually rounded base ; 1½ to 3½ ins. long, ½ to 1½ ins. wide ; both surfaces, but especially the lower one, softly downy. Racemes pendulous 4 to 6 ins. long, 3 to 4 ins. wide, the stalks densely downy. Flowers white, opening in May and June, slightly fragrant, 1 to 1¼ ins. long ; standard petal roundish, 1 in. wide, stained with yellow at the base. Calyx downy, cup-shaped, about ½ in. wide, the lobes triangular or awl-shaped ; flower-stalks about 1½ ins. long at the base of the raceme, becoming shorter towards the end. Pods 6 to 8 ins. long, velvety.

This species, named and described in 1916 (*Plantæ Wilsonianæ*, vol. ii., p. 514) was first introduced to England in May 1912, when it was shown in bloom in the Japanese section of the International Horticultural Exhibition at Chelsea. It then bore the very wrong name of " W. brachybotrys " (see W. floribunda). It differs from W. sinensis, its nearest ally, in its larger, white, more outstanding flowers, the short broad racemes, the awl-shaped lower lobes of the calyx, and the persistent down on the foliage. It has been found in Japan only as a cultivated plant, but a plant with bluish-violet blossom, collected on the hills near Nagasaki by Richard Oldham in 1863, evidently represents the wild type. Dr Rehder has named it var. VIOLACEA ; not yet in cultivation.

W. venusta is quite hardy and grows most luxuriantly in Mr Hugh Wormald's garden in Norfolk, but some badly grafted plants from Japan have been short-lived. Like W. sinensis and the forms of W. floribunda, it can be kept permanently to a shrubby state by shortening the long shoots once or twice in summer and then pruning them to within an inch or two of the base in winter. The plants originally shown at Chelsea, grown in vases, had been treated in this way.

Var. PLENA, *Rehder*, has more or less " double " white flowers. It appears to have been in cultivation previous to the introduction of the " single " flowered type in 1912 as " W. sinensis alba plena."

XANTHOCERAS SORBIFOLIA, *Bunge*. SAPINDACEÆ

(Bot. Mag., t. 6923)

A deciduous shrub or small tree up to 20 ft. high, of rather stiff, erect habit, with a large quantity of pith in the young branches. Leaves pinnate, alternate, 5 to 8 ins. long, glabrous ; leaflets nine to seventeen, borne on the upper two-thirds of the main-stalk, $1\frac{1}{2}$ to $2\frac{1}{2}$ ins. long, lanceolate, deeply and sharply toothed. Flowers produced during May in erect panicles at the end of the shoots of the previous year, and from the side buds; the terminal panicle is considerably the largest, and up to 8 ins. long; the side ones about half as large. Each flower is 1 to $1\frac{1}{4}$ ins. across, the five white petals having a carmine stain at the base. Fruit a top-shaped capsule 2 ins. wide at the top, tapering to a stout stalk at the base; it is three-valved, and as the valves open they release the rather numerous seeds, which resemble chestnuts, but are only $\frac{1}{3}$ to $\frac{1}{2}$ in. wide. The tree is a close ally of the horse-chestnut, and is the only species known.

Native of N. China; introduced to France by the Abbé David in 1868. Although at its best there are few more beautiful small trees than this, the flowers, which come with the young leaves, are liable to be injured by spring frosts in the open ground. It is admirable against a wall, as on the curator's house in the Cambridge Botanic Garden, and it is now also largely imported to this country for forcing early into flower. It is best propagated from seeds, but, failing these, cuttings of roots may be used, placing them in gentle heat in April. The plant is rather subject (like other pithy branched shrubs and trees) to the attacks of the coral-spot fungus. Branches attacked with it should be cut off as soon as noticed, and burnt, the wounds being coated over with coal-tar.

XYLOSMA RACEMOSUM, *Miquel*. TUNG-CHING TREE.
BIXACEÆ

(Hisingera japonica, *Siebold*, Fl. Jap., i., t. 88)

The typical form of this species is found wild in Japan, Korea, and the Chekiang Province of China. It does not appear to be in cultivation, and according to Wilson is only represented in Western and Central China by the

Var. PUBESCENS, *Rehder and Wilson* (Myroxylon racemosum, *Diels*), of which a good number of plants of Wilson's introduction are now in gardens. It is an evergreen tree up to 80 ft. high in nature, but small plants seem inclined to be bushy; young shoots covered with short pale hairs. Young plants are armed with straight, sharp, axillary spines $\frac{1}{2}$ to over 1 in. long. Leaves alternate, ovate to roundish ovate, toothed except near the base, which is rounded or broadly wedge-shaped, apex acuminate; $\frac{3}{4}$ to 3 ins. long, $\frac{1}{2}$ to $1\frac{1}{2}$ ins. wide, firm in texture, dark glossy green, glabrous on both surfaces; leaf-stalk $\frac{1}{8}$ to $\frac{1}{4}$ in. long, downy like the shoots. Flowers unisexual, small, yellow, fragrant, produced from the leaf-axils in short racemes $\frac{1}{4}$ to 1 in. long. Fruit about the size of small peas, black-purple, the style adhering at the top.

The cultivated plants make sturdy, bushy, well-armed evergreens, and seem to be perfectly hardy. In Japan the species flowers in August.

YUCCA. LILIACEÆ

Yucca is a genus of liliaceous trees and shrubs exclusively confined to N. and Central America. About half a dozen species are grown in the open air in the south of England, probably more in the mildest counties. The leading characteristics of these plants are a cylindrical stem, in some species not rising above ground-level, in others many feet high, fibrous and fleshy, naked of foliage below, and marked by horizontal scars of fallen leaves. Leaves long, narrow and pointed, crowded in a spherical or hemispherical head. Flowers white or greenish, drooping, produced in erect panicles or racemes, and composed of three outer segments, and three inner ones. Stamens six. Fruit an ovoid or oblong capsule up to 2 or 3 ins. long. Seeds black.

In their general aspect the yuccas are quite distinct from any other group of hardy shrubs. Their foliage is essentially of a tropical or subtropical character, which, combined with a peculiar stateliness and beauty of flower, gives the genus a unique value in gardens. They are especially suitable in formal arrangements, either isolated or in groups, and their effectiveness in flower is enhanced if a dark background can be given them.

Considering the regions of which the species described below are native, it is remarkable that they are so hardy and adaptable to our climate. The commonest species come from the coast regions of the south-eastern United States, yet they withstand 30° or 32° of frost uninjured. Compared with wild plants, our garden ones have longer, larger leaves, but smaller inflorescences. They appear to thrive in any soil, but prefer a sandy loam in a position fully exposed to the south. In such a position they never suffer from drought, nor do they, except for a diminished crop of blossom, appear to be affected by cold, wet seasons. As the stems lengthen, they ultimately decay at the older part, and fall over by their own weight. The tops can be made to strike root by trimming off half the leaves, and placing the stem in a pot of sandy soil, giving it a place in a greenhouse until rooted. The dwarf species like flaccida can be increased by division, and most of the species produce rhizomatous underground stems which make plants when cut off and potted.

There are numerous hybrids between the following species in cultivation.

Y. FILAMENTOSA, *Linnæus*

(Bot. Mag., t. 900)

A low evergreen shrub, the stem of which does not rise above ground-level, and which increases and spreads by means of side growths from the base. Leaves stiffly erect or spreading, 1 to 2½ ft. long, 1 to 2 ins. wide, pointed, but rarely spine-tipped, slightly glaucous green, roughish at the back. From the margins of the leaves, curly thread-like filaments 2 to 3 ins. long break away, and are especially numerous towards the base. Flowers pendulous, yellowish white, 2 to 3 ins. across, produced during July and August in erect, conical, glabrous panicles 3 to 6 ft. high, looser and broader than in either gloriosa or recurvifolia. Fruits 2 ins. long; seeds glossy, ¼ in. long.

Native of the south-eastern United States ; introduced in the seventeenth century, and said to have first flowered at Oxford in 1675. This is a very hardy and beautiful yucca, forming low tufts from which the stately panicles spring in profusion. It should be planted in broad masses with, if possible, a dark evergreen background. It flowers in a small state. Easily propagated by division. Allied to flaccida.

Var. VARIEGATA.—Leaves margined and striped with yellow or white. Not so hardy and vigorous as the type.

Y. FLACCIDA, *Haworth*

(Bot. Reg., t. 1895)

A low evergreen shrub, whose stem, like that of Y. filamentosa, does not arise above ground-level, spreading by sucker growths. Leaves 1 to 1¾ ft. long, 1 to 1½ ins. wide ; green or glaucous, and bent downwards above the middle, long-pointed with straightish, thread-like fibres separating from the margin, and 2 ins. or more long. Flowers as in Y. filamentosa, but borne on a downy, shorter panicle. Seeds dull, ⅓ in. long, produced in a capsule 2 to 3 ins. long.

Native of the south-eastern United States, with a more inland distribution than Y. filamentosa. It is no doubt closely allied to that species, and between them forms occur which are difficult to assign to one in preference to the other. It differs in the bent back apices of the leaves, downy panicle, larger fruit, and dull seeds. Its garden value is about the same as that of Y. filamentosa, and it is propagated in the same way.

Var. INTEGRA, *Trelease* (Y. glauca, *Sims*, not *Nuttall*; Bot. Mag., t. 2662), is without fibres on the leaf-margins, the leaves are smaller, the flower-stalks glabrous.

Var. ORCHIOIDES, *Trelease* (Y. orchioides, *Carrière*).—From the typical Y. flaccida this differs in having stiffer more erect nearly threadless leaves, and a stiffly erect, unbranched inflorescence—that is, a raceme, not a panicle. In reducing this yucca to a variety of Y. flaccida, I follow Prof. Trelease, the last monographer of the genus. It does not appear to exist in a wild state, and he describes it as " a depauperate garden form."

The Yucca figured in *Bot. Mag.*, t. 6316, as Y. orchioides major, *Baker*, is according to Trelease merely another form of Y. flaccida. He calls it Y. FLACCIDA GLAUCESCENS, and describes it as having broader, more glaucous leaves, erect until a later period, an almost tomentose panicle, and narrower petals. It is the form commonly grown in American gardens, and very probably exists under one or other of these names in ours.

Y. GLAUCA, *Nuttall*, not *Sims*

(Y. angustifolia, *Pursh* ; Bot. Mag., t. 2236)

An evergreen shrub with a low, often prostrate stem carrying a hemi-spherical head of leaves 3 to 4 ft. across. Leaves narrow linear, 1 to 2½ ft. long, ½ to ¾ in. wide, tapering to a long fine point, of a glaucous green the margins white, and beset with a few threads. Raceme, erect, 3 to 4½ ft. high, rarely branched. Flower dull greenish white, 2½ to 3 ins. long, pendulous.

Native of the south central United States ; introduced early in the nineteenth century. It is quite hardy at Kew, and several plants have grown on a south slope in the Bamboo Garden for over twenty years. They flower occasionally, but not with the freedom and regularity of Y. gloriosa and recurvifolia. Neither is the inflorescence so striking, being of a pale green, rather than truly white. Still, it is quite handsome.

Var. STRICTA, *Trelease* (Y. stricta, *Sims* ; Bot. Mag., t. 2222).—This

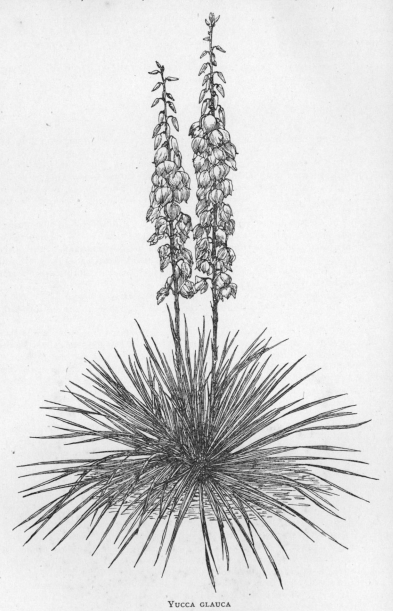

YUCCA GLAUCA

differs from typical glauca in its more vigorous growth, in its stems being more developed, and in the regularly branched inflorescence.

The yucca figured as Y. glauca in *Bot. Mag.*, t. 2662, is now called Y. flaccida integra, *Trelease* (*q.v.*).

Y. GLORIOSA, *Linnæus*. ADAM'S NEEDLE

(Bot. Mag., t. 1260)

An evergreen shrub up to 6 or 8 ft. high in this country, sometimes branched, but oftener consisting of a single, thick, fleshy stem, crowned with a cluster of numerous stiff, straight, spine-tipped leaves 1½ to 2 ft. long, by 2 to 3 ins. wide ; glaucous green when young, quite glabrous. Flowers produced from July to September, crowded on an erect, narrowly conical panicle, 3 to 8 ft. high, and 1 ft. wide. The flowers are pendulous, creamy white, sometimes tinged with red or purple outside, the six parts of the perianth oblong-lanceolate and pointed. The fruit is an oblong capsule 2 to 2½ ins. long, six-ribbed ; seeds glossy, ¼ in. long.

Native of the coast region of eastern N. America, from S. Carolina to N.E. Florida, often on sand-dunes. It was cultivated by Gerard in his garden at Holborn late in the sixteenth century, and has long been a favourite in the gardens of south and western Britain. Even now, in the twentieth century, gardens can show no more striking a feature than a group of plants in flower. It is closely allied to Y. recurvifolia, but easily distinguished by the straight, rigid leaves. It is not so common as that species, and although quite hardy in not being affected by frost, is apparently more subject to decay and injury by winter damp and snow. In Lord Ilchester's garden at Abbotsbury, Dorset, a plant has borne a panicle 12 ft. high.

Var. ELLACOMBEI, *Baker* (var. nobilis, *Carrière* ; Y. Ellacombei, *Baker*). —Leaves persistently glaucous, the outer ones recurving, and sometimes twisted on one side ; not, or scarcely ribbed. Petals red at the back. It approaches Y. recurvifolia in habit. The original plant was said by Canon Ellacombe to have been obtained from Loddiges' nursery at Hackney by his father. It is a fine yucca, perhaps from gloriosa crossed with recurvifolia.

Var. MEDIO-STRIATA has a whitish stripe down the centre of the leaf.

Var. VARIEGATA.—Leaves striped with dull yellow.

Y. RECURVIFOLIA, *Salisbury* (Plate 40)

(Y. recurva, *Haworth*)

An evergreen shrub up to 6 or 8 ft. high, more or less branched. Leaves at first glaucous, 2 to 3 ft. or even more long, 1½ to 2¼ ins. wide ; tapering to a fine stiff point, all but the upper leaves much recurved. Flowers creamy-white, 2 to 3 ins. across, in an erect panicle 2 to 3 ft. high, not so tall nor, standing so clear of the leaves as in Y. gloriosa, and with the flowers more loosely arranged ; the parts of the flower as in Y. gloriosa. Fruit 2 to 2½ ins. long ; seeds not glossy, about ⅛ in. long.

Native of the coast region of the south-eastern United States, especially of Georgia ; introduced in 1794. This is the commonest and most easily cultivated of yuccas, and although not so striking as Y. gloriosa in flower, is a more graceful plant and hardier—or, at any rate, resists snow and damp better. It flowers in late summer, and withstands the smoke of London admirably. It associates well with a formal arrangement of paths and lawns, and gives a very pleasing exotic effect. There are several varieties such as MARGINATA, whose leaves are bordered with yellow ; and VARIEGATA, with a yellow line down the centre.

III   S

Y. RUPICOLA, *Scheele*

(Bot. Mag., t. 7172)

A nearly stemless plant, consisting above ground mainly of a dense rosette of leaves, which are 2 to 2½ ft. long, 1 to 1½ ins. wide ; pale glaucous green, the margins finely toothed, cartilaginous, and yellowish. Flowers in a much-branched, glabrous panicle 4 to 6 ft. high, the branches slender, semi-erect. Flowers pendulous, somewhat bell-shaped, milky white ; the three outer parts of the perianth oblong, ¾ in. wide ; the inner ones broader (1 in. wide) ; all 2¼ ins. long, and pointed.

Native of S. Texas ; introduced about 1850. It flowered with Canon Ellacombe at Bitton, in 1890, but at present it is extremely rare in cultivation in this country. The yellowish or brownish horny margin of the leaves mentioned above distinguishes this from all other hardy species.

Y. WHIPPLEI, *Torrey*

(Bot. Mag., t. 7662 ; Gardeners' Chronicle, 17th Feb. 1912—Supplement)

An evergreen, mostly stemless shrub, producing from a rootstock a hemi-spherical rosette of much crowded leaves up to 6 ft. in diameter. Leaves 1 to 3 ft. long, ½ to 1¼ ins. wide at the base, terminated by a sharp slender spine, margins very finely toothed ; the whole leaf is rather glaucous. Flowers pendent, fragrant, closely packed on the upper part of a perfectly erect, stout stem 8 to 15 ft. high and 3 to 5 ins. in diameter at the base ; the inflorescence itself as much as 7 ft. long and 1 to 2 ft. wide. The six segments (" petals ") of the perianth are ovate-lanceolate, pointed, greenish-white tipped and edged with purple, more or less incurved, and give the flower a diameter of 2½ to 3 ins.

Native of California ; discovered during Lieut. A. W. Whipple's exploration for a railway route from the Mississippi to the Pacific in 1853-4. I believe it flowered for the first time in the open air in England with Mr Fletcher at Alnwick Manor, Bognor Regis, in 1910. But it had previously blossomed under glass in Mr Peacock's garden at Hammersmith in 1876, also at Kew. A very magnificent example flowered with Mr W. M. Christy at Watergate, Chichester, in May and June 1921. The inflorescence was 15 ft. high, the uppermost 7 ft. numerously branched and crowded with thousands of blossoms. The flowers vary in colour, and one of the best forms, called var. VIOLACEA, *André*, was figured in the *Revue Horticole* for 1884 ; this has nearly the whole of the perianth tinged more or less deeply with violet. Sargent observes that this yucca surpasses all others in the height and beauty of its panicles. It is not hardy at Kew, but Messrs Hillier have found it able to withstand 27° of frost in their nursery at Winchester. It should be well worth planting in sunny places on the south coast. Unfortunately it is apt to die after flowering.

ZANTHORHIZA APIIFOLIA, *L'Héritier*. YELLOW ROOT.
RANUNCULACEÆ

(Bot. Mag., t. 1736)

A deciduous shrub with creeping roots and erect stems from 1 to 2 ft. high. The handsome leaves are pinnate, consisting of three or five stalkless leaflets which are themselves deeply and irregularly toothed, 1 to 3 ins. long, the basal pair two- or three-lobed. The naked base of the main leaf-stalk varies from 3 to 6 ins. in length. Flowers produced in March and April, along with the young leaves in a cluster of more or less drooping panicles 3 to 5 ins. long; individually the flowers are very small ($\frac{1}{8}$ to $\frac{1}{4}$ in. wide), lurid purple, petals five, triangular, pointed.

ZANTHORHIZA APIIFOLIA

This interesting little shrub is a native of the eastern United States, where it extends from Pennsylvania to Florida, being most abundant in Virginia and N. Carolina; introduced to England about 1776, but, on account of its lack of any striking beauty of flower, has never become common. The foliage, however, is attractive, and the flowers are amongst the first to appear in spring. Easily increased by division in February. In the milder parts of the country it would appear to be suitable for naturalising in woods and moist shady spots, spreading rapidly as it does. The popular name refers to the bright yellow of the roots and stem when cut. The generic name is sometimes spelt " Xanthorhiza."

ZANTHOXYLUM. RUTACEÆ

A widely spread genus of shrubs and trees belonging to the Rue family, of which some half a dozen hardy species are in cultivation. Their leading characteristics are the strong, aromatic, sometimes unpleasant odour of the crushed leaves, the spiny young branches and leaf-stalks, the trifoliolate or pinnate, alternate leaves, the small, mostly unisexual flowers, the two-valved roundish capsules which split downward, and the shining black or blue seeds which, after the bursting of the capsules, often remain for some time attached by a short thread.

These species are not in the first rank of ornamental shrubs, but wellgrown specimens are handsome in foliage. They like a good deep soil, and are best propagated by seeds ; when these are not available they may be increased by cuttings made of the young wood in July, or of the roots in spring. The fruits and seeds of some species have a pungent pepperlike taste and are used as a condiment, and the bark contains a powerful stimulant and tonic principle sometimes employed in medicine. The generic name, sometimes spelt Xanthoxylum, refers to the yellowness of the wood of some species.

Z. AILANTHOIDES, *Siebold and Zuccarini*

A deciduous tree, 50 to 60 ft. high in Japan, the branchlets very stout, not downy, densely set with short, stiff spines. Leaves pinnate and variable in size ; on young trees at Kew they have been 3 ft. long, but ordinarily are from 10 to 18 ins. Leaflets in from five and a half to eleven and a half pairs, each one 2 to 5 ins. long, ovate or ovate-lanceolate, finely toothed, smooth, dark green. Flowers in a flat corymb 5 ins. or more across, whitish with yellow stamens ; two or more corymbs are associated at the end of the branch. Seeds black, compressed and tapering to one end.

Native of Japan and Formosa ; often introduced, but unfortunately tender and only adapted for the south-west counties. It rarely survives more than one or two winters at Kew. As its name implies, this tree resembles an Ailanthus in its long, handsome, pinnate leaves.

Z. AMERICANUM, *Miller*. PRICKLY ASH. TOOTHACHE TREE

(Z. fraxineum, *Willdenow*)

A spreading, round-headed, deciduous shrub, usually 6 to 10 ft. high in this country, but capable of growing twice as high ; young shoots brown, downy, becoming smooth and grey with age ; armed with stiff spines ½ in. or less long, in pairs. Leaves pinnate, 6 to 8 ins. long with usually five to eleven, but sometimes thirteen, leaflets, often with one or two spines on the main-stalk where the leaflets are attached. Leaflets 1½ to 2½ ins. long, ovate or oval, downy beneath especially on the midrib, minutely or not at all toothed. Flowers crowded at the joints of the previous season's shoots, very small, yellowish green. Fruit a blackish, fragrant, two-valved capsule ; seeds black and shining.

Native of the eastern United States; introduced during the middle years of the eighteenth century. This shrub is said to have been at one time common in gardens; it is no longer so. The bark and capsules have a pungent, acrid taste, and one of the popular names is given because they have been chewed to alleviate toothache. It is very easily distinguished from the other species here included by the very downy under-surface of the leaves.

Z. BUNGEI, *Planchon*

(Z. simulans, *Hance*)

A deciduous bush of graceful, spreading habit 10 ft. or more high; said sometimes to be a small tree over 20 ft. high. Branchlets downy or glabrous, armed with broad, flat spines ¼ to ¾ in. long. Leaves pinnate, 3 to 5, sometimes 9 ins. long, aromatic; leaflets seven to eleven, broadly ovate, ½ to 2 ins. long, slightly toothed; there are often a few spiny bristles on the upper surface, also on the midrib below; the main-stalk is armed beneath with short spines, also above, where the leaflets are attached. The inflorescence is a small panicle produced at the end of short, axillary twigs. Fruit reddish, with dark dots.

Native of China; introduced to Kew in 1869. One of the hardiest of the genus.

Z. PIPERITUM, *De Candolle*. JAPAN PEPPER

A compact, rounded, deciduous shrub; young shoots more or less downy when young, armed with flattish spines ½ in. long arranged in pairs at each node. Leaves pinnate, from 3 to 6 ins. long, with eleven to twenty-three leaflets, the main-stalk downy, having a few small spines on the lower side, and slightly winged. Leaflets ¾ to 1½ ins. long, ovate, stalkless, toothed, with an occasional prickle on the midrib which is also downy above; dark green, but often yellow in the centre when young. Flowers in panicles 2 ins. long at the end of short axillary twigs; small, green. Fruits reddish, dotted with glands. Seeds black, about the size of large shot.

Native of China and Japan, this shrub is, on the whole, the prettiest of these hardy species. Its neat, bushy habit and graceful foliage consisting of numerous small leaflets, render it quite distinct among hardy shrubs. It most nearly resembles Z. schinifolium, but is easily distinguished by having its spines in pairs. It is said to become occasionally a small tree in Japan. The seeds when ground are used by the Japanese as pepper.

Z. PLANISPINUM, *Siebold and Zuccarini*

(Bot. Mag., t. 8754; Z. alatum planispinum, *Rehder and Wilson*)

A deciduous shrub up to 12 ft. high, with glabrous, spiny branches; spines in pairs, thin, broad and flat at the base, ¼ to ¾ in. long, shining. Leaves 5 to 10 ins. long, trifoliolate or pinnate, with usually three or five, rarely seven stalkless leaflets, the main-stalk distinctly winged, often ⅜ in. wide. Leaflets increasing in size towards the end of the leaf, the terminal one largest and as much as 5 ins. long; others are only half as long; ovate or lanceolate, finely toothed, acuminate. Flowers yellowish, in small panicles ½ to 1½ ins. long produced from the leaf-axils in spring. Fruit red, warted; seeds black, shining, about the size of large shot.

Native of China and Japan, and nearly allied to the Z. ALATUM, *Roxburgh*, found in the Himalaya. Probably they are geographical forms of one species. The late Daniel Hanbury recorded the existence of a specimen 12 ft. high in his garden at Clapham. It is easily recognised among the other hardy species by its very distinctly winged main leaf-stalk and broad spines. Although deciduous, it will in mild seasons retain its leaves up to Christmas fresh and green. After a hot summer it bears the red fruit freely, and is then very handsome. It suffers in severe winters.

Z. SCHINIFOLIUM, *Siebold and Zuccarini*

A deciduous shrub, whose glabrous branches are armed with solitary spines up to ½ in. long. Leaves pinnate, 3 to 7 ins. long, spiny on the main-stalk, and composed of eleven to twenty-one leaflets, which are ¾ to 1½ ins. long, lanceolate, shallowly toothed, nearly or quite glabrous, deep green above, paler beneath. Flowers in a terminal flattish cluster, 2 to 4 ins. across ; each flower about ⅛ in. across. Fruit green ; seeds blue.

Native of China, Korea, and Japan. It very much resembles Z. piperitum in leaf, but differs in its spines being solitary (not in pairs), and in its flatter inflorescence produced at the end of the current year's shoot in August.

ZELKOVA.   ULMACEÆ

Nearly allied to the elms, the four species of Zelkova at present in cultivation are amongst the most interesting and handsome of hardy trees. They have smooth, beech-like trunks with a scaling bark, and deciduous, alternate, coarsely toothed, feather-nerved leaves, usually harsh to the touch like those of elm. Flowers unisexual ; both sexes produced on the same twig, the males at the base, the females solitary or few in the leaf-axils above them ; both sexes small, green, and of no beauty. Seed-vessel roundish, ⅙ to ¼ in. long, with the calyx adhering at the base, slightly horned at the top (winged in Z. Davidiana).

The zelkovas should be grown in deep, moist, loamy soil where the position is moderately sheltered. Z. crenata is the best known of them, and appears to be adapted to all but the most inclement parts of Britain. Both it and Z. acuminata should be raised from imported seed, although they can probably be grafted on elm, as are the other two species.

Z. CRETICA, *Spach*, not in cultivation, is a shrubby species found in Crete and Cyprus, whose small leaves are thickly downy beneath and coarsely, angularly toothed.

Z. CARPINIFOLIA, *K. Koch* (Plate 41)

(Z. crenata, *Spach* ; Planera Richardii, *Michaux*)

A tree 100 ft. high, with a smooth, beech-like trunk, usually comparatively short (10 to 20 ft. high), dividing into a great number of erect, crowded branches ; bark peeling off in flakes ; young twigs very downy. Leaves 1½ to 3 ins. long, ¾ to 1¾ ins. wide ; ovate or oval, rounded or slightly heart-shaped at the base, with seven to eleven coarse sharp teeth down each side ; dark green and with scattered hairs above, paler and more downy beneath ; stalk about ⅛ in. long. Flowers on short twigs, the males at the naked base of the twigs, the females in the leaf-axils above them. Fruit about the size of a small pea, distinctly ridged above.

Native of the Caucasus ; introduced in 1760. This remarkable tree is undoubtedly one of the most picturesque and distinct of any that can be grown in this country. It is slow-growing and long-lived, and might very well be used as a commemorative tree in preference to many of the exotic conifers so frequently planted for this purpose. Trees at Kew planted about 1760 are now about 60 ft. high. The densely clustered branches, much divided at their extremities, suggest a monstrous besom. The timber is of good quality, being tough and durable, but is apparently unknown in the timber trade. The largest tree in the country appears to be at Wardour Castle, in Wiltshire, about 100 ft. high. It has no distinct trunk, but a clustered group of more than a dozen stems. There is also a fine one at Holm Lacy, Hereford, whose height Mr Elwes gives as 95 ft., its trunk 19 ft. in girth. The species occasionally flowers in this country, and sometimes bears imperfect fruit, which for its proper development needs more summer heat than we experience.

Z. DAVIDII, *Hemsley*

(Hemiptelea Davidii, *Planchon* ; Planera Davidii, *Hance*)

A deciduous tree, apparently not large, armed with stout thorns ; young shoots hairy. Leaves oval, $\frac{3}{4}$ to $2\frac{1}{4}$ ins. long, $\frac{1}{2}$ to 1 in. wide ; pointed, slightly heart-shaped at the base, with seven to fifteen teeth along each side ; upper surface dark green and at first beset with pale, scattered hairs, each springing from a curious circular depression which, after the hair falls away, turns dark ; lower surface glabrous except for a few scattered hairs on the midrib and chief veins at first. Fruit conical, $\frac{1}{4}$ in. long, scarcely so wide, two-edged, slightly winged, shortly but distinctly stalked ; stalk $\frac{1}{12}$ in. long.

Native of N. and Central China and Korea ; introduced to France by Mr Maurice de Vilmorin, and from his garden at Les Barres to Kew in 1908. It is a promising tree and grows freely, being very distinct from the other species in its thorns and stalked, winged fruit. It is often regarded as generically distinct from Zelkova. Its fruits have not been produced with us, but I have seen them in great quantity on the tree at Les Barres in France. The thorns in wild trees are very formidable, sometimes 4 or 5 ins. long, but they become much less so on our cultivated trees.

Z. SERRATA, *Makino*

(Z. acuminata, *Planchon* ; Z. Keaki, *Mayr*)

A tree 100 or even 120 ft. high in Japan, with a tall, smooth, grey trunk, 5 to 10 ft. in diameter ; young shoots at first slightly downy, soon becoming almost glabrous. Leaves ovate or ovate-lanceolate, 2 to $4\frac{1}{2}$ ins. long, $\frac{3}{4}$ to 2 ins. wide ; long and taper-pointed, rounded or slightly heart-shaped at the base, with six to thirteen coarse teeth at each side ; each tooth with a short, slender point ; dark green and furnished with short, scattered hairs above, paler and glabrous beneath ; stalk $\frac{1}{8}$ to $\frac{1}{4}$ in. long. Flowers produced in April and May on short twigs, the males being borne two or more together at each joint of the leafless bases of the twigs, the females solitary in the axils of the leaves at the end ; both small, green, and of no beauty. Fruit roundish, about $\frac{1}{8}$ in. diameter. Fading leaves often good red and orange.

Introduced from Japan to England by John Gould Veitch in 1861 ; native also of Korea. Although this distinct tree is described as producing the most highly esteemed of all timbers in its native country—tough, elastic, and durable —in Great Britain it has not proved a great success, and during the fifty years that have elapsed since its introduction, few trees have reached more than 30 ft. in height. Judging by the trees at Kew, which have been growing in a favoured situation in good soil, its branches have a tendency to spread rather than grow in height in an open position. It is at the same time an elegant and interesting tree. In a young state it appears liable to injury by spring frosts. From Z. carpinifolia, it is distinguished readily by the glabrous twigs and under-surface of the leaves, and by the taper-pointed, thinner leaves with longer-pointed teeth.

Z. SINICA, *C. K. Schneider*

A deciduous tree 50 to 60 ft. high, with a trunk up to 6 ft. in girth ; young shoots greyish woolly in the early part of the season, becoming bright brown and glabrous by autumn. Leaves firm in texture, alternate, ovate to ovate-lanceolate, rounded at the base, the apex mostly slenderly pointed, the margins coarsely toothed, ciliate ; veins seven to twelve each side of the midrib, each one running out to the point of a marginal tooth ; 1 to 2½ ins. long, ⅝ to 1¼ ins. wide ; dark dull green and harsh to the touch above, greyish beneath and downy especially on the midrib and veins ; stalk very short, downy. Flowers not known to me. Fruit solitary as a rule, produced from the under side of the leaf-axils, veined, very shortly stalked, roughly obovoid, ⅕ to ¼ in. wide.

Native of W. Hupeh, Shensi, and other provinces of China. Wilson describes the bark of the trunk as smooth and pale grey, peeling off in thin flakes. Seeds were received at Kew from Messrs Vilmorin of Paris in 1920, which germinated freely. They represent probably the first introduction of the tree to England. Z. sinica has been described as a new species since the first edition of this work was published ; previously it was confused with Z. serrata, a species which is not known to be wild in China, and whose leaves have often many more veins and are even longer and more slenderly pointed. Z. sinica, evidently very hardy, is growing freely at Kew and is a welcome addition to this interesting genus.

Z. VERSCHAFFELTI, *Nicholson*

(Ulmus Verschaffelti, *Hort.*)

A small tree, or unless trained to a single stem, often a bush, with slender spreading shoots, slightly hairy when quite young ; winter buds often in pairs. Leaves 1½ to 2½ ins. long, ¾ to 1¾ ins. wide ; oval or ovate, with usually six to nine coarse, triangular teeth at the sides (usually fewer on one side than on the other), the larger teeth ¼ in. deep ; upper surface dark green and with stiff, short hairs ; lower surface with more numerous, softer hairs ; stalk ⅛ to 3/16 in. long. Fruit (according to Henry) like that of Z. carpinifolia, but somewhat smaller.

There is no wild specimen of this tree in the Kew Herbarium, and its origin is not definitely known. Dippel, who first distinguished it as a Zelkova, and figured it in his *Handbuch der Laubholzkunde*, ii., fig. 14, in 1892, suggests an Eastern Asiatic origin for it. It appears, however, to have considerable affinity with Z. carpinifolia, and is more likely to be of Caucasian origin. Henry suggests it may be a hybrid between Z. cretica, a native of Crete and Cyprus, not in cultivation, and Z. carpinifolia ; but does not explain how such a cross can have been effected. It is a pretty and distinct shrub or tree, well marked by the deep angular cutting of the leaf-margins. It has been cultivated at Kew since 1886, and is perfectly hardy, slow growing, and forming a bushy head. It was long thought to be an elm, but it fruited at Paris in 1908, and was conclusively shown to be a zelkova.

ZENOBIA SPECIOSA, *D. Don.* ERICACEÆ

(Andromeda cassinifolia, *Sims* ; Bot. Mag., t. 970)

A deciduous or sub-evergreen shrub of somewhat irregular, thin habit, 4 to 6 ft. high, devoid of down or hairs. Leaves alternate oblong-ovate, tapering at the base, pointed or rounded at the apex, shallowly toothed ; 1 to 2¼ ins. long, ½ to 1¼ ins. wide ; of a dark shining green. Flowers pendent ; produced, often in fours or fives, in axillary clusters on the terminal portion of the shoots of the previous year, each on a stalk ½ to ¾ in. long, forming leafy or naked racemes 4 to 8 ins. long. Corolla pure white, bell-shaped, ⅜ in. wide, with five shallow lobes ; calyx-lobes five, triangular, persisting at the base of the dry, flattish-globose (or orange-shaped) seed-vessel.

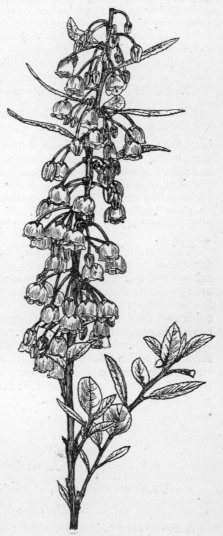

Native of the eastern United States from N. Carolina to Florida ; introduced in 1801. This beautiful shrub, whose pendent blossoms resemble large lily-of-the-valley flowers, is, after long neglect, becoming more frequent in gardens. It can be forced into bloom early (it flowers naturally in June and July), and potted plants profusely in flower may be seen at most Spring Shows. It needs a peaty soil, or a light loamy one, with which decayed leaves have been freely incorporated. It can be propagated by cuttings of half-ripened wood placed in gentle heat about July, or by seeds treated as advised for rhododendrons. The flowering part of the shoot, from beneath which

ZENOBIA PULVERULENTA

the young shoots spring, should be cut off as soon as the flowers are faded, if seed is not required.

Var. QUERCIFOLIA has the leaf-margins set with shallow wavy lobes. A curiosity.

Z. PULVERULENTA, *Hort.* (Z. speciosa pulverulenta, *Nicholson,* Andromeda pulverulenta, *Bartram*).—For garden purposes it is more convenient to treat this as a species, as some authors do, but in all essential characters it is identical with Z. speciosa. Beautiful as that shrub is, this is still more lovely. It is easily distinguished from it by having very glaucous foliage and young shoots. It blossoms with even greater freedom, and the mixture of young, blue-white leaves and pure white flowers is very attractive. Native of the same area as Z. speciosa.

ZIZYPHUS SATIVA, *Gaertner.* JUJUBE. RHAMNACEÆ

(Z. vulgaris, Lamarck ; Z. jujuba, *Miller*)

A small deciduous tree up to 30 ft. high, with glabrous, spiny branches ; spines in pairs, the longer one up to $1\frac{1}{4}$ ins. long, straight, the shorter one decurved. Leaves alternate, oval, ovate to ovate-lanceolate, shallowly round-toothed, blunt or rounded at the apex, glabrous, or downy only on the veins beneath ; three-veined at the base. Flowers less than $\frac{1}{4}$ in. across, yellowish, borne two or three together on short stalks in the leaf-axils. Fruit fleshy and rather like a small plum, roundish egg shaped, $\frac{1}{2}$ to 1 in. long, dark red, or almost black when ripe.

This interesting tree is not very hardy. At Kew it has lived outside for several years, but does not grow vigorously ; it is worth trying in the milder counties. The fruits have a pleasant acid taste when fresh, but are more agreeable when dried ; they are commonly eaten in both states in the Mediterranean region. The species now extends, both wild and cultivated, from S.E. Europe to Afghanistan, China, and Japan, but may have become naturalised in Europe. It was in cultivation in England in 1640, but its tenderness has always kept it rare. The only other hardy shrub with which it is likely to be confused is Paliurus australis, which it resembles in leaves and spines ; but the larger and prettier flowers of the paliurus, produced in short branched umbels, and especially the dry, flat, winged fruits, are very distinct.

ADDENDUM

ULMUS CORITANA, *Melville.* CORITANIAN ELM

(Journ. Linn. Soc. liii. p. 263, 1949.)

A tree up to 65 ft. in height with an open head of spreading and ascending branches. Trunk up to 4 ft. diameter, with coarsely furrowed bark. First-year branchlets $\frac{1}{12}$ in. diameter, smooth, shining brown. Spur shoots with 3 to 5 leaves. Leaves leathery, glabrous and shining above, paler below, glabrous except for axillary tufts and numerous glands ; narrowly to broadly ovate, acute, unequal at the base, with 8 to 12 pairs of veins ; margins doubly-serrate :

petiole $\frac{1}{12}$ to $\frac{3}{8}$ in. long, pubescent above, glabrous below. Flowers and fruit similar to those of *U. carpinifolia.*

Var. MEDIA, *Melville.* Leaves of the short shoots broadly ovate acute $1\frac{3}{8}$ to $2\frac{3}{4}$ ins. long, very unequal at the base, the long side meeting the petiole $\frac{1}{8}$ to $\frac{1}{3}$ in. below the short side ; petiole $\frac{1}{8}$ to $\frac{3}{8}$ in. long.

Var. ANGUSTIFOLIA, *Melville.* Leaves of the short shoots narrowly ovate to ovate lanceolate $1\frac{1}{2}$ to $3\frac{1}{2}$ ins. long, very unequal at the base, the long side meeting the petiole $\frac{1}{8}$ to $\frac{3}{5}$ in. below the short side ; petiole $\frac{1}{4}$ to $\frac{3}{5}$ in. long.

Var. ROTUNDIFOLIA, *Melville.* Leaves of the short shoots broadly ovate, acute, 1 to $2\frac{1}{8}$ ins. long, subcordate at the base, the long side meeting the petiole $\frac{1}{24}$ to $\frac{1}{8}$ in. below the short side ; petiole $\frac{1}{12}$ to $\frac{2}{5}$ in. long.

Native of Eastern and Central England. Its distribution extends through East Anglia to the Midlands between the valleys of the Thames and Trent. This description is based on a paper by Dr R. Melville published in the Journal of the Linnean Society, volume 53, p. 263, which gives illustrations and a distribution map.

ULMUS DIVERSIFOLIA, *Melville.* EAST ANGLIAN ELM

(Journ. Bot. lxxvii. p. 140, 1939).

A tree up to about 65 ft. in height with spreading branches and slender wiry branchlets. First-year branchlets $\frac{1}{24}$ to $\frac{1}{12}$ in diameter, hairy at first becoming nearly glabrous by the autumn. Spur shoots of three kinds, the majority having leaves with unequal bases, a lesser number with bases equal or nearly so, and a few with both types of leaf together. Leaves with unequal bases, elliptical to obovate acute, veins 8 to 11 pairs. Leaves with equal bases, elliptical acute, veins 5 to 9 pairs. Blade of leaf $2\frac{1}{8}$ to $3\frac{1}{8}$ ins. long slightly rough above, downy below ; margin doubly-serrate. Stalk $\frac{1}{8}$ to $\frac{2}{5}$ in. long, downy above. Sucker shoots hairy, with leaves $\frac{2}{5}$ to $2\frac{1}{4}$ ins. long. Flowers 15 to 25 in a cluster. Fruit $\frac{1}{2}$ to $\frac{3}{4}$ in. long, $\frac{3}{10}$ to $\frac{1}{2}$ in. broad, ovate to obovate, seed near the notch.

Native of England with a restricted distribution in Hertfordshire, and East Anglia. This description is based on that published in 1939 by Dr R. Melville in the Journal of Botany, volume 77, p. 140.

INDEX

WHERE the names adopted in this work differ from those accepted by Rehder in the second edition of his " Manual of Cultivated Trees and Shrubs " (1940), the latter are included below in round brackets, *e.g.* " Abies Webbiana (A. spectabilis)," implies that Rehder preferred the name Abies spectabilis to Abies Webbiana. The specific epithets printed in small capitals, *e.g.* " VEITCHII," are of trees and shrubs illustrated in the text. The trees, etc. illustrated by plates may be found by reference to the lists given at the beginning of volume I. The leading generic names are printed in heavy type, *e.g.* " **Abelia**."

PRINTED IN GREAT BRITAIN BY OLIVER AND BOYD LTD., EDINBURGH

Plate I.—Rhododendron arboreum cinnamomeum

PLATE 2.—RHODODENDRON BAILEYI (Flowers reddish-purple)

PLATE 3.—RHODODENDRON CALOSTROTUM (Flowers pale pink to purplish)

Plate 4.—Rhododendron campylocarpum

PLATE 5.—RHODODENDRON CEPHALANTHUM (Flowers white)

PLATE 6.—RHODODENDRON CHASMANTHOIDES (Flowers rose-lavender)

PLATE 7.—RHODODENDRON CROCEUM (Flowers soft yellow), at Borde Hill, Sussex

PLATE 8.—RHODODENDRON GLAUCUM

PLATE 9.—RHODODENDRON HABROTRICHUM (Flowers pale rose or white)

PLATE 10.—RHODODENDRON LACTEUM (Flowers creamy-yellow)

PLATE 11.—RHODODENDRON LADY ROSEBERY (Flowers brilliant pink)

PLATE 12.—RHODODENDRON MYRTILLOIDES (Flowers plum-coloured)

PLATE. 13—RHODODENDRON OBTUSUM, Kurume Azalea (Flowers varying from white to scarlet and crimson)

PLATE 14.—RHODODENDRON OXYPHYLLUM (Flowers pure white)

PLATE 15.—RHODODENDRON SINOGRANDE (Flowers creamy-yellow)

PLATE 16.—RHODODENDRON WARDII (Flowers yellow)

PLATE 17.—RHODODENDRON WILLIAMSIANUM (Flowers rosy-red)

PLATE 18.—SALIX BABYLONICA, Weeping Willow

PLATE 19.—SALIX CŒRULEA, Cricket-bat Willow

PLATE 20.—SALIX MATSUDANA at Kew

PLATE 21.—SALIX SALAMONI

PLATE 22.—SASSAFRAS OFFICINALE, Sassafras, at Claremont

PLATE 23. SCHIZANDRA RUBRIFLORA (Fruits red)

PLATE 24.—SCIADOPITYS VERTICILLATA, Umbrella Pine

PLATE 25.—SEQUOIA SEMPERVIRENS, Redwood at Claremont

PLATE 26.—SOPHORA JAPONICA at Kew

PLATE 27.—SORBUS INTERMEDIA, Swedish Whitebeam

PLATE 28.—SORBUS PRATTII. (Fruits white)

PLATE 29.—SPIRÆA ARGUTA

PLATE 30.—SPIRÆA TRICHOCARPA (Flowers white)

PLATE 31.—STEWARTIA KOREANA (Flowers white)

PLATE 32.—TAIWANIA CRYPTOMERIOIDES

PLATE 33.—TRACHYCARPUS FORTUNEI, Chusan Palm

PLATE 34.—TSUGA ALBERTIANA, at Murthly Castle, Perth

PLATE 35.—ULMUS STRICTA var. WHEATLEYI, Jersey Elm

PLATE 36.—VERONICA BRACHYSIPHON

PLATE 37.—VIBURNUM BITCHIUENSE (Flowers pinkish-white)

PLATE 38.—VIBURNUM FRAGRANS (Flowers white or pinkish)

PLATE 39.—WISTARIA FLORIBUNDA ALBA

PLATE 40.—YUCCA RECURVIFOLIA